PLANT PHOTOSYNTHETIC PRODUCTION
MANUAL OF METHODS

PLANT PHOTOSYNTHETIC PRODUCTION

MANUAL OF METHODS

Edited by Z. Šesták, J. Čatský & P.G. Jarvis

Dr W. Junk N.V. Publishers The Hague 1971

Typography, cover and dust jacket designed by T. Goedewaagen, Bennekom
Printed in the Netherlands by
Zuid-Nederlandsche Drukkerij N.V., 's-Hertogenbosch

SCHEME OF CONTENTS

CHAPTERS' CONTENTS

FOREWORD

The value of any piece of scientific research depends on the type and accuracy of the methods used. With the development of any branch of science the methods needed to achieve reliable results become more and more complex.
Complete standardization of methods is neither possible nor desirable in creative science, but, at the same time, it is extremely useful if the results obtained by different methods are mutually comparable. For all of these reasons, it is of great value and help to the development of any branch of science for the investigators exploring the same or similar problems to share their methodological experiences. Methodological manuals are designed to serve this purpose. This manual has been produced to serve all those investigating the problems of the ecology and physiology of photosynthesis. The importance of these problems is well-known and has been stressed by creating a special subsection for Photosynthesis and Solar Energy Conversion within the Section of Production Processes (PP) of the International Biological Programme (IBP).

The IBP – apart from endeavouring to produce valuable results – has greatly helped to bring together useful methods and to develop new ones in several branches of environmental biology, including research into the photosynthetic basis of productivity. It is therefore natural that the IBP/PP Photosynthesis Subcommittee gave its vote of support to the publication of this Manual. It is also significant that more than a half of the 36 authors of the various parts of this Manual are actively engaged in IBP research. It is hoped that the Manual will be used in many investigations of photosynthetic production – regardless of whether or not they form part of IBP and that it will retain at least a part of its usefulness after IBP has terminated, becoming used in research carried out in other programmes such as the Man and Biosphere (MAB) programme of UNESCO, and that it will provoke and initiate new methodological and technical developments.

Writing a manual is always an uneasy task requiring a great deal of mutual understanding, goodwill and efficient co-operation. It is also very time-consuming and is regarded by some scientists to be not as rewarding as writing original papers. But the reward is here. In general terms, manuals, including this one, represent a service by scientists to their fellows. It is, indeed, this very spirit of service which guided the authors and editors of this Manual that deserves our thanks and high appreciation. But the best reward to all those who have contributed to the creation of this Manual will be if it becomes a book that will be really used.

Ivan Málek

IBP/PP Convenor

Prague, 31 January 1971

PREFACE

The rapid growth and development of photosynthesis research during the last 20 years has depended to a large extent on the development of new methods. Surprisingly, no manual of methods for photosynthesis research has been written in English until now. This gap has been felt especially in studies of photosynthesis in relation to the physiology and ecology of plant production, *e.g.* within the framework of the International Biological Programme. Therefore it was decided to prepare a manual of proved methods to provide guide lines for such studies. The aim of this book is not to review all existing methods and equipment and their modifications, but to choose and comprehensively describe a number of techniques found useful by the authors of the individual chapters. The bases of all the chapters are descriptions of the techniques and their advantages and disadvantages, as well as the description of commercial and work-shop produced equipment and, in some cases, the location and repair of common faults. These data are complemented with figures, suggestions and recommendations for the treatment of certain problems and the evaluation of experimental data, and lists of references.
This manual is based on a Czech predecessor [Z. Šesták and J. Čatský (ed.): Metody studia fotosynthetické produkce rostlin. – Academia, Praha 1966] the size and number of chapters of which have been more than doubled. All the chapters have been rewritten with contributions from 35 authors from 10 countries of Europe, America and Australia. The names of the authors are given in the Contents with the title of the appropriate Chapter or its Section and their full addresses are supplied in an alphabetical list. The majority of the authors read, commented and frequently supplemented the chapters of other authors. In addition some chapters were reviewed and supplemented by other scientists the addresses of whom may be found in a separate list. This widespread cooperation amongst researchers in the field of photosynthesis has made this manual as comprehensive as possible at the moment. On the other hand, the reader will find that the individualities of the authors and their various conceptions of methodology are reflected in the style of the individual Chapters. The editors have tried to unify the text as far as possible but without distorting the individual authors' approach. This has necessarily involved a certain amount of rewriting to avoid duplication and to fit the various contributions together. Terms and units have been standardised to some extent but time has not permitted complete standardisation throughout. The editors invite any addenda, comments and methodological discussion in the field covered by this Manual from its readers. The importance and usefulness of any method is often a matter of opinion. Nevertheless, we have tried to give some general guide lines and useful data in Chapter 1, which we hope will be read by everyone who is going to use this Manual.
More than a half the text was written by authors who are not native English speakers. The revision of those manuscripts was undertaken by one of the editors (P.G.J.) and his wife, Dr. Margaret S. Jarvis. The editors highly appreciate the technical help of Mrs. Drahomíra Těžká who retyped the majority of the manus-

cript pages and helped in the preparation of indexes and reading the proofs, and Miss Jarmila Veverková, who has redrawn most of the figures.
The editors are thankful to all the authors and to everyone who helped in the preparation of the Manual. They hope that it will help scientists, teachers and students working in photosynthesis and plant productivity studies.

Z. Šesták, J. Čatský and P. G. Jarvis

AUTHORS' ADDRESSES

M. C. Anderson, C.S.I.R.O., Division of Plant Industry, P.O. Box 109, Canberra City, A.C.T. 2601, Australia.

R. B. Austin, National Vegetable Research Station, Wellesbourne, Warwick, Great Britain.

J. E. Begg, C.S.I.R.O., Division of Land Research, Canberra, A.C.T., Australia.

O. Björkman, Carnegie Institution of Washington, Department of Plant Biology, Stanford, California 94305, U.S.A.

K. W. Brown, A. & M. University, Department of Soil and Crop Sciences, College Station, Texas, U.S.A.

**J. Čatský*, Institute of Experimental Botany, Czechoslovak Academy of Sciences, Flemingovo nám. 2, Praha 6, Czechoslovakia.

M. V. Chulanovskaya, Komarov Botanical Institute, Academy of Sciences of the U.S.S.R., Ul. Popova, 2, Leningrad P-22, U.S.S.R.

O. T. Denmead, C.S.I.R.O., Division of Plant Industry, P.O. Box 109, Canberra City, A.C.T. 2601, Australia.

F. E. Eckardt, Centre National de la Recherche Scientifique, B.P. 1018, 34-Montpellier, France.

H. Fock, Botanisches Institut der J.W. Goethe-Universität, 6000 Frankfurt a.M., Siesmayerstraße 70, Germany (BRD).

E. Gauhl, Botanisches Institut der J.W. Goethe-Universität, 6000 Frankfurt a.M., Siesmayerstraße 70, Germany (BRD).

J. Janáč, Fuel Research Institute, Běchovice, Czechoslovakia.

P. G. Jarvis, University of Aberdeen, Department of Botany, St. Machar Drive, Aberdeen AB9 2UD, Great Britain.

W. Koch, Forstbotanisches Institut, 8 München 13, Amalienstraße 52, Germany (BRD).

D. Koller, Department of Botany, The Hebrew University, Jerusalem, Israel.

Š. Kubín, Laboratory of Algology, Institute of Microbiology, Czechoslovak Academy of Sciences, Opatovický mlýn, Třeboň, Czechoslovakia.

J. Květ, Institute of Botany, Czechoslovak Academy of Sciences, Stará 18, Brno, Czechoslovakia.

J. V. Lake, Rothamsted Experimental Station, Harpenden, Herts., Great Britain.

M. M. Ludlow, C.S.I.R.O., Division of Tropical Pastures, Mill Road, St. Lucia, Q'ld, 4067, Australia.

J. K. Marshall, C.S.I.R.O., Division of Plant Industry, Riverina Laboratory, P.O. Box 226, Deniliquin, N.S.W. 2710, Australia.

I. C. McIlroy, C.S.I.R.O., Division of Meteorological Physics, Aspendale, Victoria, Australia.

H. Metzner, Institut für chemische Pflanzenphysiologie der Universität, 74 Tübingen, Auf der Morgenstelle, Germany (BRD).

J. Nečas, Laboratory of Algology, Institute of Microbiology, Czechoslovak Academy of Sciences, Dukelská 145, Třeboň, Czechoslovakia.

J. P. Ondok, Institute of Botany, Czechoslovak Academy of Sciences, Ecological Station, Opatovický mlýn, Třeboň, Czechoslovakia.

A. Perrier, Station Centrale de Bioclimatologie Agricole, I.N.R.A., Route de St-Cyr, 78-Versailles, France.

G. A. Pieters, Laboratorium voor Plantenphysiologisch Onderzoek van de Landbouwhogeschool, Generaal Foulkesweg 72, Wageningen, The Netherlands.

H. Schaub, Botanisches Institut der J.W. Goethe-Universität, 6000 Frankfurt a.M., Siesmayerstraße 70, Germany (BRD).

O. A. Semikhatova, Komarov Botanical Institute, Academy of Sciences of the U.S.S.R., Ul. Popova, 2, Leningrad P-22, U.S.S.R.

* During preparation of this book partly at leave in the Station Centrale de Bioclimatologie Agricole, I.N.R.A., Route de St. Cyr, 78 – Versailles, France.

Z. Šesták, Institute of Experimental Botany, Czechoslovak Academy of Sciences, Flemingovo nám. 2, Praha 6, Czechoslovakia.

I. Šetlík, Laboratory of Algology, Institute of Microbiology, Czechoslovak Academy of Sciences, Opatovický mlýn, Třeboň, Czechoslovakia.

B. Slavík, Institute of Experimental Botany, Czechoslovak Academy of Sciences, Flemingovo nám. 2, Praha 6, Czechoslovakia.

W. Starzecki, Laboratory of Plant Physiology, Polish Academy of Sciences, Grodzka 53, Kraków, Poland.

V. L. Voznesenskiĭ, Komarov Botanical Institute, Academy of Sciences of the U.S.S.R., Ul. Popova, 2, Leningrad P-22, U.S.S.R.

O. V. Zalenskiĭ, Komarov Botanical Institute, Academy of Sciences of the U.S.S.R., Ul. Popova, 2, Leningrad P-22, U.S.S.R.

J. Zurzycki, Laboratory of Plant Physiology, University of Cracow, Grodzka 53, Kraków, Poland.

ADDRESSES OF REVIEWERS*

J. S. Brown, Carnegie Institution of Washington, Department of Plant Biology, Stanford, California 94305, U.S.A. (Chapter 18.)

P. Chartier, Station Centrale de Bioclimatologie Agricole, I.N.R.A., Route de St-Cyr, 78-Versailles, France. (Chapters 1, 2, 3, 13, 16.)

C. S. French, Carnegie Institution of Washington, Department of Plant Biology, Stanford, California 94305, U.S.A. (Chapter 18.)

P. Gaastra, Centre for Plant Physiological Research, Bornsesteeg 47, P.O. Box 52, Wageningen, The Netherlands. (Chapter 3.)

A. Hager, Botanisches Institut der Universität, 8 München 19, Menzingerstraße 67, Germany (BRD). (Chapter 18.)

O. L. Lange, Botanisches Institut II, Botanische Anstalten der Universität, 87 Würzburg, Mittlerer Dallenbergweg 64, Germany (BRD). (Chapter 17.)

W. Larcher, Institut für allgemeine Botanik der Universität, Sternwartestraße 15, A-6020 Innsbruck, Austria. (Chapters 2, 3.)

G. Meinl, Deutsche Akademie der Landwirtschaftswissenschaften zu Berlin, Institut für Pflanzenzüchtung, Groß Lüsewitz, Post Rostock 2, Germany (DDR). (Chapter 3.)

J. L. Monteith, Department of Physiology and Environmental Studies, School of Agriculture, University of Nottingham, Sutton Bonington, Loughborough, Leics., Great Britain. (Chapter 12.)

L. Nátr, Cereal Research Institute, Havlíčkova 2787, Kroměříž, Czechoslovakia. (Chapter 9.)

S. de Parcevaux, Station Centrale de Bioclimatologie Agricole, I.N.R.A., Route de St-Cyr, 78-Versailles, France. (Chapters 15, 16.)

N. J. Rosenberg, Department of Horticulture and Forestry, University of Nebraska, Lincoln, Nebr. 68503, U.S.A. (Chapter 3.)

G. Thorne, Rothamsted Experimental Station, Harpenden, Herts., Great Britain. (Chapter 10.)

* The reviewers who are simultaneously authors of another chapter are not listed here.

1 | CRITERIA FOR THE SELECTION OF SUITABLE METHODS

1.1 | Recent views on photosynthesis

Recent views on photosynthesis regard this unique event in nature as a part of a catenary process in green plants starting with the entry of radiative energy and carbon dioxide into the leaf, and ending with the efflux of oxygen and organic matter from the photosynthesizing chloroplasts. The fundamental process of photosynthesis itself is therefore often investigated together with the accompanying processes of transfer of carbon dioxide from atmosphere (the bulk air) to carboxylation sites, and transfer of radiant energy to photoreceptors[1].

Photosynthesis literally means the combining of separate parts into a whole by the action of light. However, light acts directly on only a few links in the complex process of photosynthesis: the absorption of photons results in the creation of primary oxidants and reductants which represent the conversion of radiant energy into chemical energy. The fixation of CO_2 and production of carbohydrates and other organic substances, processes of extreme importance to man, can take place in the dark and are not exclusive to green plants and photosynthetic bacteria, but also proceed in animal homogenates to which $NADPH_2$ and ATP are added. Similarly the splitting of water together with the evolution of oxygen, and photophosphorylation, may proceed in the dark using intermediates formed in the photoreactions.

Hence photosynthesis *sensu stricto* may be defined purely from the point of view of its energy turnover, *e.g.* 'Photosynthesis is a series of processes in which electromagnetic energy is converted to chemical free energy which can be used for biosynthesis' (Kamen 1963), or as a combination of biophysical (quantum absorption and conversion) and biochemical processes (formation of $NADPH_2$ and ATP accompanied by oxygen production from the splitting of water) driven by radiation of wavelengths *ca.* 400–700 nm absorbed in the photosynthetic apparatus of chloroplasts.

However, the processes by which water is split and carbon fixed supply the ultimate donors and acceptors, respectively, necessary for continuous activity of the photosynthetic electron transfer system. This system is commonly represented by the Hill-Bendall 'Z-scheme' (see Fig. 1.1) in which each of the two series-linked light reactions is driven by a separate photosystem. The photosystems are made up of photosynthetic pigments and electron carriers. The most common pigment – chlorophyll *a* – is present *in vivo* in various forms which differ mainly in their binding with proteins, in the position of absorption maxima in the red region of the spectrum, and in their photoactivity. Forms of chlorophyll *a* occur in both

1. As shown in Section 1.2, these processes only can be easily measured when studying the photosynthesis of an intact canopy, plant or leaf; the rates of these processes can then be compared with the rate of production of dry matter by the anabolic activity of green plants.

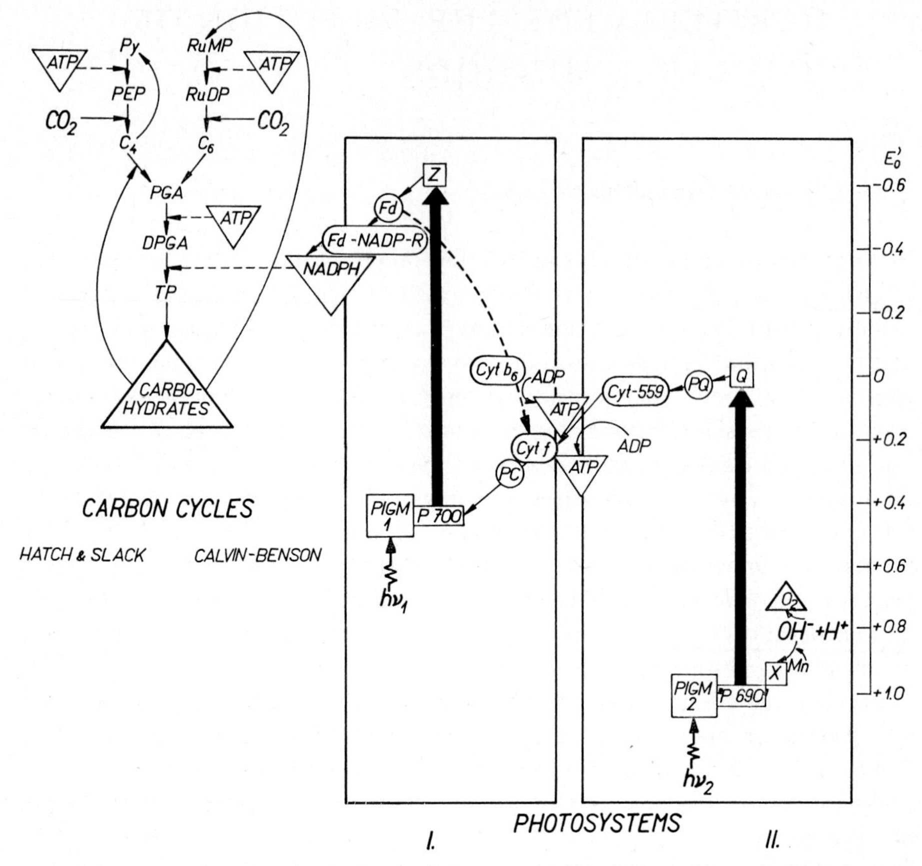

Fig. 1.1 Scheme of reaction mechanisms of photosynthesis in higher plants, showing the two photosystems and both possible types of CO_2 fixation. The text should be consulted for detailed explanation. *X* primary oxidant of photosystem II; *Q* primary reductant of photosystem II; *Z* primary reductant of photosystem I; P 700 and 'P 690' electron traps of photosystems I and II, respectively; PIGM 1, PIGM 2 pigment systems of photosystems I and II, respectively; $h\nu_1$, $h\nu_2$ quanta absorbed by photosystems I and II, respectively; PQ plastoquinone; Cyt cytochromes of the type shown; PC plastocyanin; Fd ferredoxin; Fd-NADP-R ferredoxin-NADP-reductase; NADPH reduced nicotineamide adenine dinucleotide phosphate; ADP adenosine diphosphate; ATP adenosine triphosphate; RuMP ribulose-5-monophosphate; RuDP ribulose-1,5-diphosphate; Py pyruvate; PEP phosphoenolpyruvate; C_4, C_6 intermediates of Hatch & Slack or Calvin-Benson cycles, respectively; PGA 3-phosphoglyceric acid; DPGA 1,3-diphosphoglyceric acid; TP triose phosphate.

photosystems, but the long-wavelength forms predominate in photosystem I, while the short-wavelength forms together with most of chlorophyll *b* (or *c* or *d*) and other accessory pigments (carotenoids and phycobilins) are components of photosystem II. The energy of photosynthetically active radiation absorbed by photosynthetic pigments is in both photosystems transferred gradually from shorter-wavelength to longer-wavelength absorbing pigments and finally to the so-called energy trap, probably a special form of chlorophyll. The energy trap of photosystem I is a porphyrin (chlorophyll?) pigment, known as P 700 (there is *ca.* 1 molecule present for every 500–600 chlorophyll molecules); the energy trap of photosystem II is still hypothetical and is called 'P 690' (or 'P 680' or chl-a_{II}). Excitation of the trapping molecule results in the transfer of an electron against the gradient of electrochemical (redox) potential (*i.e.* uphill transfer) and thus in the formation of highly active oxidants and reductants. Hence the absorption of energy in pigments of photosystem II leads to the photoreaction 2 which creates a primary oxidant X^+ and a primary reductant Q^-. The primary oxidant X^+ (probably with the help of the inevitable redox system Mn^{3+}/Mn^{2+}) induces splitting of water and evolution of oxygen and thus restoration of unexcited 'P 690'. The electron from the primary reductant Q^- is transferred through the chain of electron carriers joining the two photosystems which is composed of plastoquinone, cytochromes and plastocyanin. During this passage (downhill transfer) a part of the energy of the electron is expended in the formation of ATP from ADP and inorganic phosphate. Quanta absorbed by the light-harvesting pigments of photosystem I excite P 700, which in the second uphill transfer (photoreaction 1) donates an electron to an acceptor Z (ferredoxin-reducing substance). The oxidized molecule of P 700 is brought back to its ground (unexcited) state by accepting the low-energy electron transferred from photosystem II. The reduced acceptor Z^- transfers the electron *via* the Fe-protein ferredoxin and the flavoprotein ferredoxin-NADP-reductase to nicotinamide adenine dinucleotide phosphate $NADP^+$. $NADPH_2$ formed in this last step is the 'reducing power' which is used in reduction of the carboxyl group originating from the fixation of carbon dioxide.

Carbon dioxide is bound either to phosphoenolpyruvate (in the C_4-dicarboxylic acid pathway typical for tropical grasses and some other plants[1]) or to ribulose-1,5-diphosphate (in the Calvin-Benson cycle). In both cases the intermediary product of this reaction (a C_4- or C_6-compound) is split and after a few steps, including phosphorylation, 1,3-diphosphoglyceric acid is produced. Reduction of this compound by $NADPH_2$ yields the primary carbohydrate resulting from the photosynthetic conversion of radiant energy into chemical energy. The remainder of the enzymatic reactions of the carbon cycles serves to regenerate the CO_2 acceptors and to form alternative carbohydrates.

In addition to the above-mentioned photophosphorylation (*i.e.* phosphorylation induced by photosynthetic electron transfer) probably situated in the cytochrome link between the photoreactions 1 and 2 (known as non-cyclic photophosphorylation), a shortened electron transfer chain with one phosphorylating site presents an alternative pathway for energy captured by photosystem I. This cyclic pathway probably includes P 700, intermediate Z, ferredoxin, cytochrome b_6, cytochrome f and plastocyanin. This phosphorylation (known as cyclic photophosphorylation) is probably also situated in the cytochrome link.

This short account of the mechanism of photosynthesis, as it is currently thought

1. First species in which this pathway has been claimed are: *Saccharum officinarum*, *S. spontaneum*, *S. sinense*, *Zea mays*, *Sorghum halepense*, *Paspalum dilatatum*, *Axonopus argentinus*, *Digitaria*, *Chloris gayana*, *Erianthus maximus*, *Eragrostis brownii*, *Cynodon dactylon*, *Amaranthus viridis*, *A. edulis*, *A. palmeri*, *A. retroflexus*, *Gomphrena celosoides*, *Cyperus rotundus*, *Panicum bulbosum*, *P. capillare*, *P. miliaceum*, *Atriplex rosea*, *A. spongiosa*, *A. semibaccata*, *A. angulata*, *A. inflata*, *A. lindleyi*, *A. vesicaria*, *A. nummularia*, *Salsola kali*, *Kyllinga monocephala* (see Hatch & Slack 1966, 1968; Hatch, Slack & Johnson 1967; Downton & Tregunna 1968; Johnson & Hatch 1968; Downton, Berry & Tregunna 1969; Osmond 1970).

to operate, shows that photosynthesis in its broader conception may be considered as a tripartite reaction: the dehydrogenation of water with the evolution of oxygen, the transfer of electrons or H-atoms from water to $NADP^+$, and the reduction of CO_2 by the reduced NADP to form a carbohydrate with the aid of energy of ATP formed in the electron transfer chains. All these reactions proceed in a stoichiometric ratio: the only possible exception is ATP formation in cyclic phosphorylation which may take place in plants with closed stomata, without gas exchange, as a result of the activity of photosystem I only[1].

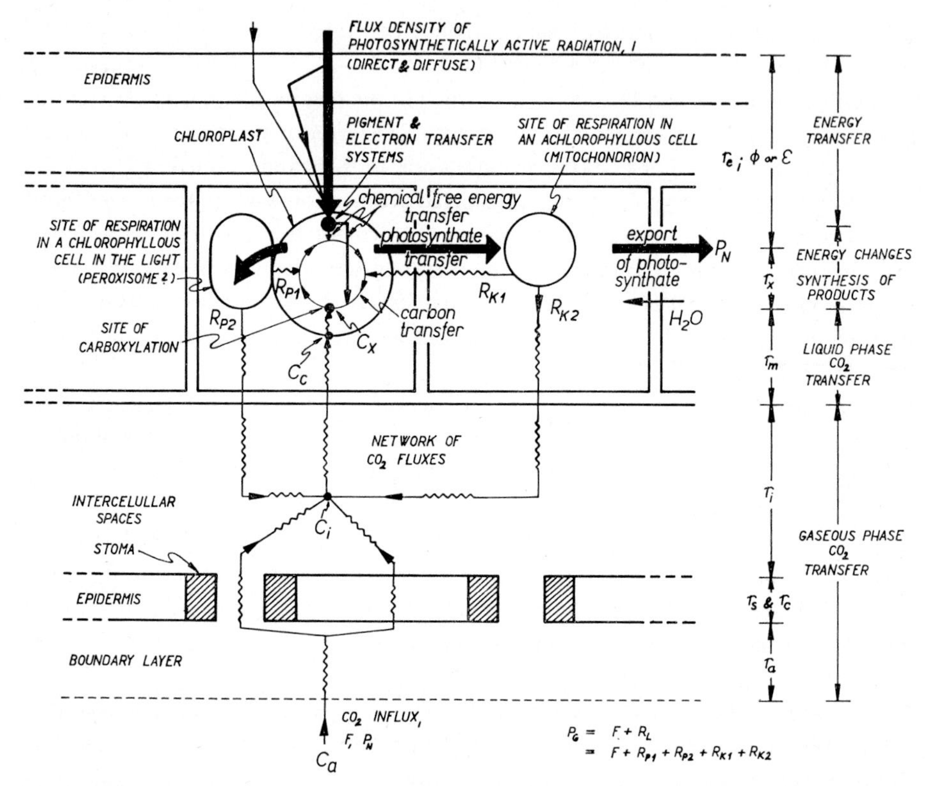

Fig. 1.2 Scheme of mass and energy transfers in photosynthesis and related processes illustrating the symbols recommended in Table 1.3 (consult also Chapter 16).

1. More detailed information concerning the development of views on photosynthesis is concentrated in the three volumes of the well-known monograph by Rabinowitch (1945, 1951, 1955) and in Vol. V/1 and V/2 of the 'Encyclopedia of Plant Physiology' edited by Ruhland (1960). The present state of knowledge of the biochemistry and biophysics of photosynthesis is summarized in the books by Kamen (1963), Clayton (1965) and Rabinowitch & Govindjee (1969) as well as in the proceedings of the recent conferences and symposia edited by Thomas & Goedheer (1966), Goodwin (1966, 1967), San Pietro, Greer & Army (1967), Sironval (1967), Shibata *et al.* (1968) and Metzner (1969) and 'Energy Conversion by the Photosynthetic Apparatus' (1967). Photosynthesis is discussed from the physiological point of view by Heath (1969) and from the point of view of crop productivity in the proceedings 'Prediction and Measurement of Photosynthetic Productivity' (1970). Review papers devoted to different fields of photosynthesis are regularly announced in the bibliography sections of the journals 'Photosynthetica' and 'Photochemistry and Photobiology'.

A narrow definition of photosynthesis might be restricted to include only the fundamental photochemical events. However, as seen above, the most convenient parameters to measure and those most widely used in practice are associated with related processes set in train as a result of the photochemical reactions. Photosynthesis in broader terms may therefore be considered as consisting of a number of closely interconnected, mutually dependent, partial processes. These include the absorption and transfer of radiant energy of appropriate wavelength, the transfer of CO_2 to the chloroplasts and of O_2 in the reverse direction, the interrelated transfers of O_2 and CO_2 consumed and evolved simultaneously in photosynthesis and in respiration in the light, the carboxylation of CO_2, the reduction and interconversion of the resulting carbon compounds and the export of the products of photosynthesis from the leaf. A scheme of photosynthesis embracing such a broad definition is shown in Fig. 1.2.

1.2 | Types of methods of photosynthetic rate determination in higher plants

The stoichiometry of the various processes shown in Section 1.1 which together represent photosynthesis in the broader sense enables one to choose from about nine possibilities when looking for an appropriate method of determining photosynthetic rate in the organs of higher green plants[1]. Some of them may be deduced from the classic summary equation of photosynthesis:

$$CO_2 + 2H_2O + 472.8\ \text{kJ}\ (112.3\ \text{kcal}) \rightarrow [CH_2O] + O_2 + H_2O$$

taking into account the initial and final components and the energetic changes in the system.

The nine possible ways of measuring photosynthesis will now be discussed:

1. The change in energy. The most exact criterion of photosynthetic rate is the direct determination of energetic changes in the intact closed photosynthesizing system. This is the only procedure for the absolute evaluation of photosynthetic efficiency and the yield of energy transformation. It requires an exact knowledge of the amount of radiant energy absorbed by the photosynthesizing system, the portion converted to sensible heat (and appearing as a change in temperature of the system), and the amount reradiated or dissipated as latent heat of vaporization of water.

1. Surprisingly there is no previous book written in English, German or French which is devoted exclusively to *methods* of photosynthesis research. In the Russian literature the booklet written by Nichiporovich *et al.* (1961) describes methods of studying plant stands; the book by Semikhatova & Chulanovskaya (1965) is devoted to manometric methods for the determination of respiration and photosynthesis; and the book of Voznesenskiĭ, Zalenskiĭ & Semikhatova (1965) reviews various methods for determining photosynthesis and respiration. The ancestor of the present manual is a Czech manual edited by Šesták & Čatský (1966), similar in style to the present book but much more limited in its scope. Papers describing new methods for the determination of photosynthesis are regularly listed in the bibliography section of the journal 'Photosynthetica'.

Measurements of this type are very difficult and hence are made only rarely and in extremely exact laboratory experiments. They require special, very sensitive calorimeters. For example, the calorimeter used by Arnold (1949) was made up of a tiny silver cup containing a leaf disc or algal suspension. The cup was supported by a number of fine wire thermocouples the other ends of which were connected to a copper ring in thermal contact with an aluminium block so that the system was totally enclosed. Photosynthetically active radiation fell onto the assimilating tissue or suspension through a quartz window. Temperature differences between the cup and the block were annulled by passing a measured current through the thermocouples and thus heating or cooling the cup. The temperature changes thus measured with the aid of the Peltier effect indicated exactly the energetic changes in the whole system and in the irradiated plant material.

2. The consumption of water. It is very difficult to determine the consumption of water in the photosynthetic process. To do this would require the use of deuterated or tritiated water, the physiological behaviour of which is different from that of normal water. This is the main reason why water uptake has not been used to measure the rate of photosynthesis.

3. Oxygen efflux. The amount of oxygen produced reflects the rate at which water is split in photosynthesis and hence the activity of photosystem II and of the whole process. The stoichiometry of photosynthesis requires that the net amount of oxygen produced is equivalent to the net amount of carbon dioxide taken up, fixed and reduced. The photosynthetic quotient, *i.e.* $+O_2/-CO_2$, is generally equal to 1. Hence preference for the determination of O_2 or of CO_2 is largely governed by technical considerations, and by the type of plant studied.

Oxygen determination is most common with submerged plants. The solubility of oxygen in water is very low (see Table 1.5), and oxygen determination is not complicated by different equilibrium states accompanying dissolution as is the case with CO_2 dissolved in water or solution (see Table 16.1 and *cf.* Section 4.3.1). In land plants O_2 production is determined less often, largely because of the high concentration of oxygen in air (20.99 vol. %). As a consequence very sensitive methods are required to determine the small changes in oxygen concentration, relative to that in air, which result from photosynthesis. On the other hand, equivalent absolute variation in carbon dioxide content (normal concentration in air is *ca.* 0.03 %) represents a big change in CO_2 concentration relative to that of air. For example, consumption of 0.003 % CO_2 represents a 10.0 % reduction in its concentration, while the equivalent rise in O_2 content is only an increase of 0.014 3 % relative to the normal amount in air.

The oxygen production of land plants has usually been determined by methods restricted to the use of small isolated leaves or pieces of tissue (frequently immersed in or floating on water or buffer). More recently paramagnetic, thermal conductivity and zirconium oxide oxygen analysers with adequate resolution and useful with intact leaves and plants have become available. Various physical, physicochemical and chemical methods of O_2 determination are reviewed in Table 1.1 and also by Lund & Talling (1957), Egle (1960) and Simonis (1960).

4. Influx of carbon dioxide. Carbon dioxide influx is a measure of photosynthetic rate, on a molecular basis equal to or similar to the efflux of O_2. For the reasons given in paragraph *3* the measurement of carbon dioxide influx is the method most frequently used with higher plants (see Table 1.2). The most frequently used instrument for the determination of CO_2 exchange by intact plants – the infra-red gas analyser – is adequately exact and generally available.

5. Dry matter accumulation. Dry matter accumulation and increase in the assimilatory surface of a plant community are the basis of methods used to determine the production of the entire stand in the natural environment. Using the procedures of growth analysis these methods yield estimates of net assimilation rate from the relations between photosynthate accumulation and growth of the plant. Net assimilation rate provides an integrated estimate of the net photosynthetic and respiratory activity of the whole plant over a minimum period of several days. It is therefore a simple measure of the integrated response of a large number of processes which differ in their individual response to the varying environment.

6. Accumulation of products. The amount of photosynthate produced is a measure of photosynthesis similar in some respects to the amount of CO_2 absorbed. However the quantity of products formed (or energy fixed) is not uniquely related to the amount of carbon dioxide bound but varies according to the chemical composition and energy content of the products. For example, one g CO_2 may be transformed into *ca.* 0.4 g fat with an energy content of 37.7 kJ g^{-1} (9 kcal g^{-1}) and a final energetic yield of *ca.* 15.1 kJ g^{-1} (3.6 kcal g^{-1}) CO_2. Alternatively one g CO_2 may be transformed into 0.62 g starch with an energy content of 17.6 kJ g^{-1} (4.2 kcal g^{-1}) and an energetic yield of 10.9 kJ g^{-1} (2.6 kcal g^{-1}) CO_2. Proteins are intermediate: one g CO_2 produces 0.5 g protein with an energetic yield of 12.6 kJ g^{-1} (3.0 kcal g^{-1}) CO_2. Thus diverse amounts of photosynthates as well as energy fixed result from the assimilation of the same amount of CO_2. Unfortunately, measurement of changes in the quantities of individual products of photosynthesis is not yet a common procedure.

The increase in total photosynthates in a leaf or sample of isolated tissue (*e.g.* discs or segments) may be directly measured with $^{14}CO_2$ techniques, preferably by using procedures which include the simultaneous determination of changes in radioactivity in the tissue and atmosphere. Data obtained from measurement of ^{14}C accumulated in the tissue alone are usually not sufficiently reliable because of the reassimilation of CO_2 produced in photorespiration from newly formed or old photosynthates (*e.g.* Goldsworthy 1966).

Alternatively, the amount of photosynthate produced can be determined from the increase in dry weight or in specific products of photosynthesis in a sample of tissue carrying on photosynthesis over a period of hours. Samples of the tissue are taken at the beginning and at the end of the period for analysis. Their difference is then taken as a measure of photosynthesis.

7. Accumulation of energy. The accumulation of energy in the tissue may be determined as the increase in the heat of combustion resulting from the production of organic matter in photosynthesis. Comparability of results obtained by this procedure and their conversion to gas exchange data is limited because of the different energy contents of leaves of various plant species, *e.g.* 16.0 kJ g^{-1} (3.82 kcal g^{-1}) dry weight in *Helianthus annuus* and *ca.* 19.5 kJ g^{-1} (4.65 kcal g^{-1}) in *Lespedeza* species. Because of this, the determination of energy content is more relevant than the determination of dry matter although in practice the errors in the determination of dry matter changes may outweigh the difference.

Table 1.1 Review of selected methods of continuous oxygen measurement applicable to photosynthet

Type of methods	Characteristics		Recording possibility	Range of permissible O_2 partial pressures	Sensitivity Δp_{O_2}	Sensitivity $\Delta mol\ O_2$ s
Physical methods	Warburg manometry		Yes		10^{-4}	10^{-10}
	Cartesian diver		No		3×10^{-6}	10^{-17}
	Recording volumetry		Yes	10^{-4} to 1	10^{-4}	$5\times10^{-}$
	Microrespirometry		No	5×10^{-6} to 1	5×10^{-6}	10^{-13}
	Thermal conductivity		Yes	10^{-6} to 1	10^{-6}	
	Mass spectrometer		Yes	10^{-7} to 1	2×10^{-8}	$3\times10^{-}$
	Quenching of phosphorescence of trypaflavin adsorbed to silica gel		Yes	10^{-9} to 10^{-6}	10^{-9}	$3\times10^{-}$
	Paramagnetic analyser		Yes	2×10^{-2} to 5×10^{-1}	10^{-5}	
Physico-chemical methods	O_2 cathode (Pt or Au, usually with Ag/AgCl or Ag/Ag_2O anode)	Clark type	Yes	10^{-5} to 1	10^{-5}	$3\times10^{-}$
		Joliot type	Yes	10^{-6} to 1	10^{-6}	10^{-16}
	Galvanic cell	Pt cathode, Fe or Pb anode	Yes	10^{-5} to 1	10^{-5}	
		Ag cathode, Pb anode	Yes	10^{-6} to $10^{-4}(10^{-1})$	10^{-7}	10^{-10}
	O_2 voltaic with calcium stabilized zirconium oxide ceramic cell		Yes	2×10^{-7} to 2×10^{-3}	2×10^{-7}	
	Spectrophotometry after conversion to O_3		Yes	10^{-4} to 1	10^{-4}	
Chemical methods	Haemoglobin – oxyhaemoglobin		Yes	10^{-3} to 4×10^{-2}	10^{-3}	$8\times10^{-}$
	Luminous bacteria (*e.g. Photobacterium fischeri*)		Yes	10^{-7} to 10^{-4}	10^{-7}	
	Luminometer with luminol solution		Yes	10^{-8} to 1	10^{-8}	$5\times10^{-}$

* Half response time = response constant

stems. (Compiled using some data of Burr & Mauzerall 1968.)

nction of O_2 ncentration	Usual half (full) response time*	Usual air-flow rate [cm^3 min^{-1}]	Appropriate for land higher plants	References
near, tegrative	1 min	0	Exceptionally	Chapter 5
near, tegrative	5 min	0	No	Lövlie & Farfaglio (1965)
near, tegrative	1 min	0	No	Kok (1955)
near, tegrative	1 min	0	Yes (leaf discs)	Chapter 6
near	(20 s)	10 to 40	Yes	Section 3.15
near	< 5 s	up to 1 500	Yes	Hoch & Kok (1963); Volk & Jackson (1964)
on-linear	20 s (2 min)	10 to 50	Yes	Pollack, Pringsheim & Terwood (1944); Allen (1955)
near	(15 s)	200 to 450	Yes	Section 3.14.1
near	(→ 0.1 s)	0	No	Clark *et al.* (1953); Carritt & Kanwisher (1959); Carey & Teal (1965); Robinson & Stocking (1968)
		450	Exceptionally with leaf discs	Vidaver (1964); Sahlström (1967); Heytler (1969)
near	5×10^{-3} s	0	No	Joliot (1967); Joliot & Joliot (1968)
near	(*ca.* 1 s)		Not yet used	Tödt *et al.* (1952); Tödt, Damaschke & Rothbühr (1954)
turates near up to 10^{-4})	4 min	80 to 100	Not yet used	Hersch (1952, 1960); Whittingham (1956)
garithmic	(1 ms; cell only)	700 to 1 000	Yes	Section 3.14.2
near	< 1 s	150	Yes	Kaye & Koency (1969)
turates, tegrative	5 s	0	No	Whittingham (1954)
turates, tegrative			Yes	Hastings (1952); Schindler (1964)
near	1 min (3 min)	10	Yes	Burr & Mauzerall (1968)

Table 1.2 Review of methods for determining CO_2 concentration in air (modified from Čatský 197
construction of the analyser.

Type of methods	Change in the air passing through	Characteristics		Re-cording	Conti-nuous analysis	Full scale ran of CO_2 conce trations corr sponding to t maximum se sitivity[1] [$\mu l\ l^{-1}$]
Chemical methods	Absorption of CO_2	Absorption in dry absorbent		No	No	0–1 500
		Gas chromatography with katharometer		Yes	No	*ca.* 1 000
	Absorption of CO_2, saturation with H_2O	Absorption + titration	Classical	No	No	0–500 (1 000)
			Spectrophoto-metric titration	No	No	1–<50 [5] up to 1–10
		Absorption + conductimetry	Classical	No	No	0–500
			Continuous	Yes	Yes	0–50 [8]
Physico-chemical methods	No change in CO_2, saturation with H_2O	pH-metry	Potentiometry	Yes[9]	Yes	100–800
			Photocolorimetry	Yes[9]	Yes	100–800
			Visual colorimetry	No	Yes	100–800
		Conductimetry	H_2O	Yes	Yes	
Physical methods	No change	Optical interferometer		No	No	*ca.* 1%
		Thermal conductivity (katharometer)	Pt or Wo wire	Yes	Yes	0–50
			Thermistor	Yes	Yes	(0–1 000)
		Infra-red analysis	Detector chambers in parallel	Yes	Yes	0–20 dif.[13]
			Detector chambers in series	Yes	Yes	0–50 dif.
		Mass spectrometer		Yes	Yes	0–2

1. To increase the sensitivity the zero can be offset by means of a counter-current (*e.g.* thermal conductivity, IRGA), by differential measurement (*e.g.* IRGA), or in another manner (*e.g.* by changing the colour indicator when using the colorimetric procedures). The values in this column give the size of scale usually used.
2. The systematic error due to calibration is not taken into account. The errors of calibration can introduce a considerable error to both absolute and differential values (*cf.* Section 3.10.1).
3. Maximum sensitivity of 10 $\mu l\ l^{-1}$ was attained by Carpenter, Fox & Sereque (1929).
4. In ± % of the value found.
5. This method has not been developed for plant research.
6. In a sample of 20 l.
7. For differential measurement using two analysers see Stocker & Vieweg (1960).
8. The normality of NaOH solution used (*Microgas, Wösthoff*) is sufficient only for CO_2 concentrations up to 5 ml l^{-1}. For higher concentrations, the gas to be

nly average performances are presented which can be improved using a very special procedure or

aximum ensitivity[2]	Discrimination[2] [% of the full scale range]	Function of CO_2 concentration (in the range given above)	Differential measurement	Usual response time (or time for one determination)	Usual air-flow rate [ml min^{-1}]	Reference (if data for a particular apparatus are presented) or Section in this Manual
0 $\mu l\ l^{-1}$	—	Integrative, colour scale	No	3 min	Sample 300 ml	Bowman (1968)
0 $\mu l\ l^{-1}$	—	Integrative	No	120 s	Sample 1 ml	Bowman (1968)
.01 mg [3]	2–7 [4]	Linear integrative	No	5–15 min	100–500	Bowman (1968)
$\mu l\ l^{-1}$ [6]	2–7 [4]	Linear integrative	No	2–4 h	up to 100	Loveland *et al.* (1959)
.01 mg	2–4 [4]	Linear integrative	No[7]	2–10 min	100–500	(Section 4.4.2)
.5 $\mu l\ l^{-1}$	1	Linear	No	30–120 s	35– 75	'*Microgas*' *Wösthoff* (Section 4.4.3)
–5 $\mu l\ l^{-1}$	2–5 [4]	Logarithmic	No[10]	5–10 min	100–500	
a. 5 $\mu l\ l^{-1}$	3–5 [4]	Logarithmic	No[11]	5–10 min	100–500	
a. 10 $\mu l\ l^{-1}$	4–7 [4]	Logarithmic	No	5–10 min	100–500	(Section 4.3.3)
< 1 $\mu l\ l^{-1}$	—	Linear to 600 $\mu l\ l^{-1}$	No[10]	20 s	500	Begg & Lake (1968) (Section 4.2)
0 $\mu l\ l^{-1}$	—	Linear	No	30 s	Sample 100 ml	Bowman (1968)
.5 $\mu l\ l^{-1}$ [12]	*ca.* 1	Linear to 5%	No[10]	*ca.* 20 s	10–40	(Section 3.15)
		Linear to 5%	No[10]	8–12 s	80	Semenenko (1958)
< 0.5 $\mu l\ l^{-1}$ [13]	*ca.* 1	Quasilinear[14]	Yes	10–60 s	500–1 000	(Section 3.4.1)
a. 0.5 $\mu l\ l^{-1}$	*ca.* 2	Quasilinear[14]	Yes	10–120 s	500–1 000	(Section 3.4.2)
.02 $\mu l\ l^{-1}$	1	Linear	No	15 s	up to 1 500	Volk & Jackson (1964)

analysed should be mixed with CO_2 free gas using a mixing pump.
9. Maximum sensitivity is reached, however, when compensation procedures are used. In such an arrangement, recording is difficult.
10. The principle of the method would allow construction of a circuit for differential measurement.
11. For differential measurement using two analysing units see Gulyaev (1965).
12. 2.5×10^{-11} mol CO_2 ml^{-1}.
13. More sensitive infra-red gas analysers with absorption tubes $\gg$ 30 cm are made by a number of manufacturers on request. Tranquillini (1964) obtained a *Super-URAS* from *Hartmann & Braun* with a maximum sensitivity of 0.01 $\mu l\ l^{-1}$, for work at very low CO_2 differentials (but *cf.* Chapters 2 and 3 for discussion pertaining to its general usefulness in photosynthesis research).
14. Depends on the construction used.

8. Rate of formation of energy rich intermediates. The determination of simultaneous changes in the ATP and $NADPH_2$ contents of assimilating tissues is not practical because of the small concentrations of these substances present and their participation in metabolic processes other than photosynthesis. Such changes are more often measured in experiments with isolated chloroplasts or algae than with whole plant tissues or leaves.

9. Properties of the photochemical apparatus. Changes induced by photosynthesis in the optical properties of the photosynthetic apparatus, mainly those of absorption, reflection and fluorescence, measured at wavelengths of the maximum spectral difference for oxidized and reduced forms of the photosynthetic pigments and substances in the electron transfer chain (P 700, cytochromes, plastocyanin, plastoquinone, ferredoxin, *etc.*) are extremely small and transient and hence can be measured only with complicated apparatus and very often with specially pretreated plant material (isolated cell layers, solvent treatment, *etc.*).

From the survey of possibilities given above it can be concluded that only methods *3* to *7* are suitable for routine measurement of photosynthesis in higher plants. The methods discussed in *3* and *4* are usually called gasometric. These, the most frequently used methods, analyse changes in the atmosphere surrounding the assimilating crop, plant, leaf or other organ (inflorescence, fruit, stem), or sample of assimilating tissue, and caused by its presence. Using gasometric methods as described in Chapters 2 to 4, the characteristics and properties of the experimental material are not necessarily changed by the measurement (although they may be if the period of measurement is long or the conditions extreme), which may be repeated at intervals throughout the growing season. Modern gasometric methods, *e.g.* those using infra-red analysers (Chapter 3) give very exact estimates of photosynthetic rate. Their main disadvantage is that photosynthesis of only a small amount of material can be measured at any one time because of the cost and complexity of the apparatus. Gasometric methods also include the methods of determining photosynthesis in undisturbed, intact stands in the field, by the aerodynamic or energy balance methods (Chapter 13). In some special variants of the gasometric methods such as manometric (Chapter 5) and volumetric (Chapter 6) methods, the material is usually enclosed in a small volume. This limits the use of these methods with higher plants to very small plants *(Lemnaceae)* or to detached organs or their parts (*e.g.* leaf discs or segments). In more elaborate gasometric methods changes in the isotopic composition of the air passing over or through the photosynthesizing tissue, especially with regard to differences in the relative proportions of carbon and oxygen isotopes (Chapters 7 and 8) are measured in addition to the changes in total CO_2 and oxygen concentration. Because of the accumulation of labelled assimilates in the tissue and their possible consumption in respiratory processes at a later date, ^{14}C methods are not suitable for exact repetitive measurements on the same material.

Simultaneous measurements on a large amount of tissue or number of treatments are possible (and necessary because of considerable variability in the results) with methods mentioned in *5* to *7*. These methods mostly do not need expensive apparatus, but are laborious and time consuming. They are very useful for measurements in large plant stands, where it is possible to sample and destroy some of the

plants and repeat the sampling throughout the whole of the growing season. Method *5* uses the simplest procedures and gives an integrated estimate of the net photosynthesis of the whole plant over periods of days or weeks (Chapter 10). Methods *6* and *7* use isolated, representative samples of assimilatory tissue which may be irradiated in a controlled or natural environment for periods of a few hours. Mass analyses (mostly dry weight increment determinations) are characteristic of method *6* (Chapter 9) while the analysis for energy content, method *7*, is more time-consuming and requires sensitive calorimeters. For this reason it is not used routinely in plant production studies and is not included in this manual. A summary of calorimetric procedures is given by Lieth (1968).
Methods described in *6* and *7* always require a large amount of material which is destroyed in the process of analysis. Thus they are not well suited for the determination of the time course of photosynthesis.

Because each method determines a different parameter of the overall complex photosynthetic process, it is very valuable and desirable that more than one method should be used on the same plant material in any investigation, *e.g.* methods of growth analysis might be complemented with short-term measurements of CO_2 exchange (Muramoto, Hesketh & El-Sharkawy 1965); measurements in stands in the field by the aerodynamic or energy balance methods might be complemented with determination of the photosynthetic rate of individual leaves (Lemon 1967); results obtained as dry matter increment might be complemented with determination of changes in energy content of the tissues (Nátr 1968), *etc.* Such parallel measurements are, unfortunately, very rare in the literature and deserve more attention. For example, there is a shortage of parallel data of growth analysis, gasometrically determined photosynthetic rate of individual leaves in near natural environmental conditions, and photosynthetic capacity determined in controlled environment assimilation chambers in the laboratory, together with exact information about the environmental conditions and physiological and biochemical state of the plant. Such a complex of values would undoubtably represent a bigger contribution to the development of knowledge about plant production than any number of scattered observations on the rate of photosynthesis measured in 'natural' conditions, so abundant in the literature.
A combination of several methods is also of considerable advantage in studying basic physiological problems. Some measuring circuits include both an infra-red CO_2 gas analyser, and/or a device for ^{14}C determination together with an oxygen analyser (*cf.* Sections 3.14, 3.15). In submerged plants CO_2 exchanges may be determined potentiometrically and O_2 content polarographically (Kok & Spruit 1956; Spruit & Kok 1956). Parallel measurement of both gases is also possible with mass spectrometry (see Brown, Nier & van Norman 1952; Volk & Jackson 1964). Carbon dioxide influx and dry matter increment in the same leaf segments may be measured in the chamber of Nátr & Gloser (1967).

1.3 | Choice of method

The principal methods available and their main advantages and disadvantages have been outlined in Section 1.2. The choice of the most appropriate method is

largely governed by the following three criteria:
1. the aim of the study,
2. the availability of equipment,
3. how laborious the method is and the man-power requirement.

1.3.1 | The aim of the study

In choosing a method a number of interrelated aims of the research must be taken into account:
a. the problem to be studied and the plant material used;
b. the required sensitivity, accuracy and response time of the measurements;
c. whether instantaneous photosynthesis or integrated photosynthesis is to be measured;
d. whether photosynthetic rate is to be measured under natural or controlled environmental conditions and at what level it is desired to achieve a mechanistic interpretation of the phenomena observed.

These four points will be considered in turn:

a. The appropriate method is usually suggested by the problem being studied. Thus, many ecological problems demand methods which can be used in the field with portable apparatus and without mains electricity. On the other hand, genetic problems require methods capable of supplying numerous data suitable for statistical analysis, whereas studies of basic physiological problems require extremely exact methods. Some problems (*e.g.* the influence of environmental factors on photosynthetic rate) require the study of the same plant material over an extended period and thus a non-destructive method is desirable. Investigation of interrelations between photosynthesis and the properties of the photochemical and enzymatic apparatus requires the destruction of the material after the measurement of photosynthesis or analysis of similar pieces of the tissue.
If there is a choice of material, plant species or varieties with broad, flat and smooth-surfaced leaves are to be preferred, since it is then relatively easy to determine the irradiated and assimilating leaf area, to cut out numerous sets of leaf discs of a given area, to measure simultaneously two or more parts of the same leaf blade, *etc.*
In selecting plant material both genetic constitution and previous environmental history must be taken into account: both influence the current rate of photosynthesis. Studies on different *genotypes and ecological or geographical races* show large differences in photosynthetic rates even when they are cultured under identical conditions (*e.g.* Björkman & Holmgren 1963; Milner & Hiesey 1964a, b; Elmore, Hesketh & Muramoto 1967; Fousová & Avratovščuková 1967; Irvine 1967; Mousseau 1967, 1968; Avratovščuková 1968; Cukrová & Avratovščuková 1968; Duncan & Hesketh 1968; Apel & Lehmann 1969, *etc.*). *Previous environmental history* influences the development of the photosynthetic organs and apparatus, thereby affecting their photosynthetic activity. Furthermore, the environmental conditions of the preceding hours and days may also have a large effect upon current photosynthetic rates (*e.g.* Björkman & Holmgren 1963; Mooney & Har-

rison 1970). *The age* of the plant material and its position on the plant may also strongly influence photosynthesis and must be taken into account especially in comparative studies and in collecting data for use in models (*e.g.* Hopkinson 1964; Jewiss & Woledge 1967; Šesták & Čatský 1967; Hardwick, Wood & Woolhouse 1968; Pearce, Brown & Blaser 1968; Wada 1968).

b. The sensitivity, accuracy and response times of various methods are usually given by their inventors or by the manufacturers of the equipment. Examples of these parameters for methods of O_2 and CO_2 determination may be found in Tables 1.1 and 1.2, respectively, and are discussed in more detail in the appropriate chapters (see Chapters 3 to 7). The magnitude of these parameters is naturally influenced also by the size (volume) of the whole measuring circuit. In addition, in biological measurements the parameters of the methods must be evaluated in conjunction with the properties of the experimental material.

c. The most commonly used gasometric methods measure the *instantaneous* rate of photosynthesis from changes in the concentration of gases in the air passing over or through the leaf which is usually enclosed in a chamber. These are the only methods which can be used in studies of transient or instantaneous reactions to changes in irradiance, detachment of the leaf, *etc.* To avoid any effects of injury to the plant material, or cumulative effects of enclosure in the chamber, the measurements should be made as rapidly as possible. This usually means that measurements are made as soon as 'steady state photosynthesis' is reached, *i.e.* with 10–30 min measuring periods in favourable cases but with periods of an hour or more when the response is slow.
Integrating methods sum changes in the atmosphere surrounding the photosynthetic material or in the material itself over short periods (min) in the manometric, volumetric and CO_2 absorption methods, or long periods (hours, days or weeks) in the dry matter accumulation and growth analysis methods. The length of the period of integration depends on the following: the accuracy required; the photosynthetic rate determining the smallest measurable change; the period over which the plant retains physiological uniformity within prescribed limits; and the period over which the environmental conditions retain sufficient uniformity for the purpose of the experiment.

d. Interpretation of measurements of photosynthesis at the physiological or production ecology level requires different kinds of methods and a different approach to the measurements than does interpretation at the level of fundamental biophysical or electron transfer processes. The methods described in this manual are largely concerned with measurements at the physiological level of investigation. None the less there is a wide range of sophistication and complexity within the range of methods discussed, and in general the more complex and demanding methods provide more detailed and precise information on which to base an interpretation of the activity and behaviour of the photosynthetic process.
Experiments in controlled environments may be done either in conditions simulating the natural ones or with the majority of environmental conditions as near optimum as possible and with programmed changes (usually step functions) in

selected variables.

Measurements in natural conditions in the field, or in simulated natural conditions in the laboratory, provide information on the *rate* of photosynthesis attainable in a range of ecologically relevant but restricted conditions which occur in the field. The advantages of determining the rate of photosynthesis in simulated field conditions in the laboratory rather than in the field are: *1.* Rooting conditions can be isolated and defined and hence some separation achieved between the influence of the edaphic and aerial environment on photosynthesis. *2.* The influence of the previous environmental history on the current rate of photosynthesis can be controlled and investigated. *3.* In a short space of time a wide range of combinations of conditions can be simulated and investigated, whereas it might take months to achieve the more extreme sets of conditions in the field. However, a danger is that the cultivated plants are or soon become so unlike the plants in the field that the information obtained is no longer of ecological relevance. Furthermore, conditions naturally limiting photosynthesis in the field may inadvertently be avoided in the laboratory.

A recent surge of interest in measurements in natural conditions is focused on the evaluation of the photosynthesis and productivity of whole plant communities. When using methods of growth analysis for this purpose some information about the total response of the plant to average weather conditions over a period is provided, thus assisting in the interpretation of the environmental factors determining the final yield. However, a mechanistic interpretation of the influence of the environment on physiological processes is not obtained because of the wide fluctuations in weather and the diurnal variations in conditions which occur between harvests. Over a period of several days variations in weather tend to be correlated one with another so that the separate influence of weather elements on the plants cannot be determined. Furthermore, problems arise as to what weather elements to select and which quantitative aspects (*e.g.* daily mean, maximum or minimum temperature) to use in attempting to interpret plant response.

To establish correlations between plant response and weather elements useful in interpreting behaviour of the plant at the physiological level, it is necessary to measure the response of the plant with a frequency and periodicity related to the naturally occurring changes in the weather, *i.e.* over periods of the order of minutes or less. Only in this way can the influence on photosynthesis of closely related weather elements such as temperature and radiation be separated by examination of plant response to strictly natural conditions. This is one reason why modern computer-evaluated energy balance and aerodynamic methods have recently achieved prominance.

The *rate* of photosynthesis itself is a characteristic of dubious value (Jarvis 1970). The majority of laboratory studies of photosynthesis are not concerned with the measurement of rate of photosynthesis in relation to natural conditions but aim at determining characteristics of the photosynthetic apparatus and elucidating the rates of the various partial processes.

Determination of characteristics of photosynthesis such as the photosynthetic capacity, the efficiency of the photochemical partial process, the total effective resistance to CO_2 transfer, the light and CO_2 compensation points, the temperature coefficient (and that of dark and light respiration) requires the measurement of the response of photosynthesis (and in some cases respiration) to wide ranges of radiation, temperature, ambient CO_2 and O_2 concentration. Furthermore if these characteristics are to be used to relate the plant to its environment, they must be determined on material which has been cultivated in a range of environmental conditions.

The normal procedure used in obtaining such response curves is to vary one environmental factor at a time in a series of step functions making precise observations of the environment and plant performance as each 'steady state' is attained. However, in many cases, especially when the environmental conditions are extreme in relation to the cultivation conditions, a 'steady state' is never reached (see Fig. 9.2). The maximum value attained after equilibration of the plant and measuring system with the new environmental conditions is often followed by a slow decline in the rate of photosynthesis or by oscillations, accompanied by changing stomatal aperture, which may take several hours to die away. Another problem is the influence of the previous treatments; *e.g.* even short exposures of only a few minutes to high or low temperatures have a large effect on the photosynthetic capacity.

1.3.2 | Availability of equipment

Only a few methods of studying photosynthesis, such as growth analysis procedures, require no complex equipment. The equipment for measuring a biological process usually has two functions:

a. Measurement of physical or chemical changes that characterise the process and serve as a basis for assessing its kinetic parameters.

b. Enclosure of the experimental material during the measurement in an environment that keeps the external conditions constant or their changes definable. This requires equipment to control the properties of the air entering the chamber and prevent its variation in the chamber, and equipment to measure and to maintain constant properties of the experimental material. Alternatively, less control may be exercised and all changes in the atmosphere and the object recorded with precise sensors. However the latter alternative is less satisfactory as the variations which might occur could confound the experiment; *e.g.* changes in leaf temperature with changing irradiance. All these requirements induce serious problems discussed in detail in Chapter 2.

In general, there is insufficient commercial production of apparatus suitable for measuring photosynthesis. Many devices used in photosynthesis research are multi-purpose ones. Hence the selection of a type fulfilling the exact requirements of a certain problem is usually necessary. Proved items of equipment, their suitability and performance, together with the names of the manufacturers, are given in the separate chapters of this Manual. There are certainly other makes of appropriate devices in existence: description of any particular item does not imply advertisement, but recommendation based upon good experience of it by the authors.

Equipment, chambers and tools often have to be produced individually in institute workshops. As much information as possible is given to facilitate this: where this information is not sufficient more detailed information may often be obtained from the authors.

In practice the availability of the equipment and its price, and the tediousness of the method must often be taken into account. If the choice of a method is limited for these reasons, the reliability and precision of the information obtained, as well as the possibilities of interpretation of the results, may also be limited.

1.3.3 | Laboriousness of methods

Some methods produce a small number of exact data (*e.g.* gas exchange systems with infra-red gas analysers), while with other methods a large number of less exact measurements can be made in the same period. However, the possible simplicity and rapidity of some simple methods does not justify their use even in 'natural' ecological or production studies. An example of such an out of date but still occasionally used method is that of Ivanov & Kossovich (1946) in which a leaf is enclosed in an Erlenmayer flask. After 5 to 15 min of irradiation the leaf is taken out, a solution of barium hydroxide is added to the flask to absorb CO_2 from the enclosed atmosphere and the surplus hydroxide is titrated with HCl. Such a method does not respect the basic requirements of controlling the environmental conditions in which the photosynthesis by the leaf occurs (see Chapter 2) and thus even very large amounts of data so obtained cannot form the basis of reliable research.

Laboriousness of the method is not necessarily a sign of its exactness or perfection; it is often caused by incomplete automatisation of the experimental equipment and might be easily remedied in better financial circumstances. Efficiency of a method for photosynthesis research might be measured by the number of results with an ensured standard error of less than $\pm$ 5%, measured by one person in a given period of time. Modern methods for studying crop production require either considerable manual labour (growth analysis, Chapter 10) or considerable equipment, and computer evaluation of the measured data (energy balance- and aerodynamic methods, Chapter 13).

1.3.4 | A simple key for choosing the method

We would not presume to give general directions about which methods should be used for particular kinds of research. Preliminary information may be obtained from the following key:

1. *a.* Measurements on intact plants or excised shoots or branches – 2.
   b. Measurements involving destruction of plant material – 7.
2. *a.* Measurements made repeatedly on the same material over long periods without the induction of experimental error – 3.
   b. Measurements suitable for single determinations only, *e.g.* $^{14}CO_2$ consumption from the air passing over the leaf – Section 7.4.
3. *a.* Measurements in the field or in other natural plant communities – 4.
   b. Measurements on potted plants or excised shoots or

branches, in the laboratory – 6.

4. *a.* Measurements on individual leaves or small groups of plants – 5.

   b. Measurements on a plant community as a whole – energy balance and aerodynamic methods (Chapter 13)
   and non-destructive growth analysis methods (Chapter 11).

5. *a.* Exact measurements – require rather expensive fixed or mobile field laboratories with infra-red gas analysers – (Section 3.13).

   b. Methods giving many but less exact data – cheaper portable (or mobile) equipment for conductimetric or colorimetric measurements of partial pressure of CO_2 – (Chapter 4).

6. *a.* Measurement of CO_2 exchanges between leaf and air in laboratory equipment
   using infra-red gas analysers (Chapter 3).
   or continuous conductimetric analysers (Section 4.2)

   b. Measurement of O_2 exchange between leaf and air
   using the paramagnetic oxygen analyser (Section 3.14.1)
   or zirconium oxide analyser (Section 3.14.2).

   c. Measurements of CO_2/O_2 ratio – katharometers (Section 3.15).

7. *a.* Determination of O_2 evolution from detached leaves or parts of leaves – 8.

   b. Determination of photosynthate production – 9.

8. *a.* Measurements on leaves or parts of leaves smaller than *ca.* 6 mm in diameter – microrespirometric method (Chapter 6).

   b. Measurements usually on larger leaves or parts of leaves – manometric methods (Chapter 5).

9. *a.* Determination of assimilate production from ^{14}C accumulation – (Section 7.3).

   b. Determination of dry matter increment – 10.

10. *a.* Determination of integrated changes in dry matter and leaf area of leaves and plants – methods of growth analysis (Chapter 10).

    b. Determination of dry matter accumulation in leaf discs or segments under constant conditions – (Chapter 9).

Individual methods are naturally very often modified, combined or improved and thus their character changed. For example, measurements on intact individual leaves in a plant community may be improved by enclosing the leaf into a chamber with partially controlled conditions, and by separate artificial irradiation of the enclosed leaf (see Chapter 2). Measurements of dry weight increase of leaf discs may be made after exposure to natural irradiation in the field instead of in a fully climatised chamber (Section 9.3.2).

1.4 | The expression of photosynthetic rate

1.4.1 | Net and gross photosynthesis

In terms of a net balance of gases, energy, carbohydrate or dry matter, the measurable rate of photosynthesis may be equal to, greater than or less than zero. When photosynthetic production and respiratory degradation are in balance, there is no net exchange of gases and no change in dry matter. The tissue is said to be at the *compensation point.* In the case of a leaf, carbon dioxide and oxygen continue to diffuse in both directions through the stomata but there is no *net* flux in either direction. In the case of more complex organs or with whole plants in which the sites of respiration and photosynthesis are more distantly separated the same situation may arise if the net efflux of a gas from one part balances the net influx into another. This state of equilibrium is reached as the result of a balance between certain environmental and internal factors and can be attained in several ways. In the classic interpretation, the compensation point is defined as a certain low irradiance at which net photosynthesis is equal to zero. This compensation point is now more explicitly called the light compensation point to distinguish it from other compensation points described in the literature such as the CO_2 compensation point (Heath 1951), the humidity compensation point (Butin 1954), the chlorophyll compensation point (Šesták 1964), *etc.*

All common methods of measuring photosynthesis estimate the values of '*net (or apparent) photosynthesis*', *i.e.* the net difference between the total production of photosynthates (or CO_2 consumption or O_2 evolution) and the simultaneous respiratory breakdown of products (or CO_2 production or O_2 consumption) for the tissue investigated.

In earlier experiments the rate of '*gross (true) photosynthesis*' was very often calculated by summing the rates of net photosynthesis and of respiration determined in darkness. Dark respiration can usually be measured with the same equipment as photosynthesis either by darkening the plant material before or after the determination of photosynthesis or by making simultaneous measurements on parallel samples in a dark chamber. The measurement procedure is usually simple, but the values thus obtained are representative only of respiration proceeding in darkness, the rate of which is quite different from respiration in light. Respiration from chlorophyll-containing cells in light, the so-called photorespiration, has been intensively studied in the last few years because of its extreme importance for plant metabolism. Methods for the determination of photorespiration are discussed in Chapter 8. It is now clear that estimates of gross assimilation rate calculated as the sum of net photosynthetic and dark respiration rates do not express the real full photosynthetic activity and are meaningless. At the moment it is not possible to estimate gross photosynthesis without making considerable, as yet unjustified assumptions about photorespiration (see Chapter 8).

1.4.2 | Recommended symbols and units

A wide variety of terms and symbols exists in the photosynthesis literature. Recently the terminology of primary production has been defined in IBP News

10 : 6 – 8, 1968, and Larcher (1969b) has defined some basic terms relating to measurement of photosynthesis. We would like to recommend symbols and units listed in Table 1.3 and Fig. 1.2. The recommended units are based on the Système International d'Unités (SI). Units based on their decimal fractions or multiples are permissible in practice, and are used in parts of this manual. Units of other systems should be converted using Table 1.4.

For interconversion of values of dry matter increase or gas exchange the data for a range of temperatures given in Tables 1.5 and 1.6 may be used. Composition of dry air is given in Table 1.7 and its properties in Table 1.8. Some properties of water and water vapour are given in Table 1.9. Some useful constants are listed in Table 1.10. A nomogram for a rapid comparison of photosynthetic and respiratory rates given in different dimensions is also provided (Fig. 1.3). Naturally only values based on the same unit of plant area or weight and measured under similar experimental conditions may be legitimately compared.

Conversion tables for radiant energy and irradiance may be found in Chapter 12 (Table 12.1). A nomogram for comparing irradiance and illuminance values is also provided (Fig. 19.3).

The general usefulness of data is greatly reduced if they are expressed as per cent of control or initial state. Such data should always be accompanied by absolute values.

1.4.3 | Bases for the expression of photosynthetic rate

The first result obtained in the measurement of photosynthetic or respiration rate is usually in the form of a flux of gas (*e.g.* in units of $cm^3\ s^{-1}$) or a change in amount of dry matter or photosynthate (*e.g.* in units of $g\ s^{-1}$) in the plant material present. To make the data obtained comparable with other work and to assist in its interpretation, it is usual to further modify such rates by expressing them on the basis of unit amount or dimension of plant material present, or some characteristic of the material present (*e.g.* in units of $cm^3\ cm^{-2}\ s^{-1}$, $g\ cm^{-2}\ s^{-1}$, $g\ g^{-1}\ s^{-1}$ *etc.*, see Section 3.12.2). Herein lies an unresolved problem. What is the most appropriate plant characteristic on which to base the quantitative expression of photosynthetic rate?

In the case of leaves and stems, the most frequently used unit is the surface area, although with leaves or leaf-like structures with all three dimensions of the same order, such as the linear leaves or needles of conifers, dry weight is often used for convenience. Fresh weight has also been used sometimes and other bases include number and volume of cells, chlorophyll *a* or ($a + b$), protein or nitrogen content, number of chloroplasts and size of the grana, and activity of the carboxylation enzymes. If the main criterion is to achieve comparability with other data in the literature then it is logical to accept the most widely used basis, which is surface area. However, more rational criteria for selection may be sought in specific investigations.

The rate of a process yields maximum information about the process itself if it is expressed on the basis of a plant characteristic which limits or at least strongly influences the process.

Thus if the irradiance is such that the amount of photochemically active radiation

Table 1.3 A list of recommended symbols and units. (For other lists of symbols see Sections 12.2.1, 13.7.1, 16.6 and 17.1.2.).

Process or Parameter	Symbol	Units: Basic	Units: Acceptable
Net photosynthetic rate*	P_N	$m^3\ m^{-2}\ s^{-1}$, $kg\ m^{-2}\ s^{-1}$	$cm^3\ cm^{-2}\ s^{-1}$, $mg\ dm^{-2}\ h^{-1}$
Gross photosynthetic rate	$P_G(P_T)$		
Dark respiration rate	R_D		
Total rate of respiration in light	R_L		
Rate of respiration in achlorophyllous cells in light or dark	R_K		
Photorespiration rate in chlorophyll containing cells in light	R_P		
Net volume flux of CO_2 (or O_2) exchange	$F(F_v)$	$m^3\ m^{-2}\ s^{-1}$	$cm^3\ cm^{-2}\ s^{-1}$
Net mass flux of CO_2 (or O_2) exchange	$F(F_m)$	$kg\ m^{-2}\ s^{-1}$	$mg\ cm^{-2}\ s^{-1}$, $mg\ dm^{-2}\ h^{-1}$
Leaf area	A	m^2	cm^2, dm^2
Total CO_2 transfer resistance	r_{CO_2}	$s\ m^{-1}$	$s\ cm^{-1}$
Total water vapour transfer resistance	r_{H_2O}		
Boundary layer diffusion resistance	r_a		
Stomatal diffusion resistance	r_s		
Cuticular diffusion resistance	r_c		
Intercellular space diffusion resistance	r_i		
Total equivalent mesophyll transfer resistance	r_M		
Mesophyll, or liquid phase, transfer resistance	r_m		
Excitation resistance	r_e		
Carboxylation resistance	r_x		
Ambient CO_2 concentration	C_a	$m^3\ m^{-3}$	$\mu l\ l^{-1}$, $cm^3\ m^{-3}$, v p m, vol. %
Average intercellular CO_2 concentration	C_i		
CO_2 concentration at chloroplast surface	C_c		
CO_2 concentration at sites of carboxylation	C_x		
CO_2 compensation concentration	Γ		
Irradiance	I	$J\ m^{-2}\ s^{-1}$	$W\ m^{-2}$, $mW\ cm^{-2}$
Illuminance	I	lx	—
Illuminance or irradiance at the light compensation point ($F = 0$)	I_0	$J\ m^{-2}\ s^{-1}$, lx	$W\ m^{-2}$, $mW\ cm^{-2}$
Photon flux**	I_P	—	$nEinstein\ cm^{-2}s^{-1}$
Efficiency of radiant energy conversion $\left(= \frac{\text{chemical energy of photosynthates formed}}{\text{radiant (PhAR) energy absorbed}}\right)$	ε	$J\ J^{-1}$, %	$kg\ J^{-1}$, $m^3\ J^{-1}$, (cal cal^{-1})
Quantum yield $\left(= \frac{\text{mol } CO_2 \text{ fixed or } O_2 \text{ evolved}}{\text{Einstein absorbed}}\right)$	Φ	dimensionless	$mol\ Einstein^{-1}$
Quantum requirement	Φ^{-1}	dimensionless	$Einstein\ mol^{-1}$

* This widely used term is rather general. Other terms relating to the process actually measured, *e.g.* F, are preferable.

** 1 Einstein = N_A quanta, where N_A is Avogadro's number (see Table 1.10).

Table 1.3 (contd.)

Process or Parameter	Symbol	Units	
		Basic	Acceptable
Transpiration or evaporation rate	E	$m^3\ m^{-2}\ s^{-1}$	$cm^3\ cm^{-2}\ s^{-1}$
		$kg\ m^{-2}\ s^{-1}$	$mg\ dm^{-2}\ h^{-1}$
Net mass flux of water vapour exchange	$Q(Q_m)$	$kg\ m^{-2}\ s^{-1}$	$mg\ cm^{-2}\ s^{-1}$
Ambient water vapour pressure	e_a	$N\ m^{-2}$, Pa	mb
Saturation water vapour pressure (at leaf temperature)	e_s	—	—
Ambient absolute humidity	χ_a	$kg\ m^{-3}$	—
Ambient specific humidity	q_a	$kg\ kg^{-1}$	—
Air temperature	T_a	K	°C
Leaf temperature	T_l	K	°C
Barometric pressure	P	$N\ m^{-2}$, Pa	b (bar)
Molecular diffusion coefficient	D	$m^2\ s^{-1}$	$cm^2\ s^{-1}$

Table 1.4 Some conversion factors for units not now permissable under Système International d'Unités (or SI). Conversions which are exact are in heavy type. (Adapted from Gray 1963, List 1963 and Socrates & Sapper 1969.)

Length, the metre, m
1 inch, in = **25.4** mm = **0.025 4** m
1 foot, ft = 12 in = **304.8** mm = **0.304 8** m
1 yard, yd = 36 in = **0.914 4** m
1 mile = 1 760 yd = 1.609 34 km
1 international nautical mile (n mile) = **1.852** km

Area, m^2
1 in^2 = **6.451 6** cm^2 = **6.451 6** $\times 10^{-4}$ m^2
1 ft^2 = **929.030 4** cm^2 = **9.290 304** $\times 10^{-2}$ m^2
1 yd^2 = **8 361.273 6** cm^2 = **0.836 127 36** m^2
1 acre = 4 046.86 m^2 = 0.404 686 ha

Volume, m^3 (in SI 1 litre, l, = **1** dm^3 = **10^{-3}** m^3 and 1.0 ml = **1** cm^3)
1 in^3 = 16.387 1 cm^3 = 1.638 71 $\times 10^{-5}$ m^3
1 ft^3 = 28.316 8 dm^3 (l) = 0.028 316 8 m^3
1 pint, pt = 0.568 261 dm^3 (l) = 5.682 61 $\times 10^{-4}$ m^3
1 quart, qt = 1.136 52 dm^3 (l) = 1.136 52 $\times 10^{-3}$ m^3
1 gallon (US), USgal = 3.785 41 dm^3 (l) = 3.785 41 $\times 10^{-3}$ m^3
1 gallon (UK), gal = 4.546 09 dm^3 (l) = 4.546 09 $\times 10^{-3}$ m^3

Mass, kg
1 ounce, oz = 28.349 5 g = 0.028 349 5 kg
1 ounce, fluid; fl oz = 28.413 1 cm^3 = 2.841 31 $\times 10^{-5}$ m^3
1 pound, lb = 453.592 39 g = 0.453 592 39 kg
1 quarter = 12.700 6 kg
1 hundred weight, cwt = 50.802 3 kg
1 ton = 1 016.05 kg

Velocity, m s^{-1} (1 m s^{-1} = 3.6 km h^{-1})
1 ft/s (fps) = **0.304 8** m s^{-1} = **1.097 28** km h^{-1}
1 ft/min (fpm) = **0.005 08** m s^{-1} = **0.018 288** km h^{-1}
1 mile/h (mph) = 0.447 04 m s^{-1} = 1.609 344 km h^{-1}
1 cusec = 0.028 316 8 m^3 s^{-1}

Density, kg m^{-3}
1 lb/ft^3 = 0.016 018 5 g cm^{-3} = 16.018 5 kg m^{-3}
1 ft^3/lb = 62.428 0 cm^3 g^{-1} = 6.242 80 $\times 10^{-2}$ m^3 kg^{-1}

Force, the Newton, N, kg m s^{-2} = J m^{-1}
1 dyn = 10^{-5} N

Pressure, N m^{-2}, kg m^{-1} s^{-2} or bar, b = 10^5 N m^{-2} (the SI unit may become the Pascal, 1 Pa = 1 N m^{-2})
1 in Hg = **25.4** mm Hg = 33.863 9 mb = 3 386.9 N m^{-2}
1 in H_2O (4°C) = 2.491 mb = 249.1 N m^{-2}
1 ft H_2O = 29.890 7 mb = 2 989.07 N m^{-2}
1 atm = **760** torr = **760** mm Hg = **1 013.25** mb = **101 325** N m^{-2}
1 b = **1 000** mb = **10^5** N m^{-2}

Table 1.4 (contd.)

1 pound-force/in^2 (p.s.i.) = 51.715 mm Hg = 68.948 mb = 6 894.76 N m^{-2}
1 kgf (kilogramme force) m^{-2} = 9.806 65 N m^{-2}
1 dyn cm^{-2} = 0.1 N m^{-2}

Energy, the joule, J, kg m^2 s^{-1} or watt, W = J s^{-1}; and
energy flux, J m^{-2} s^{-1} = W m^{-2}
1 British thermal unit (Btu) = 1.055 06 kJ
1 Btu/ft^3 = 37.258 9 kJ m^{-3}
1 Btu/ft^3 °F = 67.066 1 kJ m^{-3} K^{-1}
1 Btu/h = 0.293 071 W
1 Btu/ft^2 h = 3.154 59 W m^{-2}
1 Btu/ft h °F = 5.678 26 W m^{-2} K^{-1}
1 Btu/lb = **2 326** J kg^{-1}
1 Btu/lb °F = **4 186.8** J kg^{-1} K^{-1}
1 calorie (international table), cal = **4.186 8** J
1 cal (15 °C), cal_{15} = **4.185 5** J
1 cal (thermochemical) = **4.184** J
1 cal cm^{-2} s^{-1} = **41.868** kW m^{-2}
1 cal cm^{-2} min^{-1} = 1 ly (langley) min^{-1} = 69.78 mW cm^{-2} = 697.8 W m^{-2}
1 cal cm^{-2} s^{-1} °C^{-1} = 41.868 kW m^{-2} K^{-1}
1 cal g^{-1} = **4.186 8** kJ kg^{-1}
1 cal g^{-1} °C^{-1} = **4.186 8** J g^{-1} K^{-1}
1 erg = **10^{-7}** J

Illumination lx, cd sr m^{-2}
1 foot-candle, lm/ft^2 = 10.763 9 lx

Temperature, Kelvin, K
1 degree Celsius (centigrade), °C = (T(°C) + 273.15)K
1 degree Fahrenheit, °F = 5/9(T(°F) + 459.67)K
1 degree Rankine, °R = 5/9(T(°R))K

°F	°C	K	°F	°C	K	°F	°C	K
120	48.89	322.03	65	18.33	291.48	20	−6.67	266.48
110	43.33	316.48	60	15.56	288.70	15	−9.44	263.70
100	37.78	310.92	55	12.78	285.92	10	−12.22	260.92
95	35.00	308.15	50	10.00	283.15	0	−17.78	255.37
90	32.22	305.37	45	7.22	280.37	−10	−23.33	249.81
85	29.44	302.59	40	4.44	277.59	−20	−28.89	244.26
80	26.67	299.81	35	1.67	274.82	−30	−34.44	238.70
75	23.89	297.03	30	−1.11	272.03	−40	−40.00	233.15
70	21.11	294.26	25	−3.89	269.26	−60	−51.11	222.03

Time, s
in mean solar units
1 day, d = 24 h = 1 440 min = 86 400 s

Table 1.5 Some properties of carbon dioxide and oxygen at atmospheric pressure (1 013.25 mb = 760 torr or mm Hg = 101 325 N m^{-2}). (From Hodgman, Weast & Selby 1955, Kohn 1965 and other sources.)

	Temperature [°C]					
	0	10	15	20	25	30
Carbon dioxide						
Density [kg m^{-3}]	1.977	1.907	1.874	1.842	1.811	1.781
1/density [m^3 kg^{-1}]	0.506	0.524	0.534	0.543	0.552	0.561
Solubility in pure water*,**						
[dm^3 m^{-3} (cm^3 l^{-1})]	1 713	1 194	1 019	878	759	665
[mol m^{-3}]	76.4	51.4	43.1	36.5	31.1	26.7
[mg kg^{-1}]	3 346	2 318	1 970	1 688	1 449	1 257
Diffusivity in water [cm^2 s^{-1}]					1.7×10^{-5}	
Diffusivity in air***, D_C, D_H/D_C*** = 1.606 [cm^2 s^{-1}]	0.134	0.143	0.147	0.152	0.156	0.161
Mean free path in air+ [m] (at 1 bar)				6.15×10^{-8}		
Oxygen						
Density [kg m^{-3}]	1.429	1.378	1.355	1.331	1.309	1.287
1/density [m^3 kg^{-1}]	0.700	0.726	0.738	0.751	0.764	0.777
Solubility in pure water*						
[dm^3 m^{-3} (cm^3 l^{-1})]	48.89	38.02	34.15	31.02	28.31	26.08
[mol m^{-3}]	2.17	1.68	1.50	1.36	1.23	1.12
[mg kg^{-1}]	69.45	53.68	48.02	43.39	39.31	35.88
Maximum content in air-saturated water++ [dm^3 m^{-3}]	—	7.88	7.05	6.36	5.77	5.28
Diffusivity in water [cm^2 s^{-1}]					2.92×10^{-5}	
Diffusivity in air***, D_O [cm^2 s^{-1}]	0.169	0.180	0.186	0.191	0.197	0.203
Mean free path in air+ [m] (at 1 bar)				9.93×10^{-8}		

* Gas volumes are reduced to 0 °C.
** For information on the dependence of the concentration of different ionic species of CO_2 in water on pH see Table 16.1.
*** From Fuller, Schettler & Giddings (1966).
+ From Weast (1968).
++ From Murray & Riley (1969); the paper also contains data for water of various chlorinity. For density calculations at various barometric pressures and temperatures the nomogram of Davis (1957) may be used.

Table 1.6 Conversion coefficients for the calculation of photosynthesis at atmospheric pressure (1 013.25 mb = 760 torr and mm Hg = 101 325 N m^{-2}).

	10 °C	15 °C	20 °C	25 °C	30 °C
CO_2					
weight of O_2 evolved per unit weight of CO_2 assimilated	0.727	0.727	0.727	0.727	0.727
weight of O_2 evolved per unit volume of CO_2 assimilated	1.378	1.355	1.331	1.309	1.287
approx. weight of saccharides formed per unit weight of CO_2 assimilated	0.648	0.648	0.648	0.648	0.648
approx. weight of saccharides formed per unit volume of CO_2 assimilated	1.236	1.214	1.194	1.174	1.154
O_2					
weight of CO_2 assimilated per unit weight of O_2 evolved	1.375	1.375	1.375	1.375	1.375
weight of CO_2 assimilated per unit volume of O_2 evolved	1.907	1.874	1.842	1.811	1.781
approx. weight of saccharides formed per unit weight of O_2 evolved	0.891	0.891	0.891	0.891	0.891
approx. weight of saccharides formed per unit volume of O_2 evolved	1.227	1.206	1.185	1.165	1.146
Saccharides [the average of the molecular weight of a starch unit and glucose was taken as the basis: ½(162.14 + 180.16) = 171.15]					
weight of CO_2 assimilated in the formation of unit weight of saccharides	1.543	1.543	1.543	1.543	1.543
volume of CO_2 assimilated in the formation of unit weight of saccharides	0.809	0.823	0.838	0.852	0.866
weight of CO_2 evolved in the formation of unit weight of saccharides	1.122	1.122	1.122	1.122	1.122
volume of CO_2 evolved in the formation of unit weight of saccharides	0.815	0.829	0.843	0.858	0.872

absorbed by the leaf is limiting, *the area of the leaf* intercepting radiation provides a suitable basis on which to calculate the photosynthetic rate. Since the radiation falling on a leaf is usually highly directional, falling predominantly on one side, the relevant area is the projected area in the case of an essentially three dimensional leaf and the area of one surface in the case of a flat leaf. However, if a flat leaf is uniformly irradiated on both surfaces and the influence of the two sources of irradiation on photosynthesis is additive as found by Moss (1964, but *cf.* Starzecki 1962) either both fluxes of radiation should be separately measured and summed, or else the rate of photosynthesis should be expressed on the basis of the sum of the areas of both leaf surfaces (Pisek 1960). Similarly, if the absorption of radiation is limiting, *the amount of chlorophyll present* or other characteristics of the chloroplasts affecting the trapping of energy also provide suitable bases for calculation. If, on the other hand, photosynthesis is saturated with radiation and strongly limited by the supply of CO_2 to the chloroplasts, these bases are not appropriate. In such a case an appropriate basis would be the surface area of the leaf in which the stomata occur or the area of stomatal pores or the diffusive conductance of the stomata, or perhaps the number (Wilson & Cooper 1967) or surface area (Holm-

Table 1.7 Composition of dry air. The average molecular weight of dry air is 28.97 kg $kmol^{-1}$. (From McIntosh 1963).

	Specific gravity (O = 16)	Proportional composition By volume [%]	By weight [%]
Dry air	14.48	100.0	100.0
Nitrogen	14.01	78.09	75.54
Oxygen	16.00	20.95	23.14
Argon	19.97	0.93	1.27
Carbon dioxide	22.01	0.03	0.05
Neon	10.09	1.8×10^{-3}	1.2×10^{-3}
Helium	2.00	5.2×10^{-4}	7.2×10^{-5}
Methane	8.00	2.0×10^{-4}	1.0×10^{-4}
Krypton	41.85	1.0×10^{-4}	3.0×10^{-4}
Hydrogen	1.01	5.0×10^{-5}	4.0×10^{-6}
Nitrous oxide	22.01	5.0×10^{-5}	7.6×10^{-5}
Xenon	65.65	8.0×10^{-6}	3.6×10^{-5}
Ozone	24.00	1.0×10^{-6}	1.7×10^{-6}

Table 1.8 Some physical properties of dry air at atmospheric pressure (1013.25 mb = 760 mm Hg = 101 325 N m^{-2}) adapted from Batchelor (1967).

	Temperature [°C] 0	10	15	20	30
Density, ρ[mg cm^{-3}]	1.293	1.247	1.225	1.205	1.165
Viscosity, μ[mg cm^{-1} s^{-1}]	0.171	0.176	0.178	0.181	0.186
Kinematic viscosity, ν[cm^2 s^{-1}]	0.132	0.141	0.145	0.150	0.160
Thermal diffusivity, κ_H[cm^2 s^{-1}]	0.184	0.196	0.202	0.208	—
Specific heat at constant pressure, C_p[J g^{-1} $°C^{-1}$]			1.012		
Specific heat at constant volume, c_v[J g^{-1} $°C^{-1}$]			0.718		

gren 1968) of the mesophyll cells. Hence in the case of hypostomatous leaves the area of one surface is appropriate and in the case of amphistomatous leaves with stomata equally distributed on both surfaces, the sum of the two surface areas would be appropriate. Difficulties arise, however, when the stomata are unevenly distributed or localised to only a part of the surface area as in *Calluna vulgaris* for example. In circumstances in which photosynthesis may be strongly limited by the rate of the carboxylation reaction, at low temperature for example, calculation on the basis of *the amount or activity of the carboxylating enzymes* present would also seem to be appropriate. However *protein or nitrogen content* of the leaves seems only to be a logical choice in cases of extremely disturbed metabolism or pronounced nitrogen deficiency. *Leaf dry weight* also does not seem to be a very logical basis on which

Table 1.9 Some properties of pure water and water vapour at atmospheric pressure (1 013.25 mb = 760 torr = 760 mm Hg = 101 325 N m^{-2}). (From List 1963, Kohn 1965, Batchelor 1967 and other sources.)

	Temperature [°C]					
	0	10	15	20	25	30
Saturation vapour pressure over water, e_0[mb]	6.108	12.272	17.044	23.373	31.671	42.430
Density of vapour in saturated air*, χ_0[g m^{-3}]	4.847	9.399	12.83	17.30	23.05	30.38
Latent heat of vaporization, L[J g^{-1}]	2 501	2 477	2 465	2 454	2 442	2 430
Specific heat at constant pressure, C_p[J g^{-1} °C^{-1}]	4.217	4.192	4.186	4.182	4.179	4.178
Viscosity, μ[mg cm^{-1} s^{-1}]	17.87	13.04	11.37	10.02	8.91	7.98
Thermal conductivity, k_H[mJ cm^{-1} s^{-1} °C^{-1}]	5.6	5.8	5.9	5.9	—	6.1
Diffusivity of water vapour in air**, D_H[cm^2 s^{-1}]	0.224	0.239	0.247	0.255	0.262	0.270
	0.216	0.230	0.237	0.244	0.251	0.259
Surface tension, r[g s^{-2}]	75.64	74.22	73.4	72.75	71.9	71.18

* Approximately $e_0 \times 0.736$ g m^{-3}.

** From Lee & Wilke (1954); using the best value at 25 °C and (second line) the temperature coefficient of approximately

$$D_H = 0.224 \left(\frac{T}{273}\right)^{1.82}.$$

The data of the second line are from Fuller, Schettler & Giddings (1966).

to express photosynthetic rate since it has little or no direct relationship with radiation absorption, CO_2 uptake or enzyme activity. It is generally used purely for convenience for leaves the area of which is difficult to estimate. Fresh weight would seem to be the most useless basis of all since it varies widely from leaf to leaf and is readily changed both by water strain and by environmental conditions during development.

The above considerations indicate that in routine measurements a compromise must be made between the most logical basis and the basis which is of the greatest practical convenience. The projected surface area, or the surface area of one surface of a flat leaf is a logical choice in a number of the cases discussed above and is a suitable compromise. It has been found to be a convenient basis by the majority of investigators. Clearly it would be confusing to change the basis during the course of an experiment, although the above considerations suggest that with amphistomatous leaves illuminated from one side, the area of one surface would be appropriate at low irradiance and the area of both surfaces at high irradiance. To get the maximum possible information out of measurements of photosynthesis in different environmental conditions, it is clearly advantageous to have the information available to be able to calculate the rate of photosynthesis on the basis of several plant characteristics.

Table 1.10 Some useful constants pertaining to the Système International d'Unités (largely from Socrates & Sapper 1969).

Gas constant, R = Lk	8.314 3 J K^{-1} mol^{-1}
	83.143 b cm^3 K^{-1} mol^{-1}
	[62 361.1 (mm Hg) cm^3 K^{-1} mol^{-1}]
$RT_{273.15K}$	2.271 06 × 10^3 J mol^{-1}
Molar volume of ideal gas at 101 325 N m^{-2} (1 atm) and 273.15K	2.241 36 × 10^{-2} m^3 mol^{-1}
Boltzmann constant, k	1.380 54 × 10^{-23} J K^{-1}
Avogadro constant, N_A, L	6.022 52 × 10^{23} mol^{-1}
[Einstein, E*	6.022 52 × 10^{23} quanta]
Ice point, T_{ice}	273.150 K
Planck constant, h	6.625 6 × 10^{-34} J s
Velocity of light, c_o	2.997 925 × 10^8 m s^{-1}
Electron volt, eV	1.602 1 × 10^{-19} J
Stefan-Boltzmann constant, = $2\pi^5 k^4/15 h^3 c_o^2$	5.669 7 × 10^{-8} W m^{-2} K^{-4}
	[8.14 × 10^{-11} cal cm^{-2} min^{-1} K^{-1}]
Acceleration due to gravity at sea level, latitude 45°, g	9.806 7 m s^{-2}
π	3.141 59
π^{-1}	0.318 30
π^2	9.869 6
Base of natural logarithms, e	2.718 28
M = $\log_{10}e$	0.434 29
M^{-1} = $\log_e 10$	2.302 58

* Not a recognised SI unit.

1.5 | Limiting factors of photosynthesis

The literature on photosynthesis presents a wide range of values of rates of photosynthetic CO_2 influx, O_2 efflux or dry matter accumulation measured in various units. When converted to a common denominator, considerable variation remains, the upper limit of which is set by an optimum combination of genetic, internal and environmental factors for photosynthesis. High values of net photosynthesis have previously been reported but for one reason or another have been suspect on account of the methods used. However, with careful control of nutrition and water supply during development, high values can regularly be obtained with *Zea mays* and other tropical grasses in which the C_4-dicarboxylic acid pathway of carbon dioxide fixation has been found recently. Thus reliable values of an influx of over 100 or 70 mg CO_2 dm^{-2} h^{-1} were found at increased or normal CO_2 concentrations, respectively (*e.g.* Wilson & Ludlow 1970; Mc Pherson unpublished). Table 1.11 shows that the maximum values for other groups of plants are lower. Similar tables of photosynthetic rates were compiled by Verduin (1953, 1959), Verduin, Whitwer & Cowell (1959), Larcher (1969c), Wolf (1969), *etc.*

It is certainly very difficult to predict or explain the photosynthetic rate of a plant, because it is influenced by the simultaneous action of many external and internal

Table 1.11 Normal maximum values of net photosynthetic rate of different herbaceous and woody plants measured as CO_2 uptake at light saturation, optimum temperature and water saturation, normal (0.03%) content of CO_2 in the air and atmospheric pressure. Modified from Larcher (1963).

Plant type	CO_2 uptake [mg CO_2 h^{-1}]	
	per 1 dm^2 leaf area (single surface)	per 1 g leaf dry weight
A. Herbaceous plants		
1. Cultivated plants with Calvin cycle	20 – 35	30 – 60
2. Tropical grasses and plants with C_4-dicarboxylic acid cycle	30(40) – 70(80)*	40–120(140)*
3. Herbs from sunny habitats (heliophytes)	15 – 60(65)*	30 – 90
4. Herbs from shaded habitats (sciophytes)	4 – 16	20
5. Succulents	4 – 12	8
6. Submersed higher fresh-water plants	4 – 6	—
B. Woody plants		
1. Deciduous broad-leaved trees		
sun leaves	10 – 25	15 – 30
shade leaves	6 – 15	—
2. Evergreen broad-leaved trees		
sun leaves	10 – 16	6 – 10
shade leaves	3 – 8	—
3. *Ericaceae* and semi-arid sclerophyllous shrubs	4 – 12	4 – 6
4. Evergreen conifers	4 – 12(15)*	3 – 15(18)*

* Values in brackets reported for one species only.

factors a short review of which is given in Table 1.12. All these factors should be taken into account and measured or controlled during the determination of photosynthesis. Hence six chapters of this Manual are devoted to methods of determination of some of the more important factors: Chapter 14 to the measurement of leaf area, Chapter 15 to the determination of stomatal aperture, Chapter 16 to the determination of diffusion resistances to CO_2 transfer, Chapter 17 to the measurement of leaf temperature, Chapter 18 to basic methods of chlorophyll analysis, and Chapter 19 to methods of measuring photosynthetically active radiation.

Table 1.12 Review of rate-limiting factors of photosynthesis.
This table summarizes the main factors which affect the rate of photosynthesis. The importance of th factors, their mode of action (during the whole previous ontogeny of the plant, during one or sev of its phases or during the measurement only), and the interrelationships amongst them cannot be defi

Factor		Reason
Genetic factors[2]		
A Existence of stomatal resistance	A_1 In both leaf surfaces	CO_2 diffusion resistance
	A_2 High resistance in upper surface of the leaf	
B Differences in pathways of anabolism and catabolism of carbon substances	B_1 Pathways of carbon fixation	C_4-dicarboxylic acid pathway CO_2 fixation (typical for trop grasses and related plant spec or the more common Calvin cy
	B_2 Activity of the carboxylating enzymes	
	B_3 Presence of photorespiration[3]	Photorespiration present in pl with Calvin cycle destroys pa the newly formed photosynth
C Composition of photosystems and activity of photoreactions	C_1 Amount of chlorophyll *a* and its distribution between the *in vivo* forms, amounts of accessory pigments	Rate of radiant energy fixa formation of $NADPH_2$ and
	C_2 Amount of limiting components of electron transfer chain (cytochrome *f*, plastocyanin, P 700, ferredoxin, compounds *Q*, *X*, *etc*.)	
	C_3 Arrangement of pigments and electron carriers, ultrastructure of thylakoid membrane	
	C_4 Variation in activity of individual reactions of the electron transfer chain	
D Shape, structure and number of chloroplasts and their position in the cells		CO_2 diffusion resistance in mesophyll

ecisely. Nevertheless, the table illustrates that measured rates of photosynthesis must be regarded as e result of numerous effects. See Ruhland (1960) and Heath (1969) for more detailed information on e individual factors.

emarks	Reference[1]
rror in partitioning diffusion resistances. Gas change rates through upper and lower leaf rfaces should be determined separately.	Chapters 2, 15, 16. Raschke (1958); El-Sharkawy & Hesketh (1964); Holmgren (1968); Moreshet, Koller & Stanhill (1968)
onounced stomatal limitation of gas exchange te at saturating irradiance. Assimilation amber not separating the leaf surfaces utilisable. orometry not reliable.	Holmgren, Jarvis & Jarvis (1965); Bertsch & Domes (1969); Domes & Bertsch (1969); Zelitch (1969a)
pper limits of CO_2 influx (see Table 1.11) as ell as the level of saturating irradiance much wer in Calvin cycle plants.	Kortschak, Hartt & Burr (1965); Hatch & Slack (1966); Bassham & Jensen (1967); Ludlow & Wilson (1968); Bull (1969); Björkman (1970); Hatch (1970); Hatch & Slack (1970)
	Huffaker *et al.* (1966); Slack & Hatch (1967); Björkman (1968a); Wareing, Khalifa & Treharne (1968); Björkman & Gauhl (1969); Eagles & Treharne (1969); Treharne & Cooper (1969); Preiss & Kosuge (1970); Treharne & Eagles (1970); Walker & Crofts (1970)
igh CO_2 compensation concentration. P_G annot be determined as the sum of $P_N + R_D$. omparison of P_N with the activity of dark nzymatic reactions of photosynthesis not reliable.	Chapter 8. Forrester, Krotkov & Nelson (1966a, b); Moss (1966, 1968); Hesketh (1967); Lake (1967a, b); Downton & Tregunna (1968); Johnson & Hatch (1968); Jolliffe & Tregunna (1968); Zelitch (1969b); Ludlow (1970); Walker & Crofts (1970)
$_N$ usually better correlated with the amount of hlorophyll *a* than total chlorophylls.	Butler (1965); Deroche & Costes (1966); Schmid & Gaffron (1967); Briantais (1968); French *et al.* (1968); Hager (1969)
otential indicators of photosynthetic activity	Hill (1965); Boardman (1967, 1968, 1969, 1970); Levine (1968, 1969); Fork & Amesz (1969); Cheniae (1970)
	Park (1966); Bogorad (1967); von Wettstein (1967); Frey-Wyssling (1968)
	Hoffmann & Miller (1966); McNaughton (1967); Olson (1970)
O_2 diffusion in liquid phase may be changed vith light dependent chloroplast movements in ells. Light distribution within the leaf.	Laetsch & Stetler (1965); Haupt (1966, 1969); Homann & Schmid (1967); Mousseau (1967); Thomas, van Lierop & Ten Ham (1967); Laetsch (1968, 1969); Laisk (1968, 1970); Leech (1968); Mousseau & Bourdu (1968)

Factor				Reason
E	Leaf structure	E_1	Leaf anatomy	CO_2 diffusion resistances
		E_2	Optical properties	Efficiency of energy absorptio factor C_1
Environmental and internal factors				
F	Energy supply	F_1	Radiation 400–700 nm, its quality and duration	Energy supply to photochemical reactions; factor *N*
		F_2	Radiation 400–700 nm, flux density and duration	Photoinhibition – precise causes uncertain
		F_3	Radiation <400 nm, and >700 nm, its quality and duration	Changes in ultrastructure and th changes in other factors; facto *E* and *N*
		F_4	Photoperiod during development and immediate photoperiod history	Formative effects on plant ont genesis as well as on their phot synthetic apparatus; factor *P*
G	CO_2 supply	G_1	CO_2 concentration in the ambient air	CO_2 gradient; CO_2 concentratio near sites of carboxylation; CC dependent control of stomat opening
		G_2	Ventilation	Effect on diffusion resistance in th boundary layer, thus on transfe of CO_2, O_2 ,water vapour and hea
H	Leaf and air temperatures			Rate of chemical reactions; effec on transpiration rate and thu interrelationships with factor also influence on other factors
I	Plant water relations	I_1	Water content	Rate of translocation of photo synthates; effect on factor *J*
		I_2	Water potential in chloroplasts	Enzymatic activity in gels; suppl of water to photosystem II and en zymatic reactions of CO_2 fixatio
		I_3	Water potential along the diffusion paths (also presence of water in liquid phase in intercellular spaces)	CO_2 diffusion resistances; H_2C dependent control of stomata, an thus factor *G*
J	Concentration of photosynthates and translocation rate			Equilibrium of chemical reactions osmotic potential

Remarks	Reference[1]
Affected by growing conditions and pretreatment	McClendon (1962); Björkman & Holmgren (1963); El-Sharkawy & Hesketh (1965); Wilson & Cooper (1967, 1969a, b, c, d); Pearce *et al.* (1969); Hesketh & Baker (1970)
May change even during slight wilting; affected by deposits on the leaf surface.	Gates *et al.* (1965); Loomis (1965); Björkman (1968b)
Effect on ε of different sources of radiation and of their filtration (*e.g.* by water). Effect of irradiance during growing period.	Chapter 19. Talling (1961); Kriedeman, Neales & Ashton (1964); Hiesey & Milner (1965); Mousseau (1966, 1967, 1968); Loach (1967); Mousseau, Coste & de Kouchkovsky (1967); Pearce, Brown & Blaser (1967); Eagles & Treharne (1969); Hatch, Slack & Bull (1969); Larcher (1969c); Wilson & Cooper (1969a, d)
	Klein & Bogorad (1964); Kok, Gassner & Rurainski (1965)
Change in leaf energy balance when using different light sources.	
	Cockshull (1966); Šesták (1966); Park & Drury (1967); Sironval & Englert (1967); Thomas, van Lierop & Ten Ham (1967)
Control of CO_2 concentration in the assimilation chamber according to outlet concentration preferable.	Hesketh (1963); Holmgren & Jarvis (1967); Bishop & Whittingham (1968); Heath & Orchard (1968); Holmgren (1968); Fock *et al.* (1969); Wilson & Cooper (1969a)
Decrease in photosynthetic rate and large CO_2 gradients in the assimilation chamber at low ventilation rates.	Chapter 2. Avery (1966); Takakura (1966); Nevins & Loomis (1970a)
Difficulties in measuring the actual leaf temperature.	Chapters 16 and 17. Kozlowski & Keller (1966); Kriedemann (1968a, b); Hesketh & Baker (1969); Hew, Krotkov & Canvin (1969); Hofstra & Hesketh (1969a, b); Larcher (1969c); Pisek *et al.* (1969); Wilson & Cooper (1969c); Woledge & Jewiss (1969); Mooney & Harrison (1970); Treharne & Eagles (1970)
Sufficient water supply to the object difficult at high irradiances. Leaf energy balance important.	Clements (1964); Roberts (1964); Slavík (1966); Crafts (1968); Wardlaw (1967, 1968); Larcher (1969c)
	Packer (1966); Santarius & Ernst (1967); Santarius & Heber (1967); Crafts (1968)
	Brix (1962); El-Sharkawy & Hesketh (1964); Crafts (1968); Kriedemann (1968a); Slatyer (1969); Troughton (1969); Troughton & Slatyer (1969)
Effect of photosynthate accumulation in detached objects (leaves, discs, segments).	Chapter 9. King, Wardlaw & Evans (1967); Neales & Incoll (1968); Haapala (1969); Hofstra & Nelson (1969a, b)

Factor		Reason
K	Soil moisture	Water potential in the plant (factors *I*, *J*)
L	Mineral nutrition and contents of mineral elements in the tissue	Effects on factors *E* (*e.g.* nitroger phosphorus), *B* (*e.g.* phosphorus *I* (including permeability of mem branes, *e.g.* potassium), *C*, *J*, *etc*
M	Pathological state	Effect of other factors
N	Endogenous diurnal cycle	Stomatal CO_2 diffusion resistance rate of translocation of assimilate
O	Seasonal cycle	Effect on other factors
P	Developmental stage of the plant	Effect on other factors
R	Age of leaf	Effect on other factors
S	Age of meristem when leaf primordia were produced	Effect on other factors
T	Effect of growing conditions, adaptation and pretreatment	Effect on other factors

1. The respective chapter of this manual or examples of reviews or recent original papers dealing with the relevant factor are given. For further references see also Larcher (1969c) and Ledig (1969).
2. Factors *A* to *E* can also be influenced quantitatively by the environment.

:emarks	Reference[1]
ack of oxygen supply to roots in fully watered otted plants.	Šesták & Václavík (1965); Kozlowski & Keller (1966); Negisi (1966)
quilibrated and steady mineral nutrition during ultivation important.	Clements (1964); Keller & Koch (1964); Murata (1965); Ozbun, Volk & Jackson (1965); Kozlowski & Keller (1966); Bourdu *et al.* (1967); Hartt & Burr (1967); Keller (1968); Meinl (1969); Ryle & Hesketh (1969); Nátr (1970); Nevins & Loomis (1970b); Walker & Crofts (1970)
ffect of latent disease (*e.g.* viruses).	Livne (1964); Scott & Smillie (1966); Harding, Williams & McNabola (1968)
:omparative measurements should be done at e same time of day. Influence on prolonged easurements.	Gates (1965); Kluge (1968); Hoffmann & Miller (1966); Kozlowski & Keller (1966); Kortschak & Forbes (1969); Jones & Mansfield (1970)
ll comparative measurements on plants of the ime age	Kozlowski & Keller (1966); Shiroya *et al.* (1966); Bamberg, Schwarz & Tranquillini (1967); Gordon & Larson (1968); Larcher (1969a)
hotoperiodic influences. Existence of vegetative ycle with two peaks of photosynthetic activity, e second often at the time of flowering.	Thorne (1965); Sweet & Wareing (1966); Kortschak & Forbes (1969)
:omplex factor. Also differences in area of one af blade	Šesták & Čatský (1967); Hardwick, Wood & Woolhouse (1968); Kriedemann (1968b); Pearce, Brown & Blaser (1968); Wada (1968); Walker & Waygood (1968); Wilson & Cooper (1969b)
ffect of initial growth rate of seedlings	Bormann (1956)
lso adaptation to the quality of light source	Tranquillini (1964); Loach (1967); Mousseau, Coste & de Kouchkovsky (1967); Björkman (1968a, b); Duncan & Hesketh (1968); Hesketh (1968); Holmgren (1968); Eagles & Treharne (1969); Wilson & Cooper (1969c, d) and other papers cited in the previous sections

3. Discussing various experiments Hesketh & Baker (1967) suggest that the apparent photorespiration rate in leaves exposed to intense light and normal air, could reach *ca.* 20–30% of gross photosynthetic rate. Other authors, *e.g.* Hatch (1970) calculate losses of up to 50% (*cf.* Chapter 8).

1.6 | References

Allen, F. L.: Observations on photosynthesis and related systems. I. Influence of anaerobiosis on photosynthetic rates during continuous irradiation. – Arch. Biochem. 55: 38-53, 1955.

Apel, P., Lehmann, C. O.: Variabilität und Sortenspezifität der Photosyntheserate bei Sommergerste. – Photosynthetica 3: 255-262, 1969.

Arnold, W.: A calorimetric determination of the quantum yield in photosynthesis. – In: Franck, J., Loomis, W. E. (ed.): Photosynthesis in Plants. Pp. 273-277. Iowa State College Press, Ames 1949.

Avery, D. J.: The supply of air to leaves in assimilation chambers. – J. exp. Bot. 17: 655-677, 1966.

Avratovščuková, N.: Differences in photosynthetic rate of leaf disks in five tobacco varieties. – Photosynthetica 2: 149-160, 1968.

Bamberg, S., Schwarz, W., Tranquillini, W.: Influence of daylength on the photosynthetic capacity of stone pine (*Pinus cembra* L.). – Ecology 48: 264-269, 1967.

Bassham, J. A., Jensen, R. G.: Photosynthesis of carbon compounds. – In: San Pietro, A., Greer, F. A., Army, T. J. (ed.): Harvesting the Sun. Pp. 79-110. Academic Press, New York – London 1967.

Batchelor, G. K.: An Introduction to Fluid Dynamics. – Cambridge Univ. Press, Cambridge 1967.

Begg, J. E., Lake, J. V.: Carbon dioxide measurement: A continuous conductimetric method. – Agr. Meteorol. 5: 283-290, 1968.

Bertsch, A., Domes, W.: CO_2-Gaswechsel amphistomatischer Blätter. I. Der Einfluss unterschiedlicher Stomaverteilungen der beiden Blattepidermen auf den CO_2-Transport. – Planta 85: 183-193, 1969.

Bishop, P. M., Whittingham, C. P.: The photosynthesis of tomato plants in a carbon dioxide enriched atmosphere. – Photosynthetica 2: 31-38, 1968.

Björkman, O.: Carboxydismutase activity in shade-adapted and sun-adapted species of higher plants. – Physiol. Plant. 21: 1-10, 1968a.

Björkman, O.: Further studies on differentiation of photosynthetic properties in sun and shade ecotypes of *Solidago virgaurea*. – Physiol. Plant. 21: 84-99, 1968b.

Björkman, O.: Characteristics of the photosynthetic apparatus as revealed by laboratory measurements. – In: Prediction and Measurement of Photosynthetic Productivity. Pp. 267–281. PUDOC, Wageningen 1970.

Björkman, O., Gauhl, E.: Carboxydismutase activity in plants with and without β-carboxylation photosynthesis. – Planta 88: 197-203, 1969.

Björkman, O., Holmgren, P.: Adaptability of the photosynthetic apparatus to light intensity in ecotypes from exposed and shaded habitats. – Physiol. Plant. 16: 889-914, 1963.

Boardman, N. K.: Chloroplast structure and development. – In: San Pietro, A., Greer, F. A., Army, T. J. (ed.): Harvesting the Sun. Pp. 211-230. Academic Press, New York–London 1967.

Boardman, N. K.: The photochemical systems of photosynthesis. – Advances Agron. 30: 1-79, 1968.

Boardman, N. K.: The photochemical systems of photosynthesis. – Austral. J. Sci. 32: 36-45, 1969.

Boardman, N. K.: Physical separation of the photosynthetic photochemical systems. – Annu. Rev. Plant Physiol. 21: 115–140, 1970.

Bogorad, L.: Chloroplast structure and development. – In: San Pietro, A., Greer, F. A., Army, T. J. (ed.): Harvesting the Sun. Pp. 191-210. Academic Press, New York–London 1967.

Bormann, F. H.: Ecological implications of changes in the photosynthetic response of *Pinus taeda* seedlings during ontogeny. – Ecology 37: 70-75, 1956.

Bourdu, R., Champigny, M.-L., Lefort, M., Maslow, M., Rémy, R., Moyse, A.: Hétérogénéité structurale et fonctionnelle de l'appareil photosynthétique mise en évidence par des variations de nutrition azotée. – In: Sironval, C. (ed.): Le Chloroplaste, Croissance et Viellissement. Pp. 298-305. Masson, Paris 1967.

Bowman, G. E.: The measurement of carbon dioxide concentration in the atmosphere. – In: Wadsworth, R. M. *et al.* (ed.): The Measurement of Environmental Factors in Terrestrial Ecology. Pp. 131-139. Blackwell Sci. Publ., Oxford–Edinburgh 1968.

Briantais, J.-M.: Isolement de structures liées aux deux systèmes photochimiques des chloroplastes. – Bull. Soc. franç. Physiol. vég. 14: 227-244, 1968.

Brix, H.: The effect of water stress on the rates of photosynthesis and respiration in tomato plants and loblolly pine seedlings. – Physiol. Plant. 15: 10-20, 1962.

Brown, A. H., Nier, A. O. C., van Norman, R. W.: Measurement of metabolic gas exchange with a recording mass spectrometer. – Plant Physiol. 27: 320-334, 1952.

Bull, T. A.: Photosynthetic efficiencies and photorespiration in Calvin cycle and C_4-dicarboxylic acid plants. – Crop Sci. 9: 726-728, 1969.

Burr, A., Mauzerall, D.: The oxygen luminometer. An apparatus to determine small amounts of oxygen, and application to photosynthesis. – Biochim. biophys. Acta 153: 614-624, 1968.

Butin, H.: Physiologisch-ökologische Untersuchungen über den Wasserhaushalt. – Biol. Zentralbl. 73: 459-502, 1954.

Butler, W. L.: Development of photosynthetic systems 1 and 2 in a greening leaf. – Biochim. biophys. Acta 102: 1-8, 1965.

Carey, F. G., Teal, J. M.: Responses of oxygen electrodes to variables in construction, assembly, and use. – J. appl. Physiol. 20: 1074-1077, 1965.

Carpenter, T. M., Fox, E. L., Sereque, A. F.: The Carpenter form of the Haldane gas analysis apparatus. – J. biol. Chem. 83: 201-230, 1929.

Carritt, D. E., Kanwisher, J. W.: An electrode system for measuring dissolved oxygen. – Anal. Chem. 31: 5-9, 1959.

Čatský, J.: Méthodes et techniques de mesure de la concentration en anhydride carbonique dans l'air. – In: Techniques d'Étude des Facteurs Physiques de la Biosphère. Pp. 181-188. I.N.R.A. Paris 1970.

Cheniae, G. M.: Photosystem II and O_2 evolution. – Annu. Rev. Plant Physiol. 21: 467–498, 1970.

Clark, L. C. Jr., Wolf, R., Granger, D., Taylor, Z.: Continuous recording of blood oxygen tensions by polarography. – J. appl. Physiol. 6: 189-193, 1953.

Clayton, R. K.: Molecular Physics in Photosynthesis. – Blaisdell Publ. Co., New York–Toronto–London 1965.

Clements, H. F.: Interaction of factors affecting yield. – Ann. Rev. Plant Physiol. 15: 409–442, 1964.

Cockshull, K. E.: Effects of night-break treatment on leaf area and leaf dry weight in *Callistephus chinensis*. – Ann. Bot. 30: 791-806, 1966.

Crafts, A. S.: Water deficit and physiological processes. - In: Kozlowski, T. T. (ed.): Water Deficits and Plant Growth. Vol. II. Pp. 85-133. Academic Press, New York–London 1968.

Cukrová, V., Avratovščuková, N.: Photosynthetic activity, chlorophyll content and stomata characteristics in diploid and polyploid types of *Datura stramonium* L. – Photosynthetica 2: 227-237, 1968.

Davis, D. S.: Solubility of oxygen in water. – Water & Sewage Works 104: 478, 1957.

Deroche, M.-E., Costes, C.: Hétérogénéité des chlorophylles. – Ann. Physiol. vég. 8: 223-254, 1966.

Domes, W., Bertsch, A.: CO_2-Gaswechsel amphistomatischer Blätter. 2. Ein Vergleich von diffusivem CO_2-Austausch der beiden Blattepidermen von *Zea mays* mit dem im Porometer gemessenen viscosen Volumfluß. – Planta 86: 84-91, 1969.

Downton, W. J. S., Tregunna, E. B.: Carbon dioxide compensation – its relation to photosynthetic carboxylation reactions, systematics of the *Gramineae*, and leaf anatomy. – Can. J. Bot. 46: 207-215, 1968.

Downton, J., Berry, J., Tregunna, F. B.: Photosynthesis: Temperate and tropical characteristics within a single grass genus. – Science 163: 78-79, 1969.

Duncan, W. G., Hesketh, J. D.: Net photosynthetic rates, relative leaf growth rates, and leaf numbers of 22 races of maize grown at eight temperatures. – Crop Sci. 8: 670-674, 1968.

Eagles, C. F., Treharne, K. J.: Photosynthetic activity of *Dactylis glomerata* L. in different light regimes. – Photosynthetica 3: 29-38, 1969.

Egle, K.: Landpflanzen. – In: Ruhland, W. (ed.): Handbuch der Pflanzenphysiologie. Vol. V/1. Pp. 115-163. Springer Verlag, Berlin–Göttingen–Heidelberg 1960.

Elmore, C. D., Hesketh, J. D., Muramoto, H.: A survey of rates of leaf growth, leaf ageing and leaf photosynthetic rates among and within species. – J. Arizona Acad. Sci. 4: 215-219, 1967.

El-Sharkawy, M. A., Hesketh, J. D.: Effect of stomatal differences among species on leaf photosynthesis. – Crop Sci. 4: 619-621, 1964.

El-Sharkawy, M., Hesketh, J.: Photosynthesis among species in relation to characteristics of leaf anatomy and CO_2 diffusion resistances. – Crop Sci. 5: 517-521, 1965.
Energy Conversion by the Photosynthetic Apparatus. – Brookhaven Symp. Biol. No. 19. Brookhaven Nat. Lab., Upton, N.Y. 1967.
Fock, H., Schaub, H., Hilgenberg, W., Egle, K.: Über den Einfluss niedriger und hoher O_2-Partialdrucke auf den Sauerstoff- und Kohlendioxidumsatz von *Amaranthus* und *Phaseolus* während der Lichtphase. – Planta 86: 77-83, 1969.
Fork, D. C., Amesz, J.: Action spectra and energy transfer in photosynthesis. – Ann. Rev. Plant Physiol. 20: 305-328, 1969.
Forrester, M. L., Krotkov, G., Nelson, C. D.: Effect of oxygen on photosynthesis, photorespiration and respiration in detached leaves. I. Soybean. – Plant Physiol. 41: 422-427, 1966a.
Forrester, M. L., Krotkov, G., Nelson, C. D.: Effect of oxygen on photosynthesis, photorespiration and respiration in detached leaves. II. Corn and other monocotyledons. – Plant Physiol. 41: 428-431, 1966b.
Fousová, S., Avratovščuková, N.: Hybrid vigour and photosynthetic rate of leaf disks in *Zea mays* L. – Photosynthetica 1: 3-12, 1967.
French, C. S., Michel-Wolwertz, M. R., Michel, J. M., Brown, J. S., Prager, L. K.: Naturally occurring chlorophyll types and their function in photosynthesis. – In: Goodwin, T. W. (ed.): Porphyrins and Related Compounds. Pp. 147-162. Academic Press, London–New York 1968.
Frey-Wyssling, A.: Structure and chemistry of plastids. – Photosynthetica 2: 314-318, 1968.
Fuller, E. N., Schettler, P. D., Giddings, J. C.: A new method for prediction of binary gas-phase diffusion coefficients. – Ind. eng. Chem. 58(5): 18-27, 1966.
Gates, D. M.: Energy, plants, and ecology. – Ecology 46: 1-13, 1965.
Gates, D. M., Keegan, H. J., Schleter, J. C., Weidner, V. R.: Spectral properties of plants. – Appl. Optics 4: 11-20, 1965.
Goldsworthy, A.: Experiments on the origin of CO_2 released by tobacco leaf segments in the light. – Phytochemistry 5: 1013-1019, 1966.
Goodwin, T. W. (ed.): The Biochemistry of Chloroplasts. Vol. 1, 2. – Academic Press, London–New York 1966, 1967.
Gordon, J. C., Larson, P. R.: Seasonal course of photosynthesis, respiration, and distribution of ^{14}C in young *Pinus resinosa* trees as related to wood formation. – Plant Physiol. 43: 1617-1624, 1968.
Gray, D. E. (ed.): American Institute of Physics Handbook. 2nd Ed. – McGraw-Hill Book Co., New York–Toronto–London 1963.
Gulyaev, B. I.: Primenenie kolorimetricheskogo metoda dlya nepreryvnogo izmereniya intensivnosti fotosinteza i dykhaniya. [Use of the colorimetric method for continuous determination of photosynthetic and respiration rates.] – In: Fotosintez i Produktivnost' Rasteniï. Pp. 195-212. Naukova Dumka, Kiev 1965.
Haapala, H.: Starch metabolism of chloroplasts as influenced by light. – Aquilo, Ser. bot. 8: 42-65, 1969.
Hager, A.: Lichtbedingte pH-Erniedrigung in einem Chloroplasten-Kompartiment als Ursache der enzymatischen Violaxanthin- → Zeaxanthin-Umwandlung; Beziehungen zur Photophosphorylierung. – Planta 89: 224-243, 1969.
Harding, H., Williams, P. H., McNabola, S. S.: Chlorophyll changes, photosynthesis, and ultrastructure of chloroplasts in *Albugo candida* induced 'green islands' on detached *Brassica juncea* cotyledons. – Can. J. Bot. 46: 1229-1234, 1968.
Hardwick, K., Wood, M., Woolhouse, H. W.: Photosynthesis and respiration in relation to leaf age in *Perilla frutescens* (L.) Britt. – New Phytol. 67: 79-86, 1968.
Hartt, C. E., Burr, G. O.: Factors affecting photosynthesis in sugar cane. – Proc. 12th I.S.S.C.T. Congress Puerto Rico 1965. Pp. 590-608. Elsevier Publ. Co., Amsterdam 1967.
Hastings, J. W.: Oxygen concentration and bioluminescence intensity. I. Bacteria and fungi. – J. cell. comp. Physiol. 39: 1-30, 1952.
Hatch, M. D.: Chemical energy costs for CO_2 fixation by plants with differing photosynthetic pathways. – In: Prediction and Measurement of Photosynthetic Productivity. Pp. 215-220. PUDOC, Wageningen 1970.

Hatch, M. D., Slack, C. R.: Photosynthesis by sugar-cane leaves. A new carboxylation reaction and the pathway of sugar formation. – Biochem. J. 101: 103-111, 1966.

Hatch, M. D., Slack, C. R.: New enzyme for the interconversion of pyruvate and phosphopyruvate and its role in the carbon (4) dicarboxylic acid pathway of photosynthesis. – Biochem. J. 106: 141-146, 1968.

Hatch, M. D., Slack, C. R.: Photosynthetic CO_2-fixation pathways. – Annu. Rev. Plant Physiol. 21: 141-162, 1970.

Hatch, M. D., Slack, C. R., Bull, T. A.: Light-induced changes in the content of some enzymes of the C_4-dicarboxylic acid pathway of photosynthesis and its effect on other characteristics of photosynthesis. – Phytochemistry 8: 697-706, 1969.

Hatch, M. D., Slack, C. R., Johnson, H. S.: Further studies on a new pathway of photosynthetic carbon dioxide fixation in sugar-cane and its occurrence in other plant species. – Biochem. J. 102: 417-422, 1967.

Haupt, W.: Phototaxis in plants. – Int. Rev. Cytology 19: 267-299, 1966.

Haupt, W.: Bewegungen. – Fortschr. Bot. 31: 164-171, 1969.

Heath, O. V. S.: Assimilation by green leaves with stomatal control eliminated. – Symp. Soc. exp. Biol. 5: 94-114, 1951.

Heath, O. V. S.: The Physiological Aspects of Photosynthesis. – Stanford Univ. Press, Stanford, Calif. 1969.

Heath, O. V. S., Orchard, B.: Carbon assimilation at low carbon dioxide levels. II. The processes of apparent assimilation. – J. exp. Bot. 19: 176-192, 1968.

Hersch, P.: Galvanic determination of traces of oxygen in gases. – Nature 169: 792-793, 1952.

Hersch, P. A.: Trace monitoring in gases using galvanic systems. – Anal. Chem. 32: 1030–1034, 1960.

Hesketh, J. D.: Limitations to photosynthesis responsible for differences among species. – Crop Sci. 3: 493-496, 1963.

Hesketh, J.: Enhancement of photosynthetic CO_2 assimilation in the absence of oxygen, as dependent upon species and temperature. – Planta 76: 371-374, 1967.

Hesketh, J. D.: Effects of light and temperature during plant growth on subsequent leaf CO_2 assimilation rates under standard conditions. – Austr. J. biol. Sci. 21: 235-241, 1968.

Hesketh, J., Baker, D.: Light and carbon assimilation by plant communities. – Crop Sci. 7: 285-293, 1967.

Hesketh, J. D., Baker, D. N.: Relative rates of leaf expansion in seedlings of species with differing photosynthetic rates. – J. Arizona Acad. Sci. 5: 216-221, 1969.

Hesketh, J. D., Baker, D. N.: The relationship between leaf anatomy and photosynthetic CO_2 assimilation among and within species. – In: Prediction and Measurement of Photosynthetic Productivity. Pp. 317-322. PUDOC, Wageningen 1970.

Hew, C.-S., Krotkov, G., Canvin, D. T.: Effects of temperature on photosynthesis and CO_2 evolution in light and darkness by green leaves. – Plant Physiol. 44: 671-677, 1969.

Heytler, P. G.: Polarographic measurement of respiration and photosynthesis. – Fed. Proc. 28: 533, 1969.

Hiesey, W. M., Milner, H. W.: Physiology of ecological races and species. – Ann. Rev. Plant Physiol. 16: 203-216, 1965.

Hill, R.: The biochemists' green mansions: the photosynthetic electron-transport chain in plants. – Essays Biochem. 1: 121-151, 1965.

Hoch, G., Kok, B.: A mass spectrometer inlet system for sampling gases dissolved in liquid phases. – Arch. Biochem. Biophys. 101: 160-170, 1963.

Hodgman, C. D., Weast, R. C., Selby, S. M. (ed.): Handbook of Chemistry and Physics. 37th Ed. – Chemical Rubber Publ. Co., Cleveland, Ohio 1955.

Hoffman, F. M., Miller, J. H.: An endogenous rhythm in the Hill-reaction activity of tomato chloroplasts. – Amer. J. Bot. 53: 543-548, 1966.

Hofstra, G., Hesketh, J. D.: The effect of temperature on stomatal aperture in different species. – Can. J. Bot. 47: 1307-1310, 1969a.

Hofstra, G., Hesketh, J. D.: Effects of temperature on the gas exchange of leaves in the light and dark. – Planta 85: 228-237, 1969b.

Hofstra, G., Nelson, C. D.: The translocation of photosynthetically assimilated ^{14}C in corn. –

Can. J. Bot. 47: 1435-1442, 1969a.
Hofstra, G., Nelson, C. D.: A comparative study of translocation of assimilated ^{14}C from leaves of different species. – Planta 88: 103-112, 1969b.
Holmgren, P.: Leaf factors affecting light-saturated photosynthesis in ecotypes of *Solidago virgaurea* from exposed and shaded habitats. – Physiol. Plant. 21: 676-698, 1968.
Holmgren, P., Jarvis, P. G.: Carbon dioxide efflux from leaves in light and darkness. – Physiol. Plant. 20: 1045-1051, 1967.
Holmgren, P., Jarvis, P. G., Jarvis, M. S.: Resistances to carbon dioxide and water vapour transfer in leaves of different plant species. – Physiol. Plant. 18: 557-573, 1965.
Homann, P. H., Schmid, G. H.: Photosynthetic reactions of chloroplasts with unusual structures. – Plant Physiol. 42: 1619-1632, 1967.
Hopkinson, J. M.: Studies on the expansion of the leaf surface. IV. The carbon and phosphorus economy of a leaf. – J. exp. Bot. 15: 125–137, 1964.
Huffaker, R. C., Obendorf, R. L., Keller, C. J., Kleinkopf, G. E.: Effects of light intensity on photosynthetic carboxylative phase enzymes and chlorophyll synthesis in greening leaves of *Hordeum vulgare* L. – Plant Physiol. 41: 913-918, 1966.
Irvine, J. E.: Photosynthesis in sugarcane varieties under field conditions. – Crop Sci. 7: 297-300, 1967.
Ivanov, L. A., Kossovich, N. L.: Polevoï metod opredeleniya fotosinteza v assimilyatsionnoï kolbe. [Field method for determination of photosynthesis in an assimilation flask.] – Bot. Zh. 31: 3-12, 1946.
Jarvis, P. G.: Characteristics of the photosynthetic apparatus derived from its response to natural complexes of environmental factors. – In: Prediction and Measurement of Photosynthetic Productivity. Pp. 353-367. PUDOC, Wageningen 1970.
Jewiss, O. R., Woledge, J.: The effect of age on the rate of apparent photosynthesis in leaves of tall fescue (*Festuca arundinacea* Schreb.). – Ann. Bot. 31: 661-671, 1967.
Johnson, H. S., Hatch, M. D.: Distribution of the C_4-dicarboxylic acid pathway of photosynthesis and its occurrence in dicotyledonous plants. – Phytochemistry 7: 375-380, 1968.
Joliot, P.: Oxygen evolution in algae illuminated by modulated light. – In: Energy Conversion by the Photosynthetic Apparatus. Brookhaven Symp. Biol. No. 19. Pp. 418-433. Brookhaven Nat. Lab., Upton, N.Y. 1967.
Joliot, P., Joliot, A.: A polarographic method for detection of oxygen production and reduction of Hill reagent by isolated chloroplasts. – Biochem. biophys. Acta 153: 625-634, 1968.
Jolliffe, P. A., Tregunna, E. B.: Effect of temperature, CO_2 concentration, and light intensity on oxygen inhibition of photosynthesis in wheat leaves. – Plant Physiol. 43: 902-906, 1968.
Jones, M. B., Mansfield, T. A.: A circadian rhythm in the level of the carbon dioxide compensation point in *Bryophyllum* and *Coffea*. – J. exp. Bot. 21: 159-163, 1970.
Kamen, M. D.: Primary Processes in Photosynthesis. – Academic Press, New York–London 1963.
Kaye, S., Koency, J. E.: Spectrophotometric method for determining oxygen in gases. – Anal. Chem. 41: 1491-1494, 1969.
Keller, T.: Influence de la nutrition minérale sur les échanges gazeux des arbres de forêt. – Phosphorus Agric. 22: 25-37, 1968.
Keller, T., Koch, W.: The effect of iron chelate fertilization of poplar upon CO_2-uptake, leaf size, and content of leaf pigments and iron. – Plant Soil 20: 116-126, 1964.
King, R. W., Wardlaw, I. F., Evans, L. T.: Effect of assimilate utilization on photosynthetic rate in wheat. – Planta 77: 261-276, 1967.
Klein, S., Bogorad, L.: Fine structure changes in proplastids during photodestruction of pigments. – J. Cell Biol. 22: 443-451, 1964.
Kluge, M.: Untersuchungen über den Gaswechsel von *Bryophyllum* während der Lichtperiode. II. Beziehungen zwischen dem Malatgehalt des Blattgewebes und der CO_2-Aufnahme. – Planta 80: 359-377, 1968.
Kohn, P. G.: Tables of some physical and chemical properties of water. – In: Fogg, G. E. (ed.): The State and Movement of Water in Living Organisms. Symp. Soc. exp. Biol. 19: 3-16, 1965.
Kok, B.: Some sensitive and recording volumeters. – Biochim. biophys. Acta 16: 35-44, 1955.
Kok, B., Spruit, C. J. P.: High initial rates of gas-exchange in respiration and photosynthesis of *Chlorella*. – Biochim. biophys. Acta 19: 212-223, 1956.

Kok, B., Gassner, E. B., Rurainski, H. J.: Photoinhibition of chloroplast reactions. – Photochem. Photobiol. 4: 215-227, 1965.
Kortschak, H. P., Forbes, A.: The effects of shade and age on the photosynthesis rate of sugarcane. – In: Metzner, H. (ed.): Progress in Photosynthesis Research. Vol. I. Pp. 383-387. Tübingen 1969.
Kortschak, H. P., Hartt, C. E., Burr, G. O.: Carbon dioxide fixation in sugarcane leaves. – Plant Physiol. 40: 209-213, 1965.
Kozlowski, T. T., Keller, T.: Food relations of woody plants. – Bot. Rev. 32: 293-382, 1966.
Kriedeman, P. E., Neales, T. F., Ashton, D. H.: Photosynthesis in relation to leaf orientation and light interception. – Austr. J. biol. Sci. 17: 591-600, 1964.
Kriedemann, P. E.: Some photosynthetic characteristics of *Citrus* leaves. – Austr. J. biol. Sci. 21: 895-905, 1968a.
Kriedemann, P. E.: Photosynthesis in vine leaves as a function of light intensity, temperature, and leaf age. – Vitis 7: 213-220, 1968b.
Laetsch, W. M.: Chloroplast specialization of dicotyledons possessing the C_4-dicarboxylic acid pathway of photosynthetic CO_2 fixation. – Amer. J. Bot. 55: 875-883, 1968.
Laetsch, W. M.: Relationship between chloroplast structure and photosynthetic carbon-fixation pathways. – Sci. Progr. 57: 323-351, 1969.
Laetsch, W. M., Stetler, D. A.: Chloroplast structure and function in cultured tobacco tissue. – Amer. J. Bot. 52: 798-804, 1965.
Laisk, A.: Perspektivy matematicheskogo modelirovaniya funktsii fotosinteza lista. [Prospects of mathematical modelling of leaf photosynthesis function.] – In: Fotosintez i Produktivnost' Rastitel'nogo Pokrova. Pp. 5-45. Akad. Nauk Eston. SSR, Tartu 1968.
Laisk, A.: Leaf photosynthesis considering stomatal adaptation and light profile. – In: Prediction and Measurement of Photosynthetic Productivity. Pp. 295-306. PUDOC, Wageningen 1970.
Lake, J. V.: Respiration of leaves during photosynthesis. I. Estimates from an electrical analogue. – Austr. J. biol. Sci. 20: 487-493, 1967a.
Lake, J. V.: Respiration of leaves during photosynthesis. II. Effects on the estimation of mesophyll resistance. – Austr. J. biol. Sci. 20: 495-499, 1967b.
Larcher, W.: Die Leistungsfähigkeit der CO_2-Assimilation höherer Pflanzen unter Laboratoriumsbedingungen und am natürlichen Standort. – Mitt. Floristisch-soziolog. Arbeitsgemeinsch., N.F. 10: 20-33, 1963.
Larcher, W.: Die Bedeutung des Faktors 'Zeit' für die photosynthetische Stoffproduktion. – Ber. Deut. bot. Ges. 82: 71-80, 1969a.
Larcher, W.: Physiological approaches to the measurement of photosynthesis in relation to dry matter production by trees. – Photosynthetica 3: 150-166, 1969b.
Larcher, W.: The effect of environmental and physiological variables on the carbon dioxide gas exchange of trees. – Photosynthetica 3: 167-198, 1969c.
Ledig, F. T.: A growth model for tree seedlings based on the rate of photosynthesis and the distribution of photosynthate. – Photosynthetica 3: 263-275, 1969.
Lee, C. Y., Wilke, C. R.: Measurements of vapor diffusion coefficient. – Ind. eng. Chem. 46: 2381-2387, 1954.
Leech, R. M.: The chloroplast inside and outside the cell. – In: Pridham, J. B. (ed.): Plant Cell Organelles. Pp.137-162. Academic Press, London–New York 1968.
Lemon, E.: Aerodynamic studies of CO_2 exchange between the atmosphere and the plant. – In: San Pietro, A., Greer, F. A., Army, T. J. (ed.): Harvesting the Sun. Pp. 263-290. Academic Press, New York–London 1967.
Levine, R. P.: Genetic dissection of photosynthesis. – Science 162: 768-771, 1968.
Levine, R. P.: The analysis of photosynthesis using mutant strains of algae and higher plants. Ann. Rev. Plant Physiol. 20: 523-540, 1969.
Lieth, H.: The measurement of calorific values of biological material and the determination of ecological efficiency. – In: Eckardt, F. E. (ed.): Functioning of Terrestrial Ecosystems at the Primary Production Level. Pp. 233-242. UNESCO, Paris 1968.
List, R. J.: Smithsonian Meteorological Tables. – Smithson. misc. Collection No. 114. 6th Ed., 2nd Repr. Washington, D.C. 1963.

Livne, A.: Photosynthesis in healthy and rust-affected plants. – Plant Physiol. 39: 614-621, 1964.
Loach, K.: Shade tolerance in tree seedlings. I. Leaf photosynthesis and respiration in plants raised under artificial shade. – New Phytol. 66: 607-621, 1967.
Loomis, W. E.: Absorption of radiant energy by leaves. – Ecology 46: 14-17, 1965.
Loveland, J. W., Adams, R. W., King, H. H. Jr., Nowak, F. A., Cali, L. J.: Spectrophotometric titration of parts per million of carbon dioxide in gases. – Anal. Chem. 31: 1008-1010, 1959.
Lövlie, A., Farfaglio, G.: Increase in photosynthesis during the cell cycle of *Euglena gracilis*. – Exp. Cell Res. 39: 418-434, 1965.
Ludlow, M. M.: Effect of oxygen concentration on leaf photosynthesis and resistances to carbon dioxide diffusion. – Planta 91: 285-290, 1970.
Ludlow, M. M., Wilson, G. L.: Studies on the productivity of tropical pasture plants. I. Growth analysis, photosynthesis, and respiration of Hemil grass and Siratro in a controlled environment. – Austr. J. agr. Res. 19: 35-45, 1968.
Lund, J. W. G., Talling, J. F.: Botanical limnological methods with special reference to the algae. – Bot. Rev. 23: 489-583, 1957.
McClendon, J. H.: The relationship between the thickness of deciduous leaves and their maximum photosynthetic rate. – Amer. J. Bot. 49: 320-322, 1962.
McIntosh, D. H.: Meteorological Glossary. – H.M.S.O., London 1963.
McNaughton, S. J.: Photosynthetic system II: Racial differentiation in *Typha latifolia*. – Science 156: 1363, 1967.
Meinl, G.: Assimilationsvermögen als Sortenmerkmal. II. Trockenmassenproduktion, apparente Assimilation, Respiration und Transpiration von Kartoffelklonen unterschiedlichen Valenzstufen und Sorten bei unterschiedlich hoher NPK-Versorgung. – Photosynthetica 3: 9-19, 1969.
Metzner, H. (ed.): Progress in Photosynthesis Research. Vol. I, II, III. – Tübingen 1969.
Milner, H. W., Hiesey, W. M.: Photosynthesis in climatic races of *Mimulus*. I. Effect of light intensity and temperature on rate. – Plant Physiol. 39: 208-213, 1964a.
Milner, H. W., Hiesey, W. M.: Photosynthesis in climatic races of *Mimulus*. II. Effect of time and CO_2 concentration on rate. – Plant Physiol. 39: 746–750, 1964b.
Mooney, H. A., Harrison, A. T.: The influence of conditioning temperature on subsequent temperature-related photosynthetic capacity in higher plants. – In: Prediction and Measurement of Photosynthetic Productivity. Pp. 411-417. PUDOC, Wageningen 1970.
Moreshet, S., Koller, D., Stanhill, G.: The partitioning of resistances to gaseous diffusion in the leaf epidermis and the boundary layer. – Ann. Bot. N.S. 37: 695-701, 1968.
Moss, D. N.: Optimum lighting of leaves. – Crop Sci. 4: 131-136, 1964.
Moss, D. N.: Respiration of leaves in light and darkness. – Crop Sci. 6: 351-354, 1966.
Moss, D. N.: Photorespiration and glycolate metabolism in tobacco leaves. – Crop Sci. 8: 71-76, 1968.
Mousseau, M.: Influence de l'éclairement sur l'assimilation journalière et annuelle du *Teucrium scorodonia* L. en conditions naturelles. – Oecol. Plant. 1: 103-116, 1966.
Mousseau, M.: Les phénomènes de régulation structurale et fonctionnelle de l'appareil photosynthétique de *Teucrium scorodonia:* un mécanisme d'adaptation aux conditions d'éclairement. – Oecol. Plant. 2: 15-26, 1967.
Mousseau, M.: Action comparée de la lumière sur l'intensité photosynthétique de feuilles entières coupées ou sur pied, selon les conditions d'éclairement pendant la croissance. – C.R. Acad. Sci. (Paris) D 266: 1391-1393, 1968.
Mousseau, M., Bourdu, R.: Influence des conditions écologiques d'éclairement pendant la croissance sur la structure et l'activité des chloroplastes de *Teucrium scorodonia* L. – Bull. Soc. franç. Physiol. vég. 14: 307-315, 1968.
Mousseau, M., Coste, F., de Kouchkovsky, Y.: Influence des conditions d'éclairement pendant la croissance sur l'activité photosynthétique de feuilles entières et de chloroplastes isolés. – C.R. Acad. Sci. (Paris), D 264: 1158-1161, 1967.
Muramoto, H., Hesketh, J., El-Sharkawy, M.: Relationships among rate of leaf area development, photosynthetic rate, and rate of dry matter production among American cultivated cottons and other species. – Crop Sci. 5: 163-166, 1965.
Murata, Y.: Photosynthesis, respiration, and nitrogen response. – In: The Mineral Nutrition of

the Rice Plants. Pp. 385-400. J. Hopkins Press, Baltimore, Md. 1965.
Murray, C. N., Riley, P. J.: The solubility of gases in distilled water and sea water – II. Oxygen.- Deep-Sea Res. 16: 311-320, 1969.
Nátr, L.: La mesure de l'intensité de la photosynthèse dans les conditions naturelles par une méthode gravimétrique. – In: Eckardt, F. E. (ed.): Functioning of Terrestrial Ecosystems at the Primary Production Level. Pp. 345-348. Unesco, Paris 1968.
Nátr, L.: The influence of mineral nutrient supply to barley leaf segments on their rate of CO_2 absorption. – Photosynthetica 4: 21-30, 1970.
Nátr, L., Gloser, J.: Carbon dioxide absorption and dry weight increase in barley leaf segments. – Photosynthetica 1: 19-27, 1967.
Neales, T. F., Incoll, L. D.: The control of leaf photosynthesis rate by the level of assimilate concentration in the leaf: A review of the hypothesis. – Bot. Rev. 34: 107-125, 1968.
Negisi, K.: Photosynthesis, respiration and growth in 1-year-old seedlings of *Pinus densiflora*, *Cryptomeria japonica* and *Chamaecyparis obtusa*. – Bull. Tokyo Univ. Forests 62: 1-115, 1966.
Nevins, D. J., Loomis, R. S.: A method for determining net photosynthesis and transpiration of plant leaves. – Crop Sci. 10: 3-6, 1970a.
Nevins, D. J., Loomis, R. S.: Nitrogen nutrition and photosynthesis in sugar beet (*Beta vulgaris* L.). – Crop Sci. 10: 21-25, 1970b.
Nichiporovich, A. A., Strogonova, L. E., Chmora, S. N., Vlasova, M. P.: Fotosinteticheskaya Deyatel'nost' Rasteniĭ v Posevakh. [Photosynthetic Activity of Plants in Crops.] – Izd. Akad. Nauk SSSR, Moskva 1961.
Olson, J. M.: The evolution of photosynthesis. – Science 168: 438-446, 1970.
Osmond, C. B.: C_4 photosynthesis in the *Chenopodiaceae*. – Z. Pflanzenphysiol. 62: 129-132, 1970.
Ozbun, J. L., Volk, R. J., Jackson, W. A.: Effect of potassium deficiency on photosynthesis, respiration and the utilization of photosynthetic reductant by immature bean leaves. – Crop Sci. 5: 69-75, 1965.
Packer, L.: Evidence of contractility in chloroplasts. – In: Goodwin, T. W. (ed.): Biochemistry of Chloroplasts. Vol. I. Pp. 234-242. Academic Press, London–New York 1966.
Park, R. B.: Subunits of chloroplast structure and quantum conversion in photosynthesis. – Int. Rev. Cytol. 20: 67-95, 1966.
Park, R. B., Drury, S.: The effects of daylength on quantasome structure and chloroplast photochemistry in *Spinacia oleracea* L. var. Early Hybrid # 7. – In: Sironval, C. (ed.): Le Chloroplaste, Croissance et Vieillissement. Pp. 328-334. Masson, Paris 1967.
Pearce, R. B., Brown, R. H., Blaser, R. E.: Photosynthesis in plant communities as influenced by leaf angle. – Crop Sci. 7: 321-324, 1967.
Pearce, R. B., Brown, R. H., Blaser, R. E.: Photosynthesis of alfalfa leaves as influenced by age and environment. – Crop Sci. 8: 677-680, 1968.
Pearce, R. B., Carlson, G. E., Barnes, D. K., Hart, R. H., Hanson, C. H.: Specific leaf weight and photosynthesis in alfalfa. – Crop Sci. 9: 423-426, 1969.
Pisek, A.: Die photosynthetische Leistungen besonderer Standorte. *a*) Pflanzen der Arktis und des Hochgebirges. – In: Ruhland, W. (ed.): Handbuch der Pflanzenphysiologie. Vol. V/2. Pp. 376-414. Springer Verlag, Berlin–Göttingen–Heidelberg 1960.
Pisek, A., Larcher, W., Moser, W., Pack, I.: Kardinale Temperaturbereiche der Photosynthese und Grenztemperaturen des Lebens der Blätter verschiedener Spermatophyten. III. Temperaturabhängigkeit und optimaler Temperaturbereich der Netto-Photosynthese. – Flora, Abt. B 158: 608-630, 1969.
Pollack, M., Pringsheim, P., Terwood, D.: A method for determining small quantities of oxygen. – J. chem. Phys. 12: 295-299, 1944.
Prediction and Measurement of Photosynthetic Productivity. – PUDOC, Wageningen 1970.
Preiss, J., Kosuge, T.: Regulation of enzyme activity in photosynthetic systems. – Annu. Rev. Plant Physiol. 21: 433-466, 1970.
Rabinowitch, E. I.: Photosynthesis and Related Processes. Vol. I, II/1, II/2. – Intersci. Publ., New York 1945, 1951, 1955.
Rabinowitch, E., Govindjee: Photosynthesis. – J. Wiley & Sons, New York–London–Sydney–Toronto 1969.
Raschke, K.: Über den Einfluß der Diffusionswiderstände auf die Transpiration und die Tempe-

ratur eines Blattes. – Flora 146: 546-578, 1958.
Roberts, B. R.: Effects of water stress on the translocation of photosynthetically assimilated carbon-14 in yellow poplar. – In: Zimmermann, M. H. (ed.): The Formation of Wood in Forest Trees. Pp. 273-288. Academic Press, New York 1964.
Robinson, J. M., Stocking, C. R.: Oxygen evolution and the permeability of the outer envelope of isolated whole chloroplasts. – Plant Physiol. 43: 1597-1604, 1968.
Ruhland, W. (ed.): Handbuch der Pflanzenphysiologie. Vol. V/1, V/2. Die CO_2-Assimilation. – Springer-Verlag, Berlin–Göttingen–Heidelberg 1960.
Ryle, G. J. A., Hesketh, J. D.: Carbon dioxide uptake in nitrogen-deficient plants. – Crop Sci. 9: 451-454, 1969.
Sahlström, H.: The photosynthetic effect with *Begonia* × *cheimantha* and some temperature observations under different greenhouse shadings. – Lantbrukshögskolans Ann. 33: 737-749, 1967.
San Pietro, A., Greer, F. A., Army, T. J.: Harvesting the Sun: Photosynthesis in Plant Life. – Academic Press, New York–London 1967.
Santarius, K. A., Ernst, R.: Das Verhalten von Hill-Reaktion und Photophosphorylierung isolierter Chloroplasten in Abhängigkeit vom Wassergehalt. I. Wasserentzug mittels konzentrierter Lösungen. – Planta 73: 91-108, 1967.
Santarius, K. A., Heber, U.: Das Verhalten von Hill-Reaktion und Photophosphorylierung isolierter Chloroplasten in Abhängigkeit von Wassergehalt. II. Wasserentzug über $CaCl_2$. – Planta 73: 109-137, 1967.
Schindler, F. J.: Oxygen kinetics of the cytochrome oxidase–oxygen reaction. – Fed. Proc. 23: 322, 1964.
Schmid, G. H., Gaffron, H.: Light metabolism and chloroplast structure in chlorophyll-deficient tobacco mutants. – J. gen. Physiol. 50: 563-582, 1967.
Scott, K. J., Smillie, R. M.: Metabolic regulation in diseased leaves. I. The respiratory rise in barley leaves infected with powdery mildew. – Plant Physiol. 41: 289-297, 1966.
Semenenko, V. E.: Ustanovka dlya izucheniya kinetiki induktsionnogo perioda fotosinteza s differentsial'nym gazoanalizatorom uglekisloty na termistorakh. [Apparatus for measuring kinetics of induction period of photosynthesis with a differential gas analyser of carbon dioxide using thermistors.] – Fiziol. Rast. 5: 561-568, 1958.
Semikhatova, O. A., Chulanovskaya, M. V.: Manometricheskie Metody Izucheniya Dykhaniya i Fotosinteza Rasteniĭ. [Manometric Methods of Studying Plant Respiration and Photosynthesis.] – Nauka, Moskva–Leningrad 1965.
Šesták, Z.: Age- and chlorophyll-dependent changes in the photosynthetic activity of leaves. – 4th Int. Photobiol. Congr., Authors' Abstracts. P. 134. Oxford 1964.
Šesták, Z.: Limitations for finding a linear relationship between chlorophyll content and photosynthetic activity. – Biol. Plant. 8: 336-346, 1966.
Šesták, Z., Čatský, J. (ed.): Metody Studia Fotosynthetické Produkce Rostlin. [Methods of Studying Photosynthetic Production of Plants.] – Academia, Praha 1966.
Šesták, Z., Čatský, J.: Sur les relations entre le contenu en chlorophylle et l'activité photosynthétique pendant la croissance et le vieillissement des feuilles. – In: Sironval, C. (ed.): Le Chloroplaste, Croissance et Vieillissement. Pp. 213-262. Masson, Paris 1967.
Šesták, Z., Václavík, J.: Relationship between chlorophyll content and photosynthetic rate during the vegetation season in maize grown at different constant soil water levels. – In: Slavík, B. (ed.): Water Stress in Plants. Pp. 210-218. Publ. House Czechosl. Acad. Sci., Praha, and Dr. W. Junk N.V. – Publ., The Hague 1965.
Shibata, K., Takamiya, A., Jagendorf, A. T., Fuller, R. C. (ed.): Comparative Biochemistry and Biophysics of Photosynthesis. – Univ. Tokyo Press, Tokyo, and Univ. Park Press, State Coll., Pennsylvania 1968.
Shiroya, T., Lister, G. R., Slankis, V., Krotkov, G., Nelson, C. D.: Seasonal changes in respiration, photosynthesis, and translocation of the ^{14}C labelled products of photosynthesis in young *Pinus strobus* L. plants. – Ann. Bot. N.S. 30: 81-91, 1966.
Simonis, W.: Wasserpflanzen. – In: Ruhland, W. (ed.): Handbuch der Pflanzenphysiologie. Vol. V/1. Pp. 164-181. Springer-Verlag, Berlin–Göttingen–Heidelberg 1960.
Sironval, C. (ed.): Le Chloroplaste, Croissance et Vieillissement. – Masson, Paris 1967.

Sironval, C., Englert, E.: Action de la durée des jours sur la croissance et le contenu des chloroplastes d'épinard. – In: Sironval, C. (ed.): Le Chloroplaste, Croissance et Vieillissement. Pp. 335-348. Masson, Paris 1967.

Slack, C. R., Hatch, M. D.: Comparative studies on the activity of carboxylases and other enzymes in relation to the new pathway of photosynthetic carbon dioxide fixation in tropical grasses. – Biochem. J. 103: 660-665, 1967.

Slatyer, R. O.: Physiological significance of internal water relations to crop yield. – In: Physiological Aspects of Crop Yield. Pp. 53-88. Amer. Soc. Agron., Madison, Wisc. 1969.

Slavík, B.: Hydration level and photosynthetic activity. – Acta Univ. Carolinae – Biol. 1966 (Suppl. 1/2): 45-52, 1966.

Socrates, G., Sapper, L. J.: SI and Metrical Conversion Tables. – Newnes-Butterworths, London 1969.

Spruit, C. J. P., Kok, B.: Simultaneous observation of oxygen and carbon dioxide exchange during non-steady state of photosynthesis. – Biochim. biophys. Acta 19: 417-424, 1956.

Starzecki, W.: The role of the palisade and spongy parenchymas of leaves in photosynthesis. – Acta Soc. Bot. Polon. 31: 419-436, 1962.

Stocker, O., Vieweg, G. H.: Die Darmstädter Apparatur zur Momentanmessung der Photosynthese unter ökologischen Bedingungen. – Ber. Deut. bot. Ges. 73: 198-208, 1960.

Sweet, G. B., Wareing, P. F.: Role of plant growth in regulating photosynthesis. – Nature 210: 77-79, 1966.

Takakura, T.: The effect of room ventilation on net photosynthesis rate. – Bot. Mag. (Tokyo) 79: 143-151, 1966.

Talling, J. F.: Photosynthesis under natural conditions. – Ann. Rev. Plant Physiol. 12: 133-154, 1961.

Thomas, J. B., Goedheer, J. C. (ed.): Currents in Photosynthesis. – Ad. Donker-Publ., Rotterdam 1966.

Thomas, J. B., van Lierop, J. H., Ten Ham, M.: Dichroism in spinach chloroplasts. – Biochim. biophys. Acta 143: 204-220, 1967.

Thorne, G. N.: Photosynthesis of ears and flag leaves of wheat and barley. – Ann. Bot. N.S. 29: 317-329, 1965.

Tödt, F., Damaschke, K., Rothbühr, L.: Die elektrochemische Messung von Sauerstoffumsätzen bei der Photosynthese. – Biochem. Z. 325: 210-222, 1954.

Tödt, F., Teske, G., Windisch, F., Heumann, W., Goslich, C.: Elektrochemische Messung der in Flüssigkeiten gelösten Sauerstoffmengen bei oxy- und anoxybiotischen Stoffwechselprozessen. – Biochem. Z. 323: 192-213, 1952.

Tranquillini, W.: The physiology of plants at high altitudes. – Ann. Rev. Plant Physiol. 15: 345-362, 1964.

Treharne, K. J., Cooper, J. P.: Effect of temperature on the activity of carboxylases in tropical and temperate *Graminae*. – J. exp. Bot. 20: 170-175, 1969.

Treharne, K. J., Eagles, C. F.: Effect of temperature on photosynthetic activity of climatic races of *Dactylis glomerata* L. – Photosynthetica 4: 107-117, 1970.

Troughton, J. H.: Plant water status and carbon dioxide exchange of cotton leaves. – Austr. J. biol. Sci. 22: 289-302, 1969.

Troughton, J. H., Slatyer, R. O.: Plant water status, leaf temperature, and the calculated mesophyll resistance to carbon dioxide of cotton leaves. – Austr. J. biol. Sci. 22: 815-827, 1969.

Verduin, J.: A table of photosynthetic rates under optimal, near natural conditions. – Amer. J. Bot. 40: 675-679, 1953.

Verduin, J.: Photosynthesis in conifers computed per unit leaf area, dry weight, volume, chlorophyll content and respiratory rate. – Ecology 40: 738, 1959.

Verduin, J., Whitwer, E. E., Cowell, B. C.: Maximal photosynthetic rates in nature. – Science 130: 268-269, 1959.

Vidaver, W.: Gas-flow electrode assembly for measurements of rate of O_2 exchange. – Carnegie Inst. Washington Year Book 63: 466-468, 1964.

Volk, R. J., Jackson, W. A.: Mass spectrometric measurement of photosynthesis and respiration in leaves. – Crop Sci. 4: 45-48, 1964.

Voznesenskiĭ, V. L., Zalenskiĭ, O. V., Semikhatova, O. A.: Metody Issledovaniya Fotosinteza i

Dykhaniya Rasteniĭ. [Methods of Studying Plant Photosynthesis and Respiration.] – Nauka, Moskva–Leningrad 1965.
Wada, Y.: Changes of photosynthetic and respiratory activities and of chlorophyll content in growing leaves of some tobacco varieties. – Bot. Mag. (Tokyo) 81: 25-32, 1968.
Walker, D. A., Crofts, A. R.: Photosynthesis. – Annu. Rev. Biochem. 39: 389-428, 1970.
Walker, J. M., Waygood, E. R.: Ecology of *Phragmites communis*. I. Photosynthesis of a single shoot *in situ*. – Can. J. Bot. 46: 549-555, 1968.
Wardlaw, I. F.: The effect of water stress on translocation in relation to photosynthesis and growth. I. Effect during grain development in wheat. – Austr. J. biol. Sci. 20: 25-39, 1967.
Wardlaw, I. F.: The control and pattern of movement of carbohydrates in plants. – Bot. Rev. 34: 79-105, 1968.
Wareing, P. F., Khalifa, M. M., Treharne, K. J.: Rate-limiting processes in photosynthesis at saturating light intensities. – Nature 220: 453-457, 1968.
Weast, R. C. (ed.): Handbook of Chemistry and Physics. 49th Ed. – Chemical Rubber Co., Cleveland, Ohio 1968.
von Wettstein, D.: Chloroplast structure and genetics. – In: San Pietro, A., Greer, F. A., Army, T. J. (ed.): Harvesting the Sun. Pp. 153-190. Academic Press, New York–London 1967.
Whittingham, C. P.: Photosynthesis in *Chlorella* during intermittent illumination of long periodicity. – Plant Physiol. 29: 473-477, 1954.
Whittingham, C. P.: Induction phenomena of photosynthetic algae at low partial pressure of oxygen. – J. exp. Bot. 7: 273-289, 1956.
Wilson, D., Cooper, J. P.: Assimilation of *Lolium* in relation to leaf mesophyll. – Nature 214: 989-992, 1967.
Wilson, D., Cooper, J. P.: Effect of light intensity and CO_2 on apparent photosynthesis and its relationship with leaf anatomy in genotypes of *Lolium perenne* L. – New Phytol. 68: 627-644, 1969a.
Wilson, D., Cooper, J. P.: Apparent photosynthesis and leaf characters in relation to leaf position and age, among contrasting *Lolium* genotypes. – New Phytol. 68: 645-655, 1969b.
Wilson, D., Cooper, J. P.: Effect of temperature during growth on leaf anatomy and subsequent light-saturated photosynthesis among contrasting *Lolium* genotypes. – New Phytol. 68: 1115-1123, 1969c.
Wilson, D., Cooper, J. P.: Effect of light intensity during growth on leaf anatomy and subsequent light-saturated photosynthesis among contrasting *Lolium* genotypes. – New Phytol. 68: 1125-1135, 1969d.
Wilson, G. L., Ludlow, M. M.: Net photosynthetic rates of tropical grasses and legume leaves. – Proc. XI Int. Grassland Congr. Pp. 534-538. Univ. Queensland Press, 1970.
Woledge, J., Jewiss, O. R.: The effect of temperature during growth on the subsequent rate of photosynthesis in leaves of tall fescue (*Festuca arundinacea* Schreb.). – Ann. Bot. N.S. 33: 897-913, 1969.
Wolf, F. T.: Plants with high rates of photosynthesis. – Biologist 51: 147-155, 1969.
Zelitch, I.: Stomatal control. – Ann. Rev. Plant Physiol. 20: 329-351, 1969a.
Zelitch, I.: Mechanisms of carbon fixation and associated physiological responses. – In: Eastin, J. D. *et al.* (ed.): Physiological Aspects of Crop Yield. Pp. 207-226. Amer. Soc. Agron., Madison, Wisc. 1969b.

2 | GENERAL PRINCIPLES OF GASOMETRIC METHODS AND THE MAIN ASPECTS OF INSTALLATION DESIGN

It is clear from the discussion of different kinds of methods in Chapter 1, that gasometric methods are eminently suitable for estimating photosynthesis in many kinds of investigation, and that they are particularly suitable in circumstances which require regular measurement and continuous recording. Consequently, it is not suprising that gasometric methods are the most widely used methods for determining the gas exchange rates and photosynthetic activity of plants and parts of plants. In a general sense, all methods based on measuring gas exchange should be included in a discussion of gasometric methods. Some such methods, such as the manometric and aerodynamic methods of estimating gas exchange are discussed in detail in later chapters of this volume. In this chapter only those methods will be considered in which changes in gas composition of a limited, measured volume of air result from the activity of the plant, *i.e.* methods using assimilation chambers. As discussed in Chapter 1, gasometric methods based on the exchange of carbon dioxide are most frequently used for measurements of photosynthesis. Determination of oxygen exchange has been used less frequently with leaves and organs of higher plants (although the O_2 exchange of algae is frequently measured). The overall system in which oxygen exchange can be measured is in principle similar to that for carbon dioxide although the instruments for detecting oxygen are somewhat different. Specific examples of systems in which both carbon dioxide and oxygen exchange have been measured are described in Section 3.14. In this chapter the main emphasis will be on the measurement of carbon dioxide exchange.

2.1 | Major components of gas exchange systems

First acquaintance with a gas exchange system is frequently awe-inspiring because of its apparent complexity and large number of components. For convenience the system can be considered as made up of four groups of components.

1. The assimilation chamber[1]. This is a chamber in which the plant or part of the plant is enclosed to facilitate the measurement of gas exchange. The rate of gas exchange is determined from the changes in concentration of the gas in the ambient air surrounding the plant material and caused by the presence of the plant material. The plant material may be a leaf or other organ, or parts of the plant, the whole plant or part of a stand. A reliable determination of carbon dioxide exchange can be obtained if the assimilating (or respiring) plant material is placed in an enclosure within which no exchange of air with the surrounding atmosphere occurs, or where such an exchange occurs at a controlled and measured rate. It is most usual to completely isolate the plant material from the surroundings by enclosing it in a chamber in which water vapour and gas exchanges occur in well defined conditions of irradiance, temperature, humidity, ambient carbon dioxide concentration, and

1. This term is preferred; but terms as irradiation chamber, exposure chamber, leaf chamber *etc.* are often used for special designs (see, *e.g.*, Chapters 7 and 9).

air movement. This is the assimilation chamber, discussed in more detail in Sections 2.4 to 2.7.

2. Carbon dioxide analyser. The change in gas concentration of the air caused by the plant material is determined from measurements of the gas concentration of the air entering the chamber (the reference air stream) and that leaving the chamber (the sample air stream). Carbon dioxide and oxygen analysers suitable for this are discussed in Section 2.3 and Chapters 3 and 4.

3. Gas handling system. This system transports air through various air conditioning procedures to the assimilation chamber and thence transports the reference and sample air streams to the gas and humidity analysers. It consists of leak-proof, CO_2-inert pumps of appropriate capacity (Section 3.8.3), CO_2-impermeable and inert tubing of low resistance to air movement (Section 3.8.2), flow meters (Section 3.8.4) and auxiliary attachments to the gas analysers, such as solenoid valves, air filters *etc.*

4. Air conditioning system. The air entering the assimilation chamber is treated beforehand to have known, predetermined temperature, humidity, CO_2, and in some cases O_2, concentration. Since it is the conditions within the chamber which it is actually desired to control, the air conditioning components which regulate the properties of the air entering the chamber may be controlled by feed-back from sensors within the assimilation chamber, or from the sensors analysing the sample air stream. This system will be discussed in more detail in Section 2.6.

2.2 | Gas exchange systems

Gas exchange systems may be classified into three types (Brown 1968; Larcher 1969): closed, semi-closed, and open.

2.2.1 | Closed system

In a closed system (see *e.g.* Orchard & Heath 1964; Stout 1967) both the air input to and output from the assimilation chamber are connected to the gas analyser(s) with a pump in the interconnecting air line. The total volume of gas circulating may be passed through the gas analyser (Fig. 2.1*a*) or, if the volume that must be circulated is too large, a part may be drawn off with a second pump and passed to the gas analyser (Fig. 2.1*b*).

It is essential that the entire system of assimilation chamber, pump, tubing and gas analyser(s) be completely air-tight. The enclosed air circulates between analyser and chamber where its composition is changed by the plant material. The CO_2 concentration in the air changes gradually because of CO_2 exchange by the plant. The rate of CO_2 exchange is obtained from a curve of CO_2 concentration against time at selected ambient CO_2 concentrations; alternatively the time required for the CO_2 concentration in the system to change by a certain amount, is recorded. The rate of CO_2 exchange is given by

$$F = \frac{\Delta C}{t} \cdot \frac{V}{A} \qquad (2.1)$$

 where

F = influx or efflux of CO_2 [$kg\ m^{-2}\ s^{-1}$],
$\Delta C/t$ = rate of change in CO_2 concentration [$kg\ m^{-3}\ s^{-1}$],
V = the volume of air enclosed in the system [m^3],
A = the area of one surface of the leaf [m^2].

Closed systems have a practical advantage in that they are relatively simple. The whole system must be free of leaks and this is not always easy to obtain. One gas analyser is required for each chamber, and this can prove expensive in replicated experiments, but precise measurements of flow rate are not required.

On the other hand they suffer from two serious failings:

Firstly, steady state observations are not obtained. This is particularly relevant with regard to measurements of photosynthesis because stomatal aperture may take anything up to an hour to respond completely to quite small changes in ambient CO_2 and this significantly influences the estimate of photosynthetic rate.

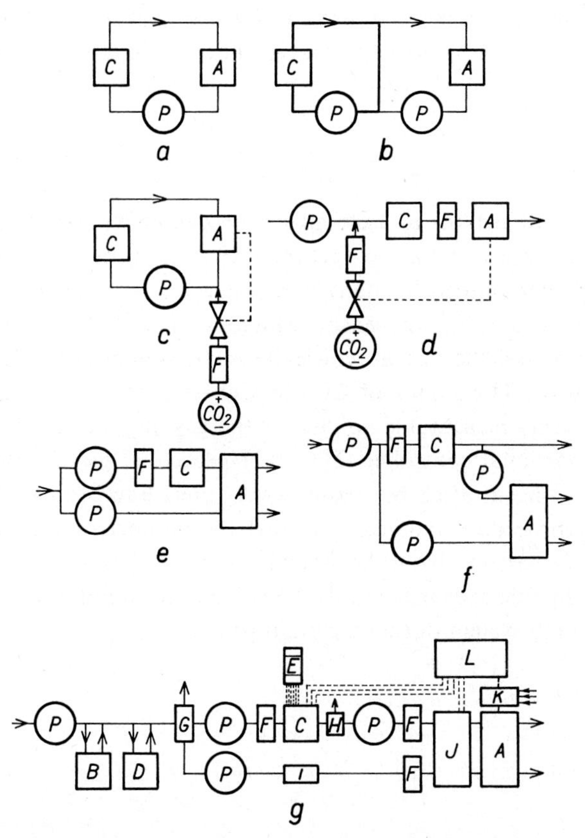

Fig. 2.1 Diagram to show the main features of different kinds of gas exchange systems. *a* and *b* closed systems; *c* and *d* semi-closed systems; *e*, *f*, *g* open systems. In *a* to *f* only the principal components are shown: *A* infra-red gas analyser; *C* assimilation chamber; *F* flow meter; *P* pump. In *g* additional components which may be found in a simple working system are shown: *B* carbon dioxide control unit; *D* humidity control unit; *E* temperature, lighting and ventilation control units; *G* manifold reservoir with blow off to atmospheric pressure; *H* blow off chamber; *I* by-pass; *J* humidity or oxygen measuring instrument; *K* gas analyser calibration unit; *L* data recorder. The positions of the various components, the pumps especially, can be varied to suit individual needs.

Secondly, photosynthesis is not linearly related to ambient carbon dioxide concentration except in the region of about 100 to 200 $\mu l\ l^{-1}$. Consequently it is extremely difficult to define the ambient concentration at which the measurements have been made when the time taken for the concentration to change over a certain CO_2 concentration range is measured. It is clearly erroneous to measure the time for the ambient concentration to fall from say 400 to 200 $\mu l\ l^{-1}$ and to consider the rate of photosynthesis obtained representative of that at the normal ambient concentration of 300 $\mu l\ l^{-1}$.
Hence the system should be used over only small changes in ambient CO_2 concentration, and when the concentration is changing slowly, to provide estimates of photosynthetic rate. Even then the results should not be regarded as very precise. The system is no more acceptable for comparative experiments because the response of stomata in different species or treatments may vary widely.
A closed system is particularly useful in the determination of the CO_2 compensation concentration and gives a more accurate result than that obtained from linear extrapolation of photosynthesis at CO_2 concentrations above the compensation concentration.

2.2.2 | *Semi-closed system*

The two most serious objections to a closed system can be eliminated by adding CO_2 to the system (or removing it) so that the CO_2 concentration in the system is maintained at a predetermined constant level (Fig.2.1*c*, *d*). In such a system the gas analyser operates as a null-point sensor regulating the supply of CO_2 or CO_2-free air to the system, and the rate at which the gas is supplied is recorded (*e.g.* Koller & Samish 1964). The supply of CO_2 or CO_2-free air may be in repeated doses of a certain, easily measurable volume or the gas may be supplied continuously using a proportional controller. The latter procedure gives closer control of the ambient CO_2 concentration but requires very precise recording flowmeters, whereas the former procedure requires only that the number of volumes added is counted. Surplus air escapes from the system *via* an overflow.
The rate of carbon dioxide exchange is calculated from the amount of CO_2 added to or removed from the system during a certain period:

$$F = \frac{V'}{t} \cdot \frac{(C' - C'')}{A} \tag{2.2}$$

where
V' is the volume of gas added to the system $[m^3]$ in time t $[s]$,
C' is the concentration of CO_2 in the gas added to the system $[kg\ m^{-3}]$,
C'' is the concentration of CO_2 in the air in the system at the analyser $[kg\ m^{-3}]$.
An alternative procedure available when respiration is being measured is to circulate a part of the air in the system at a measured rate through a by-pass which contains an agent, such as '*Ascarite*' or '*Carbosorb*', which removes CO_2 from the air at a rate just sufficient to maintain the CO_2 concentration in the system constant. The rate of respiration is then given by

$$F = J' \cdot \frac{C''}{A} \qquad (2.3)$$

where

J' is the flow rate through the by-pass $[m^3\ s^{-1}]$

The semi-closed system can be used advantageously with large assimilation chambers for whole plants or groups of plants (*e.g.* Musgrave & Moss 1961; Moss 1963; Baker & Musgrave 1964; Eckardt 1968; Wolf 1969) and in such cases pure CO_2 can be metered into the system. For leaves and small plants, however, the amount of CO_2 required to maintain the concentration in the system is so small that the rate of addition of pure CO_2 is difficult to regulate and measure with the required precision. Hence a mixture of CO_2 in air of the order of 0.2% by volume is added (Koller & Samish 1964).

The same principles of control and measurement can also be applied to humidity. Dry air can be added to the system at a controlled and measured rate to offset the increase in humidity resulting from transpiration and to maintain the humidity in the system constant. To some extent this must occur when dry CO_2 or CO_2-free air is added to the system. In this case the flux of water vapour is given by an expression similar to equation (2.2). A humidity sensor is used as a null-point sensor as in the case of CO_2. Alternatively, a part of the air can be circulated through a by-pass containing a desiccant or other water vapour trap at a measured controlled rate so as to maintain the humidity in the system constant. In this case the flux of water vapour is given by an expression similar to equation (2.3). If both methods of removing humidity from the air are employed, as in the case of simultaneous measurement of CO_2 and water vapour flux, the water vapour flux is given by:

$$Q = \frac{\chi}{A}\left(J' + \frac{V'}{t}\right) \qquad (2.4)$$

where

Q is water vapour flux $[kg\ m^{-2}\ s^{-1}]$,

χ is absolute humidity at the humidity sensor $[kg\ m^{-3}]$.

The semi-closed system integrates the flux of CO_2 over a period of time. Consequently the system is not as sensitive to transient, short-term fluctuations in the rate of CO_2 exchange as the open system but it does provide easier regulation of the ambient CO_2 concentration.

2.2.3 | *Open system*

In an open system an air stream of known, and in many cases conditioned, properties is passed through the assimilation chamber at a measured, constant flow rate. All or part of it is then passed through the gas analyser(s) before it exhausts from the system (Fig. 2.1*e,f*). In a completely open system there is no recirculation. The carbon dioxide flux is then given by:

$$F = J \cdot \frac{\Delta C}{A} \qquad (2.5)$$

where
J is the rate of flow of air through the assimilation chamber [$m^3\ s^{-1}$],
ΔC is the change in CO_2 concentration of the air as a result of passage through the chamber [$kg\ m^{-3}$].
This calculation is discussed in more detail in Section 3.12.2. The water vapour flux is estimated in an analogous manner.
In some circumstances the rate of evaporation from the plant material may be such that there is risk of condensation in the chamber or in the tubing. For this reason, it is common practice to add a recirculation loop to an open system for the removal of water vapour. A part of the air leaving the chamber is recirculated at a known flow rate through a water vapour trap before re-entering the chamber. The total water vapour flux is then given by:

$$Q = \frac{1}{A}(J \cdot \Delta\chi + J' \cdot \chi_a) \qquad (2.6)$$

where
$\Delta\chi$ is the change in absolute humidity of the air as a result of passage through the chamber [$kg\ m^{-3}$],
χ_a is the ambient humidity in the chamber [$kg\ m^{-3}$] and equal to the humidity at the humidity sensor if the air in the chamber is well stirred.
The rate of flow of air through the chamber is regulated in relation to the amount of plant material in the chamber and its photosynthetic activity. If CO_2 exchange with the air passing through the chamber is rapid a high air flow rate is used; if CO_2 exchange is slow a low air flow rate is used. In this way the CO_2 differential, ΔC, is usually maintained at about 20 $\mu l\ l^{-1}$. The accuracy with which such a differential can be measured is discussed in Sections 3.9 and 3.12.2. The differential should not be much larger than this because of the non-linearity of gas analyser response and because, if normal atmospheric air is being used, a large differential leads to an artificially low photosynthetic rate because of the strong dependence of photosynthesis upon ambient CO_2 concentration under many conditions. If the CO_2 content of the air stream is conditioned before it reaches the chamber, the size of the differential is less important since the ambient CO_2 concentration in the chamber can be adjusted to any predetermined level by regulating the mixing system and the flow rate through the chamber (Fig. 2.1*d*).
In a well stirred chamber the rate of photosynthesis is independent of flow rate through the chamber. In unstirred chambers, however, the boundary layer thickness is strongly dependent on the flow rate and so therefore is the photosynthetic rate:

$$F = f(r_a) = f(J^{-0.5}) \qquad \text{(Raschke 1960)}$$

where
r_a is the boundary layer resistance (see Chapter 16).
[The exponent rises to 0.7 in fully turbulent conditions but these are most unlikely to be met with even in well stirred chambers.] Hence in unstirred chambers a certain flow rate is required to reduce the boundary layer thickness to a reasonable level. It is highly desirable that the boundary layer resistance be kept both low

and reproducible, otherwise photosynthesis is strongly limited by CO_2 supply to the intercellular spaces, and changes in the physiological activity of the leaf are only insensitively reflected in the photosynthetic rate.
High ventilation rates and low boundary layer resistances can lead to excessive transpiration and the development of internal water deficits in imperfectly air-conditioned chambers. However this can be prevented by adjusting the ambient humidity or the temperature of the plant material.
The open system is particularly useful for investigation of single leaves, parts of plants or small plants. It allows the continuous recording of small rapid fluctuations and changes in photosynthetic rate with considerable accuracy.
From a technical point of view the open system is more complex because it has more components and because it requires the accurate measurement of flow rate. However it has the advantage that it does not have to be completely leak-proof and does not necessarily require a leak-free assimilation chamber. If the air flow circuit is so arranged that air is pushed through the chamber rather than sucked through, slight leakage is of little significance. This also applies to semi-closed systems (Koller & Samish 1964). A particularly useful consequence of this is that the air pressure in the assimilation chamber remains close to atmospheric pressure. This can be readily ensured by collecting the air flowing from the chamber into a vessel which is open to atmospheric pressure and from which a sample is taken for analysis. In the closed and semi-closed systems a considerable and often unknown elevation of pressure above atmospheric pressure may occur. This affects the

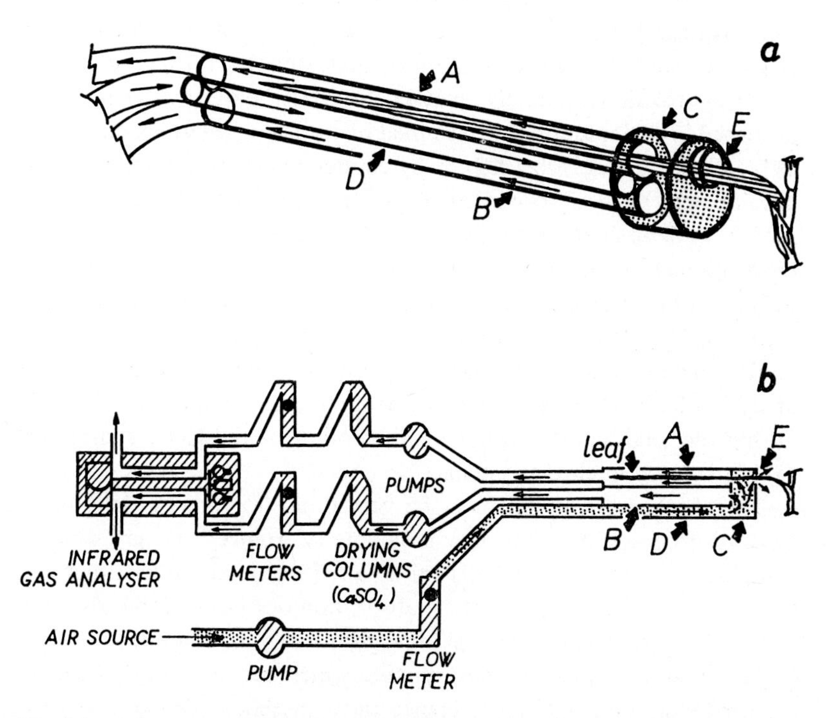

Fig. 2.2 *a:* A narrow air-seal chamber for leaves of cereals and grasses (after Wolf *et al.* 1969). *A* leaf compartment; *B* reference air compartment; *C* air-seal compartment; *D* air supply tube; *E* leaf port. Total length of chamber is 30 cm.
b: Arrangement of the air-seal chamber in a gas exchange system (symbols as above).

partial pressure of the gases and the measurement of flow rates. [All flow rates mentioned should be corrected to standard temperature and pressure (see Section 3.12.2).]

These features of open systems have been further developed into the use of the 'air seal'. A frequent troublesome problem is to seal a leaf into a chamber in a leak- and damage-free manner. Controlled leakage of air from the air stream which is on its way into the chamber, away from the chamber along the petiole, prevents unconditioned, unmonitored air from entering the chamber and thus provides an air seal (Fig. 2.2). This principle has recently been put to practical use in the field where it is particularly useful because it allows quick, simple insertion of the leaf into the chamber (*e.g.* Wolf *et al.* 1969).

2.3 | Types of carbon dioxide analysers

Reviews of different kinds of methods of CO_2 analysis have recently been provided by Bowman (1968) and Čatský (1970) (*cf.* also Davies 1969). Both integrating and continuously recording gas analysers may be used in gas exchange systems.

2.3.1 | Integrating analysers

Integrating analysers determine the total amount of carbon dioxide in a given volume of air: from this the CO_2 concentration can be calculated if desired. Both eudiometric and absorption methods are of this kind but in practice only absorption methods have been used. In the absorption methods, the air to be analysed is passed over or, finely divided into small bubbles, through a dilute solution of alkali hydroxide (*e.g.* KOH, NaOH, $Sr(OH)_2$, $Ba(OH)_2$). The amount of CO_2 absorbed in this solution is determined by titration (see for example Boysen-Jensen 1918, 1932; Lundegårdh 1922) or by conductimetry (see Section 4.4). Prior to the development of the infra-red gas analyser in the 1950s, these were the most commonly used methods of analysis and quite recently new modifications to these methods have been proposed (Fujiwara & Suzuki 1957; Loveland *et al.* 1959; Sanadze 1963; Bowman 1968). Notwithstanding the continuing interest in these methods, they do have some definite limitations:

a. Both eudiometric and absorption methods were originally devised for the analysis of air samples of a given volume, the composition of which changes during the analysis as a result of absorption of the CO_2. Hence such methods cannot be used in closed systems.

b. The absorbing solution must be very dilute for precise determination of the CO_2 absorbed by titration or conductimetry. Hence it is very difficult to realise complete absorption of all CO_2 in the air. In general the best that can be hoped for is that a repeatable percentage absorption occurs, and this also depends upon the flow rate of the analysed air through or over the solution.

c. The total amount of carbon dioxide which can be absorbed by a volume of absorbing solution is limited. Hence these methods can only be used for short term experiments unless the absorbing solution is regularly replaced or continuously regenerated.

d. Determination of the CO_2 absorbed by titration is prone to appreciable errors.

Conductimetric determination is more exact but even in this case it is difficult to obtain sufficient precision.

e. With an open system, either all the air leaving the assimilation chamber must pass through the absorber (Fig. 2.1*d*), and the assimilation chamber must be air-tight, or a sample of measured volume of the air leaving the chamber, is passed through the absorber (Fig. 2.1*f*). In the former case, the maximum air flow rate through the assimilation chamber is limited by the rate of flow allowable through the absorber. Furthermore a slight error in the estimate of this flow rate introduces a considerable error into the estimation of photosynthetic rate. Consider the following example:

- ambient CO_2 concentration = 0.6 mg l^{-1}
- amount of CO_2 absorbed = 5 mg
- actual flow rate = 10.0 l min^{-1}

then the rate of photosynthesis = $(10 \times 0.6) - 5 = 1.00$ mg CO_2 min^{-1}
however, if flow rate determined = 10.5 l min^{-1}
rate of photosynthesis calculated = $(10.5 \times 0.6) - 5 = 1.30$ mg CO_2 min^{-1}

Thus an error in the measurement of the flow rate of 5% results in an error in the estimate of photosynthesis of 30%. [Such an error in flow rate measurement results in a final error of only 5% in the case of continuous analysis (Section 2.3.2).] In the latter case, the calculation of CO_2 flux in the chamber depends upon the estimation of *two* volume flow rates, and this considerably enhances the error. The greatest accuracy is obtained with the absorption method if it is used in such a way that identical, known volumes of reference and of sample air are passed through absorbers in approximately equal time intervals. The CO_2 flux in the assimilation chamber is then given by the difference in the amounts of CO_2 absorbed in the two instances, largely independent of the flow rate (*cf.* Section 4.4). To achieve this, volumes of air are passed through the system from aspirators of precisely known and easily measured volume (Boysen-Jensen 1932; Lundegårdh 1954).

2.3.2 | *Continuous analysers*

Continuous analysers enable continuous analysis to be made of the CO_2 concentration in the atmosphere. In most cases the composition of the air passing through the analyser is not altered but some exceptions occur. Modifications to the absorption conductimetric method of Thomas (1933) (*e.g.* Thomas & Hill 1937) to enable continuous analysis to be made put that method in this category too (see Section 4.4). As noted previously, since CO_2 is absorbed from the air, such methods cannot be used in closed or semi-closed systems.

The more commonly used continuous analysers are based either upon physical principles (IR-spectroscopy, Chapter 3; heat conductivity, Section 3.15) or physico-chemical principles (conductimetric [Begg & Lake 1968] and electrometric methods, Sections 4.2 and 4.3). Most of the analysers discussed in detail in this manual belong to this group.

Such continuous analysers have facilitated the development of the closed and semi-closed gas exchange systems. They also have undeniable advantages in open systems and have replaced absorption methods in investigations on photosynthesis. The main advantages of continuous analysers are the following:

a. The estimate of gas concentration is independent of air flow rate over an appreciable range (*e.g.* from 50 to 5000 cm^3 min^{-1} for many instruments).
b. Continuous indication of gas concentration allows adjustments to be made, to the flow rate through the chamber for example, during the course of the experiment, to obtain maximum precision of measurement.
c. The precision of determination of photosynthetic rate is much less dependent upon the accuracy of the flow rate measurement than in the case of the absorption measurements. (*cf.* Section 2.3.1 *e*).

2.4 | Assimilation chambers and the scope and limitation of their application

The need to enclose plant material in an assimilation chamber to measure its gas exchange has in the past often been regarded as a major shortcoming of all gasometric methods. Whilst enclosure in assimilation chambers certainly does have definite disadvantages and creates difficulties of interpretation, it can provide an extremely convenient way of obtaining basic information about the characteristics of the photosynthetic apparatus. In general assimilation chambers are used in two main ways.
In the laboratory, plants are put into assimilation chambers to investigate the mechanisms of physiological processes by observing the response of gas exchange processes and the energy balance of the plant to closely controlled, step function changes in the external environment (*e.g.* irradiance, temperature, humidity, CO_2 and O_2 concentration) and internal environment (*e.g.* salt content, sugar content, hormone level, water potential).
For such experiments it is highly desirable to use plants with a well defined previous environmental history. The environmental conditions which the plants experience in the days preceeding the measurements have a large influence on photosynthesis and may indeed be a most useful experimental variable (*e.g.* Björkman & Holmgren 1963; Mooney & Shropshire 1967; Mooney & Harrison 1970).
From the observed responses to environmental conditions, the adaptation of the plant to the environment can be deduced and inferences drawn regarding the limiting rôle of the various partial processes which go to make up photosynthesis, *i.e.* the photochemical reaction, CO_2 transfer, carboxylation reaction, activity of the photosystems, photorespiration *etc.* (*e.g.* Björkman & Holmgren 1963; Björkman 1968a, b; Holmgren 1968a). The information obtained can also be combined with data about the microclimate and the structure of the stand in the field into models of photosynthesis in stand canopies which can be used to predict performance in the field (*e.g.* Monteith 1965a; de Wit 1965; Budyko & Gandin 1966; Duncan *et al.* 1967; Chartier 1970).
Since the object of such experiments is usually to elucidate processes rather than to simulate natural conditions, the environmental conditions in the chamber may be as artificial as is found useful in relation to the problem, and the enclosure of the plant presents no conceptual problems.
In the field, on the other hand, plants are frequently enclosed within chambers in attempts to describe their physiological behaviour in response to the naturally occurring variations in weather.
 The environmental conditions within the chamber, particularly air movement and

the fluxes of short and long wave radiation, can never be identical in all respects with those outside (Jarvis 1970). Hence enclosure of plants or part of a plant within a chamber in the field must be regarded as undesirable in principle if the object is to describe the physiological response of the plant to the naturally occurring weather (Philip 1966). With appropriate servo-operated, proportional control systems, external conditions of carbon dioxide concentration, humidity and air temperature averaged over periods of the order of seconds or tens of seconds can be closely simulated within the chamber (*e.g.* Bosian 1955, 1960, 1964b, 1965a, b, 1968; Eckardt 1966; Lange, Koch & Schulze 1969). However little or nothing can be done at present to simulate the more rapid, naturally occurring fluctuations in these properties, or the natural variations in air movement, and the energy balance of the plant material in the chamber is unavoidably very different from that of the free, unenclosed plant in several significant respects (Jarvis 1970). Consequently the conditions in the chamber must be regarded as unnatural although they may simulate the external conditions closely in many respects, and a decision, almost entirely subjective at the present time, must be made by each investigator, in each case, as to whether the artificial conditions in the chamber are likely to have physiological consequences not experienced by the adjacent unenclosed leaves. As a result considerable caution should be exercised in the interpretation of data obtained from chambers in the field, even when modern, sophisticated chambers have been used (Philip 1966; Jarvis 1970). Extremely unnatural micro-climatic conditions, especially temperature and humidity, arising in simple assimilation chambers have undoubtably led to many erroneous conclusions in the past (Bosian 1968). To some extent these problems have been overcome by the recent development of new chambers with control of temperature and humidity by sophisticated air conditioning techniques (see Sections 2.6 and 2.7.3). However few of the chambers in current use have been designed with the energy balance of the plant material in mind and it is certain that new types of chambers will be seen in the next few years (*cf.* Lee 1966; Jarvis 1970).

2.5 | Chamber microclimate and principles of assimilation chamber design

For a precise measurement of the rate of photosynthesis in relation to various environmental properties leading to an assessment of the relative rôles of the various partial processes of photosynthesis, it is essential to define the environmental conditions at the surface of the leaf as closely as possible. Indeed in some investigations this has been taken a stage further and certain environmental conditions, notably the CO_2 concentration, have been defined at the surface of the mesophyll cell wall by inducing a mass flow of air through a leaf held in an extremely specialised design of chamber (Troughton & Slatyer 1969) (see Section 2.7.3). On the other hand, the precise definition of conditions in the chamber may not be so important for general ecological purposes. To some extent then, design criteria must vary with the purpose to which the chamber is to be put.

The design of a functional assimilation chamber, which is as far as possible satisfactory both conceptually and in practice, depends upon a thorough understanding of the processes underlying and regulating the exchanges of energy and matter within the chamber. It is therefore highly pertinent to consider the supply to the plant material, and the exchanges, of carbon dioxide, water, heat and radiant energy within the chamber in relation to the mass movement of air within and through the chamber.

2.5.1 | Ventilation

A freely exposed leaf in the field is ventilated by eddies of air, usually completely turbulent in character and varying rapidly in size and mean velocity. The ventilation of any particular leaf is a function of the free movement of air above the vegetation and the aerodynamic roughness or drag coefficient of the ground and vegetation. (A simple description of the interactions between wind and vegetation is given by McIntosh & Thom 1969, Chapter 9.) This results in a complex pattern of rapidly changing ventilation around the leaves which can never be completely simulated either quantitatively or qualitatively in an assimilation chamber. Nevertheless there are a number of good reasons for having a controlled, known rate of air movement in assimilation chambers both in the field and in the laboratory. The ventilation rate determines the thickness of the boundary layer around the leaf, or the boundary layer resistance (for a definition see Chapter 16):

$$r_a = \mathrm{k} \cdot u^{-0.5}$$

where
u is the mean ventilation rate [m s^{-1}],
r_a is the boundary layer resistance [s m^{-1}],
k is a constant (see Raschke 1960; Monteith 1965b; Thom 1968; Parlange, Waggoner & Heichel 1970).
The boundary layer resistance controls, to a greater or lesser degree, the transfer of CO_2, O_2, water vapour, heat and momentum, between the ambient air and the leaf (see Chapter 16 for references) and hence influences the gas exchange and energy balance of the leaf. In particular changes in ventilation rate may be expected to either increase or decrease the flux of water vapour from the leaf in transpiration depending upon the relative magnitude of the boundary layer and other resistances, notably the stomatal resistance, in the water vapour pathway and hence on the relative amounts of energy going into convective and latent heat transfer (Raschke 1958; Monteith 1963; Gates 1968). That the thickness of the boundary layer can have a direct, rapid influence on photosynthetic rate is readily shown by measuring the rate of light saturated photosynthesis in relation to the rate of ventilation in the chamber (*e.g.* Hesketh & Musgrave 1962; Björkman & Holmgren 1963; Tranquillini 1964a, b; Avery 1966). Photosynthesis is found to be asymptotically related to increases in wind speed or ventilation rate in the chamber (Fig. 2.3) and the relationship between photosynthesis and $\sqrt{u}$ is approximately linear at low ventilation rates up until other limiting factors predominate (*cf.* also Tranquillini 1969). Hence it is highly desirable that the boundary layer resistance should be maintained constant throughout any one experiment and as reproducible as possible from one experiment to the next. This can be achieved by introducing stirring and circulation of air within the chamber by use of a propeller, fan or blower of some kind. With adequate stirring the boundary layer resistance can be reduced to a value of

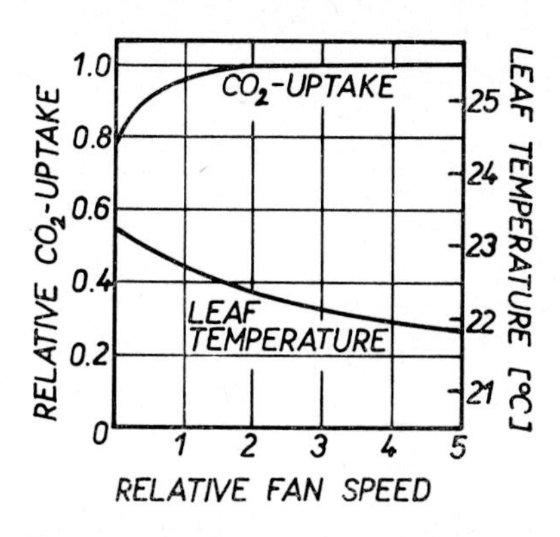

Fig. 2.3 The effect of rate of ventilation within an assimilation chamber upon rate of net photosynthesis and leaf temperature (from Björkman & Holmgren 1963).

the order of 0.1 s cm^{-1} and the air flow rate through the chamber can be varied over quite wide limits, to provide a suitable CO_2 differential (see Section 2.2.3) at different CO_2 fluxes, without any significant effect on the boundary layer resistance.

An additional valuable consequence of stirring the air is that gradients of CO_2, O_2 and water vapour across the chamber are eliminated. In unstirred chambers appreciable gradients of these properties occur so that it is extremely difficult if not impossible to define precisely the concentration of water vapour, CO_2, O_2 or other gases (in diffusion porometry, for example) close to the surface of the leaf: it is some complex, basically exponential, function of the concentration of the gases entering and leaving the chamber (see Section 2.5.2). With adequate stirring, however, the ambient concentration in the chamber may be taken as equal to that of the sample taken from the chamber for analysis. From a practical point of view it is necessary, in addition to introducing stirring, to ensure, by appropriate placement of the air intake and exhaust parts relative to the stirrer, that air entering the chamber is rapidly mixed into the bulk air and that eddies of unmixed air do not get swept into the exhaust port. This can be facilitated by reducing the size of the inlet port so that air enters the chamber in a jet and by reducing the exhaust port to a diameter only slightly larger (to prevent a pressure rise) than the inlet port. The introduction of smoke into the chamber demonstrates the extremely efficient, rapid mixing which results.

Whilst most systems of stirring in assimilation chambers provide perfectly adequate mixing, fully developed turbulence is not usually induced (Monteith 1965b).

2.5.2 | *Concentration of CO_2, water vapour and other gases*

The carbon dioxide concentration will be discussed: analogous considerations apply to water vapour and other gases. Air flowing through an unstirred assimilation chamber across a leaf is progressively impoverished in carbon dioxide (Egle & Schenk 1952; Fig. 2.4). Thus the part of the leaf farthest from the air inlet experiences the lowest ambient CO_2 concentration and hence may have an appreciably lower rate of photosynthesis at high irradiance because of the dependence of CO_2 uptake on the ambient CO_2 concentration.

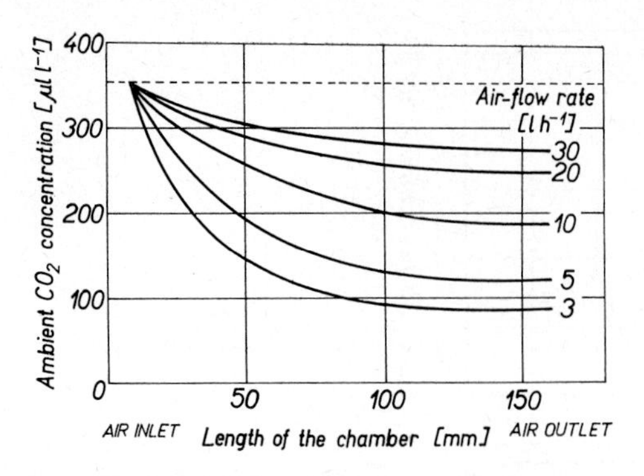

Fig. 2.4 The fall in ambient CO_2 concentration across a leaf in an unstirred assimilation chamber supplied with air from one side at different air flow rates (after Egle & Schenk 1952).

The mean ambient CO_2 concentration in an unstirred chamber is a function of the CO_2 concentration of the air entering the chamber, *i.e.* the CO_2 concentration of the reference and sample air streams, respectively. If the front of the air stream moves uniformly across the leaf and if the air stream is turbulent, an exponential reduction in CO_2 concentration would be expected (Egle & Schenk 1952; Gaastra 1959; Avery 1966) so that:

$$\bar{C}_a \approx \frac{C_r - C_s}{\ln C_r - \ln C_s}$$

where
$\bar{C}_a$ is the mean ambient CO_2 concentration [kg m^{-3}],
C_r is the reference air CO_2 concentration [kg m^{-3}],
C_s is the sample air CO_2 concentration [kg m^{-3}].
Others have assumed a linear decrease in CO_2 concentration across the leaf (*e.g.* Decker 1947; Negisi & Satoo 1961) and estimated $\bar{C}_a$ from

$$\bar{C}_a \approx \frac{C_r + C_s}{2}$$

However, if $C_r < 2C_s$ the difference between the two estimates is less than 4% so that it makes little difference which is used. Both these relationships represent a considerable over-simplification. In adequately stirred chambers the above approximations are not necessary and it may be assumed that $\bar{C}_a = C_s$.
In the past there has been a certain amount of interest in calculating a 'corrected' rate of net photosynthesis at a standard ambient CO_2 concentration, for example at 300 μl l^{-1}, from the rate measured at the mean ambient concentration, $\bar{C}_a$. The corrected rate has sometimes been calculated by simple proportion on the basis of a linear relationship between net CO_2 influx and ambient CO_2 concentration passing through the origin. Calculation of such a corrected rate of net photosynthesis is fraught with difficulties.
In the first place, it depends on an accurate knowledge of $\bar{C}_a$. As already mentioned,

this is not readily available in unstirred assimilation chambers. Gaastra (1959) developed a model of the gas exchange of a leaf in an unstirred chamber to investigate the conditions influencing the estimation of $\bar{C}_a$ for this purpose. He concluded that the estimation of $\bar{C}_a$ depends on the following factors:
- the air flow rate through the chamber
- the position of the leaf in the chamber
- the proportions of the volume flow passing over each surface
- the distance of the edges of the leaf from the chamber walls and the relative distribution of stomata on the two surfaces of the leaf.

Variation and uncertainties in these factors can lead to large variation in the estimation of $\bar{C}_a$ and errors in the determination of the corrected photosynthetic rate of 70% or more. Since unstirred chambers are not now commonly used this problem will not be discussed in more detail here, and the reader is referred to the monograph by Gaastra (1959). In stirred chambers a reliable estimation of $\bar{C}_a$ can be made.

Secondly, given an accurate estimate of $\bar{C}_a$, accurate estimation of a corrected rate of net photosynthesis at a standard ambient CO_2 concentration of 300 $\mu l\ l^{-1}$ depends upon accurate knowledge of the relationship between CO_2 influx and ambient CO_2 concentration for the particular plant material concerned. For most plants this relationship is linear over only a small range of ambient CO_2 concentration, *e.g.* 100 to 200 $\mu l\ l^{-1}$ (*cf.* Fig. 16.3), and for many species it does not pass through the origin but cuts the ambient CO_2 axis at around 50 $\mu l\ l^{-1}$. Hence estimation of a corrected rate of photosynthesis based on the two assumptions of a linear relationship passing through the origin cannot be justified in the majority of cases. Furthermore, the shape of the relationship between net CO_2 influx and ambient CO_2 concentration, and the intercept on the CO_2 concentration axis are influenced by the previous environmental history and the physiological state of the plant as well as the current environmental conditions. Hence it is not even sufficient to base such a correction on a once determined relationship for the experimental material: it must be known for the plant material to which the correction is to be applied. If the relationship is known for the plant material, then, of course, an arbitrary correction procedure is not required.

2.5.3 | *Radiation balance*

Placing an assimilation chamber around a leaf influences the radiant and convective exchanges of energy between the environment and the leaf and thereby affects the rate of photosynthesis, the temperature of the leaf and the rate of transpiration. In the laboratory this is of no great conceptual consequence, although it may be of practical significance in achieving the range of conditions required, because the response of the plant to closely defined conditions of the experimenter's own choosing within the assimilation chamber is observed. In some investigations this may also be the case in the field, but in many field investigations, plants or leaves are enclosed in assimilation chambers as a means to observe the physiological responses of the plant to natural variations in the weather and other environmental conditions. In such experiments, it is clearly essential that the physiological processes observed are not significantly influenced by the act of enclosing the leaves in an assimilation chamber. It is therefore of considerable importance to consider the consequences of enclosing the leaves in an assimilation chamber on the exchange of energy and the likely influence of disturbance to the energy exchanges on physiological processes. The implications of disturbance to the supply of radiation for photosynthesis and to the thermal energy balance are considered below.

In passing it may be noted that enclosing leaves in assimilation chambers creates a sampling problem. In the laboratory the problem is relatively straightforward and is concerned with the distribution of variation in physiological properties within the plant (*e.g.* Šesták & Čatský 1967) and within the population of plants being studied. In the field these sampling problems also arise, often to a greater degree, and are further complicated by the naturally occurring variation in leaf orientation and inclination. In the majority of studies with small assimilation chambers in the field this variability has not been taken into account: the leaves and chamber have usually been arbitrarily placed horizontally.

2.5.3.1 | The flux density of photosynthetically active radiation

For green leaves, the activity of the photochemical partial processes of photosynthesis depends upon the number of quanta absorbed within the wavelength range 400 to 700 nm. Over this range little wavelength specificity is shown (Hoover 1937; Gabrielsen 1940; Gaastra 1959; Björkman 1968b; Bulley, Nelson & Tregunna 1969). However routine measurement of absorption of quanta is not practical and generally the flux density of radiation (400 to 700 nm) incident upon the leaf is measured (but *cf.* McPherson 1969; Norman, Tanner & Thurtell 1969). Given the absorptance of the leaf and preferably the absorption spectrum, this may then be converted to the number of quanta absorbed if desired (Gaastra 1959, 1962; Rackham 1966; Björkman 1968b). Methods of measuring the flux density of radiation are described in Chapter 19. Reference may also usefully be made to the reviews by Withrow & Withrow (1956) and Anderson (1964).

To determine the response of net photosynthesis to irradiance, and in particular the photochemical efficiency or quantum requirement, the flux density of radiation incident upon the leaf must be defined precisely (see for example Björkman & Holmgren 1963). Since the window material of the chamber (*e.g.* glass, acrylic plastic) reduces the irradiance at the leaf surface as a result of reflection and absorption, the flux density of photosynthetically active radiation incident on the leaf should be measured with a sensor in the chamber in the plane of the leaf. Provided the sensor is calibrated against a standard thermopile for the appropriate light source and wavelength range (see Gaastra 1959), the kind of sensor is not important and a variety of photon sensitive and thermal sensors have been used. Silicon photovoltaic cells have proved very suitable and can be cut down to very small size, *e.g.* 1 mm^2, and yet have sufficient sensitivity. With a single leaf in the chamber, the incident flux density (and other conditions) at the leaf surface can be defined quite precisely and accurate estimates of photochemical efficiency obtained (*e.g.* Björkman & Holmgren 1963). Even then a problem arises as to how much irradiation the leaf receives on its under surface from reflection within the chamber.

 Because, at low irradiance, the effect on photosynthesis of incident radiation on the two surfaces of the leaf tends to be additive (Moss 1964), irradiance on the lower surface should be well defined or, preferably, zero. This can largely be achieved by adjusting the diameter of the chamber to be much the same as that of the leaf and by painting the interior of the chamber matt black (excluding the window, of course).

The problem of definition of the incident flux density of radiation is much more acute with plant material which cannot, because of its morphology, be exposed in one plane, *e.g.* the shoots of conifers, heaths and succulents. With such material it is generally not possible to obtain accurate response curves, relating photosynthesis to irradiance, which have a clear cut interpretation. The shoots or plants cannot be exposed so that all leaves receive the same, known total radiation flux density. For example, the apparent photochemical efficiency of a spruce shoot in a cylindrical chamber is increased if the radiation entering the chamber is diffused and reflected at all surfaces of the chamber, including the window through which it enters (Fig. 2.5). This suggests that a suitable chamber for accurate definition of photochemical efficiency for complex, and perhaps all, kinds of plant material, might be a sphere with internally reflecting walls and the source of radiation so arranged that the radiant flux is diffuse and omnidirectional, as in the Ulbricht sphere.

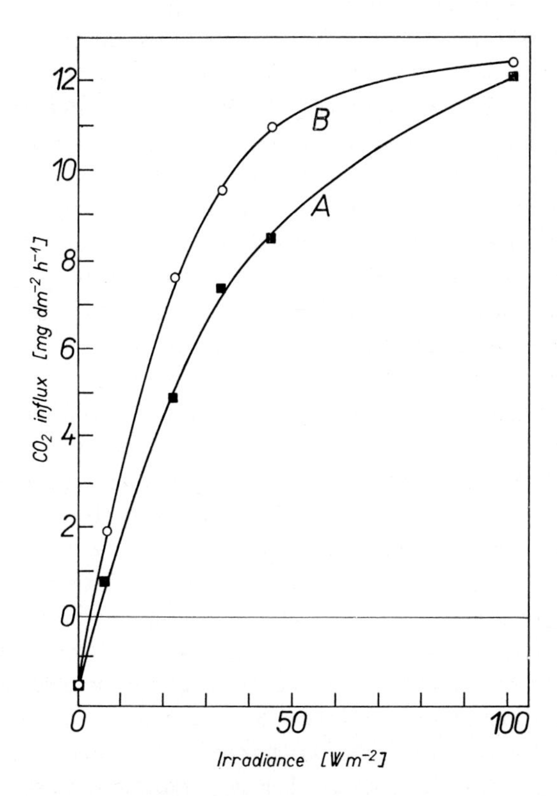

Fig. 2.5 The effect of diffusing the source of radiation incident upon a spruce shoot in an assimilation chamber upon the relationship between the rate of net photosynthesis and the flux density of radiation incident upon a horizontal surface normal to the direction of the radiation. Curve *A* source undiffused; curve *B* source diffused and internally reflected within the chamber.

Assimilation chambers of this kind are still in the embryonic stage of development and, in general, uniform irradiation of the leaf or plant in the laboratory is achieved by ensuring an even distribution of irradiance in the direct beam from the light source. Two methods are commonly used. One is to use a large source which irradiates a large area more or less homogeneously, such as a bank of closely packed high output fluorescent tubes, mercury vapour fluorescent lamps or photofloods, or, on a small scale, high wattage, cylindrical xenon (6 to 10 kW) or quartz-halide (2 to 5 kW) lamps, for example (for details of the properties and photosynthetic efficiencies of modern kinds of lamps see Gaastra 1970). Alternatively, a small lamp (*e.g.* various kinds of projection lamps, quartz-halide, mercury and xenon lamps) approximating to a point source, can be used with a system of lenses to provide parallel irradiation to uniformly illuminate a small chamber. The latter kind of arrangement has certain distinct advantages especially if the components of lamps, lenses and chamber are mounted on an optical bench: the flux density incident on the leaf is largely independent of the distance between source and leaf and it can be very sensitively controlled with shutters or a diaphragm to reduce the aperture without alteration of its spectral composition; in addition, solution, glass and interference filters can be readily introduced into the radiation path (*e.g.* Raschke 1967). Filters may be introduced both to reduce the amount of thermal radiation entering the chamber (see Section 2.5.3.2) and for the rough determination of action spectra. For the definition of wavelength bands within the range 400 to 700 nm, at high irradiance, glass and interference filters made by *Balzers* (Liechtenstein) have been used successfully in an optical system (Björkman 1968b).

In addition to the use of shutters and diaphragms, the flux density of radiation at the leaf can also be controlled by: varying the lamp output; varying the distance between lamp and leaf; and by interposing neutral filters. Varying the distance between lamp and leaf is simple and does not result in any changes in spectral composition (unless any stray light from other sources or from reflection reaches the leaf). However, it may result in a cumbersome mechanical hoist, unnecessary overheating of the laboratory and strain on the eyes if the system is not totally enclosed. Reducing irradiance by interposing neutral filters avoids the need to remove the lamp an appreciable distance from the leaf to obtain low irradiances, but suffers from the danger that many so-called neutral filters are not in fact neutral. Matt black netting, ground glass and cheese cloth (Brown 1968) are acceptably neutral. The radiant intensity from most kinds of lamps (excluding mercury vapour lamps) can now be readily controlled over a very wide range using modern thyristor or triac controllers. Some change in spectral composition may result and it is therefore desirable that the radiation sensor in the chamber be calibrated at a range of irradiances obtained in the same manner as in the experiments. If two of the methods of control discussed above are used in combination, for example varying position to give a range of high irradiances and voltage regulation to give a range of low irradiances, then two separate sensor calibration curves should be used.

In the field, the total photosynthetically active radiation incident upon a leaf may be very considerably changed by enclosing the leaf in an assimilation chamber. Some change is inevitable and cannot be avoided, but the degree of additional disturbance depends upon the design of the chamber. The physiological consequence of a decrease in incident radiation depends of course on whether photosynthesis by the leaf is light saturated or not, and this depends on the incident irradiance and physiological state of the tissue.

Consider a freely exposed horizontal leaf in the upper stratum of a plant canopy. The flux density of direct and diffuse photosynthetically active radiation on its upper surface from sun and sky is I_0 W m^{-2}. On its lower surface it will receive by reflection from leaves in its vicinity a flux density of about 0.07 I_0 (Bray, Sanger & Archer 1966) so that the total incident flux density of photosynthetically active radiation is 1.07 I_0. The reflectance (α) by the leaf for this incident radiation is 0.07 and the transmittance (β) by the leaf about 0.03 (Gates *et al.* 1965; Bray, Sanger & Archer 1966). Hence the absorptance of photosynthetically active radiation is $[1 - (\alpha + \beta)] = 0.9$ and the amount absorbed is $0.9 \times 1.07\ I_0 = 0.96\ I_0$. That is to say, the amount of photosynthetically active radiation absorbed is very nearly equal to the total incident flux density of such radiation.

If now the leaf is placed in an assimilation chamber such that the radiation incident upon it must first pass through a window of glass, acrylic plastic *('Plexiglass', 'Lucite'* or *'Perspex')* or other transparent plastic such as polyvinyl chloride, the short wave radiation balance is appreciably altered. With normal incidence of parallel irradiation, about 0.04 I_0 is lost by reflection at each of the two surfaces of the window and a further one or two per cent or more may not be transmitted, depending upon the optical properties and cleanliness of the material. In this respect acrylic plastic is a very suitable material. '*Perspex*' has a very low absorptance of less than 0.2% per cm in the body of the material and almost uniform transmittance of 0.92 from 400 to 800 nm (*ICI* handbook 'The Properties of '*Perspex*' Acrylic Materials', published anonymously and undated by *Imperial Chemical Industries Ltd.*, Plastics Division, Welwyn Garden City, Herts, U.K.). However the surfaces are readily scratched and abraded so that larger losses at the surfaces may occur. Thus a flux density of something less than 0.92 I_0, say 0.9 I_0, is incident upon the upper surface of the leaf, at normal incidence of parallel irradiation (Withrow & Withrow 1956). As the angle of incidence departs from the normal the reflection losses of direct radiation rise slowly at first and then, beyond

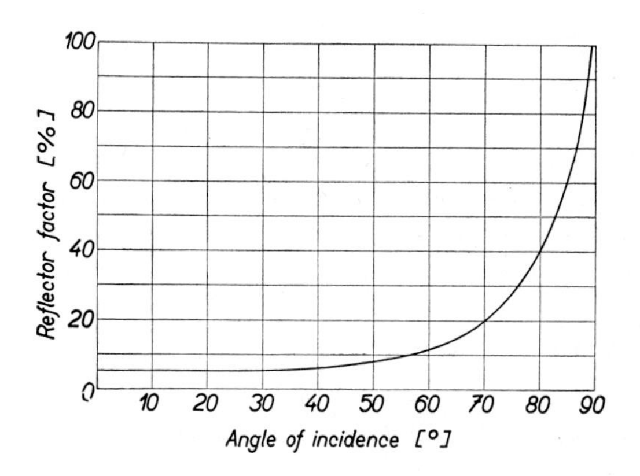

Fig. 2.6 The relationship between the angle of incidence of a beam of light striking a '*Perspex*' surface and the reflectance (from *ICI* handbook 'The Properties of "*Perspex*" Acrylic Materials').

60°, very rapidly (Fig. 2.6). Thus the flux density of radiation incident upon the upper surface of the leaf in the chamber is very much less than that incident upon the free, unenclosed leaf when the sun is near the horizon in the mornings and evenings, and, in the winter months, throughout the day. The integrated transmittance of diffuse radiation from the hemisphere of a sky of uniform brightness is *ca.* 0.85 (*ICI* Handbook). Hence the overall transmittance of new '*Perspex*' may be less than 0.9 in the middle of the day and very much less for used '*Perspex*' and for low angles of direct incident radiation.

The flux density of photosynthetically active radiation incident upon the lower surface of a leaf enclosed in an assimilation chamber depends upon the material of which the underside of the chamber is made. Three possibilities will be considered: a mirror, a matt black surface and a transparent window.

A mirror below the leaf will reflect photosynthetically active radiation efficiently so that the lower surface of the leaf may receive an appreciable fraction of I_0, perhaps 0.6 I_0. The exact amount depends upon the reflectance ($\approx$ 0.95) and proximity of the mirror and the extent to which it is shaded by the leaf, the solar altitude and relative proportions of direct and diffuse irradiance. At large angles of incidence, with the sun near the horizon, the flux incident upon the lower surface will become a large fraction of I_0 whereas the flux incident upon the upper surface becomes a smaller fraction of I_0. In the most usual conditions then the total flux of photosynthetically active radiation incident upon the leaf ($0.9\ I_0 + 0.6\ I_0 = 1.5\ I_0$) may be much larger than that incident upon the free, unenclosed leaf. Furthermore, it is divided between the upper and lower surfaces in a ratio of about 2 : 1, rather than *ca.* 14 : 1 for the free leaf. This, as shown by Moss (1964), may be expected to result in a much greater rate of photosynthesis than obtained by the free leaf if photosynthesis is not light saturated by an irradiance of 1.07 I_0. As the solar altitude and proportion of direct and diffuse radiation change, the total income of photosynthetically active radiation will vary in a manner difficult to predict. At times it will be greater than the flux density incident on the free leaf; at times it will be less: only infrequently will it coincide with the income of the free leaf, 1.07 I_0.

If the back of the chamber is painted with matt black paint (reflectance $\approx$ 0.05), the total flux density of photosynthetically active radiation incident on the leaf will always be less than that incident on the freely exposed leaf, though usually only by a small amount (*ca.* 10%) when the sun is near the zenith.

If the back of the chamber is also a window like the front, the total flux density incident on the leaf will also always be less than that incident on the free leaf. If radiation incident on the lower window is all diffuse and losses amount to about 15%, the maximum total incident flux density when the sun is near the zenith is $0.90\ I_0 + 0.06\ I_0 = 0.96\ I_0$, as opposed to 1.07 I_0 for the freely exposed leaf. At angles of incidence greater than about 50° the disparity rises rapidly.

This could be largely avoided by making the windows of hemispheres and the chamber spherical so that the cosine law is obeyed, but chambers of this design have not been used commonly, probably because of technical difficulties associated with introducing the necessary air conditioning. In any event, the fluxes of photosynthetically active radiation incident on both surfaces of the leaf should be measured continuously *in situ* in the assimilation chamber.

The problems associated with an artificial surface below the leaf do not arise when an area of vegetation is enclosed in a tent-like enclosure (*e.g.* Musgrave & Moss 1961; Baker 1965). Other problems arise, however, associated with sealing the chamber at the soil surface and gas exchange from the soil surface. Irradiance in the chamber will be lower than outside as with the single leaf chamber and for the same reasons. If the leaf area index is appreciable, photosynthesis of the lower canopy strata will be depressed even at midday, and more severely when the sun is nearer the horizon.

One can conclude this section by saying that the flux density of photosynthetically active radiation incident on leaves in assimilation chambers is generally unlike that incident on similarly exposed but unenclosed leaves, and sufficiently different, especially at large angles of incidence, to influence photosynthesis appreciably.

2.5.3.2 | Radiation balance and plant temperature

The temperature of leaves influences photosynthesis, largely by affecting the rates of the biochemical processes, and transpiration, largely by affecting water vapour pressure at the liquid-air interface in the leaf, and both processes to some extent by affecting the transfer resistances to CO_2 and water vapour. Methods of measuring leaf temperature are discussed in Chapter 17. In assimilation chambers thermocouples and thermistors inserted into the leaf or adpressed against the leaf surface are widely used for monitoring leaf temperature.

Leaf temperature is the resultant of the energy balance of the leaf (Section 17.6) and hence quantitative changes in the components of the energy balance result in changes in leaf temperature. These include the income and losses of solar and thermal radiation and the convective exchanges of sensible and latent heat, all of which are likely to be changed as a result of enclosing the leaf in an assimilation chamber.

As previously, consider a freely exposed, horizontal, broad leaf in the upper strata of a canopy receiving fluxes of direct and diffuse solar radiation from the sun, near its zenith, and the sky, equal to R_s W m^{-2}. On its lower surface it will receive by reflection from leaves in the vicinity about 0.20 R_s (Monteith 1959) making a total short-wave income of about 1.20 R_s. Short-wave reflectance of leaves is about 0.2 and transmittance of moderately thick leaves about 0.1 (Gates *et al.* 1965), and hence the absorptance of the leaf for this short-wave radiation is about 0.7. The amount absorbed is therefore $0.7 \times 1.20\ R_s = 0.84\ R_s$. The leaf also receives thermal radiation on both surfaces and radiates thermal radiation from both surfaces. The flux density of thermal radiation incident on the upper surface from the sky can be approximated from a variety of empirical equations, for example, from $(-\ \mathrm{a} + \mathrm{b}\,\sigma\, T_a^4)$ where a and b are empirical constants, σ is the Stefan-Boltzmann constant [5.70×10^{-8} W m^{-2} K^{-4}] and T_a [K] is the temperature of the ambient air (Swinbank 1963). The flux density incident on the lower surface is given by the Stefan-Boltzmann equation to be $\varepsilon\, \sigma\, T_a^4$ where ε is the emittance of the surrounding leaves taken as *ca.* 0.95 (Gates & Tantraporn 1952) and T_s [K] their temperature. The absorptance of the leaf for these fluxes of radiation is 0.95, equal to its emittance. The leaf radiates thermal radiation from each surface in relation to its own temperature, T'_l [K], so that the net exchange of thermal radiation is

$$0.95(-\ a + b\,\sigma\, T_a^4 + 0.95\,\sigma\, T_s^4 - 2\,\sigma\, T_l'^4)$$

Hence the radiation balance (R_n) of the leaf is given by

$$R'_n = 0.84\, R_s - 0.95\ a + 0.95\,\sigma\,(bT_a^4 + 0.95\ T_s^4 - 2T_l'^4)$$

Consider now the same leaf enclosed in an assimilation chamber. The transparent window material influences the total short-wave balance in much the same way as has been previously indicated for the photosynthetically active component of short-wave radiation. Hence the short-wave radiation balance, when the sun is near the zenith, may reach a maximum of $(0.7 \times 1.5)R_s = 1.05\ R_s$ in chambers with a mirror behind the leaf, or be much less if the back of the chamber is black ($\approx 0.63\ R_s$) or if both sides of the chamber are transparent ($0.63\ R_s + 0.14\ R_s = 0.77\ R_s$), as compared with $0.84\ R_s$ for the unenclosed leaf. When the angle of incidence is large, the short-wave balance will be much less than indicated because of the great increase in reflectance at the surfaces of the windows.
While some of the short-wave radiation absorbed is used in photosynthesis and some is lost from the leaf in sensible and latent heat transfer, a large part of it is irradiated from each surface of the leaf as thermal radiation according to the Stefan-Boltzmann equation. The transmittance of many window material ssuch as glass and acrylic plastic to thermal radiation is virtually zero (Withrow & Withrow 1956; Trickett & Goulden 1958; Avery 1967; Fig. 2.7). Others such as thin film polyethylene and polypropylene may be highly transparent to thermal radiation with a transmittance of 0.9 or more, and yet others like thin film polyvinylchloride (transmittance $\approx$ 0.25) are intermediate. If the window material is opaque to thermal radiation, thermal radiation emanating from the enclosed leaf, other structures and sensors in the chamber, as a result of absorption of short-wave and thermal radiation, cannot pass directly out of the chamber but is absorbed by the windows from which some of it may again be irradiated to the leaf. At the same time thermal radiation from the sky cannot pass directly to the leaf in the chamber but is also absorbed by the windows, thereby contributing to a rise in window temperature and irradiation of the leaf by the windows. Thus there is a short circuit of thermal radiation set up between the chamber windows and chamber contents, leading to a rise in temperature of the leaves and walls of the chamber. This is commonly known as the 'glasshouse effect' or the 'cuvette effect' and less commonly and specifically as the 'chamber microclimate'. The temperature rises until the additional heat load imposed on the chamber and its contents by the absorption of thermal radiation by the windows is balanced by increased losses by irradiation and convection of sensible heat from the walls of the chamber and from the leaf and by latent heat transfer from the leaf.
This situation can be represented as follows. If the window in the upper surface of the chamber, and the window or mirror or black wall below the leaf behave as black bodies, the thermal radiation balance of the leaf is

$$0.95\,\sigma(T_p^4 + T_m^4 - 2T_l^4)$$

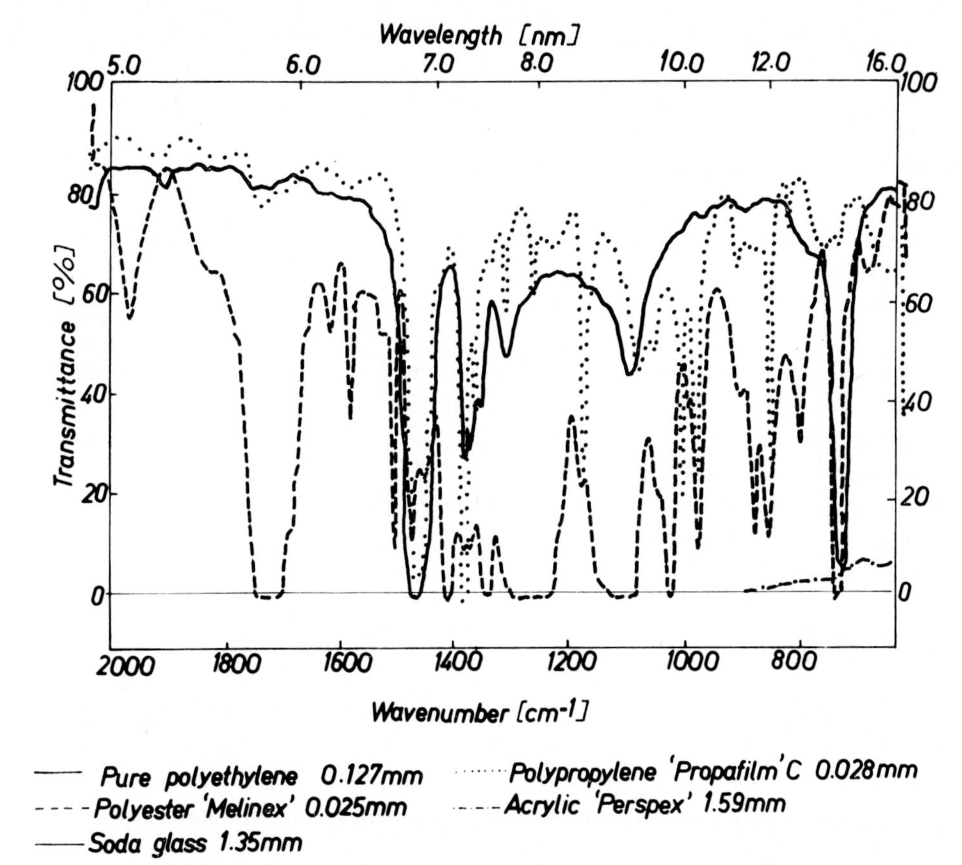

Fig. 2.7 The transmittance of various materials to thermal radiation. Transmittance was measured with a *Perkin-Elmer 237* grating, infra-red spectrophotometer without provision of special optics and is therefore not precise quantitatively.

where T_p is the upper window temperature and T_m is the lower wall (mirror or window) temperature [K]. If the short-wave balance is taken as maximum as $(0.7 \times 1.5)R_s$, the net radiation balance of the enclosed leaf is

$$R_n = 1.05\, R_s + 0.95\, \sigma(T_p^4 + T_m^4 - 2T_l^4)$$

The increased radiation absorbed by the leaf in the chamber is then

$$R_n - R_n' = 0.21\, R_s + 0.95\, \mathrm{a} + 0.95\, \sigma(T_p^4 + T_m^4 - \mathrm{b}T_a^4 - 0.95\, T_s^4) + 1.9\, \sigma(T_l'^4 - T_l^4) \tag{2.7}$$

The rather large number of terms in this equation make it difficult to state explicitly what the temperature elevation $(T_l - T_l')$ amounts to. However, some simplification can be achieved by making some simple assumptions. If by the use of air conditioning techniques, the rate of ventilation inside the chamber and the rate of transpiration of the leaf inside the chamber are made equal to the respective rates outside, the potential rise in temperature of the leaf is derived from equation (2.7) (Jarvis 1970) to be

$$T_l - T_l' = \frac{0.21R_s + 0.95a + 0.95\,\sigma(T_p^4 + T_m^4 - bT_a^4 - 0.95T_s^4)}{C_p\rho/r_a - 7.6\,\sigma\bar{T}^3} \tag{2.8}$$

where
r_a is the leaf boundary layer resistance [s m^{-1}],
$\bar{T}$ is the mean of T_l and T_l' [K],
C_p is the specific heat of air at constant pressure [J kg^{-1} $°C^{-1}$],
ρ is the density of moist air [kg m^{-3}],
and other symbols are as used previously.

It should not be forgotten that this equation has been derived by assuming identical transpiration of the leaves within and without the chamber. This is an arbitrary assumption since the transpiration rate is itself a function of the energy balance and can not easily be known for the unenclosed leaf. None the less it allows the derivation of an expression which shows that the potential rise in temperature depends upon the boundary layer resistance of the leaf in the chamber (r_a) *i.e.* the ventilation rate in the chamber, the short-wave radiation balance, and the temperature of the window (T_p) and wall, mirror or window (T_m) behind the leaf.

Since in practice the boundary layer resistance of a leaf in a stirred chamber is usually much less more that of a free, unenclosed leaf, the above equation yields an underestimate of the potential rise in temperature. By putting appropriate values into equation (2.8) the temperature difference can be estimated. This has been done to show its marked dependence upon r_a (Fig. 2.8). If the rate of ventilation is sufficiently rapid, in practice little or no temperature elevation need occur, as has been elegantly demonstrated by Tranquillini (1964a, b) (Fig. 2.9).

The short-wave radiation term may contribute numerically more than half the numerator of equation (2.8) as given as 0.21 R_s for the condition with a mirror behind the leaf. If the mirror is replaced by a transparent or coloured surface the short-wave radiation term is reduced to a little less than zero and hence the potential

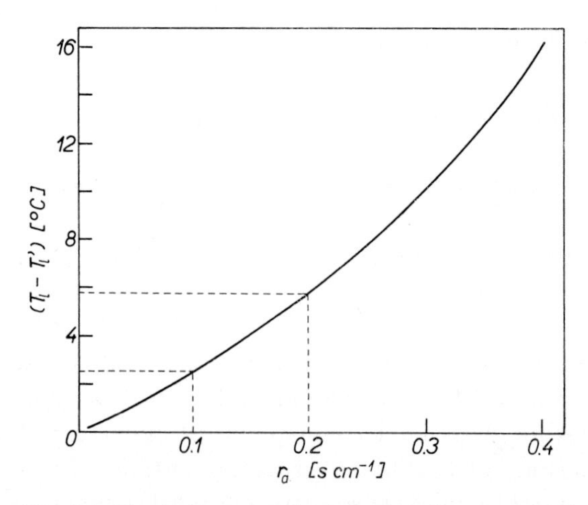

Fig. 2.8 The influence of the boundary layer resistance to sensible heat transfer, r_a, on the difference in temperature between a leaf enclosed in an assimilation chamber and a similarly exposed, free leaf ($T_l - T_l'$).

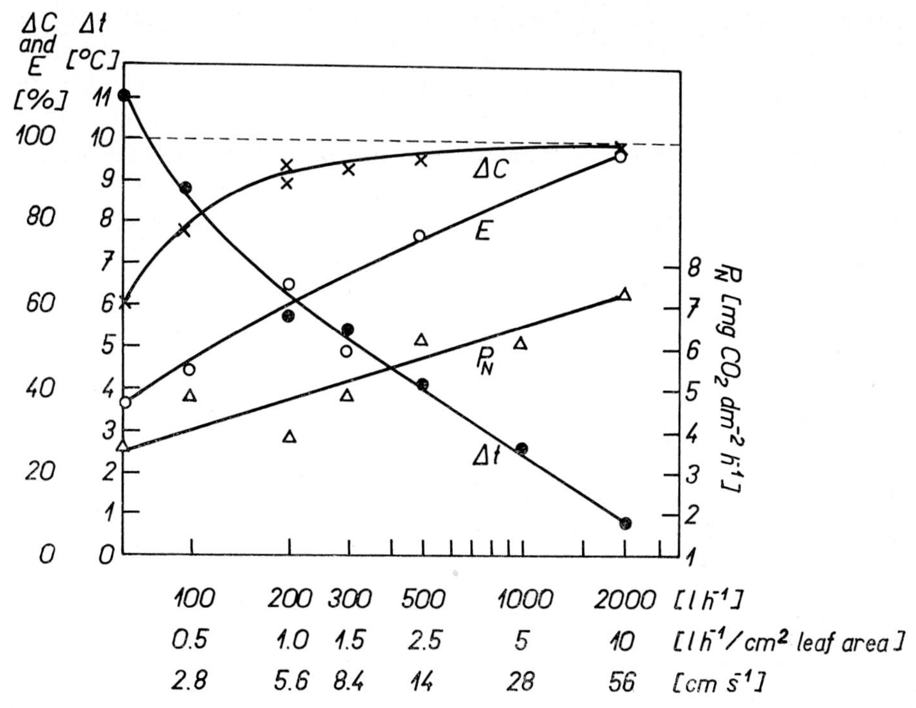

Fig. 2.9 Net photosynthetic rate (P_N) of a larch twig, outlet CO_2 concentration (ΔC, % of the inlet concentration), evaporation rate measured by Piche evaporimeter (E, % of E measured outside), and needle temperature (Δt, °C above the temperature of freely exposed needles), in an unstirred assimilation chamber at different air flow rates (abscissa, 1 h^{-1}, or, 1 h^{-1} cm^{-2} leaf area) and linear air velocities [cm s^{-1}]. Irradiance with sunlight of 1045 W m^{-2}. (After data of Tranquillini 1964a, b.)

rise in temperature also becomes reduced by more than half. This condition also obtains with tent-like enclosures (see Lee 1966).

It is clear from the above analysis and from equation (2.8) that the temperature of the upper window especially and other walls of the assimilation chamber has a big effect on the extra amount of energy absorbed by the leaf in the chamber. Clearly from the above analysis too, the temperature of the window depends upon its own complex energy balance and in particular upon its absorptance of short-wave and thermal radiation and the loss of sensible heat from it by convection both inside and outside the chamber. By analogy with the above analysis for the leaf, the temperature of the wall will be higher, and hence also the radiation load on the leaf, if its absorptance for short-wave and thermal radiation is high, and if the boundary layer resistances of the two surfaces of the window and the air temperature inside and outside the chamber are high. [The thermal conductivity of a thick window may also be important if the air temperatures of each side of it are widely different.]

The net flux of thermal radiation from wall or window to leaf may be reduced by cooling down the walls and window(s) of the chamber to below leaf temperature. This may be largely achieved by ventilating the outside of the chamber with cool air. The combined effect of reduction in boundary layer thickness and air temperature may be sufficient to bring the window and wall temperature down towards leaf temperature (Etherington 1967). Alternatively a more familiar solution is to cool the chamber walls and window with a water jacket through which a thermostatically controlled flow of cold water or other coolant is passed (Bosian 1959a, b, 1965b). However it is impractical to cool the wall to a temperature similar to that of the sky (*e.g.* 200 K) so that the naturally occurring heat sink is not simulated. Cooling of the wall by passing water or other coolant through it is related to the temperature of the coolant, its rate of flow and the efficiency of heat exchange between wall and coolant. The rate of heat removal is given by:

$$C_p \rho \frac{J}{A} (T_{out} - T_{in})$$

where
J = flow rate of coolant [$m^3\ s^{-1}$],
C_p = specific heat of coolant [$J\ kg^{-1}\ K^{-1}$],
ρ = density of coolant [$kg\ m^{-3}$],
A = area of wall surface [m^2].
At any point on the wall the rate of heat exchange between the wall and the coolant is given by

$$C_p \rho\, K_c \left(\frac{dT}{dz} \right)$$

where K_c is the diffusivity of heat between wall and bulk coolant [$m^2\ s^{-1}$]. The boundary layer resistance of the wall is given by

$$r_w = \int_{z_1}^{z_2} \frac{dz}{K_c} \qquad [s\ m^{-1}]$$

and hence the temperature of the wall at any point T_w [K] is given by

$$T_w = T_c + \frac{J}{A} \frac{(T_{out} - T_{in})}{r_w}$$

where T_c is the corresponding bulk coolant temperature.
Another practical alternative perhaps more frequently used in the laboratory, is to deflect or absorb much of the incident flux of thermal radiation before it reaches the assimilation chamber. Filters of water and of solutions of $CuSO_4$ and $FeSO_4$ are effective in absorbing thermal radiation (Baumeister 1952; Withrow & Withrow 1956). Considerable thickness of the water layer is needed. Gaastra (1959) points out that 68% of the radiation from an incandescent, tungsten filament source is still in the infra-red after transmission through an 8 cm water filter (unfiltered radiation from such a source is about 95% infra-red). Glass filters, interference filters, and infra-red mirrors which cut off around 800 nm can also be used to filter out thermal radiation. Glass filters made by *Schott & Gen.* (Mainz, BRD; Jena, DDR) are widely used (*e.g. BG 17, BG 19, BG 21, KG 1, KG 2 etc.*).

The filter must be cooled by ventilation or by immersion in a flowing water bath. The latter is effective but the coatings become damaged with time.
Covering the window with a water jacket or introducing filters into the radiation pathway has the serious disadvantage that the flux density of photosynthetically active radiation reaching the leaf is reduced a further 8 % or more.
A simple method of avoiding the problem altogether is to eliminate the chamber window. This can be done by enclosing the leaves or vegetation only intermittently in the assimilation chamber using an automatically operated hinged lid or pivoting chamber as described by Lange (1962) and Eckardt (1966, 1968), for example (see also Section 2.7.2). However, steady state and continuous observations are not obtained: the temperature of the leaves rises rapidly throughout the period during which the window is in place to allow the measurement of CO_2 exchange to be made (Lange 1962).
Perhaps the simplest and most practical alternative, and yet one which is rarely used in modern systems, is to make the chamber window (and all walls) of materials which have a high thermal radiation transmittance. Some thin plastic films such as polyethylene and polypropylene have high infra-red transmittance with low combined absorptance and reflectance of about 10 % (Fig. 2.7; Trickett & Goulden 1958; Funk 1959; Dirmhirn 1966). Polyethylene, for example, is widely used in the construction of radiation balance meters because of its high infra-red transmittance and the familiar polythene bag has been used to make simple assimilation chambers for use in the field by Polster and his associates (*e.g.* Polster 1961). Polythene is rather permeable to CO_2 (Woolley 1967) and a more suitable film with good radiation transmittance and low permeability to CO_2 is coated polypropylene marketed by *ICI* under the trade name of '*Propathane C*'.
A leaf in such a chamber absorbs considerably less heat energy in excess of that absorbed by a free leaf than does the leaf in the previously considered examples. Applying the same analysis as previously leads to the conclusion that the 'cuvette effect' will not exist – although in practice it may because of the rather higher boundary layer resistance to be expected in the chamber (Jarvis 1970).

2.5.4 | Water status of the plant material

If the environmental conditions in the chamber are such that the potential rate of transpiration is high (*i.e.* if the radiation load on the leaf leads to a high temperature, or if the ambient humidity is low), a large reduction in leaf water potential may be necessary to give a sufficient drop in water potential across the plant and soil to support the required mass flow of water from soil to leaf. A low leaf water potential is associated with a loss in turgor and a rise in solute concentration in the cells of the leaf, both of which may result in a reduced rate of photosynthesis. Conversely, stomatal opening and rate of photosynthesis is sometimes not maximum in a fully turgid leaf but is in leaves with a volumetric water content of about 92 to 97 % of maximum as a result of the so-called hydropassive closing of stomata (Stålfelt 1932). In practice, however, this is rarely a problem.
In the field the water status of the plant material is a result of the immediate environmental history and of the current environmental conditions. Provided that leaf temperature and ambient vapour pressure are adequately simulated in the

chamber, the influence of the resulting water stress on photosynthesis must be considered as the consequence of a constellation of interacting, natural environmental conditions.

In the laboratory, on the other hand, it is usually not desirable that water strain should influence the measured rates of photosynthesis. This can be fairly readily prevented by ensuring that the water potential of water reaching the cells in the leaves is as close to zero as possible, and by preventing excessive rates of potential transpiration. Considering the latter first, it is general experience that stomatal aperture is reduced in many species, and photosynthesis also if other conditions are such that CO_2 supply is partially limiting, by leaf-air vapour pressure differences of greater than about 16 mb or 12 mm Hg (Rufelt, Jarvis & Jarvis 1963; Bierhuizen & Slatyer 1964a; Skidmore & Stone 1964; Whiteman & Koller 1964, 1967a, b; Gale, Kohl & Hagan 1966; Jarvis & Slatyer 1970). Thus judicious control of ambient humidity in relation to leaf temperature to maintain the leaf-air vapour pressure difference at around 8 mb is sufficient to prevent reduction in photosynthesis on this account. Technical problems may arise if leaf temperature is high, *e.g.* 35 °C. At this temperature, an ambient vapour pressure of 48.2 mb is necessary to prevent the leaf-air vapour pressure difference exceeding 8 mb (assuming that the water vapour pressure at the liquid-air interface in the leaf is equal to the saturation vapour pressure at leaf temperature). At such a vapour pressure, saturation obtains at *ca.* 32.2 °C. Clearly then, there is a definite risk of condensation in parts of the gas exchange system and precautions must be taken to prevent this occurring.

The limits given above pertain to plants rooted in water culture or in well aerated soil, close to pot (field) capacity and at temperatures of more than about 15 °C. If the water potential of the soil, its temperature or air filled porosity is reduced, the potential of water entering the leaves is also lower and photosynthesis is reduced at much lower leaf-air vapour pressure differences (*e.g.* Brix 1962; El-Sharkawy & Hesketh 1964; Cox & Boersma 1967; Troughton 1969). In other words, the supply of water to the roots must be adequate but not excessive and high permeability of the roots must be maintained. Special precautions must be taken when using detached leaves and shoots to ensure that the potential of water entering the leaves is not reduced as the result of detachment. To prevent the development of a significant resistance in the xylem and tracheids resulting from cavitation, air embolism and blockage of the cut surface, the initial excision should be made under water and additional sections removed from the cut shoot or petiole under water at subsequent intervals.

It may be concluded from these considerations that it is highly desirable that the water status of the tissue be kept under continuous observation during the course of the experiment. This can be done quite conveniently for broad leaves by building a suitable sensor into the chamber. A β-gauge has proved very suitable for this since the small radioactive source can be placed above the leaf where it need not shade more than about 1 mm^2 and the larger G.M. detector can be placed below the leaf at a sufficient distance from it not to interfere with the boundary layer (Jarvis & Slatyer 1966b; Section 2.7.3).

2.5.5 | Assimilation chamber design

From the preceeding sections, certain general principles regarding chamber design may be deduced. In general it is desirable, if not essential, that the environmental conditions affecting photosynthesis to which the leaf is exposed should be known by, and under the control of, the investigator. These environmental conditions include:
- the flux density of photosynthetically active radiation incident on the leaf from all directions
- the leaf temperature
- the ambient carbon dioxide concentration
- the ambient oxygen concentration
- the ambient water vapour pressure
- the atmospheric pressure in the chamber and
- the leaf water content (perhaps not strictly in the same category as the others).

In the first place a prime consideration in the design of a chamber for use in the field must be the energy balance of the enclosed leaf, including separate consideration of the balance of both thermal and photosynthetically active radiation. A leaf chamber for use in the laboratory also designed on energy balance principles has certain advantages in respect of ease of control of temperature and irradiance. Consideration of the leaf energy balance leads to the conclusion that many chambers currently used are less satisfactory than they might be and, as a direct result of their design, generate problems of temperature and irradiance control which are not altogether necessary.

It has been suggested in previous sections that one of the most severe, and generally least appreciated problems is the proper definition of the fluxes of photosynthetically active radiation incident on the leaf in the chamber. In the field this problem is particularly acute when photosynthesis in the chamber is being taken as indicative of that occurring outside. There is no obvious solution to this problem, but it may be reduced by enclosing the leaf in as near as possible a spherical chamber of transparent material so that irradiation from the sun and sky and by reflection from surrounding leaves is as natural as possible. In the laboratory the problem is somewhat different since unnatural conditions pertain in any case. The problem then is to know precisely the total photosynthetically active radiation incident on the leaf from all directions. One solution to this problem may be to enclose the leaf in a spherical chamber with reflective walls and illuminate the interior through a port-hole so that the leaf receives uniform, diffuse irradiance from all directions.

The chamber must also be designed so that the control of leaf temperature is possible. In both the field and laboratory this may be achieved by air conditioning or other heat exchange techniques (Section 2.6) but the problem can be reduced by suitable design. In the field the problem of overheating can be minimised by making the chamber of a material which is transparent to thermal radiation and enabling the leaf to radiate without restriction in all directions. In the laboratory it is more convenient to filter out the thermal radiation before it reaches the chamber. In both cases considerable control is also achieved by ventilating the leaf to improve convective exchanges of heat between leaf and air.

For this reason and to achieve a proper definition of ambient carbon dioxide and humidity, it is essential to include controllable ventilation in chambers for use both in field and laboratory.

Other practical aspects of chamber design which should be borne in mind include a construction which allows ready introduction and removal of attached leaves or plants, and the placement of appropriate sensors to monitor the prevailing conditions, including leaf water content.

2.6 | Principles of chamber air conditioning

It is a prerequisite of the majority of experiments done in assimilation chambers that the temperature, humidity and CO_2 content of the air in the chamber can be kept constant or within narrow limits and, in many cases, controlled to predetermined values. Recently it has also become desirable to control the ambient oxygen concentration in the chamber. In general, control of conditions within the chamber may be effected in one of two ways. Either the conditions are controlled within the chamber itself, for example by adjustment of chamber wall temperature or by direct injection of CO_2, or control is achieved by air conditioning the air stream entering the chamber. In the latter case it is often possible to use commercial, packaged air conditioning units for temperature and humidity control (*e.g.* Musgrave & Moss 1961). In both cases conditions within the chamber are monitored and compared with pre-set values. If deviations from the pre-set values occur the control system is activated so as to restore the required conditions. This may be done either manually or with servo-operated controls. Modern servo systems with anticipation and proportional control can operate on very small deviations from pre-set values and hence can give very close control of conditions within the chamber. Consequently they are increasing rapidly in usefulness and popularity. Recording the fluctuations of the input value about the pre-set value is advisable. Some correction of errors due to hunting in the control system may then be possible. Some hunting is in fact unavoidable. It is impossible to obtain both high accuracy and high stability. Increasing the gain of the controller, *i.e.* the output signal/error ratio, will often bring about a decrease in stability.

However in many experiments, such as the determination, in the laboratory, of the response curve relating photosynthesis to irradiance or temperature, it is sufficient that the experimental variable be constant and accurately known at any one time, whilst its exact value is unimportant. In such circumstances manual control of the conditions may be equally or (since hunting of the control system is avoided) more effective. In principle with servo-operated control systems the course of an entire experiment can be programmed for automatic operation from start to finish. The conditions in the chamber can be set to follow environmental conditions or they can be changed from one pre-set value to another as steady state photosynthesis is attained (Eckardt 1966; 1968; Parkinson 1968; Lange, Koch & Schulze 1969). With automatic control of the environmental conditions in the chamber, automatic recording of the data onto charts and tape, and regular automatic recalibration of the infra-red gas analyser (Section 3.10.3) much of the tediousness can be removed from measurements of photosynthesis. It should not be forgotten though, that a living plant is at the centre of the equipment and a close watch must be kept on its appearance and behaviour (see also the relevant discussion in Chouard & de Bilderling 1969).

2.6.1 | *Control of temperature*

From the point of view of the physiology of the plant, it is the temperature of the leaf which is important rather than the temperature of the air, although the latter is of course important in relation to heat transfer (Chapter 17). As emphasised earlier (Section 2.5) control of leaf temperature is greatly facilitated by design of the assimilation chamber to minimise trapping of thermal radiation and the consequent rise in temperature, and by removal of thermal radiation from the radiation source with appropriate filters (Section 2.5.3.2). The temperature of the leaf may be controlled by regulating the exchanges of sensible heat and/or thermal radiation between the leaf and its surroundings. In the majority of installations, leaf temperature is largely controlled by regulating the temperature of the ambient air in the chamber and hence by controlling the exchange of sensible heat between leaf and air. This can be achieved either by conditioning the air entering the chamber or by conditioning the air within the chamber.

Techniques used to regulate the temperature of the air entering the chamber depend upon the volume flow required for other purposes. For small chambers and for small flow rates in the laboratory the temperature of the air stream may be regulated by passing it through heat exchangers immersed in a temperature controlled water bath (*e.g.* Björkman & Holmgren 1963). For large chambers and flow rates, particularly in the field, commercial air conditioning units can be used (Musgrave & Moss 1961).

The temperature of the air within the chamber can be conditioned by circulating it over temperature controlled heat exchangers within the chamber. These may consist of the walls of the chamber which may be heated or cooled, over which the air is moved by fans, or of free standing heat exchangers around which the air is circulated. The temperature of the leaf is then controlled by regulating the temperature of the heat exchangers and the rate at which they are ventilated, thereby controlling the exchanges of sensible heat between leaf and air, and air and heat exchangers. In addition, thermal radiation exchange between the leaf and the heat exchangers will also occur and contribute to the flux of heat between the two.

Many methods can be used to regulate the temperature of the walls of the chamber or of heat exchangers within the chamber. These include: total immersion of the chamber in a water bath (*e.g.* Raschke 1965); total immersion of the chamber in a refrigerator (*e.g.* Hardwick, Lumb & Woolhouse 1966); jacketing the chamber so that water or refrigerants can be circulated over the chamber walls (*e.g.* Bosian 1959a, b; Gaastra 1959; Björkman & Holmgren 1963; Bierhuizen & Slatyer 1964b; Parkinson 1968); attaching cooling coils to the external walls of the chamber or introducing them into the chamber; attaching Peltier modules to the external walls of the chamber (Bosian 1964a; Koch, Klein & Walz 1968). In all cases heat exchange is facilitated by a large area of exchanging surface such as results from the addition of fins: these help to prevent cold spots and local condensation on the internal chamber walls when working at low temperatures. In the case of Peltier modules, a heat sink in the form of fins or a water jacket must also be provided on the side of the module away from the chamber to facilitate removal of the heat pumped out of the chamber by the module. It is also desirable in all such heat exchange methods that the thermal conductivity of the chamber walls be as high as possible.

As an alternative to control of leaf temperature by regulation of sensible heat exchange, leaf temperature can be rapidly and effectively controlled solely by regulation of thermal radiation exchange between the leaf and a heat sink (Lake 1967).

2.6.2 | *Control of humidity*

Control of humidity in the assimilation chamber is effected by regulating the humidity of the air entering the chamber. Since plants tend to raise the ambient humidity as a result of transpiration, humidity control usually involves the removal of water vapour from the chamber. This is effected by diluting the humid air in the chamber with dried air. However, transpiration increases as a result of a reduction in ambient humidity. Because of this compensation by the plant, large changes in the humidity of the air entering the chamber and in the flow rate through the chamber are needed to change effectively the ambient humidity.

In an open system at normal temperatures and with a high flow rate through the chamber, adequate control of humidity may be achieved by regulating the humidity of the air entering the chamber by any one of the following methods:

1. The air is saturated at a given dew point temperature. This is best achieved by passing the air in fine bubbles first through a column of water somewhat warmer than the required dew point temperature (*e.g.* room temperature) and then through a column of water at the required dew point temperature. [It is more effective to condense out water in the final stage than to take it up.]. Simple apparatus for this consists of columns of water each with a sintered glass or metal plate at the bottom through which the air is forced, immersed in a stirred water bath the temperature of which is precisely controlled by circulating coolant and a thermostatically controlled heater (Went 1957).

This method is effective but cumbersome. Its main disadvantage is that it takes a long time to alter the temperature of the bath and so obtain a different humidity. Greater flexibility is obtained with the *Siemens* Peltier-cooled condensor units (Koch, Klein & Walz 1968).

2. The air is passed over the surface of sulphuric acid solutions or saturated salt solutions in long, wide-bore (∅ 3 cm) tubing (*e.g.* Anderson, Hertz & Rufelt 1954; Björkman & Holmgren 1966; Jarvis & Slatyer 1966a). This method provides a source of air of constant humidity over periods of about a day. Over longer periods the changes in concentration of the sulphuric acid solutions must be taken into account. Saturated salt solutions are not as satisfactory in practice because the unstirred solution does not remain saturated at the surface. The great advantage of the method is that it is very quick and simple to change humidity by switching from one tube to another containing a different solution. A battery of such tubes should be thermostated in a water bath or ventilated box. The tubes should be about 1½ m long for flow rates of up to about $2\ l\ min^{-1}$.

3. A dry air stream and a humid air stream are mixed in fixed proportions. The air stream is divided in two. One part is dried approximately by passing it over a condensor at low temperature or over a desiccant. The other part is humidified either as in *1* above or by the injection of steam (*e.g.* van den Driessche & Wareing 1966) to a dew point temperature a few degrees below room temperature. The two streams are mixed in any desired proportions by passing them through flow meters (precision is not required) controlled by needle valves. The proportions of the mixture are adjusted in relation to the humidity of air in the chamber. The method can readily be servo-operated to give any desired humidity (*e.g.* Cross 1968).

However at low leaf and air temperatures in the chamber or at low flow rates, the vapour pressure in the chamber can readily exceed the dew point. In such circumstances, control of humidity in the chamber can only be achieved by circulating a part of the chamber air through a by-pass in which water vapour is removed by a desiccant or by condensation in a temperature controlled condenser. The amount of transpired water removed from the system in this way can readily be calculated from knowledge of the vapour pressure of the air entering the by-pass (equal to the water vapour pressure of the air in the chamber), the water vapour pressure of the air rejoining the chamber (effectively zero if the air is dried over an effective desiccant or to a dew point appreciably below zero) and the rate of volume flow through the by-pass (see Section 3.8.5). In a closed system control of humidity is achieved entirely in this way (*e.g.* Koller & Samish 1964).
In practice the humidity of the air leaving the assimilation chamber is monitored and compared with a pre-set value. Deviations from the pre-set value cause a change either in the flow rate through the by-pass (D. Koller) or in the dew point

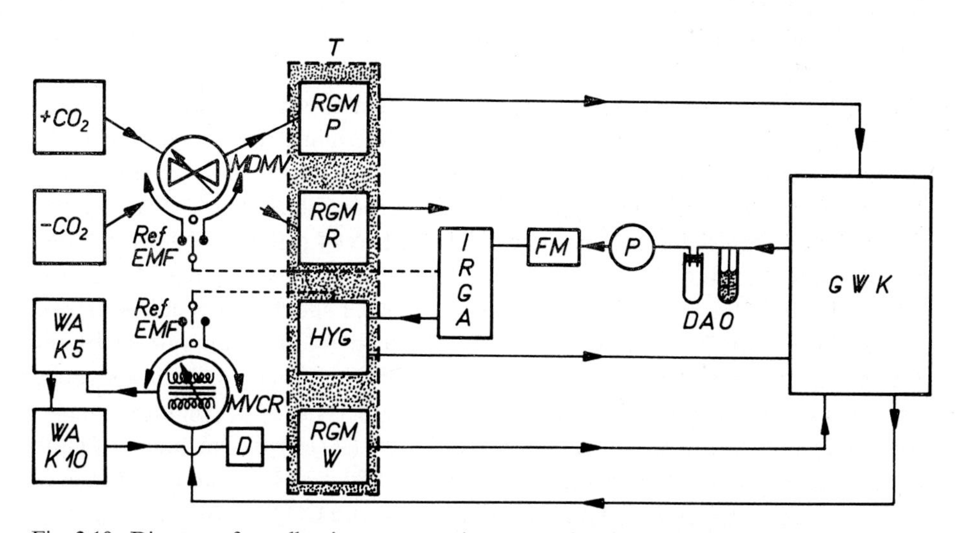

Fig. 2.10 Diagram of a null-point compensating system for simultaneous measurement of gas exchanges in photosynthesis and transpiration (D. Koller, unpublished).
D chemical desiccant; *DAO* oil trap outlet; *FM* flow meter; *GWK* Siemens assimilation chamber; *HYG* hygrometer; *IRGA* infra-red gas analyser; *MDMV* motor driven micrometer valve; *MVCR* motorized variac controlled pump; *P* pump; *RGM* recording gas flow meter; *T* water bath; *WA* water absorber. For further details see text.

temperature of the condenser (Koch, Klein & Walz 1968). If the flow rate is varied it must be recorded to give an integrated volume flow through the by-pass over the period for which transpiration is calculated. If the dew point is varied, the flow rate must be maintained completely constant, by means of a special pump or regulator, and the humidity of the air recorded after having passed through the condenser. In both cases the hygrometer used to monitor the humidity of the air leaving the chamber is used solely as a null-point instrument.

Examples of humidity control systems of this type are shown in Figs. 2.10 and 2.23. In Fig. 2.10 the error signal from the hygrometer *(HYG)* activates a motorized variac-controlled *Reciprotor* pump *(MVCR)* which increases or decreases the air flow rate through two *Siemens* water absorbers (*WA/K5*, + 5°C dewpoint and *WA/K10* − 15°C dewpoint) and a chemical desiccant (*D*, self-indicating granular magnesium perchlorate). The integrated volume flow of air through the by-pass is recorded by the recording gas flow meter *(RGM/W)* immersed in the water bath *(T)* at constant temperature. The system shown in Fig. 2.23 differs in that the flow rate through the condenser *(WA2)* is kept constant by the pump *(P)*. The error signal obtained as the difference in output between the lithium chloride sensor *(EFF)* monitoring the humidity of the air entering the chamber and the similar sensor *(AFF)* monitoring the humidity of the air leaving the chamber is the input signal to the *PID*-controller *(FR)* which adjusts the dew point of the condenser in the by-pass. For set valve control of humidity, the air is moistened before entering the chamber and is then dried to the desired dew point by the water vapour trap *(WA1)*.

2.6.3 | *Control of carbon dioxide (and oxygen) concentration*

With an open system, the CO_2 concentration in the chamber is readily controlled by varying either or both the volume flow of air through the chamber and the CO_2 content of the air entering the chamber. In many experiments, such as the determination of temperature response curves, it is sufficient to supply normal air to the chamber provided that its CO_2 concentration is determined at intervals during the course of the experiment so that the concentration in the chamber at any time is known. Air entering the gas system for this purpose should be drawn through reservoirs of appreciable volume (*e.g.* 400 l, *i.e.* two 44 gallon oil drums in series) to eliminate transitory fluctuations of CO_2 concentration in the air stream. Ideally the air in the reservoir(s) should be stirred. Air should not be taken in from outside in this way in large towns since the CO_2 content of the air varies with the traffic density. The source of the intake should be positioned as high above the ground as possible and well away from sources of CO_2 such as chimneys.

To obtain precise control of the concentration of CO_2 in the air and to obtain concentrations outside the normal range, air from which all CO_2 has been removed (CO_2-free air) is mixed in fixed proportions with pure CO_2 (or 10% or 1% CO_2) from a gas cylinder.

Carbon dioxide-free air can be obtained in several ways. The air stream may be passed through CO_2-absorbing liquids in fine bubbles. To break the air stream up into fine bubbles it is forced under pressure through sintered glass or metal plates.

 Solutions used to absorb the CO_2 include diethanol-amine which can be regenerated

by heating (Koch 1957) and 40% KOH (*e.g.* Oorschot & Belksma 1961; Bierhuizen & Slatyer 1964b). A certain risk attaches to the use of this method and precautions must be taken to avoid being showered in 40% KOH on occasion. It is somewhat simpler but more expensive in materials to absorb all CO_2 from the air by passing it over coarsely granular (6–16 mesh) soda-lime (a solid mixture of NaOH and $Ca(OH)_2$) or soda-asbestos, or similar proprietary products such as '*Ascarite*' and '*Carbosorb*' (see Section 3.16) which can be obtained in self-indicating forms.
In principle mixing CO_2 with CO_2-free air is simple but in practice certain difficulties occur. If pure CO_2 (or almost pure – the usual purity of inexpensive bottled CO_2 is approx. 99.98%) is used as the source of CO_2, the two flow rates are widely disparate. The very low flow rate of the CO_2 is difficult to measure and the physical nature of the two flows is different. In capillary flow meters, for example, the flow of CO_2 is laminar whereas the flow of CO_2-free air is partly turbulent. As a result the two flow rates respond differently to changes in atmospheric pressure (Holmgren 1968b). If, on the other hand, air reputed to contain 10% or 1% CO_2 is used as the source, a problem arises as to what is the real concentration of CO_2 in the air. It must be determined since the usual limits on such a specification of $\pm$ 10% leave too wide a margin of error.
Alternatively CO_2 can be obtained from a solution of bicarbonate by addition of an acid. Continuous, quantitative production of CO_2 can be obtained by supplying the acid through a motor-driven syringe with proportional controller (*e.g.* Goldsworthy 1966). Carbon dioxide generated in this way can be fed directly into the assimilation chamber to replace CO_2 taken up in photosynthesis.
Carbon dioxide and CO_2-free air can be mixed together in fixed proportions in several ways. Perhaps the simplest and most convenient is to use commercial high precision gas-mixing pumps (*H. Wösthoff*, Bochum, BRD). Metered amounts of CO_2 and CO_2-free air are obtained from precisely calibrated cylinders. The proportions of the two components entering the mixture can be readily varied by changing the gear-ratios, thus changing the rate at which the cylinders are filled and emptied. With three or four pumps (Type *SA 27* or *SA 18*) cascaded in series or with the more flexible single pump (Type *M 100*) any concentration required for the normal run of physiological experiments can be obtained. The pumps yield highly reproducible mixtures of acceptable accuracy. A series of gear-ratio changes amongst four cascaded pumps yielded reproducible mixtures with an absolute accuracy of $\pm$ 2 μl l^{-1} (Bate, D'Aoust & Canvin 1969). The single most important characteristic of the pumps limiting their usefulness is their inability to deliver mixtures at flow rates larger than 87 l h^{-1}.
Capillary flow meters have been widely used to mix CO_2 and CO_2-free air in fixed proportions (*e.g.* Gaastra 1959; Björkman & Holmgren 1963; Bierhuizen & Slatyer 1964b) and they are commonplace features of the majority of systems. Constant mixtures can be obtained especially if the CO_2 is supplied at a pressure of about 8 b. A very satisfactory mixing system is described by Holmgren (1968b). It should be emphasised that the theory of mixing with capillary flow meters is not as simple as it may appear superficially because of the different nature of the flows of the two gas streams in the capillaries, and hence that it is difficult to calculate the composition of the mixture precisely (see Holmgren 1968b).

A fine-control injection system is described by Redshaw & Meidner (1970). Another method of mixing CO_2 into CO_2-free air is to allow it to diffuse through a silicone rubber membrane into the CO_2-free air stream (Apel 1966). By stretching the membrane so as to change its area and thickness, the rate of diffusion of the CO_2 and hence the composition of the mixture can be varied.

In closed or semi-closed systems such as those shown in Figs. 2.10 and 2.23, the gas analyser (or hygrometer – see previous section) acts as a null-point instrument in a feed-back loop control system. Deviations from the pre-set value result in an error signal which, after amplification, activates a controller to produce an output which changes the input in the desired way. In the case of CO_2 or humidity control the amplified error signal may activate a proportional valve controlling the injection of CO_2 into the circuit or the flow of air from the circuit through a by-pass in which water vapour or CO_2 is removed.

In the system shown in Fig. 2.10 deviations from the pre-set value result in an error signal which activates a motor driven micrometer valve *(MDMV)* to increase or decrease the supply of CO_2-free or CO_2-enriched air until the error signal is cancelled. Displaced air is released from the system through the oil trap outlet *DAO*. The flow rates of CO_2-free and CO_2-enriched air are recorded by the recording gas meters (*RGM/R* and *RGM/P*, respectively) at constant temperature. The system shown in Fig. 2.23 is similar in many respects. Photosynthesis or respiration is calculated from the amount of CO_2 or CO_2-free air fed into the circuit to maintain the concentration in the assimilation chamber constant. Alternatively as the plant respires, the excess CO_2 produced is absorbed by soda lime in a by-pass, the flow of air through which is controlled by an automatic valve, as with humidity control.

For humidity control, ordinary continuous on-off controllers are often suitable, whereas for CO_2 control, more complex types of controllers are desirable. The best type for CO_2 control seems to be the 'periodically discontinuous action controller'. This is a continuous control system which is switched on periodically by means of an interrupter key actuated by a cam driven by a synchronous motor. When the system is switched on, the valve controlling CO_2 input will either open or close at a speed proportional to the error signal. This type of controller performs better than normal continuous controllers in feed-back systems characterised by large time lags. The controller can be set so as to minimise the difference between CO_2 or water vapour content of the air inside and outside the chamber, or to maintain a constant difference between these. Constant CO_2 and water vapour content can be obtained by stopping the air flow in the reference cell of the IRGA and by using the optical shutter of the instrument for setting.

2.7 | Examples of assimilation chambers in current use

It follows from Section 2.5 that different designs of chamber are required for use in the field and in the laboratory. In the laboratory it is a fairly simple matter to create the desired conditions of leaf temperature, ambient gas and vapour concentrations, and irradiance within the assimilation chamber. In routine work, in the field, on the other hand, it may not be possible to use laboratory chambers because of the complexity of the associated equipment, and indeed it is not

desirable to do so if the aim is to obtain as near natural conditions as possible within the chamber. A chamber of a different design is required.
Assimilation chambers in current use may be classified in the following manner:

A without control of the chamber microenvironment
A.1 without an independent ventilation system
A.1.a simple box-like chamber (*e.g.* Negisi 1961; Avery 1967)
A.1.b box-like chamber with high air flow rate and infra-red filter (*e.g.* Tranquillini 1954, 1957, 1959, 1964b)
A.1.c small, shallow, 'pincer' chamber (*e.g.* Čatský & Slavík 1960)
A.1.d plastic bag chamber (*e.g.* Polster 1961)
A.1.e plastic tent enclosure (Decker, Gaylor & Cole 1962; Lee 1966)
A.1.f intermittent, short period exposure in a 'trap' chamber (*e.g.* Lange 1962)
A.2 with independent ventilation achieved by
A.2.a stirring the chamber air by fan or turbine in the chamber (*e.g.* Decker 1959; Bosian 1960; Polster & Weise 1962)
A.2.b recirculation of air through the chamber using a supplementary pump in a by-pass
B partial control of chamber microenvironment, *e.g.* temperature only (Clark 1961; Avery 1967; Wolf *et al.* 1969) or humidity only (Etherington 1967)
C with control of the major components of chamber microenvironment (see Section 2.5.5)
C.1 without an independent ventilation system
C.1.a leaf temperature controlled by conditioning of the air before entry into the chamber only (*e.g.* Musgrave & Moss 1961; Koller & Samish 1964; Baker 1965)
C.1.b leaf temperature controlled by air conditioning and by regulating the temperature of chamber walls and window (*e.g.* Gaastra 1959)
C.2 with an independent ventilation system – leaf temperature controlled by air conditioning and by regulating the temperature of chamber walls and window by:
C.2.a water cooling (*e.g.* Bosian 1959a, b, 1960, 1965b; Björkman & Holmgren 1963; Nátr & Špidla 1963; Jarvis & Slatyer 1966a; Parkinson 1968; Gloser 1970; Chartier & Chartier 1971)
C.2.b Peltier plates (*e.g.* Bosian 1964a, b; Eckardt 1968; Lange, Koch & Schulze 1969)
C.2.c temperature control of air in the surrounding room (Louwerse & van Oorschot 1969)

As discussed earlier not all of these kinds of chambers are altogether suitable for the purposes for which they were used and some of them are of historical interest only.
A selection of assimilation chambers of present day importance are described below. A review of chamber types has been made by Eckardt (1968).

2.7.1 | *Assimilation chambers with uncontrolled microenvironment*

For routine field measurements very simple chambers are frequently used to obtain quantitative estimates of the rate of photosynthesis. A convenient type of chamber of this kind is the 'pincer' chamber which can be quickly and easily attached to an area of leaf of about 10 cm^2 (Pochinok 1958; Nichiporovich *et al.* 1961). Such a chamber usually consists of two rectangular, chromed brass jaws (*1*, Fig. 2.11*A*) with plastic film or acrylic windows *(2)* (Čatský & Slavík 1960). Air enters the chamber through the pores *(5)* and is sucked out through the perforations *(7)* in the tubing *(6)*. The perforations in the tubing increase in size along its length to ensure an even flow of air across the chamber. Reference air is independently passed to the analyser. Both jaws of the chamber are interconnected and lock onto

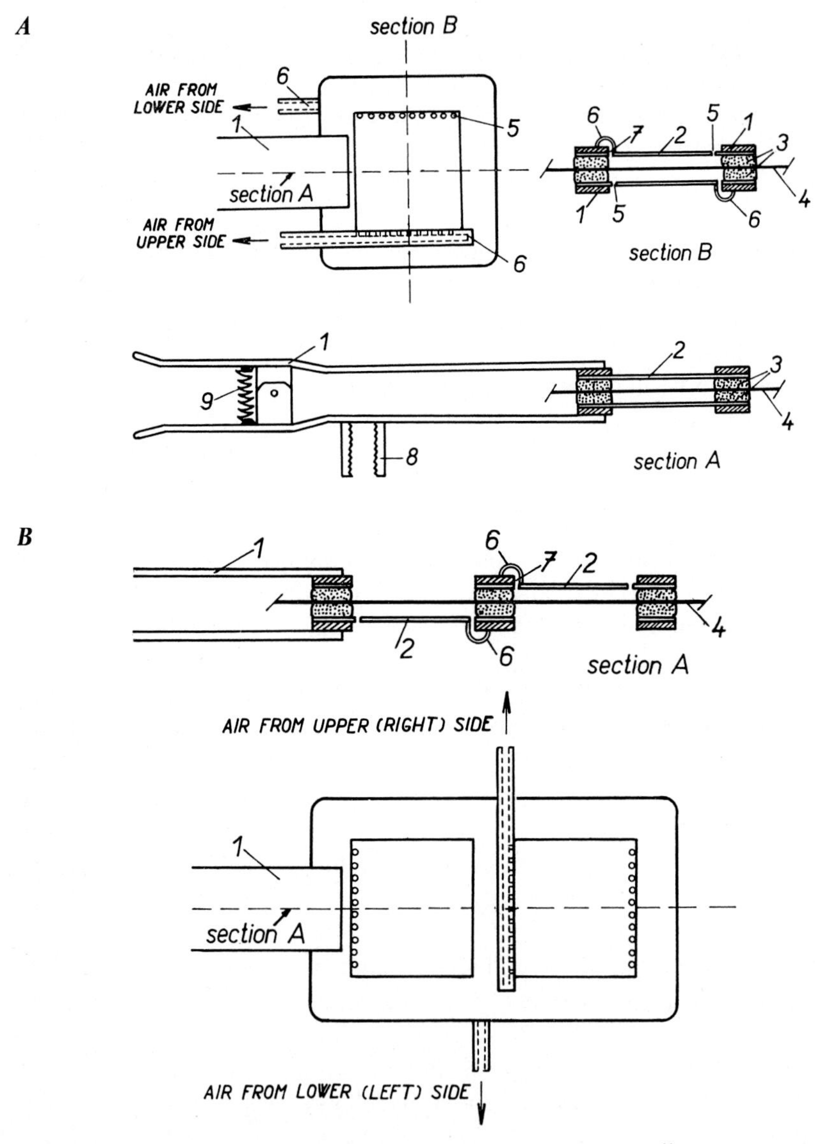

Fig. 2.11 Pincer assimilation chambers (modified from Čatský & Slavík 1960 *[A]* and from Okanenko, Gulyaev & Pochinok 1965 *[B]*). *1:* chromed brass jaws, *2:* windows of plastic film or acrylic plastic, *3:* polyurethane foam, *4:* leaf, *5:* air inlet, *6, 7:* air outlet (see text), *8:* sockets for an infra-red filter and for a support.

the leaf with variable pressure controlled by a spring *(9)*. Foam plastic *(3)* around the periphery of the chambers seals them against the leaf *(4)*, even over large veins, sufficiently tightly to ensure that air does not leak into the chamber. The chamber may be supported on a camera tripod with a ball joint attachment if an appropriate socket *(8)* is fitted to the lower clamp (Romashko 1959).
Overheating of the leaf in such a chamber may be reduced by making the windows of an appropriate plastic film (Section 2.5.3) and by filtering incident radiation through an infra-red filter before it reaches the chamber. Such a filter should not be placed closer than 10 cm to the chamber and should be cooled itself to reduce reradiation of thermal radiation to the chamber (Tranquillini 1957). The dangers of overheating may be further reduced by redesigning the chamber so that only one surface of the leaf is enclosed at any point (Okanenko, Gulyaev & Pochinok 1965). In the modification shown in Fig. 2.11*B* both halves of the clamps *(1)* are divided into two parts, one of which is covered by a transparent window *(2)* and the other left open. The area on the lower surface of the leaf corresponding to the covered area on the upper surface is not enclosed and *vice versa*. The air from both halves removed through tubes *(7)* can be analysed separately or together.
In the investigation of certain problems, such as the influence of internal factors on the rate of photosynthesis, it may be desirable to eliminate irradiance as a variable and to ensure that photosynthesis of the enclosed leaf is light saturated. Because of the small area of leaf enclosed in the 'pincer' chamber, this can conveniently be done by irradiating the leaf with a small, 100 W incandescent lamp (*e.g.* a quartz-halide or krypton lamp) enclosed in a cooled, reflector housing.
Another interesting solution to leaf chamber design for use in the field is the '*Ansaugplatte*' devised by Koch (1956, 1957). The experimental leaf is freely placed, with no window present, in an open chamber on a flat bed. The surface of the chamber below the leaf is regularly perforated with conical holes through which *all* CO_2-impoverished air which has passed over the leaf is exhausted to the analyser. A leaf so exposed experiences much less disturbance to its microenvironment and radiation balance than a leaf completely enclosed in a chamber and does not tend to overheat to the same extent. This method has not, however, been widely used perhaps because of the difficulty of ensuring that all impoverished air is sucked off to the analyser and because it is restricted in practice to hypostomatous leaves.

2.7.2 | *Intermittent enclosure in 'trap' type chambers*

The long term influence of the chamber microenvironment on the physiology of the plant in the field can be reduced if the plant or leaf is only enclosed for short periods during which measurements are taken. This can be realised by designing the chamber so that the window over the leaves or vegetation can be removed when measurements are not being made, thereby enabling the plant to exchange radiation, CO_2 and water vapour with its surroundings in an unhampered, almost natural manner. Prior to CO_2 analysis, the window is reimposed and the chamber flushed with air long enough for a steady state concentration of CO_2 to be obtained. Whilst this approach minimises the long term influence of enclosure, short-term consequences may still occur. The period of enclosure necessary to obtain a

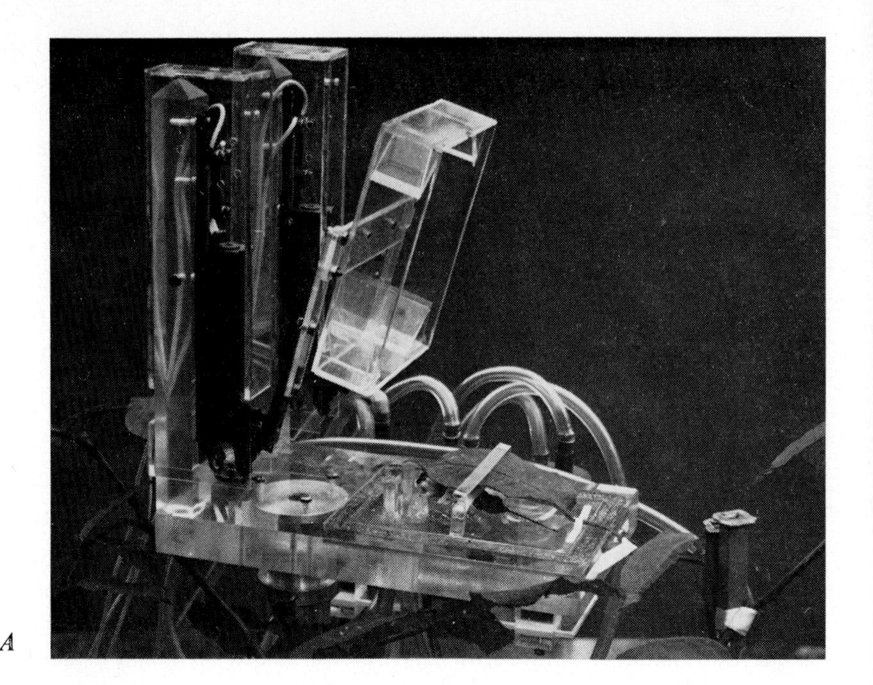

Fig. 2.12 Trap chamber of Lange (1962) *[A]* and its section *[B]*. *1:* hinged transparent lid of acrylic plastic, *2:* solenoids, *3:* polyurethane foam saturated with liquid paraffin, *4:* air inlet and outlet, *5:* thermocouple leads, *6:* spring, *7:* leads to solenoids.

steady state CO_2 concentration depends upon the nature of the chamber and the rate of air flow through it. During this period, which may amount to one or more minutes, the temperature of the leaf may rise several degrees if air conditioning is not also provided (Lange 1962; Hellmuth 1967; Eckardt 1968). The first practical chamber of this kind was the '*Klappküvette*' (Lange 1962), a tiltable, trap-type chamber which is used in combination with an infra-red gas analyser and with a six-way sequential valve (Section 3.8.8). The original chamber (Fig. 2.12) is not air-conditioned. It is made of a thick '*Plexiglass*' plate to which the leaf is attached by means of a '*Plexiglass*' strip. This plate is covered by a hinged lid *(1)* of thin '*Plexiglass*' held down by two solenoids *(2)*. The edges of the lid are trimmed with polyurethane foam *(3)* saturated with liquid paraffin to provide an air-tight seal. In one of the side walls of the lid there is an opening through which the petiole passes and which also serves as the fresh air inlet. In the lower part of the chamber there are two outlet tubes through which the air passes to the infra-red gas analyser *(4)* in such a way as to ensure uniform air flow across the chamber. Closure of the chamber is controlled by the sequential valve *(Hartmann & Braun)* which also switches current *(7)* to the solenoids. When the lid is closed, air is at first exhausted from the chamber for 20 s through one aperture to flush the chamber and then for 1 min through the other. The latter air stream is analysed by the IRGA. Then the sequential valve disconnects the current supply to the solenoids and the lid is returned to the normal position by a spring *(6)*. The leaf remains for 4 min 40 s in the open chamber at near natural conditions. The CO_2 impoverished air from the second outlet remains during this period and for the following 20 s flushing period in the tubing between the chamber and the analyser. Overheating of the leaf during a one-minute exposure in the closed chamber reaches about 2 °C.

The success of Lange's chamber indicated a new line of chamber development, and the possibility of long-term use of chambers on the same material in the field. The main disadvantage of Lange's prototype was the rapidly changing conditions of leaf temperature, ambient humidity and CO_2 concentration in the chamber during the measurement period, and the logical solution was to complement the chamber with an air conditioning system. Several kinds of chambers based on these principles have been developed at Montpellier (Eckardt 1966, 1967, 1968). Fundamentally the chambers used at Montpellier are based on the principle of the closed circuit wind tunnel. They comprise a strong turbine which forces air round in a circuit into which is inserted the chamber containing the part of the plant or area of vegetation studied.

The equipment, at present, exists in two versions, one for measurement at ground level and one for measurement within the crown layer of trees. The ground level chamber (Figs. 2.13 and 2.14) covers one square meter of vegetation. Regulation of humidity and temperature is obtained by cooling and then heating the air after it has passed through the chamber, the automatic control unit operating in conjunction with two sets of sensors (lithium chloride dew cell and platinum resistance thermometer) located within and outside the chamber, respectively.

Carbon dioxide concentration during the day is regulated automatically by introducing pure carbon dioxide, kept in liquid form, into the chamber through a remotely controlled valve which opens and closes at a speed proportional to the

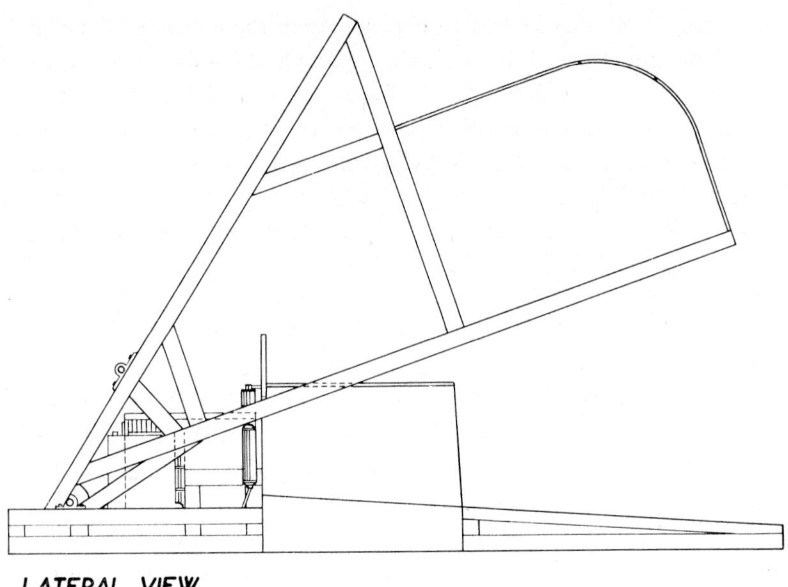

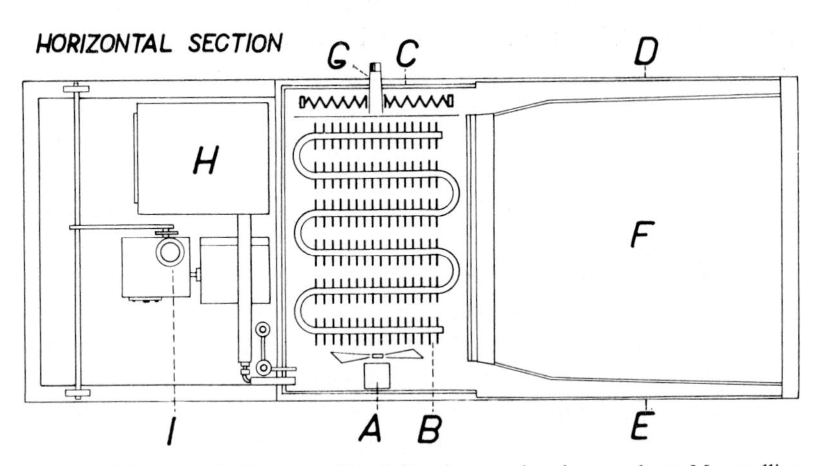

Fig. 2.13 Diagram of the ground-level 'trap' type chamber used at Montpellier (from Eckardt 1968). *A* turbine; *B* cooling coils; *C* heating element; *D* inlet and *E* outlet of air from the assimilation chamber *F; G* outlet for water condensed on cooling coils; *H* compressor unit; *I* motor for opening and closing the chamber. Temperature and humidity sensors are located between *E* and *A*. At this level too air is taken in for CO_2 analysis.

concentration difference between the outside and the inside air. Carbon dioxide concentration is measured with a differential infra-red gas analyser, to which air samples are continuously conducted from the sites of the temperature and humidity sensors. Radiant energy flux is regulated by sets of screens adapted to the transparent plastic walls of the chamber, or by mirrors.

Three regimes are possible: 1. temperature, humidity and CO_2 content are kept constant, 2. temperature, humidity and CO_2 content are kept at the same level as outside, and 3. temperature, humidity and CO_2 content differ from the outside

Fig. 2.14 The ground level assimilation chamber in action (from Eckardt 1968).

conditions, but the deviations are kept constant. When functioning in the second regime the deviations between conditions inside and outside the chamber do not exceed a temperature of 1 °C and concentrations of 500 mg m^{-3} water vapour and 30 mg m^{-3} carbon dioxide, except when rapid changes occur in the external environment.

Apparent photosynthesis is evaluated from the measurement of the amount of CO_2 added, using a heat transfer flow meter, and transpiration from the determination of the amount of water vapour condensed in the cooling system, using a rain gauge type of recorder. Night respiration is calculated from the increase in CO_2 content of the chamber immediately after closing it.

The crown level chamber (Figs. 2.15 and 2.16) is based on the same principle as that of the ground level chamber with the exception that humidity is measured by means of lithium chloride resistance probes situated in the circuit just prior to the CO_2 analyser and that temperature is measured by thermocouples inserted into the leaves. When used in the surface layer of the vegetation and under high irradiance, apparent photosynthesis is evaluated from the drop in CO_2 concentration in an open system.

When no measurements are carried out, the chambers are kept open in order to expose the plant organs to natural conditions.

The control and data recording devices necessary for the simultaneous functioning of these chambers are centralised in a self-contained, mobile laboratory (Eckardt 1968). Data are recorded onto magnetic tape in unworked form. At the end of a measuring campaign in the field, they are corrected for non-linearity of the transducers, converted from analogue to digital form and stored on punched cards.

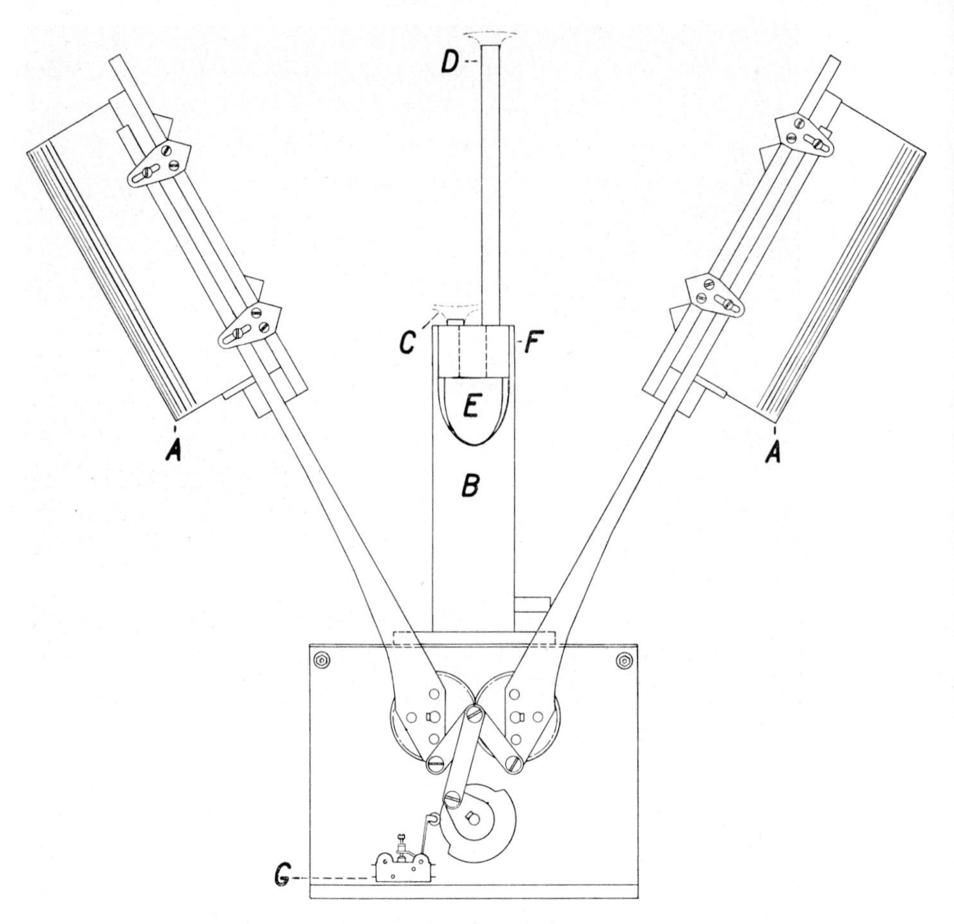

Fig. 2.15 Diagram of the crown level assimilation chamber used at Montpellier (from Eckardt 1968) (air conditioning unit not shown). The two hemicylindrical windows *(A)* close around the plant organ attached to the support *(B)*, containing the air inlet *(C)* and air outlet *(D)* tubes. The stem of the branch enters the chamber through *(E)* and is held by means of the sliding lid *(F)*. The chamber is opened and closed by the reversing switch *(G)* operated remotely.

2.7.3 | *Fully air-conditioned chambers with independent ventilation*

The 'trap' chambers of Eckardt described in the previous section are fully air conditioned and might well have been included here. They are separated because of the unique way in which they are used.

Air conditioned chambers fall into two broad categories: the air-conditioning equipment may be built into the chamber in all or part (*e.g.* Lange, Koch & Schulze 1969) or it may be entirely separate from the chamber (*e.g.* Musgrave & Moss 1961; Koller & Samish 1964). The latter approach has the obvious advantage that the same air conditioning and control units can readily be used with a wide range of kinds of chamber without major reconstruction, whereas little flexibility of use exists when the components of the air conditioning system are built in. On the other hand, a built in system has considerable advantages in achieving a close control of conditions in the chamber. In the first place the distance and volume of

Fig. 2.16 The crown level assimilation chamber in action: *(a)* operating in the normal position, *(b)* a general view showing the air conditioning unit and the tubes through which circulates the coolant from the refrigerator located at ground level.

conduit between chamber and site of air conditioning can be kept very small, thus facilitating a rapid response to changes in conditions (Lange, Koch & Schulze 1969), and secondly the possibility of changes in the composition of the air, because of condensation or leakage of CO_2 (either by mass flow or diffusion) for example, between the site of air conditioning and the chamber is largely eliminated. The majority of air conditioned chambers compromise between these two extremes.

Conditioning of the air with regard to CO_2 concentration is almost invariably done at a distance from the chamber: conditioning for water vapour concentration is also usually done at a distance from the chamber (although not in the case of Eckardt's and Koch's chambers): conditioning of the air for temperature may be partly done at a distance but, because of the low heat capacity of air and the change in temperature in transit, the final stage of temperature control is usually done at or in the chamber. The majority of laboratory systems and some field systems conform to this pattern of air conditioning and many complementary chambers, all variations on the same basic theme, have been devised for investigations with specific kinds of material or problems (*e.g.* Gaastra 1959; Bosian 1959a, b; 1965b; Björkman & Holmgren 1963; Nátr & Špidla 1963; Bierhuizen & Slatyer 1964a; Jarvis & Slatyer 1966a; Parkinson 1968).

An example of a simple chamber for use with air conditioning of this kind is shown in Fig. 2.17 (Nátr & Špidla 1963). The chamber shown has been designed especially for measurements of gas exchange by attached spikes and leaves of

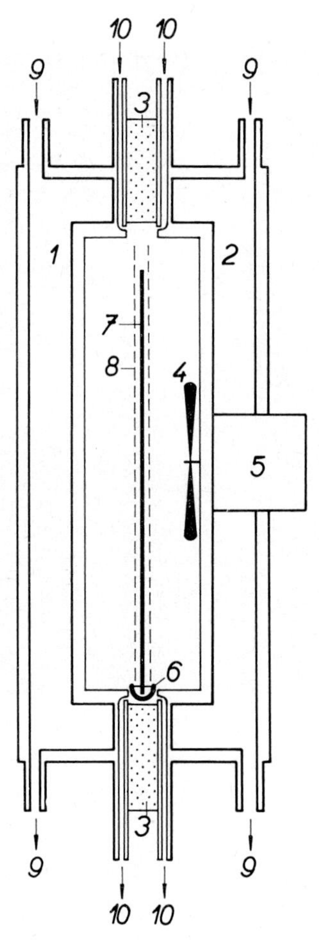

Fig. 2.17 Assimilation chamber with temperature control using water jackets (after Nátr & Špidla 1963). *1, 2:* water jackets, *3:* foam silicon rubber, *4:* propeller, *5:* motor, *6:* trough containing the water supply to excised leaves, *7:* leaf or spike, *8:* nylon net support, *9:* water inlets, *10:* air inlets.

cereals. The shape and size of the chamber may be varied to suit other material. The chamber is made of two parts each with a water jacket *(1, 2)* of acrylic plastic. Within the chamber a propeller *(4)* mixes the air. The propeller is coupled to a small motor fixed to the outside of the chamber *(5)* by strips of magnetic rubber (40 × 10 mm) on the propeller and motor shafts. In this way the propeller is driven without risk of leakage along the propeller shaft (see also Nishida 1962). The temperature of leaves in the chamber is controlled by means of temperature conditioned water flowing through the two halves of the water jacket. For temperatures close to 0 °C an ethanol-water mixture can be substituted (Bourdeau & Woodwell 1965).

The plant material to be measured is held in position between a double net of nylon threads *(8)*. If cut spikes, leaves or internodes are measured, water is supplied from a trough in the chamber *(6)*. Thick foam rubber *(3)* between the two halves of the chamber provides an effective seal, even if spikes are positioned across it. To prevent possible damage to brittle straw, it is advantageous to leave some gaps in the rubber lining, where the stalks enter the chamber. Cotton wool, foam plastic, wax or Swedish putty is then sufficient to seal the stalks into the chamber.

An example of a more complex assimilation chamber designed for a special purpose is that described by Jarvis & Slatyer (1966a). The chamber was designed to allow separate estimates of the fluxes of CO_2 and water vapour to and from each surface of a flat leaf and an independent estimate of stomatal resistance, so that differences in the gas flow pathways across each leaf surface could be quantitatively evaluated. The main requirements of the chamber were:

1. that it would enable the continuous measurement of water vapour and carbon dioxide exchange between each surface of an attached leaf and the surrounding atmosphere;

2. that the concentration of any gas introduced into the chamber could be controlled to predetermined levels;

3. that an independent estimate of stomatal aperture could be obtained for the portion of the leaf under study;

4. that leaf temperature could be controlled and measured and that variation in leaf temperature should be as small as possible;

5. that gradients of air temperature and gas concentration in the leaf chamber would be insignificant;

6. that the water content of the leaf in the chamber could be continuously monitored;

7. that the thickness of the leaf surface boundary layer would be small and independent of the rate at which air was removed from the chamber for analysis;

8. that the flux density of photosynthetically active radiation at the leaf could be controlled to predetermined levels and continuously monitored;

9. that the necessary measuring instruments would shade the surface of the leaf as little as possible;

10. that the leaf chamber be made in such a way that it could be readily dismantled for additions and modifications in relation to the performance and dimensions of the various instruments that were included.

The leaf chamber was made of '*Perspex*' acrylic plastic. One disadvantage commonly experienced with leaf chambers made with this material is the difficulty of obtaining

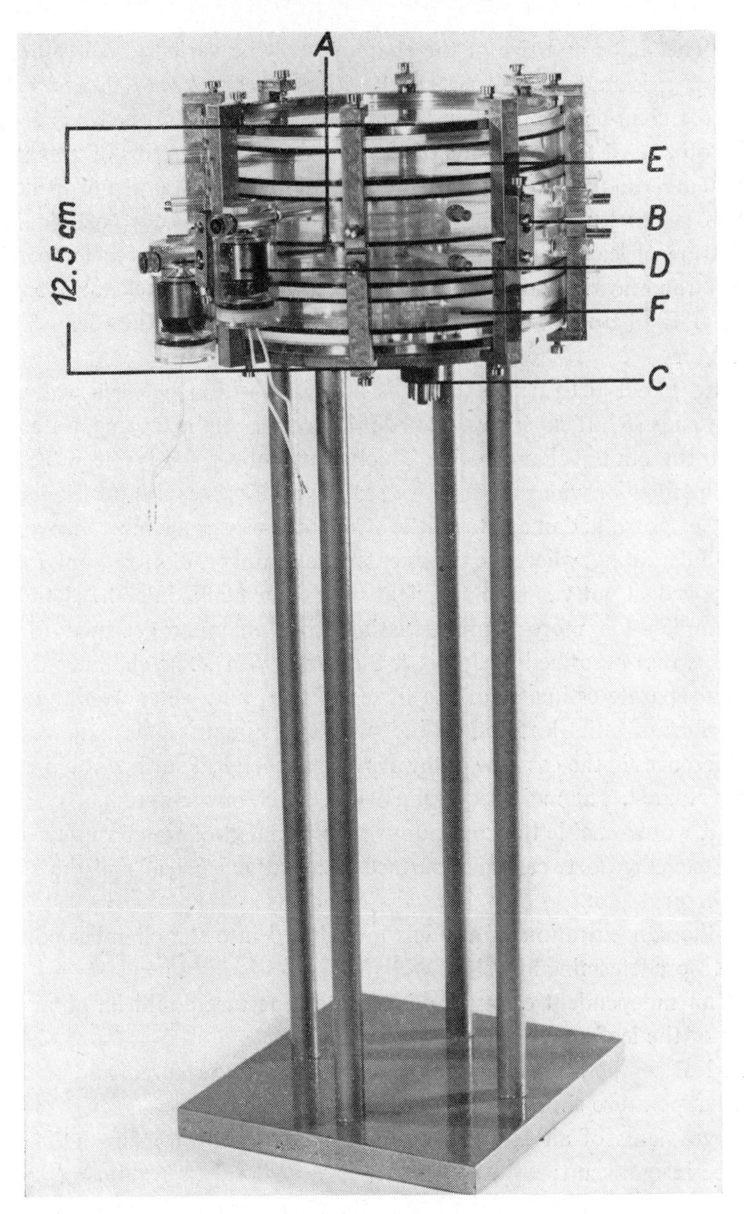

Fig. 2.18 Side view of a bilateral assimilation chamber (from Jarvis & Slatyer 1966a by courtesy of C.S.I.R.O., Division of Land Research). *A* slot for petiole; *B* clamps holding upper and lower halves together; *C* base of Geiger-Müller tube; *D* motor housings with 3 V, d.c. motors; *E* upper water jacket 2 cm across; *F* lower water jacket 2 cm across.

joints that remain properly watertight and airtight over a period of more than a few months. Another is that glued joints often create stresses in the material, which subsequently crazes and cracks. These difficulties were avoided by virtually eliminating glued and cemented joints from the construction. Out of about 60 joints only 2 were glued. The remainder were clamped or tapped and sealed with sheet neoprene or with O-rings.

 The chamber is illustrated in Figs. 2.18, 2.19 and 2.20. The photographs were

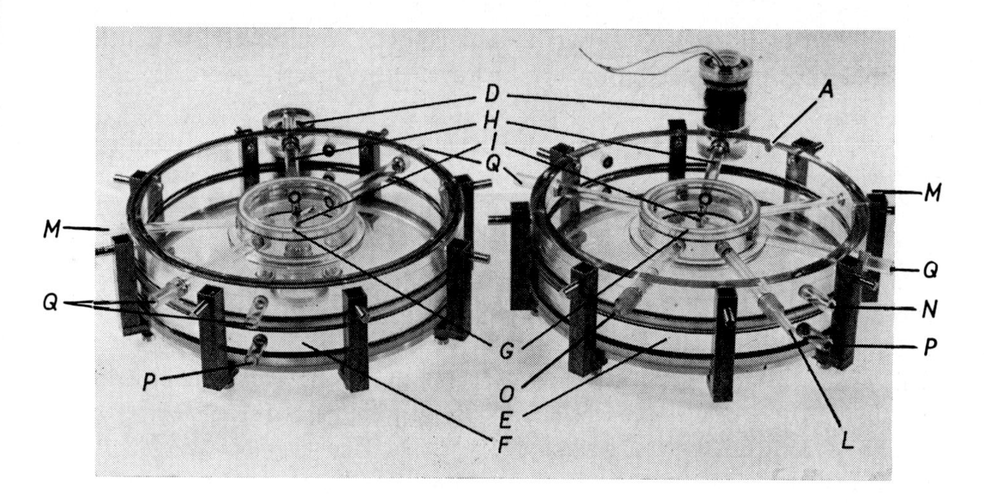

Fig. 2.19 The lower (left) and upper (right) halves of the chamber. *A* slot for petiole; *D* motor housings with 3 V, d.c. motors; *E* upper water jacket 2 cm across; *F* lower water jacket 2 cm across; *G* inflatable rubber gaskets; *H* neoprene belt drive; *I* '*Perspex*' propellers; *L* inlet tube for β-gauge source; *M* inlet tube to inflate gaskets; *N* inlet tube for photovoltaic cell; *O* reserve inlet tube; *P* water inlet or exit tubes; *Q* air inlet or exit tubes. (From Jarvis & Slatyer 1966a by courtesy of C.S.I.R.O., Division of Land Research.)

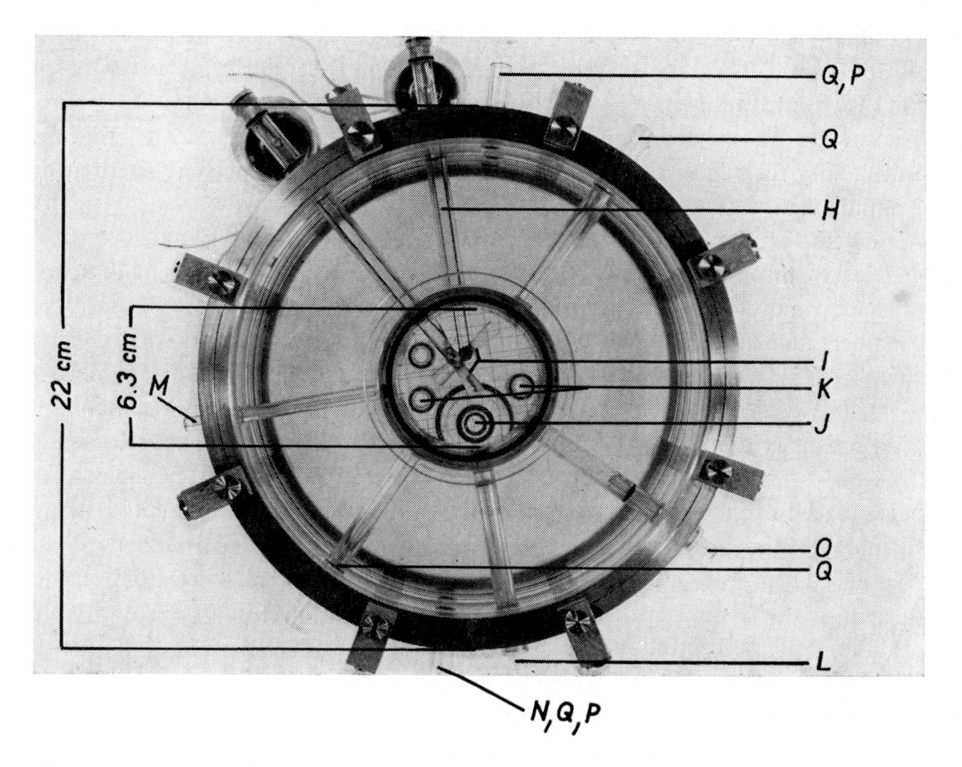

Fig. 2.20 Plan of chamber from above. *J* entry port for Geiger-Müller tube; *K* entry port for thermocouples; other symbols as in Figs. 2.18 and 2.19. (From Jarvis & Slatyer 1966a by courtesy of C.S.I.R.O., Division of Land Research.)

taken before the insertion of most of the air and water supply lines. The dimensions of the chamber were chosen to suit the leaves of plants with large broad leaves and long petioles.

The chamber opens into two halves. It consists of a cylindrical outer ring surrounding a central cylinder, which is divided by the leaf lamina into subchambers above and below the leaf. The internal diameter of the central cylinder is 6.3 cm, so that approximately 31 cm^2 of leaf upper and lower surface are isolated in the central cylindrical subchambers with the remainder of the leaf in the peripheral subchamber. Each of the three chambers has entry and exit ports providing independent air circulation.

This arrangement enables the environmental conditions around the peripheral part of the leaf to be maintained similar to those in the central subchambers, unless otherwise desired. The air leaving the peripheral subchamber can be readily connected into the analysis circuits and the flow rate into the peripheral subchamber can be adjusted to maintain the concentration of water vapour and carbon dioxide similar to that in the central subchambers. This provision was made to minimize the occurrence of stimuli in the peripheral part of the leaf, which might be transmitted laterally to the central portion under study.

When the leaf is in position the two halves of the chamber are held together with four clamps (Fig. 2.18). The petiole passes out through a slot sealed with 'plastic putty'. The lamina of the leaf can be sealed into the central chambers by inflating (to about 300 mb pressure) two annular rubber membranes opposed on each side of the leaf. These seals consist of thin, high quality surgical rubber (0.075 mm thick) cemented to the faces of the central cylinders across a 1.5 mm wide groove. The two grooves are connected to a pressure reservoir with a mercury manometer. Satisfactory seals have also been obtained using sponge silicone rubber rings of 2 mm diameter.

Air enters the two central subchambers through small ports 0.8 mm diameter, and leaves through holes of twice the diameter to ensure that no build-up of pressure can occur in the chambers. The small entry ports create turbulence in the chambers and this is augmented by two small '*Perspex*' propellers, one in each chamber. These are run at a rapid reproducible rate, the supply of current to each motor (3 V d.c.) being metered. Under standard operating conditions the boundary layer resistance of a piece of wet blotting paper in the chamber was approximately 0.4 s cm^{-1} for each side. The propellers are driven by neoprene belts, the motors being placed outside the chamber to minimize interception of the radiant energy to the leaf, and interference with the various sensors inserted below the leaf. Neoprene O-rings are used to seal the motors into '*Perspex*' housings and to isolate them from the tubes containing the fan belts (while these tubes are inevitably extensions of the central subchambers, their volume was only about 3.5 cm^3). These seals are completely tight up to pressures of more 80 cm water.

A silicon solar cell mounted in the peripheral chamber 2 cm from the central cylinder and approximately at leaf level, continuously monitors the incident radiation flux density. The solar cell was calibrated *in situ* (*i.e.* with a *Schott KG 2* filter and the water jacket in position) against a Moll-Gorczynski solarimeter placed in the position normally occupied by the leaf.

Temperature control is achieved by passing the air stream through heat-exchanging coils in a thermostatically controlled water bath before it enters the chamber. In addition, water from the bath is pumped through the two water jackets bounding the leaf chamber on the top and bottom. By changing the water bath temperature, and hence the temperature of the water jackets and of the air entering the three leaf chambers, the temperature of the leaf can be maintained constant at varying radiation loads, or varied for experimental purposes.

The temperature of the leaf, or of the lower-chamber air if required, is monitored by three thermocouples inserted vertically through the base of the central chamber and touching the under surface of the leaf. O-ring seals enable easy raising and lowering of the thermocouple holders. The thermocouples (copper-constantan 40 wire-gauge) are cemented into the tips of tapered '*Perspex*' holders with RTV silicone rubber.

Leaf water content is continuously monitored using β-particle gauging (Nakayama & Ehrler 1964; Jarvis & Slatyer 1966b). A thin mica end-window Geiger-Müller tube 1.2 cm maximum diameter, is inserted through the floor of the lower central chamber and held in position with O-ring seals (Fig. 2.18). The mica end-window is approximately 8 mm from the leaf surface so that ventilation of the lower leaf surface is not impeded. The radioactive source, which had to be above the leaf, is adsorbed on to a bead of resin or encased in a glass bead and mounted on a support, which is as small as possible to minimize shading of the leaf. The support consists of a thin steel wire, 0.8 mm diameter, threaded on the source end to take a small brass cylinder, 1.8 mm outside diameter, which can be screwed up and down past the source to provide collimation. The steel wire bends through a right angle just above the brass cylinder and passes out of the central chamber in an O-ring sealed '*Perspex*' holder. The position of the source can thus be adjusted to avoid veins and it can be withdrawn into a niche at the side of the chamber when not in use. A number of different sources can be used with leaves of different thickness. They include ^{147}Pm, of 0.3, 0.6, and 3 mc, for leaves of density thickness 10–30 mg cm^{-2} and ^{204}Th, of 1 mc, for thicker leaves.

Independent estimates of stomatal resistance can be obtained by using the two opposing central chambers as a mass flow porometer or as a diffusion porometer. To make estimates of stomatal resistance by mass flow porometry, air on the way to one of the central chambers is diverted through a pressure regulating valve and a capillary flow meter before reaching the chamber. A wide-bore tap on the chamber outlet is closed so that any air flux out of the chamber occurs through the leaf, or through leaks. The pressure regulating valve delivers a slow flow of air at constant pressure and the choice of a suitable capillary between the two manometers of the capillary flow meter allows observations over a range of fluxes and stomatal resistances (Bierhuizen, Slatyer & Rose 1965).

In operation the pressure difference across the leaf does not need to exceed 30 cm of water and leakage is negligible. There was no difficulty in completely sealing the upper surface of a cotton leaf; the lower surface was sometimes more difficult to seal completely because of the large veins (up to 1.5 mm diameter). Hence the direction of air flow generally used is from upper to lower chambers. This direction is preferable for a cotton leaf also because of the smaller number of stomata on the upper surface (approximately two-thirds of that on the lower surface) and hence the reduced tendency for lateral leakage through the leaf. When the lower surface was also sealed completely, the same resistance was obtained for flow in either direction.

The two central chambers can be used as a diffusion porometer by introducing a gas, *e.g.* nitrous oxide, to one side of the leaf and continuously monitoring the amount diffusing through the leaf to the air stream on the other side (Slatyer & Jarvis 1966). This air is passed through one channel of an infra-red gas analyser fitted with a nitrous oxide detector; the reference air by-passing the chamber is passed through the other channel of the analyser. Since nitrous oxide is not a normal constituent of air, control and measurement are simpler than with carbon dioxide. Nitrous oxide, 100%, is fed from a cylinder *via* reducing valves, a precision pressure regulator, and a capillary flow meter at a rate to give the required concentration on mixing with the air stream to one of the central subchambers. In normal use, air containing 1 000–5 000 $\mu l\ l^{-1}$ N_2O is supplied to the lower surface of the leaf, the concentration chosen depending on the leaf diffusion resistance. The concentration of nitrous oxide in air leaving the upper chamber can be determined with an accuracy better than 2 $\mu l\ l^{-1}$. The flux of nitrous oxide through the leaf is obtained from its concentration in the air leaving the upper chamber and the air flow rate through the upper chamber. Because of the efficient stirring in the chambers, the nitrous oxide concentration leaving the upper chamber is representative of the concentration close to the leaf, so that the nitrous oxide gradient across the leaf is obtained from the difference between the concentration applied to the lower surface and that concentration indicated by the infra-red gas analyser (see Slatyer & Jarvis 1966).

Chambers of this kind have been used in both open and closed systems (Troughton & Slatyer 1969; Jarvis & Slatyer 1970) and simpler versions based on the same general principles have also been constructed (Gale, Poljakoff-Mayber & Kahane 1967).

By applying a small pressure difference across the two central subchambers, the intercellular spaces of the leaf can be flushed with air containing a known, predetermined concentration of CO_2. This can be useful in the determination of mesophyll resistance to CO_2 transfer (Lake 1967; Troughton & Slatyer 1969).

An assimilation chamber suitable for gas exchange measurements in both field and laboratory has been developed as a result of years of collaboration between the Institute of Forest Botany, Munich, and the *Siemens A.G.*, Erlangen (BRD) (Koch, Klein & Walz 1968). The objective was the development of an apparatus which meets the diverse requirements of plant physiologists and ecologists and which could be used both in the field and the laboratory. The main design criteria of the system were that it should be constructed on the unit module principle so as to be readily adaptable and it should also be suitable for quantity production. In design and construction, the assimilation chamber meets most of the ten design criteria listed as essential requirements for the previous chamber discussed (page 95) (the special requirements *3* and *6* relating to the measurement of stomatal aperture and leaf water content are not included in the basic design) and has certain unique features of its own. A notable feature of the design of the chamber and the control systems is the use of thermoelectric cooling by Peltier modules. These have a number of advantages over conventional components: A stepless adjustable

Fig. 2.21 *Siemens* assimilation chamber (Type *PK-GWK 12*).

temperature is obtained by changing size and direction of the electric current to the modules; there is little or no maintenance or wear as there are no moving parts; they are insensitive to mounting position and mechanical shocks; they are of small volume and weight and automatic control is possible with electronic controllers. However some provision must be made to remove the heat pumped out of the chamber from the Peltier modules.

The assimilation chamber is shown in Figs. 2.21 and 2.23, and appears as *GWK* in Fig. 2.22. The Peltier modules are mounted on the back of the chamber, and are connected on both sides to heat exchangers. The outer heat exchanger can be cooled by ventilation with an axial fan; its cooling power can be further increased by additional water or brine cooling. A metal baseplate separates the internal heat exchanger from the useful space above. A radial fan provides air circulation within the chamber and forces the air through the fins of the heat exchanger on one side and passes it over the plant material in the useful space above. As a result, the temperature of the air is controlled and gradients of carbon dioxide, water vapour and temperature in the vicinity of the plant material are largely avoided. The ventilation rate inside the chamber can be adjusted by varying the speed of the radial fan. The '*Plexiglas*' casing is closed by a removable '*Plexiglas*' cover.

The useful space inside the chamber of 15 litres is suitable for fairly small plants, *e.g.* lichens or mosses and/or leaves or shoots of larger plants which can be inserted through a slot in the narrow side of the casing. The slot can be readily sealed with a non-hardening mastic (*e.g. Terostat*, *Apioson*). The plants are held in position in the chamber with nylon threads. There are connections and entry points provided

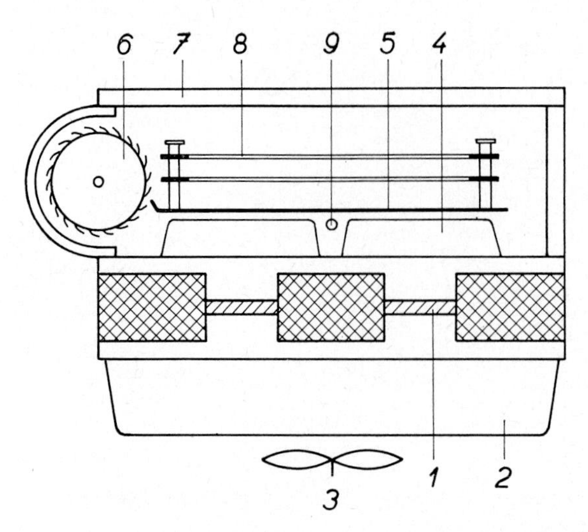

Fig. 2.22 Cross sectional diagram of the assimilation chamber. *1:* Peltier blocks; *2:* external heat exchanger; *3:* fan; *4:* internal heat exchanger; *5:* base plate; *6:* squirrel edge fan; *7:* '*Plexiglass*' top; *8:* mounting frame; *9:* platinum resistance thermometer (100 Ω). (From Koch, Klein & Walz 1968.)

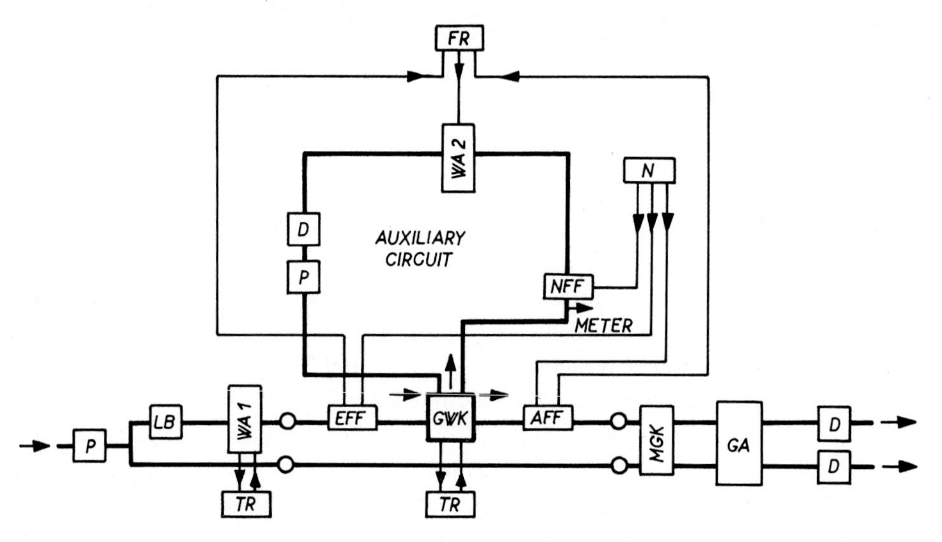

Fig. 2.23 Block diagram of a humidity and temperature controlled assimilation chamber for gas exchange measurements. *GWK* chamber; *EFF* humidity sensor for incoming air; *AFF* humidity sensor for air leaving the chamber; *NFF* humidity sensor in the re-circulating air stream; *FR* humidity controller; *TR* temperature controller; *D* flow meter; *P* pump; *WA* water vapour trap; *N* power supply for humidity sensors; *MGK* cooler for drying the air for CO_2 measurement; *GA* gas analyser; *LB* air humidifier. ▬▬ pneumatic connections; —— electrical connections. (From Koch, Klein & Walz 1968.)

in the walls for additional electrical transducers in the chamber, such as photocells and thermocouples. In the side walls interchangeable tubing connections connect the chamber to the CO_2 and humidity measurement and control systems. Bars at the side of the chamber enable it to be mounted in any position. The Peltier modules control the chamber temperature within the ecologically important

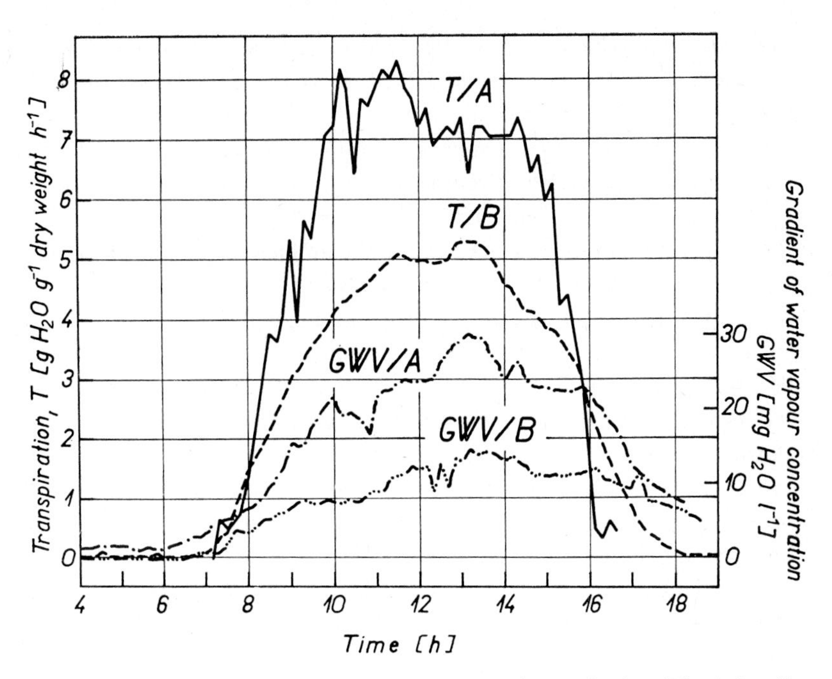

Fig. 2.24 A comparison between the daily course of transpiration *(T)* of *Citrullus colocynthis* and the gradient of water vapour concentration of the air (*GWV*) in a *Siemens* chamber with uncontrolled humidity *(A)* and in a similar chamber with control of humidity *(B)*. (From Lange, Koch & Schulze 1969.)

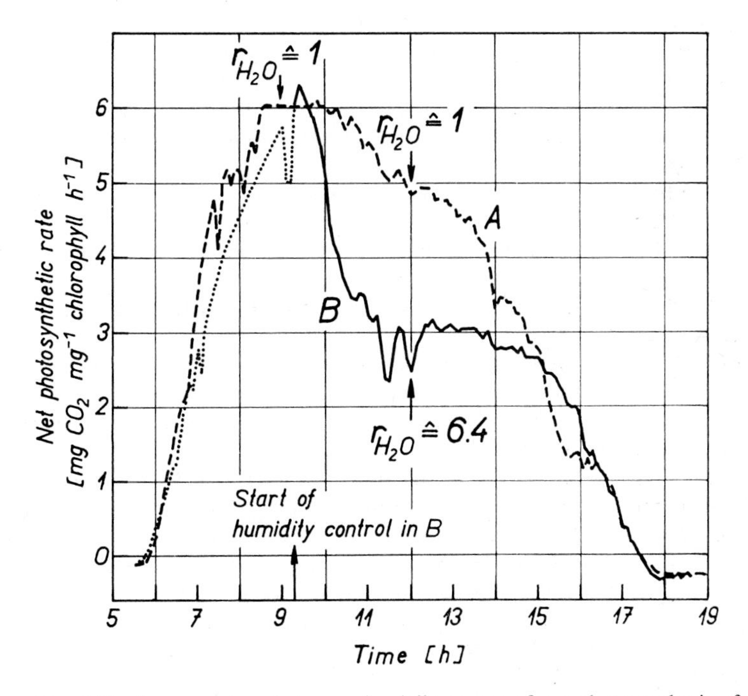

Fig. 2.25 A comparison between the daily course of net photosynthesis of *Datura metel* in a humidity controlled *Siemens* chamber *(B)* and in a similar chamber with uncontrolled humidity *(A)*. r_{H_2O} - total diffusion resistance of the leaves to water vapour transfer. (From Lange, Koch & Schulze 1969.)

range of about −20 to +50 °C. In the absence of a radiation load the temperature in the chamber can be lowered 20 °C below the ambient temperature with full cooling power. If the thermal load on the chamber is increased as a result of irradiation, this maximum temperature difference is reduced. As discussed earlier, it will depend on the rate of ventilation in the chamber because this influences the flux of convective heat between the heat exchangers and ambient air.
The temperature in the chamber and in the ambient air is measured with platinum 100 Ω resistance thermometers. The output of these thermometers is transmitted to a PID-controller (Fig. 2.23 *TR*) which adjusts the temperature in the chamber in one of three different ways. The air temperature in the chamber is either kept the same as the ambient temperature (follow-up-control), or it is kept constant (set-value-control), or it is varied according to a pre-set programme (programme control).
The chamber may be used in an open or closed system. In Fig. 2.23 the chamber is shown in a typical measurement and control system. A large number of these chambers are now in use. Good examples of their use in obtaining ecologically relevant data in an extreme environment are given by Lange, Koch and Schulze (1969), some of whose data are shown in Figs. 2.24 and 2.25.

2.8 | References

Anderson, M. C.: Light relations of terrestrial plant communities and their measurement. – Biol. Rev. 39: 425-486, 1964.

Anderson, N. E., Hertz, C. H., Rufelt, H.: A new fast recording hygrometer for plant transpiration measurements. – Physiol. Plant. 7: 753-767, 1954.

Apel, P.: Herstellung CO_2-haltiger Gasgemische für Photosynthesemessungen mit dem URAS. – Flora 157 A: 330-333, 1966.

Avery, D. J.: The supply of air to leaves in assimilation chambers. – J. exp. Bot. 17: 655-677, 1966.

Avery, D. J.: The temperatures of leaves in assimilation chambers, and in the open. – J. exp. Bot. 18: 379-396, 1967.

Baker, D. N.: Effects of certain environmental factors on net assimilation in cotton. – Crop Sci. 5: 53-56, 1965.

Baker, D. N., Musgrave, R. B.: Photosynthesis under field conditions. V. Further plant chamber studies of the effects of light on corn (*Zea mays* L.). – Crop Sci. 4: 127-131, 1964.

Bate, G. C., D'Aoust, A., Canvin, D. T.: Calibration of infra-red CO_2 gas analyzers. – Plant Physiol. 44: 1122-1126, 1969.

Baumeister, W.: Zur Anwendung des Ultrarotabsorptionsschreibers für CO_2-Assimilationsmessungen an abgeschnitteten Blättern im Laboratorium. – Ber. deut. bot. Ges. 65: 361-368, 1952.

Begg, J. E., Lake, J. V.: Carbon dioxide measurement: A continuous conductimetric method. – Agr. Meteorol. 5: 283-290, 1968.

Bierhuizen, J. F., Slatyer, R. O.: Photosynthesis of cotton leaves under a range of environmental conditions in relation to internal and external diffusive resistances. – Austr. J. biol. Sci. 17: 348-359, 1964a.

Bierhuizen, J. F., Slatyer, R. O.: An apparatus for the continuous and simultaneous measurement of photosynthesis and transpiration under controlled environmental conditions. –CSIRO Div. Land Res., Regional Surv. tech. Pap. 24: 1-16, 1964b.

Bierhuizen, J. F., Slatyer, R. O., Rose, C. W.: A porometer for laboratory and field operation. – J. exp. Bot. 16: 182-191, 1965.

Björkman, O.: Carboxydismutase activity in shade-adapted and sun-adapted species of higher plants. – Physiol. Plant. 21: 1-10, 1968a.

Björkman, O.: Further studies on differentiation of photosynthetic properties in sun and shade ecotypes of *Solidago virgaurea*. – Physiol. Plant. 21: 84-99, 1968b.

Björkman, O., Holmgren, P.: Adaptability of the photosynthetic apparatus to light intensity in ecotypes from exposed and shaded habitats. – Physiol. Plant. 16: 889-914, 1963.
Björkman, O., Holmgren, P.: Photosynthetic adaptation to light intensity in plants native to shaded and exposed habitats. – Physiol. Plant. 19: 854-859, 1966.
Bosian, G.: Über die Vollautomatisierung der CO_2-Assimilationsbestimmung und zur Methodik des Küvettenklimas. – Planta 45: 470-492, 1955.
Bosian, G.: Die vollautomatische Regulierung der relativen Feuchtigkeit in der Assimilationsküvette für Standortsversuche. – Ber. deut. bot. Ges. 71 (Gen.-Vers. H.): 26, 1959a.
Bosian, G.: Zum Problem des Küvettenklimas: Temperatur und Feuchteregulierung. – Ber. deut. bot. Ges. 72: 391-397, 1959b.
Bosian, G.: Zum Küvettenklimaproblem: Beweisführung für die Nichtexistenz 2-gipfeliger Assimilationskurven bei Verwendung von klimatisierten Küvetten. – Flora 149: 167-188, 1960.
Bosian, G.: Der Peltier-Effekt im Einsatz zur Küvettenklima-Regulierung. – Ber. deut. bot. Ges. 77 (Gen.-Vers.H.): 22-23, 1964a.
Bosian, G.: Assimilations- und Transpirationsbestimmungen an Reben im Freiland mit klimatisierten Küvetten. – Weinwissenschaft 19: 265-271, 1964b.
Bosian, G.: The controlled climate in the plant chamber and its influence upon assimilation and transpiration. – In: Eckardt, F. E. (ed.): Methodology of Plant Eco-Physiology. Pp.225-232. Unesco, Paris 1965a.
Bosian, G.: Control of conditions in the plant chamber: Fully automatic regulation of wind velocity, temperature and relative humidity to conform to microclimatic field conditions. – In: Eckardt, F. E. (ed.): Methodology of Plant Eco-Physiology. Pp. 233-238. Unesco, Paris 1965b.
Bosian, G.: Die Bedeutung der Stomata, der Luftfeuchte und der Temperatur für den CO_2- und Wasserdampfgaswechsel der Pflanzen. – Photosynthetica 2: 105-125, 1968.
Bourdeau, P. F., Woodwell, G. M.: Measurements of plant carbon dioxide exchange by infrared absorption under controlled conditions and in the field. – In: Eckardt, F. E. (ed.): Methodology of Plant Eco-Physiology. Pp. 283-289. Unesco, Paris 1965.
Bowman, G. E.: The measurement of carbon dioxide concentration in the atmosphere. – In: Wadsworth, R. M. *et al.* (ed.): The Measurement of Environmental Factors in Terrestrial Ecology. Pp. 131-139. Blackwell Sci. Publ., Oxford-Edinburgh 1968.
Boysen-Jensen, P.: Studies on the production of matter in light- and shadow-plants. – Bot. Tidskr. 36: 219-262, 1918.
Boysen-Jensen, P.: Die Stoffproduktion der Pflanzen. – G. Fischer, Jena 1932.
Bray, J. R., Sanger, J. E., Archer, A. L.: The visible albedo of surfaces in central Minnesota. – Ecology 47: 524-531, 1966.
Brix, H.: The effect of water stress on the rates of photosynthesis and respiration in tomato plants and loblolly pine seedlings. – Physiol. Plant. 15: 10-20, 1962.
Brown, K. W.: Experimental considerations for the measurement of photosynthetic rates by means of carbon dioxide exchange in leaf chambers. – Nebraska Coll. Agr. Home Econ., Agr. exp. Sta. Lincoln, Progr. Rep. 66: 1-40, 1968.
Budyko, M. I., Gandin, L. S.: Vliyanie klimaticheskikh faktorov na rastitel'nyĭ pokrov. [The influence of climatic factors on plant cover.] – Izv. Akad. Nauk SSSR, Ser. geogr. 1966(1): 3-10, 1966.
Bulley, N. R., Nelson, C. D., Tregunna, E. B.: Photosynthesis: Action spectra for leaves in normal and low oxygen. – Plant Physiol. 44: 678-684, 1969.
Čatský, J.: Méthodes et techniques de mesure de la concentration en anhydride carbonique dans l'air. – In: Techniques d'Étude des Facteurs Physiques de la Biosphère. Pp. 181-188. I.N.R.A., Paris 1970.
Čatský, J., Slavík, B.: Polevoĭ pribor dlya opredeleniya intensivnosti fotosinteza. [A field apparatus for the determination of photosynthetic rate.] – Biol. Plant. 2: 107-112, 1960.
Chartier, M., Chartier, P.: Design of an air-conditioned assimilation chamber for detached leaves. – Photosynthetica 5 74-75, 1971.
Chartier, P.: Assimilation nette d'une culture couvrante. I. Définition d'un schéma d'expérimentation à partir d'une analyse théorique. – Ann. Physiol. vég. 12: (in press), 1970.
Chouard, P., de Bilderling, N. (ed.): Phytotronique. – Éd. C.N.R.S., Paris 1969.

Clark, J.: Photosynthesis and respiration in white spruce and balsam fir. – State Univ. Coll. Forestry, Syracuse Univ. Tech. Publ. No. 85: 1–72, 1961.
Cox, L. M., Boersma, L.: Transpiration as a function of soil temperature and soil water stress. – Plant Physiol. 42: 550-556, 1967.
Cross, N. L.: A humidity control system for a small chamber. – J. sci. Instr. (J. Phys. E) Ser. 2, 1: 65-68, 1968.
Davies, D. H.: A review of non-gravimetric methods of determining carbon dioxide and monoxide. – Talanta 16: 1055-1065, 1969.
Decker, J. P.: The effect of air supply on apparent photosynthesis. – Plant Physiol. 22: 561-571, 1947.
Decker, J. P.: Some effects of temperature and carbon dioxide concentration on photosynthesis of *Mimulus*. – Plant Physiol. 34: 103-106, 1959.
Decker, J. P., Gaylor, W. G., Cole, F. D.: Measuring transpiration of undisturbed Tamarisk shrubs. – Plant Physiol. 37: 393-397, 1962.
Dirmhirn, I.: Das Strahlungsfeld in Lebensraum. – Akademische Verlagsges., Frankfurt a/M. 1966.
van den Driessche, R., Wareing, P. F.: Dry-matter production and photosynthesis in pine seedlings. – Ann. Bot. N.S. 30: 673-682, 1966.
Duncan, W. G., Loomis, R. S., Williams, W. A., Hanau, R.: A model for simulating photosynthesis in plant communities. – Hilgardia 38: 181-205, 1967.
Eckardt, F. E.: Le principe de la soufflerie climatisée, appliqué à l'étude des échanges gazeux de la couverture végétale. – Oecol. Plant. 1: 369-399, 1966.
Eckardt, F. E.: Mécanisme de la production primaire des écosystèmes terrestres sous climat méditerranéen. Recherches entreprises à Montpellier dans le cadre du Programme Biologique International. – Oecol. Plant. 2: 367-393, 1967.
Eckardt, F. E.: Techniques de mesure de la photosynthèse sur le terrain, basées sur l'emploi d'enceintes climatisées. – In: Eckardt, F. E. (ed.): Functioning of Terrestrial Ecosystems at the Primary Production Level. Pp. 289-319. Unesco, Paris 1968.
Egle, K., Schenk, W.: Untersuchungen über die Reassimilation der Atmungskohlensäure bei der Photosynthese der Pflanzen. – Beiträge Biol. Pfl. 29: 75-105, 1952.
El-Sharkawy, M. A., Hesketh, J. D.: Effects of temperature and water deficit on leaf photosynthetic rates of different species. – Crop Sci. 4: 514-518, 1964.
Etherington, J. R.: Measurement of photosynthesis and transpiration in controlled environments with particular reference to microclimate control in leaf cuvettes. – Ann. Bot. N.S. 31: 653-660, 1967.
Fujiwara, A., Suzuki, M.: Studies on the carbon metabolism in the higher plant. I. On the newly deviced apparatus for the measurement of the photosynthesis. – Tohoku J. agr. Res. 7: 383-389, 1957.
Funk, J. P.: Improved polythene-shielded net radiometer. – J. sci. Instr. 36: 267-270, 1959.
Gaastra, P.: Photosynthesis of crop plants as influenced by light, carbon dioxide, temperature and stomatal diffusion resistance. – Meded. Landbouwhogesch. Wageningen 59(13): 1-68, 1959.
Gaastra, P.: Photosynthesis of leaves and field crops. – Neth. J. agr. Sci. 10: 311-324, 1962.
Gaastra, P.: Climate rooms as a tool for measuring physiological parameters for models of photosynthetic systems. – In: Prediction and Measurement of Photosynthetic Productivity. Pp. 387-398. PUDOC, Wageningen 1970.
Gabrielsen, E. K.: Einfluss der Lichtfaktoren auf die Kohlensäureassimilation der Laubblätter. – Dansk bot. Arkiv 10: 1-177, 1940.
Gale, J., Kohl, H. C., Hagan, R. M.: Mesophyll and stomatal resistances affecting photosynthesis under varying conditions of soil, water and evaporation demand. – Israel J. Bot. 15: 64-71, 1966.
Gale, J., Poljakoff-Mayber, A., Kahane, I.: The gas diffusion porometer technique and its application to the measurement of leaf mesophyll resistance. – Israel J. Bot. 16: 187-204, 1967.
Gates, D. M.: Transpiration and leaf temperature. – Annu. Rev. Plant Physiol. 19: 211-238, 1968.
Gates, D. M., Tantraporn, W.: The reflectivity of deciduous trees and herbaceous plants in the infra-red to 25 microns. – Science 115: 613-616, 1952.
Gates, D. M., Keegan, H. J., Schleter, J. C., Weidner, V. R.: Spectral properties of plants. – Appl. Optics 4: 11-20, 1965.

Gloser, J.: A set of leaf chambers suitable for gas exchange measurements in grasses. – Photosynthetica 4: 312-313, 1970.

Goldsworthy, A.: A simple apparatus for generating an air stream containing a constant concentration of $^{14}CO_2$. – J. exp. Bot. 17: 147-150, 1966.

Hardwick, K., Lumb, H., Woolhouse, H. W.: A chamber suitable for measurements of gas exchange by leaves under controlled conditions. – New Phytol. 65: 526-531, 1966.

Hellmuth, E. O.: A method of determining true values for photosynthesis and respiration under field conditions. – Flora 157 B: 265-286, 1967.

Hesketh, J. D., Musgrave, R. B.: Photosynthesis under field conditions. IV. Light studies with individual corn leaves. – Crop Sci. 2: 311-315, 1962.

Holmgren, P.: Leaf factors affecting light-saturated photosynthesis in ecotypes of *Solidago virgaurea* from exposed and shaded habitats. – Physiol. Plant. 21: 676-698, 1968a.

Holmgren, P.: A device to procure air mixtures with accurate carbon dioxide concentrations. – Lantbrukshögsk. Ann. 34: 219-224, 1968b.

Hoover, W. H.: The dependence of carbon dioxide assimilation in a higher plant on wave length of radiation. – Smithsonian misc. Coll. 95(21): 1-13, 1937.

ICI Ltd.: The properties of '*Perspex*' acrylic materials. – *ICI Ltd.*, Plastics Div., Welwyn Garden City, U.K.

Jarvis, P. G.: Characteristics of the photosynthetic apparatus derived from its response to natural complexes of environmental factors. – In: Prediction and Measurement of Photosynthetic Productivity. Pp. 353-367. PUDOC, Wageningen 1970.

Jarvis, P. G., Slatyer, R. O.: A controlled-environment chamber for studies of gas exchange by each surface of a leaf. – CSIRO Div. Land Res. tech. Paper 29: 1-16, 1966a.

Jarvis, P. G., Slatyer, R. O.: Calibration of β-gauges for determining leaf water status. – Science 153: 78-79, 1966b.

Jarvis, P. G., Slatyer, R. O.. The role of the mesophyll cell wall in leaf transpiration. – Planta 90: 303-322, 1970.

Koch, W.: Eine neue Methode zur Lösung des Küvettenproblems bei der Registrierung des Gaswechsels. – Naturwissenschaften 43: 64, 1956.

Koch, W.: Der Tagesgang der 'Produktivität der Transpiration'. – Planta 48: 418-452, 1957.

Koch, W., Klein, E., Walz, H.: Neuartige Gaswechsel-Meßanlage für Pflanzen in Laboratorium und Freiland. – Siemens-Z. 42: 392-404, 1968.

Koller, D., Samish, Y.: A null-point compensating system for simultaneous and continuous measurement of net photosynthesis and transpiration by controlled gas-stream analysis. – Bot. Gaz. 125: 81-88, 1964.

Lake, J. V.: Respiration of leaves during photosynthesis. II. Effects on the estimation of mesophyll resistance. – Aust. J. biol. Sci. 20: 495-499, 1967.

Lange, O. L.: Eine 'Klapp-Küvette' zur CO_2-Gaswechselregistrierung an Blättern von Freilandpflanzen mit dem URAS. – Ber. deut. bot. Ges. 75: 41-50, 1962.

Lange, O. L., Koch, W., Schulze, E. D.: CO_2-Gaswechsel und Wasserhaushalt von Pflanzen in der Negev-Wüste am Ende der Trockenzeit. – Ber. deut. bot. Ges. 82: 39-61, 1969.

Larcher, W.: Physiological approaches to the measurement of photosynthesis in relation to dry matter production by trees. – Photosynthetica 3: 150-166, 1969.

Lee, R.: Effects of tent type enclosures on the microclimate and vaporization of plant cover. – Oecol. Plant. 1: 301-326, 1966.

Louwerse, W., van Oorschot, J. L. P.: An assembly for routine measurements of photosynthesis, respiration and transpiration of intact plants under controlled conditions. – Photosynthetica 3: 305-315, 1969.

Loveland, J. W., Adams, R. W., King, H. H. Jr., Nowak, F. A., Cali, L. J.: Spectrophotometric titration of parts per million of carbon dioxide in gases. – Anal. Chem. 31: 1008-1010, 1959.

Lundegårdh, H.: Neue Apparate zur Analyse des Kohlensäuregehalts der Luft. – Biochem. Z. 131: 109-115, 1922.

Lundegårdh, H.: Klima und Boden. 4th Ed. – G. Fischer, Jena 1954.

McIntosh, D. H., Thom, A. S.: Essentials of Meteorology. – Wykeham Publ. (London) Ltd., London 1969.

McPherson, H. G.: Photocell-filter combinations for measuring photosynthetically active radiation. – Agr. Meteorol. 6: 347-356, 1969.
Monteith, J. L.: The reflection of short wave radiation by vegetation. – Quart. J. roy. meteorol. Soc. 85: 386-392, 1959.
Monteith, J. L.: Calculating evaporation from diffusive resistances. – In: Investigation of Energy and Mass Transfers near the Ground including the Influences of the Soil-Plant-Atmosphere System. Pp. 177-189. Univ. California, Davis 1963.
Monteith, J. L.: Light distribution and photosynthesis in field crops. – Ann. Bot. N.S. 29: 17-37, 1965a.
Monteith, J. L.: Evaporation and environment. – Symp. Soc. exp. Biol. 19: 205-234, 1965b.
Mooney, A. H., Harrison, A. T.: The influence of conditioning temperature on subsequent temperature-related photosynthetic capacity in higher plants. – In: Prediction and Measurement of Photosynthetic Productivity. Pp. 411-417. PUDOC, Wageningen 1970.
Mooney, H. A., Shropshire, F.: Population variability in temperature-related photosynthetic acclimation. – Oecol. Plant. 2: 1-13, 1967.
Moss, D. N.: The effect of environment on gas exchange of leaves. – In: Zelitch, I. (ed.): Stomata and Water Relations in Plants. Conn. agr. exp. Sta. Bull. 664: 86-101, 1963.
Moss, D. N.: Optimum lighting of leaves. – Crop Sci. 4: 131-136, 1964.
Musgrave, R. B., Moss, D. N.: Photosynthesis under field conditions. I. A portable, closed system for determining net assimilation and respiration of corn. – Crop Sci. 1: 37-41, 1961.
Nakayama, F. S., Ehrler, W. L.: Beta ray gauging technique for measuring leaf water content changes and moisture status of plants. – Plant Physiol. 39: 95-98, 1964.
Nátr, L., Špidla, J.: Assimilation chambers for studying the photosynthetic rates of leaves and spikes of cereals. – Biol. Plant. 5: 284-286, 1963.
Negisi, K.: A simple assimilation chamber for measurement of photosynthesis of forest tree seedlings. – J. Jap. For. Soc. 43: 261-262, 1961.
Negisi, K., Satoo, T.: Effect of air supply on apparent photosynthesis of Akamatu *(Pinus densiflora)*, Sugi *(Cryptomeria japonica)* and Hinoki *(Chamaecyparis obtusa)*. – J. Jap. For. Soc. 43: 354-355, 1961.
Nichiporovich, A. A., Strogonova, L. E., Chmora, S. N., Vlasova, M. P.: Fotosinteticheskaya Deyatel'nost' Rasteniĭ v Posevakh. [Photosynthetic Activity of Crop Plants.] – Izd. Akad. Nauk SSSR, Moskva 1961.
Nishida, K.: Studies on the re-assimilation of respiratory CO_2 in illuminated leaves. – Plant Cell Physiol. 3: 111-124, 1962.
Norman, J. M., Tanner, C. B., Thurtell, G. W.: Photosynthetic light sensor for measurements in plant canopies. – Agron. J. 61: 840-843, 1969.
Okanenko, A. S., Gulyaev, B. I., Pochinok, Kh. N.: Mnogokanal'naya ustanovka dlya izmereniya intensivnosti fotosinteza. [Multichannel apparatus for measuring photosynthetic rate.] – In: Fotosintez i Produktivnost' Rasteniĭ. Pp. 103-112. Zinatne, Riga 1965.
van Oorschot, J. L. P., Belksma, M.: An assembly for the continuous recording of CO_2 exchange and transpiration of whole plants. – Weed Res. 1: 245-257, 1961.
Orchard, B., Heath, O. V. S.: Carbon assimilation at low carbon dioxide levels. I. Apparatus and technique. – J. exp. Bot. 15: 314-330, 1964.
Parkinson, K. J.: Apparatus for the simultaneous measurement of water vapour and carbon dioxide exchanges of single leaves. – J. exp. Bot. 19: 840-856, 1968.
Parlange, J.-Y., Waggoner, P. E., Heichel, G. H.: Boundary layer resistance and temperature distribution on still and flapping leaves. – Plant Physiol. 45: (in press), 1970.
Philip, J. R.: Plant water relations: Some physical aspects. – Annu. Rev. Plant Physiol. 17: 245-268, 1966.
Pochinok, Kh. N.: Ustanovka dlya gazometricheskogo opredeleniya fotosinteza v estestvennykh usloviyakh. [A device for the gasometric determination of photosynthesis in natural conditions.] – Fiziol. Rast. 5: 200-205, 1958.
Polster, H.: Neuere Ergebnisse auf dem Gebiet der standortsökologischen Assimilations- und Transpirations-Forschung an Forstgewächsen. – Sitzungsber. deut. Akad. Landwirtschaftswiss. Berlin 10: 1-43, 1961.
Polster, H., Weise, G.: Vergleichende Assimilationsuntersuchungen an Klonen verschiedener

Lärchenherkünfte *(Larix decidua* und *Larix leptolepis)* unter Freiland- und Klimaraumbedingungen. – Züchter 32: 103-110, 1962.
Rackham, O.: Radiation, transpiration, and growth in a woodland annual. – In: Bainbridge, R., Evans, G. C., Rackham, O. (ed.): Light as an Ecological Factor. Pp. 167-185. Blackwell Sci. Pub., Oxford 1966.
Raschke, K.: Über den Einfluss der Diffusionswiderstände auf die Transpiration und die Temperatur eines Blattes. – Flora 146: 546-578, 1958.
Raschke, K.: Heat transfer between the plant and the environment. – Annu. Rev. Plant Physiol. 11: 111-126, 1960.
Raschke, K.: Eignung und Konstruktion registrierender Porometer für das Studium der Schliesszellenphysiologie. – Planta 67: 225-241, 1965.
Raschke, K.: Eine Anlage zur monochromatischen Bestrahlung biologischer Objekte, ausgerüstet mit Interferenzfiltern und einer elektronisch geregelten 2,5 kW-Xenonlampe. – Planta 75: 55-72, 1967.
Redshaw, A. J., Meidner, H.: A fine-control carbon dioxide injection circuit for the measurement of rates of net photosynthesis by infra-red gas analysis. – J. exp. Bot. 21: 410-413, 1970.
Romashko, Ya. D.: Do metodyky vyznachennya gazoobminu v kroni dereva. [On methods for determining gas exchange in the tree top.] – Ukr. bot. Zh. 16(5): 48-54, 1959.
Rufelt, H., Jarvis, P. G., Jarvis, M. S.: Some effects of temperature on transpiration. – Physiol. Plant. 16: 177-185, 1963.
Sanadze, G. A.: Primenenie titrometricheskogo gazoanalizatora dlya opredeleniya fotosinteza i dykhaniya. [Use of titrimetric gas analyser for determination of photosynthesis and respiration.] – Bot. Zh. 48: 1796-1799, 1963.
Šesták, Z., Čatský, J.: Sur les relations entre le contenu en chlorophylle et l'activité photosynthétique pendant la croissance et le vieillissement des feuilles. – In: Sironval, C. (ed.): Le Chloroplaste, Croissance et Vieillissement. Pp. 213-262. Masson & Cie, Paris 1967.
Skidmore, E. L., Stone, J. F.: Physiological role in regulating transpiration rate of the cotton plant. – Agron. J. 56: 405-410, 1964.
Slatyer, R. O., Jarvis, P. G.: Gaseous-diffusion porometer for continuous measurement of diffusive resistance of leaves. – Science 151: 574-576, 1966.
Stålfelt, M. G.: Die stomatäre Regulation in der pflanzlichen Transpiration. – Planta 17: 22-32, 1932.
Stout, M. B.: Photosynthesis and respiration studies with sugar beets. I. Equipment and methods. – J. amer. Soc. Sugar Beet Technol. 14: 302-308, 1967.
Swinbank, W. C.: Long wave radiation from clear skies. – Quart. J. roy. meteorol. Soc. 89: 339-348 and 90: 488-493, 1963.
Thom, A. S.: The exchange of momentum, mass and heat between an artificial leaf and the airflow in a wind-tunnel. – Quart. J. roy. meteorol. Soc. 94: 44-55, 1968.
Thomas, M. D.: Precise automatic apparatus for continuous determination of carbon dioxide in air. – Ind. eng. Chem., Anal. Ed. 5: 193-198, 1933.
Thomas, M. D., Hill, G. R.: The continuous measurement of photosynthesis, respiration and transpiration of alfalfa and wheat growing under field conditions. – Plant Physiol. 12: 285-307, 1937.
Tranquillini, W.: Über den Einfluss von Übertemperaturen der Blätter bei Dauereinschluss in Küvetten auf die ökologische CO_2-Assimilationsmessung. – Ber. deut. bot. Ges. 67: 191-204, 1954.
Tranquillini, W.: Standortsklima, Wasserbilanz und CO_2-Gaswechsel junger Zirben (*Pinus cembra* L.) an der alpinen Waldgrenze. – Planta 49: 612-661, 1957.
Tranquillini, W.: Die Stoffproduktion der Zirbe (*Pinus cembra* L.) an der Waldgrenze während eines Jahres I. Standortsklima und CO_2-Assimilation. – Planta 54: 107-129, 1959.
Tranquillini, W.: Photosynthesis and dry matter production of trees at high altitudes. – In: The Formation of Wood in Forest Trees. Pp. 505-518. Academic Press, New York 1964a.
Tranquillini, W.: Blattemperatur, Evaporation und Photosynthese bei verschiedener Durchströmung der Assimilationsküvette. Mit einem Beitrag zur Kenntnis der Verdunstung in 2000 m Seehöhe. – Ber. deut. bot. Ges. 77: 204-218, 1964b.
Tranquillini, W.: Photosynthese und Transpiration einiger Holzarten bei verschieden starkem Wind. – Centralbl. ges. Forstw. 86: 35-48, 1969.

Trickett, E. S., Goulden, J. D. S.: The radiation transmission and heat conserving properties of glass and some plastic films. – J. agr. Eng. Res. 3: 281-287, 1958.

Troughton, J. H.: Plant water status and carbon dioxide exchange of cotton leaves. – Aust. J. biol. Sci. 22: 289-302, 1969.

Troughton, J. H., Slatyer, R. O.: Plant water status, leaf temperature, and the calculated mesophyll resistance to carbon dioxide of cotton leaves. – Aust. J. biol. Sci. 22: 815-827, 1969.

Went, F. W.: The Experimental Control of Plant Growth. – Chron. bot. Co., Waltham, Mass. 1957.

Whiteman, P. C., Koller, D.: Environmental control of photosynthesis and transpiration in *Pinus halepensis*. – Israel J. Bot. 13: 166-176, 1964.

Whiteman, P. C., Koller, D.: Interactions of carbon dioxide concentration, light intensity and temperature on plant resistances to water vapour and carbon dioxide diffusion. – New Phytol. 66: 463-473, 1967a.

Whiteman, P. C., Koller, D.: Species characteristics in whole plant resistances to water vapour and CO_2 diffusion. - J. appl. Ecol. 4: 363-377, 1967b.

de Wit, C. T.: Photosynthesis of leaf canopies. – Agr. Res. Rep. (Wageningen) 663: 1-57, 1965.

Withrow, R. B., Withrow, A. P.: Generation, control, and measurement of visible and near-visible radiant energy. – In: Hollaender, A. (ed.): Radiation Biology. Vol. III. Pp. 125-258. McGraw-Hill, New York 1956.

Wolf, D. D., Pearce, R. B., Carlson, G. E., Lee, D. R.: Measuring photosynthesis of attached leaves with air sealed chambers. – Crop Sci. 9: 24-27, 1969.

Wolf, F.: New climatic measuring chambers for plant physiological research. Technical description. – In: Chouard, P., de Bilderling, N. (ed.): Phytotronique. Pp. 12-16. Éd. C.N.R.S., Paris 1969.

Woolley, J. T.: Relative permeabilities of plastic films to water and carbon dioxide. – Plant Physiol. 42: 641-643, 1967.

3 | INFRA-RED GAS ANALYSERS AND OTHER PHYSICAL ANALYSERS

3.1 | Characteristics of methods using infra-red gas analysers

The general application of gasometric methods for the determination of CO_2 exchange was described in the previous chapter. It was stated that the reliability and accuracy of these methods are essentially determined by two elements of the equipment – the assimilation chamber and the CO_2 analyser. While there are many chamber types and new ones are constantly being devised, infra-red gas analysers (IRGA) are now the most commonly used type of CO_2 analyser. They are produced in large numbers throughout the world, to a suitable specification and of good quality. They are popular because of their accuracy and reliability of performance, as well as the simplicity of their operation. Their undeniable advantages are that they continuously and directly measure the carbon dioxide density (*i.e.*, the concentration), they can be used with many types of recorders, and their output can be processed automatically by means of a computer. Therefore they are almost ideal instruments to use in laboratory systems for making possibly the most precise measurements of the rate of CO_2 exchange.
On the other hand, IRGAs and their accessories are rather complicated and expensive devices. This prevents their utilisation for serial work which in practice is possible only by using a sequential switching system (see Section 3.8.8). However, then the advantage of continuous analysis is lost in investigations of short term changes in the CO_2-exchange rate (*i.e.*, changes lasting only a few minutes). Chapter 4 will therefore be devoted to methods which allow easy and inexpensive application to serial work.

3.2 | Infra-red analysis of gases and vapours

The analysis of substances in the infra-red region of the spectrum is one of the most common methods based on the interaction of matter and electromagnetic radiation. There is a direct relation between the infra-red absorption spectrum of a substance and its molecular structure. This relation is determined by kind, number and mass of atoms, mutual bonding forces and symmetry of the molecule. Different molecules have different spectra. Complicated molecules with very similar structures can have almost identical spectra because individual atom groups in different molecules have absorption bands in the same position. However, some variation in absorption can practically always be found and used for the analysis.
Gases and vapours that usually exhibit very complex spectra are especially suitable for infra-red analysis. The so-called intermediate infra-red region of the spectrum, ranging from 2.5 to 25 μm, is used in the infra-red analysis of gases. Vibration and vibration-rotation spectra of molecules, with similarities and differences between them which make it possible to measure gas mixtures selectively, lie within this range. At normal temperatures and pressures, these spectra are characterized by a very fine structure of individual spectral lines forming characteristic absorption

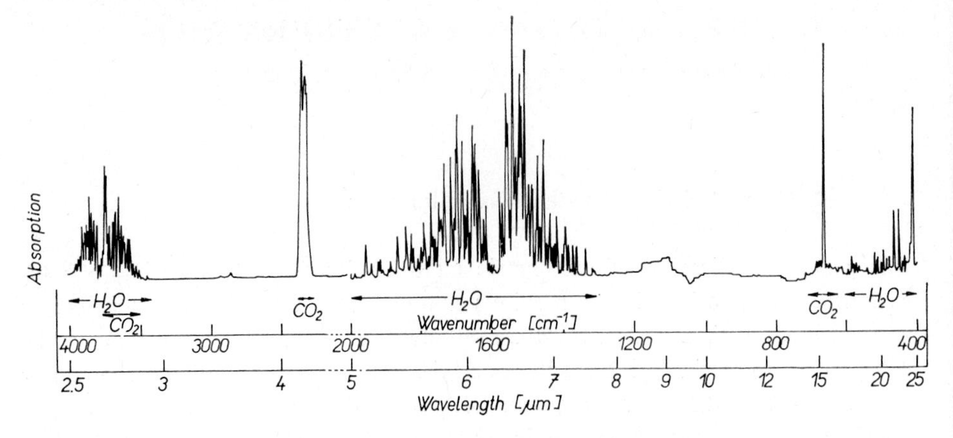

Fig. 3.1 Absorption spectra of atmospheric carbon dioxide and water vapour.

bands of the form which is registered by spectroscopes of moderate resolution. Good selectivity in measurements of gas mixtures is thus ensured. The gases CO_2, H_2O, CO, SO_2, NO, N_2O, HCN, NH_3, CS_2, CH_4, and all higher hydrocarbons, are among the most common compounds which absorb in the infra-red region. On the other hand, molecules made up of two identical atoms (*e.g.* O_2, N_2, H_2) and gases not exhibiting dipole moment, do not absorb infra-red radiation (for details see *e.g.* Brügel 1962; Banwell 1966).
Carbon dioxide is one of the most intensely absorbing gases, and therefore particularly suitable for determination in very low concentrations by means of infra-red analysis. Absorption spectra of atmospheric carbon dioxide and of water vapour are illustrated in Fig. 3.1. It is very important to stress from the outset that the absorption bands of CO_2 and H_2O overlap in the region around 2.7 μm. The determination of CO_2 in trace concentration can therefore be affected by the presence of water vapour if all absorption bands are used unselectively.

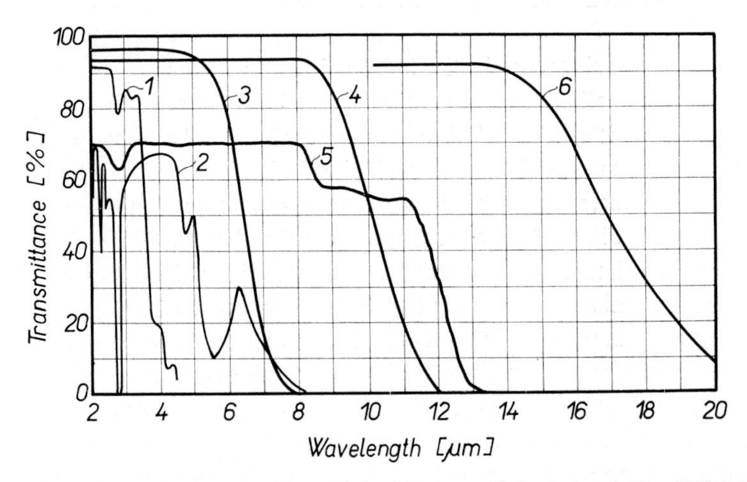

Fig. 3.2 Spectral transmittance of IR optical materials. *1:* fused silica (SiO_2) 10 mm thick; *2:* mica 0.06 mm thick; *3:* lithium fluoride (LiF) 10 mm thick; *4:* calcium fluoride (CaF_2) 10 mm thick; *5:* arsenic trisulfide glass (As_2S_3) 3 mm thick; *6:* sodium chloride (NaCl) 10 mm thick.

Continuous, quantitative gas analysis is carried out by infra-red gas analysers (IRGAs) which are simpler than infra-red spectrographs, because they operate without dispersion. They have no monochromators and they are therefore also appreciably cheaper. The range of wavelengths which can be used for measurements by IRGA is determined by the properties of the optical materials used in the construction. Calcium fluoride, which is not hygroscopic, is the most commonly used window material; it transmits infra-red radiation up to *ca.* 8 μm (Fig. 3.2). However, for measuring CO_2, the main absorption band of which is near 4.26 μm (Fig. 3.1, Table 3.1), even cheap mica windows may be used for the tubes.

Table 3.1 Main absorption bands of carbon dioxide in the intermediate infra-red region.

Wavelength $\lambda[\mu m]$	Wavenumber $v[cm^{-1}]$	Band intensity* $S[atm^{-1}\ cm^{-2}]$	Average absorption coefficient $k[atm^{-1}\ cm^{-1}]$
2.69	3 716	54 ± 10	0.54 ± 0.10
2.77	3 609	37 ± 8	0.31 ± 0.07
4.26	2 349	2 500 ± 400	23.2 ± 3.71
14.99	667	330 ± 90	3.1 ± 0.85

* At standard conditions (after Burch, Gryvnak & Williams 1962).

3.3 | Theory of radiation absorption

Infra-red radiation can be defined by its frequency $\bar{v}$, wavelength λ, or wavenumber v:

$$v[cm^{-1}] = \bar{v}[s^{-1}]/c[cm\ s^{-1}] = 1/\lambda[cm]$$

where c is the velocity of light propagation equal to 2.998×10^{10} [cm s^{-1}] in vacuum. The total absorptance A, also called integral absorptance, over a finite spectral interval Δv is given by the expression

$$A \equiv \int_{\Delta v} A_v\, dv = \int_{\Delta v} [1 - \exp(-k_v w)]dv \qquad (3.1)$$

where A_v is the fractional absorptance, k_v is the absorption coefficient at wavenumber v, and w is the so-called optical thickness. Optical thickness is given by the expression

$$w = l\rho \qquad (3.2)$$

where l is the path length traversed by the radiation and ρ is the density of the absorbing medium[1]. Also, for gases:

$$w = lp \tag{3.3}$$

where p is the partial pressure of the absorbing gas.
The value of the integral in Eq. (3.1) depends upon the function relating k_ν to ν. The solution is simple only when the absorption coefficient is constant:

$$A = \Delta\nu[1 - \exp(-kw)] \tag{3.4}$$

This is the well-known Beer's law. If kw is sufficiently small so that the exponential can be replaced by the first two terms in its series expansion, then

$$A \simeq \Delta\nu \cdot kw \tag{3.5}$$

In gases, except at very high pressures and low temperatures, k_ν is a rapidly varying function of ν in the infra-red region, and Beer's law is not generally valid. With certain approximation (for details see *e.g.* Penner 1959) we reach two simple limiting cases. For a band consisting of many non-overlapping lines of Lorentz shape (this condition is fulfilled by CO_2), the total absorptance of the band of 'weak lines' is given by

$$A = \Sigma_i S_i w \tag{3.6}$$

where S_i is line intensity, and the total absorptance of the band of 'strong lines' is given by

$$A = 2(wP)^{\frac{1}{2}}\, \Sigma_i(\beta S_i)^{\frac{1}{2}} \tag{3.7}$$

where β is a quantity related to the half-width of lines and P is the total pressure of the gas.
Eq. (3.6) describes the linear region of the total absorptance. In this region Beer's law is valid. Hence from Eqs. (3.5) and (3.6) the average absorption coefficient of the band can be described by

$$k = S/\Delta\nu \tag{3.8}$$

where $S = \Sigma_i\, S_i$ is band intensity[2]. Band intensities and average absorption

1. Whilst weight per unit weight is a more conservative measure and is therefore preferable, concentrations of gases are usually given in units of volume per unit volume and expressed as vol.% or volume per million [vpm], or less precisely as parts per million by volume [ppm]. More appropriate units are ml l^{-1} or $\mu l\ l^{-1}$ (= vpm).
2. The units most frequently employed in spectroscopy are: S[atm^{-1} cm^{-2}], k[atm^{-1} cm^{-1}].

coefficients of CO_2 are given in Table 3.1. Most of the absorptance is by the 4.26 μm band of CO_2.

Eq. (3.7) describes the 'square-root' region. The total absorptance depends also on the total pressure of the gas and, through the quantity β, on the composition of the gas mixture to be analysed.

Eq. (3.6) for 'weak lines' is applicable for small values of $S \cdot w/2\pi\beta P$, while Eq. (3.7) is applicable for large values of $S \cdot w/2\pi\beta P$, (for details see *e.g.* Howard, Burch & Williams 1956; Burch, Gryvnak & Williams 1962; Anderson, An-Ti Chai & Williams 1967).

An approximately linear IRGA response is required. For the region where Beer's law is valid, it was found that about $(kw)_{max} \leq 0.1$ (Janáč 1966).

The expression $(kw)_{max}$ represents kw at full-scale deflection. The maximum deviation from linearity d_{max} is observed approximately in the middle of scale. For $d_{max} = 1\%$, $(kw)_{max} = 0.083$; for $d_{max} = 2\%$, $(kw)_{max} = 0.174$; and for $(kw)_{max} = 0.1$, $d_{max} = 1.3\%$. Hence in practice, work is carried out at a low value of the product $(kw)_{max}$. A value of 0.1 can be achieved when analysing low to high concentrations by selecting a suitable length absorption path. Frequently, in analysis of traces of a gas, tubes of the desirable length cannot be used: for constructional reasons the usual maximum length of absorption tubes in IRGAs is 30 cm (but longer tubes can be provided to special order by most manufacturers). Then the value of $(kw)_{max} \simeq 0.1$ cannot be achieved and $(kw)_{max}$ may be lower by one order of magnitude or more[1]. Hence, Eqs. (3.5) and (3.6) are applicable to the calculation of the absorption of infra-red radiation under the conditions of an IRGA in analysis of traces of gases.

3.4 | Principles of infra-red radiation detection

In IRGAs the principle of positive filtration is most commonly used because of its sensitivity. Practically all analysers used for the study of CO_2 exchange in plants are based on this principle. IRGAs based on other principles will not be described in this chapter (for further details see, *e.g.*, McAlister 1937; Dingle & Pryce 1940; Scarth, Loewy & Shaw 1948; Hengstenberg, Sturm & Winkler 1957; Kenndall 1966; Hill & Powell 1968).

An analyser using positive filtration contains a selective radiation detector. Essentially, this detector is a gas thermometer having one or two absorption chambers filled with the same gas component the concentration of which is to be determined in the sample tube.

These analysers are of two types, differing in the arrangement of the absorption chambers in the detector:

1. with absorption chambers arranged optically in parallel,
2. with absorption chambers arranged optically in series.

3.4.1 | Detector with absorption chambers in parallel

This type is the one most commonly produced at present. It is most generally

1. This is one of the main factors limiting the minimum range of present day IRGAs.

used, mainly because of its high sensitivity and selectivity of measurement, easy adaptability to analyses of various substances, and small response time. However, as compared with analysers based on other more simple physical principles, stability is less, requiring more frequent recalibration of the output during long-term measurement.
This analyser, known as the conventional type (Fig. 3.3), is arranged as follows:

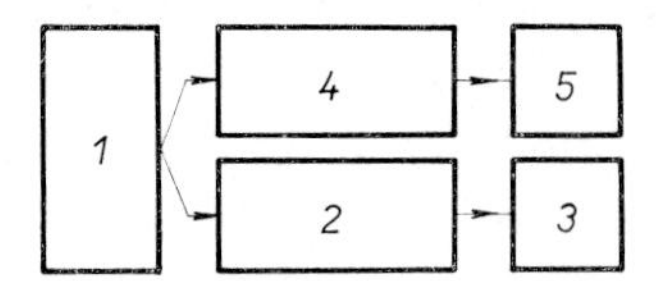

Fig. 3.3 Scheme of IRGA with detector with absorption chambers in parallel. *1:* non-selective source of infra-red radiation, *2:* reference tube, *3:* absorption chamber of the detector, *4:* sample tube, *5:* absorption chamber of the detector.

a non-selective source *1* emits infra-red radiation both through a reference tube *2*, filled with a gas which does not absorb infra-red radiation (*e.g.* nitrogen)[1], and through a sample tube *4* containing the mixture to be analysed, one component of which is the gas the concentration of which is to be determined. The gas in the sample tube absorbs radiation of the appropriate wavelengths, to an extent depending on its concentration. Residual non-absorbed radiation passes through the tube *(4)* and enters the absorption chamber *(5)* of the detector. Radiation passing through the reference tube *(2)* with unreduced flux density over the whole of the spectrum enters the absorption chamber *(3)* of the detector. The signal given by the detector results from the difference between the constant amount of energy absorbed by chamber *(3)* and the variable amount of energy dependent upon the concentration of the gas in tube *(4)*, absorbed by chamber *(5)*.
Selectivity of measurement is based on the selection of the same gas, the concentration of which is to be determined in the sample tube, as the energy absorber in chambers *3* and *5* (*i.e.*, the absorption chambers of the detector are filled with CO_2 when analysing for CO_2). From the whole continuous spectrum emitted by the non-selective source, this gas absorbs only radiation in its own absorption bands; this 'selective' detector does not therefore respond to radiation of other wavelengths. This ensures that the measurement will not be affected by other gases in the sample tube absorbing infra-red radiation of other wavelengths. The energy absorbed by the gas in the detector increases the temperature, pressure and volume of this gas. Thus these properties, measured by various means, depend on the concentration of the gas being analysed in the sample tube.

1. The simplest type of system is described here, to allow the clearest explanation of basic terms and technical principles. However, one feature must be stressed at the beginning to avoid misunderstanding. In the most modern types of IRGAs, a reference gas (a standard mixture or the 'control' air) flows through one of the absorption tubes. The gas with lower CO_2 concentration is always passed through the reference tube, irrespective of whether it is the actual reference gas or the sample gas. In this chapter the term reference tube always refers to the tube which contains the gas with the lower CO_2 concentration.

It was assumed above that the mixture being analysed does not contain other gases which absorb infra-red radiation at the same wavelengths as the gas being studied. However, the mixture may often contain a gas which shares some spectral lines with the one being analysed, and is therefore called an interfering gas[1]. A change in concentration of such a gas in the mixture contained in the sampling tube would then affect the measurement because of the overlapping spectral lines and would lead to incorrect results. A filter can be built into the optical system of the analyser, to remove absorption frequencies of the interfering gas from the continuous spectrum of the source, in both the paths of radiation. Gas filters, *i.e.* tubes filled with the interfering gas, are generally used. However, absorption or interference filters are used for removal of the effect of water vapour when measuring low concentrations of CO_2 (see Section 3.8.6).

3.4.2 | Detector with absorption chambers in series

The IRGA with the detector of this type has been developed and produced only recently. It has greater stability and better selectivity of measurement than the conventional type. The main feature of this analyser is that the radiation passing through the sample tube is absorbed by two successive layers of gas in the detector. The physical principle of the measurement is the fact that the gas absorbs radiation more intensively in the centre of the spectral line than at its tails (a more detailed explanation of this phenomenon is given by Luft, Kesseler & Zörner 1967).

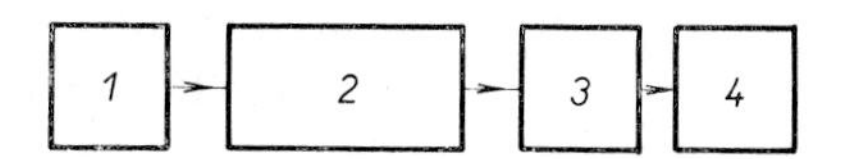

Fig. 3.4 Scheme of IRGA with detector with absorption chambers in series. *1:* non-selective source of infra-red radiation, *2:* sample tube, *3:* first absorption chamber of the detector, *4:* second absorption chamber of the detector.

This type of IRGA (Fig. 3.4) is constructed in such a way that the infra-red radiation emitted by a non-selective source *1* passes first through the sample tube *2* containing the mixture of gases to be analysed. The gas to be measured, present in the mixture, absorbs radiation of the appropriate wavelengths to an extent which depends on its concentration. Other non-absorbed radiation from the sample tube passes through the first absorption chamber *(3)* and then enters the second absorption chamber *(4)* of the detector. Both absorption chambers are filled with the gas to be analysed. The gas in the absorption chamber *(3)* of the detector absorbs radiant energy predominantly in the centre of the absorption lines, whereas the gas in the absorption chamber *(4)* of the detector absorbs the

1. Traces of water vapour, carbon monoxide, methane *etc. can* interfere in CO_2 determinations. Sulphur dioxide in the low concentrations normally present in the atmosphere cannot be considered to be an interfering gas although one of its absorption bands overlaps with that of CO_2 near 4.3 μm. However, when measuring CO_2 exchange in air with a particularly high SO_2 concentration its effect should be checked experimentally.

residual radiation in the tails of the absorption lines; the latter changes only slightly with changing concentration of the analysed gas in the sample tube. Thus the presence of the analysed gas in the sample tube brings about particularly a decrease in energy absorbed by the first chamber of the detector. The difference or ratio of energies absorbed by the detector chambers is then a measure of concentration of the gas. Absorption by the gas in both absorption chambers should be adjusted in such a way that the energy absorbed in both chambers of the detector is equal, if the sample tube does not contain any of the gas. If the partial pressures of the absorbing gas are equal in both chambers, the first chamber must be shorter than the second one. In other respects this analyser does not differ from the conventional one. Its advantages are greater stability of measurement (approximately by one order) and better selectivity (approximately five times).

3.5 | Construction of infra-red CO_2 analysers

The most commonly used type of construction of infra-red CO_2 analysers of the conventional type[1] (Section 3.4.1) is shown in Fig. 3.5. Two nichrome spirals (or one with the beam split by mirrors) in reflectors, heated by low-voltage current to about 600–800 °C (dark red glow), serve as sources of radiation (*1* and *2*). Radiation from heater *2* passes through the sample tube *4*, containing the analysed air, and enters the absorption chamber *6*. Radiation from heater *1* passes through reference tube *3*, filled with nitrogen or with air freed of CO_2 and H_2O, and enters the chamber *5*. The two chambers of the detector *(7)* are separated from one another by a thin membrane (usually of aluminium alloy) about 5 to 10 μm thick, which forms one electrode of the diaphragm condenser (the opposite plate is usually placed about 50 μm from the membrane). The paths of radiation are interrupted by a rotational shutter *(10)* (usually with a constant frequency between 2 and 20 Hz), causing periodical pressure changes in the detector, with simultaneous vibration of the membrane. The amplitude of vibration of the membrane is determined by the pressure difference between the two absorption chambers causing a variation of the condenser capacity. Voltage changes across the condenser

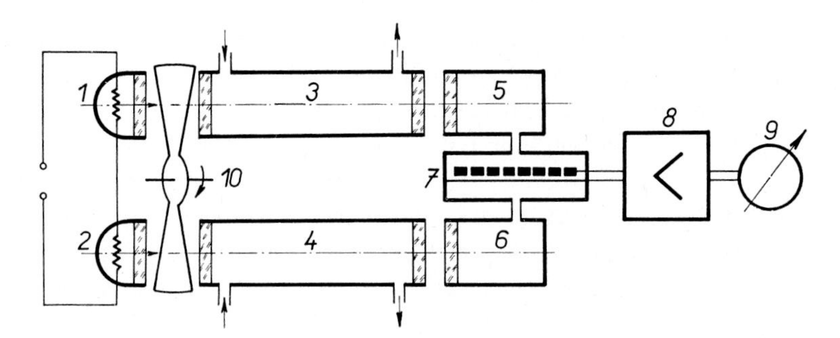

Fig. 3.5 Construction of IRGA with detector absorption chambers in parallel. *1*, *2*: sources of radiation, *3*: reference tube, *4*: sample tube, *5*, *6*: absorption chambers, *7*: detector, *8*: amplifier, *9*: meter, *10*: rotational shutter.

1. Similar analysers are used to measure other gases and vapours, *e.g.* H_2O; they differ from the CO_2 analyser only in the gas filling the detector.

(charged usually with 100–200 V D.C.) are inversely proportional to capacity changes. It is amplified by the amplifier *8*, rectified and measured by the output meter (recorder) *9*.

The use of interrupted radiation which brings about the necessary stability of measurement, is a basic feature of this type of construction, originally designed by Luft (1943). Periodical pressure changes in the detector make it possible to connect both absorption chambers by means of an acoustic filter[1], which prevents the passage of gas during vibration of the membrane at the working frequency (*i.e.* 2 to 20 Hz) and maintains static pressure equilibrium between the two absorption chambers. Interrupted radiation also makes it possible to use an alternating current amplifier, which is simpler and much more stable than a D.C. one.

The type of construction of the IRGA with the absorption chambers of the detector arranged *in series*, designed originally by Luft (1962), is in practice more complicated than the simplified arrangement described in Section 3.4.2. This arrangement would not allow zero to be set, with zero concentration of the measured gas in the sample tube, by means of an optical shutter, as it is in the conventional type of IRGA. The analyser is therefore equipped with a reference tube, the reason for which is seen from the description of the analyser presented schematically in Fig. 3.6.

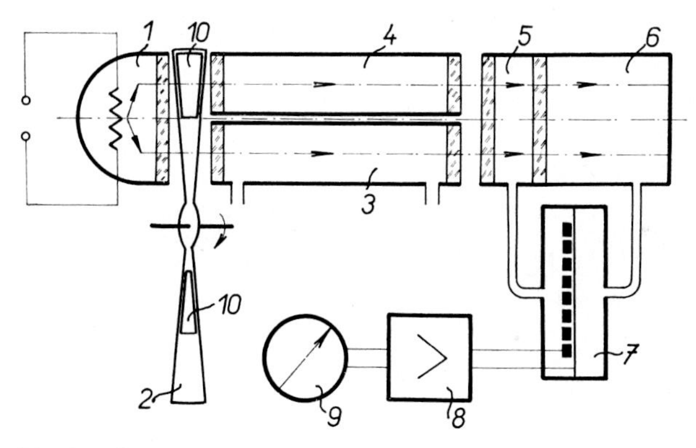

Fig. 3.6 Construction of IRGA with detector absorption chambers in series. *1:* source of radiation, *2:* rotational shutter, *3:* sample tube, *4:* reference tube, *5:* first absorption chamber, *6:* second absorption chamber, *7:* detector, *8:* amplifier, *9:* meter, *10:* openings in the shutter.

Radiation from the source *1* is interrupted by the rotational shutter *2* in such a way that it passes alternately through the sample tube *3* and the reference tube *4*. The reference tube is filled with a gas which does not absorb infra-red radiation. Therefore, when no sample gas is present in the sample tube, the energies absorbed in chambers *5* and *6* from the reference radiation path are the same as those absorbed from the sample path. Any small discrepancy between the energies absorbed from the reference and the sample paths is compensated electrically,

1. An acoustic filter is a narrow slit, of a rectangular or circular shape; its size is determined primarily by the working frequency.

and thus a zero signal of the detector is achieved. Other aspects of the operation of this analyser are in principle the same as with the conventional type.
The IRGAs which operate on the so-called *deflection principle* have been described above. For control of CO_2 concentration where long-term operating stability is the fundamental requirement, *null-balance* IRGAs are often used. In a manner similar to double-beam spectrometers, these IRGAs use an optical system with an optical null. Usually, a balancing shutter is mounted before the detector in the reference path of radiation, and its position is controlled by a servomotor.

3.6 | Examples of types of IRGA in production

Infra-red analysers with positive filtering suitable for measuring low CO_2 concentrations in air are produced by a number of manufacturers. An example is analyser *URAS 2* (*Hartmann & Braun A.G.*, Frankfurt/Main, B.R.D.), an improved version of *URAS 1* which, at present, is one of the most common. This analyser (Figs. 3.7 and 3.8) is of a modular construction. All its principal components may be easily taken out of a double dust- and water-tight box. The bottom half of the box contains the optical system of the analyser, the upper half the electronics.
The source of radiation consists of two heaters placed in a parabolic reflector. The heaters are connected in series and fed by D.C. voltage of 8 V 1.5 A. The frequency of chopping is 12.5 Hz with a 50 Hz line frequency or 15 Hz with a 60 Hz line frequency.

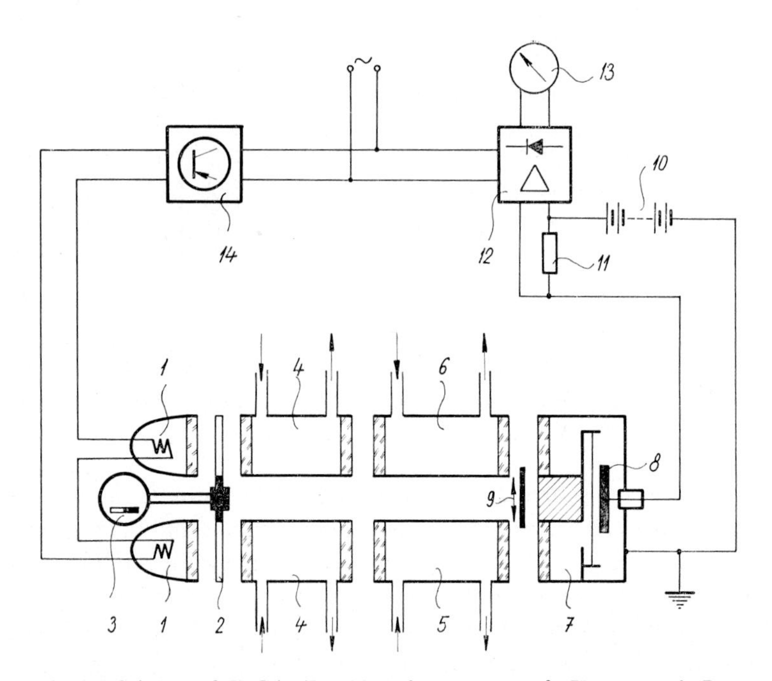

Fig. 3.7 Scheme of IRGA (*URAS 2*, by courtesy of *Hartmann & Braun A.G.*, Frankfurt/Main). *1:* heater, *2:* rotation shutter, *3:* electric motor, *4:* filter tube, *5:* reference tube, *6:* sample tube, *7:* detector, *8:* membrane condenser, *9:* optical shutter, *10:* source of D.C. voltage, *11:* input high impedance resistor, *12:* amplifier, *13:* output meter, *14:* line voltage stabiliser.

Fig. 3.8 Internal view of URAS 2 (by courtesy of *Hartmann & Braun A.G.*, Frankfurt/Main).

The sample and reference tubes are placed in a common holder on an optical bench. The tubes are replaceable and their lengths vary, as required, in the range of 0.2 up to 250 mm. The tubes shorter than 50 mm are of aluminium, the longer ones are of glass with gilt inner surface.
The detector is placed on the optical bench and its position is adjusted according to the length of the tubes. It also incorporates an optical shutter which is used to adjust the flux density of the two radiating beams. The pre-amplifier is withdrawably connected with the body of the detector, and is equipped with an input valve in the electronic circuit.
Under the optical bench there are two heating resistances with a total input of 100 W, a ventilator and thermostat which keeps the temperature at 59 ± 1.5°C. In the upper half of the box is a four-stage amplifier. The output signal of the amplifier rectified by two diodes is transferred to a measuring device ranging from 0 to 100 μA/1200 Ω. In the output circuit there is a potentiometer for regulating the intensity of the counter-current, thereby adjusting the zero of the meter, in the range of 15 to 150 μA.
Analyser URAS 2 has a minimum measuring range from 0 to 50 vpm of CO_2 in air (or, if required, from 0 to 20 vpm). According to the manufacturer the zero drift is less than 2% of the full scale range per week, and the sensitivity change is less than 2% of the deviation per week.
Approximately the same results are achieved by infra-red analyser *SB 2*, Fig. 3.9 (*Sir Howard Grubb Parsons & Co. Ltd.*, Newcastle upon Tyne, U.K.). When using tubes 300 mm long, the minimum measuring range for CO_2 in air is 0 to 50 vpm. Reproducibility, according to the manufacturer, is 1% of the full scale range, and stability of the deviation is also 1% of the full scale range, in 24 hours. The analyser may be equipped with an optical semiconductive filter not penetrated by radiation

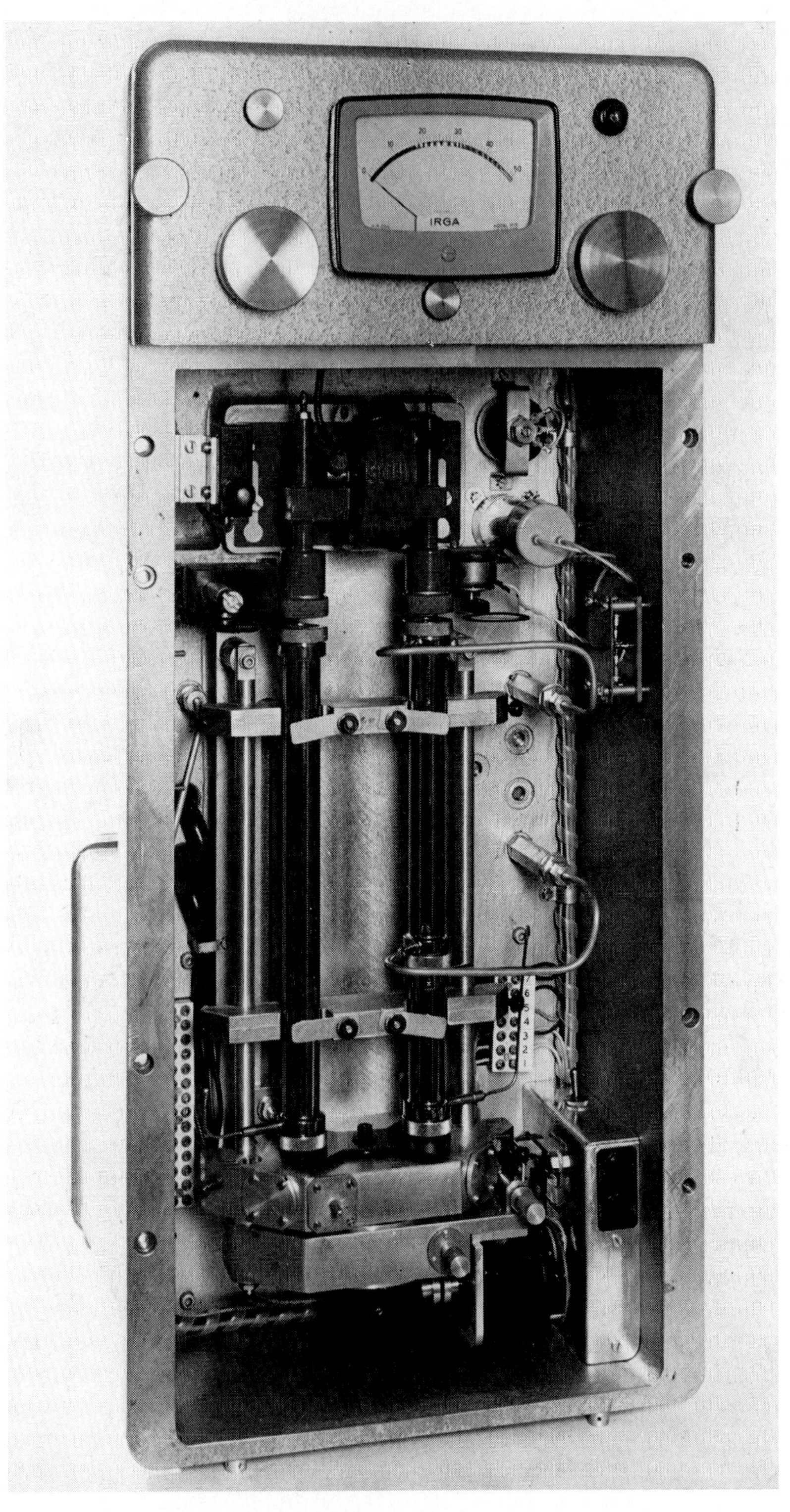

Fig. 3.9 Internal view of IRGA *SB 2* (by courtesy of *Grubb Parsons & Co. Ltd.*, Newcastle upon Tyne).

of wavelength 2.7 μm, so that water vapour cannot exert any influence on measurements of CO_2 and the gas sample being analysed need not be dried. The transmittance of optical filters supplied by the manufacturer is shown in Fig. 3.10. Infra-red analyser *Hilger – I.R.D.* type *SC/F* (*Hilger & Watts Ltd.*, London,

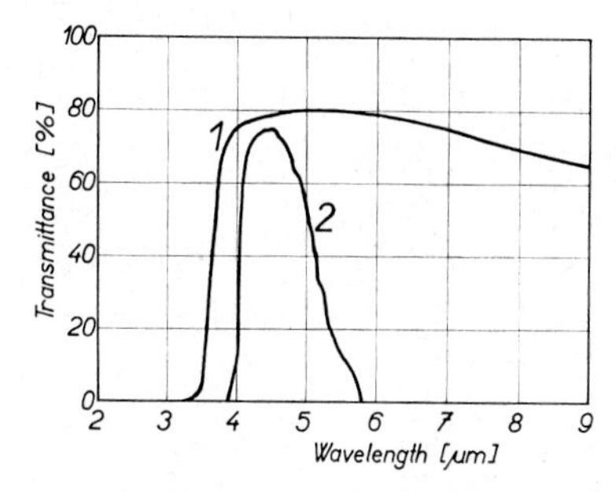

Fig. 3.10 Spectral transmittance of the filters used for determining CO_2 in the presence of water vapour. *1:* indium arsenide, *2: Grubb Parsons* filter (by courtesy of *Grubb Parsons & Co. Ltd.*, Newcastle upon Tyne).

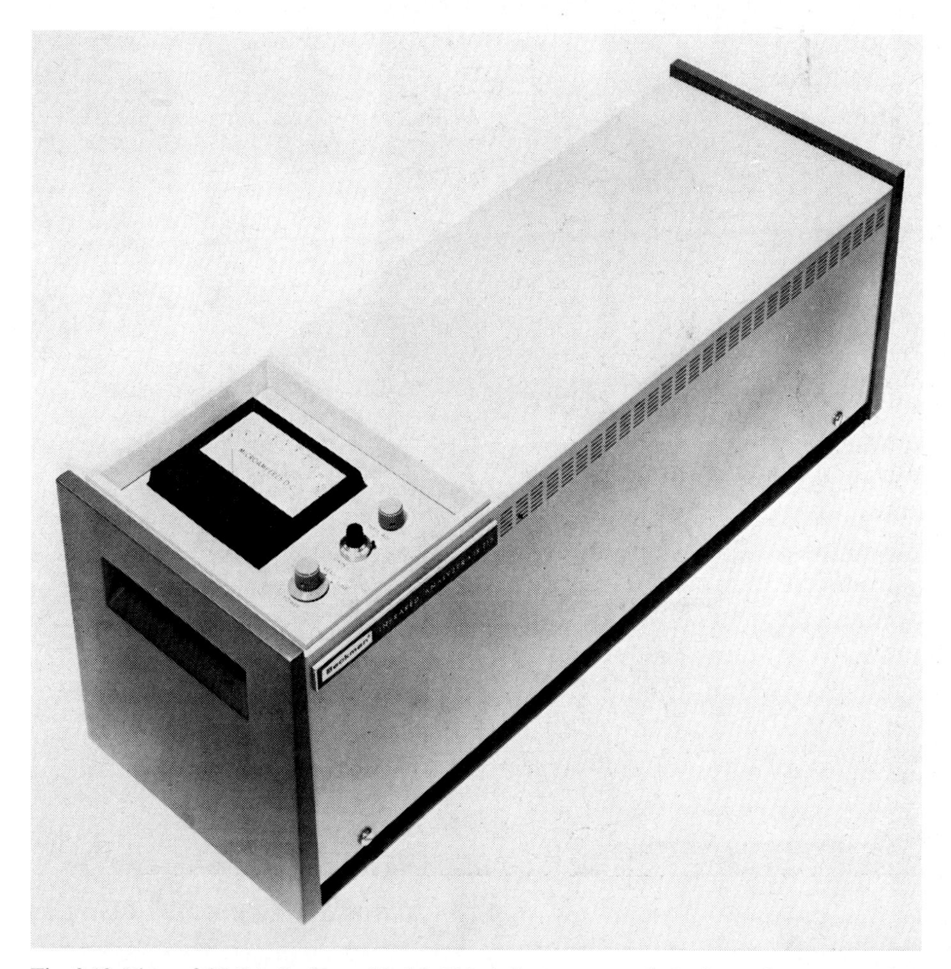

Fig. 3.12 View of IRGA *Beckman* Model *215 A* (by courtesy of *Beckman Instruments Inc.*, Fullerton).

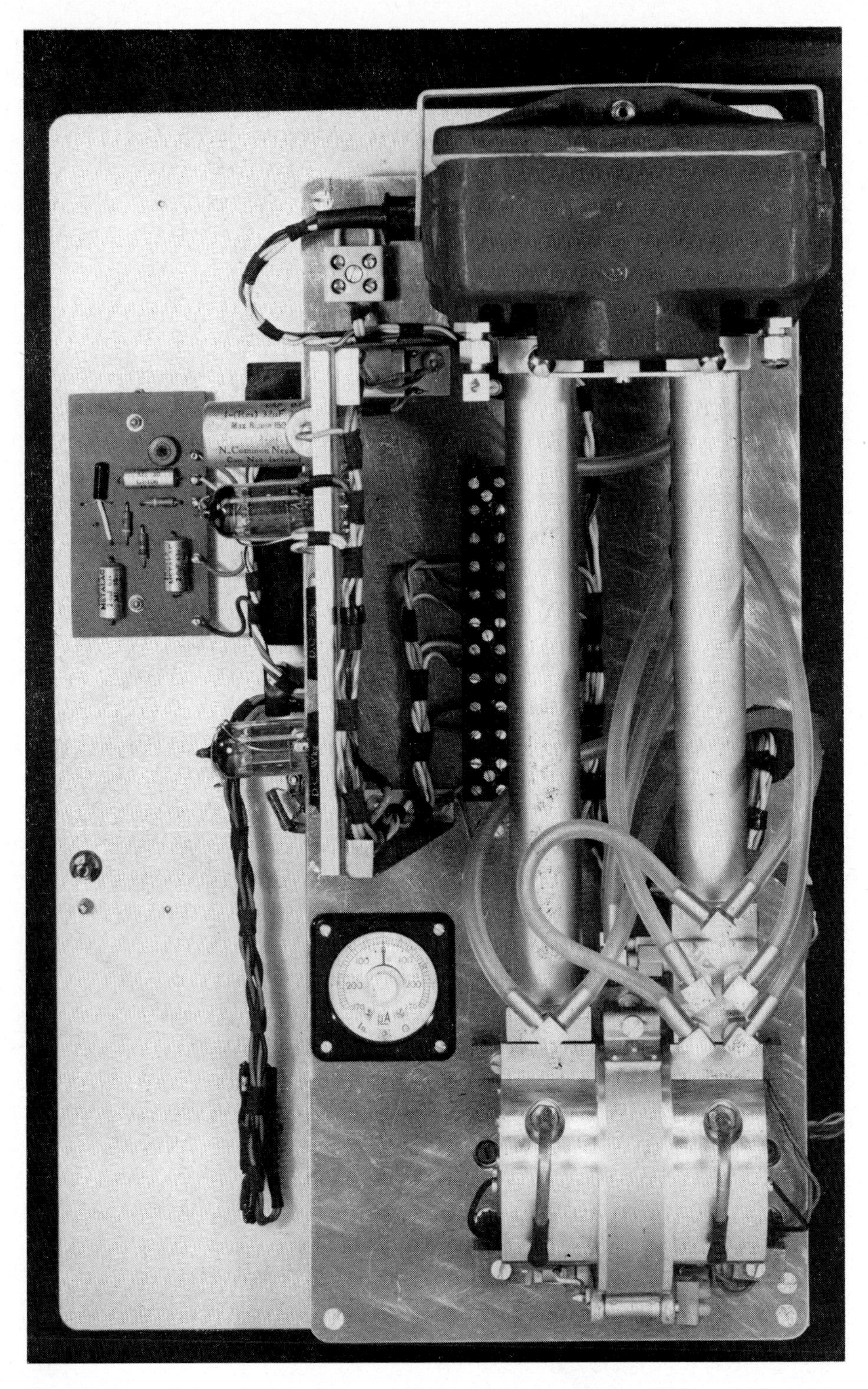

Fig. 3.11 Internal view of IRGA *Hilger – IRD* Type *SC/F* (by courtesy of *Hilger & Watts Ltd.*, London).

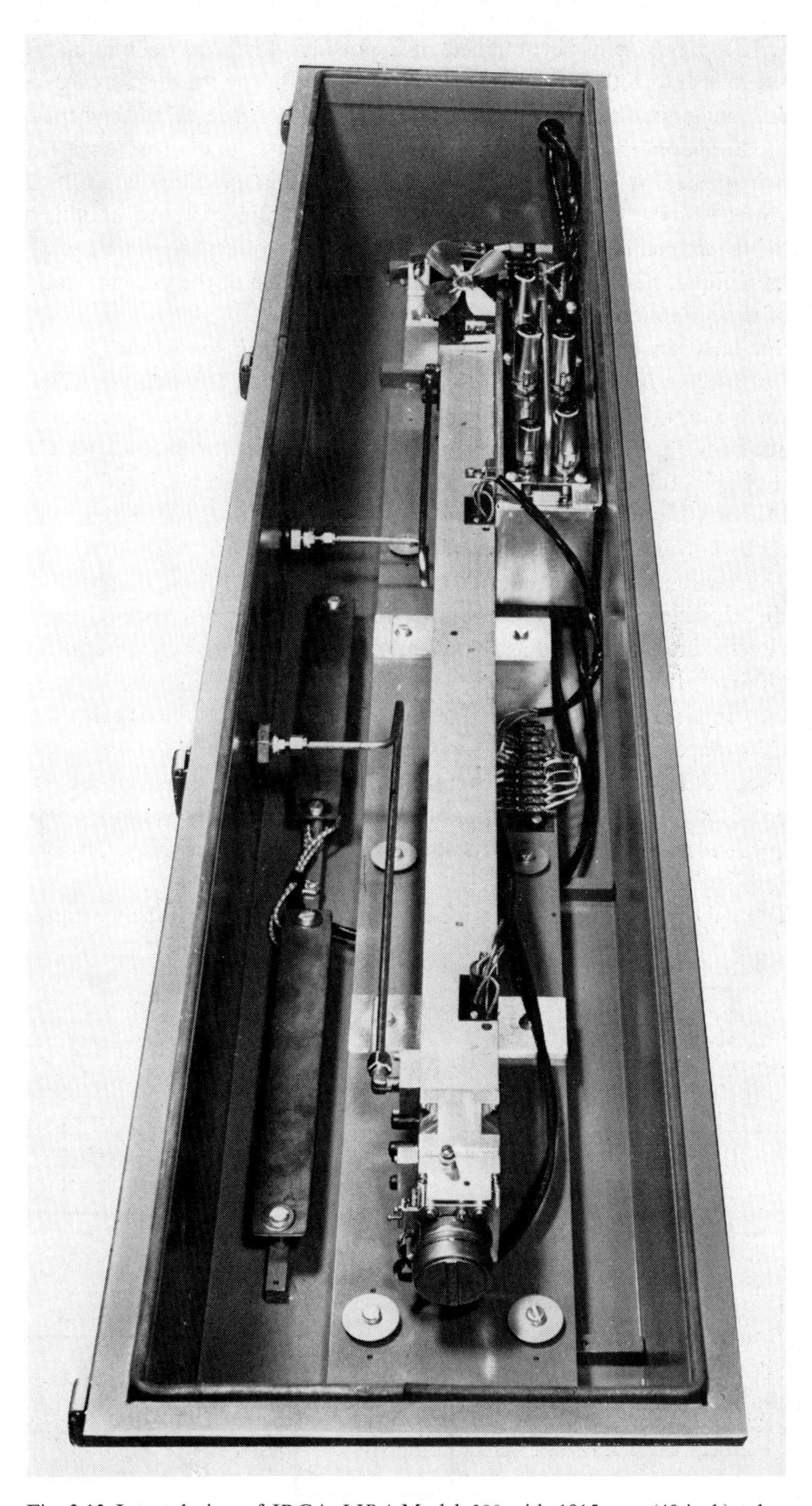

Fig. 3.13 Internal view of IRGA *LIRA* Model *200* with 1015 mm (40-inch) tubes (by courtesy of *MSA Research Corp.*, Evans City).

U.K.), which may be obtained in a portable form, has a minimum measuring range of 0 to 100 vpm of CO_2 in air (Fig. 3.11). The main difference between this instrument and the two above is in the method of measuring the capacity changes of the diaphragm condenser which forms part of a discriminator circuit fed by a frequency of 1.7 MHz. Periodical capacity changes modulate a high-frequency voltage in the discrimination circuit which continues to be amplified and after being rectified is led into the meter. This method offers an advantage which cannot be ignored, namely that high insulation resistance of the detector and input parts of the amplifier is no longer required.

Similarly, in research on photosynthesis the *Beckman* Model *215 A* (*Beckman Instruments Inc.*, Fullerton, USA) is often utilized. This analyser (Fig. 3.12) with *ca.* 343 mm (13.5-inch) sample tube for 250–350 vpm CO_2 differential range has an accuracy ± 3% of full scale range. The accuracy for 0–600 vpm CO_2 range is ± 1% of full scale range. This type of IRGA is also produced by *Schlumberger et Cie* (Clamart, France), by *Elliot-Automation Ltd.* (Borhamwood, U.K.), by *Analytic System Co.* (Pasadena, USA), and by *VEB Junkalor* (Dessau, DDR). The analyser *LIRA* Model *200* (*M.S.A. Research Corp.*, Evans City, USA) is slightly different. In this type, beams from sample and reference tube are alternately directed into the single detector chamber. For high sensitivity applications 1,015 mm (40-inch) tubes are used (Fig. 3.13). In this case the minimum range is 0–10 vpm CO_2 in air. In the standard instruments, *ca.* 203 mm (8-inch) tubes for 0–50 vpm CO_2 range are used.

The *LIRA* Model *100* is an example of the null-balance instrument. This analyser operates on the principle of null-balance feedback by varying voltage on one infra-red source (Fig. 3.14). Its advantage is extreme sensitivity, very high stability, and linearity.

The only infra-red analyser with absorption detector chambers arranged in series

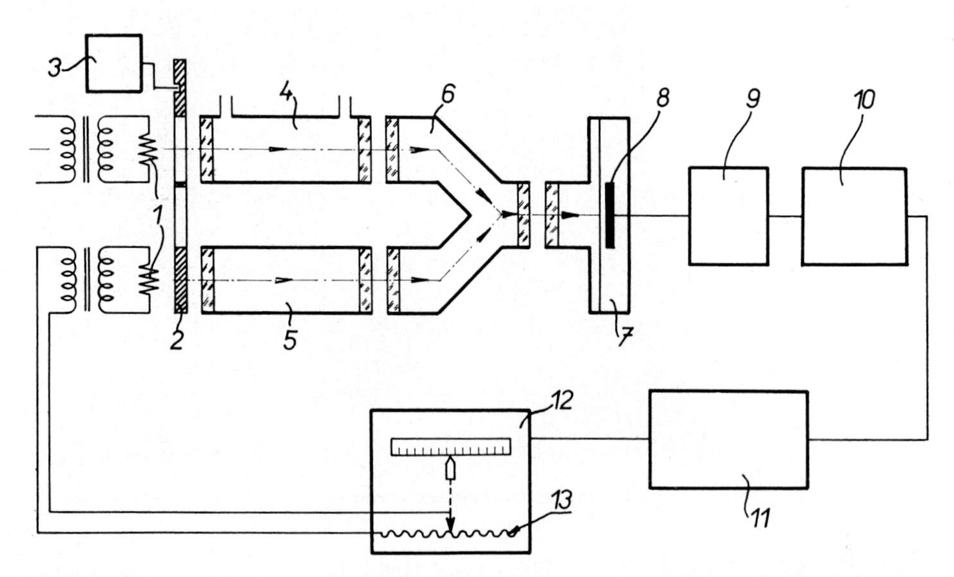

Fig. 3.14 Scheme of IRGA *LIRA* Model *100*. *1:* heaters, *2:* beam chopper, *3:* electric motor, *4:* sample tube, *5:* reference tube, *6:* beam combiner, *7:* detector, *8:* membrane condenser, *9:* pre-amplifier, *10:* amplifier, *11:* control box, *12:* recorder, *13:* resistor geared to recorder chart.

which is manufactured on a commercial scale is the apparatus *UNOR 2* (*Maihak A.G.*, Hamburg) (Fig. 3.15). The radiation from a single source is divided into two beams, one of which passes through the reference tube, the other through the sample tube. The rotating shutter interrupts both beams in turn, with a frequency of 6.25 Hz. By means of a diffuser, the radiation leaving the tubes is concentrated in the detector consisting of two subsequent absorption chambers. These chambers are separated by a diaphragm, which is a part of the condenser. The diaphragm condenser in the bridge circuit is fed by a high-frequency voltage, as in the analyser *Hilger-I.R.D.* type *SC/F*. The amplifier is of a transistor type with electronic compensation for temperature changes of the analysed gas in the sample tube so that no thermostat is needed.
With this analyser the minimum measuring rage is from 0 to 50 vpm of CO_2 in air. The instrument achieves an accuracy of 2% of the full scale range. Like the conventional types of analysers, it can also be used for differential measurement of concentration.

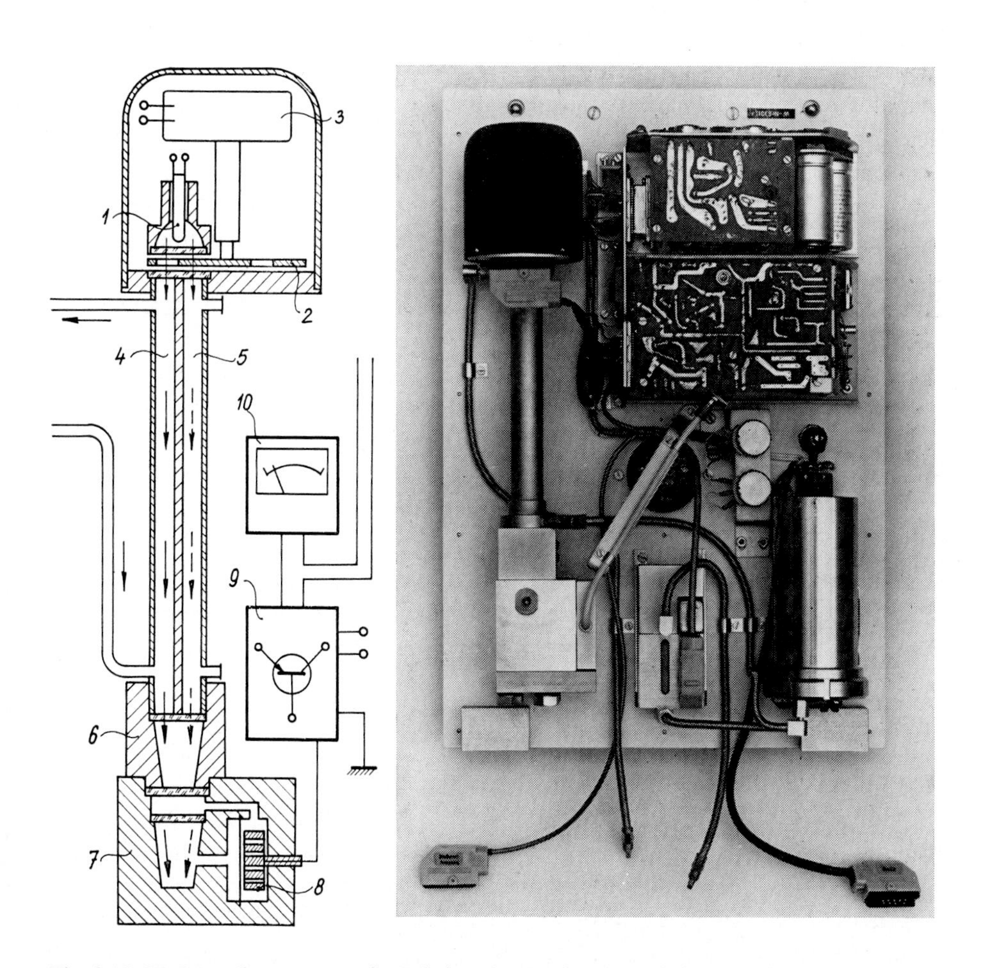

Fig. 3.15 *UNOR 2* (by courtesy of *Maihak A.G.*, Hamburg). *A:* Scheme. *1:* heater, *2:* rotation shutter, *3:* electric motor, *4:* sample tube, *5:* reference tube, *6:* diffuser, *7:* detector, *8:* membrane condenser, *9:* amplifier, *10:* output meter.
B: Internal view.

3.7 | Installation of the IRGA

3.7.1 | Effect of environment, and mechanical installation of IRGA

When installing an IRGA it is necessary to exclude all effects of the local environment which would interfere with its operation. The instrument can be unfavourably affected by vibration, temperature or pressure changes and unsuitable composition of the atmosphere (*cf.* also Čatský, Chartier & Chartier 1970).
If a building is not completely free from vibration, it is advisable to fix the analyser on a main wall or a pier of the building (possibly even using rubber supports). The place for the analyser must be chosen in such a way that it is not subjected to direct effects of sources of heat, *i.e.* radiators, steam pipes, sunshine, *etc.*, especially when it is not equipped with a thermostat. Placing the IRGA in a temperature-controlled (*ca.* 40 °C) box is often recommended when measuring very small CO_2 differentials, even for IRGAs with their own temperature control.
Unsuitable composition of the atmosphere has several consequences. If the atmosphere contains harmful compounds (H_2S, mercury vapour) the working life of the amplifier is substantially decreased. Under conditions of high relative humidity (*e.g.* in a glasshouse), the quality of the high-impedance insulation of the detector and input stage of the amplifier is decreased, resulting in decreased accuracy of measurement or even defects in the instrument. Results can also be distorted when the atmosphere contains an excess of CO_2. High CO_2 concentration within the IRGA box results in a decrease in the amount of radiation reaching the detector. Brown (1968) and Brown & Rosenberg (1968) found that with the IRGA used (*Beckman* Model *IR 315*, 140 mm tubes) the apparent concentration decreased linearly at a rate of 0.6 vpm per 100 vpm increase in the CO_2 concentration in the box (*cf.* also effect of background concentration on the IRGA sensitivity, p. 150). If it is not possible to achieve suitable conditions in the room used, the box of the IRGA must be flushed with a neutral gas (*e.g.* nitrogen or dry CO_2-free air); when analysing small differentials (*e.g.* 50 vpm f.s.d.), this is always necessary. In some cases, air with constant CO_2 concentration (*e.g.* control air) is sufficient. The excess pressure and flow-rate of the flushing gas should be as low as possible, so as not to interfere with temperature control inside the box.
The installation of accessory devices and a gas handling system will be presented in Section 3.8.

3.7.2 | Electric installation

IRGAs are sensitive to mains voltage fluctuations. A voltage stabiliser should therefore be used if the fluctuation in voltage is greater than $\pm$ 5%. It is recommended that a stabilised power supply should always be used when analysing traces of CO_2, if this is not built into the IRGA. Magnetic stabilisers may be used only if the mains frequency does not vary. Preferably magnetic stabilisers with frequency compensation (constructed always for a particular type of IRGA) should be used.
Largely because of the mechanical chopper, IRGAs are extremely sensitive to fluctuations in the frequency of the supply. Normal mains frequency is usually

sufficiently stable. However the variations in frequency from temporary or portable supplies from generators even of quite large capacity (*e.g.* 6 kVA), may result in output fluctuations equivalent to 1 or 2% of full scale. Whilst the fitting of expensive hydraulic flywheels to such generators may reduce this error, it cannot eliminate it. The only sure answer is to supply the IRGA from batteries through a commercial solid state D.C./A.C. converter, and to charge the batteries from the generator. To reduce the power output needed from the batteries, it is convenient to separate the power supply to the heating circuit and to supply that directly from the generator supply. Approximately 150 VA is then required from the battery supply to operate the IRGA. This can be supplied continuously from several car batteries of moderate capacity (*e.g.* 90 Ah). The voltage of the supply from such generators is usually at least as stable as the mains supply. With a stable battery supply of this kind, the standard error of the mean of 30 sequential observations at half minute intervals with a *URAS 2* (f.s.d. 100 vpm) was approximately 0.05 vpm (Jarvis, unpubl., Lange & Schulze, unpubl., *cf.* also Polster & Fuchs 1956).
The IRGA also requires a dead earth. The earthing conductor must be of a sufficient section, 5 mm^2 being the minimum, and may be connected only to a designated place on the instrument.

3.7.3 | Commissioning the IRGA

A certain procedure – usually given by the manufacturer in the instructions for use – must be followed when putting the IRGA into operation. Only a few general remarks will therefore be given here.
The IRGA is switched on at a reduced amplifier output and allowed to operate for several hours (preferably overnight) in order to stabilize its temperature. The amplification is then increased up to the degree which approximately corresponds to normal working operation of the analyser. The sample tube is filled with dry neutral gas (in absolutely measuring IRGAs), or both tubes are filled with the control standard gas (*e.g.* air) (in differentially measuring IRGA), the deflection of the meter is adjusted to the centre of the scale by means of the optical shutter, and the output is followed for several hours until it is steady. In some cases the initial output is unsteady. This need not be a sign of a direct failure of the IRGA, especially if the analyser had been stored for long periods of time and may result from moistening of the high-impedance insulation. If this effect occurs, the analyser should be allowed to operate continuously for several days until the defect disappears.
Zero setting. With the tubes filled as above, the amplification is set so that the measuring instrument deflection attains *ca.* 3/4 of the scale. This deflection is first reduced by the optical shutter. On attaining zero deflection the amplification is increased and the procedure repeated. When zero cannot be attained, the minimum deflection is further reduced by correcting the phase displacement (by changing the position of the rotating shutter in relation to the tubes).
In the case of most IRGAs operating by the deflection principle, the amplifier rectifier is insensitive to phase changes; the instrument thus only records the absolute value of the energy difference between the two radiation paths. Further,

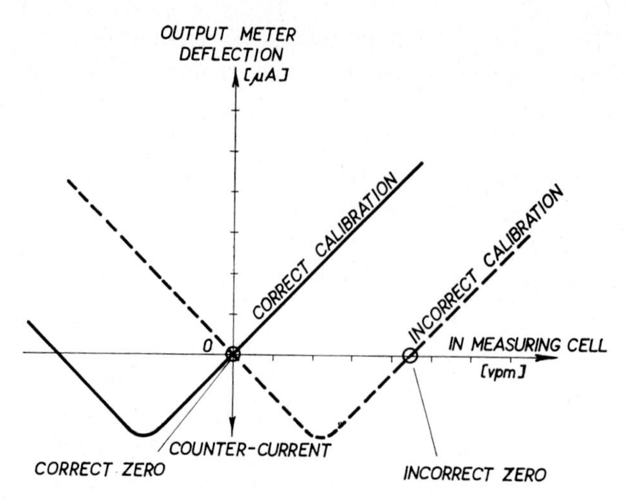

Fig. 3.16 Scheme of phase adjustment of IRGA.

the amplifier characteristic is not usually linear in the proximity of the zero signal value. For these reasons these analysers operate either with a zero suppressed by a counter-current, or the zero concentration is made to correspond to a certain initial deflection on the instrument scale. It is very important to carry out correct phase adjustment of the IRGA, so that the counter-current equalizes the detector signal brought about by reducing the radiant energy in the sample tube path by means of the optical shutter (with respect to the radiant energy in the reference tube path). Then, during absorption by the gas in the sample tube, there is a correct further radiant energy decrease in the sample tube path, as indicated in Fig. 3.16. If the counter-current were incorrectly equalized by the detector signal, then an increase in absorption in the sample tube would first result in a fall of the deflection below zero, and only then, on a further concentration increase, would there be a positive deflection. The correctness of the phase adjustment can be checked by slightly screening off the sample tube path at a set zero value. When the adjustment is correct the indicator immediately exhibits a positive movement. **Sensitivity adjustment.** After setting zero, the sensitivity of the IRGA must be adjusted in relation to the required scale. With IRGAs of moderate sensitivity, only the highest concentration indicated on the scale (often directly in vpm CO_2 or % CO_2) is adjusted, usually after filling the sample tube with a standard gas containing this concentration. However, more accurate calibration is necessary for the most sensitive IRGAs (10 to 100 vpm for full scale). The calibration procedures will therefore be discussed in detail in Section 3.10.2.

3.7.4 | Connecting IRGA to recorder

Millivolt or digital voltmeter type recorders are commonly utilized to measure the signals generated by the IRGA. In order to prevent distorted signals resulting from transient line pickup, the signal wires should be physically isolated from power conductors, and an earthed shielding should be provided. Care must also be taken to select recorders with input impedances which are compatible with the

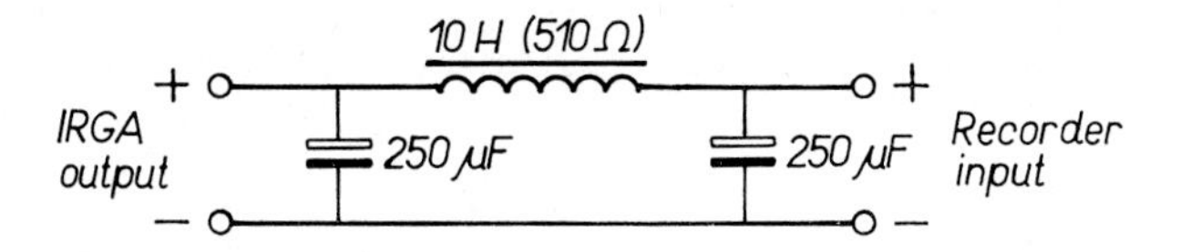

Fig. 3.17 An LC filter for removing noise between IRGA and recorder.

output from the IRGA. Poorly matched impedances will result in increased time response of the recorder, and may result in erroneous recordings.

In some cases the electrical noise generated by the IRGA or induced by the environment may cause the indicator, or pen on the recorder to vibrate, resulting in a wide trace. A simple one-stage RC filter may be used to remove this noise. Such a filter can easily be constructed by placing two variable resistors in series with one of the signal wires; a capacitor is then connected between the junction of the two resistors and the other signal wire. The values of the resistors and capacitor must be selected to prevent impedance incompatibilities as discussed above. The values of the filter components will be dependent on the IRGA and the recorder to be used. Multiple filters consisting of several stages may be used if one stage is not adequate.

Alternatively an LC filter may be used. This is likely to be more suitable for operation at frequencies as low as 6.6 Hz as obtained with some makes of IRGA (*e.g. Sir Howard Grubb Parsons & Co. Ltd.*, *Hilger-I.R.D. Ltd.*). The filter shown in Fig. 3.17 was developed at the National Institute of Agricultural Engineering (Bedford, U.K.) and is now fairly widely used.

Sometimes measuring periods of several days or months are desirable. In such long-term measurements, it is highly desirable that the data are collected automatically and in a form suitable for subsequent processing by digital computer. This is also becoming desirable for routine purposes in laboratory experiments involving a lot of measurements and subsequent calculations of H_2O and CO_2 fluxes and transfer resistances, and in some laboratories data-logging facilities have been installed to facilitate subsequent handling of the data. The experimental data can be recorded simultaneously in analogue form on recorder charts and some forms of magnetic tape and in digital form on electric typewriters, magnetic tape, punched paper tape and punched cards. The recorder chart and typewriter output provide the permanent visual display which allows the data to be seen and checked as it is recorded. The digital magnetic tape, punched paper tape or punched cards can be fed to the computer for data processing. A combination of a display and a record which can be computer processed without further manipulation is desirable. In this way errors associated with the transference of data from charts to punched cards or tape for processing is avoided. Furthermore if fluctuations, oscillations and other non-steady state phenomena are being followed, calculations can readily be made as frequently as required. Alternatively if step functions are being employed, attainment of the steady state can be followed on the chart and the digital recording equipment be switched on only when it is desired to obtain a set of records.

Many commercial data-loggers are widely used in industry to monitor many environmental parameters, including CO_2 and humidity, and can be used for

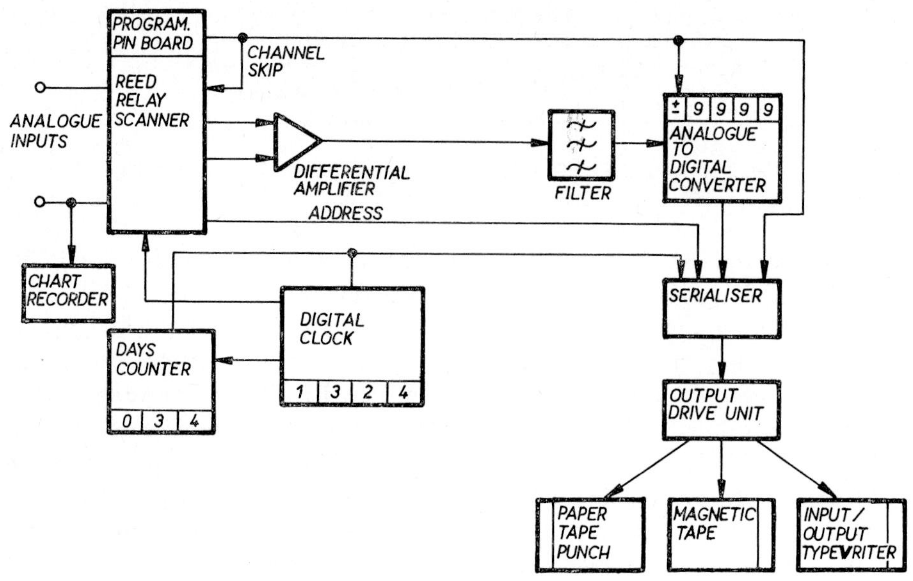

Fig. 3.18 Block diagram of a typical data-logger.

recording photosynthesis and transpiration with little or no modification. Alternatively systems can be built especially for a particular purpose. Eckardt (1966) describes a system developed for recording data from IRGAs and other equipment onto magnetic tape, and Cernusca (1968) and Cernusca and Moser (1969) describe battery-fed equipment suitable for recording IRGA and micro-climatic data onto punched paper tape automatically in remote places.

In general most data-logging systems involve the same basic modules although the precise manner in which a function is achieved may vary widely. A block-diagram of a typical data-logger is shown in Figure 3.18. Signals from a number of sensors, perhaps several hundred including the IRGAs, are switched sequentially and rapidly; they are converted to digital and measured on a digital voltmeter and the record is punched out on the tape and recorded by the typewriter and chart recorder simultaneously. A digital clock is also included to initiate a scan of the inputs and it also provides a record of the data and time which goes onto the tape. Trigger signals are provided by the logger to activate relays which control solenoid valves which switch the sample gases through the IRGA. Thus with a 100 channel logger making one scan every 10 min, solenoids can be activated every tenth channel to switch a fresh sample gas through the IRGA. In this way eight separate samples can be analysed, a zero check carried out and a comparison between the flowing reference gas and a bottled standard gas made. If the IRGA is fitted with an automatic calibration unit such as the *Hartmann & Braun CGMS*, recalibration can also be arranged to occur automatically at intervals.

3.8 Gas handling system

A sample of the analysed air must be transferred into the IRGA in the required state, *i.e.* suitable amount, temperature, pressure, humidity and purity. A gas handling system (also called sampling system), which can vary considerably in structure, is used for this purpose. However, the system used when measuring CO_2 exchange in plants generally contains: tubing (connected to a probe), a pump, drying device with a filter, flow meter, pressure regulator and a sequential valve, respectively. After connecting all elements, the entire system must be checked precisely for leaks. A good procedure is to introduce nitrogen as a test gas at the sampling end of the system (Brown & Rosenberg 1968). (Consult also Pinkava 1970 for unit operations and basic equipment.)

3.8.1 | *Probe*

It is a purpose of the probe to take a typical sample (*cf.* also Section 3.8.9) of the air to be analysed. In the study of CO_2 exchange a probe is used only in some cases, *e.g.* when taking air samples from big assimilation chambers containing plant communities, or when using aerodynamic methods (Chapter 13) *etc.* In these cases the correct placing of the probe is of primary importance.
To obtain spatially integrated samples in the field, probes with orifices spaced at 25 or 50 cm have been used both in and above crop canopies. Such orifices should be covered with fine mesh nylon (*e.g.* hose) to prevent insects or dirt from entering.

3.8.2 | *Gas sample line*

Metal or glass tubing of an internal diameter of 4 to 6 mm is to be preferred. Copper tubing, after heating to a dull red glow, is convenient (*cf.* also Brown & Rosenberg 1970). High density nylon tubing may also be used. In lead tubing, there may be microscopic holes which allow diffusion through the wall. Rubber tubing or some brands of plastic tubing (especially polyethylene and tygon) absorb gases and are permeable to CO_2, and so are not suitable. Short sections of these thick-walled (vacuum) plastic tubes may be used to provide flexibility of the line. However, considerable lengths of such tubes should not be used. Brown & Rosenberg (1968) tested PVC garden hose in the field and found that when air was drawn at 4 l min^{-1} from an intake near the top of a sugar beet canopy (50 cm) and passed to the IRGA through a hose lying on the ground, the

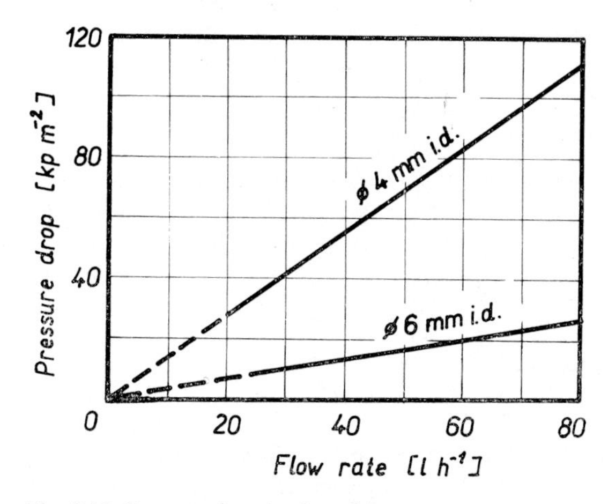

Fig. 3.19 Pressure drop in the tubing.

concentration of CO_2 in the incoming sample was increased by 6 vpm per 30 m of hose.

To limit the contact of the gas with plastic tubing, connections should be of 'metal to metal' type. The transport path and gas volumes of all elements of the handling system should not be too large in order to minimize the response time. Conversely the bore of the tubing should not be too small, otherwise there will be a large pressure drop along the tubing (for assessment of the pressure drop see Fig. 3.19). Condensed water (at places colder than the dew-point of the air) may act as a source and sink for CO_2. The condensation of water in the tubing can be prevented most easily by use of a heater, *e.g.* constantan wire threaded through the tubing and heated by low voltage current (Koch 1957) or commercial heating tape wound externally. Also warm water or air can be used (see Bosian 1965). The tubing must be then insulated, most easily by polyurethane foam tubing.

3.8.3 | Pump

The pump is usually inserted between the assimilation chamber and the IRGA because of the greater accuracy and stability of measurement when the IRGA is placed at the end of the gas sample line (see Section 3.13). Pumps which neither leak nor contaminate the air sample must therefore be used. Membrane (diaphragm) pumps, usually provided by manufacturers of the IRGA and commonly available are most suitable (optimal flow is about 30 to 60 $l\ h^{-1}$) providing that sudden changes of CO_2 concentration are not to be studied. Small membrane pumps are usually driven by an electromagnet, bigger ones by an electromotor (an example of construction of this type and its characteristics are shown on Fig. 3.20; *cf.* also Fig. 4.12). The pressure provided is dependent on the amount of pumped gas, which is controlled by a change of the amplitude of the membrane.

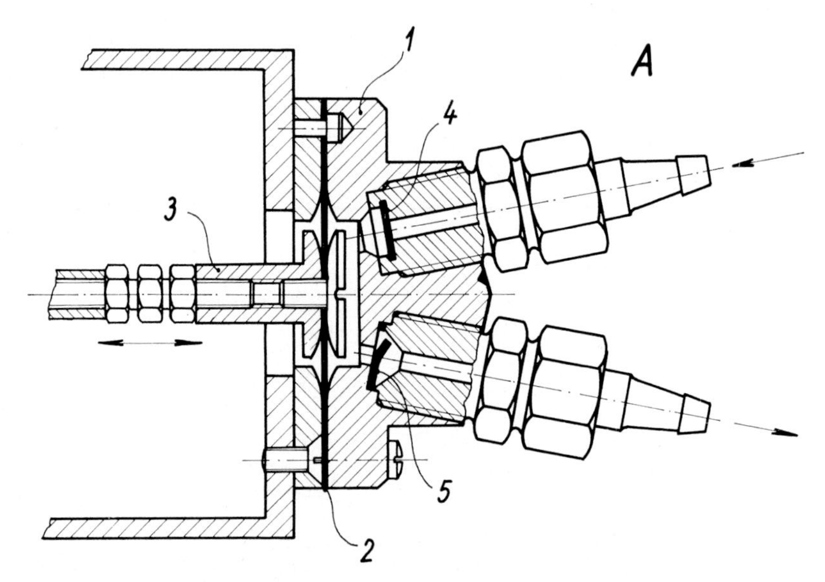

Fig. 3.20 Membrane pump (*A*) and its characteristics (*B*). (By courtesy of *Maihak A.G.*, Hamburg). *1:* valve body, *2:* flexible membrane, *3:* drive rod, *4:* inlet valve, *5:* outlet valve.

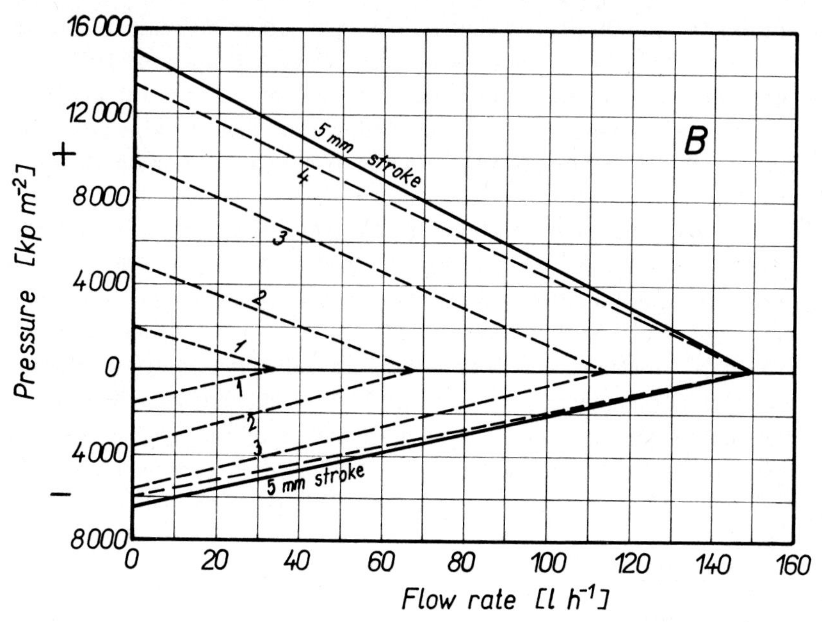

Fig. 3.20B.

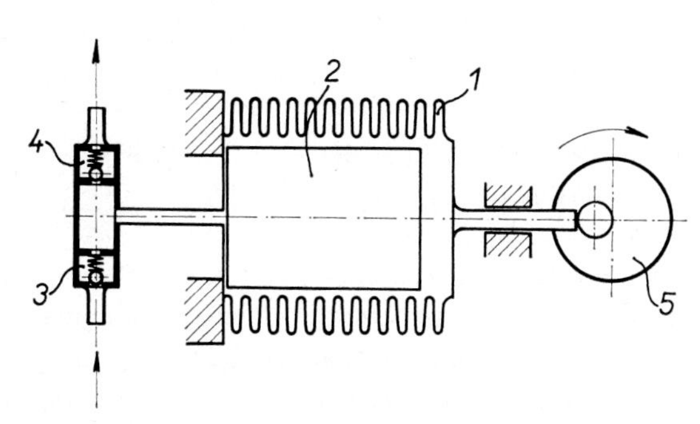

Fig. 3.21 Peristaltic pump. *1:* bellows, *2:* displacer, *3:* inlet valve, *4:* outlet valve, *5:* cam.

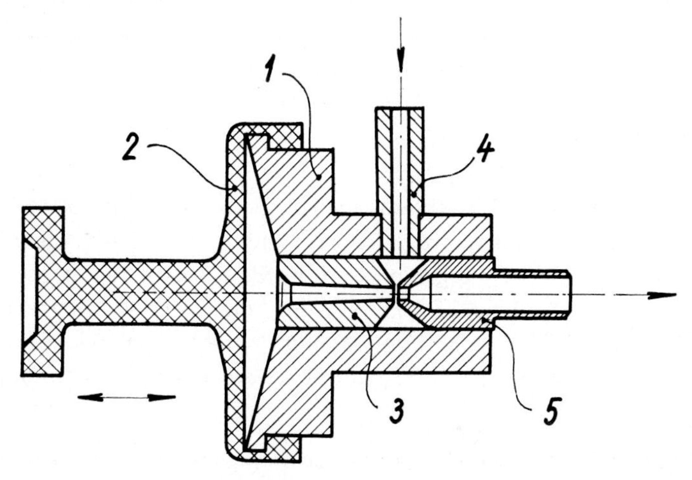

Fig. 3.22 Jet pump. *1:* pump body, *2:* flexible rubber membrane, *3:* jet, *4:* gas inlet, *5:* gas outlet.

Piston or other pumps containing oil in their compressors are not suitable for some systems. They may be used only if they are placed after the IRGA (this is undesirable) or if they are supplied with a good filter. Many oil-less types of pumps commonly available are designed to allow small leaks. These pumps are therefore not suitable. Peristaltic pumps with metal bellows (Orchard & Heath 1964), which are less porous to CO_2 than the membrane type, are useful (Fig. 3.21). Peristaltic pumps commercially available are also convenient for using in a closed circuit, *e.g.* a circuit containing ^{14}C (Lister, Krotkov & Nelson 1961). Another suitable type is the 'jet-pump' *(Taumelscheibenpumpe)*, the principle of which is shown in Fig. 3.22. The fluctuations of the rubber membrane are provided by a tiltable plate driven by an electromotor. This plate is usually common to four or more pumps; connecting them in series or in parallel allows change of the required pressure and amount of air pumped. The main advantage of this type is that no valves are present. Another widely used completely leak free pump suitable for continuous running is made by *Reciprotor A/S* (Copenhagen, Denmark).

3.8.4 | Flow meter

A rotameter with a range of 3 to 40–60 $l\ h^{-1}$, often supplied with the analyser, is most frequently used to measure the air flow. It has the advantage of only slight pressure drop, and the disadvantage that a precisely vertical position is required. The commercially available rotameters supplied with IRGAs usually have a needle valve attached. These rotameters are designed to be connected immediately before the IRGA. Instead of rotameters, capillary (manometric) flow meters can also be used (*e.g.* Fig. 4.8; Leblond & Carlier 1965; Holmgren 1968).
The accuracy of the measurement of CO_2 exchange is most often limited by the accuracy with which the flow rate through the assimilation chamber is known. In general this is much less accurately known than the CO_2 concentrations of the air, supposing that the IRGA is calibrated very precisely (*cf.* Section 3.10.1, p. 152, and Chartier 1970). Flow meters of all types should be very carefully calibrated *in situ* in the system. For flow rates of up to about 2 $l\ min^{-1}$ the soap bubble method is satisfactory (Levy 1964, *cf.* also van Oorschot & Belksma 1961). For larger flow rates, acceptable accuracy can be obtained with commercial Wet Test Gas Meter (*cf.* Ower & Pankhurst 1966).

3.8.5 | Pressure and flow regulators

It is desirable to add a pressure (flow) regulator before the point of entry into the gas analyser, as the flow resistance in the gas handling system may change and the IRGA output depends on the gas pressure in the tubes of IRGA (according to functions shown in Section 3.9). The pressure (and hence the flow rate) should therefore be identical for calibration and all sample analyses. Commercially available low-pressure membrane regulators are most convenient[1]. Simple liquid

1. *E.g.*, *Flostat Minor II* (*Ecoflow II*) manufactured by *Endress und Hauser* (Maulburg/ Baden, West Germany) or *G. A. Platon* (Croydon, Surrey, U.K.) maintains a constant flow of 1.5 to 1500 $l\ h^{-1}$ regardless of the incoming air pressure (0.14–7 atm).

regulators (Fig. 3.23) are usually combined in laboratory devices with negative pressure regulators providing an efficient stabilisation of suction capacity of the pumps. The pressure regulators are often combined with flow regulators. An example of a flow regulator providing constant air flows from 6 to 60 $l\ h^{-1}$ irrespective of the pressure on the air outlet is shown schematically on Fig. 3.24. The inlet pressure must be *ca.* 20% higher than that in the outlet. Equipment based on another principle is described by Le Chevallier & Leleu (1956); the air flow of 0.1 to 100 $l\ h^{-1}$ is governed by a manometric flow meter controlling a fine needle valve by means of a small electromotor. As a check against a systematic error arising from pressure differences between the reference and sample tubes of the IRGA, it is convenient to place a simple differential U-tube manometer across the reference and sample tube outlets. This is particularly desirable, if not essential, if the IRGA is not at the end of the gas lines and other tubing and sensors, such as a psychrometer or another IRGA, come after it.

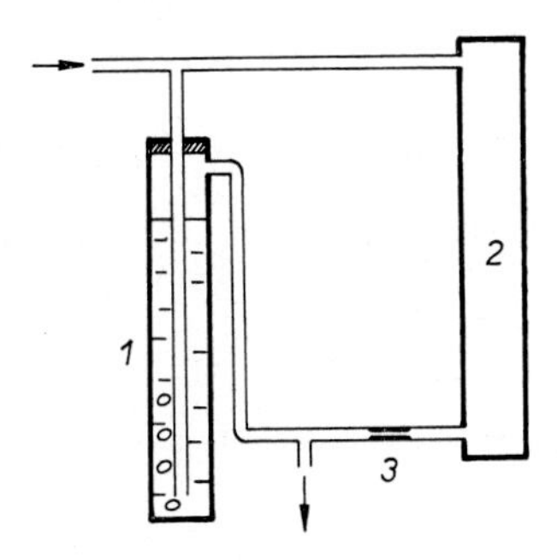

Fig. 3.23 Liquid pressure regulator. *1:* regulator, *2:* IRGA, *3:* nozzle (capillary). The level of the liquid in the regulator (*1*) can be changed according to the pressure required.

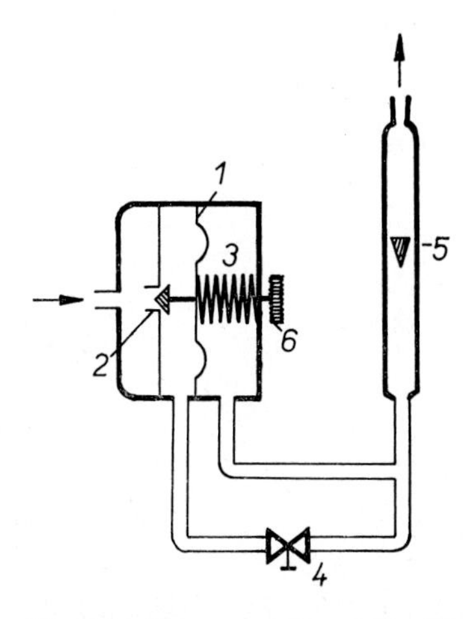

Fig. 3.24 Flow regulator. *1:* flexible membrane, *2:* valve, *3:* spring the pressure of which is regulated by the screw (*6*) according to the flow rate required, *4:* handle valve, *5:* flow meter.

If the 2.7 μm waveband is not optically filtered out, air must be well dried if traces of CO_2 are to be analysed accurately, because of overlap between absorption bands for CO_2 and H_2O in this region (*cf.* Fig. 3.1). When chemical desiccants are used, the quality and selectivity of the drying agent are essential; it must neither absorb nor emit CO_2 and must not create an environment conducive to growth of microorganisms. Common desiccants (*e.g.* silica gel, *Ascarite*) are not suitable for this application. Tamm & Krzysch (1959) using silica gel found that a period of 30 minutes or more is required to re-establish equilibrium following a change in the CO_2 concentration. Indicating *Drierite* ($CaSO_4$) also absorbs CO_2 to reach an equilibrium with the air (Koller & Samish 1964) although it is commonly used and recommended. Magnesium perchlorate *(Dehydrite)* is regarded as the most useful (*cf.* Table 3.2 and Slavík 1972). However, for drying an air stream,

Table 3.2 Efficiency of various desiccants usable for drying gas before the IRGA.

Desiccant	Formula	Residual water [$\mu g \cdot l^{-1}$]
Magnesium perchlorate, anhydrous	$Mg(ClO_4)_2 \cdot 0.12\ H_2O$	0.2*
Anhydrone	$Mg(ClO_4)_2 \cdot 1.48\ H_2O$	1.5*
γ-Aluminium oxide	γ-Al_2O_3	3.0**
Phosphorus pentoxide	P_2O_5	{ 3.6* 0.02**
Magnesium perchlorate, anhydrous, indicating	88% $Mg(ClO_4)_2 \cdot 0.86\%\ KMnO_4$	4.4*
Drierite		5.0**
Calcium chloride, anhydrous	$CaCl_2 \cdot 0.18\ H_2O$	67*
Calcium chloride	$CaCl_2 \cdot 0.28\ H_2O$	99*
Calcium chloride, anhydrous, dried at high temperature	$CaCl_2 \cdot 0.00\ H_2O$	137*
Calcium oxide	CaO	200**
Sulphuric acid	H_2SO_4 100%	3.0
	95%	300
	84.5%	1 800
Gas cooled at −30 °C		330
−20 °C		880
−10 °C		2 140
0 °C		4 840
10 °C		9 400

* After Trusell and Diehl (1963). Test temperature 25 °C, flow rate 1.35 l h^{-1}, U-tube 14 mm i.d. and 150 mm deep.
** After Luck (1964). Test temperature 25 °C.

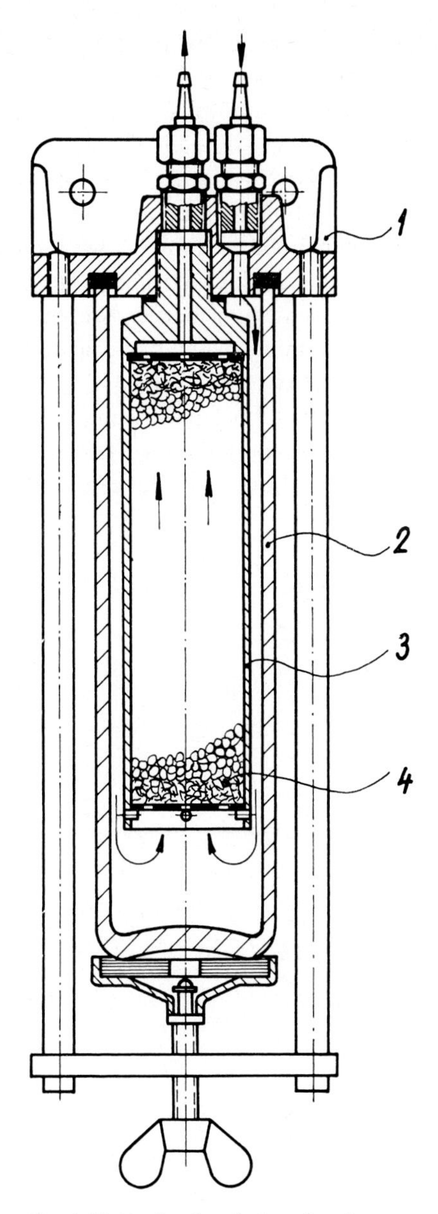

Fig. 3.25 Device for drying the air stream with a solid desiccant. *1:* body, *2:* glass vessel, *3:* container for granulated desiccant (*4*).

zinc chloride is more suitable, because it absorbs water faster than magnesium perchlorate (Voznesenskiï, pers. comm.) in spite of the fact that the equilibrium water vapour pressure is higher[1]. If a drying agent with low absorption capacity has to be used because of its high drying efficiency, some other desiccant with sufficient capacity but low efficiency should precede it. An example of a drying device for a granulated desiccant is shown in Fig. 3.25.

1. Zinc chloride deliquesces by absorbing water. The air inlet should therefore be located on the side of the drying flask.

If the drying agent can be regenerated it is convenient to double up the drying device to enable the exchange of used desiccant merely by switching from one absorption tube to another. This is also a convenient way of testing if the desiccant is still performing satisfactorily.

Sulphuric acid is the most useful of the liquid drying agents. The firm *Hartmann & Braun A.G.*, recommends a one-litre washing bottle with a fine sintered glass inlet containing 800 ml of sulphuric acid, which may be used for 2–3 weeks at a normal air flow (*i.e.* 30 l h^{-1}). A glass wool filter trapping any fine drops of the acid carried in the air stream is added after the washing bottle. Nielsen & Madsen (1964) described a glass drying apparatus containing sulphuric acid and absorbing more than 99.5% humidity at air flow rates up to 60 l h^{-1} (Fig. 3.26). It seems that molecular sieves (see, *e.g.*, Thomas & Mays 1961, for details) with a suitable size of adsorption pores (4 A, 5 A) at an increased temperature may also be used to dry air; however, available molecular sieves also adsorb CO_2 and cannot therefore be used without precise testing.

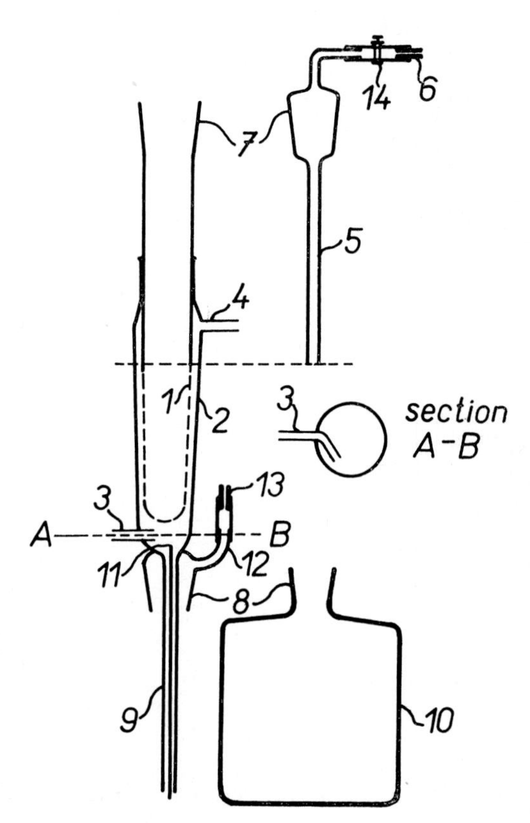

Fig. 3.26 Device for drying the air stream with sulphuric acid (after Nielsen & Madsen 1964). *1:* glass filter *Jena 112*, *2:* glass tube, *3:* air inlet, *4:* air outlet, *5:* pressure regulating tube, *6:* interchangeable capillary, *7, 8:* glass joint *NS 29*, *9:* glass tube (inner ø 4 mm), *10:* two-liter flask, *11:* loose glass rod 1 mm in diameter, *12:* outlet tube for pressure equilibration, *13:* capillary, *14:* clamp. The vessel with filter *(1)* is filled with concentrated sulphuric acid; this passes through the filter with a rate controlled by the capillary (*6*) and the length of the tube (*5*), forming a thin, constantly renewed layer of acid on the outer surface of the filter. The acid diluted by humidity absorbed from the air passing through the device is collected in the vessel (*10*).

Freeze-drying (*e.g.* in a Dewar flask with ice-water mixture) to a constant humidity (*e.g.* 10–20% rel. humidity), which has only a negligible effect on the data obtained, is sometimes used. A compressor-operated cooling unit can also be used; the temperature of the heat exchanger is controlled usually from -10 to $+10\,°C$ with an accuracy *ca.* $\pm$ 0.5 °C (*cf.* Table 3.2). Drying the air by means of a semiconductor freezing device cooled by the Peltier effect (Koch, Klein & Walz 1968) is more convenient and very simple, but the device manufactured by *Siemens A.G.* (Erlangen, West Germany) under the name *Meßgaskühler PK-WAK* is rather expensive.
However, CO_2 IRGAs insensitive to water vapour are available. As was mentioned above, the firm of *Sir Howard Grubb Parsons & Co. Ltd.* (Newcastle upon Tyne, U.K.) provides optical filters with their analysers, transmitting only radiation of 3.8 to 5.7 μm, so that the main absorption bands of water vapour are removed (see Fig. 3.10). It is not necessary to dry the sample when using such analysers; on the other hand, the sensitivity of the IRGA is diminished because only one CO_2 absorption band is used for the determination. Such filters can be bought separately from *Grubb Parsons* and fitted to almost any IRGA. Similar filters are also available from other companies (*e.g. Standard Telephones and Cables*).

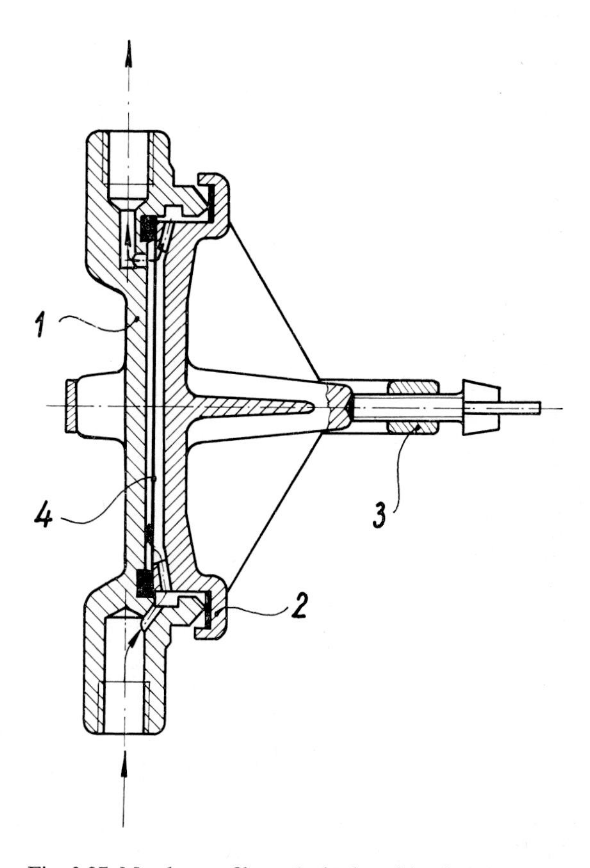

Fig. 3.27 Membrane filter. *1:* body with air inlet and outlet, *2:* cap, *3:* screw, *4:* porous membrane.

3.8.7 | *Dust filters*

Infra-red gas analysers, like all photometric instruments, are particularly sensitive to the presence of solid particles in the sample. Hence microporous dust filters must always be used to prevent dust, some of which may derive from the desiccant, entering the tubes. Membrane filters (Fig. 3.27) with a pore size of about 1 μm formed by a thin porous membrane (about 0.1 mm thick) made of glass wool or of vinyl or acetate cellulose are very effective (*e.g.* from *Gelman Instrument Co.*, Ann Arbor). Filters of this kind removed from gas-masks have been used successfully. Ceramic filters (Fig. 3.28) or sintered glass or metal filters should be used if large amounts of dust are present. These can be obtained in a range of pore sizes down to about 5 μm (*e.g.* from *Hoke International Inc.*, Cresskill, N.J.; *C. A. Norgren Ltd.*, Shipston on Stour, Warwicks, U.K.; *Aerox Ltd.*, Chalford, Stroud, Glos., U.K.). The pore size and area of the filter should not be so small as to introduce a large pressure drop into the system.

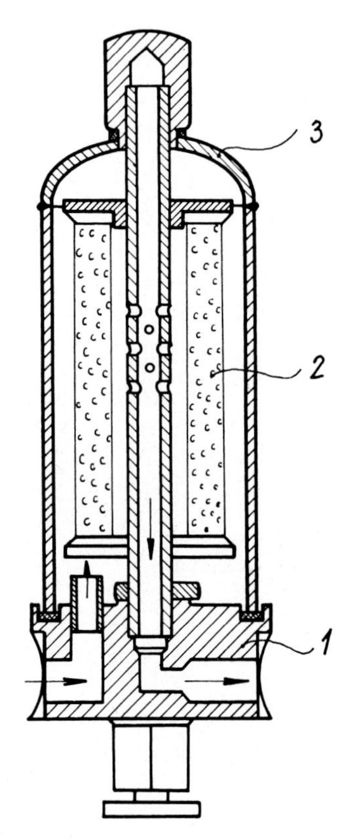

Fig. 3.28 Ceramic filter. *1:* body, *2:* ceramic cylinder, *3:* cap.

3.8.8 | *Sequential valve*

Commercially available three-, six- and twelve-point sequential valves (gas-current switch; *Gasumschalter*) make it possible to analyse more gas streams with one analyser at short time intervals. These devices sequentially (at 20 to 120 s intervals) introduce one of 3, 6 or 12 gas streams into the analyser (*cf.* also Orchard & Heath 1964 for a manually controlled tap system). In sequential valves used for measurements of gas exchange in plants, the remaining streams are sucked off without being analysed and without change of flow rate. Switching the gas streams is synchronised with switching the contacts and printing identification (colours, points, figures) of a multiple recorder.

When switching systems are used they must be designed to insure that, at the flow rate used, the sample reaches and flows through the analyser long enough to achieve equilibrium before a reading is taken. This depends upon the flow rate and volume of tubing and IRGA tubes after the gas switch. It may be about 30 seconds.

Sequential valves are formed either by a system of channels in metal blocks, the relative positions of which are changed by an electric motor (*e.g. Hartmann & Braun* – Fig. 3.29, *Drallim Industries Ltd.*, Bexhill on Sea, Sussex, U.K., *cf.* also

Fig. 3.29 Sequential switching system of *Hartmann & Braun A.G.* (Frankfurt am Main).

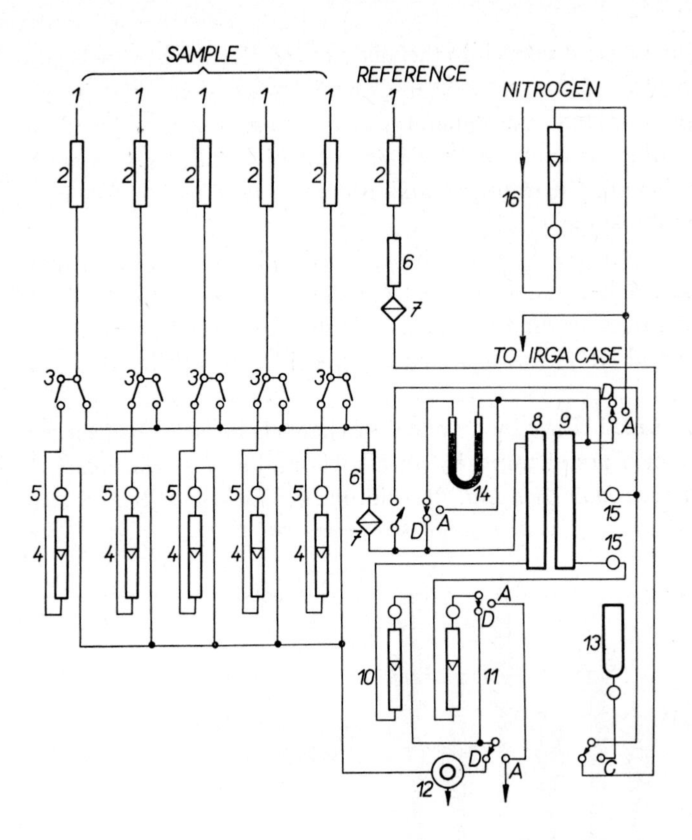

Figs. 3.30A and B.

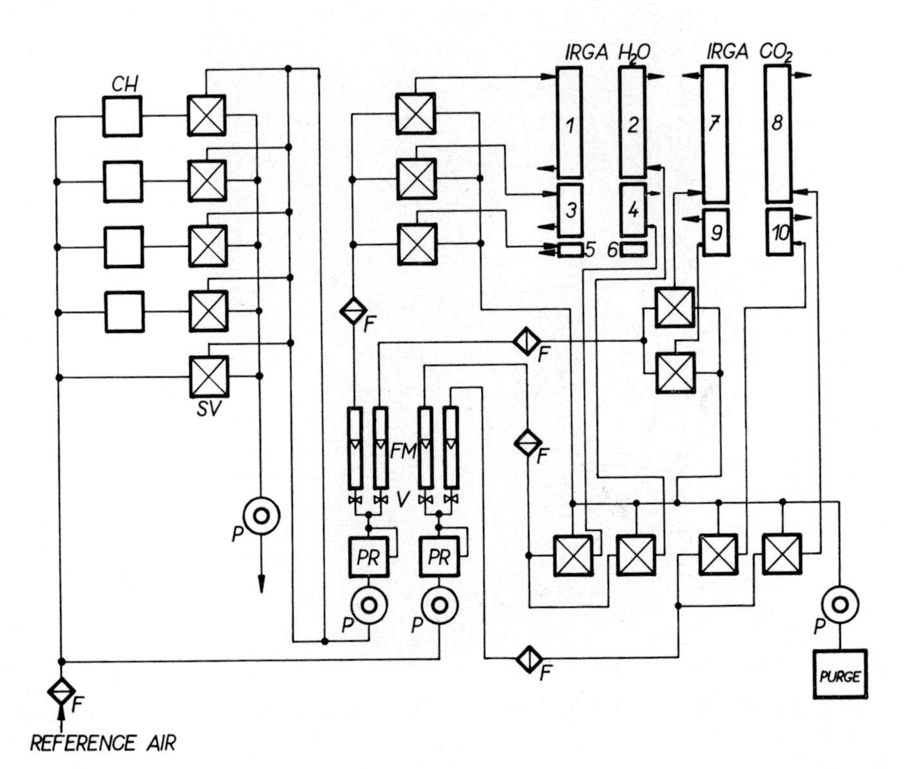

Young & Biale 1962) or by a set of solenoid valves (*e.g. Hilger IRD* – Fig. 3.30). There are two systems used to synchronize sequential opening of the gas tubing with changes in the corresponding printing identification in the multichannel recorder. Either the sequential valve controls switching of the channels of the recorder (*e.g. Hartmann & Braun*), or the recorder controls the operation of the sequential valve (*e.g. Junkalor*).

It is very important when rapidly switching individual gas streams to remove completely a previous gas sample from the whole tubing and sample tube prior to further measurement. This is possible when using a device described by Meinl & Gössler (1965). Gas samples which are not being analysed at the time are collected in glass vessels while displacing a liquid (*e.g.* Brodie solution). The stored gas always rapidly flushes the whole tubing when individual gas streams are connected sequentially with the analyser. The operation of the device is shown in Fig. 3.31 and 3.32.

Fig. 3.30 *A:* Scheme of multi-stream measurement (by courtesy of *Hilger & Watts Ltd.*, London). *1:* inlets of samples, *2:* absorbers, *3:* solenoid valves, *4:* flow meters, *5:* throttle valve, *6:* drying devices, *7:* sintered-glass filters, *8:* sample tube of IRGA, *9:* reference tube of IRGA, *10:* flow meter for sample gas, *11:* flow meter for reference gas during differential measurement or for nitrogen during absolute measurement, *12:* membrane pump, *13:* cylinder with standard gas, *14:* manometer, *15:* equaliser valve, *16:* nitrogen inlet. Position of valves: *A:* in absolute measurement, *D:* in differential measurement, *C:* in calibration. For calibration, the position of the six valves is changed to pass the appropriate gases through the IRGA tubes as required.

B: Modified version of a five-channel system designed by *Grubb Parsons Ltd.* (Newcastle upon Tyne). The IRGAs are provided with several tubes of different lengths enabling the IRGA range to be changed automatically (see the table of tube length and gas concentration). The IRGAs monitor the concentration difference between sample and reference gas irrespective of whether the lower concentration is in the sample or reference tube.

F: filter, *CH:* assimilation chambers, *SV:* 3-way solenoid valves, *P:* pump, *PR:* differential pressure regulator, *FM:* flow meters, *V:* needle valves, *PURGE:* nitrogen.

Kind of measurement	IRGA tube content					
H_2O	*1*	*2*	*3*	*4*	*5*	*6*
diff., range 1	*S*	*R*	*S*	*R*	*P*	*P*
diff., range 2	*S*	*R*	*P*	*P*	*P*	*P*
diff., range 3	*P*	*P*	*S*	*R*	*P*	*P*
absolute	*P*	*P*	*P*	*P*	*S*	*P*
zero	*P*	*P*	*P*	*P*	*P*	*P*
CO_2	*7*	*8*	*9*	*10*		
diff.	*S*	*R*	*S*	*R*		
absolute	*P*	*P*	*S*	*P*		
zero	*P*	*P*	*P*	*P*		

S: sample gas, *R:* reference (background) gas, *P:* purge (nitrogen).

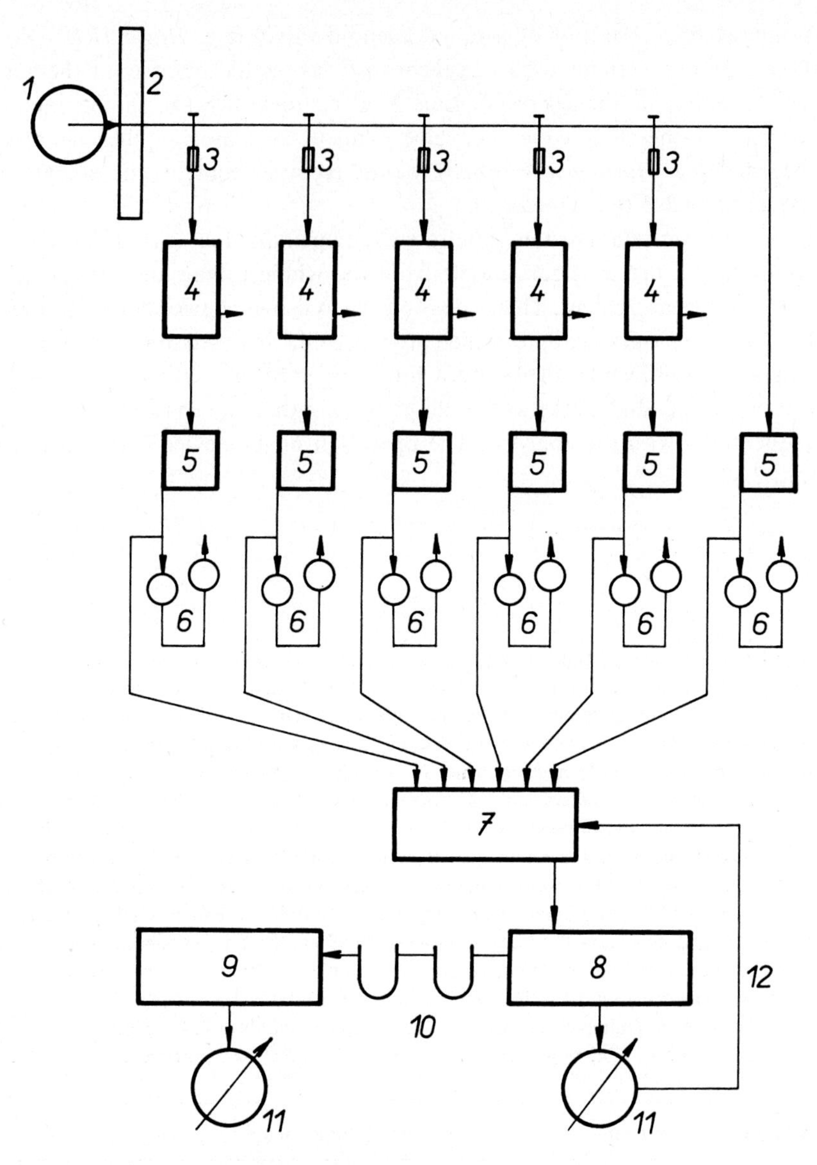

Fig. 3.31 Scheme of multi-stream measurement after Meinl & Gössler (1965). *1:* compressor, *2:* pressure regulator, *3:* flow meters, *4:* assimilation chamber, *5:* membrane pumps, *6:* solenoid valves with air sample containers, *7:* sequential valve, *8:* IRGA for H_2O, *9:* IRGA for CO_2, *10:* drying device, *11:* six-channel recorders, *12:* synchronous control of the sequential valve.

3.8.9 | *Mixing and collecting chambers*

When an IRGA is used to measure gradients of CO_2 for field determinations of net photosynthetic rate (see Chapter 13), time averaged values are required. Averages for periods of the order of 10 or 20 min from several locations or heights are usually desired. Since only one analyser is generally available some means of collecting and mixing samples to eliminate short term fluctuation is generally used.

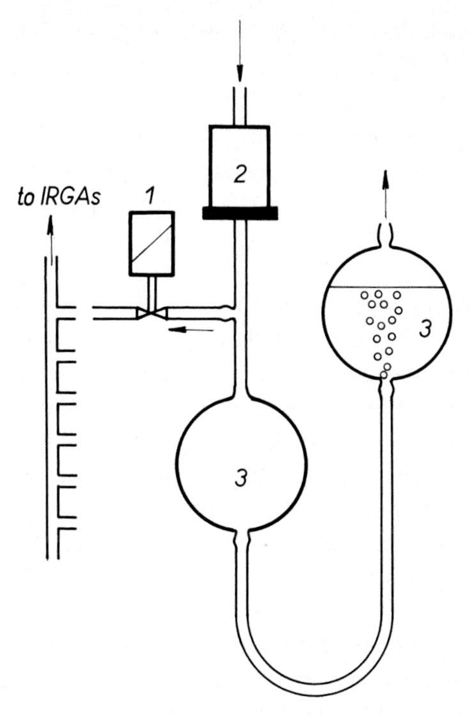

Fig. 3.32 Scheme of the solenoid valve with air sample container (after Meinl & Gössler 1965). *1:* solenoid valve, *2:* membrane pump, *3:* glass containers.

Among the methods which have been used are: 1. inflation of sample bags, 2. filling of evacuated solid wall containers, and 3. the use of continuous flow mixing chambers. The considerations for each type of system will be discussed (see also Section 3.13).

1. Inflation system. The construction of an inflation system requires bags which are not porous to CO_2, and which will not develop leaks after repeated use. Air storage bags can be made from laminated polyethylene and mylar (Lemon, pers. comm.) or from polypropylene (*Propathane C*, *I.C.I.*, U.K.). Such bags may be made just slightly larger than a solid walled container in which they are housed. Such an arrangement eliminates the possibility of over-inflation, which weakens the bags. Flow rates may be adjusted to fill the bags during the desired time interval. After inflation, the bags can be isolated with solenoid valves. A sequential valve is then used to supply air from one bag at a time to the analyser. Among the economic considerations for such a system are the requirement for one air tight pump for each sampling line, in addition to the pump used between the sequential valve and the analyser. Plexiglass cylinders with pistons may also be used (A. Perrier, unpubl.).

2. Evacuated container system. Solid wall evacuated cylinders may be equipped with flow regulators and solenoid valves which allow the sample air to be bled into the evacuated container. Care must be taken to ensure constant flow rates, even at varying pressure differentials. A pump must be utilised to draw the samples from

the container, and pass it through the analyser at a constant flow rate for a period of time which is adequate for the IRGA to reach an equilibrium reading.
The plumbing for such a system must be of a better quality than that required for other systems because of the pressure differentials which develop. The pumps must also be of special design and are thus more expensive. Either of the above systems may be arranged to provide simultaneous average samples over the time desired.

3. Continuous flow system. A solid wall container may be utilised in the lines either before or after a pump to eliminate the short term fluctuations. The size of the chamber and the flow rate may be adjusted to achieve the desired time constant. Where a small chamber (5 liter) is used, positioning the inlet and outlet on opposite ends will generally provide enough mixing when the flow rates are of about $1 \, l \, min^{-1}$. When larger chambers are used some means of stirring may be required, if flow rates are low. The time constant introduced by such an arrangement will depend on the flow rate and the volume of the container. As a rule of thumb the time constant for an unstirred chamber is approximately the volume divided by the flow rate.
The continuous flow mixing system may be operated with a minimum number of pumps. Any available large volume pump may be used to draw samples continuously through all the lines and mixing chambers simultaneously. When the samples are to be analysed, solenoid valves may be used to switch the samples to the sample pumps which deliver them to the analyser.
Although simultaneous samples are not obtained with a continuous flow system, if the mixing chambers are subsampled several times during the time for which an average is desired the average of the results will very closely approximate the results of simultaneous sampling.

3.9 | Accuracy of IRGA

The accuracy of an IRGA, like that of other measuring instruments, is influenced partly by its internal properties, and partly by the effect of external conditions. The errors arising may be divided into *random errors* ΔX_r and *systematic errors* ΔX_s defined by the following relations:

$$\Delta X_r = \frac{\partial X_r}{X_r}, \qquad \Delta X_s = \frac{\partial X_s}{X_s} \tag{3.9}$$

where ∂X_r, ∂X_s are partial derivatives.
During long term measurement, the accuracy is not constant. If at the beginning of the measurement period we set the output, for example, with a standard gas, we eliminate all systematic errors. Hence we can obtain the so-called short term accuracy indicated only by random errors. After subsequently readjusting the analyser the systematic error increases. The magnitude of the error before the new adjustment indicates the so-called long term accuracy. It is evident from what has been said that the long term accuracy is always related to the length of a certain period. The longer this period or the smaller the error arising in a certain

period, the better is the accuracy of the analyser. The total relative error of the analyser is then given by the expression

$$\Delta X = \Delta X_r + \Delta X_s \tag{3.10}$$

For the relative random error of an IRGA of conventional type Janáč (1965) derived the approximate equation:

$$\Delta X_r \simeq [\Delta G^2 + \alpha^2 \Delta U^2 + \Delta M^2 + \Delta P^2 + \Delta T^2]^{\frac{1}{2}} \tag{3.11}$$

valid for small changes, where ΔG is the change in gain of the IRGA amplifier, ΔU the change in mains voltage, ΔM the accuracy of the measuring apparatus, ΔP the change in total pressure, and ΔT the fluctuation in absolute temperature of the analysed gas. The value of the coefficient α is dependent on the stability and the construction of the source of radiation, on the stability of the polarising voltage on the membrane condenser of the detector and on the ratio of the wavelength of maximum radiation of the source to the wavelength at which the analysis is carried out. The quantities ΔG and α depend on the quality of the analyser. Accuracy of an IRGA according to the manufacturer is usually in the range of 1 to 2%.
If in equation (3.11) we substitute an approximate estimate of the various terms, in per cent, for the analysis of CO_2 we obtain:

$$\Delta X_r = (0.5^2 + 1.35^2 + 1^2 + 0.3^2 + 0.2^2)^{\frac{1}{2}} = 1.8\%$$

If instead of a measuring instrument with an accuracy of 1% we use one with an accuracy of 0.25%, the accuracy of the analysis improves only from 1.8% to 1.5%.
Systematic errors include all errors which exert a slow and one-sided influence upon the output signal of the analyser. They are, first of all, the errors caused by changes in the resistances of the heaters and the changes in the optical quality of the sample or reference path of radiation. A systematic error is also caused by differences between the pressure and temperature of the analysed gas as compared with the conditions pertaining when the analyser was adjusted.
In Janáč's paper (1965), an equation has been derived for the relative systematic error of an IRGA of the conventional type when small changes are taking place:

$$\Delta X_s \simeq \frac{1}{kw}(\Delta\Psi + \beta\Delta R) + \Delta P - \Delta T \tag{3.12}$$

where $\Delta\Psi$ is the change in the difference between the optical quality of the two radiation paths of the analyser, ΔR the change in the difference between the resistances of the two heaters, ΔP the change in total pressure of the analysed gas mixture and ΔT the change in its absolute temperature. Coefficient β is given by the construction of the radiation source and by the wavelength at which the analysis is carried out. The values of the variables $\Delta\Psi$ and ΔR cannot be determined in advance, but by analysing the problem one can find that the changes in these variables are mainly responsible for the low stability of conventional IRGAs. This results from the fact that both the variables are multiplied by $1/kw$

(as already shown in Section 3.3, the value of $1/kw$ is 10 with an IRGA for normal analyses, and 100 or more for trace analyses). Eq. (3.12) may well be used for determining the influence of deviations of gas pressure and temperature from the conditions under which the analyser has been adjusted.

The signs in equation (3.12) indicate the direction of the action of the variable: a pressure increase results in a positive error, a temperature increase in a negative one. Under normal ambient conditions (1013 mb, 20 °C) a pressure change of 10 mb causes an error of *ca.* 1 %, a temperature change of 10 °C an error of 3.4 %. (Assuming that the measurement and the calibration with standard gas is made at the same altitude, only the fluctuation of barometric pressure affects the error – see Lascombes 1963.)

The type of IRGA discussed is very often also used differentially as described in Section 3.12. In this case it is possible to derive the following equations for estimating relative errors valid for small deviations.

For the influence of a relative change in CO_2 concentration in the reference air, ΔC_1, upon the relative error of the analyser, ΔX_s, Janáč (1970) derived the following aproximate relation:

$$\Delta X_s \simeq - K n_1 C_1 \Delta C_1 \tag{3.13}$$

where C_1 is the CO_2 concentration in the reference air; $n_1 = T_0 P_1 / P_0 T_1$ where T_0, P_0 are absolute temperature and total pressure of the gas under normal condi-

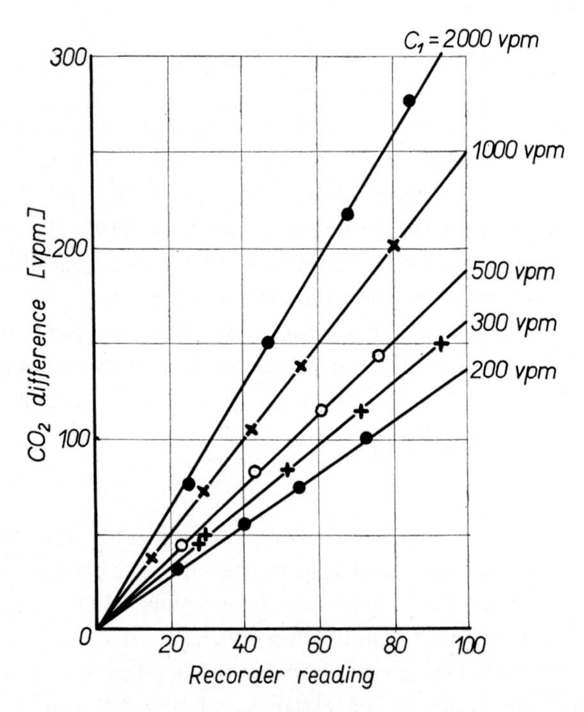

Fig. 3.33 The influence of the CO_2 concentration of the reference air (the so-called background concentration) on the calibration curves of the IRGA (after Bierhuizen & Slatyer 1964). Abscissa: recorder reading, ordinate: CO_2 difference in sample and reference air samples, c_1: the background concentration.

tions, and T_1, P_1 are absolute temperature and total pressure of gas in the reference tube. As a first approximation K may be considered as constant with a value for CO_2 analysis of $K = 7 \times 10^{-4}$ [vpm^{-1}].
Assuming that n_1 does not differ much from unity, the relative error is given by the concentration of CO_2 in the reference air and the change in it. This is shown in Fig. 3.33 based on measurements by Bierhuizen & Slatyer (1964). From Eq. (3.13) a change of 15 vpm CO_2 in the reference air results in a 1% error in the analysis.
For the influence of relative changes in the absolute temperatures and total gas pressures in the reference and sample tube on the error of the analyser the following approximate relation holds (Janáč 1970):

$$\Delta X_s = \underbrace{C_1/\Delta C(\Delta P_1 - \Delta P_2 + \Delta T_2 - \Delta T_1)}_{II} + \underbrace{\Delta P_2 - \Delta T_2}_{I} \tag{3.14}$$

where ΔC is the measured difference in CO_2 concentration between reference and sample tube, C_1 is CO_2 concentration in the reference air, T_1, P_1 are absolute temperature and total gas pressure in the reference tube, and T_2, P_2 are absolute temperature and total gas pressure in the sample tube. This equation is valid if the higher CO_2 concentration is in the reference tube and the lower CO_2 concentration is in the sample tube. When the lower 'background' CO_2 concentration is in the reference tube, the expression II has the form $C_1/\Delta C\,(\Delta P_2 - \Delta P_1 + \Delta T_1 - \Delta T_2)$.
Eq. (3.14) shows that for the same change of temperature and pressure in the reference tube and in the sample tube, the relative error of the analyser only arises from the expression indicated as I. The expression I corresponds to Eq. (3.12) and is equivalent to the error of the direct measurement. If the changes of temperature and pressure in both tubes are different the additive error of the analyser is given by expression II. This additive error depends on the ratio $C_1/\Delta C$ having a considerably value.
Therefore the precise control of temperatures and gas pressures in the tubes is of great importance in the case of differential measurement of CO_2.
When dealing with the problems of differential measurement it is also important to point out that with increasing CO_2 concentration in the reference air the sensitivity of measurement decreases. For the ratio of sensitivity of differential measurement S[1] to sensitivity of direct measurement S_0, Janáč (1970) derived the following relation:

$$S/S_0 \simeq \exp(-K\, n_1\, c_1) \tag{3.15}$$

Eq. (3.15) shows that the decrease in sensitivity of differential measurement depends in the first place on the CO_2 concentration in the reference air. The theoretical consequence of Eq. (3.15) and experimental results of Gaastra (1959), and Bierhuizen & Slatyer (1964) are given in Fig. 3.34. It is evident that for $C_1 = 500$ vpm,

1. Sensitivity S is defined as a ratio of elementary increase in the deviation of the analyser meter to the elementary increase in concentration C in the sample tube.

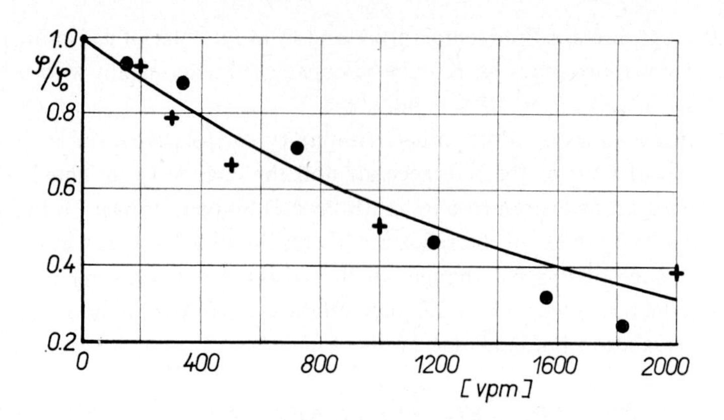

Fig. 3.34 Sensitivity of differential measurement. The experimental points were calculated after Gaastra (1959) (●), and after Bierhuizen & Slatyer (1964) (+). The solid line is calculated from Eq. (3.15). Abscissa: CO_2 concentration in the reference tube of IRGA, ordinate: S/S_0 (see Eq. 3.15 for details).

for example, the sensitivity of differential measurement decreases approximately to 3/4 that of direct measurement.

A further error of measurement may occur when the absorption bands of the analysed and interfering gases present in the sample tube overlap. The influence of an interfering gas is expressed by means of the so-called discrimination ratio given by the equation:

$$Q = A\,C_R/A_R\,C \tag{3.16}$$

where A is the deviation of the measuring device, caused by the analysed gas in the sample tube with concentration C, A_R is the deviation of the measuring apparatus caused by the interfering gas in the sample tube with concentration C_R. The discrimination ratio indicating the selectivity of the analyser is, first of all, dependent on the nature of the analysed and interfering gases, their concentrations and the type of the analyser. Necessarily, it must be determined experimentally. When measuring the CO_2 exchange of plants this problem is solved by removing water vapour from the sample being analysed or by using an optical filter to remove the radiation of interfering frequency.

3.10 | Calibration of IRGA

There are two main ways of calibrating the IRGA:
by using standard gases with known CO_2 concentration, prepared in various ways (see Sections 3.10.1 and 3.10.2), or by pressurisation technique (see Section 3.10.3).

3.10.1 | Preparation of standard gas mixtures

The CO_2 analyser has to be calibrated with precisely defined gas mixtures. If, for example, 5% error in CO_2 concentrations in standard gases is assumed (*i.e.* if gases 250 − 12.5 vpm, and 300 + 15 vpm are used to set the scale), this can

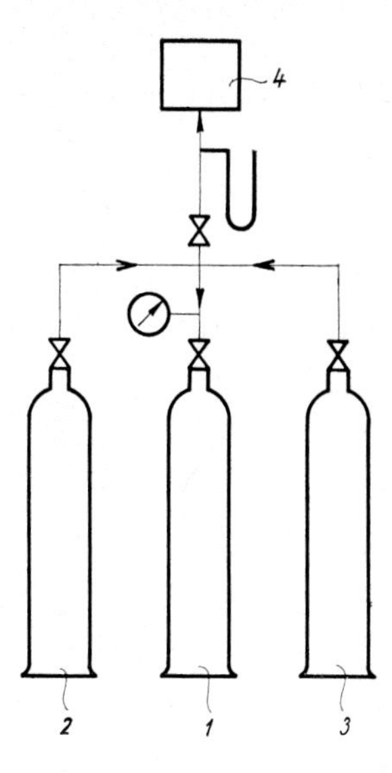

Fig. 3.35 Preparation of a standard gas mixture by means of the high-pressure method. *1:* cylinder for stocking the prepared standard gas, *2:* cylinder with nitrogen, *3:* cylinder with CO_2, *4:* vacuum pump.

introduce an error of 55% (!) in a differential IRGA with 50 vpm scale (Chartier 1970). The standard gas mixtures consisting of the required CO_2 concentration in a neutral gas (usually nitrogen) can be prepared in several ways, generally by the pressure, volume or flow methods.

The pressure method. Of these methods, that involving preparation of the mixture in a pressure cylinder (usually of a capacity of 2 to 10 litres) is the most suitable one. Cylinders of this kind with standard gases are commercially available, usually from the manufacturer of the IRGA. Some chemical supply houses sell CO_2 and air (nitrogen) mixtures to be used as standards for CO_2 analysis. Experience has shown that the analysis by several such companies may be in error by as much as 30 vpm. Thus any such standards should be checked before use. A schematic diagram of the equipment for the high-pressure preparation of standard gases is shown in Fig. 3.35. The pressure cylinder is first evacuated completely, and pure CO_2 is then added from another cylinder until pressure p_1 is attained. The cylinder is then made up with nitrogen or CO_2-free air to a final pressure P. Both pressures are determined according to Dalton's law:

$$C_1 = 100 \frac{p_1}{P} \qquad (3.17)$$

where C_1 is the required concentration of CO_2 in vol. %. A two-stage method is employed when preparing CO_2 concentrations below 0.1%, *i.e.* 1000 vpm. The concentration of the standard mixture is chosen somewhat below the value of the final measuring range. In view of the requirement for high-pressure manometer accuracy, the mixture thus obtained has to be checked by a suitable analytical method. A chemical (absorption) method is usually used. Brown & Rosenberg (1968) recommended passing a measured volume of dry standard gas mixture

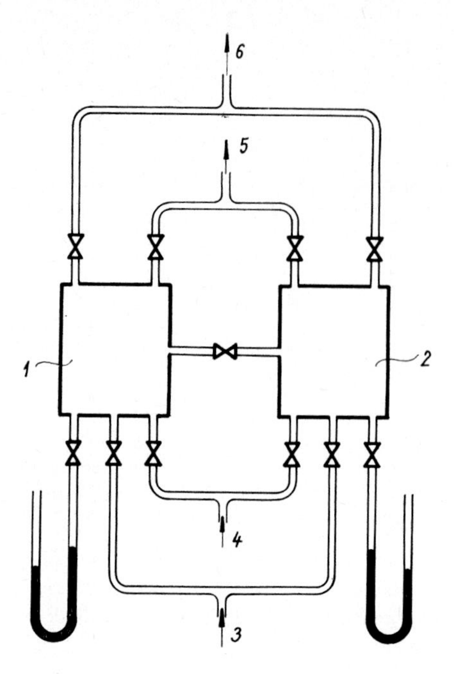

Fig. 3.36 Preparation of a standard gas mixture by the low-pressure method. *1* and *2:* vessel for preparation of the standard gas, *3:* nitrogen inlet, *4:* CO_2 inlet, *5:* to vacuum pump, *6:* to IRGA.

over dry indicating *Ascarite* (sodium hydrate asbestos). The absolute CO_2 concentration can then be estimated to within 10 vpm from the change in the weight of *Ascarite.* A reliably calibrated IRGA may also be used for checking newly prepared gas mixtures. This may introduce a systematic error equal to the calibration error of this IRGA.

The internal surface of pressure cylinders intended for a long term storage of mixtures should be suitably coated (*e.g.* with epoxy resin). It is recommended to wait several days before analysing the gas so that a completely homogeneous mixture is formed by diffusion[1]. The CO_2 concentration in the cylinders should be checked after storage for long periods because changes can occur. Changes in CO_2 concentration in the last third of the cylinder content have been observed. The standard mixture in a 10-litre cylinder is sufficient for 200 to 500 IRGA adjustments.

When it is necessary to avoid work with high pressures, the low-pressure method (Fig. 3.36) can be used. After first evacuating vessel *(1)* a certain amount of pure CO_2 is introduced into it from vessel *(2)*. The pressure is measured by a precision mercury manometer (*e.g.* filling to a pressure of 40 mb). Then the vessel is filled with nitrogen (*e.g.* to a pressure of 2000 mb, thus giving a concentration of 2%). The concentration is further decreased by evacuating vessel *(2)*, introducing to it a part of the mixture from vessel *(1)* and making up the pressure with nitrogen.

1. In order to accelerate mixing the gas by shaking, some objects of suitable shape could be placed in the cylinders. Differential heating of the cylinder, achieved with an electrical heater strip attached to one side, also hastens mixing.

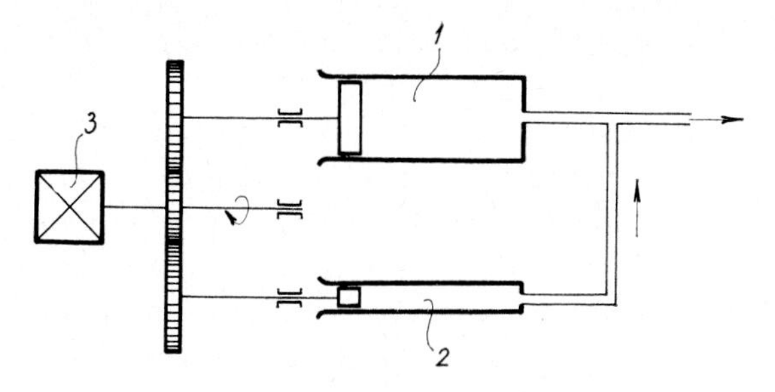

Fig. 3.37 Preparation of a standard gas mixture by the volume method. *1:* piston device with nitrogen, *2:* piston device with CO_2, *3:* electromotor.

The procedure is repeated until the required concentration is obtained. The accuracy of this method depends primarily on the measuring accuracy of the mercury manometers. A dilution ratio of 1 : 100 should not be exceeded in one stage. When working carefully it is possible to prepare the standard mixture with an accuracy of about 2% in one dilution stage (*i.e.*, *e.g.* 500 ± 10 vpm). This method has the disadvantage of providing only a small stock of the standard mixture. A

Fig. 3.38 Mixing pump (by courtesy of *H. Wösthoff*, Bochum).

description of a device for preparing mixtures by this method is given by Fonselius & Wärme (1960).

The volume method allows preparation of the standard mixture in the simple way shown in Fig. 3.37, for example. A piston metering device *(1)* filled with nitrogen, and another *(2)* filled with carbon dioxide, are jointly driven by an electric motor *(3)*. This ensures a precisely identical displacement of the two pistons. When the ratio of the piston areas is 1 : 99, a mixture with 1% CO_2 is obtained. Still lower concentrations require the filling of metering device *(2)* with pre-diluted gas, or the use of two devices connected in series. Commercially available mixing pumps (*e.g. Gasmischpumpe, H. Wösthoff*, Bochum, BRD) are widely used at present (Fig. 3.38; *cf.* also Müller & Nauck 1965 for other types of mixing pumps).

The flow method is schematically illustrated in Fig. 3.39. Nitrogen (or CO_2-free air) and carbon dioxide pass from pressure cylinders *(1* and *2) via* capillaries or nozzles *(4)* into the mixing chamber *(3)*. The flow rate is checked according to the pressure drop at the nozzle by means of precisely calibrated differential manometers *(5)*. The flow rate ratio chosen should not exceed 1 : 100, so that

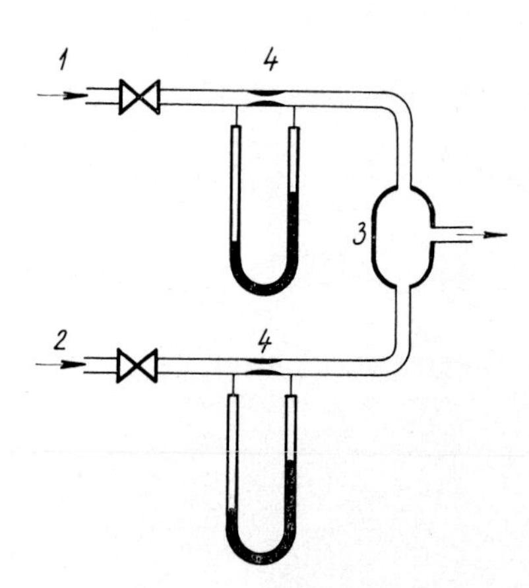

Fig. 3.39 Preparation of a standard gas mixture by the flow method. *1:* nitrogen inlet, *2:* CO_2 inlet, *3:* mixing chamber, *4:* capillaries.

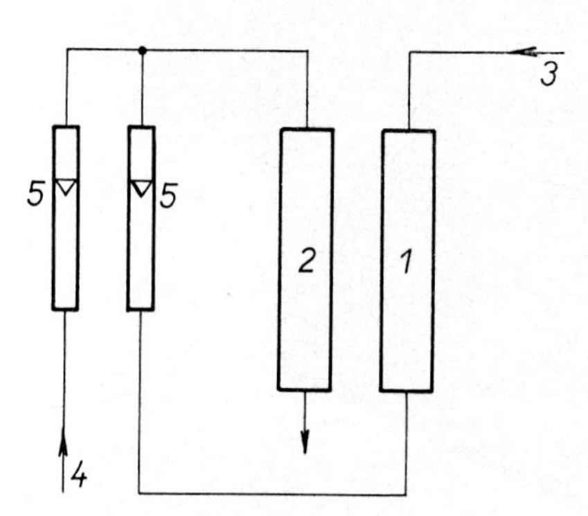

Fig. 3.40 Scheme of a device for calibrating a differentially measuring IRGA. *1:* sample tube of IRGA, *2:* reference tube of IRGA, *3:* inlet of standard gas, *4:* inlet of nitrogen, *5:* flow meters.

pre-mixing is necessary when low concentrations are required. The method is accurate to about 1% of the mixture concentration value when it is carried out with sufficient precision. Other air-flow mixing devices have been described by several authors (*e.g.* Schnelle 1957, *cf.* also Apel 1966; Holmgren 1968). A similar procedure can also be used for calibrating differentially measuring IRGAs (Fig. 3.40, Bierhuizen & Slatyer 1964; Nátr 1964).

Carbon dioxide added to the stream of CO_2-free gas can also be obtained by electrolysis of oxalic acid (a device and conditions are described by Přibyl 1966) or by evolution from bicarbonate by means of acid (Nátr 1964). The latter method is suitable when calibrating an IRGA in a closed system.

Standard mixtures of trace concentrations should be prepared by the methods described above from absolutely pure gases only. Current technical grade gases supplied in pressure cylinders could contain impurities which have to be checked before use.

The preparation of a gaseous standard has recently been the subject of a review by Roccanova (1968).

3.10.2 | Calibration of IRGA using standard gases

After setting zero (see Section 3.7.3), the standard gas, with a CO_2 concentration corresponding to the maximum of the measuring range, is introduced into the sample tube and the amplification is adjusted so that the deflection of the measuring instrument corresponds to this concentration. In differentially measuring IRGAs, standard gases providing the required CO_2 differentials are used, the gas with lower CO_2 concentration being used in the reference tube. The zero position is then checked again. The final zero and deflection setting is carried out from outside the IRGA, in order to prevent the thermal equilibrium from being affected by opening the door. Finally, the course of the complete calibration curve may be checked, when necessary, by using three to five standard mixtures with various CO_2 concentrations, in turn.

Alternatively, three calibration gases, *A*, *B*, and *C*, may be used. Zero is set by comparing *A* with *B* (*B* in the sample tube), and range by comparing *A* with *C* (*C* in the sample tube). This principle is employed by the *Hartmann & Braun* automatic calibration unit referred to below.

The IRGA should be calibrated after connecting it into the system to prevent differences in pressure between calibration and measurement conditions.

As already mentioned in Section 3.9, long term accuracy of the IRGA depends on the frequency with which adjustments are made. The accuracy can be increased considerably by adjusting the IRGA several times a day. This can be carried out automatically by a commercially available device (*e.g. CGMS – Messumformer, Hartmann & Braun A.G.*, Frankfurt/Main) which fills the IRGA tubes with standard gases at the required times and sets the correct amplifier output by means of potentiometers controlled by servomotors.

All changes which affect the CO_2 density in the IRGA tubes also affect the slope of the calibration curve. Thus barometric pressure and temperature have a considerable effect on the calibration curve. Some types of IRGAs therefore include an automatic correcting device which eliminates the effects of pressure on the data. The effect of gas temperature is eliminated in temperature-controlled analysers.

3.10.3 | *Pressurisation technique of calibration of IRGA*

When measuring small CO_2 differentials (below 50 vpm) the error in the determination of the CO_2 concentration in standard mixtures is relatively high. For this reason, pressurisation calibration has been widely used. A single standard gas with known background concentration is used to fill both analyser tubes, and the pressure in the sample tube is increased by restricting the outflow from this tube. A mercury manometer is coupled to the IRGA exhaust with a glass T and the outflow from the third branch of the T is restricted while maintaining a constant flow rate. The tube pressure can easily be doubled in such a way (Brown & Rosenberg 1968). The "background" CO_2 concentration, *i.e.* the constant CO_2 concentration, is then the *lower* one. This is different from the arrangement usually used for measuring photosynthesis, in which the *higher* CO_2 concentration (*i.e.* the concentration in the control air) is regarded as the background. This difference could be a source of error since there is a change in the slope of the calibration curves in response to a change in background CO_2 concentration (Fig. 3.33).
The unknown concentration is given by the equation

$$\Delta C = [(P_2/P_1) - 1]C_1 \tag{3.18}$$

where
ΔC is the difference in CO_2 concentrations in the sample and reference tubes
C_1 is the CO_2 concentration in the reference tube
P_1 is the total pressure in the reference tube
P_2 is the total pressure in the sample tube.
A condition for using the above equation is that there is only a small increase of the tube pressure, so that the pressure extension of the absorption bands is negligible (*cf.* Legg & Parkinson 1968). A device for the pressurisation technique for calibrating IRGA is described by Girshovich (1967), for example.
Although this technique has been used fairly frequently, there is as yet no reliable evidence that it is as adequate for all types of IRGAs as calibration with standard gas mixtures. Indeed Legg & Parkinson (1968) have shown a large discrepancy between pressure and true calibrations. Furthermore there is no universally applicable correction factor and hence the pressure method cannot be recommended.

3.11 | Repair of defects in IRGA

In the case of a defect it is first necessary to find out which part of the system is responsible. When the reason is not apparent at once it is necessary to proceed by elimination, first checking the parts which have the highest failure rate and those which can be checked easily. The correct function of the gas handling system is therefore checked first. In the case of the IRGA itself, the various components – the measuring instrument (recorder), the amplifier and the optical part of the IRGA (including the detector) – can be checked separately. The measuring instrument is replaced by another one or it is checked by an adequate source (*e.g.* a battery and a suitable resistor). In order to check the amplifier the detector can be replaced, *e.g.* by a 'capacity change generator'[1]. In the optical part there may be defects in the radiation source, in the tubes, or in the detector; the most frequent defects are listed in Table 3.3.

The kind of record is often a good guide to spotting the defect. A gradual change in deflection may indicate that there is a leak in the reference tube (in absolutely measuring IRGAs) or the detector (or may be the desiccant exhausted!). The cause of periodic fluctuations of the deflection around the mean is usually a defect in the IRGA's thermostat. A low analyser sensitivity is usually due to escape of the detector filling, and sometimes can be caused by soiling of the windows or the sample tube reflecting areas. A dependence of the sensitivity of the IRGA on the flow rate can be the result of dust present in the tube(s). In the case of too small an analyser deflection, a test operation with a standard mixture is the only reliable check.

During long term operation, some optical parts of the IRGA (inner surface of the tubes and windows) can be polluted with fine dust. Because of the poor mechanical properties of the optical materials used in IR-technique, careful cleaning procedures must be used:

Tube cleaning. The insides of the tubes can be cleaned using a very soft cloth, followed by blowing out any dust and fluff in a stream of dry air. Distilled water may be used but organic solvents are not advisable. Extreme care must be taken to avoid damage to the bores of the tubes and, during re-assembly, to ensure that the ends of each tube fit correctly inside the seals in the window housings.

Window cleaning. The materials from which the tubes, detector unit and radiator unit windows are made will depend upon the application for which the IRGA is calibrated (*cf.* Section 3.2). Whatever material the windows are made from, the greatest possible care must be taken not to scratch or chip them, as even slight scratching will affect the calibration. The necessity for cleanliness must be emphasised, all possible precautions should be taken to exclude dust, fluff and grit whenever the tubes are dismantled. The cleaning procedures for the various window materials are as follows:

Calcium fluoride: clean with acetone. Fluoride should be carefully handled as it shatters easily.

Mica: Clean by dipping in acetone, then shake off the surplus and allow to dry. Mica must not be rubbed or wiped with cotton wool or cloth as this will certainly scratch the surface.

Sodium chloride: Clean with a dry camel hair brush. Sodium chloride must be kept dry as otherwise it will absorb moisture and become cloudy. For this reason it must not be fingered, or exposed to a damp atmosphere.

1. This consists of a synchronous motor on the shaft of which a disc, constituting one capacitor plate, is excentrically attached so that it is electrically insulated from the shaft. Against this disc it is possible to position a screw forming the other capacitor plate. The whipping of the disc against the screw brings about capacity changes. Their size is given by the distance between the screw and the disc, the frequency by the speed of the motor (*e.g.* 375 r.p.m. are used for 6.25 Hz).

Table 3.3 Detection of usual faults in the IRGA.

Symptom	Cause	Remedial Action
1. No reading on meter	1.1 *Source failure* (heaters are cold)	
	Filament broken	– Replace heater
	Heaters circuit fault	– Check circuit
	1.2 *Rotating shutter not rotating*	
	Bearing fault	– Check bearing lubrication
	Electromotor circuit fault	– Check circuit
	1.3 *Detector failure*	
	Insulation fault	– Test high impedance input circuit
	Membrane condenser fault	– Replace membrane condenser or detector
	Detector leakage	– Refill with absorption gas or replace detector
	1.4 *Amplifier failure*	
	Valves fault	– Check by interchanging valves
	Rectifier fault	– Check rectifier
	Amplifier circuit fault	– Replace amplifier
	1.5 *Meter failure*	
	External fault	– Check meter circuit
	Internal fault	– Replace meter
2. Meter shows full scale deflection	2.1 *Analyser section failure*	
	Zero control shutter incorrectly set	– Adjust zero control
	Faulty phasing adjustment	– Adjust phasing
	One heater fault	– Replace both heaters with matched pair
	Membrane condenser short circuit	– Replace membrane condenser or detector
	Dirt in sample tube	– Dismantle and clean
	2.2 *Electrical section failure*	
	High gain of amplifier	– Reduce gain settings to minimum
	Noisy valves	– Check by interchanging valves
	Amplifier circuit fault	– Replace amplifier
3. Zero is not obtainable on meter by using zero control	3.1 *Phasing incorrectly set*	– Re-set phasing
	3.2 *Unequal radiation in both paths*	– Check source or dismantle and clean sample tube
	3.3 *Too high gain of amplifier*	– Reduce gain
	3.4 *Noisy amplifier*	– Check and replace
4. Record permanently increases	4.1 *Detector leakage*	– Replace detector
	4.2 *Drying agent failure*	– Drying tube re-charge with fresh desiccant
5. Unstable record	5.1 *Membrane condensor short circuit*	– Replace detector
	5.2 *High impedance insulating fault*	– Check detector insulating and amplifier input (humidity)
	5.3 *Irregular speed of rotating shutter*	– Lubricate bearings or gear box

Table 3.3. *(continued)*

Symptom	Cause	Remedial Action
6. Low sensitivity of analyser	6.1 *Detector leakage*	– Replace detector
	6.2 *Amplifier fault*	– Check gain
	6.3 *Dirt in sample tube*	– Dismantle and clean
7. Meter reading varies with sample flow	7.1 *Dirt in sample tube*	– Dismantle and clean
8. Meter reading varies with humidity of sample gas	8.1 *Detector leakage*	– Replace detector
	8.2 *Drying agent failure*	– Re-charge drying tube with fresh desiccant

Fused silica: Clean with acetone. Cotton wool or a soft cloth may be used.
Arsenic trisulphide: As calcium fluoride. Arsenic trisulphide is poisonous if swallowed. The hands should be washed after handling it.

3.12 | General principles of using IRGA for measuring CO_2 exchange rates

3.12.1 | Absolutely and differentially measuring IRGA

Systems with IRGAs are designed as generally shown in Chapter 2. Only a short review with a few remarks is therefore given here.
One of two measurement arrangements – absolute or differential – is generally used in systems with IRGA, the second one being most popular recently for determinations of CO_2 exchange in plants. The flow of the reference gas through one of the tubes of the differentially measuring IRGA is the only difference from an IRGA for absolute measurement.
Absolutely measuring IRGAs monitoring the CO_2 concentration in the flowing air stream were used in the first measurements of the CO_2 exchange rate in plants (for details see *e.g.* Egle & Ernst 1949; Huber 1950, 1957, 1958, 1964; Egle & Schenk 1951; Strugger & Baumeister 1951; Tranquillini 1952; Huber & Polster 1955). The sensitivity of those analysers usually allowed only the range from 0 to 500 vpm CO_2. The CO_2 concentration in the control air and that in the air from the assimilation chamber were therefore measured alternately, the difference between them being a measure of CO_2-exchange rate of the experimental material. In this arrangement, however, the errors of the two determinations made up a large part of the difference between them, so that the total error of the measurement of the CO_2-exchange rate was significantly large. In addition, short term fluctuations in CO_2 concentration of the control air were another source of errors, especially when a sequential valve was used. More recently absolutely measuring IRGAs with optically suppressed zero have been used covering only the range *e.g.* 250–350 vpm CO_2, or, alternatively, IRGAs with flowing reference gas (*i.e.* control air) (*cf. e.g.* Gaastra 1959; Björkman & Holmgren 1963; Hesketh & Moss 1963; Slavík & Čatský 1963; Bierhuizen & Slatyer 1964). The important advantage of the latter is that the accuracy of the results is governed by the analyser error alone and not by the sum of two errors.

IRGAs with an 'open' reference tube through which flows the reference gas are used at present for measuring CO_2 differentials as well as for absolute measurements of CO_2 concentration; for the latter differences in CO_2 concentration between one or several standard gas streams and the reference gas are measured. More detailed methodological information can be found also in Ormrod (1961), Hesketh & Musgrave (1962), Bourdeau & Woodwell (1965), Stoy (1965), van den Driessche & Wareing (1966), Jarvis & Slatyer (1966), Etherington (1967), Woolhouse (1967/8), Parkinson (1968), Lange, Koch & Schulze (1969), Louwerse & van Oorschot (1969), Chartier, Chartier & Čatský (1970), and in other original papers cited in the relevant sections of the bibliographies published in the journals Photosynthetica, Photochem. Photobiol., and Agric. Meteorol.

3.12.2 | *Calculations of the rate of CO_2 exchange and their errors*

The IRGA measures the CO_2 concentration [vpm or $\mu l\ l^{-1}$] or partial pressure. The flux density of CO_2 or the CO_2 exchange rate, F, has sometimes been expressed in volumetric units of $cm^3\ CO_2 \cdot cm^{-2}$ leaf area · unit time^{-1} (*e.g.* Gaastra 1959) from a simple expression of the following kind:

$$F = \frac{\Delta C \cdot J}{A} \tag{3.19}$$

where
F = flux density of CO_2 [$cm^3\ cm^{-2}\ s^{-1}$],
J = air flow rate through the assimilation chamber [$cm^3\ s^{-1}$],
A = leaf area (usually the area of one surface) [cm^2],
ΔC = the difference in CO_2 concentration of the air streams before and after the assimilation chamber measured at the same temperature and pressure [$cm^3\ cm^{-3}$].

However, it is frequently desirable to express the CO_2 exchange rate in terms of the mass flux of CO_2. To do this it is necessary to know the temperature and pressure in the laboratory at the time of the observations and the temperature and pressure at which the flow meter was calibrated. Equation (3.19) then becomes

$$F = \frac{\Delta C}{A} \frac{J \cdot 44}{22\,414} \frac{273}{T} \frac{P}{1013} [g\ cm^{-2}\ s^{-1}] \tag{3.20}$$

where
T = both the temperature [K] at which the flow meter was calibrated and the temperature of the flow meter at the time of observation; if these are different, an additional temperature correction is necessary;
P = barometric pressure [mb] at the time of observation, the calibration of the flow meter having been corrected to 1 013 mb (*i.e.* 760 torr).

This expression is satisfactory for capillary flow meters. Baker and Musgrave (1964) give an analogous expression for rotameters, taking into account the theory of rotameters (hence the square roots; see *e.g.* Ower & Pankhurst 1966). Equation (3.19) then becomes

$$F = \frac{\Delta C}{A} \frac{J \cdot 44}{22\,414} \frac{273}{T} \frac{P}{1\,013} \sqrt{\frac{T}{T^1}} \sqrt{\frac{P^1}{P}} \; [\text{g cm}^{-2}\,\text{s}^{-1}] \qquad (3.21)$$

where

P^1 = pressure at which the rotameter was calibrated [mb],
T^1 = temperature at which the rotameter was calibrated [K],
P = barometric pressure at the time of observation [mb],
T = temperature of the flow meter at the time of observation [K].

Similar considerations apply to the calculation of the ambient CO_2 concentration within the assimilation chamber. If the assimilation chamber is well stirred internally, the concentration of CO_2 in the sample of air continuously drawn off for analysis, C_0 [vpm or $\mu l\ l^{-1}$], may be assumed equal to the ambient concentration in the chamber. The mass concentration of CO_2 in the chamber, C_a is given by:

$$C_a = C_0 \frac{44}{22\,414} \frac{273}{T''} \frac{P}{1\,013} \cdot 10^{-6} \qquad [\text{g cm}^{-3}] \qquad (3.22)$$

where T'' = the air temperature in the assimilation chamber [K].

For practical purposes, Table 3.4 can be used to convert volumetric to mass units. It is based on experimentally found values, and differs slightly from the theoretical coefficients following from the equations (3.21) and (3.22).

This expression is satisfactory if optical filters are being used to suppress interference by water vapour. However, if the air is dried before analysis, allowance must be made for variations in the water vapour pressure in the assimilation chamber:

$$C_a = C_0 \frac{44}{22\,414} \frac{273}{T''} \frac{P}{1\,013} \frac{(P - e)}{P} \qquad (3.23)$$

where e is the ambient water vapour in the assimilation chamber in the same units as P. If stirring is adequate, e may also be taken as the vapour pressure of the air leaving the chamber[1].

The results obtained by various calculation procedures differ slightly according to the accuracy of the individual calculations and correction factors, but the deviation is small.

The evaluation of the standard deviation associated with the measurement of photosynthetic rate differs slightly depending upon whether the difference in CO_2 concentration is measured directly by means of a differential IRGA or determined by subtraction from two estimations of CO_2 concentration by an absolute IRGA (*cf.* Brown & Rosenberg 1968)[2].

The standard deviation of the calculated photosynthetic rate is given by Brown & Rosenberg (1968) as follows:

1. If the water vapour pressures of the reference and sample air streams differ widely, a correction of this kind should also be applied to the determination of ΔC in Eqs. (3.19) to (3.21).
2. For a calculation of the error of F determination in an unstirred assimilation chamber see also Gulyaev, Manuil'skiĭ & Okanenko 1970.

Table 3.4 The amount of CO_2 in mg per litre in air of different CO_2 concentration [$\mu l\ l^{-1}$ = vpm] at different temperatures and a pressure of 1 013.25 mb, *i.e.* 760 torr (calculated after data in Weast 1968).

$\mu l\ l^{-1}$ (= vpm)	mg $CO_2\ l^{-1}$ (= 10^{-6}g CO_2 cm^{-3} = 10^{-3} kg CO_2 m^{-3})					
	10°C	15°C	20°C	25°C	30°C	35°C
180	0.343	0.337	0.332	0.326	0.321	0.315
200	0.381	0.375	0.368	0.362	0.356	0.350
220	0.420	0.412	0.405	0.398	0.392	0.385
240	0.458	0.450	0.442	0.435	0.427	0.420
260	0.496	0.487	0.479	0.471	0.463	0.456
280	0.534	0.525	0.516	0.507	0.499	0.491
300	0.572	0.562	0.553	0.543	0.534	0.526
320	0.610	0.600	0.589	0.580	0.570	0.561
340	0.648	0.637	0.626	0.616	0.606	0.596
360	0.686	0.675	0.663	0.652	0.641	0.631
380	0.725	0.712	0.700	0.688	0.677	0.666
400	0.763	0.750	0.737	0.724	0.712	0.701
420	0.801	0.787	0.774	0.761	0.748	0.736
440	0.839	0.825	0.810	0.797	0.784	0.771
460	0.877	0.862	0.847	0.833	0.819	0.806
480	0.915	0.900	0.884	0.869	0.855	0.841
500	0.954	0.937	0.921	0.906	0.891	0.876
520	0.992	0.974	0.958	0.942	0.926	0.911
540	1.030	1.012	0.995	0.978	0.962	0.946
560	1.068	1.049	1.032	1.014	0.997	0.981
580	1.106	1.087	1.068	1.050	1.033	1.016
600	1.144	1.124	1.105	1.087	1.069	1.051
650	1.240	1.218	1.197	1.177	1.158	1.139
700	1.335	1.312	1.289	1.268	1.247	1.226
750	1.430	1.405	1.382	1.358	1.336	1.314
800	1.526	1.499	1.474	1.449	1.425	1.402
850	1.621	1.593	1.566	1.539	1.514	1.489
900	1.716	1.687	1.658	1.630	1.603	1.577
950	1.812	1.780	1.750	1.720	1.692	1.664
1000	1.907	1.874	1.842	1.811	1.781	1.752
1100	2.098	2.061	2.026	1.992	1.959	1.927
1200	2.288	2.249	2.210	2.173	2.137	2.102
1300	2.479	2.436	2.395	2.354	2.315	2.278
1400	2.670	2.623	2.579	2.535	2.493	2.453
1500	2.861	2.811	2.763	2.717	2.672	2.628
1600	3.051	2.998	2.947	2.898	2.850	2.803
1700	3.242	3.186	3.131	3.079	3.028	2.978

Table 3.4 *(continued)*

Correction of the above values for different atmospheric pressures. The above values are to be multiplied by the factors given below:

torr	= mb	0	2	4	6	8
700	933.26	0.9211	0.9237	0.9263	0.9289	0.9316
710	946.59	0.9342	0.9368	0.9395	0.9421	0.9447
720	959.92	0.9474	0.9500	0.9526	0.9553	0.9579
730	973.25	0.9605	0.9632	0.9658	0.9684	0.9711
740	986.59	0.9737	0.9763	0.9789	0.9816	0.9842
750	999.92	0.9868	0.9895	0.9921	0.9947	0.9974
760	1013.25	1.0000	1.0026	1.0053	1.0079	1.0105
770	1026.58	1.0132	1.0158	1.0184	1.0211	1.0237

$$\sigma F = \sqrt{\left(\frac{\partial F}{\partial \Delta C} \cdot \sigma \Delta C\right)^2 + \left(\frac{\partial F}{\partial J} \cdot \sigma J\right)^2 + \left(\frac{\partial F}{\partial A} \cdot \sigma A\right)^2} \tag{3.24}$$

where σF, $\sigma \Delta C$, σJ, and σA, respectively, are standard deviations of photosynthetic rate, of the difference in CO_2 concentrations at the inlet and at the outlet of the assimilation chamber, of the flow rate, and of the leaf area.
The partial deviations for the Eq. (3.20) are as follows:

$$\frac{\partial F}{\partial \Delta C} = \frac{\mathrm{K}J}{A} \tag{3.25}$$

$$\frac{\partial F}{\partial J} = \frac{\mathrm{K}\Delta C}{A} \tag{3.26}$$

$$\frac{\partial F}{\partial A} = \frac{-\mathrm{K}J\Delta C}{A^2} \tag{3.27}$$

Substituting these expressions into equation (3.21) yields:

$$\sigma F = \sqrt{\left(\frac{\mathrm{K}J\sigma\Delta C}{A}\right)^2 + \left(\frac{\mathrm{K}\Delta C\sigma J}{A}\right)^2 + \left(\frac{-\mathrm{K}J\Delta C\sigma A}{A^2}\right)^2} \tag{3.28}$$

When ΔC is evaluated by subtraction from two measurements with an absolute IRGA, the error term must be attached to both measured values. The standard deviation associated with ΔC can thus be evaluated and substituted into the above procedure to determine the error to be attached to F:

$$\Delta C = C_{\mathrm{inlet}} - C_{\mathrm{outlet}} \tag{3.29}$$

Since

$$\frac{\partial \Delta C}{\partial C_{\mathrm{inlet}}} = 1 \tag{3.30}$$

and

$$\frac{\partial \Delta C}{\partial C_{outlet}} = -1 \tag{3.31}$$

$$\sigma \Delta C = \sqrt{(\sigma C_{inlet})^2 + (-\sigma C_{outlet})^2} \tag{3.32}$$

Assuming the same range (sensitivity) of both the differential and the absolute IRGAs, in the latter case the standard error increases by a function of the square root of 2.

Examples of standard deviations for the photosynthetic rate calculated from hypothetical values, assuming different kinds of measurement, are shown in Table 3.5.

Table 3.5 Standard deviations of the values of photosynthetic rate calculated from hypothetical values of CO_2 concentration, air flow rate, and leaf area, determined with different precision.

Scale of IRGA [vpm]	Kind of measurement	Deflection of the recorder [vpm]	Hypothetical precision of the determination of			Standard deviation of the calculated value of photosynthetic rate [%]
			CO_2 concentration (% of IRGA's full-scale reading)*	air-flow rate (% of the estimated value)	leaf area (% of the estimated value)	
0–50, background 300 vpm	differential	30	±1	±3	±1	± 3.6*
			±2	±5	±1	± 5.4**
			±2	±5	±2	± 5.7
0–100, background 300 vpm	differential	30	±1	±3	±1	± 4.6
			±2	±5	±1	± 7.9
			±2	±5	±2	± 8.1
260–310	absolute	300 (inlet)	±1	±3	±1	± 3.9
		1-270 (outlet)	±2	±5	±1	± 6.4
			±2	±5	±2	± 6.6
250–500	absolute	300 (inlet)	±1	±3	±1	±12.2
		270 (outlet)	±2	±5	±1	±22.2
			±2	±5	±2	±22.3
0–500	absolute	300 (inlet)	±1	±3	±1	±22.0
		270 (outlet)	±2	±5	±1	±47.5
			±2	±5	±2	±47.6***

* The error of the determination of CO_2 concentration is given by the precision of the IRGA, *i.e.* reproducibility (usually 1% of the full-scale reading) and by the calibration accuracy (usually ± 2% of the full-scale reading) which is not taken into account in this table. The values in this column represent the reproducibility expressed in % of full-scale reading (*e.g.* 30 ± 0.5 vpm for the first line [*] and 30 ± 1 vpm for the second line [**] and *e.g.* 300 ± 10 vpm and 270 ± 10 vpm for the last line [***]). The calibration accuracy is usually given by the manufacturer ± 2% of the full-scale reading; however, in practice, the error can be several times higher (*cf.* p. 152 and Chartier 1970).

3.13 | Use of infra-red gas analysers in the field

The problems arising in connection with the use of IRGAs in the field are of two kinds: those arising from the special working conditions prevailing in the field, and those arising from the use of the IRGA in the gas flow system in the field.

3.13.1 | Working conditions in the field

Unstable environmental conditions, a variable power supply and the need to pack instruments closely together in small mobile laboratories are the causes of some of the most serious problems arising in the field (see *e.g.* Bosian 1955; Went 1958; Friedrich & Schmidt 1963; Neuwirth 1965; Eckardt 1966, 1967, 1968; Lange, Koch & Schulze 1969; Mooney *et al.* 1971).

For the comfort and performance of both personnel and instruments it is desirable that the temperature of the laboratory be maintained within fairly narrow limits around 20 °C, and for this reason the laboratory should be equipped with normal thermostatic or air conditioning equipment. Depending on the dimensions and the insulation of the laboratory the latter may draw 2 kVA or more, in particular in a hot climate. If the laboratory is not being operated from the electrical grid but from mobile A.C. generators, it is desirable to have a separate generator for thermostatting the laboratory so as to avoid large fluctuations in both voltage and frequency if such a large load is being switched in and out at irregular intervals. In temperate environments where only intermittent heating is required, 1 kVA of heating is usually adequate. With a 6 kVA generator followed by a voltage stabiliser, the switching in and out of the load[1] does not cause the voltage to fluctuate more than 2% and a single generator will suffice. Proportional controllers can be used to eliminate large voltage fluctuations.

If the IRGA is internally thermostatted, as most are, slow fluctuations of 5 °C or more in the ambient temperature do not appreciably affect its accuracy. If the ambient conditions in the laboratory are fluctuating more than this, it may be necessary to enclose the IRGA in a thermostatted cupboard. Rack-mounting in the conventional manner also provides quite effective insulation against ambient temperature fluctuations.

Although very stable voltage supplies, often more stable than the grid, can be obtained from small A.C. generators, the output frequency (Hz) is far from stable. Stability of the frequency can be improved by the addition of expensive hydraulically controlled flywheels but the stability obtained is still unlikely to be satisfactory for frequency-dependent components, such as the mechanical chopper in most IRGAs. The fluctuating frequency from a 6 kVA generator has been found to lead to apparent rhythmic fluctuations in CO_2 concentration of 2 vpm or $\mu l\, l^{-1}$. Such fluctuations are too large to be tolerated. Hence the IRGA can be driven by batteries through a solid state DC-AC transverter. [A transverter is a transistorised D.C. to A.C. converter or inverter consisting of a transistorised oscillator and voltage regulator (produced *e.g.* by *Valradio Ltd.*, Feltham, Middx., U.K., or *Sorensen-Ard AG*, Zürich, Switzerland).] The batteries are continuously trickle-

1. A proportional controller will not have this effect.

charged by the generator, as described in Section 3.7.2. To reduce the battery and transverter capacity required to a minimum, the IRGA thermostat circuit may be supplied separately, directly by the generator. In some circumstances, the batteries may not be necessary. By connecting the converter directly to the generator a frequency stability of $\pm$ 0.1 to 0.2 Hz may be obtained when the voltage varies $\pm$ 15%.

Some makes of IRGA are quite sensitive to vibration; others are not. For use in mobile laboratories, sensitivity to vibration is a considerable disadvantage since a solid mounting is difficult to provide (it can be done by mounting the IRGA on a frame which passes through the floor into the ground). Anti-vibration mountings such as springs and rubber blocks help to reduce errors resulting from the vibrations which may occur in phase with the chopper.

As in the laboratory, the IRGA case should be flushed with nitrogen or dry air to maintain constant CO_2 and water vapour concentrations within the case. If large variations in ambient CO_2 result from the presence of a number of people working in a small space it may be necessary to seal the IRGA in a nitrogen-filled plastic sack. These precautions do not apply to IRGAs with sealed optical shutters.

Spurious signals from other electrical installations can be reduced by proper shielding and earthing of the instruments in the field laboratory, by the use of low voltage D.C. relays in preference to other types of relays, by keeping separate power- and signal-carrying cables, and by shielding the signal-carrying cables.

3.13.2 | Use of IRGAs in gas flow systems

The IRGA is commonly used in the field for the measurement or control of CO_2 or water vapour concentrations. It may be used in open, semi-open or closed circuits (Chapter 2), and in connexion with the eddy flux, profile (Chapter 13) and assimilation chamber (Chapters 2 and 3) methods. Problems associated with the use of the IRGA in the laboratory also arise, sometimes in a more exaggerated form, in the field. Only those problems particularly associated with field applications will be treated here. A more general treatment is given in Chapter 2 and other parts of this chapter.

Apart from the eddy correlation method, which is in its infancy, all methods involve transporting gas samples to the IRGA over considerable distances, in circuits consisting of long lengths of tubing, and including flow meters, valves, pumps, damping vessels *etc.*

As in the laboratory, leakage of CO_2 into or out of the circuit must be reduced to a minimum. However in the field this is not so easy because of the long lengths of tubing involved and the possibility of appreciable CO_2 diffusion through the walls of the tubing between sampling point and analyser. Hence only tubing which is extremely impermeable to CO_2 should be used (see Section 3.8.2). Small bore tubing, taps, valves *etc.* should be kept to a minimum since they may result in an appreciable pressure drop down the circuit with increased possibilities of leakage. The circuit should be designed carefully from this point of view since large sections with many junctions at pressures appreciably below atmospheric are clearly undesirable. If a number of points or chambers are being sampled sequentially by one analyser, one clearly has a choice between a single main pump continuously drawing all samples to the vicinity of the analyser, the samples being below atmospheric pressure between sampling point and pump, and a number of pumps, one per sample line, pushing the samples, at above atmospheric pressure, from sampling point to the vicinity of the analyser.

In all cases protection against dust and large pressure changes is important. Air pumps should be fitted with dust filters (see Section 3.8.7) and excess pressure valves. Flow meters and valves should be present in the circuit just before the IRGA to prevent pressure changes in the analyser cells when switching from one circuit to another. Some manufacturers will supply constant pressure regulators for the IRGA to ensure that large pressure fluctuations cannot occur. A simple alternative is a manometer connected across the outlet to ensure that both reference and sample tubes are at the same pressure.

Another considerable problem associated with the use of long lengths of tubing is the danger of condensation of water vapour which may affect measurements, not only of air humidity but also of CO_2 concentration since CO_2 is readily absorbed in water. Condensation may be prevented by placing all the sample tubes inside a wider tube through which warm air (or a liquid) is circulated. By introducing nitrogen into the wide tube and analysing it for CO_2 and H_2O it is further possible to check for leaks in the circuits. When using metal tubes, heating can be achieved by applying a low voltage current to the ends of the tubes. Alternatively a nichrome wire may be passed down each tube or industrial heating tape wound round the sample tubes, the whole bundle then enclosed in a conduit of some kind. Whilst condensation is the major problem, the absorption and desorption of water on the walls of the tubing especially poses a further problem in the precise determination of humidity. For this reason, in the laboratory it is desirable to maintain all parts of the circuit at constant temperature and this is most easily obtained by thermostatting the room. (It is readily shown with a sensitive humidity sensor that a change in room temperature of a few degrees can lead to apparent changes in transpiration resulting from this phenomenon.) In the field this is not possible and it must be accepted that changes in the amount of adsorbed water with changes in temperature may result in some loss of precision in the determination of humidity.

Because of the turbulent structure of the atmosphere, CO_2 concentration at a given point at normal working height above the ground is always characterised by large fluctuations involving a large spectrum of frequencies. These fluctuations often make it extremely difficult to compare air samples of different origin. The fluctuations can be damped by passing the air through big containers, preferably fitted inside with an electric fan. For sample collection rates of 3 l min^{-1}, containers of about 25 l capacity are usually adequate to absorb the fluctuations.

In some circumstances it may be necessary to know the concentration of CO_2 at several sample points simultaneously. This is the case if instantaneous profiles are being used in the profile method (Chapter 13). One way of solving this problem is to use circuits of different length and volume so that air samples taken in at the same time arrive at the analyser at different times and so can be analysed sequentially. Another way is to store the air between the time of sampling and the time of analysis (but see Section 3.13.3). However, when short term variations in CO_2 concentration are not of interest or the calculations of CO_2 exchange are made using mean values obtained by averaging over periods such as an hour, simultaneous measurements are less important and this source of error can be considerably reduced by the use of large damping containers.

One grave disadvantage of the use of assimilation chambers in open circuit (Section 2.2.3) in the field (not to mention changes in the radiation environment and in momentum exchange), is that two of the principal factors affecting photosynthesis and transpiration, the CO_2 and water vapour content of the air, are necessarily changed, and the influence which these changes have on the rates of the processes cannot readily be evaluated in retrospect. Hence the changes in CO_2 and water vapour concentration occurring during the passage of the air through the chamber should be kept as small as possible. This can be done to a limited extent by adjustment of the rate of air flow. However the differences in concentration cannot be made very small without resulting in relatively inaccurate estimation of the rates of the processes (see Sections 3.9 and 3.10).

Changes in CO_2 and water vapour content of the air can to some extent be reduced by pretreatment of the air (see Section 2.6). However most of the advantages of the simple open circuit are then lost and recycling of the air in a closed circuit is to be preferred.

Closed circuits (Sections 2.2.1 and 2.7) are now widely used in the field. The role of the IRGA in a closed circuit is to control, and not to measure, the concentration of CO_2 and water vapour in the assimilation chamber. In a closed system, CO_2 and water vapour concentrations in the chamber very close to those outside are attained under steady conditions although some hunting in the control system is unavoidable and it is impossible to obtain both high accuracy and high stability. Under changing, variable weather conditions, however, the construction of the IRGA, the tubing, valves, volume of the chamber *etc.* must all result in appreciable lags in the control system, leading to less than perfect simulation of ambient conditions within the chamber.

3.13.3 | The 'beach-ball' technique

In some circumstances in which taking the IRGA into the field has not been possible, perhaps because no field laboratory was available, or was not thought warranted, perhaps because it was also in use in the laboratory, samples have been collected in the field and their concentration measured back at the laboratory.

A simple way to collect the samples is to inflate empty plastic containers with the air to be analysed, using membrane pumps. The method has become known as the 'beach-ball' technique because P.V.C. beach balls were amongst the first plastic containers to be successfully used (*e.g.* Hunt, Impens & Lemon 1967). Samples can be collected at different heights above the ground for use in the profile method (Chapter 13) or they can be collected into the containers after having passed through an assimilation chamber. In either case the concentration which is measured is an average concentration integrated over the period during which the sample is collected and hence leads to a determination of average rate of the process for that period. Samples can be collected simultaneously and analysed sequentially.

Two main problems arise concerned with the plastic containers. Firstly, the material must be such that rapid diffusion of CO_2 does not occur through the walls

between the time of collection and the time of measurement. Secondly, the material must be such that CO_2 can be readily cleaned off its internal surface so that previously collected samples do not significantly influence those currently being collected. On no account should one ever breathe into such a container as it is almost impossible to remove all traces of high CO_2 concentrations.
Since the original use of P.V.C., a number of other plastics have been used singly or in a laminated construction (*e.g.* polyethylene, *Mylar* and aluminium foil; Lourence & Pruitt, 1967). Materials suitable for making storage bags for mixtures of CO_2 in air in the laboratory (*e.g. Propafilm C*; coated polypropylene from *I.C.I.*) are also suitable.

3.14 Simultaneous and continuous determination of oxygen and carbon dioxide in an open system

Simultaneous observation of oxygen and carbon dioxide exchange and the calculation of CO_2 and O_2 ratios in an open system raise experimental difficulties (for review of the appropriate methods see Tables 1.1 and 1.2).
Bassham, Shibata & Calvin (1955) and Yuan, Evans & Daniels (1955) combined an infra-red CO_2 analyser with a paramagnetic oxygen analyser in a closed circuit system, but the oxygen meter measured only a difference of 1 or 2% O_2 over the recorder scale and was not sensitive enough for open system experiments (see also Weigl, Warrington & Calvin 1951). A paramagnetic oxygen analyser of suitable sensitivity has been developed only recently (*e.g.* Luft & Mohrmann 1967; Luft, Kesseler & Zörner 1967). This has made it possible to combine it with an IRGA in an open system and obtain simultaneous, continuous, and precise oxygen and carbon dioxide readings in steady state as well as transient studies (Section 3.14.1). Another new highly sensitive oxygen analyser is zirconium oxide ceramic cell (Section 3.14.2).

3.14.1 Paramagnetic oxygen analyser

For the determination of small oxygen differences a paramagnetic oxygen analyser is usually used (for references see Egle 1960, pp. 155–158). The analyser *OXYGOR*, made by *Maihak AG.* (Hamburg, Germany), has been used in the installation described later.[1] The O_2 analyser of this kind is based on the fact that oxygen has paramagnetic properties and is attracted in the direction of an increasing non-homogeneous magnetic field. This attractive force, which is related to the volumetric oxygen concentration but is independent of nitrogen and carbon dioxide, may be utilized for measuring devices. The oxygen analyser operates on the principle of pressure differences between two oxygen-containing gases of different magnetic susceptibility.
A functional diagram of the paramagnetic oxygen analyser is shown in Fig. 3.41. The reference gas is passed through the two branches of the flow channel *(1)*. Before leaving the measuring device, the reference gas is flushed through opposite

1. The authors thank Dr. K. F. Luft of the *Berbau-Forschung GmbH*, 43 Essen-Kray, who kindly supplied a prototype oxygen analyser, for helpful advice and discussion.

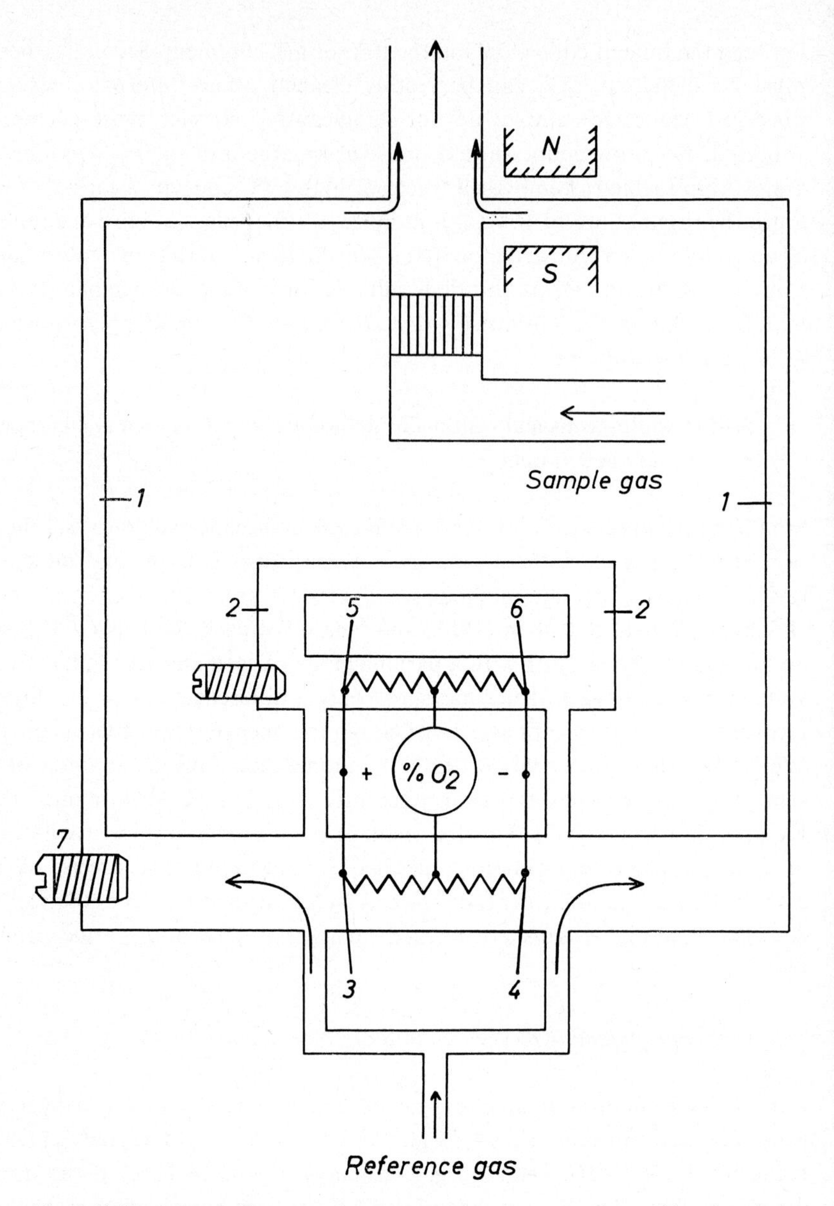

Fig. 3.41 Functional diagram of paramagnetic oxygen analyser. For description see text. (Courtesy of *Maihak A.G.*, Hamburg).

slits, one of which is located in a strong, inhomogeneous magnetic field, into the sample gas channel and is mixed together with the sample gas. The flow resistances of the two branches *(1)* are adjusted *(7)* so that the two reference gas streams are symmetrical, if sample and reference gas have the same magnetic susceptibility. As the oxygen partial pressure in the sample gas increases, it is attracted by the magnetic field and partly blocks the reference gas flowing through the outlet arranged in the magnetic field. Consequently, back-pressures are created, the flow system is unbalanced, and pressure differences between the two outlet slits are induced. These cause cross flow of reference gas over the thermo-sensor *(3, 4)*

and differential cooling across the thermo-sensor halves, which are located in two arms of a Wheatstone bridge. The temperature change unbalances the Wheatstone bridge and produces an electrical signal that is proportional to the difference in oxygen content of sample and reference gas.
Convection flow due to the location of the analyser may induce bridge resistance changes, but these are compensated by the thermo-sensor *(5, 6)* in the flow channel *(2)*.

3.14.1.1 Experimental system with a paramagnetic oxygen analyser

A system designed by Schaub, Hilgenberg & Fock (1968) will be presented here as an example (Fig. 3.42).
Gas of a definite known oxygen concentration was obtained by flushing nitrogen from one tank into another with a known volume of oxygen, the final excess pressure being 100 atm. The actual oxygen partial pressure of the gas mixture was measured with a polarographic Clark electrode, which was calibrated with standard gases delivered from accurate gas mixing pumps *(MP)*. The error of the oxygen determination did not exceed 0.1 % O_2 (Fock, Schaub & Hilgenberg 1968). A gas stream from a tank with an outlet pressure of 1.2–1.3 atmospheres, was bubbled through a CO_2 absorber *(C)* and then dried *(D_1)*. The gas stream was divided and one portion (0.6–0.7 l h^{-1}) was reduced to exactly 1 atm by means of a precision pressure regulating valve *(P)*, passed through a second drying agent (D_2), and was used as reference gas in the O_2 analyser.

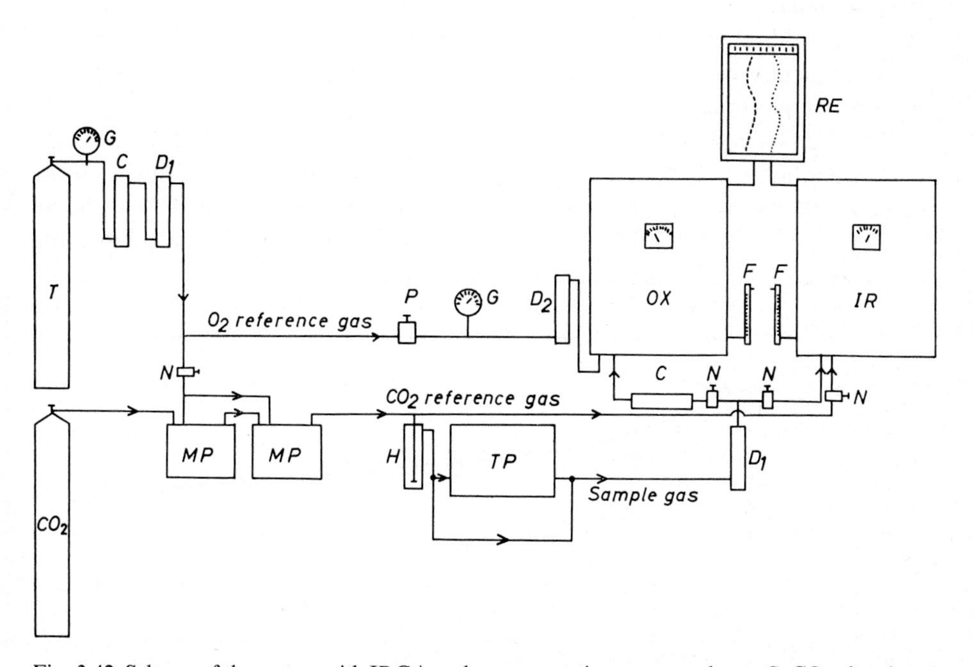

Fig. 3.42 Scheme of the system with IRGA and paramagnetic oxygen analyser. *C:* CO_2 absorber, *CO_2:* cylinder with CO_2, *D_1:* drier with $CaCl_2$, *D_2:* drier with magnesium perchlorate, *F:* flow meter, *G:* pressure gauge, *H:* wash tower with distilled water, *IR:* IRGA, *MP:* mixing pump, *N:* needle valve, *OX:* oxygen analyser, *P:* precision pressure regulating valve, *RE:* recorder, *T:* vessel with gas mixture, *TP:* assimilation chamber.

Carbon dioxide at any concentration was generated with two or three gas mixing pumps *(MP)* connected in series, and was introduced into the main gas stream at atmospheric pressure. A portion of this gas mixture ($10\ l\ h^{-1}$) served as reference gas in the IRGA, while the remainder ($28\ l\ h^{-1}$) was flushed through a wash tower with distilled water *(H)* into the transparent assimilation chamber *(TP)*, which could be by-passed. Thus pressure changes which strongly interfered with the signal of the O_2 analyser were compensated.
After leaving the assimilation chamber, the air was dried *(D_1)* and passed through the IRGA *(IR)* and the oxygen analyser *(OX)* which were connected in parallel. The CO_2 of the gas entering the oxygen analyser was absorbed *(C)* in order to avoid dilution of the oxygen partial pressure by carbon dioxide. The readings from the IRGA and from the paramagnetic instrument were continuously recorded on a two pen recorder *(RE)*.
The open system apparatus allows the simultaneous and independent operation of the CO_2 and O_2 analysers. The accuracy and reliability of this method is dependent on such factors as constancy of gas composition, of gas pressure, of flow rate, on drift of baseline, sensitivity, precision of analyser calibration, and on several other variables. With sufficient precautions, good results were obtained in laboratories with air conditioning.
The O_2 analyser responded at highest sensitivity to a difference of approximately 1000 ppm O_2 with full scale deflection, almost independently of the oxygen concentration in the reference gas (Fig. 3.43). For simultaneous CO_2 and O_2 measurements, the IRGA was adjusted to a similar range of CO_2 concentrations as the oxygen meter.
Analyser calibration charts were drawn up in the laboratory and the analysers were frequently calibrated with standard gases delivered from a series of gas mixing pumps (Fock 1965).
The above system has been used to measure the oxygen and CO_2 exchange rate (*e.g.* Brunnhöfer, Schaub & Egle 1968a, b; Fock *et al.* 1969); it was found that the response of the oxygen analyser is fast and the lag is short enough to analyse certain light-dark and dark-light transients, if the volumes of the tubing, the absorber, and the assimilation chamber are minimized.

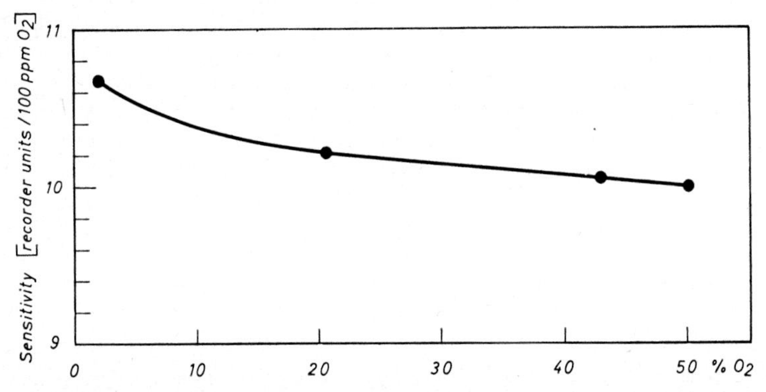

Fig. 3.43 Correlation between sensitivity of the paramagnetic oxygen analyser *Oxygor* and O_2 concentration in reference gas. In the range used (differential of 0–1 000 vpm O_2) the analyser output depends linearly on O_2 differential between sample and reference gas.

3.14.2 | Oxygen analyser with zirconium oxide ceramic cell

A new oxygen analyser, exploiting the high ionic conductivity to oxygen of calcium-stabilised zirconium, was tested and recommended for its application to measurements of higher plant photosynthesis by Björkman & Gauhl (1970).

Description of the oxygen sensor. The sensor, used also in *Model 209 oxygen monitor (Westinghouse Electr. Co.*, Pittsburgh, Pa.), consists of a nonporous tube of a calcium-stabilised zirconium oxide ceramic to which porous electrodes are attached. It is also equipped with a furnace operating at about 850 °C. This temperature is kept constant with a solid-state proportional controller.

The gas to be analysed is admitted to one side of the ceramic tube and reference gas to the other side. Oxygen molecules on the side with the higher O_2 pressure gain electrons to become ions, while simultaneously on the other side, oxygen molecules are formed by reverse action. The potential V of the cell (in volts) is then given (Burke 1968) by

$$V = \frac{\mathrm{R}T}{n\,\mathrm{F}} \ln \left(\frac{P_s}{P_r} \right) \tag{3.33}$$

where

R is the gas constant [= 8.314 4 $\mathrm{JK^{-1}\ mol^{-1}}$],

T is the operating temperature of the cell [K],

F is Faraday's constant [= 9.648 8 × 10^4 coulomb $\mathrm{mol^{-1}}$],

n is the number of equivalents per unit electrode reaction (which is equal to 4),

P_s is the partial pressure of O_2 in the sample gas,

P_r is the partial pressure of O_2 in the reference gas.

At the operating temperature used by Björkman & Gauhl (1970), 1 110 K, the open circuit potential in millivolts is then

$$V = 55 \log \left(\frac{P_s}{P_r} \right) \tag{3.34}$$

As evident from Eqs. (3.33) and (3.34) the cell voltage is a logarithmic function of the ratio between the O_2 pressure in the sample and that in the reference gas. This relationship was found to be valid over a wide range of O_2 pressures (0.05 to 760 mm Hg).

The cell voltage is unaffected by the presence of noncombustible gases such as water vapour and carbon dioxide, but care has to be taken not to introduce combustible gases into the cell since at the high operating temperature these will react with oxygen and reduce its concentration.

Since the output voltage of the cell is a logarithmic function of the ratio between the partial pressure of O_2 in the sample and that in the reference gas, O_2 concentrations over several orders of magnitude can be measured. The sensitivity of the device decreases strongly with increasing O_2 concentration. A sufficient sensitivity (of about 1 vpm) can be obtained at CO_2 concentrations of less than 2000 vpm O_2. Because of this, Björkman & Gauhl (1970) used in their open system gas from a cylinder containing 825 vpm CO_2, 1500 vpm O_2, and 99.7% N_2. At this concentra-

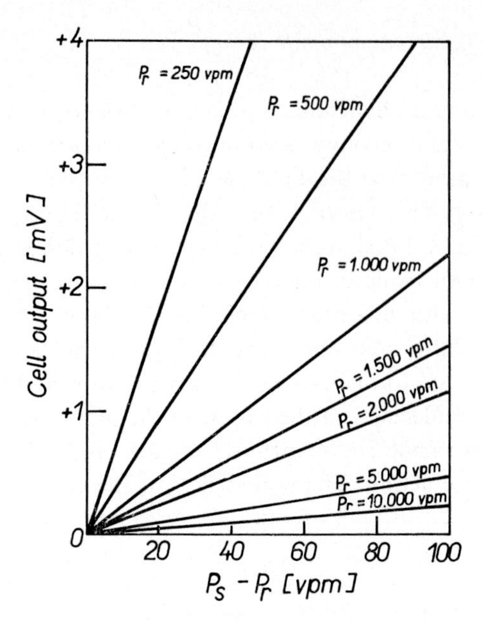

Fig. 3.44 The open cell circuit voltage (ordinate) as a function of the difference in oxygen concentrations between the sample and the reference gas (abscissa), at different O_2 concentrations in the reference gas (values P_r). (From Björkman & Gauhl 1970.)

tion the sensitivity of the device was sufficiently high (Fig. 3.44) and there was no evidence of adverse metabolic effects that might be caused by anaerobic conditions. As shown in Fig. 3.44, the relationship between the O_2 concentration and the cell voltage is very close to linear in this narrow range.

Measuring equipment. The output voltage of the O_2 cell is measured with a micro-voltmeter (*e.g. Keithley Model 150 B)* and the amplified signal displayed with a dual channel potentiometric recorder (*e.g. Hewlett-Packard 7100 BM).*

Performance of the zirconium analyser. With the above O_2 concentrations the noise level of the output voltage from the O_2 cell is very low. The estimated signal to noise ratio of the amplified and recorded signal is about 500 to 1. A change in concentration of 0.2 vpm can easily be detected when the O_2 concentration is kept at about 1500 vpm. Under these same conditions the baseline drift is 1% of f.s.d. over a 10 h period. These data suggest that a considerably higher amplification factor could be used while a tolerable noise level could still be maintained.

The zirconium oxide O_2 analyser is completely unaffected by vibrations from pumps and other equipment. It is also unaffected by considerable changes (some $\pm$ 5 °C) in the ambient temperature. Another attractive feature is that no elaborate calibrations are needed. The response of the cell to changes in O_2 concentration can readily be predicted from Eq. 3.34. The response time of the O_2 cell itself is, according to the manufacturer, only 1 millisecond.

Use in photosynthesis studies. A particularly valuable feature of the O_2 cell is its complete insensitivity to CO_2 which greatly simplifies measurements of the dependence of photosynthesis on CO_2 concentration, and of photosynthetic responses under saturating CO_2 concentrations where the infra-red CO_2 analyser has a relatively poor resolution.

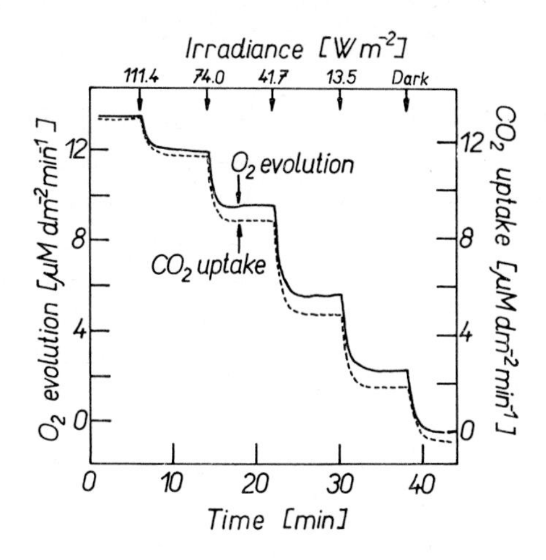

Fig. 3.45 Recorder traces of the time courses of O_2 evolution and CO_2 uptake in a *Mimulus verbenaceus* Greene leaf. The leaf was subjected to decreases in irradiance. The leaf temperature was 25 °C, the CO_2 concentration in the leaf chamber approx. 800 vpm. (From Björkman & Gauhl 1970.)

Because of its insufficient sensitivity at high O_2 concentrations, the zirconium oxide cell is of limited usefulness in photosynthesis measurements under field conditions and in studies on the inhibitory effect of O_2 on net photosynthesis ('photorespiration' studies). It is, however, probably the best instrument currently available for kinetic studies of higher plant photosynthesis under low oxygen concentrations where reoxidation of photosynthetic products in the light is inhibited. An example of measurements in an open system, in which the zirconium oxide cell and a *Beckman* Model 215 IRGA were used to measure the exchange of O_2 and CO_2, respectively, is given in Fig. 3.45.

3.15 Katharometric (diaferometric) determination of carbon dioxide, oxygen, and water vapour[1]

Gas analysis by the katharometer (diaferometer, or hot wire method) is based on differences in the thermal conductivity of gases. This apparatus has not been used intensively in plant physiological work, because of the difficulties encountered at the required high sensitivity in commercially available apparatus.

However, when adequately designed, the advantage of the katharometer is that it can be an instrument of simple design, with no moving parts, relatively cheap, trouble-free and easy to use.

The katharometer, described here, has such highly improved qualities. Its sensitivity matches that of the IRGA, and its response time is very short.

1. 278th Communication from the Laboratory of Plant Physiological Research, Agricultural University, Wageningen.

Acknowledgement: Sincere thanks may be expressed here to Dr. K. Schurer, physicist of the Technical and Physical Engineering Research Service for his interest and advice, and to the technical Staff of that Institute for manufacturing the apparatus.

3.15.1 | Principle

One of the physical properties of gases, by which they can be identified, or by which their concentration can be measured, is their thermal conductivity. A wire, heated by an electric current to incandescence, can be cooled down by replacing the surrounding air by hydrogen. This experiment of Andrews in 1840 can be regarded as the origin of the hot wire method (Daynes 1933). Further improvements of the katharometer are described by Noyons (1935), Maas (1938) and Burg & Stolwijk (1959). (For the use of a katharometer in connection with a diffusion porometer see Milthorpe & Penman 1967. For other references see Egle 1960, p. 148.)
The temperature of the wire changes as a result of changes in the composition of the gas. The change of temperature can be measured by the change of the resistance of the wire.
In addition to the conductivity of the gas mixture, many other physical and geometrical factors determine the temperature of the wire. Therefore, the system comprising the hot wire and its environment should be well defined. This can be done by stretching the wires in channels drilled in a brass block.
To eliminate variability with time, measurement is generally made of the temperature difference between two identical wires in identical channels, one flushed with a reference gas, the other with the gas of which the change in composition is to be measured. This suggests the use of the Wheatstone bridge.

3.15.2 | Theory

3.15.2.1 | The Wheatstone bridge

Comparison of the temperatures of the wires is most suitably done in a Wheatstone bridge with four hot wires (Fig. 3.46). Considering the katharometer adjusted to be fully symmetrical (see Section 3.15.3 Adjustments), we may neglect R_3,R_4, R_5, R_6, R_7 and R_8. Thus we assume that the bridge consists only of the resistances R_1 and R_2. Hence, it is easily seen that the electromotive force in the Wheatstone bridge is:

$$\mathrm{EMF} = V_1 - V_2 = V_0 \frac{R_1 - R_2}{R_1 + R_2} = V_0 \frac{\alpha(\mathrm{d}t_1 - \mathrm{d}t_2)R_t}{R_t\{2 + \alpha(\mathrm{d}t_1 + \mathrm{d}t_2)\}} \simeq V_0 \frac{\alpha(\mathrm{d}t_1 - \mathrm{d}t_2)}{2} \quad (3.35)$$

R_t the resistance of each of the four wires, when flushed with reference gas,
R_1 the resistance of each of wires 1 when flushed with the gas to be measured,
R_2 the resistance of each of wires 2 when flushed with reference gas, while the wires 1 are flushed with the gas to be measured,
$\mathrm{d}t_1$ and $\mathrm{d}t_2$ the corresponding small temperature changes,
α the temperature coefficient of the resistivity of the material of the wire (tungsten): $\alpha = 0.0045\,°\mathrm{C}$,
V_0 the stabilised supply voltage to the bridge,
V_1 the voltage drop over each of the wires 1,
V_2 the voltage drop over each of the wires 2.

3.15.2.2 Heat balance of the hot wire system

Heat dissipation by radiation and end-cooling of the wires is less than 1% and can be neglected. But free and forced convection contribute much to the heat balance and can be estimated roughly by the Nusselt number. Estimation of the Nusselt number gives in this case Nu = 2.2, which means that heat is transported by convection and conduction in the ratio (Nu–1)/1 (Gröber, Erk & Grigull 1963). We may suppose that energy transport by convection is only slightly influenced by the conductivity of the gas mixture, so that the following equations approximately describe the situation.

Measuring wire 1:

$$\frac{V_1^2}{R_1} = \frac{V_0^2(1 + \alpha \mathrm{d}t_1)}{4\,R_t} = \mathrm{k}J\{\Delta t_1 K_1 + (\mathrm{Nu}-1)\Delta t_1 K_0\} \tag{3.36}$$

Reference wire 2:

$$\frac{V_2^2}{R_2} = \frac{V_0^2(1 + \alpha \mathrm{d}t_2)}{4\,R_t} = kJ\{\Delta t_2 K_0 + (\mathrm{Nu}-1)\Delta t_2 K_0\} \tag{3.37}$$

The proportionality factor k can be estimated when the whole system is flushed with reference gas, since:

$$\frac{V_0^2}{4\,R_t} = kJ\Delta t K_0 + (\mathrm{Nu}-1)kJ\Delta t K_0 = \mathrm{Nu}\,kJ\Delta t K_0 \quad \text{or} \quad k = \frac{V_0^2}{4\,Rt\,\mathrm{Nu}\,J\Delta t K_0} \tag{3.38}$$

Subtracting (3.37) from (3.36) and substituting k, we get:

$$\alpha(\mathrm{d}t_1 - \mathrm{d}t_2) = \frac{\Delta t_1 \Delta K + \mathrm{Nu} K_0(\Delta t_1 - \Delta t_2)}{\mathrm{K}_0 \Delta t\,\mathrm{Nu}}$$

or:

$$\mathrm{d}t_1 - \mathrm{d}t_2 = -\frac{\Delta t_1 \Delta K}{\mathrm{Nu} K_0(1 - \alpha\Delta t)} \simeq -\frac{\Delta t \Delta K}{\mathrm{Nu} K_0(1 - \alpha\Delta t)} \tag{3.39}$$

in which:
k is a proportionality factor, depending on the geometry of the system,
$K_1 = K_0 + \Delta K$ is the thermal conductivity of the gas to be measured,
K_0 is the thermal conductivity of the reference gas,
$\Delta t_1 = \Delta t + \mathrm{d}t_1$ is the temperature difference between wire 1 and the block,
$\Delta t_2 = \Delta t + \mathrm{d}t_2$ is the temperature difference between wire 2 and the block,
Δt is the temperature difference between the wires 1 and 2 and the block, when all the channels are flushed with reference gas,
J is the mechanical equivalent of heat.
Δt is easily calculated from the difference in resistance of the wires when heated and not heated. With air as reference gas, for the instrument described, Δt = 80.5 C.

3.15.2.3 Thermal conductivity of gas mixtures

According to Daynes (1933) we put:

$$K_1 = K_0 + p(K' - K_0) \text{ or } K_1 - K_0 = \Delta K = p(K' - K_0) \tag{3.40}$$

p is the partial pressure of the gas to be measured,
K' is the conductivity of the pure gas to be measured.
Daynes (1933) mentions many cases of a non-linear relationship between K_1 and the partial pressures of the constituent gases. But according to our experience, for the physiologically important gases CO_2, O_2 and H_2O in the important concentration ranges, this linear relationship holds.

3.15.2.4 The EMF of the katharometer in relation to the concentration of the gas to be measured

Combining equations (3.35), (3.39) and (3.40), we get

$$\text{EMF} = -\frac{\alpha V p \dfrac{K' - K_0}{K_0} \Delta t}{2\,\text{Nu}(1 - \alpha\Delta t)} = -\frac{\alpha V p \varepsilon \Delta t}{2\,\text{Nu}(1 - \alpha\Delta t)} \tag{3.41}$$

in which $(K' - K_0)/K_0 = \varepsilon$ is the relative difference of conductivity (*cf.* Burg & Stolwijk 1959).

3.15.2.5 Properties of the katharometer

From equation (3.41) it appears that the electrical signal is proportional to α, V, p, ε and $\Delta t/(1 - \alpha\Delta t)$.
The reaction of the apparatus to a change in the reference gas is somewhat complicated, because then not only ε but also Δt changes. If we change over from air as reference gas to air + 5% CO_2, the sensitivity to changes in CO_2 concentration decreases because of decreasing ε (Table 3.7), but increases because of increasing Δt. At the same time, the relative sensitivity to O_2 changes increases, an

Table 3.6 Thermal conductivities of various gases (calculated from Weast 1968).

Gas	Temperature of gas [°C]					
	15.6	26.7	37.8	15.6	26.7	37.8
	10^{-7} cal/s cm² °C/cm			10^{-7} J cm^{-1} s^{-1} K^{-1}		
air	603.4	622.0	642.2	2 526.3	2 604.1	2 687.9
CO_2	376.1	396.7	417.4	1 574.6	1 660.9	1 747.5
O_2	615.8	636.4	659.1	2 578.2	2 664.4	2 759.5
H_2O	405.0	425.7	446.3	1 695.6	1 782.3	1 868.5
He	3 521.0	3 603.6	3 686.3	14 741.7	15 087.5	15 433.8
H_2	4 339.2	4 463.2	4 587.2	18 167.3	18 686.5	19 205.6

effect which, if neglected, can be a disturbing factor in quantitative measurements of photosynthesis. If we change over to He or H_2 as reference gas, the sensitivity ratio $\varepsilon_{O_2}/\varepsilon_{CO_2}$ increases, but the absolute sensitivity decreases, unless compensated by an increasing V_0 (van der Veen 1949; Vejlby 1959).

3.15.3 | Construction of the katharometer

In deriving the above theory of the katharometer we intentionally supposed the katharometer to be perfectly symmetrical. In the majority of katharometers this principle of symmetry has been maintained both in the mechanical and electrical construction. But this symmetry cannot be attained without special facilities for adjustment.

3.15.3.1 | Adjustments

Ambient temperature. Basically each wire records the temperature of the ambient atmosphere. Theoretically, however, the four wires balance each other in this respect, but in reality some sensitivity to ambient temperature remains. To suppress this temperature sensitivity, the dimensions of the katharometer block should be as large as practicable. The material should have a large heat capacity and heat conductivity. The block must be placed in an insulating box.
Sensitive adjustment of this thermal unbalance, however, is achieved by mounting in the block a platinum wire, which can be added to one or the other arm of the Wheatstone bridge, and shunted until temperature insensitivity is accomplished (Fig. 3.46 R_4 and R_5, Fig. 3.47).

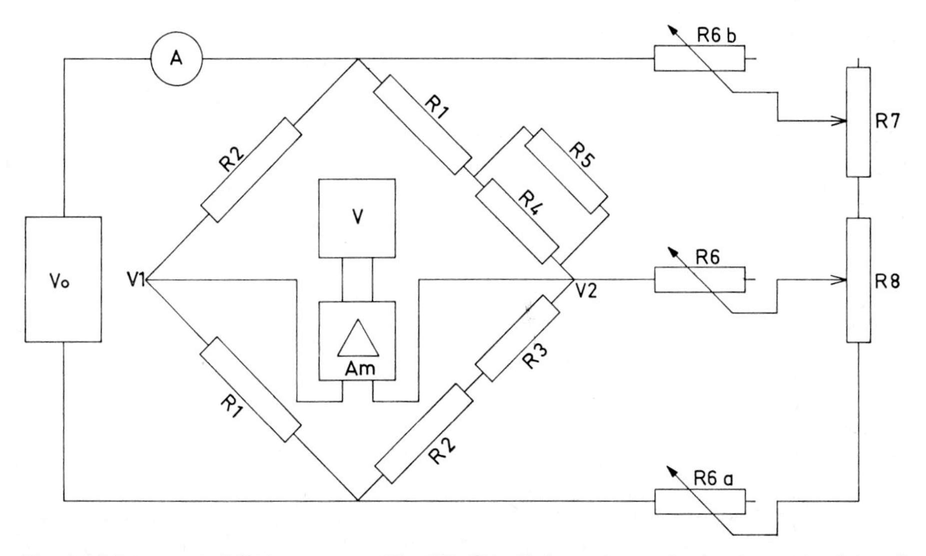

Fig. 3.46 Diagram of katharometer. *R1:* 100 Ω coiled tungsten wire in the measuring cell, *R2:* 100 Ω coiled tungsten wire in the reference cell, *R3:* manganine balancing resistor, *R4:* 10 Ω temp. correction platinum wire, *R5:* shunt temp. correction, *R6:* 20 kΩ adjustable resistor, *R7:* 500 Ω multi-turn potentiometer, *R8:* 20 kΩ multi-turn potentiometer, *Vo:* 14.3 V D.C. stabiliser *PE 4818 Philips* (Holland), *A:* 100 mA meter, *Am:* D.C. amplifier *Ri* = 2 MΩ *T.F.D.L.* Wageningen, *V:* recorder.

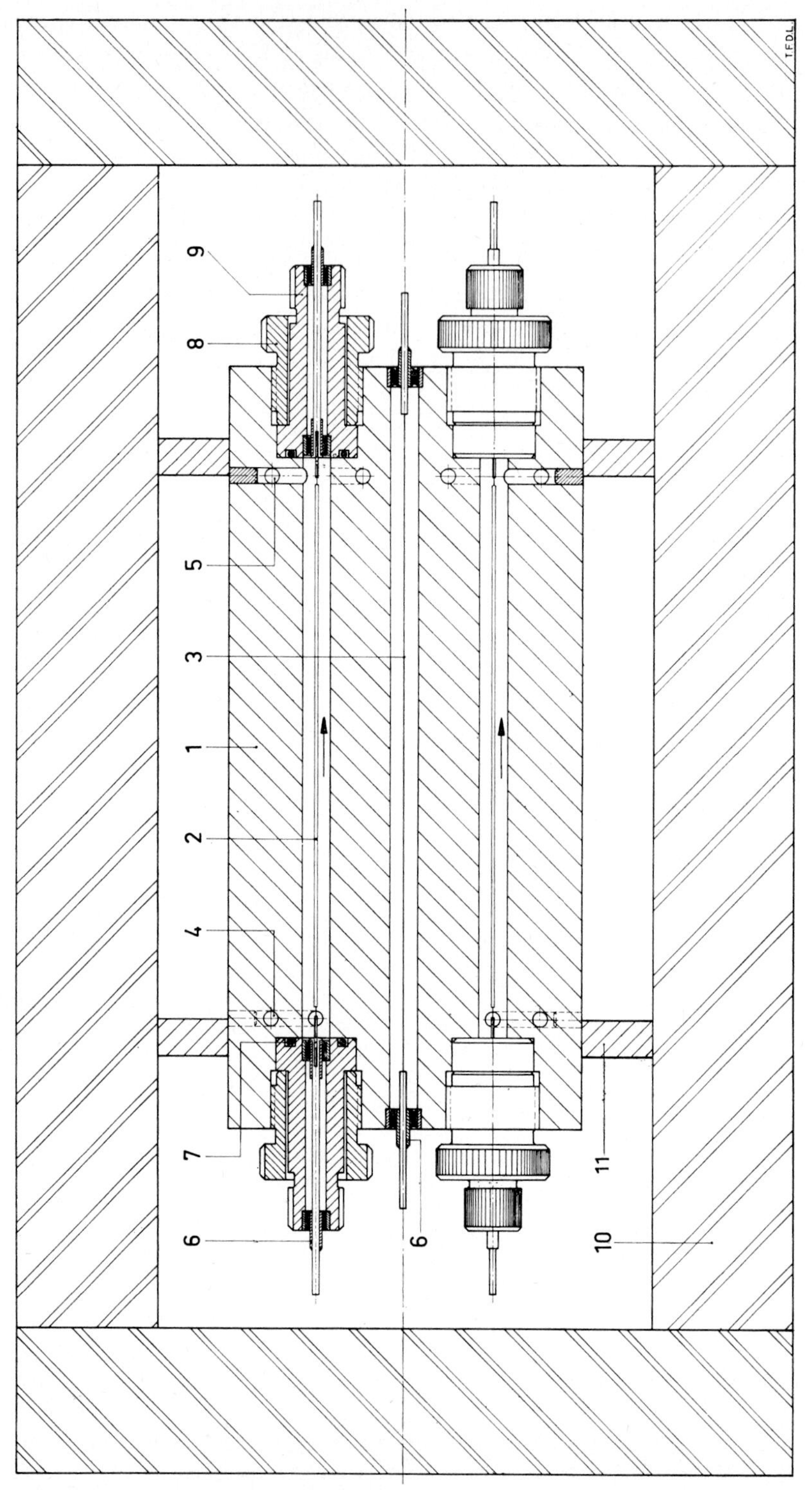

Fig. 3.47 Construction of the measuring and reference tubes of the katharometer. *1:* Brass katharometer block, *2:* coiled tungsten wire, *3:* platinum wire, *4:* gas inlet for two channels, *5:* gas outlet, *6:* glass duct, *7:* O-ring, *8:* screw cap, *9:* lead duct, *10:* insulating box, *11:* insulating block support.

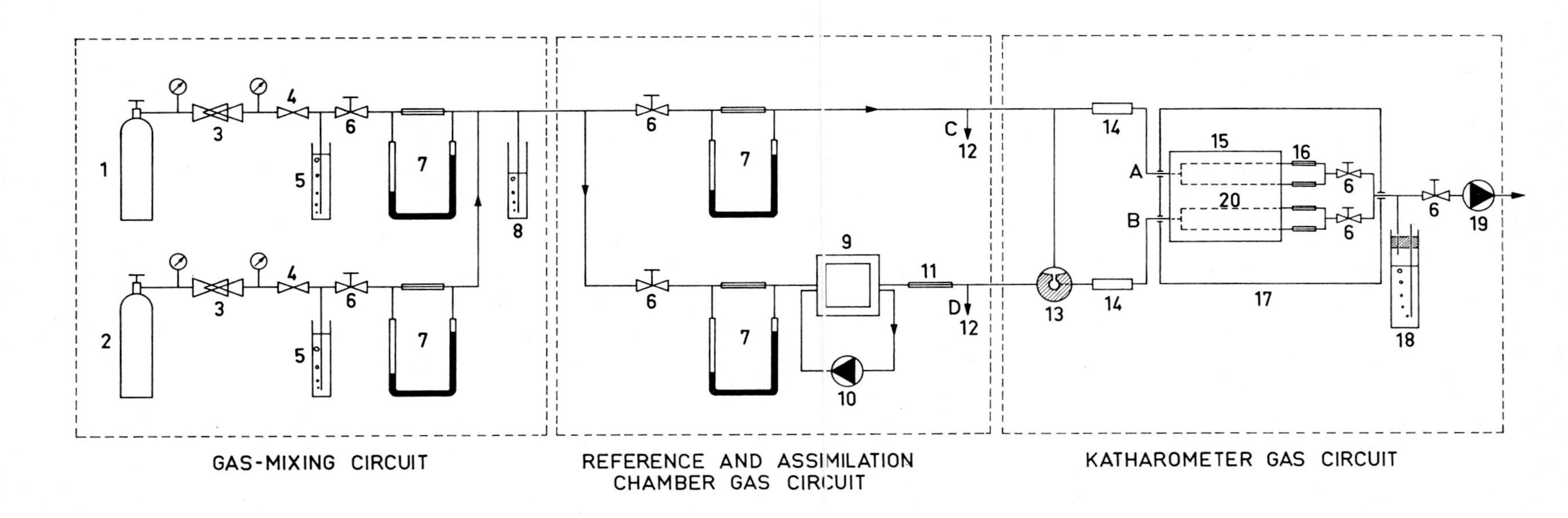

Fig. 3.48 Gas flow circuit with katharometer. *1:* cylinder with air, *2:* cylinder with CO_2 enriched (5%) air, *3:* pressure reducing valve, *4:* valve, *5:* overflow pressure regulator, *6:* needle valve, *7:* capillary flow meter, *8:* overflow pressure regulator, *9:* assimilation chamber, *10:* recirculation pump, *11:* capillary to damp pressure vibration, *12:* outflow, *13:* three-way valve, *14:* drying tube, *15:* katharometer block, *16:* capillaries, *17:* katharometer housing, *18:* suction pressure regulator, *19:* suction pump, *20:* four channels.

In this way the thermal drift of the signal can be largely suppressed.
Power supply. Without special adjustment the temperature, *i.e.* the resistances of both wire systems, will not change symmetrically when the value of V_0 changes a little with time. This results in a drift of the signal. This drift of the signal can be suppressed by correct shunting and balancing the arms of the bridge (see Fig. 3.46 R_{6a}, R_{6b} and R_3).
Gas flow. A heated wire is a well-known and very sensitive anemometer. Regulation of the four gas streams is accomplished by putting 4 glass capillaries in the plastic tubing between the four exits and the suction pressure regulator (Fig. 3.48,*16*). The dimensions of the capillaries must be chosen so that a small change in the suction pressure does not cause an electrical signal from the katharometer.
Shock. It is clear that shock or vibration of the wires influences their temperatures and causes an electrical signal acting as 'noise'. The box containing the katharometer-block is therefore mounted on rubber shock absorbers.

3.15.3.2 | Description of the block

In a brass block (Fig. 3.47) of 12 × 5 × 5 cm, 6 channels of 4 mm diameter are drilled. Four channels are closed by 8 brass plugs held in place by screw-caps. In the middle of each of the 8 plugs, glass ducts are mounted. The nickel ends of the tungsten wires are led through the central metal tubing of these glass ducts and soldered.
The other two channels are closed by soldering 4 glass ducts in their ends. Through the tubing in the centre, thin platinum wire is drawn and soldered onto brass pins. The 4 channels are connected two by two by drilling 2 holes at one side at right angles to them. On the other side, each channel has its own exit.

3.15.3.3 | Hot wires

For the hot wires, doubly coiled tungsten wires (10 μm, 99 Ω), spot-welded to nickel ends of 0.5 mm, are used. These were generously supplied by the *Philips Laboratories* (Eindhoven, the Netherlands). Four selected wires were placed carefully in the block.

3.15.3.4 | Balancing device

As can be seen from the schematic diagram (Fig. 3.46 R_7 and R_8), a very simple balancing device is applied. This is trouble-free, sufficiently sensitive, and has a large range because two ten-turn helical precision potentiometers of 20 kΩ and 500 Ω (maximum correction $\pm$ 0.5% CO_2) are used.

3.15.3.5 | Gas flow circuit

The important details are shown in the diagram of the gas flow circuit (Fig. 3.48). It should be mentioned here that, if for some reason a pressure difference develops between *A* and *B*, the gas flow in each side of the katharometer will change differently. This causes an electrical signal on the recorder. The three-way tap which allows entry either of the reference gas or of the gas to be analysed, therefore has a special cavity to prevent stagnation of the gas flow during turning. For the same reason, the gas pressure drop over the outlets *C* and *D* deserves special attention and must be lower as more gas flows out. Also, air vibrations originating from the recirculation pump must be damped by putting a capillary in the gas circuit (Fig. 3.48, *11*).

3.15.4 | *Method of use*

3.15.4.1 | Gas chromatographic analysis

Because of its non-specificity, the katharometer is particularly suitable as an analyser after a gas chromatographic column. Of course, its relative sensitivity is not the same for every constituent separated, but by choosing the appropriate carrier gas, one can also change the sensitivity for special gases.
By merely connecting the appropriate separation unit to the apparatus, normally used for photosynthesis measurement, one can detect whether other products are produced by the biological material (*cf.* Burg & Stolwijk 1959), in addition to H_2O, O_2 and CO_2.

3.15.4.2 | Pretreatment of the gas to be analyzed

The non-specific character of the instrument can be overcome in three ways:
No pretreatment. No pretreatment is necessary, if $p_1\varepsilon_1$ of the measured gas (Eq. 3.41) is large in comparison to $\Sigma p_a\varepsilon_a$ of the other changing gases, or if the ratio $p_1\varepsilon_1/\Sigma p_a\varepsilon_a$ is constant and known. Both cases occur in photosynthesis studies, *viz.*, in the measurement of transpiration and in that of the photosynthesis quotient (*viz.*, $\Delta O_2/\Delta CO_2$ = constant).

Fig. 3.49 View of tilted drying tubes and three-way stopcock.

Chemical pretreatment. *Drying of the gas mixture* is best performed with P_2O_5. The highly hygroscopic P_2O_5-powder can be filled into special drying tubes (Fig. 3.49). It is essential that these drying tubes are tilted a little to allow the solution of H_3PO_4 formed to drain off. If specific measurements of the changes in the concentrations of CO_2 and O_2 are to be made, *absorption of CO_2* is necessary. This can be accomplished by granulated soda lime, followed by drying.
Influencing the sensitivity ratio $\varepsilon_1/\varepsilon_2$. In photosynthesis measurements we can deliberately bring about insensitivity to *e.g.* O_2 by choosing for the reference gas a gas mixture with $K'_{O_2} = K_0$; this can be achieved by addition of a small amount of He or H_2.

3.15.4.3 | Measurement of gases important in gas exchange in plants

In photosynthesis, exchange of only 3 gases is involved, *viz.* CO_2, O_2 and H_2O. Whether this is valid is easily established by gas chromatographic analysis.
Transpiration. The value of $p\varepsilon_{H_2O}$ is large in comparison to $p\varepsilon_{CO_2} + p\varepsilon_{O_2}$. Transpiration can therefore be measured without pretreatment of the gas, notwithstanding the changes in O_2 and CO_2.
Photosynthesis. Photosynthesis is easily measured with the katharometer when the gas coming from the assimilation chamber is thoroughly dried before it enters the apparatus (Vejlby 1959; Pieters 1964). The concurrent change in the CO_2 and O_2 concentrations does not invalidate the measurement, when the ratio $\Delta CO_2/\Delta O_2$ is constant and known. Furthermore, the sensitivity of the katharometer to O_2 is an order of magnitude smaller than that to CO_2. The sensitivity ratio $\varepsilon_{CO_2}/\varepsilon_{O_2}$, however, changes with K_0 (see Table 3.7).
Specific measurement of O_2. If the ratio $\Delta CO_2/\Delta O_2$ is not constant or not known, we can absorb CO_2 from the gas in the assimilation chamber. The katharometer deflections are then proportional to the changes in O_2 content (van der Veen 1949; Burg & Stolwijk 1959).
Specific measurement of CO_2 (see the paragraph 'Influencing the sensitivity ratio $\varepsilon_1/\varepsilon_2$, in Section 3.15.4.2). In order to measure changes in CO_2, we can divide the gas coming from the assimilation chamber into two parts, absorb CO_2 from one of the gas streams, and lead both streams separately through the measuring and reference channels of the katharometer.
It must be stressed that this method brings about an unbalance of the katharometer bridge approximately as large as the CO_2 content of the original gas. This unbalance can be compensated for by the balancing device, up to a CO_2 content of 0.5% (see Section 3.15.3.4), thus allowing the use of the apparatus at full sensitivity.

3.15.4.4 | Calculation of the photosynthetic rate

If the sensitivity S of the apparatus is given as the difference in per cent of the volume of CO_2 in air per 100 scale units (*e.g.* f.s.d. for a change of 0.01%) we obtain for the rate of photosynthesis

$$\frac{D}{100} \times \frac{S}{100} \times L \times 10^6/A = \frac{DSL \times 10^2}{A} \; [\text{mm}^3\ \text{cm}^{-2}\ \text{h}^{-1}]$$

in which D = deflection [in scale units], L = gas flow rate through the assimilation chamber [$l\ h^{-1}$], A = leaf area [cm^2].

3.15.5 | *Technical data*

The katharometer is a non-specific instrument suitable for measuring gas concentrations.

Gas flow. A very slow gas flow is required, *viz.*, 10 – 40 ml min^{-1}.

Response time. At a flow rate of 40 ml min^{-1}, the response time is less than 20 s. Rapid changes in gas exchange can easily be measured (induction effects—van der Veen 1949; Vejlby 1959).

Sensitivity. The sensitivity of the katharometer to a particular gas depends on the relative conductivity difference $(K' - K_0)/K_0 = \varepsilon$ of the pure gas and the reference gas. When taking air or air with 5% CO_2 as reference, the EMF for CO_2 changes is *ca.* 62.5 μV/0.01% CO_2.

By choosing H_2 or He as reference gas, the sensitivity to changes in CO_2 can be increased about 2.5 times, and to O_2 more than 20 times (van der Veen 1949; Burg & Stolwijk 1959), if the right voltage V_0 is chosen (see Table 3.7).

Table 3.7 ε and $\frac{\Delta t}{1 - a\Delta t} \times \varepsilon$ of various gas mixtures at a temperature of 37.8 °C*.

Gas mixture			
Reference	To be measured	ε	$\frac{\Delta t}{1 - a\Delta t} \times \varepsilon$ (at constant V_0)
Air	CO_2	−0.3498	−44.16
Air + 5% CO_2	CO_2	−0.3382	−43.53**
Air	O_2	+0.0266	+ 3.36
Air + 5% CO_2	O_2	+0.0399	+ 5.14
90% He + 5% CO_2 + 5% O_2	CO_2	−0.8761	−14.42
90% He + 5% CO_2 + 5% O_2	O_2	−0.8045	−13.24

* The block temperature or the mean temperature of the gas during measurement is estimated to be 40 °C.

** That the theory of the katharometer is somewhat more complicated is clear from the fact that we find in reality a 3% higher sensitivity to CO_2 in air + 5% CO_2 (see the Table).

Resolution of small amounts of gas. Very small amounts of gas can be detected. The order of magnitude is at least 2.5×10^{-11} mol CO_2 ml^{-1}.

Reproducibility. Reproducibility is better than 1% of the full scale at the sensitivity of 0.01% CO_2/f.s.d.

Linearity. The EMF of the katharometer for CO_2 and H_2O differences has been shown to be practically linear in the entire physiologically important concentration

range, *e.g.* 0–5% CO_2 in air and 0–100% relative humidity (deviation + 3% over 0–5% CO_2).
Noise and drift. The noise level of the instrument is less than 0.2 μV and the drift less than 3 μV h^{-1}. The drift is mainly due to changes in ambient temperature. A slow change of the ambient temperature is tolerable.
Electrical data. The current for heating the wires is from a simple electronic D.C. stabiliser (*Philips*, PE 4818): V_0 = 14.3 V, I = 0.100 A, $R_t \simeq$ 143 Ω.

3.16 | A list of instrument manufacturers

This list contains the names and addresses of firms supplying equipment which has been used in IRGA systems. It is not intended to be a comprehensive list of all suppliers of the kinds of equipment listed. Further information regarding possible suppliers can be obtained from:
The British Instruments Directory, published annually by the Scientific Instrument Manufacturers' Association and United Trade Press, Boswell House, 9 Gough Square, Fleet Street, London E.C. 4.
The Guide to Scientific Instruments, published annually by the American Association for the Advancement of Science as a special issue of Science, *e.g.* Science 169A, No. 3951A, 23 September 1970.
Many of the manufacturers listed below are associated with manufacturing and distribution companies, agencies and agents, many bearing the same or similar names, in countries throughout the world. Generally the address given is in the country in which the company has its head quarters.

3.16.1 | Infra-red gas analysers

Analytic System Co., Pasadena, U.S.A.
The Analytical Development Co. Ltd., Southwell Grove Rd, London E. 11, U.K.
Beckman Instruments Inc., 2500 Harbor Blvd., Fullerton, Cal. 92634, U.S.A.
Elliot – Automation Ltd., Borhamwood, U.K.
Sir Howard Grubb Parsons & Co. Ltd., Walkergate, Newcastle upon Tyne, 6, U.K.
Hartmann & Braun A.G., 6 Frankfurt/Main 90, Gräfstr. 97, Postfach 900507, Germany (BRD).
Hilger – I.R.D. Ltd., no longer a supplier.[1]
V.E.B. Junkalor, Altener Str. 43, 45 Dessau, Germany (DDR).
Leeds & Northrup Co., Sumneytown Pike, North Wales, Pa. 19454, U.S.A.
Maihak A.G., 2 Hamburg 39, Semperstr. 52, Germany (BRD).
M.S.A. Research Corp., Evans City, Pa. 16033, U.S.A.
Schlumberger et Cie, Division Contrôle Industriel, 185 Av. de la Libération, 92–Clamart, France.

1. *Hilger – I.R.D. Ltd.* – this company has been taken over by *Rank Precision Industries Ltd.*, who have passed over all their interests in IRGAs to *Sir Howard Grubb Parsons & Co. Ltd.*

3.16.2 | Interference filters to increase IRGA selectivity for CO_2

Sir Howard Grubb Parsons & Co. Ltd. (address in Section 3.16.1).
Hartmann & Braun A.G. (address in Section 3.16.1).
Standard Telephones & Cables Ltd., Rectifier Division, Edinburgh Way, Marlow, Essex, U.K.

3.16.3 | Oxygen analysers

Beckman Instruments Inc. (address in Section 3.16.1).
Hartmann & Braun, A.G. (address in Section 3.16.1).
Maihak A.G. (address in Section 3.16.1).
Schlumberger et Cie (address in Section 3.16.1).
Servomax Controls Ltd., Crowborough, Sussex, U.K.
Westinghouse Electric Corporation, New Products Division, Pittsburgh, Pa. 15230, U.S.A.

3.16.4 | Calibration gases (specialist firms only)

Air Products Ltd., Stonor Street, Cobridge, Burslem, Stoke on Trent, U.K.
Hartmann & Braun A.G. (address in Section 3.16.1).
Helms, 3000 Hannover, Postfach 2703, Germany (BRD).
Matheson Gas Products Div., P.O. Box 85, East Rutherford, N.J. 07073 U.S.A.
Rank Precision Industries Ltd., Hilger & Watts Ltd., Analytical Division, Roding Works, Westwood Industrial Estate, Ramsgate Road, Margate, Kent (this company has taken over the business formerly carried on by *Hilger – I.R.D. Ltd.*).

3.16.5 | Gas mixing pumps

H. Wösthoff, Apparatebau, 463 Bochum, Hagenstr. 30, Germany (BRD).

3.16.6 | Gas sampling pumps

Charles Austen Pumps Ltd., 100 Royston Road, Byfleet, Sussex, U.K.
Cole-Parmer Instrument Co., 7425 N Oak Park Av., Chicago, Ill. 60648, U.S.A.
Edwards High Vacuum Ltd., Manor Royal, Crawley, Sussex, U.K.
Hartmann & Braun A.G. (address in Section 3.16.1).
GfG-Gesellschaft für Gerätebau, 46 Dortmund, Westfalendamm 267, Deutschland.
VEB Junkalor (address in Section 3.16.1).
Lindfors Elektriska AB, Råsundavägen 137, S 17130 Solna-Stockholm, Sweden.
Phywe AG, 34 Göttingen, Postfach 665, Germany (BRD).
Piot et Tirouflet, 89 rue de la Croix Nivert, Paris 15e, France.
Reciprotor A/S, Krogshøjvej 47, DK-2880, Bagsvaerd, Denmark.
W. Sauer, 56 Wuppertal-CR, Cronenfelderstr. 34, Germany (BRD).
Sigmamotor Inc., 3 North Main Street, Middleport, N.Y. 14105, U.S.A.
The Watson-Marlow Air Pump Co., Marlow, Bucks, U.K.

3.16.7 | *Flow regulators and valves*

Asco Dewrance & Co. Ltd., Gt Doverstreet, London S.E. 1, U.K.
Autogen Ritter, 8 München, Nymphenburgerstr. 57–61, Germany (BRD)
Black Automatic Controls Ltd., Leafield, Corsham, Wilts, U.K.
Brooks Instrument N.V., Veenendaal, The Netherlands.
Carba AG, Bern, Switzerland.
Danfoss (London) Ltd., 6 Wadsworth Road, Perivale, Greenford, Middx, U.K.
Dräger-Werk, Lübeck, Germany (BRD).
Drallim Industries Ltd., Brett Drive, De La Warr Road, Bexhill on Sea, Sussex, U.K.
Edwards High Vacuum Ltd. (address in Section 3.16.6).
Endress & Hauser GmbH & Co., Maulburg/Baden, Germany (BRD).
Ether Ltd., Control Valve Division, Caxton Way, Stevenage, Herts, U.K.
Fairchild Hiller, Stratos Industrial Products, Winston, Salem, North Carolina, U.S.A.
GFG – Becorit Electronics (address in Section 3.16.6).
Göres, 6 Frankfurt/Main, Buchrainstr. 18, Germany (BRD).
Hartmann & Braun A.G. (address in Section 3.16.1).
Herion-Werke KG, 7 Stuttgart, Postfach 2970, Germany (BRD).
Hoke International Inc., 1 Tenakill Pk., Cresskill, N.J. 07626, U.S.A.
Hone Instruments Ltd., 19 Eldon Park, London, S.E. 25, U.K.
L. Krohne, Duisburg, Germany (BRD).
Matheson Gas Products Div. (address in Section 3.16.4).
AB Mecman, Box 320 35, S 12611 Stockholm 32, Sweden.
Negretti & Zambra Ltd., Stocklake, Aylesbury, Bucks, U.K.
C. A. Norgren Ltd., Shipton on Stour, Warwicks, U.K.
L'Oxhydrique française, 8 av. J. Ferry, 92 – Malakoff, France.
G. A. Platon Ltd., Wella Rd., Basingstoke, Hants, U.K.
Simplifix Couplings Ltd., Hargrave Rd., Maidenhead, Berks, U.K.
Veriflo Corporation, 250 Canal Boulevard, Richmond, Calif., U.S.A.
Wade Couplings Ltd., Argyle St., Birmingham 7, U.K.

3.16.8 | *Flow meters*

Brooks Instrument Div., Emerson Electric Co., 407 W. Vine St., Hatfield, Pa. 19440, U.S.A.
The Cobb-Slater Instruments Co. Ltd., Cosim Works, Darley Dale Matlock, Derbyshire, U.K.
Dam, Lyon 5e, 6 Av. Appolinaire, France.
Dwyer Instruments, P.O. Box 373, Michigan City, Ind. 46360, U.S.A.
Electronic Flo-meters Ltd., 31 Cross Lancet Rd., Hounslow, Middx., U.K.
Fisher & Porter Co. Ltd., County Line Rd., Warminster, Pa. 18974, U.S.A.
Fisher & Porter GmbH., 34 Göttingen, Postfach 701, Germany (BRD).
Greiner Scientific Corp., 20 N. Moore St., New York 13, N.Y. 10013, U.S.A.
Matheson Gas Products Div. (address in Section 3.16.4).
Meterate, Glass Precision Engineering Ltd., Mark Rd., Hemel Hempstead, Hertshire, U.K.

Meterflow Ltd., North Feltham Trading Estate, Feltham, Middlesex, U.K.
G. A. Platon Ltd. (address in Section 3.16.7).
VEB Prüfgeräte-Werk, Medingen/Dresden, Germany (DDR).
Rotameter (Apparate- u. Maschinenbau), D-7867 Oeflingen, Germany (BRD).
Rotameter Manufacturing Co., 330 Purley Way, Croydon CR9 4PG, Surrey, U.K.
Société Houdec 'Le Contrôle des Fluides', 53 Bd Jean Jaures, 91-Corbeil, Essonnes, France.
Turbo-Werk, Köln, Postfach, Germany (BRD).
Wallace & Tiernan Ltd., Priory Works, Tonbridge, Kent, U.K.

3.16.9 | Gas and wet test meters

American Meter Co., Philadelphia, Pennsylvania, U.S.A.
Parkinson Cowan Measurement, P.O. Box 3, Talbot Rd., Stretford, Manchester, U.K.
Rockwell International, S. A., Genève, Switzerland.
Alexander Wright & Co. (Westminster) Ltd., 77 Glouster Road, Croydon CR9 2SA, U.K.

3.16.10 | Air filters

Aerox Ltd., Cotswold Works, Chalford, Stroud, Glos, U.K.
Gelman Instrument Co., 600 S Wagner Rd., Ann Arbor, Mich. 48106, U.S.A.
Hoke International Inc. (address in Section 3.16.7).
C. A. Norgren Ltd. (address in Section 3.16.7).
Whatman Gamma-10, Balston Ltd., Maidstone, Kent, U.K.

3.16.11 | Chemical desiccants and CO_2 absorbers

British Drug Houses Ltd., Laboratory Chemicals Div., Poole, BH12 4NN, U.K.
Dräger-Werk, Lübeck, Germany (BRD).
Fisher Scientific Company, 711 Forbes Avenue, Pittsburgh, Pa. 15219, U.S.A.
Fisons Scientific Apparatus Ltd., Bishop Meadow Rd., Loughborough, Leics, U.K.
W. A. Hammond Drierite Co., 138 Dayton Av., Xenia, Ohio 45385, U.S.A.
Mallinckrodt Chemical Works, P.O. Box 384, Jersey City, N.J. 07303, U.S.A.
E. Merck, 61 Darmstadt 2, Postfach 4119, Germany (BRD).
Sofnol Ltd., Westcombe Hill, Greenwich, London S.E. 10, U.K.
Arthur H. Thomas Co., Vine St. & Third, Philadelphia, Pa. 19105, U.S.A.

3.16.12 | Controlled dewpoint drying equipment

Siemens A. G., D-8520 Erlangen 2, Postfach 325, Germany (BRD).

3.16.13 | Infra-red mirrors and filters

Balzers A. G., FL-9496 Balzers, Fürstentum Liechtenstein.
Barr & Straud Ltd., Caxton Street, Anniesland, Glasgow W. 3., U.K.

Corning Glass Works, Laboratory Products Dept., Corning, N.Y. 14830, U.S.A.
Sir Howard Grubb Parsons & Co. Ltd. (address in Section 3.16.1).
Pilkington Bros Ltd., Chance-Pilkington Optical Works, Galscoed Road, St. Asaph, Flintshire, U.K.
Schott & Gen., Jenaer Glaswerke, D-6500 Mainz, Postfach 1327, Germany (BRD).
VEB Schott, Jena, Germany (DDR).

3.16.14 | *Assimilation chambers*

Hoefer Scientific Instruments, 2609 California Street, San Francisco, Calif. 94115, U.S.A.
Siemens A.G. (address in Section 3.16.12).
S.I.M., 18 Hartley St., Canberra, A.C.T. 2601, Australia.

3.16.15 | *Temperature controlled water baths and water circulating pumps*

Charles Austen Pumps Ltd. (address in Section 3.16.6).
B. Braun, Apparatebau, Melsungen, Germany (BRD).
Grant Instruments Ltd., Toft, Cambridge, U.K.
Haake K. G., Berlin-Steglitz, Germany (BRD).
Heto, Klinthöjvaenge 3, Birkeröd, Denmark.
Secasi, Parc Industriel de Pessac, 36 – Bordeaux, France.
Siemens A. G. (address in Section 3.16.12).
Stuart Turner Ltd., Henley on Thames, Oxon., U.K.
Techne Scientific Instruments, Duxford, Cambridge, U.K.
Townson & Mercer Ltd., Beddington Lane, Croydon CR9 4EG, U.K.

3.16.16 | *Hygrometers*

American Instrument Co. Inc., 8030 Georgia Av., Silver Spring, Md. 20910, U.S.A.
Cambridge Systems Inc., 50 Hunt St., Newton, Mass. 02158, U.S.A.
Honeywell Inc., Industrial Div., 1100 Virginia Dr., Fort Washington, Pa. 19034, U.S.A.
Hygrodynamics Inc., 949 Selim Rd., Silver Spring, Md. 20910, U.S.A.
W. Lambrecht KG, Friedländer Weg 65, Göttingen, Germany (BRD)
Salford Electrical Instruments Ltd., Peel Works, Barton Lane, Eccles, Manchester, U.K.
Shaw Moisture Meters, Rawson Road, Westgate, Bradford, U.K.
Siemens A. G. (address in Section 3.16.1.2).
Sina Ltd. Co., Zürich, Switzerland.
Karl Weiss GmbH, Grünbach am Schneeberg/N.Ö., Österreich.

3.16.17 | *Strip chart recorders*

Bristol Company of Canada Ltd., Toronto, Ont., Canada.

Control Instruments Ltd., Alfreton Rd, Derby, U.K.

Esterline Angus Div., Esterline Corp., P.O. Box 24000, Indianapolis, Ind. 40224, U.S.A.
General Electric Co., Analytical Measurement Business Section, 25 Federal Street, West Lynn, Mass. 01905, U.S.A.
Hartmann & Braun A.G. (address in Section 3.16.1).
Hewlett-Packard Co., 1501 Page Mill Rd., Palo Alto, Cal. 94304, U.S.A.
Honeywell Inc. (address in Section 3.16.16).
Geo. Kent Ltd., Luton, Bedfordshire, U.K.
Laboratorní přístroje n.p., Na okraji 335, Praha 6 – Veleslavín – Petřiny, Czechoslovakia.
Leeds & Northrup Co. (address in Section 3.16.1).
Linseis K. G., 8672 Selb, Postfach 135, Germany (BRD).
VEB Messgeräte- und Armaturenwerk (MAW), Magdeburg – Buckau, Germany (DDR).
Metrawatt AG, Schoppershofstr. 50, Nürnberg, Germany (BRD).
N.V. Philips, Eindhoven, The Netherlands.
Rustrack Instrument Co., Manchester, NH 03103, U.S.A.
Schlumberger et Cie (address in Section 3.16.1).
Siemens AG (address in Section 3.16.12).
Société Meci, 123 bd de Grenelle, Paris 15e, France.
Telsec Instruments Ltd., Sandy Lane, West Eastern By-pass, Oxford, U.K.
Texas Instruments Inc., Industrial Products Div., Box 66027, Houston, Tex. 77006, U.S.A.

3.17 | References

Anderson, A., An-Ti Chai, Williams, D.: Self-broadening effects in the infrared bands of gases. – J. opt. Soc. Amer. 57: 240-246, 1967.
Apel, P.: Herstellung CO_2-haltiger Gasgemische für Photosynthesemessungen mit dem URAS. – Flora A 157: 330-333, 1966.
Baker, D. N., Musgrave, R. B.: Photosynthesis under field conditions. V. Further plant chamber studies of the effects of light on corn (*Zea mays* L.). – Crop Sci. 4: 127-131, 1964.
Banwell, C. N.: Fundamentals of Molecular Spectroscopy. – McGraw-Hill, London 1966.
Bassham, J. A., Shibata, K., Calvin, M.: Quantum requirement in photosynthesis related to respiration. – Biochim. biophys. Acta 17: 332-340, 1955.
Bierhuizen, J. F., Slatyer, R. O.: An apparatus for the continuous and simultaneous measurement of photosynthesis and transpiration under controlled environmental conditions. – CSIRO Div. Land Res., Regional Surv. tech. Pap. 24: 1-16, 1964.
Björkman, O., Gauhl, E.: Use of the zirconium oxide ceramic cell for measurements of photosynthetic oxygen evolution by intact leaves. – Photosynthetica 4: 123-128, 1970.
Björkman, O., Holmgren, P.: Adaptability of the photosynthetic apparatus to light intensity in ecotypes from exposed and shaded habitats. – Physiol. Plant. 16: 889-914, 1963.
Bosian, G.: Über die Vollautomatisierung der CO_2-Assimilationsbestimmung und zur Methodik des Küvettenklimas. – Planta 45: 470-492, 1955.
Bosian, G.: Control of conditions in the plant chamber: Fully automatic regulation of wind velocity, temperature and relative humidity to conform to microclimatic field conditions. – In: Eckardt, F. E. (ed.): Methodology of Plant Eco-Physiology. Pp. 233-238. UNESCO, Paris 1965.
Bourdeau, P. F., Woodwell, G. M.: Measurements of plant carbon dioxide exchange by infra-red absorption under controlled conditions and in the field. – In: Eckardt, F. E. (ed.): Methodology of Plant Eco-Physiology. Pp. 283-289. UNESCO, Paris 1965.

Brown, K. W.: Experimental Considerations for the Measurement of Photosynthetic Rates by Means of Carbon Dioxide Exchange in Leaf Chambers. – Progr. Rep. 66. Univ. Nebraska Coll. Agr. Home Econ., Agr. exp. Sta., 40 pp. Lincoln 1968.

Brown, K. W., Rosenberg, N. J.: Errors in sampling and infrared analysis of CO_2 in air and their influence in determination of net photosynthetic rate. – Agron. J. 60: 309-311, 1968.

Brown, K. W., Rosenberg, N. J.: The concentrations of CO_2 in the air above a sugar beet field. – Mo. Weather Rev. 98: 75-82, 1970.

Brügel, W.: Einführung in die Ultrarotspektroskopie. – Steinkopff, Darmstadt 1962.

Brunnhöfer, H., Schaub, H., Egle, K.: Der Verlauf des CO_2- und O_2-Gaswechsels bei *Bryophyllum daigremontianum* in Abhängigkeit von der Temperatur. – Z. Pflanzenphysiol. 59: 285-292, 1968a.

Brunnhöfer, H., Schaub, H., Egle, K.: Die Beziehungen zwischen den Veränderungen der Malat- und Stärkekonzentrationen und dem CO_2- und O_2-Gaswechsel bei *Bryophyllum daigremontianum*. – Z. Pflanzenphysiol. 60: 12-18, 1968b.

Burch, D. E., Gryvnak, D. A., Williams, D.: Total absorptance of carbon dioxide in the infrared. – Appl. Optics 1: 759-765, 1962.

Burg, S. P., Stolwijk, J. A. J.: A highly sensitive katharometer and its application to the measurement of ethylene and other gases of biological importance. – J. biochem. microbiol. Technol. Eng. 1: 245-259, 1959.

Burke, J. E.: Ceramics today. – Science 161: 1205-1212, 1968.

Čatský, J., Chartier, M., Chartier, P.: Mesure de la concentration en anhydride carbonique dans l'air par absorption des rayonnements infra rouges. – In: Techniques d'Étude des Facteurs Physiques de la Biosphère. Pp. 189-199. I.N.R.A., Paris 1970.

Cernusca, A.: Der Einsatz automatischer Datenerfassungssysteme für klimaökologische Untersuchungen im Rahmen der Produktivitätsforschung. – Photosynthetica 2: 238-244, 1968.

Cernusca, A., Moser, W.: Die automatische Registrierung produktionsanalytischer Meßdaten bei Freilandversuchen auf Lochstreifen. – Photosynthetica 3: 21-27, 1969.

Chartier, P.: Étude de l'assimilation nette d'une culture couvrante. – Thesis, C.N.R.A. Versailles 1970.

Chartier, P., Chartier, M., Čatský, J.: Resistances for carbon dioxide diffusion and for carboxylation as factors in bean leaf photosynthesis. – Photosynthetica 4: 48-57, 1970.

Le Chevallier, M., Leleu, M.: Un régulateur de débits gazeux. – Électronique ind. 1955/57(7): 26-28, 1956.

Daynes, H. A.: Gas Analysis by Measurement of Thermal Conductivity. – Univ. Press, Cambridge 1933.

Dingle, H., Pryce, A. W.: The estimation of small quantities of carbon dioxide in air by the absorption of infra-red radiation. – Proc. roy. Soc. B 129: 468-474, 1940.

van den Driessche, R., Wareing, P. F.: Dry-matter production and photosynthesis in pine seedlings. – Ann. Bot. N.S. 30: 673-682, 1966.

Eckardt, F. E.: Le principe de la soufflerie climatisée, appliqué à l'étude des échanges gazeux de la couverture végétale. – Oecol. Plant. 1: 369-399, 1966.

Eckardt, F. E.: Mécanisme de la production primaire des écosystèmes terrestres sous climat méditerranéen. Recherches entreprises à Montpellier dans le cadre du Programme Biologique International. – Oecol. Plant. 2: 367-393, 1967.

Eckardt, F. E.: Techniques de mesure de la photosynthèse sur le terrain, basées sur l'emploi d'enceintes climatisées. – In: Eckardt, F. E. (ed.): Functioning of Terrestrial Ecosystems at the Primary Production Level. Pp. 289-319. UNESCO, Paris 1968.

Egle, K.: Landpflanzen. – In: Ruhland, W. (ed.): Handbuch der Pflanzenphysiologie. Vol. V/1. Pp. 115-163. Springer Verlag, Berlin–Göttingen–Heidelberg 1960.

Egle, K., Ernst, A.: Die Verwendung des Ultrarotabsorptionsschreibers für die vollautomatische und fortlaufende CO_2-Analyse bei Assimilations- und Atmungsmessungen an Pflanzen. – Z. Naturforsch. 4b: 351-360, 1949.

Egle, K., Schenk, W.: Die Anwendung des Ultrarotabsorptionsschreibers in der Photosyntheseforschung. – Ber. deut. bot. Ges. 64: 181-197, 1951.

Etherington, J. R.: Measurement of photosynthesis and transpiration in controlled environments with particular reference to microclimate control in leaf cuvettes. – Ann. Bot. N.S. 31: 653-660, 1967.

Fock, H.: Über die 'Lichtatmung' bei grünen Pflanzen. Die Wirkung von Sauerstoff und Kohlendioxyd auf die Photosynthese, die Atmung und den Glykolsäure-Stoffwechsel. – Thesis, Univ. Frankfurt a.M. 1965.

Fock, H., Schaub, H., Hilgenberg, W.: Über den Sauerstoff- und Kohlendioxidgaswechsel von *Chlorella* und *Conocephalum* während der Lichtphase. – Z. Pflanzenphysiol. 60: 56-63, 1968.

Fock, H., Schaub, H., Hilgenberg, W., Egle, K.: Über den Einfluß niedriger und hoher O_2-Partialdrucke auf den Sauerstoff- und Kohlendioxidumsatz von *Amaranthus* und *Phaseolus* während der Lichtphase. – Planta 86: 77-83, 1969.

Fonselius, S., Wärme, K.-E.: A method to make standard CO_2 samples for infrared gas analysis and the operation of an IRGA analyser for air samples from the Scandinavian network. – Tellus 12: 227-230, 1960.

Friedrich, G., Schmidt, G.: Weitere Untersuchungen über das assimilatorische und respiratorische Verhalten der Obstgehölze. – Arch. Gartenbau 11: 209-245, 1963.

Gaastra, P.: Photosynthesis of crop plants as influenced by light, carbon dioxide, temperature, and stomatal diffusion resistance. – Meded. Landbouwhogesch. Wageningen 59(13): 1-68, 1959.

Girshovich, I. E.: Isseledovanie optiko-akusticheskogo gazoanalizatora pri izmerenii malykh raznosteĭ kontsentratsii CO_2. [Studying the optico-acoustic gas analyser measuring small differentials in CO_2 concentrations.] – Pribory i Sistemy Upravleniya 12: 51-52, 1967.

Gröber, H., Erk, S., Grigull, U.: Die Grundgesetze der Wärmeübertragung. – 3rd Ed. Springer, Berlin–Göttingen–Heidelberg 1963.

Gulyaev, B. I., Manuil'skiĭ, V. D., Okanenko, A. S.: Otsenka pogreshnosteĭ izmereniya intensivnosti fotosinteza gazometricheskim metodom. [Error estimation in photosynthetic rate measurement by a gazometric method.] – Fiziol. Biokhim. kul't. Rast. 2: 34-40, 1970.

Hengstenberg, J., Sturm, B., Winkler, O.: Messen und Regeln in der chemischen Technik. – Springer, Berlin 1957.

Hesketh, J. D., Moss, D. N.: Variation in the response of photosynthesis to light. – Crop Sci. 3: 107-110, 1963.

Hesketh, J. D., Musgrave, R. B.: Photosynthesis under field conditions. IV. Light studies with individual corn leaves. – Crop Sci. 2: 311-315, 1962.

Hill, D. W., Powell, T.: Non-dispersive Infrared Gas Analysis. – Hilger, London 1968.

Holmgren, P.: A device to procure air mixtures with accurate carbon dioxide concentrations. – Lantbrukshögsk. Ann. 34: 219-224, 1968.

Howard, J. N., Burch, D. E., Williams, D.: Infrared transmission of synthetic atmospheres. II. Absorption by carbon dioxide. – J. opt. Soc. Amer. 46: 237-241, 1956.

Huber, B.: Registrierung des CO_2-Gefälles und Berechnung des CO_2-Stromes über Pflanzengesellschaften mittels Ultrarot-Absorptionsschreiber. – Ber. deut. bot. Ges. 63: 52-63, 1950.

Huber, B.: Neue Ergebnisse der pflanzlichen Gaswechselschreibung. – Ber. deut. bot. Ges. 70: 455-461, 1957.

Huber, B.: Recording gaseous exchange under field conditions. – In: Thimann, K. V. (ed.): The Physiology of Forest Trees. Pp. 187-195. Ronald Press, New York 1958.

Huber, B.: Recording photosynthesis, respiration, and transpiration. – In: Zimmerman, M. H. (ed.): The Formation of Wood in Forest Trees. Pp. 497-504. Academic Press, New York 1964.

Huber, B., Polster, H.: Zur Frage der physiologischen Ursachen der unterschiedlichen Stofferzeugung von Pappelklonen. – Biol. Zentralbl. 74: 370-420, 1955.

Hunt, L. A., Impens, I. I., Lemon, E. R.: Preliminary wind tunnel studies of the photosynthesis and evapotranspiration of forage stands. – Crop Sci. 7: 575-579, 1967.

Janáč, J.: Messgenauigkeit von Infrarot-Gasanalysengeräten. – Messen-Steuern-Regeln 9 ap: 119-122, 1965.

Janáč, J.: Otsenka velichiny poleznogo deĭstviya istochnikov izlucheniya infrakrasnykh gazoanalizatorov. [Efficiency of the radiation sources in IRGAs.] – Opt. Spektroskopiya 20: 154-162, 1966.

Janáč, J.: The accuracy of the differential measurement of small CO_2 concentration differences with the infra-red analyzer. – Photosynthetica 4: 302-308, 1970.

Jarvis, P. G., Slatyer, R. O.: A controlled-environment chamber for studies of gas exchange by each surface of a leaf. – CSIRO Div. Land Res. techn. Pap. 29: 1-16, 1966.

Kenndall, D. N.: Applied Infrared Spectroscopy. – Reinhold, New York 1966.

Koch, W.: Der Tagesgang der 'Produktivität der Transpiration'. – Planta 48: 418-452, 1957.

Koch, W., Klein, E., Walz, H.: Neuartige Gaswechsel-Meßanlage für Pflanzen in Laboratorium und Freiland. – Siemens-Z. 42: 392-404, 1968.

Koller, D., Samish, Y.: A null-point compensating system for simultaneous and continuous measurement of net photosynthesis and transpiration by controlled gas-stream analysis. – Bot. Gaz. 125: 81-88, 1964.

Lange, O. L., Koch, W., Schulze, E. D.: CO_2-Gaswechsel und Wasserhaushalt von Pflanzen in der Negev-Wüste am Ende der Trockenzeit. – Ber. deut. bot. Ges. 82: 39-61, 1969.

Lascombes, G.: Remarques sur l'utilisation des analyseurs de gaz a infrarouge pour l'étude écologique de la photosynthèse. – Ann. Sci. nat., Bot. (Paris), Ser. 12, 4: 251-264, 1963.

Leblond, C., Carlier, G.: Technique pour la mesure de l'émission de gaz carbonique par les organes végétaux sur pied, en conditions définies de température et d'humidité relative. – In: Eckardt, F. E.(ed.): Methodology of Plant Eco-physiology. Pp. 275-281. UNESCO, Paris 1965.

Legg, B. J., Parkinson, K. J.: Calibration of infra-red gas analysers for use with carbon dioxide. – J. sci. Instrum. (J. Phys. E) Ser. 2, 1: 1003-1006, 1968.

Levy, A.: The accuracy of the bubble meter for gas flow measurements. – J. sci. Instrum. 41: 449-453, 1964.

Lister, G. R., Krotkov, G., Nelson, C. D.: A closed-circuit apparatus with an infrared CO_2 analyzer and a Geiger tube for continuous measurement of CO_2 exchange in photosynthesis and respiration. – Can. J. Bot. 39: 581-591, 1961.

Lourence, F. J., Pruitt, W. O.: Flexible bags collect gas samples. – Control Eng. 1967 (September): 105, 1967.

Louwerse, W., van Oorschot, J. L. P.: An assembly for routine measurements of photosynthesis, respiration and transpiration of intact plants under controlled conditions. – Photosynthetica 3: 305-315, 1969.

Luck, W.: Feuchtigkeit. – R. Oldenbourg, München–Wien 1964.

Luft, K. F.: Über eine neue Methode der registrierenden Gasanalyse mit Hilfe der Absorption ultraroter Strahlen ohne spectrale Zerlegung. – Z. techn. Phys. 24: 97-104, 1943.

Luft, K. F.: Der *Unor*, ein neues Gasanalysengerät für den Bergbau. – Glückauf 98: 493-495, 1962.

Luft, K. F., Mohrmann, D.: Neues Gerät zur paramagnetischen Sauerstoff-Messung.–Chemie-Ingenieur-Technik 39: 575-578, 1967.

Luft, K. F., Kesseler, G., Zörner, K. H.: Nichtdispersive Ultrarot-Gasanalyse mit dem *UNOR*. – Chemie-Ingenieur-Technik 39: 937-945, 1967.

Maas, J. A.: Die visco-elastischen Eigenschaften von Kautschuk und glatten Muskeln, kontrolliert am Stoffwechsel des Helixfusses. – N.V. Noordhollandsche Uitgevers Maatschappij, Amsterdam 1938.

McAlister, E. D.: Spectrographic method for determining the carbon dioxide exchange between an organism and its surroundings. – Plant Physiol. 12: 213-215, 1937.

Meinl, G., Gössler, H.: Poznámky ke konstrukci přepínačů odběrových míst při měření fotosyntézy a transpirace rostlin infračerveným analyzátorem. [Construction of sequential valves in measurements of photosynthesis and transpiration with an IRGA.] – Rostlinná Výroba (Praha) 4: 427-435, 1965.

Milthorpe, F. L., Penman, H. L.: The diffusive conductivity of the stomata of wheat leaves. – J. exp. Bot. 18: 422-457, 1967.

Mooney, H. A., Dunn, E. L., Harrison, A. T., Morrow, P. A., Bartholomew, B., Hays, R. L.: A mobile laboratory for gas exchange measurements. – Photosynthetica 5: in press, 1971.

Müller, G., Nauck, G.: Reinste Gase. – Verlag Wissenschaft, Berlin 1965.

Nátr, L.: Stanovení příjmu a výdeje CO_2 jednotlivými orgány obilovin v konstantních podmínkách. [Determination of the uptake and release of CO_2 by different organs of cereals at constant conditions.] – Rostlinná Výroba (Praha) 10: 751-762, 1964.

Neuwirth, G.: Aufbau und Arbeitsweise eines Feldlabors zur Messung von CO_2-Assimilation und Transpiration in Pflanzenbeständen. – Biol. Plant. 7: 212-217, 1965.

Nielsen, G., Madsen, A.: An apparatus designed for drying of streaming air. – Scand. J. clin. Lab. Invest. 16: 115-118, 1964.

Noyons, A. K. M.: Eine Methode zur kontinuierlichen Registrierung des Stoffwechsels von Mensch und Tier. – Acta Brevia neerl. Physiol., Pharmacol., Microbiol. 5: 23-24, 1935.

van Oorschot, J. L. P., Belksma, M.: An assembly for the continuous recording of CO_2-exchange and transpiration of whole plants. – Weed Res. 1: 245-257, 1961.
Orchard, B., Heath, O. V. S.: Carbon assimilation at low carbon dioxide levels. I. Apparatus and technique. – J. exp. Bot. 15: 314-330, 1964.
Ormrod, D. P.: Photosynthesis rates of young rice plants as affected by light intensity and temperature. – Agron. J. 53: 93-95, 1961.
Ower, E., Pankhurst, R. C.: The Measurement of Air Flow. – Pergamon Press, Oxford – New York 1966.
Parkinson, K. J.: Apparatus for the simultaneous measurement of water vapour and carbon dioxide exchanges of single leaves. – J. exp. Bot. 19: 840-856, 1968.
Penner, S. S.: Quantitative Molecular Spectroscopy and Gas Emissivities. – Addison-Wesley Publ., Reading 1959.
Pieters, G. A.: Some aspects of the problem of sun and shade leaves. – Proc. 16th int. hort. Congr., Vol. 4. Pp. 393-399. Brussels 1964.
Pinkava, J.: Unit Operations in the Laboratory. – Academia, Prague 1970.
Polster, H., Fuchs, S.: Verwendungsmöglichkeiten des Ultrarot-Absorptionsschreibers für Assimilations- und Atmungsmessungen im Freiland. – Biol. Zentralbl. 75: 373-376, 1956.
Přibyl, M.: Coulometrische Eichung der Geräte zur Bestimmung kleiner Kohlendioxidmengen. – Fres. Z. anal. Chem. 217: 7-12, 1966.
Roccanova, B.: The present state of art of the preparation of gaseous standards. – Pittsburgh Conf. anal. Chem. Spectroscopy, 1968.
Scarth, G. W., Loewy, A., Shaw, M.: Use of the infrared total absorption method for estimating the time course of photosynthesis and transpiration. – Can. J. Res., Ser. C, 26: 94-107, 1948.
Schaub, H., Hilgenberg, W., Fock, H.: Eine neue Meßanordnung zur gleichzeitigen Messung von Sauerstoff und Kohlendioxid im offenen Gasstrom. – Z. Pflanzenphysiol. 60: 64-71, 1968.
Schnelle, P. D.: A precision gas mixer for calibrating analyzers. – ISA J. 4(4): 128-133, 1957.
Slavík, B.: Methods of Studying Plant Water Relations. – Springer Verlag, Berlin–Heidelberg–New York 1972, in press.
Slavík, B., Čatský, J.: Differentially measuring infrared analyzer with an air-conditioned exposure chamber for photosynthetic rate measurements. – Biol. Plant. 5: 135-142, 1963.
Stoy, V.: Photosynthesis, respiration and carbohydrate accumulation in spring wheat in relation to yield. – Physiol. Plant. 18 (Suppl. IV): 1-125, 1965.
Strugger, S., Baumeister, W.: Zur Anwendung des Ultrarotabsorptionsschreibers für CO_2-Assimilationsmessungen im Laboratorium. – Ber. deut. bot. Ges. 64: 5-22, 1951.
Tamm, E., Krzysch, G.: Beobachtungen des Wachstumsfaktors CO_2 in der Vegetationszone. – Z. Acker-Pflanzenbau 107: 275-300, 1959.
Thomas, T. L., Mays, R. L.: Separations with molecular sieves. – In: Berl, W. G. (ed.): Physical Methods in Chemical Analysis, Vol. 4. Pp. 45-98. New York-London 1961.
Tranquillini, W.: Der Ultrarot-Absorptionsschreiber im Dienste ökologischer Messungen des pflanzlichen CO_2-Umsatzes. – Ber. deut. bot. Ges. 65: 102-112, 1952.
Trusell, F., Diehl, H.: Efficiency of chemical desiccants. – Anal. Chem. 35: 674-677, 1963.
van der Veen, R.: Induction phenomena in photosynthesis. II. – Physiol. Plant. 2: 287-296, 1949.
Vejlby, K.: Induction phenomena in photosynthesis. Simultaneous measurements of CO_2 and O_2 exchange. – Physiol. Plant. 12: 162-172, 1959.
Weast, R. C. (ed.): Handbook of Chemistry and Physics. 49th Ed. – Chemical Rubber Co., Cleveland, Ohio 1968.
Weigl, J. W., Warrington, P. M., Calvin, M.: The relation of photosynthesis to respiration. – J. Amer. chem. Soc. 73: 5058-5063, 1951.
Went, F. W.: A mobile desert laboratory. – Plant Sci. Bull. 4: 1-3, 1958.
Woolhouse, H. W.: Leaf age and mesophyll resistance as factors in the rate of photosynthesis. – Hilger J. 11(1): 7-12, 1967–8.
Young, R. E., Biale, J. B.: Carbon dioxide effects on fruit respiration. I. Measurement of oxygen uptake in continuous gas flow. – Plant Physiol. 37: 409-415, 1962.
Yuan, E. L., Evans, R. W., Daniels, F.: Energy efficiency of photosynthesis by *Chlorella*. – Biochim. biophys. Acta 17: 185-193, 1955.

4 | PHYSICO-CHEMICAL MEASUREMENT OF pCO_2 AND CHEMICAL DETERMINATION OF CARBON DIOXIDE

4.1 | Characteristics of analysers of this group

Methods of analysing CO_2 using relatively simple equipment will be described in this chapter. These allow a large number of separate determinations to be made both in the field and the laboratory (the conductimetric analyser – Section 4.2), or in the field alone (Sections 4.3 and 4.4). The first type allows continuous, simultaneous analysis of several air streams as in the aerodynamic method. Both types can be utilised where the biological variability of the material or the variability of environmental factors is so great that a large number of simultaneous (often comparative) determinations is necessary in order that the results are statistically satisfactory. In the field, in many cases only moderate accuracy may then be acceptable. It must be pointed out, however, that the colorimetric (Section 4.3) and absorption conductimetric (Section 4.4) analysers are only of limited use in terms of present-day requirements and approaches to photosynthetic research. The value of the recently proposed continuous conductimetric analyser (Section 4.2) can be shown only by future general use.
Even the so-called serial methods for determining CO_2 exchange rate must comply with the principles of modern gasometric methods. Thus, the general requirements presented in Chapters 2 and 3 must also be met by these simpler CO_2 analysers.

4.2 | Conductimetric measurement of carbon dioxide concentration using deionized water

The use of deionized water to measure the concentration of carbon dioxide in air by conductivity was proposed by James (1966) and first developed for use with plants by Bowman (1968a). Carbon dioxide from the air dissolves in the deionized water in an absorption vessel and the electrical conductivity of the water is then measured. Both James and Bowman used a vertical absorption tube, supplied at the base with deionized water from a column of mixed-bed resin. Bubbles of air introduced near the base of the absorption tube entrain water as they rise and at the top of the tube the air escapes to waste while the water flows through a conductivity cell and re-circulates back to the deionizing column. The sensitivity of Bowman's instrument is adequate for its intended purpose, *i.e.*, incorporation in a system for controlling the carbon dioxide concentration in glasshouses where fluctuations of 5–10 % about the desired value of about 10^3 vpm (parts per million by volume) are acceptable, but it is unsuitable for photosynthesis studies in which an accuracy better than $\pm$ 1 vpm is required. An improved instrument was described by Begg and Lake (1968); we now amplify that description and give details of recent experience and modifications.

4.2.1 | *Theory*

4.2.1.1 | Exchange in parallel flow

This is essentially the process occurring in Bowman's instrument. For conservation of carbon dioxide in the absorption vessel,

$$\rho V(p_1 - p_2)/P = 2.4\, V'p_2'/\mathrm{K} \qquad [\mathrm{g\ min^{-1}}] \tag{4.1}$$

where V and V' are the volumetric flows [$\mathrm{cm^3\ min^{-1}}$] of air and water, P is the atmospheric pressure [mb], p_1 and p_2 are the partial pressures of carbon dioxide in the air entering and leaving the absorption vessel, p_2' is the partial pressure of carbon dioxide in the water leaving the absorption vessel, K is Henry's Law Constant [1.65×10^6 mb at 25 °C in dilute solution] and ρ is the density [$\mathrm{g\ cm^{-3}}$] of carbon dioxide.
The sensitivity of the instrument depends on the fraction ϕ'/ϕ, where ϕ' is the mole fraction of carbon dioxide in the outgoing water and ϕ is the concentration [vpm] in the incoming air. By analogy with heat exchange in parallel flow (Schack 1965, equation 453) under steady state conditions,

$$10^6\, \phi'/\phi = \frac{1 - \exp[-\,UA(\mathrm{K}/2.4\, V' + P/\rho V)]}{2.4\, V'/\rho V + \mathrm{K}/P} \tag{4.2}$$

where U is a transfer coefficient [$\mathrm{g\ cm^{-2}\ min^{-1}\ mb^{-1}}$] and A is the area [$\mathrm{cm^2}$] of the air-water interface. When this interface is large, *i.e.*, as $UA \rightarrow \infty$, the exponential term approaches zero and

$$10^6\, \phi'/\phi \rightarrow \frac{P}{\mathrm{K} + 2.4\, V'P/\rho V} \tag{4.3}$$

If the condition

$$V'/V \ll \mathrm{K}\rho/2.4\, P (= 1.23 \text{ at } 25°\mathrm{C} \text{ and } 1\,013 \text{ mb}) \tag{4.4}$$

can also be satisfied, the sensitivity is further improved and

$$10^6\, \phi'/\phi \rightarrow P/\mathrm{K} \tag{4.5}$$

However, in instruments such as Bowman's, where the volumetric flows of water and air are approximately equal ($V' \simeq V$), condition (4.4) is not satisfied and when UA is large (4.3) becomes $10^6\, \phi'/\phi \simeq P/1.7\,\mathrm{K}$.

4.2.1.2 | Exchange in counter-flow

Equation (4.1) remains valid for this process, but the equation upon which the sensitivity depends is changed. By analogy with the appropriate equation for steady state heat exchange in counter-flow (Schack 1965, equation 455)

$$10^6\,\phi'/\phi = \frac{1 - \exp[UA(K/2.4\,V' - P/\rho V)]}{2.4\,V'/\rho V - \dfrac{K}{P}\exp[UA(K/2.4\,V' - P/\rho V)]} \tag{4.6}$$

$$\simeq \frac{P}{K + 2.4\,V'/UA} \tag{4.7}$$

when the exponential terms are small compared with unity. An alternative form of this equation has been given by Begg and Lake (1968). When $UA \to \infty$ the exponential terms will approach infinity if

$$V'/V < K\rho/2.4\,P \tag{4.8}$$

and then (4.6) reduces to (4.5), *i.e.*, the sensitivity is the same as the best attainable with parallel flow. With $V' \simeq V$ the sensitivity exceeds that of Bowman's parallel flow instrument by a factor of $\sim$ 1.7. However, if (4.8) is not satisfied, the exponential terms in (4.6) approach zero when $UA \to \infty$ and then

$$10^6\,\phi'/\phi \to V/2.4\,V' \tag{4.9}$$

$$< P/K \tag{4.10}$$

so that the sensitivity is less than the best attainable with parallel flow.
For many applications there is an upper limit to V so that condition (4.4) or condition (4.8) can be satisfied only by adjusting V'. As the response time of the instrument is inversely related to the rate at which the conductivity cell can be flushed with water, it is desirable for V' to be large and (4.8) is thus more readily satisfied than (4.4). For maximum sensitivity, counter flow thus seems preferable to parallel flow.

4.2.1.3 | Equilibration

Conditions (4.4) and (4.8) both require water to flow slowly in the absorption vessel; in the limit, when V' is zero, full equilibration can occur and Henry's law [condition (4.5) written as an equation] is obeyed. In principle, this could be

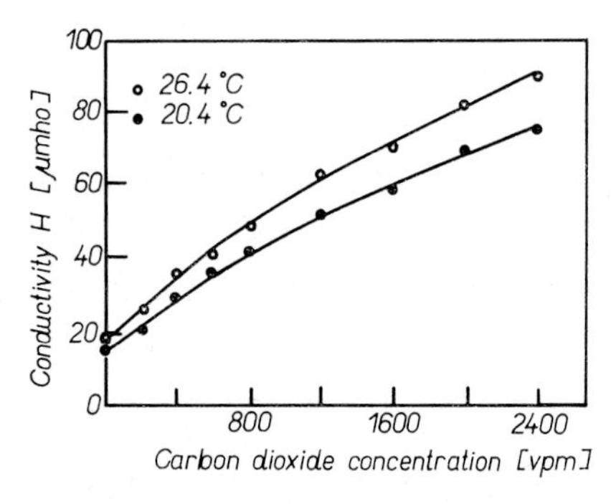

Fig. 4.1 Relationship between carbon dioxide concentration and the conductivity of the shunted conductivity cell at two temperatures.

achieved by using the conductivity cell itself as the absorption vessel and bubbling air through deionized water contained in it.

Whether the exchange is by parallel flow, counter flow, or full equilibration, the sensitivity could evidently be increased by increasing P, *i.e.*, by compressing the gas in the absorption vessel; the sensitivity of an infra-red gas analyser can be increased in a similar way (Bowman 1968a), but there are considerable practical difficulties.

An upper limit to sensitivity may be set by the need to maintain a linear calibration. The dissolved carbon dioxide combines with the water and ionizes; when ϕ' is small the resulting electrical conductivity is linearly proportional to ϕ, but as ϕ' becomes larger the linear relationship no longer holds (Fig. 4.1). Thus ϕ'/ϕ must be so adjusted that linearity is maintained at the greatest value of ϕ to be measured. In our application, this was $\sim$ 600 vpm.

4.2.2 | *Specification*

4.2.2.1 | Sensitivity

In the context of measuring the carbon dioxide exchange of plants, the greatest sensitivity is likely to be required for measuring concentration profiles in the open in and above plant communities during dull or windy weather. The difference in concentration between two levels in a profile may often be less than 10 vpm, so that in principle a sensitivity of 0.2 vpm would be desirable. In leaf chamber experiments, the rates of gas flow can often be so adjusted that the carbon dioxide concentration differences to be measured are about 50 vpm and an instrument sensitivity of 1.0 vpm is then acceptable.

4.2.2.2 | Linearity

A linear calibration is essential if the use of linearizing circuits is to be avoided and the output of the instrument is to be integrated to measure average concentrations; it also facilitates routine calibration checks. For measuring field profiles, linearity over the range 0–600 vpm is usually adequate, but when the output is to be continuously recorded, a non-linear calibration is acceptable, provided the instrument has advantages to outweigh the relative difficulty of calibration.

4.2.2.3 | Absolute and differential measurement

Both in the open and in leaf chambers, it is usually necessary to measure the absolute concentration in one air stream, together with one or more measurements of concentration differences. The instrument should be adaptable for either kind of measurement by simple electrical switching, *e.g.*, on command from a data-logging system.

4.2.2.4 | Multi-channel operation

In field profile measurements, concentrations are usually measured at about ten levels. It is desirable to be able to scan the profile at any time, *e.g.*, with a data-logging system, without the need to switch gas samples and the attendant delays in instrument response.

4.2.2.5 | Lag coefficient

If the requirement for multi-channel operation is satisfied, then for profile studies in the open it is not important that the instrument should respond rapidly to changes in the concentration provided that there is no hysteresis and provided the response time is not too long compared with the scanning interval. By contrast, in leaf chambers the responses of leaves to sudden or transient changes in environment are often studied. Typically, the lag coefficient of stomatal response is of the order of 10 min and the lag coefficient of the instrument should be negligible by comparison, *e.g.*, briefer than 1/2 min.

4.2.2.6 | Reliability

An instrument is often required to be in continuous use throughout a growing season so reliability is essential. It must also be able to operate without attention for periods up to about 12 hours.

4.2.3 | The choice of design and materials

4.2.3.1 | Flow in the absorption vessel

Of the systems considered in Section 4.2.1 that described in Section 4.2.1.3 seems at first to be the most promising. If the conductivity cell itself is used as an absorption vessel the instrument can be extremely simple. For field use, a cell could be placed at each sampling point so that the connections between field site and laboratory need only be electrical, without the need for gas sampling tubes. However, in laboratory use the deionized water became contaminated with ionizing solutes other than carbon dioxide and as the effect of the contamination was cumulative the instrument zero drifted erratically.
When the deionized water in the absorption vessel is continuously replaced, a particle of an ionizing solute carried as dust in the air stream has only a transient effect on the measured conductivity. As shown in Section 4.2.1.2 counter-flow of water and air is preferable to parallel flow.

4.2.3.2 | Counter-flow absorption vessels

The vessel must be made from inert material and it should also be trans parent or translucent so that, when setting up the apparatus, the absence of air locks can be verified. Nylon proved convenient as it is easily cut and welded.
As K is strongly temperature-dependent, the absorption vessel must be compact enough to fit into a water bath with accurate temperature control. Another requirement is that the geometry should be such as to maintain a constant area, A,

of air/water interface, although as (4.5) and (4.9) show, this becomes less important as A is increased.
A vertical nylon tube (dia. 5 cm) filled with either nylon beads, *Dixon* (stainless steel) rings or *Raschig* (porcelain) rings to increase A, gave erratic results, apparently because of variations in V' and A.
An inclined nylon tube, straight or in a helix and without beads or rings, has proved satisfactory, although to maintain A constant the slope of the tube must not change with time, and clamping to a rigid support is necessary. An absorption tube of stainless steel (medical grade) may be suitable, but it must be insulated electrically from the water bath.
We considered using the enzyme carbonic anhydrase in the absorption vessel, but although this would facilitate solution and ionization of the carbon dioxide, it is too unstable for our purpose.

4.2.3.3 | The conductivity cell

This must be of a design suitable for continuous flow and, to measure the very small conductivity of the deionized water accurately, the cell constant must be about 0.01. Two cells of this specification can be bought, but only one, made of stainless steel, proved satisfactory for the present purpose. The alternative kind was made of an epoxy resin casting with annular carbon electrodes, and when used in the instrument the signal drifted continuously, presumably because of surface effects at the electrodes.
Satisfactory cells have been made from rhodium coated brass, but they are not yet on sale.

4.2.3.4 | Flow control

The rates of flow of both air and water affect the sensitivity of the instrument (equation 4.6) although the effects become small when (4.8) is satisfied and A is large. When (4.8) holds good, the water flow rate affects the sensitivity, *via* the exponential term in equation (4.6), more than does the air flow rate. Also, water flow rate had a large effect on the reading of the conductivity cell. Thus, in the instrument described below, a change of 1% in the water flow rate of 100 cm^3 min^{-1} caused a change of 1% (3 vpm in normal air) in the apparent carbon dioxide concentration. By contrast, when the air flow rate (500 cm^3 min^{-1}) was changed by 1% the corresponding change in apparent carbon dioxide concentration was only 0.03% (0.1 vpm in normal air).
The best commercial water pumps of suitable output maintain a flow constant to $\pm$ 1%, which is inadequate for our purpose. The use of constant head and a capillary tube was therefore preferred and the flows of both water and air were controlled in this way.

4.2.3.5 | Deionization

The cartridge of mixed-bed resin used for this purpose can be bought, but the filter gauze provided fails to prevent some small resin particles from contaminating

the deionized water. It is therefore necessary to supplement this filter with a second one (pore size about 15 μm).
The conductivity of the deionized water may change slightly with time and this can be allowed for in one of two ways. A second conductivity cell can be placed between the deionizing column and the absorption tube; the cells can then be compared electrically. Alternatively and simpler, carbon dioxide-free nitrogen can be passed through the absorption tube to provide a routine check on the instrument zero.

4.2.4 | *Description of the instrument*

4.2.4.1 | Air and water circuit

The air is filtered to remove dust particles and a constant flow of 500 cm^3 min^{-1} through the absorption tube is achieved by an air pressure regulator filled with paraffin oil, *E* (Fig. 4.2) and a capillary, C_1. The air leaves the absorption tube through an outlet sloping downwards so that any water condensing on the walls is carried away from the instrument.
Control of water flow [100 cm^3 min^{-1}, satisfying condition (4.8)] through the column of mixed-bed deionizing resin, *D*, the absorption tube, *S*, and the conductivity cell, *B*, is by means of a fixed head, *h* (~ 45 cm) between the two reservoirs, H_1 and H_2, and a capillary, C_2 (~ 15 cm long and 0.14 cm internal diameter) in the

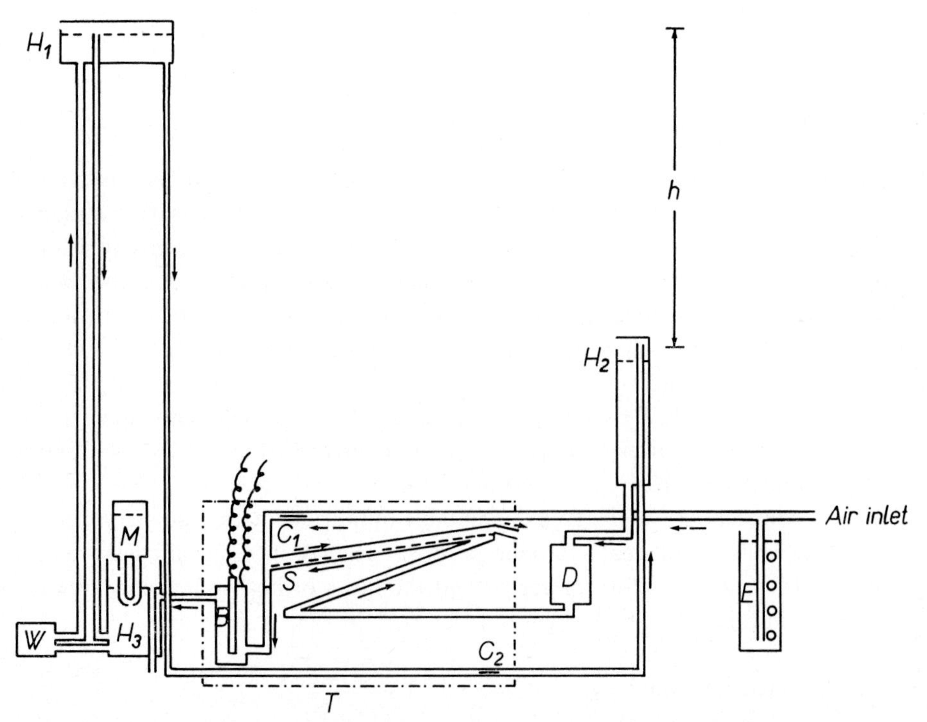

Fig. 4.2 Diagram of air and water circuits. *B:* conductivity cell, C_1, C_2: capillaries, *D:* deionizing column, *E:* air pressure regulator, H_1, H_2, H_3: reservoirs, *M:* Marriotte bottle, *S:* absorption tube, *T:* thermostat bath, *W:* water pump.

thermostat bath, *T*. New deionizing cartridges must be flushed through with about a litre of water, as recommended by the manufacturer, before fitting to the instrument.
An overflow from reservoir H_1 accommodates variations in the output of the water pump *W*. The reservoir H_2 accommodates small variations in the resistance to water flow through the deionizing column *D*.
The thermostat bath controls the temperature of the air and water passing through the capillaries and the temperature of the absorption tube and the conductivity cell with the required accuracy (see Section 4.2.7). The water from the conductivity cell passes into reservoir H_3 where the water level is controlled by a Marriotte bottle, *M*, and an overflow to waste. Reservoir H_3 supplies the pump with water and receives the overflow from H_1. To facilitate setting the apparatus up, it is useful to have an additional overflow, not shown in the drawing, from H_2 to H_3.
All fittings between the deionizing column and the conductivity cell must be of an inert material such as nylon, to avoid contamination of the deionized water. The absorption tube consists of a 75 cm length of 1 cm internal diameter nylon tubing with a fall of 4 cm, dimensions found by experiment to give a suitable sensitivity and lag coefficient. The fittings between the conductivity cell and the deionizing column need not be of inert material as any contamination of the water is removed by the deionizing resin. Ordinary tap water may be used in the Marriotte bottle to maintain the water level in the reservoir H_3.

4.2.4.2 | Electrical circuit

The principle of operation of the electrical circuit is to detect changes in the alternating current potential across a resistance, R_2 ($\sim$ 100 Ω), in series with the conductivity cell, R_1 (Fig. 4.3). These changes are amplified and rectified and the direct current in resistances R_3 and R_4 ($50\,\Omega \leq R_3 + R_4 \leq 5000\,\Omega$) is proportional to the cell conductivity, $1/R_1$. The direct current output changes from 0.1 to 1.0 mA when the conductivity changes from 10 to 100 μmho. The portion of the circuit within the dotted lines in Fig. 4.3 is available commercially (*e.g.*, *Electronic Switchgear Ltd.*, *Conductivity Transmitter TX2/F*). The value of R_3 is chosen to suit the potentiometric recorder and the desired range of carbon dioxide measure-

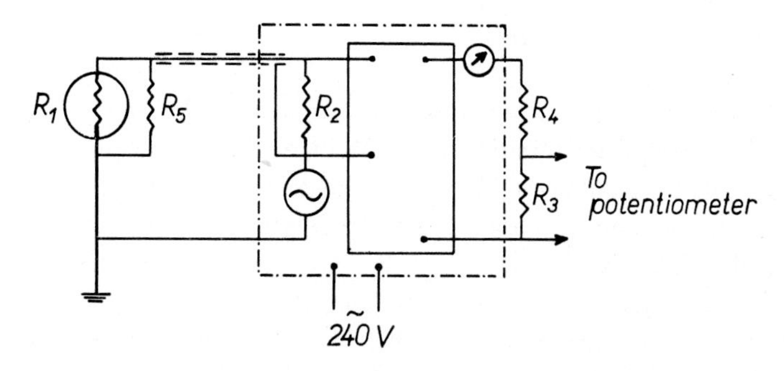

Fig. 4.3 Schematic diagram of electrical circuit. Typical values of the resistors are: R_1 (the conductivity cell) 100 kΩ, R_2 100 Ω, R_3 27 Ω, R_4 2 kΩ, R_5 100 kΩ. The part within the dotted lines is available commercially.

ment. If the recorder has a full scale deflection of 1 mV and it is desired to make this correspond to a carbon dioxide concentration change of 100 vpm, a suitable value for R_3 is 27 Ω. Over the range of measured conductivities 15 to 100 μmho, the potential across R_3 is linearly proportional to the measured conductivity. However, the conductivity of the cell when containing deionized water at 20 °C is only ~ 6 μmho and it is therefore shunted with R_5 (10 μmho). With this arrangement, the potential across R_3 is about 8 mV when measuring the carbon dioxide concentration in normal air and it is necessary to use a stable potential source of about 7.5 mV to back off the unwanted part of the signal when using a 1 mV recorder. When a data logging system with a suitable digital voltmeter is used in place of the 1 mV recorder, the backing-off potential source is not required.

4.2.4.3 | Sensitivity and lag coefficient

The calibration is shown (Fig. 4.1) in terms of the change in conductivity of the shunted conductivity cell (*i.e.*, R_1 with R_5). Corresponding values for the conductivity of the cell without a shunt are found by subtracting 10 μmho. The calibration is linear up to ~ 600 vpm.
If the conductivity changes by ΔG, the initial value being G_0, the lag coefficient λ is defined as the time taken for the value to change to

$$G_\lambda = G_0 - \Delta G(1 - e^{-1})$$

On this definition, $\lambda = 20$ s.

4.2.4.4 | Stability

The stability of the instrument zero depends mainly on the water bath temperature control and on the deionizing resin. The effective life of the resin when continuously measuring carbon dioxide in normal air is of the order of ten weeks; any deterioration is detected by periodic zero checks with carbon dioxide-free air or nitrogen.

4.2.5 | Multi-channel operation

An eight-channel instrument was made to measure concentration profiles outdoors. The components requiring multiplication include the air pressure regulator, *E*, the reservoir, H_2, the capillaries, C_1 and C_2, the deionizing column, *D*, the absorption tube, *S*, and the conductivity cell, *B*. The conductivity cells are switched into a common electrical circuit on command from a multi-point recorder or data logging system. When two *TX2/F* circuits (see Section 4.2.4.2) were connected electrically so that the difference between their direct current outputs was fed to a potentiometric recorder the signal was noisy because of common mode problems, but in a recent modification by the manufacturer this difficulty has been overcome *(TX 2/F MK II)*.

4.2.6 | *Sources of error*

4.2.6.1 | Temperature control

A rise in temperature increases the electrical conductivity of the solution, but this is partly offset by an increase in the value of Henry's Law Constant, K. The rates of flow through the capillaries and the area, A, of the surface available for exchange also depend on temperature, making exact calculation of the temperature coefficient intractable. It was therefore determined experimentally and found to be 20 vpm per °C change in thermostat bath temperature at 200 vpm and 30 vpm per °C at 400 vpm (Fig. 4.1).
Temperature also affects the density of the water in the head, h, controlling the rate of flow through C_2 which, in turn, has a direct effect on the instrument sensitivity (see Section 4.2.3.4), the coefficient being 0.02% per °C. The temperature control in the water bath should be good enough to ensure that the accuracy of the instrument depends mainly on the range of room temperature variation ΔT_{room} rather than on ΔT_{bath}. Then from the coefficients given above,

$$\Delta T_{bath} < 2 \times 10^{-3}\,\Delta T_{room}.$$

In an ordinary laboratory, ΔT_{room} is unlikely to exceed 10 °C, so $\Delta T_{bath} < 0.02$ °C. In other words, there is little point in attempting to decrease fluctuations in room temperature, except in so far as this may help to ensure that the water bath temperature is controlled to better than ± 0.01 °C, corresponding to ± 0.3 vpm carbon dioxide in normal air.

4.2.6.2 | Backing-off potential

When using a 1 mV recorder rather than a digital voltmeter, as described in Section 4.2.4.2, the absolute accuracy of the measurement depends on the stability of the source of the backing-off potential, a change of 1 μV causing an apparent change of 0.1 vpm carbon dioxide. However, adequate stability is attainable with the use of zener diodes.

4.2.6.3 | Changes in atmospheric pressure

A simple proportional correction (equation 4.5) is adequate but the effect on concentration differences in photosynthesis studies is negligibly small.

4.2.6.4 | Contamination

Gases other than carbon dioxide affect the instrument reading if they combine with water and produce ions. Sulphur dioxide is the one most likely to be encountered outdoors, but the concentration rarely exceeds 0.5 vpm, at which value it is toxic to many plants (Webster 1967).
Dust particles which ionize in solution produce a transient change of conductivity, but the effect of particles too small to be conveniently removed by filtration is trivial.

4.2.7 | *Limitations and advantages*

In some experiments, *e.g.*, when measuring the carbon dioxide concentration Γ, at which net photosynthesis is zero in bright light, it is desirable to avoid changing the composition of the gas during measurement, but change is unavoidable with the present counter-flow instrument. One based on the full equilibration principle (Section 4.2.1.3) would be more suitable for use in this context.

The instrument is much simpler in design and operation than others of comparable performance and it has the advantage over an infra-red gas analyser that it is insensitive to water vapour or to nitrous oxide, which is a gas sometimes used in photosynthesis studies. However, its principal advantage is that it is better suited for continuous multi-channel operation, as required for field studies of carbon dioxide profiles.

4.2.8 | *Addresses of manufacturers*

Several firms make suitable components; the following list is given by way of example, not as a recommendation:

Deionizing column: *Elga Products Ltd.*, Lane End, Buckinghamshire, U.K., Deionizing cartridge *C203*.

Conductivity cell and electrical circuit: *Electronic Switchgear Ltd.*, Hitchin, Hertfordshire, U.K., Cell type *CCW001* ('old pattern'), Conductivity transmitter type *TX2/F*.

Water pump: *Totton Electrical Products Ltd.*, Southampton Rd., Cadnam, Southampton, U.K., Pump unit *175 B/M/DP*.

4.3 | Colorimetric and electrometric measurements of $p\mathrm{CO}_2$

4.3.1 | *Theoretical bases of the measurements*

All modifications of electrometric and colorimetric continuous CO_2 analysers are based on the fact that the pH value of a dilute solution of a bicarbonate of an alkali metal (usually $NaHCO_3$) is proportional to the partial CO_2 pressure in the air in equilibrium with the solution, *i.e.*

$$\begin{array}{ll} \text{air:} & \mathrm{CO_2} \\ & \downarrow\uparrow \\ \text{solution:} & \underbrace{\mathrm{CO_2 + H_2O \rightleftarrows H_2CO_3}}_{(4.12)}\underbrace{\mathrm{\rightleftarrows H^+ + HCO_3^-}}_{(4.11)}\mathrm{\rightleftarrows HCO_3^- + Na^+ \rightleftarrows NaHCO_3} \end{array}$$

The equilibrium constant of the equation (4.11) is given by the expression:

$$K = \frac{[\mathrm{H^+}][\mathrm{HCO_3^-}]}{[\mathrm{H_2CO_3}]} \tag{4.13}$$

As carbonic acid is in equilibrium with the dissolved carbon dioxide (reaction 4.12), the equilibrium constant can be expressed by the equation

$$K = \frac{[H^+][HCO_3^-]}{[CO_2]} \tag{4.14}$$

where $[CO_2]$ is the molar concentration of dissolved carbon dioxide.

Then

$$\frac{1}{[H^+]} = \frac{[HCO_3^-]}{K[CO_2]} \tag{4.15}$$

Taking the logarithm of this expression,

$$-\log[H^+] = -\log K + \log\frac{[HCO_3^-]}{[CO_2]} \tag{4.16}$$

or

$$pH = pK + \log\frac{[HCO_3^-]}{[CO_2]} = pK + \log[HCO_3] - \log[CO_2] \tag{4.17}$$

This dissociation equilibrium, in the form of the Henderson-Hasselbalch equation (4.17), expresses the law that the pH value of a solution containing HCO_3^- ions depends on the molar concentration of CO_2 dissolved in the solution. The molar concentration of CO_2 in the solution is proportional to the CO_2 concentration in the gas phase (air) above the solution, *i.e.* to the partial pressure of CO_2; the pH value is therefore determined by the first dissociation constant of carbonic acid, by the concentration of bicarbonate ions in the solution and by the partial pressure of CO_2 above the solution.

The dependence of the pH value of a solution of 0.001 N $NaHCO_3$ on the partial pressure of CO_2, and thus on the CO_2 concentration in the air at various temperatures, can be calculated using the Henderson-Hasselbalch equation. For practical purposes, however, an empirical equation has been proposed (see Lange 1956). An addition of 0.099 N KCl to eliminate the salt error in colorimetric pH determination is made in some methods. The most recent form of the equation (Čatský & Šesták 1966) is:

$$pH = a - 0.934 \log p \tag{4.18}$$

where a is a coefficient dependent on the temperature and p is the partial pressure of CO_2 in the air expressed in atm.

The above principle of measuring pCO_2 and thus the carbon dioxide concentration in the air was worked out in detail for electrometric (potentiometric) measurements (*e.g.* Wilson, Orcutt & Peterson 1932; Kauko 1935; for recent modifications see *e.g.* Stow, Baer & Randall 1957; Severinghaus & Bradley 1958; Snell 1960; Gingras 1963; Martin & Pigott 1965; Lee & Woolhouse 1966)[1] which, however, can rarely be used in natural conditions. Field potentiometric determinations of

1. For further references see also Gingras (1966).

CO_2 concentration are mostly impractical because of technical difficulties (*e.g.* the necessity for a precision battery pH-meter) and their accuracy is insufficient. The expensive 'bubbling devices' with built-in or movable electrodes are the most important disadvantage of serial potentiometric measurements. In the laboratory, potentiometric measurements of CO_2 concentration also have a number of disadvantages, compared with IRGAs. They have therefore only rarely been used for determining photosynthetic rates, and they will not be discussed in this manual. Less complicated continuous procedures using visual colorimetry for pH measurement were originally described for CO_2 determination in the air in meteorology, bioclimatology, technology, *etc.* (see, *e.g.*, Higgins & Marriott 1917; McClendon 1917; Kauko 1932, 1934; Sajaniemi 1936; Kalle 1937; for recent modifications see, *e.g.*, Sharp 1964 and Bowman 1968b). However, a similar procedure can be utilised in serial continuous determination of the rate of CO_2 exchange (Čatský & Slavík 1958, 1960; Nichiporovich *et al.* 1961; Kreitsberg 1965; Slavík & Čatský 1965; Kreeb 1970).
One of the visual colorimetric CO_2 analysers will be described in detail (Section 4.3.3), as an example of an extremely simple method for serial work, namely for semiquantitative measurements of CO_2 concentration.

Attempts have been made to construct photocolorimetric CO_2 analysers for more

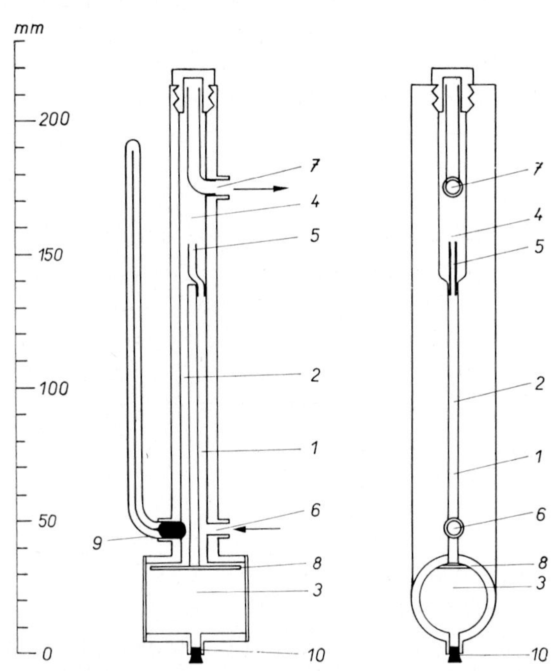

Fig. 4.4 Plexiglass bubbling device for continuous photocolorimetric CO_2 determination (after Slavík & Čatský 1965). *1, 2:* two parallel tubes bored in the plexiglass body, *3:* photocolorimetric cuvette with thin glass windows, *4:* wide tube, *5:* PVC tube, *6:* air inlet, *7:* air outlet, *8:* baffle-plate, *9:* thermometer, *10:* outlet with stopper. The cuvette (*3*) and tubes (*1*) and (*2*) are filled with the bicarbonate solution about 5 mm above the upper mouth of the tubes. The air passes through it in bubbles and carries the solution upward into the tube (*4*). The solution falls from (*5*) and returns through (*2*) to cuvette (*3*).

accurate measurements, but these are rarely used because of the rather complicated construction and the considerable advantages of IRGAs for similar applications. Some authors have designed mains-supplied photocolorimetric analysers. French, Hiesey & Milner (1959) used such an analyser for controlling the CO_2 content in an air-conditioned chamber. They used a double-beam colorimeter; one beam passed through the colorimetric cuvette containing bicarbonate solution with cresol red, the other through a neutral compensating filter (mesh). Both rays were alternately interrupted by a rotary shutter and were then in turn incident on a single photocell. Any change in the extinction in the cuvette disturbs the equilibrium between the two rays and an automatic CO_2 dosing device is activated by the photocell current.

Gulyaev (1965) has designed a mains-supplied analyser which measures the difference in the extinctions of two solutions, through one of which passes control air while the air from the assimilation chamber passes through the other. Gulyaev employs the above bicarbonate solution (0.001 N $NaHCO_3$) diluted several times (usually six times) in order to attain more rapid establishment of equilibrium. However, the dilution lowers the pH value, so that phenol red, with a more acid transition point, is employed.

A field photocolorimetric CO_2 analyser for simultaneous analysis of eight air streams has been designed by Slavík & Čatský (1965). Special bubbling devices allow continuous measurement of absorbance without interrupting the air flow (Fig. 4.4).

4.3.2 | *General principles of the visual colorimetric determination of CO_2 exchange rate*

As in procedures using IRGAs, the photosynthetic rate is determined from the difference in CO_2 concentration between the inlet and the outlet of the assimilation chamber. It must be stressed that colorimetric analysers operate continuously[1], measuring the position of the reversible equilibrium between pCO_2 and the bicarbonate solution.

The air is continuously analysed in a 'bubbling' device, the construction and material of which differs in the various modifications of the method (*e.g.* Fig. 4.5). The air sample passes in the form of small bubbles through 0.001 N $NaHCO_3$ + 0.099 N KCl solution, the pH value of which is measured by means of the added colour indicator (see p. 223). The equilibrium between the CO_2 concentration in the air and the pH of the bicarbonate solution is established after 5 to 10 min, depending on the flow rate and the difference between the original and final pH values (*i.e.* on the change in CO_2 concentration). When measuring extremely low CO_2 concentrations (*e.g.* 100 vpm), equilibrium is reached after 20 or more min, and the concentration is then determined only infrequently (Fig. 4.6, *cf.* also

1. Visual colorimetry was also used by Ålvik (1939), and a number of other authors, for determining photosynthetic rate in a closed glass chamber. Although Ålvik's procedure can, for example, be used for simple determinations of the light compensation point (Pavletić 1958; Pavletić & Lieth 1958; Lieth 1960; Souchon & Souchon 1966), it is unsuitable for measuring CO_2 exchange rate (*e.g.* Frenzel 1955).

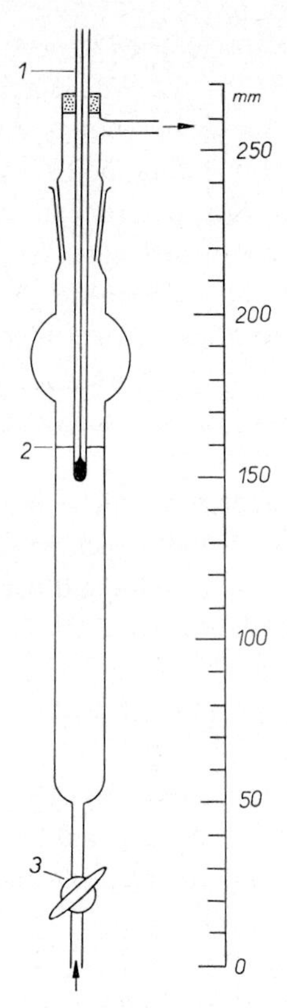

Fig. 4.5 Glass bubbling device for visual colorimetric CO_2 determination (after Čatský & Slavík 1960). *1:* thermometer, *2:* bicarbonate solution level, *3:* 'burette' tap.

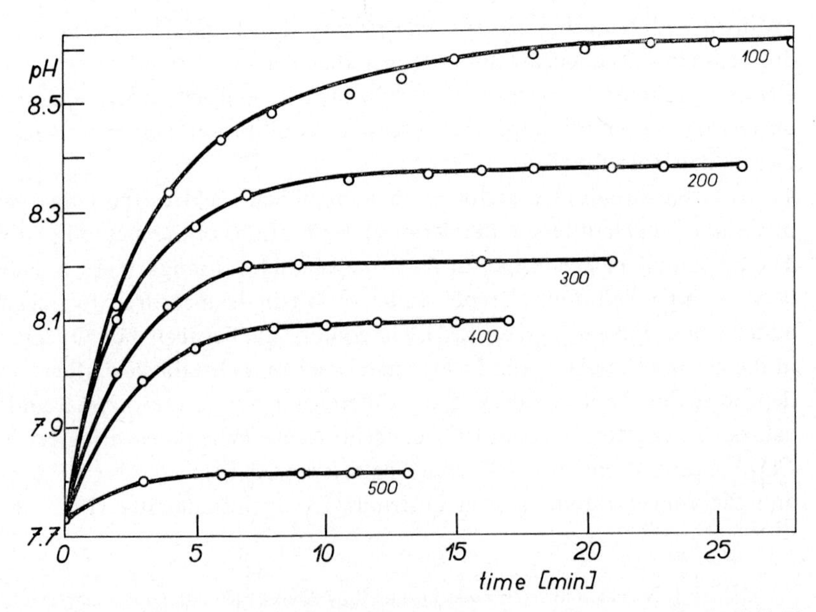

Fig. 4.6 Equilibration between CO_2 concentration in air (figures by the individual curves [vpm]) and the pH of the bicarbonate solution (ordinate). Measured by means of a pH-meter with glass electrode at 25 °C, 15 ml of bicarbonate solution, flow rate 5 l h^{-1}. After Čatský & Šesták (1966).

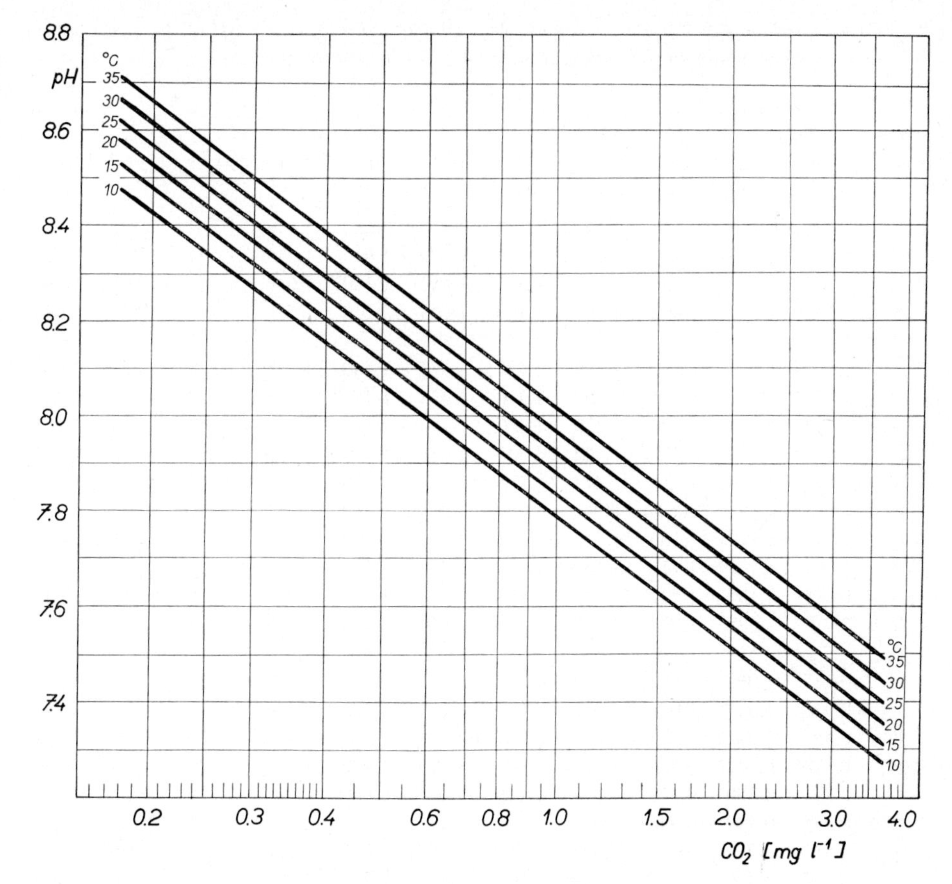

Fig. 4.7 Relationship between pH of the bicarbonate solution (ordinate) and the CO_2 concentration in the air (abscissa [mg l^{-1}]) at different temperatures and 1 013 mb (760 torr) (Čatský & Šesták 1966).

Wilson, Orcutt & Peterson 1932; Lange 1956). Gulyaev (1965) recommended speeding up equilibration (to *ca.* 5 min) by a six-fold reduction in $NaHCO_3$ normality. This decreases the pH value at corresponding CO_2 concentrations by *ca.* 0.8 pH.

At an air flow of 5 to 10 l h^{-1} through 10 to 20 ml of bicarbonate solution, the pH can be determined after *ca.* 10 min of air bubbling and the CO_2 concentration in mg CO_2 l^{-1} can be read directly from a diagram or table (Fig. 4.7, Table 4.1)[1]: both are calculated for 1 013 mb, so that corrections must be made at significantly higher or lower pressures, or the calculations must be verified experimentally.

The pH value and the colour of the bicarbonate solution does not alter after equilibrium between air and the solution has been reached. However, during prolonged air bubbling the solution gets denser by evaporation; this causes

1. The calculation formula will become more precise as it becomes technically possible to make more precise pH measurements; corrections to Table 4.1 can therefore be expected.

Table 4.1 Calculation of the CO_2 concentration in the air from the found pH of the bicarbonate solution at various temperatures and a pressure of 1 013.25 mb (760 torr).

pH	°C										
	10	15	16	17	18	19	20	21	22	23	24
7.67	1.330	1.490	1.515	1.540	1.580	1.620	1.650	1.696	1.740	1.775	1.810
7.68	1.300	1.445	1.476	1.512	1.542	1.580	1.610	1.648	1.694	1.735	1.770
7.69	1.270	1.405	1.437	1.472	1.508	1.540	1.580	1.616	1.652	1.694	1.730
7.70	1.235	1.370	1.402	1.434	1.468	1.504	1.540	1.576	1.612	1.648	1.688
7.71	1.205	1.340	1.366	1.399	1.431	1.464	1.500	1.535	1.572	1.608	1.644
7.72	1.175	1.310	1.336	1.362	1.396	1.428	1.465	1.496	1.532	1.568	1.604
7.73	1.150	1.280	1.306	1.332	1.360	1.393	1.425	1.457	1.492	1.528	1.564
7.74	1.120	1.250	1.276	1.302	1.328	1.358	1.390	1.422	1.454	1.486	1.522
7.75	1.090	1.220	1.246	1.272	1.298	1.324	1.350	1.387	1.419	1.451	1.484
7.76	1.065	1.190	1.216	1.242	1.268	1.294	1.320	1.351	1.384	1.416	1.448
7.77	1.040	1.160	1.186	1.212	1.238	1.264	1.290	1.318	1.349	1.381	1.413
7.78	1.015	1.130	1.156	1.182	1.208	1.234	1.260	1.288	1.316	1.344	1.377
7.79	0.995	1.100	1.126	1.154	1.178	1.208	1.230	1.256	1.286	1.314	1.342
7.80	0.970	1.085	1.097	1.122	1.151	1.174	1.205	1.228	1.253	1.284	1.312
7.81	0.945	1.055	1.080	1.094	1.118	1.148	1.170	1.203	1.226	1.251	1.282
7.82	0.920	1.025	1.052	1.075	1.091	1.114	1.145	1.168	1.201	1.224	1.248
7.83	0.898	1.000	1.023	1.049	1.070	1.088	1.110	1.142	1.166	1.199	1.222
7.84	0.878	0.975	0.998	1.021	1.046	1.065	1.085	1.109	1.139	1.164	1.197
7.85	0.855	0.950	0.973	0.996	1.019	1.043	1.060	1.083	1.108	1.136	1.162
7.86	0.835	0.930	0.948	0.971	0.994	1.017	1.040	1.058	1.081	1.107	1.133
7.87	0.815	0.910	0.927	0.946	0.969	0.992	1.015	1.038	1.056	1.079	1.106
7.88	0.797	0.890	0.907	0.924	0.944	0.967	0.990	1.013	1.036	1.054	1.077
7.89	0.778	0.865	0.887	0.904	0.921	0.942	0.965	0.988	1.011	1.034	1.052
7.90	0.760	0.840	0.863	0.884	0.901	0.918	0.940	0.963	0.986	1.009	1.032
7.91	0.740	0.822	0.839	0.861	0.880	0.898	0.915	0.938	0.961	0.984	1.007
7.92	0.720	0.800	0.821	0.837	0.859	0.877	0.895	0.912	0.936	0.957	0.982
7.93	0.709	0.780	0.799	0.820	0.835	0.857	0.875	0.892	0.909	0.934	0.957
7.94	0.692	0.765	0.779	0.798	0.819	0.834	0.855	0.873	0.889	0.906	0.932
7.95	0.675	0.750	0.764	0.777	0.797	0.818	0.832	0.853	0.870	0.885	0.908
7.96	0.667	0.730	0.748	0.763	0.776	0.796	0.816	0.831	0.851	0.868	0.886
7.97	0.640	0.710	0.728	0.745	0.761	0.775	0.795	0.814	0.830	0.848	0.864
7.98	0.625	0.690	0.706	0.724	0.741	0.758	0.774	0.792	0.810	0.828	0.845
7.99	0.608	0.675	0.690	0.705	0.723	0.740	0.756	0.774	0.792	0.810	0.828
8.00	0.590	0.660	0.674	0.690	0.706	0.722	0.738	0.754	0.772	0.791	0.807
8.01	0.578	0.645	0.659	0.673	0.689	0.705	0.720	0.737	0.754	0.772	0.788
8.02	0.565	0.630	0.644	0.657	0.672	0.688	0.702	0.719	0.735	0.753	0.768
8.03	0.550	0.615	0.629	0.642	0.656	0.671	0.684	0.701	0.717	0.734	0.750
8.04	0.537	0.600	0.614	0.627	0.641	0.655	0.668	0.684	0.700	0.716	0.731
8.05	0.525	0.585	0.599	0.612	0.626	0.640	0.653	0.668	0.682	0.698	0.712
8.06	0.510	0.570	0.584	0.597	0.610	0.624	0.637	0.652	0.666	0.680	0.695
8.07	0.500	0.556	0.569	0.582	0.595	0.609	0.622	0.636	0.650	0.663	0.679
8.08	0.486	0.544	0.554	0.567	0.581	0.594	0.607	0.620	0.634	0.647	0.662
8.09	0.473	0.528	0.540	0.553	0.566	0.579	0.592	0.605	0.619	0.632	0.647
8.10	0.463	0.515	0.527	0.539	0.551	0.564	0.578	0.590	0.604	0.617	0.632

Table 4.1 (continued)

°C											pH
25	26	27	28	29	30	31	32	33	34	35	
1.850	1.900	1.950	2.010	2.070	2.130	2.190	2.250	2.310	2.380	2.450	7.67
1.808	1.846	1.895	1.946	2.002	2.060	2.120	2.180	2.243	2.306	2.371	7.68
1.765	1.804	1.843	1.890	1.943	2.000	2.057	2.114	2.172	2.231	2.290	7.69
1.725	1.760	1.800	1.840	1.885	1.938	1.992	2.046	2.100	2.155	2.210	7.70
1.682	1.720	1.755	1.795	1.835	1.880	1.928	1.978	2.028	2.078	2.130	7.71
1.642	1.680	1.715	1.750	1.790	1.832	1.875	1.918	1.962	2.006	2.050	7.72
1.600	1.636	1.673	1.710	1.749	1.790	1.831	1.873	1.915	1.957	2.000	7.73
1.560	1.596	1.632	1.668	1.704	1.743	1.783	1.823	1.865	1.907	1.950	7.74
1.520	1.556	1.592	1.628	1.664	1.700	1.737	1.776	1.817	1.858	1.900	7.75
1.480	1.514	1.556	1.588	1.624	1.660	1.698	1.737	1.776	1.815	1.855	7.76
1.445	1.478	1.514	1.551	1.584	1.620	1.657	1.695	1.733	1.771	1.810	7.77
1.410	1.443	1.476	1.510	1.545	1.580	1.616	1.653	1.690	1.727	1.765	7.78
1.375	1.407	1.441	1.474	1.503	1.540	1.575	1.611	1.647	1.683	1.720	7.79
1.340	1.372	1.404	1.439	1.472	1.500	1.539	1.574	1.609	1.644	1.680	7.80
1.310	1.337	1.369	1.401	1.437	1.470	1.504	1.538	1.572	1.606	1.640	7.81
1.280	1.308	1.334	1.367	1.399	1.435	1.468	1.501	1.534	1.567	1.600	7.82
1.245	1.277	1.306	1.331	1.363	1.395	1.427	1.460	1.493	1.526	1.560	7.83
1.220	1.242	1.270	1.298	1.328	1.360	1.392	1.424	1.456	1.488	1.520	7.84
1.195	1.216	1.239	1.267	1.295	1.325	1.355	1.386	1.417	1.448	1.480	7.85
1.160	1.192	1.212	1.239	1.266	1.295	1.324	1.354	1.384	1.414	1.445	7.86
1.130	1.158	1.184	1.208	1.236	1.265	1.295	1.325	1.335	1.385	1.415	7.87
1.105	1.128	1.156	1.182	1.208	1.235	1.265	1.295	1.325	1.355	1.385	7.88
1.087	1.104	1.129	1.154	1.183	1.210	1.239	1.268	1.297	1.326	1.355	7.89
1.050	1.074	1.099	1.124	1.152	1.180	1.209	1.238	1.267	1.296	1.325	7.90
1.030	1.053	1.077	1.102	1.125	1.150	1.178	1.206	1.243	1.262	1.290	7.91
1.005	1.026	1.049	1.072	1.096	1.120	1.147	1.174	1.201	1.228	1.255	7.92
0.980	1.003	1.026	1.047	1.071	1.090	1.117	1.147	1.171	1.198	1.225	7.93
0.955	0.978	1.001	1.021	1.042	1.060	1.086	1.112	1.138	1.164	1.190	7.94
0.931	0.954	0.976	0.995	1.015	1.035	1.060	1.085	1.110	1.135	1.160	7.95
0.907	0.928	0.949	0.971	0.993	1.015	1.038	1.061	1.084	1.107	1.130	7.96
0.887	0.908	0.920	0.950	0.970	0.990	1.011	1.032	1.053	1.075	1.095	7.97
0.862	0.880	0.902	0.926	0.947	0.967	0.987	1.007	1.028	1.049	1.070	7.98
0.846	0.865	0.885	0.906	0.927	0.947	0.965	0.983	1.002	1.021	1.040	7.99
0.824	0.840	0.856	0.873	0.892	0.910	0.930	0.950	0.970	0.990	1.010	8.00
0.804	0.821	0.837	0.853	0.872	0.890	0.909	0.928	0.947	0.966	0.985	8.01
0.784	0.801	0.818	0.834	0.852	0.870	0.889	0.908	0.927	0.946	0.965	8.02
0.765	0.782	0.800	0.816	0.834	0.850	0.869	0.888	0.907	0.926	0.945	8.03
0.747	0.764	0.782	0.798	0.815	0.831	0.849	0.868	0.887	0.906	0.925	8.04
0.728	0.746	0.763	0.780	0.795	0.812	0.830	0.848	0.867	0.886	0.895	8.05
0.711	0.728	0.745	0.762	0.777	0.793	0.809	0.825	0.841	0.858	0.875	8.06
0.694	0.711	0.727	0.743	0.759	0.775	0.791	0.807	0.823	0.840	0.857	8.07
0.678	0.694	0.709	0.725	0.741	0.757	0.774	0.791	0.808	0.825	0.843	8.08
0.661	0.677	0.692	0.707	0.723	0.740	0.757	0.774	0.791	0.809	0.827	8,09
0.645	0.659	0.675	0.690	0.706	0.722	0.739	0.756	0.773	0.790	0.807	8.10

Table 4.1 (continued)

pH	°C										
	10	15	16	17	18	19	20	21	22	23	24
8.11	0.453	0.502	0.514	0.526	0.538	0.551	0.563	0.576	0.589	0.602	0.616
8.12	0.441	0.490	0.501	0.513	0.525	0.537	0.550	0.562	0.575	0.588	0.601
8.13	0.430	0.478	0.489	0.500	0.512	0.524	0.536	0.548	0.561	0.573	0.586
8.14	0.420	0.467	0.477	0.488	0.499	0.511	0.523	0.534	0.547	0.559	0.571
8.15	0.410	0.457	0.466	0.476	0.487	0.498	0.510	0.522	0.533	0.545	0.557
8.16	0.400	0.445	0.456	0.465	0.476	0.486	0.497	0.509	0.521	0.531	0.543
8.17	0.390	0.435	0.444	0.454	0.464	0.475	0.485	0.496	0.508	0.519	0.530
8.18	0.380	0.424	0.434	0.443	0.453	0.464	0.474	0.484	0.495	0.507	0.518
8.19	0.372	0.413	0.422	0.432	0.442	0.453	0.462	0.472	0.483	0.493	0.505
8.20	0.363	0.403	0.412	0.422	0.432	0.441	0.450	0.461	0.471	0.481	0.492
8.21	0.355	0.393	0.402	0.411	0.421	0.430	0.439	0.450	0.460	0.470	0.480
8.22	0.345	0.383	0.392	0.401	0.409	0.420	0.429	0.438	0.449	0.459	0.468
8.23	0.338	0.373	0.382	0.391	0.400	0.410	0.419	0.428	0.437	0.447	0.458
8.24	0.329	0.365	0.372	0.381	0.391	0.399	0.408	0.418	0.426	0.435	0.446
8.25	0.321	0.357	0.364	0.372	0.380	0.389	0.398	0.407	0.415	0.425	0.434
8.26	0.312	0.348	0.356	0.364	0.371	0.379	0.388	0.397	0.405	0.414	0.423
8.27	0.304	0.339	0.347	0.355	0.363	0.371	0.378	0.387	0.396	0.404	0.413
8.28	0.298	0.332	0.339	0.347	0.354	0.363	0.370	0.378	0.386	0.395	0.403
8.29	0.291	0.323	0.331	0.338	0.346	0.354	0.361	0.369	0.377	0.385	0.393
8.30	0.282	0.316	0.323	0.330	0.337	0.345	0.352	0.361	0.368	0.375	0.383
8.31	0.276	0.307	0.315	0.322	0.329	0.337	0.344	0.352	0.360	0.367	0.374
8.32	0.268	0.300	0.306	0.314	0.321	0.329	0.336	0.344	0.351	0.359	0.366
8.33	0.263	0.293	0.299	0.306	0.313	0.321	0.328	0.335	0.343	0.350	0.358
8.34	0.257	0.286	0.292	0.299	0.305	0.313	0.320	0.327	0.334	0.342	0.349
8.35	0.251	0.279	0.285	0.291	0.297	0.305	0.312	0.319	0.326	0.333	0.341
8.36	0.245	0.272	0.279	0.285	0.291	0.298	0.304	0.311	0.318	0.325	0.332
8.37	0.238	0.265	0.271	0.278	0.284	0.291	0.297	0.303	0.310	0.317	0.324
8.38	0.233	0.259	0.265	0.271	0.277	0.284	0.290	0.296	0.302	0.309	0.316
8.39	0.227	0.253	0.258	0.264	0.270	0.277	0.283	0.289	0.295	0.302	0.308
8.40	0.221	0.247	0.252	0.257	0.263	0.269	0.276	0.282	0.289	0.295	0.301
8.41	0.216	0.241	0.246	0.252	0.257	0.263	0.269	0.275	0.282	0.288	0.294
8.42	0.211	0.235	0.240	0.246	0.251	0.257	0.262	0.268	0.275	0.281	0.287
8.43	0.206	0.229	0.234	0.240	0.245	0.251	0.256	0.262	0.268	0.274	0.280
8.44	0.202	0.223	0.229	0.234	0.239	0.244	0.250	0.255	0.261	0.267	0.273
8.45	0.197	0.218	0.223	0.228	0.233	0.238	0.244	0.249	0.254	0.260	0.266
8.46	0.190	0.213	0.218	0.223	0.228	0.233	0.238	0.243	0.248	0.254	0.259
8.47	0.185	0.207	0.212	0.217	0.222	0.227	0.232	0.237	0.243	0.248	0.253

Table 4.1 (continued)

°C											pH
25	26	27	28	29	30	31	32	33	34	35	
0.630	0.643	0.656	0.672	0.689	0.705	0.722	0.739	0.756	0.773	0.790	8.11
0.615	0.627	0.641	0.655	0.671	0.687	0.704	0.721	0.739	0.758	0.775	8.12
0.600	0.612	0.626	0.640	0.654	0.669	0.686	0.703	0.720	0.737	0.755	8.13
0.586	0.598	0.611	0.624	0.637	0.651	0.667	0.683	0.699	0.716	0.733	8.14
0.571	0.583	0.596	0.610	0.622	0.636	0.651	0.667	0.683	0.699	0.715	8.15
0.556	0.569	0.582	0.594	0.608	0.622	0.637	0.652	0.667	0.682	0.698	8.16
0.542	0.556	0.567	0.580	0.593	0.607	0.622	0.637	0.652	0.667	0.683	8.17
0.529	0.542	0.553	0.566	0.579	0.591	0.605	0.620	0.635	0.650	0.665	8.18
0.517	0.528	0.539	0.552	0.564	0.576	0.589	0.603	0.617	0.631	0.645	8.19
0.504	0.516	0.527	0.539	0.552	0.564	0.577	0.591	0.605	0.619	0.633	8.20
0.491	0.503	0.514	0.525	0.537	0.550	0.563	0.576	0.590	0.604	0.618	8.21
0.479	0.489	0.500	0.511	0.523	0.535	0.548	0.561	0.674	0.588	0.602	8.22
0.467	0.477	0.488	0.499	0.511	0.521	0.534	0.547	0.560	0.573	0.586	8.23
0.456	0.465	0.476	0.486	0.497	0.509	0.522	0.535	0.548	0.561	0.575	8.24
0.445	0.454	0.464	0.474	0.484	0.495	0.507	0.519	0.531	0.543	0.556	8.25
0.433	0.443	0.454	0.463	0.473	0.483	0.494	0.505	0.516	0.528	0.540	8.26
0.422	0.432	0.442	0.452	0.462	0.472	0.482	0.493	0.504	0.515	0.526	8.27
0.412	0.421	0.431	0.441	0.451	0.461	0.471	0.481	0.492	0.503	0.514	8.28
0.402	0.411	0.421	0.430	0.440	0.450	0.460	0.470	0.480	0.490	0.501	8.29
0.392	0.401	0.410	0.419	0.429	0.439	0.449	0.459	0.469	0.479	0.489	8.30
0.382	0.391	0.400	0.409	0.418	0.428	0.438	0.448	0.458	0.468	0.478	8.31
0.373	0.381	0.390	0.399	0.408	0.417	0.426	0.435	0.445	0.455	0.465	8.32
0.365	0.372	0.380	0.389	0.398	0.406	0.415	0.424	0.434	0.444	0.454	8.33
0.357	0.364	0.371	0.379	0.388	0.397	0.406	0.415	0.424	0.433	0.443	8.34
0.348	0.355	0.363	0.370	0.378	0.387	0.396	0.405	0.414	0.423	0.432	8.35
0.340	0.347	0.355	0.362	0.369	0.377	0.385	0.394	0.403	0.412	0.421	8.36
0.331	0.339	0.346	0.353	0.361	0.368	0.376	0.384	0.393	0.402	0.411	8.37
0.323	0.330	0.338	0.345	0.352	0.359	0.367	0.375	0.383	0.392	0.401	8.38
0.315	0.322	0.329	0.336	0.343	0.350	0.358	0.366	0.374	0.383	0.392	8.39
0.307	0.314	0.321	0.327	0.334	0.341	0.349	0.357	0.365	0.373	0.382	8.40
0.300	0.306	0.313	0.319	0.327	0.333	0.341	0.349	0.357	0.365	0.373	8.41
0.293	0.299	0.305	0.311	0.319	0.325	0.332	0.339	0.347	0.355	0.363	8.42
0.286	0.292	0.298	0.304	0.311	0.318	0.325	0.332	0.340	0.348	0.356	8.43
0.279	0.285	0.291	0.297	0.303	0.310	0.317	0.324	0.331	0.339	0.347	8.44
0.272	0.277	0.283	0.289	0.296	0.303	0.310	0.317	0.324	0.331	0.339	8.45
0.265	0.270	0.276	0.282	0.289	0.295	0.302	0.309	0.316	0.323	0.330	8.46
0.258	0.263	0.269	0.275	0.281	0.287	0.293	0.300	0.307	0.314	0.321	8.47

Table 4.2 Selected indicators which can be used for the colorimetric determination of CO_2

Range of CO_2 concentration			Indicator	pH range of the indicator	Colour change with increase in pH[3]
[mg l^{-1}]	[vol.%]	Corresponding pH range			
0.2– 0.6	0.011– 0.033	8.7–8.2	phenolphthalein	8.3–10.0	cl → re
			o-cresolphthalein	8.2– 9.8	cl → re
			thymol blue[2]	8.0– 9.6	ye → bl
			xylenol blue	8.0– 9.6	ye → bl
			tetrabromophenolphthalein	8.0– 9.0	cl → vi
0.3– 1.5	0.016– 0.082	8.5–7.9	*m*-cresol purple	7.4– 9.0	ye → p
0.5– 3.0	0.028– 0.170	8.3–7.5	cresol red[2]	7.2– 8.8	ye → v
			m-nitrophenol	6.8– 8.6	cl → ye
1.0–10.0	0.054– 0.540	8.0–7.0	phenol red[2]	6.8– 8.4	ye → r
			quinoline blue (cyanin)	7.0– 8.0	cl → vi
			neutral red	6.8– 8.0	red →
5.0–50.0[1]	0.28 – 2.80	7.3–6.3	bromothymol blue[2]	6.0– 7.6	ye → b
30–300[1]	1.6 –16.0	6.5–5.6	alizarin	5.5– 6.8	ye → r
			bromophenol red	5.2– 6.8	ye → r
			bromocresol purple	5.2– 6.8	ye → p
100–1800[1]	5.4 –100	6.0–4.7	methyl red	4.2– 6.3	red →
			δ-dinitrophenol	4.3– 6.3	cl → ye

1. In this range, the dependence of pH on CO_2 concentration is not known precisely (Lange 1956).
2. Indicators used in measurements of CO_2 concentration in air (Čatský & Šesták 1966). For bromothymol blue see also Claypool & Keefer (1942) and Scott (1967).
3. cl: colourless.

increase in concentration of the indicator, and also increase in the normality of the bicarbonate solution and therefore in the pH value corresponding to the CO_2 concentration in the tested air. The effect of the normality of the bicarbonate solution on its pH was established experimentally by Gulyaev (1965). The colour of the solution also changes as a result of impurities from the air; it is therefore expedient to change the solution after 1–3 hours. According to Karpushkin (unpublished) colour changes can be prevented by bubbling the air through a potassium permanganate solution before it enters the bicarbonate solution. It is also advisable to decrease the surface tension of the solution by adding a small amount of paraffin.

The determination of the pH value limits the precision of the colorimetric method. The pH indicator is selected in relation to the CO_2 concentration (*i.e.* the range of pH) which is to be measured. For visual colorimetry and the most often used range of 200 to 1 000 vpm CO_2, a mixture of thymol blue and cresol red was found to be most convenient (Čatský & Slavík 1960). For other CO_2 concentrations, thymol

al con- ration he cator l^{-1}]	Wavelength for spectrophotometry [nm]	Salt error in 0.5 N–NaCl: the correction to be used [pH]	Molecular weight	Chemical composition
15		−0.17		di-*p*-dioxydiphenylphthalide
				di-*o*-cresolphthalide
	595	−0.17	466	thymolsulfonphthalein
			410	1,4-dimethyl-5-oxybenzensulfonphthalein
			382	*m*-cresolsulfonphthalein
10	572		382	*o*-cresolsulfonphthalein
				m-nitrophenol
10	558	−0.15	354	phenolsulfonphthalein
				1,1′-diisoamyl-4,4′-quinocyanineiodide
10				aminodimethylaminomethylphenaziniumchloride
20	614		624	dibromothymolsulfonphthalein
				1,2-dihydroxyanthraquinone
			512	dibromophenolsulfonphthalein
		−0.25	540	dibromo-*o*-cresolsulfonphthalein
5		+0.10		dimethylaminoazobenzene-*o*-carbonic acid
				δ-dinitrophenol

blue, phenol red, bromothymol blue *etc.* can be used (Čatský & Šesták 1966, *cf.* Table 4.2). An indicator mixture is advantageous for visual determinations because it has a broad colour range (for thymol blue and cresol red, yellow-orange-red-violet) and not only a change in the intensity of colour. A precision of ± 0.02 to 0.03 pH, within a range of pH 7.6 to 8.5, can be attained using this mixture after some practice. The mean error in estimation of CO_2 concentration then corresponds to ± 5 to 7%. According to this rather small accuracy, ΔC should not be less than 20% of the inlet CO_2 concentration; this is permissible only if a stirred assimilation chamber is used (*cf.* Section 2.5).

The precision of pH measurement is also affected by the temperature dependence of pH of the standard buffer solutions, the pH of which is measured potentiometrically, usually at 25 °C. The corrections must therefore be established by using the standards at a range of temperatures; alternatively different sets of standard buffers for different temperature ranges should be prepared (see also Gulyaev 1965).

4.3.3 | *An example of the visual colorimetric CO_2 analyser*

4.3.3.1 | Description of the instrument

A simple design of the apparatus for measuring photosynthetic rate in the field, using the visual colorimetric determination of CO_2, is shown in Fig. 4.9 (Čatský & Slavík 1960). Each of six measuring units of this apparatus consists of a glass bubbling device (Fig. 4.5) and a capillary flow meter (Fig. 4.8); the battery-driven diaphragm pumps are common to the six units. The air to be analysed is drawn from the assimilation chamber through a PVC tube to the bubbling device where it passes through the bicarbonate solution, the pH of which is determined by a mixture of colour indicators (*cf.* p. 223).

A range of borate buffers (Section 4.3.4) containing the same indicator mixture acts as the colorimetric standard; these differ in pH by 0.02 to 0.03 pH. Stock solutions, to which the mixture of indicators of suitable concentrations have already been added, are used to prepare the buffers, to ensure identical concentrations of indicators (see Section 4.3.4). The pH values of the individual buffers are determined with an accuracy of 0.005 pH, using a precision pH meter. The solutions are then sealed in glass ampoules with the same dimensions and made of the same glass as the bubbling device, and preserved by the addition of a grain of thymol. These standards can be kept for long periods in the dark in a refrigerator. Air from the bubbling device is drawn through a glass capillary flow meter to the unit of battery-driven membrane pumps (Fig. 4.10). The air flow rate is controlled

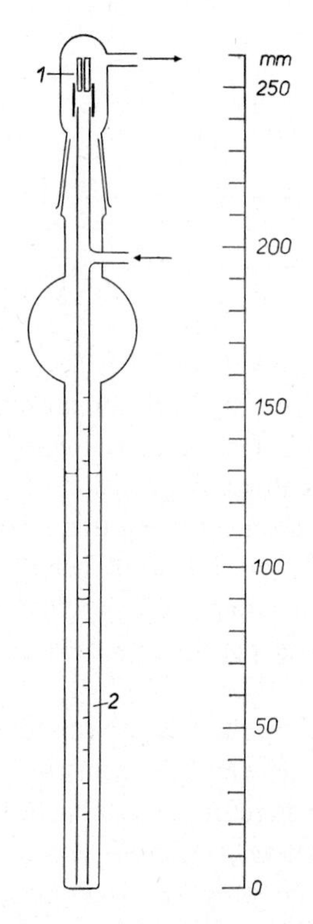

Fig. 4.8 Capillary flow meter. *1:* interchangeable capillary, *2:* ethyleneglycol.

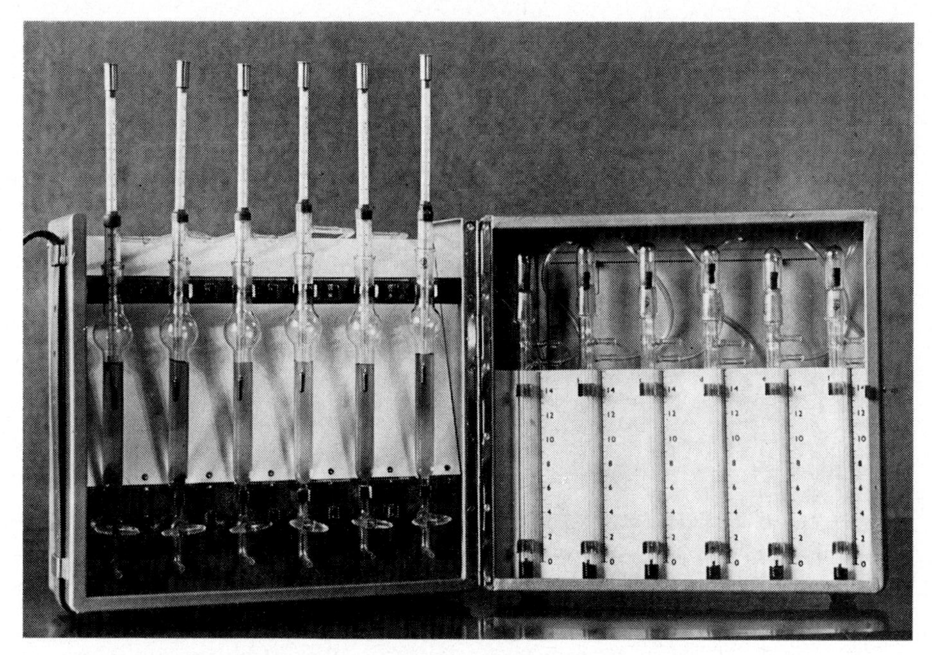

Fig. 4.9 Visual colorimetric CO_2 analyser (after Čatský & Slavík 1960).

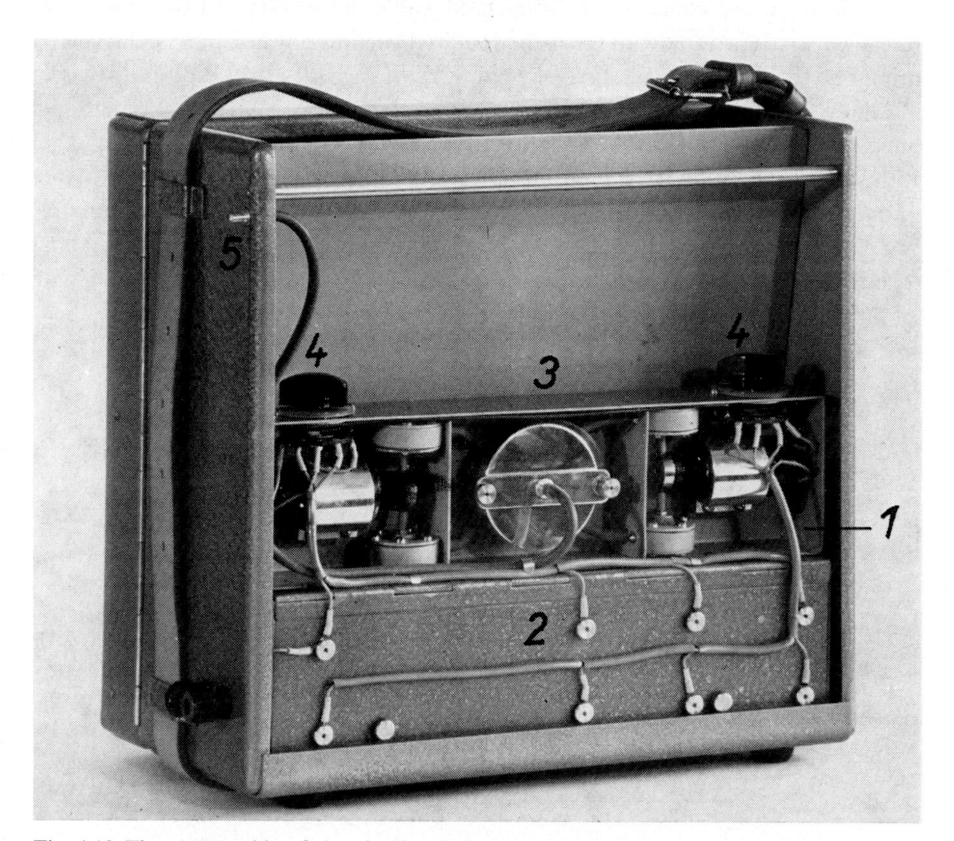

Fig. 4.10 The reverse side of the visual colorimetric CO_2 analyser with four membrane pumps. *1:* pumps and small electric motors, *2:* batteries, *3:* vessel with silica gel, *4:* switch with rheostat, *5:* air inlet (should be connected to flow meters).

Fig. 4.11 Membrane pumps (*1*) driven by electric motors (*2*) fed from 12 V accumulator. The inlets of the two pumps are connected by a common vessel (*3*) with a dust filter and silica gel.

with the so-called burette cocks at the bottom of the bubbling device. In front of the diaphragm pumps there is a vessel containing silica gel, to prevent the pump valves from getting clogged with condensed water and to even out the diaphragm pump pulses. It is an advantage if the required suction power can be achieved by using only half the total number of pumps, as this ensures operation in the event of failure and provides a reserve of output necessary for a stable flow rate. Small pumps (*e.g.* Fig. 4.10) can be used as a separate, easily detachable unit together with their batteries (20 flashlight batteries of 4.5 V each); large pumps of higher output (Figs. 4.11, 4.12) are best supplied from a separate Ni-Fe or Pb-accumulator. The six measuring units are contained in an aluminium case, 330 × 300 × 190 mm, together with accessories (a scale of standard buffers in ampoules, bicarbonate

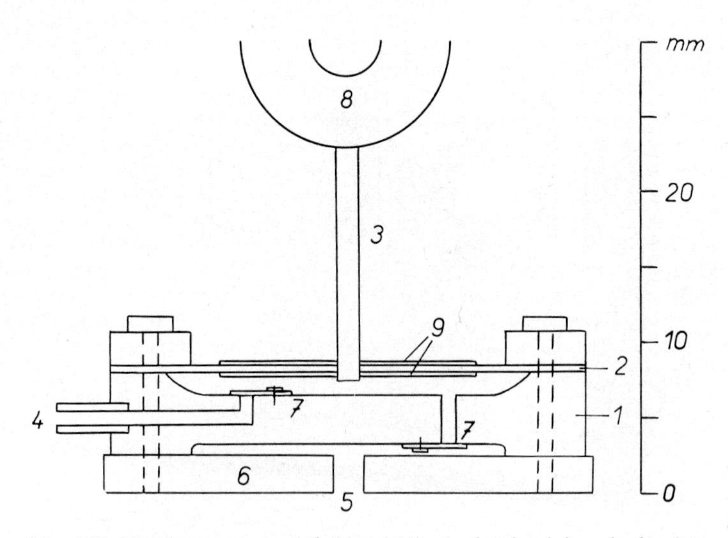

Fig. 4.12 Membrane pump (*cf.* Fig. 4.11). *1:* duraluminium body, *2:* membrane, *3:* bar with metal discs (*9*), *4:* air inlet, *5:* air outlet, *6:* support, *7:* valve of thin PVC, *8:* holder with ball bearing mounted on an excentric pin on the motor axle.

stock solution with pH indicator and the assimilation chambers – stirred preferentially – with PVC tubes); the total weight is about 9 kg, including batteries, if the small pumps (Fig. 4.10) are used. The flow meters are fitted to the front tilting face of the apparatus. Visual estimation of pH is facilitated by a matt white plate placed at an adjustable angle behind the row of bubbling devices; this illuminates the measuring tubes with reflected light.

4.3.3.2 | Operation of the apparatus

New glass bubbling devices should be well rinsed with 'chromic acid', and distilled water before use. The bicarbonate solution is then introduced into the bubbling tubes up to about two thirds of their height (the amount of the solution has no effect on pH) and the same air is allowed to pass through all the bubbling devices at a rate of about 20 l h^{-1}. After about 10 min there must not be the slightest perceptible difference in the colour of the solution in the different tubes. The apparatus must be checked daily in the same way.
Tubes from assimilation chambers are then attached to the bubbling devices and the air is drawn through at a rate of about 20 l h^{-1} (this flow rate is usually used for 10 cm^2 leaf area and high photosynthetic rates). Usually one (or several, if needed) assimilation chamber is left empty and the air from it is measured as the control sample. The flow rate and the temperature of the bicarbonate solution are recorded at 10 to 20 min intervals; the air flow is then stopped in the individual tubes in turn and the pH estimated by comparison with standard buffer solutions. In this assessment, attention is paid not only to the quality and the intensity of colour of the solution, but also to the reflection of light in the solution and the colour of the meniscus. The measuring tube and the ampoule should not be in direct sunlight but illuminated with sufficiently diffused white light of satisfactory intensity. The estimation accuracy is adversely affected by yellow or reddish light. If artificial light is used, the best results are obtained against a radiating area of white or daylight fluorescent tube. The measuring solution is usually replaced after one or two hours.

4.3.4 | *The composition of the solutions for the colorimetric determination of* pCO_2

Measuring solution
– Stock solution: 0.840 1 g $NaHCO_3$ + 73.807 g KCl dissolved and made up to 1 000 ml with distilled water. The normality of this solution is checked by titration with an acid (*e.g.* 0.2 N hydrochloric or oxalic acid) using methyl yellow as the indicator, and the factor determined.
– Solution for use: 100 ml (times the factor, eventually) of the stock solution and x ml of the stock solution of pH indicator are made up to 1 000 ml with distilled water. x for visual determination is 10 ml cresol red + 10 ml thymol blue.

Stock solutions of pH indicators
– cresol red 100 mg in 100 ml 50 % ethanol
– thymol blue 200 mg in 100 ml 96 % ethanol
– bromothymol blue 100 mg in 100 ml 96 % ethanol
– phenol red 100 mg in 100 ml 96 % ethanol

Standard buffer solutions
Stock solutions (Zeller 1951):
– Solution *a*: 19.108 g $Na_2B_4O_7 \cdot 10\ H_2O + x$ ml of the stock solution of pH indicator made up to 1 000 ml with distilled water.
– Solution *b*: 12.45 g H_3BO_3 + 2.925 g NaCl + x ml of the stock solution of pH indicator made up to 1 000 ml with distilled water (for x see above).

pH	solution *a** [ml]	pH	solution *a** [ml]	pH	solution *a** [ml]
7.300	4.5	7.775	9.8	8.250	18.6
7.325	4.8	7.800	10.3	8.275	19.2
7.350	5.0	7.825	10.6	8.300	19.8
7.375	5.3	7.850	11.0	8.325	20.4
7.400	5.5	7.875	11.4	8.350	21.0
7.425	5.8	7.900	11.8	8.375	21.6
7.450	6.0	7.925	12.2	8.400	22.3
7.475	6.3	7.950	12.6	8.425	22.9
7.500	6.5	7.975	13.1	8.450	23.5
7.525	6.8	8.000	13.5	8.475	24.1
7.550	7.0	8.025	14.0	8.500	24.8
7.575	7.3	8.050	14.4	8.525	25.5
7.600	7.5	8.075	14.7	8.550	26.1
7.625	7.8	8.100	15.3	8.575	26.8
7.650	8.1	8.125	15.7	8.600	27.5
7.675	8.4	8.150	16.4	8.625	28.2
7.700	8.8	8.175	16.8	8.650	28.9
7.725	9.1	8.200	17.5	8.675	29.6
7.750	9.5	8.225	18.0	8.700	30.3

* complete to 50 ml with the solution *b*.

4.4 Chemical determination of carbon dioxide by absorption conductimetric analysers

4.4.1 *General principles and design of absorption conductimetric analysers*

All the gasometric analysers described above are continuous ones, *i.e.* they continuously monitor the CO_2 *concentration (or partial pressure)* in the air coming through, but with a shorter or longer response time. In some cases, however, it is preferable to use analysers which measure the absolute *amount* of CO_2 [*e.g.* in short term (1–2 min) measurements of photosynthetic rate]. For this purpose, absorption titrimetric methods have often been used (*cf.* Chapter 2). All the carbon dioxide is absorbed and measured by passing known volume of the analysed air through a hydroxide solution (barium-, potassium-, or sodium hydroxide) in a so-called absorber, a device enabling as complete as possible absorption of CO_2.
In the original procedures (see *e.g.* Boysen-Jensen 1918, 1932; Lundegårdh 1924,

1954; Newton 1935) the amount of absorbed CO_2 is then determined by titration of the excess hydroxide with an acid (oxalic, hydrochloric) after precipitation of the carbonate formed by the addition of barium chloride, for example, (unless absorption is in barium hydroxide, in which case insoluble $BaCO_3$ is formed directly). This procedure, however, is not accurate enough for measuring CO_2 exchange rate in plants, and its application is very limited. Titration of the excess hydroxide has therefore been replaced by the conductimetric estimation of the course of CO_2 absorption.
The principle of the absorption conductimetric method is as follows: The conductivity of a solution depends on the concentration and type of ions. A solution of hydroxide (*e.g.* NaOH) has a higher conductivity than a solution of carbonate (*e.g.* Na_2CO_3) of the same normality. The conductivity of a hydroxide solution therefore decreases during absorption of CO_2 in proportion to the amount absorbed. The main disadvantage of this measurement is the large dependence of the conductivity on temperature, necessitating either good temperature control of the whole device or very precise measurement of temperature and subsequent correction of results (for details see the following sections).
As the absorption conductimetric methods have been reviewed in detail in many publications (*e.g.* Zalenskiĭ 1959; Egle 1960; Voznesenskiĭ, Zalenskiĭ & Semikhatova 1965) and there are no major new developments, only a few recent modifications will be included here.

4.4.2 | *Integrating absorption conductimetric CO_2 analysers*

Two examples of integrating absorption conductimetric CO_2 analysers, differing in the main principles of construction, will be presented in this section.
1. The first analyser measures the absolute amount of CO_2 in one sample only. A special measuring cell for determining the conductivity of the hydroxide solution, compensating for the effect of temperature on the measurement, is its main feature. The measurement of photosynthetic rate can be carried out either by successive determinations of CO_2 in the air sample from the inlet and the outlet of the assimilation chamber, or by simultaneous analysis of the two air samples using two analysers.
2. The second analyser measures the amount of CO_2 in the air at the inlet and at the outlet of the assimilation chamber simultaneously, the difference between them being directly proportional to the photosynthetic rate, irrespective of the amount of the air drawn through the analyser. The temperature of the hydroxide solution is measured and taken into account when calculating the results.

4.4.2.1 | Absorption conductimetric analyser with temperature compensation

The first example is the analyser designed for field work by Voznesenskiĭ (1960, 1964, 1967; Voznesenskiĭ, Zalenskiĭ & Semikhatova 1965). The analyser is constructed as a self-contained unit for determining the rate of CO_2 exchange, and includes the necessary accessories (assimilation chamber, aspirator for providing the flow of the air sample *etc.*).
Construction (see Fig. 4.13). Absorber *(1)*, measuring cell with electrodes *(2)*,

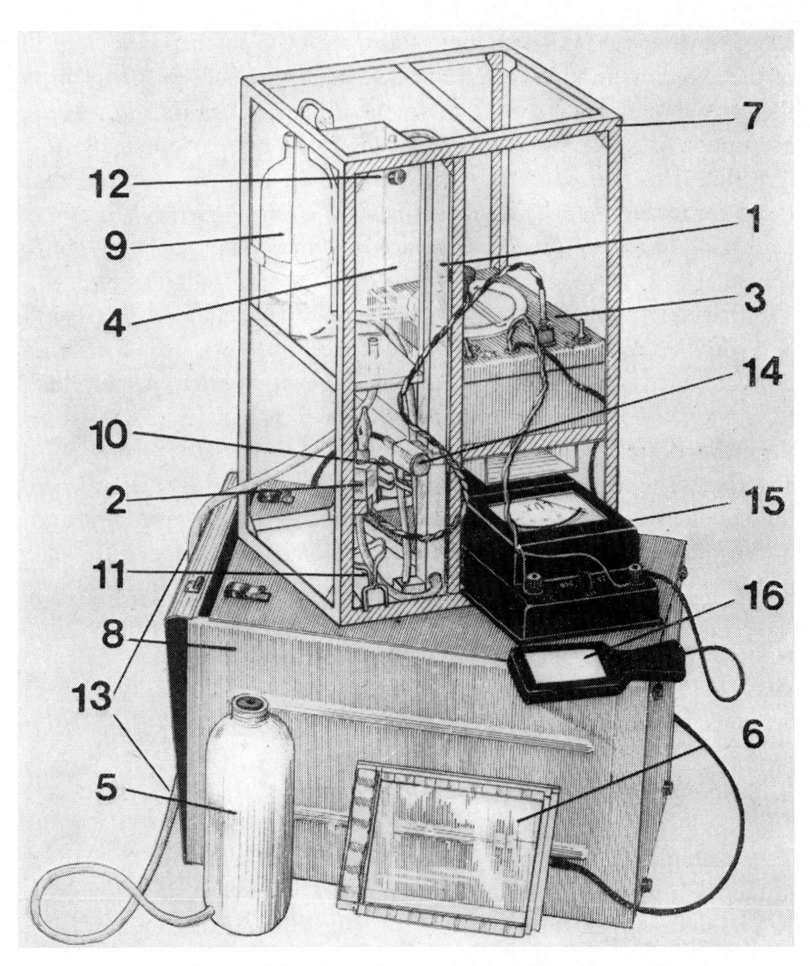

Fig. 4.13 A general view of the absorption conductimetric analyser with temperature compensation. *1:* absorber, *2:* measuring cell with electrodes, *3:* conductimeter, *4:* stationary aspirator vessel, *5:* movable aspirator vessel, *6:* assimilation chamber, *7:* body, *8:* box, *9:* flask with the reserve hydroxide solution, *10:* clamp on the rubber tube connecting vessel *9* with the absorber *1*, *11:* clamp on the rubber tube put on the inlet of the absorber (see Fig. 4.14 *B*, *4*), *12:* cork stopper, *13:* rubber tube leading to the movable aspirator vessel, *14:* needle valve, *15:* luxmeter, *16:* photoelement.

transistor conductivity meter *(3)*, and accessories [aspirator *(4, 5)*, assimilation chamber *(6)*] are the principal parts of the apparatus, mounted on a duraluminium body *(7)* and covered with the box *(8)* during transportation.

To measure CO_2 in the air, a known volume (500 ml) is drawn through the absorber by means of the *aspirator*. This consists of two vessels linked by a rubber tube. One of the vessels is firmly fixed on the apparatus, has an inner volume somewhat larger than 500 ml, and is made of plexiglass. A polyethylene bottle, 500 ml capacity, serves as the second, movable vessel of the aspirator. The *absorber* (Fig. 4.14) is a plexiglass square sectioned tube (300 × 10 × 10 mm). At the bottom there is a piece (*ca.* 4 × 4 mm) of sintered glass (no. 1) sealed in with epoxy resin. This serves to break up the air flow through the hydroxide solution. At a distance of 10–12 cm from the bottom of the absorber there is a mark on the front up to which the absorber is filled with the hydroxide solution. The volume of solution used must be sufficient for full absorption of CO_2 from the air passing through. This also depends on the concentration of the hydroxide and the degree of dispersion of the air flow. The volume of 0.02 N-hydroxide is usually 10–12 ml. To control the air flow rate through the assimilation chamber and absorber, a needle valve is placed between them.

Assimilation chambers utilised in this apparatus may be of various types of construction (see Chapter 2). A simple chamber with solid infra-red filter (*e.g. Schott BG-17*, Soviet-made filter *C3C-14)* was used by the author.

The *measuring cell* comprises two cavities with electrodes, one filled with the original hydroxide solution and the other with the exposed solution from the absorber (Fig. 4.15). The common central electrode allows rapid equilibration of the temperature of the solutions in the two cavities; this is most important for

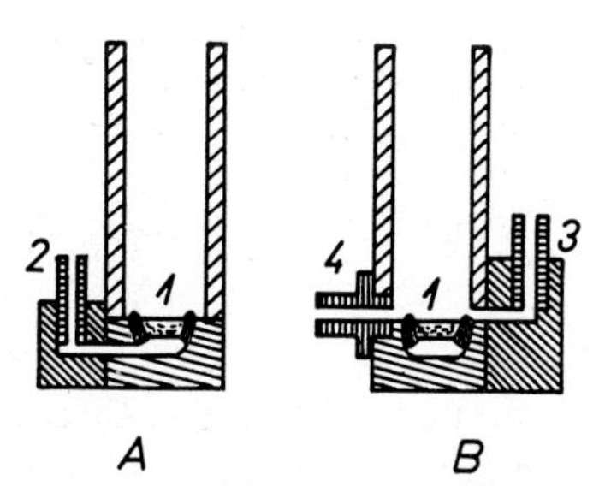

Fig. 4.14 Lower part of the absorber (*A:* front view, *B:* side view). *1:* sintered glass sealed in with epoxy resin, *2:* inlet connecting the absorber with the needle valve, *3:* inlet connecting the absorber to the vessel with reserve hydroxide solution, *4:* inlet linking the absorber and the measuring cell, used for pouring out the hydroxide solution.

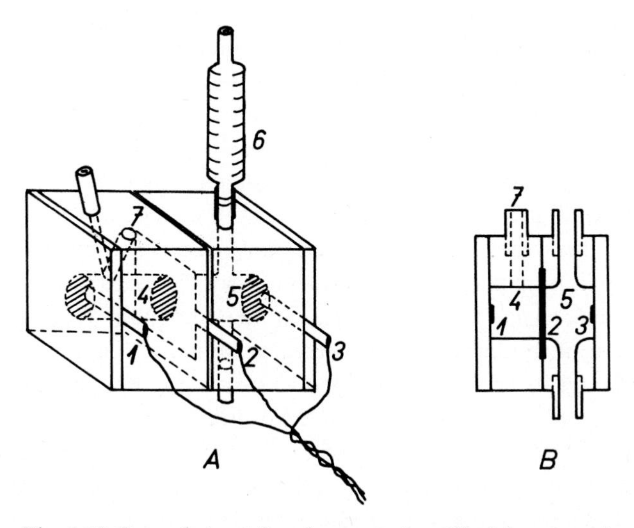

Fig. 4.15 General view (*A*) and cross-section (*B*) of the measuring cell. *1*, *2*, *3:* nickel electrodes, *4:* cavity where the hydroxide solution serving as a standard resistance is poured through opening *7* prior to measurements, *5:* cavity to which the measured hydroxide solution is introduced through the inlet from the absorber, *6:* glass balloon.

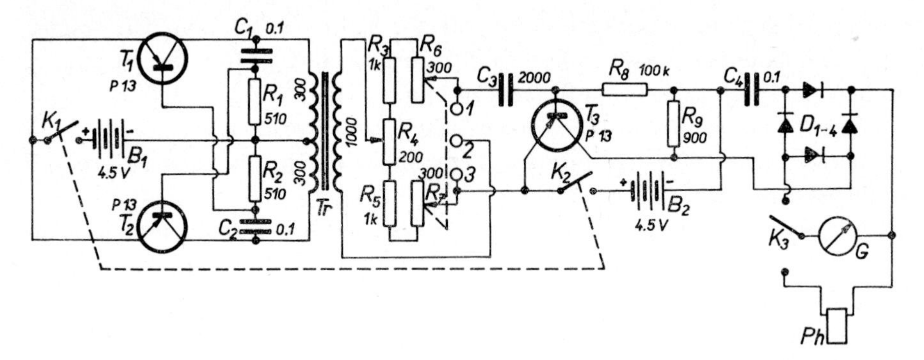

Fig. 4.16 Scheme of the conductivity meter. Electrodes of the measuring cell are connected to terminals *1*, *2*, and *3*.
T_1, T_2, T_3: Soviet-made triodes *P-13*, D_{1-4}: Soviet-made diodes *D1V*, *Tr:* transformer – I . . . 2 × 300 turns, II . . . 1000 turns; wire 0.1 mm, *G:* galvanometer of a luxmeter, *Ph:* photoelement, B_1, B_2: batteries of 4.5 V. Values of resistors R_1 and R_2 and of capacitors C_1 and C_2 depend on transformer quality and are selected so that the frequency of oscillations is about 20 kHz. Resistors R_3, R_5, and R_7 serve to establish the necessary sensitivity and the zero point.

R_1, R_2:	510 Ω	R_8:	100 Ω
R_3, R_5:	1 kΩ	R_9:	900 Ω
R_4:	200 Ω wire	C_1, C_2, C_4:	0.1 μF
R_6, R_7:	300 Ω	C_3:	200 pF

measuring the ratio of the conductivities by means of the bridge. Electrodes made of nickel proved to be most suitable for several years' work.

The *conductimeter* is an A.C. Wheatstone bridge (Fig. 4.16). The readings corresponding to the amount of CO_2 absorbed in the hydroxide solution are made from the reochord scale, while the galvanometer of a luxmeter serves as a zero device. The whole electronics of the apparatus consists of four independent units: A.C. generator, bridge, amplifier, and output unit to the zero indicator. After assembling the conductivity meter it should be checked and adjusted. Firstly, the frequency of oscillations set by the generator should be checked on an oscilloscope; if it differs appreciably from 20 kHz, the capacitors C_1 and C_2 should be changed (increased to decrease the frequency and *vice versa*). Two identical resistors from 300 to 500 Ω are then connected across terminals *1* and *2*, and *2* and *3* (Fig. 4.16). If the conductimeter works properly, a very small output must be obtainable, corresponding to equilibrium of the bridge. The slightest change (1–2 graduations) in the position of the reochord scale should cause the galvanometer needle to move from the equilibrium position. If this does not occur it is necessary to increase amplification by increasing the resistor R_9. If the minimum output is hardly perceptible the amplification should be decreased. Finally, the whole conductimeter is checked, and its sensitivity adjusted as necessary. For this purpose, the *hydroxide solution* is placed in the apparatus. For normal CO_2 concentrations in air, this is 0.02 N NaOH or KOH, with 0.5 to 0.6% of isoamylalcohol added, to aid dispersion of the air coming through and thus maximum absorption of CO_2. The normality of the hydroxide solution chosen is a compromise: high normality should be used for full CO_2 absorption, but low normality is advantageous for highest sensitivity of the measurement.

 The optimum sensitivity for ordinary determinations of CO_2 concentration in air is when the amount of CO_2 contained in one litre of normal air (*ca.* 0.6 mg) corresponds to about 50–60 graduations of the reochord scale. To change sensitivity, the resistors R_3 and R_5 should be changed equally and simultaneously. An increase in these resistances causes an increase in sensitivity, and *vice versa.*

Check of the analyser. One of the most important requirements is that the apparatus should be completely sealed, as shown by the water level in the aspirator and the absence of air bubbles in the absorber. During operation, the foam comprising the minute air bubbles in the hydroxide solution must fill about 3/4 of the absorber. No large air bubbles should move through the foaming solution, and the flow rate must be constant.

Setting the sensitivity of the analyser. The sensitivity of the apparatus should be set according to the following steps:

1. The absorber is rinsed with fresh solution, refilled, and the end of the rubber tube from the lower inlet is fitted to the upper inlet on the left hand side of the measuring cell, to the cavity which is to be filled with the original hydroxide solution. In order to fill this cavity the movable vessel of the aspirator containing water is lifted so that some of the water flows into the stationary vessel and creates an excess pressure in the absorber.
2. The clamp on the tube linking the absorber and the cell is then opened a little so that the solution flows into the cell cavity. The cavity is rinsed, filled, and stoppered. Care should be taken that there are no air bubbles on the electrode surfaces.
3. The same end of the rubber tube from the absorber is then fitted to the lower inlet of the right hand cavity of the measuring cell which is rinsed several times with the hydroxide solution from the absorber. The solution flows into the cell when there is excess pressure in the absorber, and is sucked back into the absorber when the pressure there is decreased by lowering the movable vessel of the aspirator and stoppering the stationary one.
4. After rinsing and emptying the absorber, it is again filled up to the mark with fresh hydroxide solution. The solution is made to flow into the right hand side of the measuring cell so that it completely fills (without bubbles) the electrode cavity and partly flows out into the glass balloon.
5. The initial ratio of conductivities of the hydroxide solutions in the two cavities of the measuring cell is shown on the reochord scale. By backwards and forwards movement of the slide, the point of minimum deviation of the galvanometer needle from zero is then found. By regulating the double resistors this position is adjusted to be in the range from 0 to 20 graduations, and is recorded.
6. All the solution in the aspirator is then moved to the stationary vessel. The movable vessel is lowered, the regulating needle valve is opened and 500 ml of control air is passed through the absorber.
7. The solution from the absorber is then moved to the measuring cell and the ratio of the conductivities of this solution and of the original hydroxide solution present in the left hand cell cavity is determined. If this is 20–30 graduations different from the primary record, the sensitivity of the apparatus is sufficient and calibration may begin.

Calibration of the analyser may be carried out in two ways. The first method consists in bubbling a known amount of air with a known concentration of

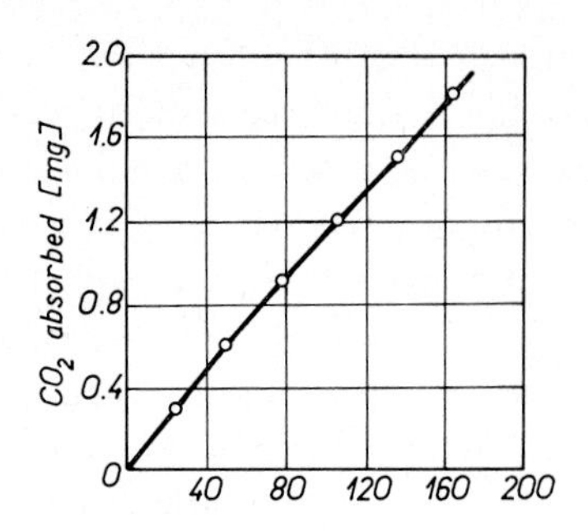

Fig. 4.17 Calibration curve of the absorption conductimetric apparatus. Abscissa: difference between reochord scale readings before and after the exposure in graduations. Ordinate: amount of CO_2 absorbed in mg.

CO_2 through the hydroxide solution and measuring the corresponding number of graduations on the reochord scale (Fig. 4.17). The second method involves the introduction into the right hand cavity of the measuring cell of a mixture of KOH and K_2CO_3 of equal concentration, 0.02 N. The apparatus is quickly calibrated by gradual increase in the amount of carbonate in the solution, using freshly-prepared solutions with different CO_3^{2-} contents. Absorption of CO_2 from the surrounding air should be avoided.

The first method of calibration is simpler and corresponds better to the conditions of measurement of CO_2 concentrations. The procedure is as follows: The absorber and the two cavities of the measuring cell are rinsed with fresh hydroxide solution. The absorber and the left hand part of the cell are filled with fresh solution. Part of this solution is transferred from the absorber to the right-hand part of the cell. The primary record on the reochord scale is made. Then the solution is returned to the absorber. All the solution from the cell and the connecting tube should be transferred and the number of air bubbles passing through into the absorber during this operation should be as small as possible. Then air of known CO_2 concentration is passed through the absorber in 500 ml samples. After each sample has passed through, the solution from the absorber is transferred to the right hand cavity, its conductivity is recorded in terms of reochord scale divisions and then it is returned to the absorber. Transfer of the solution to the cell must be performed as follows: the cell should first be filled with the solution, then the solution sucked into the absorber, then the cell filled a second time. This procedure ensures that the cell cavity is rinsed with the solution and that the solution in the absorber is well mixed so that any small differences in concentration are eliminated.

The apparatus must be re-calibrated after changing the hydroxide solution, after changing any of the parts in the conductimeter (except the batteries), after cleaning the electrodes or when the alkalinity of the solution changes for any other reason.

Determination of CO_2 concentration in the air. The procedure for determining the CO_2 concentration in the air is the reverse of that used for the calibration:

1. Connect the inlet tubing with the air sample, and pass about one litre through it.
2. Rinse and fill the left hand part of the measuring cell and the absorber up to the mark with the reserve hydroxide solution.
3. Transfer some of the hydroxide solution from the absorber to the right hand part of the cell.

4. Make an initial measurement of the conductivity of the solution.
5. Draw the hydroxide solution out of the right hand part of the cell back into the absorber, using the aspirator as before, with care to avoid too many air bubbles passing through the solution in the absorber.
6. Transfer all the water into the stationary aspirator vessel by moving the movable vessel upwards and opening the stationary vessel. After water has been poured into the stationary vessel it is corked and the movable vessel lowered.
7. Open the needle valve and pass 500 ml of air through the absorber.
8. Turn the tap and wait till the foam settles down. Rinse the right hand cell cavity and then fill it again ensuring that there are no air bubbles in the electrode spaces of the cell. This can be done by manipulating the movable aspirator vessel, the cork of the stationary vessel and the clamp of the tube connecting the absorber and the measuring cell.
9. If the solution temperature in the absorber, and consequently in the right hand part of the cell, differs from that in the left hand part (shown by the displacement of the minimum point in the reochord scale during recording), wait for 3–5 min to allow the temperature of the solutions to equilibrate.
10. Find the reochord position corresponding to a new minimum deviation of the galvanometer.
11. Transfer the hydroxide solution from the right hand part of the cell back to the absorber and make the next measurement (repeating all the operations beginning from point 5 onwards).
12. Measurements can be continued using the same hydroxide solution as long as the reochord scale allows. After this, the solution in the absorber should be replaced (*i.e.* repeating all the operations from point 2 onwards). If the work is continued on the same day the solution in the left hand part of the cell need not be replaced.

Determination of the rate of CO_2 exchange by the experimental material. The amount of CO_2 taken up by the experimental material is estimated from the difference in CO_2 content of air before and after it has passed through the assimilation chamber, measured following the procedure described above. The photosynthetic (respiration) rate is calculated taking into account the duration of exposure and the leaf area or weight (for general principles see Chapters 2 and 3):
1. The leaf is inserted in the chamber, the needle valve quickly turned and the stop-watch started. The flow rate of the air must be kept constant.
2. After the exposure (the duration of which is characterized by the time needed for air to pass through the apparatus), the reading of the reochord is recorded, and the leaf is taken out of the chamber.
3. After every 3 or 4 exposures, CO_2 concentration in the ingoing air (control) should be determined.

Sensitivity and accuracy of the apparatus. The sensitivity of the apparatus described can be expressed as the amount of absorbed CO_2 corresponding to one graduation of the reochord scale. It may be changed within rather wide limits, especially if a decreased sensitivity is demanded. The optimum sensitivity is such that approximately 0.01 mg CO_2 corresponds to one graduation. It may easily be 3 to 5 times greater. However, further increase in the sensitivity is accompanied by loss of accuracy.

Excluding large errors which may arise during the exposure (bubbles on the electrodes or in the inter-electrode spaces, temperature inequality of solutions in the cavities of the measuring cell, imperfect CO_2 absorption due to large bubbles in the absorber *etc.*), the error is rather small. It depends on the accuracy with which the minimum deviation of the galvanometer can be determined. The maximum relative error of the determination of CO_2 concentration in the air may be 2 to 3% of the value found (for further information on errors in determining rate of CO_2 exchange see Section 3.12.2).

4.4.2.2 Darmstadt apparatus for the short term determination of photosynthetic rate

Another example of an integrating absorption conductimetric CO_2 analyser is the so-called Darmstadt apparatus for the short term determination of photosynthetic rate. The apparatus to be described is the latest modification (Stocker & Vieweg 1960) of the apparatus of Holdheide, Huber & Stocker (1936). The apparatus works in principle as follows: The attached leaf is placed into the closed assimilation chamber immediately before the measurement. A certain amount of air (the amount depending on the predicted photosynthetic rate and the leaf area) is then sucked through the chamber by means of the pump (*cf.* Fig. 4.19), the leaf is removed from the chamber, and the rest of the 'impoverished' air from the chamber and the tubes is also sucked into the absorber by several revolutions of the pump. The air flows through the absorber (*cf.* Fig. 4.18) filled with 50 ml 0.02 N-NaOH to which 0.75 to 1% of n-butanol and 20 mg l^{-1} of saponin are added; these admixtures form a rich foam enabling as full as possible absorption

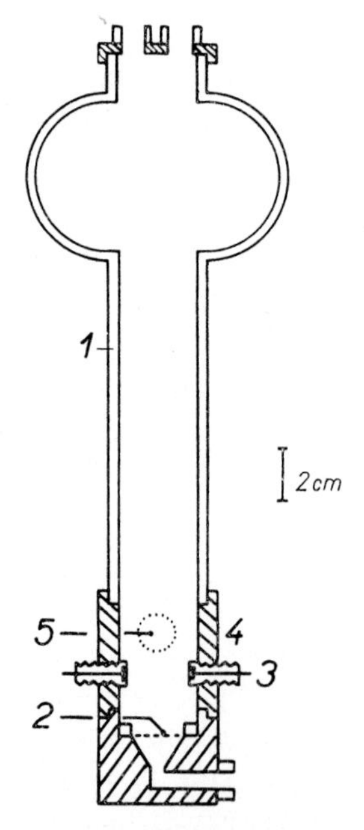

Fig. 4.18 Absorber of the Darmstadt conductimetric apparatus (after Stocker & Vieweg 1960). *1:* plexiglass tube, *2:* filter plate (see text), *3:* electrodes, *4:* ring with nickel resistance thermometer (*5*).

of CO_2. In the absorber there are two electrodes, serving to measure the conductivity of the solution by means of the Wheatstone bridge. The amount of absorbed CO_2 is calculated from the difference in conductivities before and after the exposure. During the exposure the same amount of control air is sucked simultaneously through another absorber by a second pump, synchronised with the first. The *difference* in the absorbed amounts of CO_2 in the first and the second absorbers (regardless of the total amount of air sucked through) is a measure of photosynthetic rate of the leaf during the exposure. For field work, the apparatus is built into a case which also acts as a support for the pumps and the galvanometer. The weight of the whole apparatus is 15 kg and its volume 0.2 m^3.

The absorbers (Fig. 4.18) are made of plexiglass tube *(1)* blown out to a sphere at the top. The other parts are made of polyvinylchloride, screwed together using softened PVC for sealing. At the bottom of the absorber, there is an 18 mm diameter filter *(2)* made of 0.2 mm thick PVC foil with four holes, 0.09 mm in diameter, bored regularly per square mm. The precise dimensions of these holes are necessary for the proper functioning of the filter. Silver electrodes *(3)*, 6 mm in diameter, are fixed in the PVC support, enabling the distance between the electrodes to be changed. A nickel resistance thermometer is placed in the ring *(4)*; this measures the temperature of the hydroxide solution to the nearest 0.05 °C by means of the Wheatstone bridge. In the lid *(6)* are the air outlet and the opening for filling the absorber.

The Wheatstone bridge measures the resistance from 220 to 720 Ω, on five scales.

The pumps. The volume of air sucked through the analyser is calculated from the number of revolutions of the pumps. Special construction was therefore necessary,

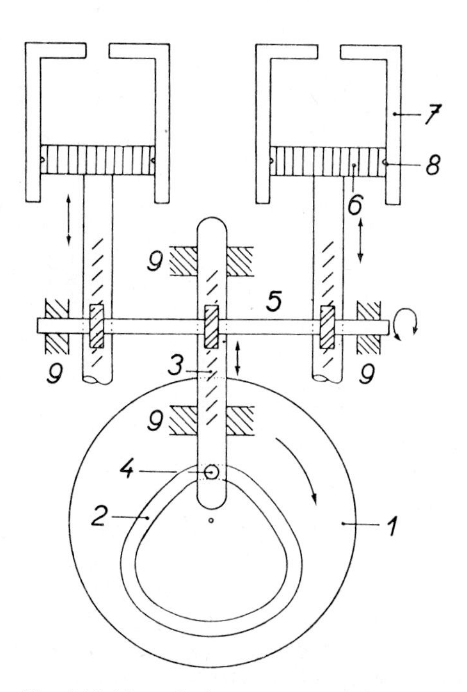

Fig. 4.19 Manual piston pumps of the Darmstadt conductimetric apparatus (after Stocker & Vieweg 1960). *1:* disc with leading groove, *2:* cog-bar with the pin *(4)*, *5:* shaft, *6:* piston with groove filled with vaseline *(8)*, *7:* cylinder, *9:* bearing.

ensuring a short stop of the piston at the down inflection point (maximum volume of the cylinder), allowing equilibration of the suction resulting from the resistances of the absorbers and the tubings. The operation of the pumps is shown in Fig. 4.19. *The assimilation chamber.* The authors used a simple chamber made of 1 to 2 mm thick plexiglass, ensuring the same composition of the air entering the chamber and the 'control air' tubing.

Calculation of results. The calculation is based on the assumption that the same amount of air is sucked through the two absorbers. The rate of CO_2 exchange is then given by: 1. the difference in the amount of carbon dioxide (in mg) absorbed in the two absorbers, and by 2. the exposure time, *i.e.* the time during which the experimental material was enclosed in the assimilation chamber.

4.4.3 | *Continuous absorption conductimetric analysers*

Relatively complicated continuous analysers have been designed on the same principle. The best-known is that of Thomas (1933), a modification of which was used for checking the CO_2 concentration in the world's first phytotron in the Earhart Laboratory in Pasadena (Went 1957). The air to be analysed is sucked at a *constant* rate into a spiral glass absorber to which the hydroxide solution is added, also at a constant rate. After leaving the absorber, the solution is removed

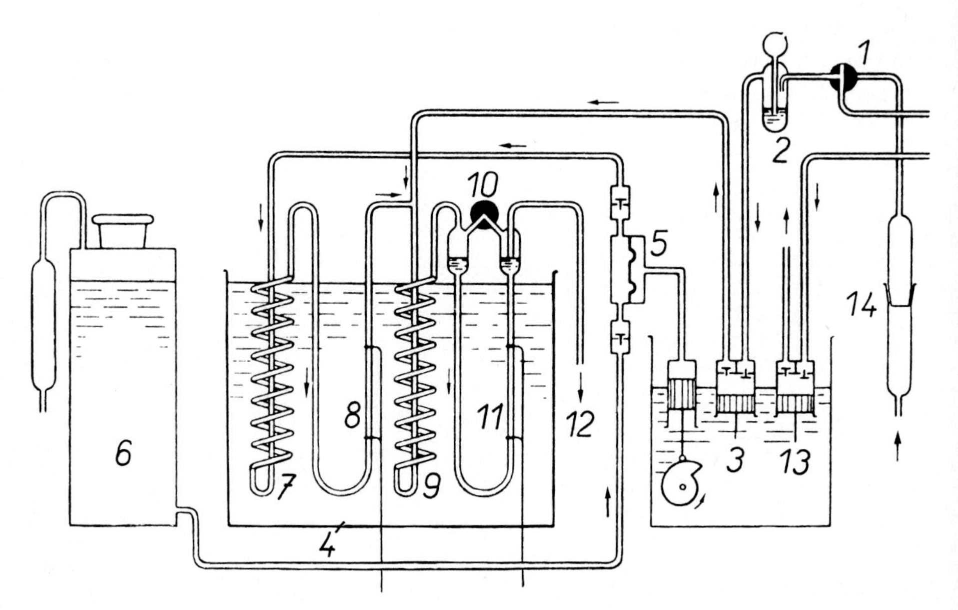

Fig. 4.20 Scheme of the continuous conductimetric CO_2 analyser *Mikrogas* (*H. Wösthoff*, Bochum/BRD). After Rüsch (1955). The air to be analysed is sucked through the tap (*1*) and the valve (*2*) by means of the pump (*3*); then it is passed to the analysing part in the temperature controlled oil bath (*4*). 0.02 N-NaOH solution is sucked by means of the pump (*5*) from the four liter vessel (*6*); its volume is sufficient for 85 hours' operation of the analyser. The solution is passed through the coil (*7*) and the conductivity of it is measured by electrodes (*8*). Then the solution is mixed with the air sample in the coil (*9*); in the vessel (*10*), the air is separated, and the conductivity of the solution measured by electrodes (*11*). The solution and the air escape through the tube (*12*). The pump (*13*) is used if a sequential valve is connected. The vessel (*14*) with NaOH is used to supply CO_2-free air to check zero.

from the air and its conductivity is continuously measured and compared with that of the solution before entering the absorber. The temperature of the apparatus is very precisely controlled so that the difference between the two conductivities is a direct measure of CO_2 concentration in the air coming through and can be recorded by a recorder calibrated directly in units of CO_2 concentration.
The analysers *Ultragas* and *Microgas* (*H. Wösthoff*, Bochum, BRD) operate on the same principle (Fig. 4.20). They have rarely been used for determining CO_2 exchange rate in plants (*e.g.* Wöhrmann & Meyer zu Drewer 1959).

4.5 | References

Ålvik, G.: Über Assimilation und Atmung einiger Holzgewächse im westnorwegischen Winter. – Meddel. No 22 Vestlandets forstlige Forsøksstation (Bergen) 6: 1-266, 1939.

Begg, J. E., Lake, J. V.: Carbon dioxide measurement: A continuous conductimetric method. – Agr. Meteorol. 5: 283-290, 1968.

Bowman, G. E.: The control of carbon dioxide in plant enclosures. – In: Eckardt, F. E. (ed.): Functioning of Terrestrial Ecosystems at the Primary Production Level. Pp. 335-343. UNESCO, Paris 1968a.

Bowman, G. E.: The measurement of carbon dioxide concentration in the atmosphere. – In: Wadsworth, R. M. *et al.* (ed.): The Measurement of Environmental Factors in Terrestrial Ecology. Pp. 131-139. Blackwell Sci. Publ., Oxford-Edinburgh 1968b.

Boysen-Jensen, P.: Studies on the production of matter in light- and shadow-plants. – Bot. Tidskr. 36: 219-262, 1918.

Boysen-Jensen, P.: Die Stoffproduktion der Pflanzen. – G. Fischer, Jena 1932.

Čatský, J., Šesták, Z.: Suitable indicators and an altered empiric equation for calculating CO_2 concentration in colorimetric determinations of photosynthetic rate. – Biol. Plant. 8: 60-72, 1966.

Čatský, J., Slavík, B.: Eine neue Anwendung der CO_2-Bestimmung nach Kauko zu Assimilationsmessungen. – Planta 51: 63-69, 1958.

Čatský, J., Slavík, B.: Polevoï pribor dlya opredeleniya intensivnosti fotosinteza. [A field apparatus for the determination of photosynthetic rate.] – Biol. Plant. 2: 107-112, 1960.

Claypool, L. L., Keefer, R. M.: A colorimetric method for CO_2 determination in respiration studies. – Proc. Amer. Soc. hort. Sci. 40: 177-186, 1942.

Egle, K.: Landpflanzen. – In: Ruhland, W. (ed.): Handbuch der Pflanzenphysiologie. Vol. V/1. Pp. 115-163. Springer Verlag, Berlin–Göttingen–Heidelberg 1960.

French, C. S., Hiesey, W. M., Milner, H. W.: Carbon dioxide control for plant growth chambers. – Carnegie Inst. Washington Year Book 58: 352, 1959.

Frenzel, B.: Einige Bemerkungen zu der CO_2-Bestimmungsmethode nach Ålvik. – Planta 46: 447-466, 1955.

Gingras, G.: Une méthode de mesure directe des vitesses d'échanges de CO_2: application à la photosynthèse. – Physiol. vég. 1: 369-373, 1963.

Gingras, G.: Étude comparative, chez quelques algues, de la photosynthèse et de la photoréduction réalisée en présence d'hydrogène. – Physiol. vég. 4: 1-65, 1966.

Gulyaev, B. I.: Primenenie kolorimetricheskogo metoda dlya nepreryvnogo izmereniya intensivnosti fotosinteza i dykhaniya. [Use of the colorimetric method for continuous determination of photosynthetic and respiration rates.] – In: Fotosintez i Produktivnost' Rasteniï. Pp. 195-212. Naukova Dumka, Kiev 1965.

Higgins, H. L., Marriott, W. M.: A colorimetric method for the determination of the CO_2 percentage in air. – J. Amer. chem. Soc. 39: 68-71, 1917.

Holdheide, W., Huber, B., Stocker, O.: Eine Feldmethode zur Bestimmung der momentanen Assimilationsgrösse von Landpflanzen. – Ber. deut. bot. Ges. 54: 168-188, 1936.

James, D. B.: British Patent No. 1018658, 1966.

Kalle, K.: Eine einfache Schnellmethode zur Bestimmung der Luftkohlensäure nach Y. Kauko. – Ann. hydrogr. mar. Meteorol. 65: 212-214, 1937.

Kauko, Y.: Das Bestimmen der Kohlensäure in der Luft. – Suomen Kemistilehti 5: 54, 1932.

Kauko, Y.: Zur Bestimmung der Kohlensäure in der Luft mit Hilfe von pH-Messungen. – Angew. Chem. 47: 164-167, 1934.
Kauko, Y.: Ein Apparat zur potenziometrischen Bestimmung der Luftkohlensäure. – Angew. Chem. 48: 539-540, 1935.
Kreeb, K.: Eine Feldmethode zur Abschätzung des CO_2-Gaswechsels. – Photosynthetica 4: 158-161, 1970.
Kreitsberg, O. E. (Kreicbergs, O.): Metody ucheta fotosinteza v polevykh usloviyakh. [Methods of studying photosynthesis in field conditions.] – In: Fotosintez i Produktivnost' Rasteniï. Pp. 91-102. Zinatne, Riga 1965.
Lange, O. L.: Zur Methodik der kolorimetrischen CO_2-Bestimmung nach Ålvik. – Ber. deut. bot. Ges. 69: 49-60, 1956.
Lee, J. A., Woolhouse, H. W.: A re-appraisal of the electrometric method for the determination of the concentration of carbon dioxide in soil atmospheres. – New Phytol. 65: 325-330, 1966.
Lieth, H.: Über den Lichtkompensationspunkt der Landpflanzen. I & II. – Planta 54: 530-554, 555-576, 1960.
Lundegårdh, H.: Der Temperaturfaktor bei Kohlensäureassimilation und Atmung. – Biochem. Z. 154: 195-234, 1924.
Lundegårdh, H.: Klima und Boden in ihrer Wirkung auf das Pflanzenleben.–4th Ed. G. Fischer, Jena 1954.
Martin, M. H., Pigott, C. D.: A simple method for measuring carbon dioxide in soils. – J. Ecol. 53: 153-155, 1965.
McClendon, J. F.: The standardization of a new colorimetric method for the determination of the hydrogen ion concentration, CO_2 tension, and CO_2 and O_2 content of sea water, of animal heat, and of CO_2 of the air, with a summary of similar data on bicarbonate solutions in general. – J. biol. Chem. 30: 265-288, 1917.
Newton, R. G.: An improved electrical conductivity method for the estimation of carbon dioxide and other reactive gases. – Ann. Bot. 49: 381-398, 1935.
Nichiporovich, A. A., Strogonova, L. E., Chmora, S. N., Vlasova, M. P.: Fotosinteticheskaya Deyatel'nost' Rasteniï v Posevakh. [Photosynthetic Activity of Plants in Crops.] – Izd. Akad. Nauk SSSR, Moskva 1961.
Pavletić, Z.: Kolorimetrijsko odreotivanje kompenzacione točke svijetla kod kormofita. [Colorimetric determination of the light compensation point in higher plants.] – Acta bot. croatica 17: 113-149, 1958.
Pavletić, Z., Lieth, H.: Der Lichtkompensationspunkt einiger immergrüner Pflanzen im Winter und im Frühjahr. – Ber. deut. bot. Ges. 71: 309-314, 1958.
Rüsch, J. D.: Der CO_2-Gehalt bodennaher Luftschichten unter Einfluss des Windschutzes. – Z. Pflanzenernährung Düngung Bodenk. 71: 113-132, 1955.
Sajaniemi, I. K.: Ilman hiilihapon määrääminen. [Determination of carbon dioxide in air.] – Acta forest. fennica 42(4): 1-11, 1936.
Schack, A.: Industrial Heat Transfer. – P.460. Chapman & Hall, London 1965.
Scott, L. E.: A procedure for the measurement of carbon dioxide evolution from individual fruits over brief time intervals. – HortScience 2: 66-68, 1967.
Severinghaus, J. W., Bradley, A. F.: Electrodes for blood p_{O_2} and p_{CO_2} determination. – J. appl. Physiol. 13: 515-520, 1958.
Sharp, R. B.: A simple colorimetric method for the in-situ measurement of carbon dioxide. – J. agr. Eng. Res. 9: 87-94, 1964.
Slavík, B., Čatský, J.: Colorimetric determination of CO_2 exchange in field and laboratory. – In: Eckardt, F. E. (ed.): Methodology of Plant Eco-Physiology. Pp. 291-298. UNESCO, Paris 1965.
Snell, F. M.: Electrometric measurement of carbon dioxide and bicarbonate ion. – J. appl. Physiol. 15: 729-732, 1960.
Souchon, C., Souchon, J.: Echanges gazeux de la respiration et de la photosynthèse mise en évidence par un réactif au rouge de crésol. – Inform. sci. 21: 118-124, 1966.
Stocker, O., Vieweg, G. H.: Die Darmstädter Apparatur zur Momentanmessung der Photosynthese unter ökologischen Bedingungen. – Ber. deut. bot. Ges. 73: 198-208, 1960.

Stow, R. W., Baer, R. F., Randall, B. F.: Rapid measurement of the tension of carbon dioxide in blood. – Arch. phys. Med. Rehabilitation 38: 646-650, 1957.
Thomas, M. D.: Precise automatic apparatus for continuous determination of carbon dioxide in air. – Ind. eng. Chem., Anal. Ed. 5: 193-198, 1933.
Voznesenskiĭ, V. L.: Izmerenie intensivnosti fotosinteza po izmeneniyu elektroprovodnosti pogloshchayushchego rastvora shchelochi. [Determination of photosynthetic rate by a change in conductivity of the absorbing hydroxide solution.] – Tr. bot. Inst. Akad. Nauk SSSR, Ser. 4, Eksper. Bot. 14: 258-283, 1960.
Voznesensky, V. L.: Conductometric apparatus for determining the photosynthetic rate. – Biol. Plant. 6: 79-83, 1964.
Voznesenskiĭ, V. L.: Konduktometricheskiĭ Pribor dlya Izmereniya Fotosinteza i Dykhaniya Rasteniĭ v Polevykh Usloviyakh. [Conductimetric Apparatus for Determining Photosynthetic and Respiration Rates in Field.] – Nauka, Leningrad 1967.
Voznesenskiĭ, V. L., Zalenskiĭ, O. V., Semikhatova, O. A.: Metody Issledovaniya Fotosinteza i Dykhaniya Rasteniĭ. [Methods of Studying Plant Photosynthesis and Respiration.] – Nauka, Moskva–Leningrad 1965.
Webster, C. C.: The Effects of Air Pollution on Plants and Soil. – P.53. Agric. Res. Council, London 1967.
Went, F. W.: The Experimental Control of Plant Growth. – Chron. bot. Co., Waltham, Mass. 1957.
Wilson, P. W., Orcutt, F. S., Peterson, W. H.: Determination of carbon dioxide in gas mixtures. A potentiometric method. – Ind. eng. Chem., Anal. Ed. 4: 357-361, 1932.
Wöhrmann, K., Meyer zu Drewer, H.: Vergleichende Untersuchungen über die CO_2-Aufnahme di- und tetraploider Pflanzen von *Trifolium incarnatum* in Abhängigkeit von Lichtintensität und Temperatur. – Züchter 29: 264-270, 1959.
Zalenskiĭ, O. V.: Obzor metodov izucheniya fotosinteza nazemnykh rasteniĭ. [Review of methods for studying photosynthesis of terrestrial plants.] – In: Lavrenko, E. M., Korchagin, A. A. (ed.): Polevaya Geobotanika. Pp. 245-330. Izd. Akad. Nauk SSSR, Moskva-Leningrad 1959.
Zeller, O.: Über Assimilation und Atmung der Pflanzen im Winter bei tiefen Temperaturen. – Planta 39: 500-526, 1951.

5 | MANOMETRIC METHOD OF PLANT PHOTOSYNTHESIS DETERMINATION

5.1 | General principles and peculiarities of the manometric method

Manometric methods for gas exchange measurements are based on determinations of pressure changes which – under constant temperature – occur as a result of gas uptake or evolution in a hermetically sealed reaction flask connected to a sensitive manometer. They may be applied to the study of all biochemical processes or chemical reactions accompanied by gas exchange, *e.g.* photosynthesis and respiration of plants. Since many chemical reactions lead to changes in hydrogen ion concentration, a great number of processes may result in a secondary release or absorption of CO_2.

Manometric readings are independent of the partial pressure of oxygen at the start of the experiment. This means that the measurements may be performed under the ordinary O_2 content of the normal atmosphere. This great advantage distinguishes the manometric procedure from many other methods, *e.g.* the electrochemical or paramagnetic measurement of oxygen.

Manometry allows rather sensitive kinetic determinations with relatively small samples of material. In contrast to several modern methods like the polarographic analysis or the IRGA procedure, manometry enables one to measure two different gases, *e.g.* oxygen and carbon dioxide, simultaneously.

Since the introduction of the manometric technique into biology and biochemistry a great number of modifications have been made, affecting the way in which the pressure measurements are made and many details of the reaction flask design. The following sections deal exclusively with the 'normal' manometric method of Warburg and some of its modifications. Many different types of apparatus are available commercially (Fig. 5.1). They differ in the number of manometers attachable, the method of shaking, the temperature regulation and, especially, the type of the irradiation system. In practice, radiation sources ranging from fluorescent lamps to xenon arcs may be used. Special attachments allow the pressure changes to be recorded automatically.

The Warburg manometer consists of a U-form capillary tube (sometimes a double capillary) with a short sidearm which connects one end with the reaction flask. A plugged rubber tube serves as reservoir for the manometer fluid, the level of which can be adjusted with a screw-clamp.

The relation between the pressure changes observed [mm] and the amount of gas evolved or taken up is expressed by the equation

$$X = H \cdot K$$

where

X is the quantity of gas exchanged by the sample [μl],

H is the pressure change observed, in mm of manometric fluid, corrected for thermobarometer changes (see below),

Fig. 5.1*A–D* Examples of different types of Warburg apparatus for photosynthesis measurements. (See also pages 240-241.) *A:* Apparatus with circular shaking of flasks around the manometer axis. The amplitude of both sets of 7 manometers is set separately, each manometer may be read individually. Irradiation of flasks with fluorescent or mercury-vapour lamps. Model *S 85 G* of *B. Braun*, Melsungen/BRD.

Fig. 5.1*B:* Apparatus with 15 stationary manometers arranged at the front of the instrument and connected by steel capillaries to the reaction flasks mounted on the shaking frame. The flasks are irradiated by fluorescent lamps or other radiation source. Model *F 166* of *B. Braun*, Melsungen, BRD.

Fig. 5.1*C:* Apparatus with circular water bath. Each of the 14 reaction flasks is irradiated by a 40 W light bulb cooled by a fan. Model *V 166* of *B. Braun*, Melsungen/BRD.

K is the so-called flask constant, *i.e.* the gas volume evolved or taken up, if the meniscus of the manometer fluid changes its position by 1 mm. This factor depends on the volume of the flask, the relation between fluid and gas phase, the gas observed and the temperature. It is given by the equation

$$K = \frac{v_g \cdot \frac{273}{T} + v_f \cdot \alpha}{P_0} \tag{5.1}$$

where

v_g is the volume of the gas phase of the flask (and the manometer to the reference point, see below [μl]),

v_f is the volume of the liquid in the flask [μl],

T is the temperature of the water bath [K],

α is the solubility coefficient of the gas involved (expressed in ml gas ml^{-1} liquid at the standard pressure of 1 013.25 mb and the temperature of the experiment) (see Table 5.1),

P_o is the standard pressure, expressed in mm of the manometer fluid used (see Table 5.2); (in the case of Brodie's solution it corresponds to 10 000).

Table 5.1 gives data for the solubility coefficients of oxygen and carbon dioxide over the range of physiologically relevant temperatures, Table 5.2 lists some

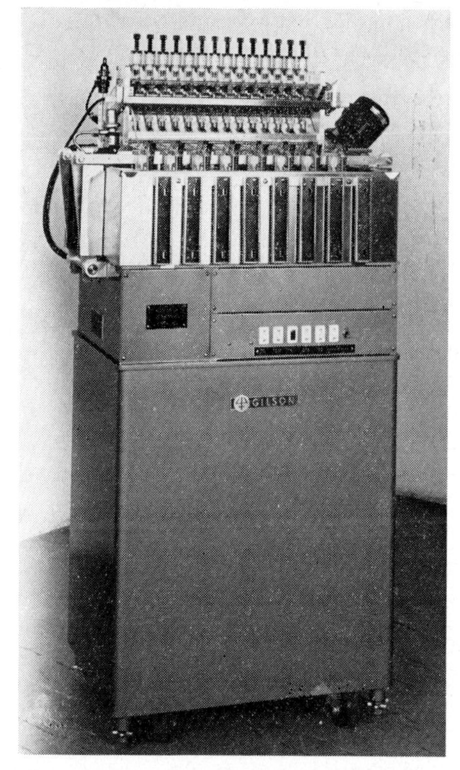

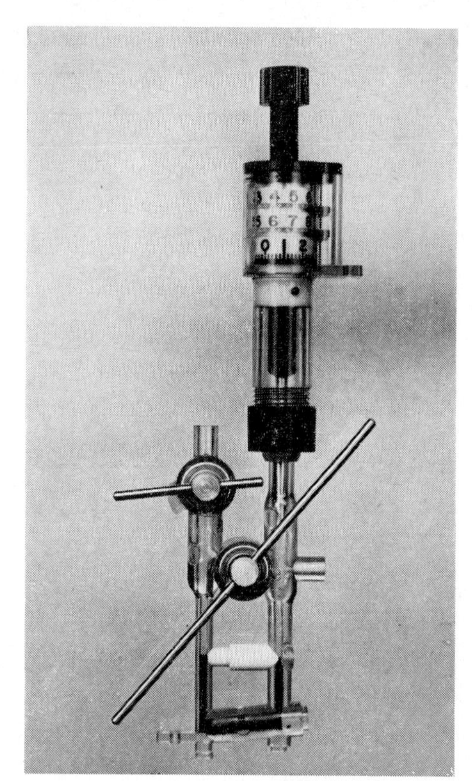

Fig. 5.1*D* (left): Differential respirometer at constant pressure uses a single reference flask for all active flasks. The volumeters combine the manometer and the micrometer. Each flask is irradiated by a 50 W spotlight placed under the plastic bottomed tank. Floor model *GP 14* of *Gilson Medical Electronics*, Villiers-le-Bel, France. Fig. 5.1*E* (right): Digital readout volumetric measuring unit used in the differential respirometer *D*. Product of *Gilson Medical Electronics*.

solutions which may be used as manometer fluids. The derivation of the equation for the flask constant may be found in all practical manuals on manometry (*e.g.* Dixon 1951; Umbreit, Burris & Stauffer 1957; Kleinzeller 1965; Semikhatova & Chulanovskaya 1965).

According to this equation the flask 'constant' is valid only for a certain combination of experimental data. An important value is the exact volume of the empty reaction flask including the volume of the manometer up to the reference point. It must be measured beforehand. For this procedure several methods have been described. In most cases a gravimetric determination using mercury to fill the flask and manometer up to the reference point is used. Details are given in the manuals listed above.

The equation

$$X = H \cdot K \tag{5.2}$$

is the basis for the so-called 'direct method'. It allows the determination of the quantity of one gas evolved or taken up under the condition that the amounts of all other gases in the flask remain unchanged. For measuring photosynthesis or respiration rates it is therefore necessary to keep the partial pressures of all gases

Table 5.1 Solubility coefficients of carbon dioxide and oxygen in water. Data expressed as ml gas ml^{-1} fluid at a gas pressure of 1 013.25 mb (760 torr).

Temperature °C	Oxygen	Carbon dioxide
0	0.048 9	1.713
10	0.038 0	1.194
15	0.034 2	1.019
20	0.031 0	0.878
25	0.028 3	0.759
30	0.026 1	0.665
35	0.024 4	0.592
40	0.023 1	0.530

Table 5.2 Manometric fluids.

Designation	Composition				Specific weight [g cm^{-3}]	P_o [mm]
	salt	surface-active substance*	dye	water		
Brodie's fluid	23 g NaCl	5 g sodium cholate	fluorescein, acid fuchsin and others	500 ml	1.033 at 0°	10 000
Krebs' fluid	44 g anhydrous NaBr	Lissapol N	Evans blue (0.3 g l^{-1})	1000 ml	1.033	10 000
Clerici's fluid	7 g thallium formate, 7 g thallium malonate			1 ml	4.0	2 500
isocapronic acid				—	0.926 at 15°	11 160
ethyl lactate			methyl violet or malachite green	—	1.031 at 20°	10 000
For differential manometry	Kerosene (heavy fraction)		Sudan	—	0.8	13 000
	Isooctane			—	0.692 at 20°	15 000

* Other surface-active substances may also be used.

except one constant. In photosynthesis studies it would be possible in principle to reduce the oxygen pressure to zero (see below) and to measure exclusively the changes of the CO_2 content. On the other hand, the CO_2 partial pressure can be adjusted to a preset value; in this case the changes in the oxygen pressure can be estimated.

Both in photosynthesis and respiration of pure carbohydrate the number of gas molecules evolved is identical to the number taken up. As equal amounts of oxygen and carbon dioxide possess equal pressure we should expect that the total pressure in a sealed vessel filled with assimilating or respiring tissue would remain constant. This is not the case if the flask contains a fluid. The observable changes are caused by the differences in the solubility coefficients of the gases involved (*cf.* Table 5.1). Since the solubility of oxygen is much lower than that of CO_2, photosynthesis – *i.e.* increase in the partial pressure of O_2 – results in a pressure increase, whereas during respiration the total pressure decreases. Thus the uptake of oxygen during respiration causes a decrease of pressure in the system and a fall in the level of manometric fluid; output of oxygen in photosynthesis increases the pressure and raises the level of manometric fluid.

The determination of the pressure changes consists of a series of measurements begining with the adjustment of the manometer fluid level to the reference point (normally the centre value of the manometer scale). Before the first reading can be taken, the flask has to adapt to the temperature of the thermostated water-bath. To facilitate the gas exchange between fluid and gas phase the flasks must be vigorously shaken. Frequency and amplitude of shaking are dependent on the

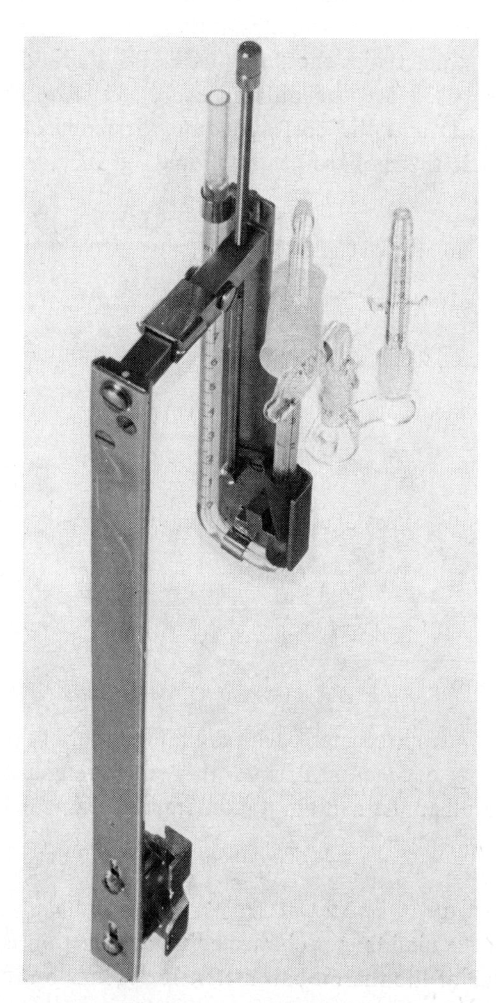

Fig. 5.2 Manometer unit for immersion in a water bath.

type of vessel used and on the sample. If the centre well of the reaction flask or a sidearm are filled with a buffer solution and/or an enzyme poison, care must be taken to avoid splashing these solutions into the main compartment.
If possible, the manometer valves should remain open during the period of temperature adaptation. If the flasks are filled by a special gas mixture, one has to hold the valves closed, and open them several times for very short periods. Normally a whole series of readings are to be made. One of the main difficulties in all manometric measurements are temperature fluctuations within the flasks. A carefully controlled water-bath is absolutely necessary, especially if small pressure changes are to be recorded. Working with extreme temperatures, it may even be necessary to immerse the manometers in the water (see Fig. 5.2). The flask-manometer combination reacts like a thermometer and a barometer, *i.e.* all changes in the temperature of the flask content and all changes in the external pressure will influence the values indicated. For this reason reference flasks – so-called thermobarometers – must be included. They consist of vessels which are filled with a few milliliter of the medium which is used in the reaction flasks. In special cases in which the suspension in the reaction flasks absorbs a considerable amount of radiant energy, *e.g.* in experiments with xenon arcs, a thermobarometer fluid with about the same absorption characteristics should be used. The data on which the pressure determinations are based are the differences between the changes in pressure of the reaction vessels and the corresponding thermobarometers (see Table 5.3). At least two such thermobarometers should be included in every

Table 5.3 Corrections for thermobarometer changes.

Pressure changes		
h_{exp}	h_{tb}	H
−21	0	−21
−16	+3	−19
−10	−2	− 8
+13	−2	+15
0	+2	− 2
0	−2	+ 2
+ 2	+1	+ 1

experiment. The modern *Gilson* respirometer – with digital readout of the pressure values – combines the entire set of reaction flasks with a single reference volume. The table of experimental results must contain the differences

$$H = h_{exp} - h_{tb} \tag{5.3}$$

where h_{exp} is the reading on the manometer connected to the reaction flasks, and h_{tb} is the corresponding value of the thermobarometer. It depends on the type of the experiment whether the total accumulated pressure change ('total method')

Table 5.4 Interval and total method of calculations.

Readings		Interval method			Total method		
Thermo-barometer	Experimental manometer	h_{tb}	h_{exp}	H	h_{tb}	h_{exp}	H
150	152						
151	138	+1	−14	−15	+1	−14	−15
149	124	−2	−14	−12	−1	−28	−27
147	108	−2	−16	−14	−3	−44	−41
149	99	+2	− 9	−11	−1	−53	−52

or the changes between the individual readings ('interval method') are evaluated (see Table 5.4).

The rate of shaking must be high enough to ensure rapid gas exchange; it depends on the intensity of the gas exchange. In most cases the amount of cells suspended or the size of the metabolizing tissue sample must be kept quite small (see p. 253). It should always be checked whether an increased rate of agitation has any influence on the pressure changes.

With most instruments shaking of all the manometers is stopped during the whole period of taking the readings. This interruption of shaking may disturb the equilibrium between gas phase and fluid of the reaction vessel. For this reason arrangements are preferred which allow the shaking of single manometers to be stopped.

The frequency with which pressure changes need to be recorded depends on the type of experiment. To keep the determination error low, subsequent values should – whenever possible – differ by not less than 10 mm. Sometimes the measurements must be extended for several hours; in other cases manometric experiments may be finished within less than one hour. In any case a number of readings at fixed intervals should be taken to get information on the kinetics of the process.

In some photosynthesis experiments control determinations in darkness are used. The pressure changes in the unirradiated flasks give the volume changes which are caused by respiration. The 'real' photosynthetic rate is then often considered to be the sum of the gas exchange values during irradiation (apparent photosynthesis) and in the dark. For such calculations it has to be assumed that the respiration rate during irradiation is the same as during darkness. This may not be so, at least not for all organisms (see Chapter 8).

Successive measurements provide a list of data which have to be converted into comparable figures. After the values have been corrected for changes in the thermobarometer, the multiplying by flask constants enables the changes in the meniscus position to be converted into real gas volume changes. Of course, the data have to be related to some characteristic of the sample: *e.g.* the surface of a leaf disc, the number or weight of cells. The gas production or consumption per unit of tissue and of time can then be calculated.

5.2 | Accuracy of the manometric method

The accuracy of the manometric method is frequently overestimated. Under normal experimental conditions the error of the pressure determinations is barely less than 5%; it may easily reach 10–20%. Equation (5.2) can be used to demonstrate how the error of the apparatus can be diminished. Since the rate of gas exchange (X) is equal to the product $H \cdot K$, its inaccuracy is equal to the sum of the errors of these two factors. The accuracy of the flask constant K (K_{CO_2} or K_{O_2}) depends on the calibration procedure applied; it may be correct within a tenth of a per cent. So the experimental error is largely determined by the readings of the pressure changes in two flasks – the reaction and the thermobarometer flasks. These readings cannot be better than 0.5 mm. So the error of a single comparison is 1 mm.

Obviously the error in the determination is smaller the larger the pressure change. If the readings of two thermobarometers are taken and their average value has an error of $\pm$ 2 mm, the error of the estimation will also be $\pm$ 2 mm. For a total pressure change of 10 mm this would be an inaccuracy of 20%. It must be noted that the error referred to above is the maximum possible error of the apparatus. To find the relative error of the photosynthetic rate of the plant under investigation one must take into consideration the accuracy of determinations of the amount of plant tissues and of the time intervals between the readings. However, the largest source of error is the biological heterogeneity of the plant samples. Thus the aim should always be to make H as large as possible. To attain this the sample may be enlarged. (A limit to this is set by the gas exchange rate between the two phases in the reaction vessel.) The time interval between the readings may be increased. This, too, has its shortcomings, because only repetitions within small time intervals may give the necessary information on the kinetics of the reaction. Another way is to decrease the flask constant. Without changing the flask itself this may be achieved by decreasing the volume of the gas phase. This, too, has its disadvantages: If the volume of the fluid phase is increased, the rate of gas exchange is slower. The gas volume can be decreased by adding glass beads to the vessel but this restricts the movement of the fluid.

5.3 | Principles of photosynthesis determinations

It was Warburg (1919) who introduced the manometric method into photosynthesis research. He developed not only the experimental technique itself, but he also recommended a suitable object: the unicellular green alga *Chlorella*. In spite of many years of experience and countless improvements in the apparatus manometric determinations of the photosynthetic rate are still a problem, and they are much more difficult than respiration measurements. This difference is caused by several factors. In the first place the flasks have to be exposed to high irradiance without disturbing their temperature equilibrium. Secondly, the partial pressure of one of the participating gases must be kept constant. We have no method of adjusting the oxygen pressure to a fixed value other than zero. It is possible to remove all the oxygen from the reaction flask by a $CrCl_2$ solution which can be put into a sidearm or into the centre well of the reaction vessel. This has been proposed by Myers (1960), but today we know that the rate of photosynthetic gas exchange depends on the O_2 content of the atmosphere (Björkman 1966). Hence all measurements made in an oxygen-free gas phase do not give results relevant to natural conditions.

Fortunately it is rather easy to keep a chosen CO_2 pressure constant. Warburg (1919) proposed the use of carbonate-bicarbonate mixtures which function as buffers of alkaline pH. Table 5.5 demonstrates that mixtures of 0.1 M $NaHCO_3$ and 0.1 M Na_2CO_3 regulate a wide range of carbon dioxide concentrations both in the solution and in the gas phase which is in equilibrium with the buffer. The CO_2 partial pressure will be even higher when the concentrations of the two solutions are increased. Table 5.6 gives the corresponding values for different concentrations of Warburg buffer No. 9.

Table 5.5 Carbonate-bicarbonate mixtures.
Data are valid for 25 °C ($T = 298$ K). pH values are measured with a glass electrode (*cf.* Umbreit, Burris & Stauffer 1957); the data for the CO_2 partial pressure in the gas phase and the buffer are taken from Smith (1937).

No.	Concentration [mmol l^{-1}]		CO_2 concentration		
	carbonate	bicarbonate	in buffer [μmol l^{-1}]	in gas phase [%]	pH
1	85	15	0.48	0.001 4	10.42
2	80	20	0.90	0.002 7	10.30
3	75	25	1.49	0.004 4	10.19
4	70	30	2.29	0.006 8	10.10
5	60	40	4.68	0.013 9	9.93
6	50	50	8.67	0.025 8	9.79
7	35	65	20.50	0.061 1	9.51
8	25	75	37.50	0.112 0	9.32
9	15	85	78.70	0.235 0	9.08
10	10	90	131.00	0.390 0	8.91
11	5	95	290.00	0.865 0	8.69

Table 5.6 Dependence of CO_2 concentration in buffer and gas phase upon the absolute concentration of the buffer components. (Data given for Warburg buffer No. 9.)

Concentration of the buffer [M]	Concentration [mmol l^{-1}]		CO_2 concentration	
	carbonate	bicarbonate	in buffer [μmol l^{-1}]	in gas phase [%]
0.1	15	85	78.7	0.235
0.2	30	170	174	0.5
0.3	45	255	276	0.8
0.4	60	340	390	1.2
0.5	75	425	510	1.5

Table 5.7 'CO_2-buffers'.

Composition[1]						References
Diethanolamine		$KHCO_3$	HCl[2]		H_2O	
concentration [%]	quantity [ml]	[g]	concentration [N]	quantity [ml]	[ml]	
60	10	3	6	from 0 to 6	up to 15	Pardee (1949)
concentrated	36	18	concentrated	30	42	Burk *et al.* (1951)
concentrated	6	3	6	2.2	6.8 [3]	Umbreit, Burris & Stauffer (1957)

1. Thiourea may be added to decrease auto-oxidation.
2. The CO_2 concentrations in the gas phase depends on the quantity of HCl added.
3. CO_2 concentration maintained by this buffer in the flask with $K_{CO_2} = 1\text{–}2$ and $V_f = 0.6$ ml is approximately 1%.

Other CO_2 buffers are often used (see Table 5.7). Organic bases, *e.g.* diethanolamine, with $KHCO_3$ and HCl (Pardee 1949; Krebs 1951) maintain the CO_2 partial pressures in the gas phase of a closed system between 1 and 5%.
Several authors have used these buffers as the suspension medium. In many cases, however, buffers of this rather high pH value are harmful. It has proved possible

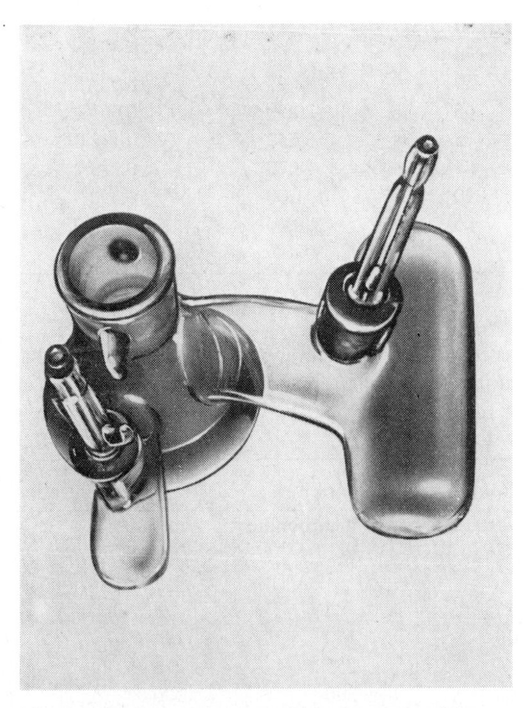

Fig. 5.3 Special manometer flask for maintaining a constant CO_2 pressure in the atmosphere (designed by Warburg & Krippahl 1960).

to use the buffers in closed systems as regulators for maintaining a constant carbon dioxide partial pressure in the atmosphere. For this purpose they are placed in a special attachment connected to the main compartment by a bridge (see Fig. 5.3). The organisms remain in their nutrient solution or in another suitable medium. This modification requires specially designed flasks. It is essential to have the buffers in a sidearm with an unusually large surface. To facilitate the gas exchange it may be necessary to add a small amount of carbonic anhydrase to the buffer (Burk 1961).

In 1924 Warburg described a second manometric procedure which he called the 'indirect method'. It allows the simultaneous determination of two gases in one experiment. It is based on measurements of pressure changes in two flasks with different flask constants, *i.e.* the reaction vessels differ either in their volume or in the relative contents of gas and fluid. To get the exchange rates for two gases, two independent equations are necessary. Their derivation and interpretation is given *e.g.* by Umbreit, Burris & Stauffer (1957). Usually they are written in the form

$$X_{CO_2} = \frac{H \cdot K_{O_2} - h \cdot k_{O_2}}{\frac{K_{O_2}}{K_{CO_2}} - \frac{k_{O_2}}{k_{CO_2}}}; \qquad X_{O_2} = \frac{H \cdot K_{CO_2} - h \cdot k_{CO_2}}{\frac{K_{CO_2}}{K_{O_2}} - \frac{k_{CO_2}}{k_{O_2}}}$$

where

X_{CO_2} is the quantity of carbon dioxide exchanged,
X_{O_2} is the quantity of oxygen exchanged,
K_{CO_2} and k_{CO_2} are the flask constants for carbon dioxide,
K_{O_2} and k_{O_2} are the flask constants for oxygen,
H and h are the changes of pressure in the flasks, corrected for changes in the thermobarometers.

The capital letter symbols are used for the flask containing a large volume of liquid, the small letter symbols for the flask with a small volume of liquid.

The main shortcoming of the indirect method is the accumulation of the reading errors with the result that the data are less accurate than with the direct method. On the other hand, it allows the calculation of the assimilatory quotient.

Myers (1960) used two identical flasks – one filled with an oxygen-absorbing $CrCl_2$ solution, one free of the chromic salt – to calculate the assimilatory quotient *(AQ)* by comparison between the two different pressure changes. This method suffers from the dependence of the photosynthetic rate on the O_2 partial pressure (see above). It is, however, possible to determine the *AQ* in a single reaction flask. Metzner (1967) designed a special vessel which permits subsequent measurements first in the presence of a CO_2 buffer, then in an atmosphere in which the partial pressure of both oxygen and carbon dioxide change. A movable connection between the flask itself and the manometer joint allows one to switch from one condition to the other (Fig. 5.4).

It should be mentioned that one or more sidearms enable addition of solutions to the main compartment without any interruption of the experiment. Special attachments may be also used to mix two solutions and to change the gas atmos-

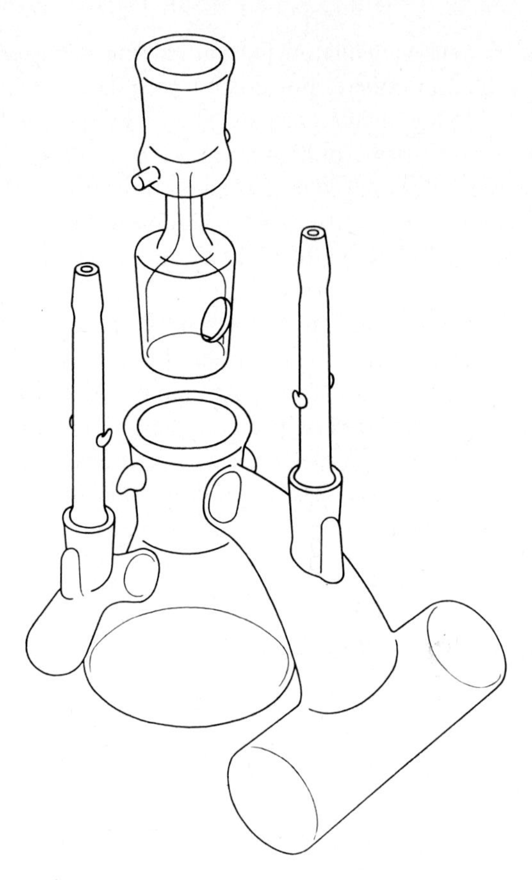

Fig. 5.4 Special manometer flask for the determination of the assimilatory quotient (designed by Metzner 1967).

phere. These possibilities are mainly used in biochemical studies, where countless pieces of valuable information have been obtained from the application of the Warburg procedure.

5.4 | Manometric measurements with algal suspensions

Reaction vessels like the one demonstrated in Fig. 5.5 are most suitable for work with unicellular algae. Many other types, too, have been used with great success. With suspended organisms it is in principle much easier than with leaves to provide the cells with sufficient amounts of CO_2. It is, of course, necessary to choose a suspension density which, per unit of time, absorbs less CO_2 than the buffer can release. If the algae are suspended in the buffer itself, one has to take into account its salt concentration and pH. Whereas the osmotic values of the 'Warburg buffers' (0.1 M) correspond to those of the commonly used nutrient solutions, their pH values are rather high. The buffer No. 9 for example has a pH value above 9. This is not dangerous for *Chlorella* (Rabinowitch 1951), but it may damage some other species.

Cell density, buffer volume and irradiance are determined by the physiological activity of the cells and by the duration of the experiment. In dense suspensions

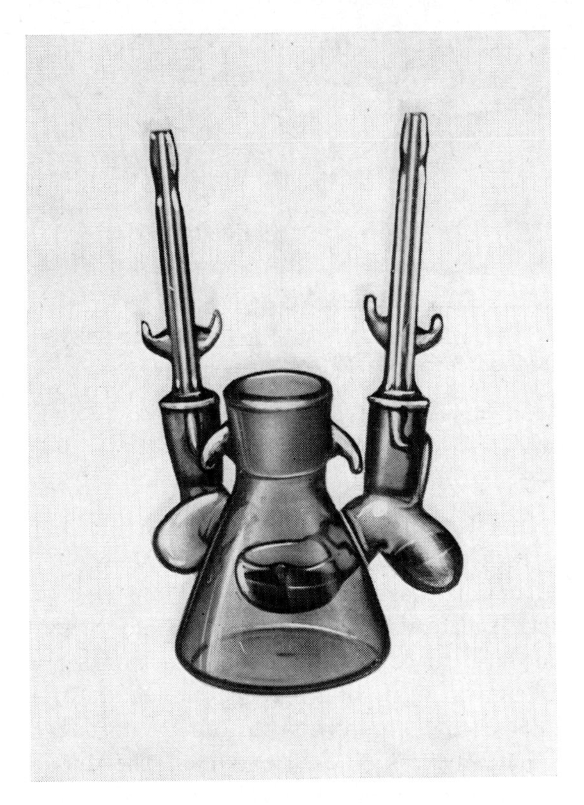

Fig. 5.5 Special manometer flask for photosynthesis experiments with suspended algal cells (designed by Warburg & Krippahl 1958).

the cells shade each other. This makes the cell number critical. The indirect method of Warburg postulates identical irradiation of the two suspensions to be compared. Hence, the application of identical flasks with different suspension volumes is not desirable. Thus two vessels of different volume should be used. The volume difference can be obtained by varying the height of the flasks. Since conical vessels of different sizes have different diameters, it is better to use rectangular flasks.

In most cases it is desirable to determine the photosynthetic rate under conditions of saturating irradiance. This limits the density of the suspensions (see Fig. 5.6) and also requires a rather intense radiation source. Many commercially available apparatuses are equipped with fluorescent lamps. These seldom supply the necessary irradiance. Usually it is better to replace these low energy sources by incandescent or special high output lamps. This is unavoidable if the gas exchange is to be measured in monochromatic radiation. In this case the reaction flasks can be covered by interference filters.

The range of optimal CO_2 concentrations depends on the species and conditions. The CO_2 content of normal air is too low to saturate the photosynthetic process. Hence partial pressures corresponding to a CO_2 percentage of between 0.5 and 2.0% should be used if photosynthesis is to be CO_2 saturated. If the algae are suspended in buffers with pH values > 5.0, the gas exchange data must be corrected

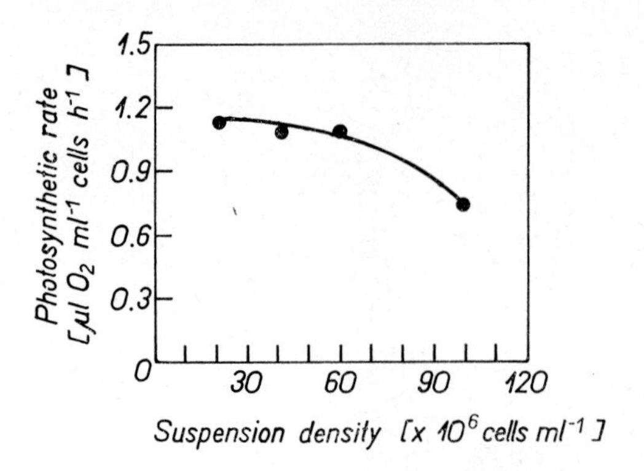

Fig. 5.6 Dependence of photosynthetic rate of *Chlorella* on the suspension density (illuminance 10 000 lux, thickness of suspension layer 1 cm).

for losses by CO_2 retention (Warburg 1954). Only if the pH value remains below this critical limit, do the exchange values need no further correction.

Many experiments need unusual gas atmospheres, *e.g.* rare gases or nitrogen-CO_2 mixtures. The practical manuals give several methods by which the normal atmosphere in the reaction flask can be replaced either by flushing or by evacuation. On switching from darkness to light, or from light to darkness, the rate of oxygen exchange does not change abruptly. Algal cells go through a so-called 'induction period' with quite atypical gas exchange rates. The duration of this slow shift from one steady state to another depends on the alga chosen and on its pretreatment. Contrary to other methods, the Warburg procedure is too sluggish to demonstrate the time course of this phenomenon; the pressure determinations show only a slow shift to a new exchange rate (*cf.* Fig. 5.9). To avoid disturbances resulting from this induction period, it is recommended that the lamps be switched on some 5–15 min prior to the closure of the vents on the manometers and after the period of temperature equilibration in the system. Saturation of the solution with carbon dioxide is generally also completed during this time.

5.5 | Manometric measurements with terrestrial plant leaves

The adaptation of the manometric procedure to the measurement of leaf photosynthesis is much more difficult than in the case of unicellular algae. There are so many sources of error that other methods are usually preferred. It is, of course, possible to use small water plants like *Spirodela* or *Lemna*. However, terrestrial plants are in quite unusual surroundings if suspended in a buffer solution (see Wassink 1946). Since it is also possible to keep high CO_2 concentrations of the gas phase constant, it seems much better to separate the buffer from the leaf, as already van der Paauw (1932) had suggested, by placing the leaves on nets above the solution (*cf.*, *e.g.*, Drautz 1936; Bode 1942; Simonis 1947). Some of the earlier measurements were performed with specially adapted manometric instruments. In many cases, however, the ordinary Warburg method was chosen (*cf.* Ostapenko 1946; Wedding, Riehl & Rhoads 1952; Brilliant & Gorbunova 1955; Nixon & Wedding 1956; Turner, Todd & Brittain 1956). It proved necessary to design special flasks which allow intense irradiation of the sample and a large buffer

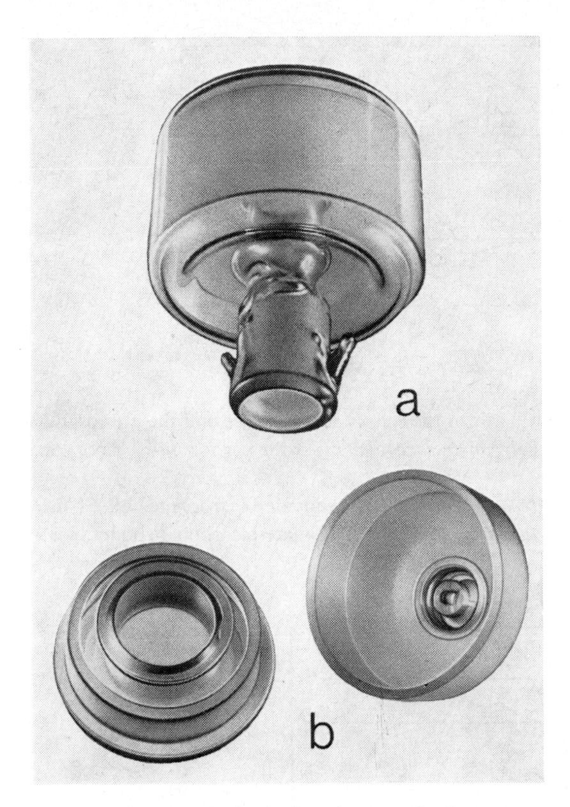

Fig. 5.7 Manometric flasks for photosynthesis measurements on leaves of terrestrial plants: the flask of Katunskiï (*a*), the flask of Arkadev (*b*).

surface area for fast CO_2 exchange (Fig. 5.7). At high irradiances a rather high CO_2 partial pressure is necessary if photosynthesis is not to be CO_2 limited.

As has already been stated, the principal requirement for correct manometric measurement of photosynthetic O_2 output is the maintenance of absolute constancy of the CO_2 partial pressure in the flask. The presence of the buffer solution alone is not sufficient: the rate of CO_2 absorption in photosynthesis must not exceed the rate of CO_2 evolution from the buffer. Since the latter rate is relatively low, only a small leaf disc should be taken for the experiment. To secure constancy of CO_2-concentration, a test should be made to see whether proportionality between the surface of the sample and the gas exchange rate exists. A linear relation holds only for small leaf samples (Fig. 5.8) (*cf.* Ensgraber 1954).

Inside a Warburg flask a typical artificial 'cuvette climate' is obtained. There is always the danger that the gas exchanges are affected by stomatal closure, high temperature and thick boundary layer of the leaf. As irradiation raises the temperature of the leaf and of the surrounding air (Fig. 5.9), the manometer valves should not be closed before a short period (3–5 min) of irradiation has elapsed. Before the manometer valves are closed, equilibrium of CO_2 concentration in the buffer and in the gas phase within the flask must be attained. It is desirable to flush the flask with a gas mixture containing a CO_2 concentration equal to that maintained by the buffer used.

For special purposes the manometric measurements of O_2 output – either for

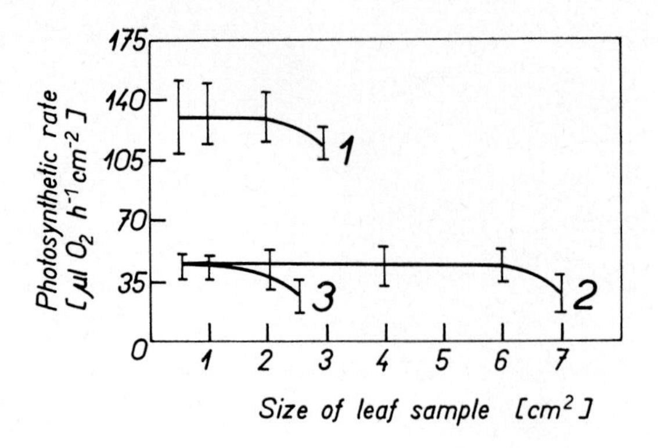

Fig. 5.8 Relation between the size of leaf samples and the photosynthetic rate:
1: for a leaf of *Polygonum sacchalinense* with carbonate-bicarbonate buffer No. 9 (0.5 mol l^{-1}),
2: for a leaf of *Musa sapientum* with carbonate-bicarbonate buffer No. 9 (0.5 mol l^{-1}),
3: for a leaf of *Musa sapientum* with carbonate-bicarbonate buffer No. 9 (0.1 mol l^{-1}).

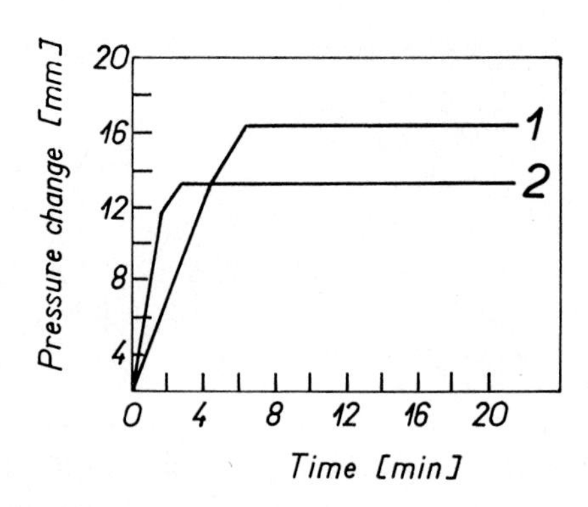

Fig. 5.9 Changes of pressure in the flask caused by the switching on of the lights after the closure of manometer vents: in the flask of Katunskiï (*1*) or in the flask of Arkadev (*2*).

leaves or for algae – can be combined with other measurements, *e.g.* the radioassay of the incorporated carbon. In this case either the carbonate or bicarbonate of the buffer solution are labelled with ^{14}C (Zalenskiï, Semikhatova & Voznesenskiï 1955).

5.6 | General considerations

A critical comparison of the manometric procedures with other methods demonstrates their advantages and their shortcomings. The dependence of the photosynthetic rate on the physiological state of the plant, the effect of certain environmental factors and especially the influence of enzyme poisons and other inhibitors may be preferentially solved by the manometric method. A severe limitation lies in the low exchange rate between gas and fluid phase, *i.e.* the fast kinetics of photosynthetic reactions cannot be investigated by this method (Emerson & Chalmers 1955).

Environmental conditions in the Warburg flask are such that the rates measured may bear no relation to rates of gas exchange occurring in natural conditions. Furthermore only few of the environmental parameters can be varied in a precisely controlled manner over a range of physiologically interesting conditions. Nevertheless data obtained with cell suspensions have given the most interesting and valuable information about the biochemistry of photosynthetic processes as well as reliable data on the quantum requirement of these reactions. These data may not be compared with productivity measurements on mass cultures, but they may demonstrate the maximal efficiency of the photosynthetic process.

5.7 | References

Björkman, O.: The effect of oxygen concentration on photosynthesis in higher plants. – Physiol. Plant. 19: 618-633, 1966.

Bode, O.: Über Zusammenhänge zwischen CO_2-Assimilation und Photoperiodismus bei *Kalanchoë blossfeldiana*. – Planta 33: 278-289, 1942.

Brilliant, V. A., Gorbunova, G. S.: Ekologo-fiziologicheskaya napravlennost' v izuchenii fotosinteza i ego produktivnosti. [Ecologo-physiological trend in studying photosynthesis and its productivity.] – Tr. Inst. Fiziol. Rast. K.A. Timiryazeva 10: 139-149, 1955.

Burk, D.: On the use of carbonic anhydrase in carbonate and amine buffers for CO_2 exchange in manometric vessels, atomic submarines and industrial CO_2 scrubbers. – Ann. N.Y. Acad. Sci. 92: 372-400, 1961.

Burk, D., Schade, A. L., Hunter, J., Warburg, O.: Three-vessel and one-vessel manometric techniques for measuring CO_2 and O_2 gas exchanges in respiration and photosynthesis. – Symp. Soc. exp. Biol. 5: 312-335, 1951.

Dixon, M.: Manometric Methods. – 3rd Ed. Cambridge Univ. Press, Cambridge 1951.

Drautz, R.: Über die Wirkung äusserer und innerer Faktoren bei der Kohlensäureassimilation. – Jahrb. wiss. Bot. 82: 171-232, 1936.

Emerson, R., Chalmers, R.: Transient changes in cellular gas exchange and the problem of maximum efficiency of photosynthesis. – Plant Physiol. 30: 504-529, 1955.

Ensgraber, A.: Über den Einfluß der Austrocknung auf die Assimilation und Atmung von Moosen und Flechten. – Flora 141: 432-475, 1954.

Kleinzeller, A.: Manometrische Methoden und ihre Anwendung in Biologie und Biochemie. – Publ. House Czechosl. Acad. Sci., Praha 1965.

Krebs, H. A.: The use of 'CO_2-buffers' in manometric measurements of cell metabolism. – Symp. Soc. exp. Biol. 5: 336-342, 1951.

Metzner, H.: Über eine Eingefäß-Methode zur kontinuierlichen Messung von Photosynthese- und Atmungsquotienten. – Photosynthetica 1: 249-252, 1967.

Myers, J.: Culture of unicellular algae. Manometric techniques for measuring photosynthesis. – In: Ruhland, W. (ed.): Handbuch der Pflanzenphysiologie. Vol. V/1, pp. 211-233. Springer Verlag, Berlin–Göttingen–Heidelberg 1960.

Nixon, R. W., Wedding, R. T.: Age of date leaves in relation to efficiency of photosynthesis. – Proc. Amer. Soc. hort. Sci. 67: 265-269, 1956.

Ostapenko, L. A.: Vliyanie udaleniya chasti list' ev na produktivnost' i intensivnost' fotosinteza. [Effect of partial removal of leaves on the productivity and rate of photosynthesis.] – Dokl. Akad. Nauk SSSR 54: 81-83, 1946.

Paauw, F. van der: The indirect action of external factors on photosynthesis. – Rec. trav. bot. néerl. 29: 497-620, 1932.

Pardee, A. B.: Measurement of oxygen uptake under controlled pressures of carbon dioxide. – J. biol. Chem. 179: 1085-1091, 1949.

Rabinowitch, E. I.: Photosynthesis and Related Processes. Vol. II/1. – Intersci. Publ., New York 1951.

Semikhatova, O. A., Chulanovskaya, M. V.: Manometricheskie Metody Izucheniya Dykhaniya i

Fotosinteza Rasteniĭ. [Manometric Methods of Studying Plant Respiration and Photosynthesis.] – Nauka, Moskva – Leningrad 1965.

Simonis, W.: CO_2-Assimilation und Stoffproduktion trocken gezogener Pflanzen. – Planta 35: 188-224, 1947.

Smith, E. L.: The influence of light and carbon dioxide on photosynthesis. – J. gen. Physiol. 20: 807-830, 1937.

Turner, J. S., Todd, M., Brittain, E. G.: The inhibition of photosynthesis by oxygen. I. Comparative physiology of the effect. – Austr. J. biol. Sci. 9: 494-510, 1956.

Umbreit, W. W., Burris, R. H., Stauffer, J. F.: Manometric Techniques. – 3rd Ed. Burgess Publ. Co., Minneapolis 1957.

Warburg, O.: Über die Geschwindigkeit der photochemischen Kohlensäurezersetzung in lebenden Zellen. – Biochem. Z. 100: 230-270, 1919.

Warburg, O.: Verbesserte Methode zur Messung der Atmung und Glykolyse. – Biochem. Z. 152: 51-63, 1924.

Warburg, O.: Über die Berücksichtigung der Retention der Kohlensäure bei Messungen der Photosynthese in Kulturlösungen. – Z. Naturforsch. 9b: 302-303, 1954.

Warburg, O., Krippahl, G.: Weiterentwicklung der manometrischen Methoden. – Z. Naturforsch. 13b: 434-437, 1958.

Warburg, O., Krippahl, G.: Weiterentwicklung der manometrischen Methoden (Carbonatgemische). – Z. Naturforsch. 15b: 364-367, 1960.

Wassink, E. C.: Experiments on photosynthesis of horticultural plants, with the aid of the Warburg method. – Enzymologia 12: 33-55, 1946.

Wedding, R. T., Riehl, L. A., Rhoads, W. A.: Effect of petroleum oil spray on photosynthesis and respiration in citrus leaves. – Plant Physiol. 27: 269-278, 1952.

Zalenskiĭ, O. V., Semikhatova, O. A., Voznesenskiĭ, V. L.: Metody Primeneniya Radioaktivnogo Ugleroda C^{14} dlya Izucheniya Fotosinteza. [Methods Using Radioactive Carbon ^{14}C for Photosynthesis Investigations.] – Izd. Akad. Nauk SSSR, Moskva–Leningrad 1955.

6 | VOLUMETRIC METHODS

6.1 | Review of volumetric methods

The oldest quantitative method of photosynthesis measurement is the bubble method, which is volumetric in principle. It was as early as 1837 that Dutrochet established that fronds and leaves of water plants emit gas bubbles from the cut surface if they are exposed to light. Sachs (1864) showed that the gas emission rate can be taken as a measure of photosynthesis. This method can be applied if the assumption is made that the volume of bubbles is constant per unit of time. This assumption is, however, not exactly fulfilled, because the volume of individual bubbles depends on temperature and other physical properties of the medium, and because at a high rate of bubble production the bubbles are usually smaller. Modifications of the bubble method have aimed at a more precise determination of the emitted gas volume. Kohl (1897) suggested measuring the volume of an individual bubble in contact with the leaf. A leaf of a water plant (*e.g. Elodea*) cut off with a fragment of the stem, was placed at the bottom of a basin and the diameter of the escaping bubbles was measured using a microscope with a micrometer ocular. Wilmott (1921) constructed a special apparatus in which the gas emitted from the cut base of a stem was collected in a capillary and then passed through the bent and narrowed end of the capillary into distilled water. As the diameter of the capillary and the surface tension of the distilled water were constant, Wilmott thought that the error in determination of the volume of the bubbles was eliminated. Other modifications included the use of micropipettes, which made gas collection in a measured time possible and allowed the determination of its volume (Kniep & Minder 1909; Górski 1931). Uspenskaya (1951) applied measurement of bubble diameter to calculating the amount of the emitted gas as a measure of photosynthetic activity.

If the volume of gas bubbles produced is to be taken as a real measure of photosynthetic rate, another assumption is necessary, *viz.* that the gas emitted in bubbles is exclusively oxygen. Pfeffer (1871) and Godlewski (1874), from theoretical considerations and from detailed experiments, showed that this assumption was not justified. Diffusive exchange of gases in water causes a partial loss of oxygen from the bubbles and a simultaneous diffusion of nitrogen and carbon dioxide present in the water into the intracellular spaces. In consequence the emitted gas contains from 20–60% O_2 and from 80–40% N_2. The content of oxygen in the bubbles depends on a series of factors, one of which is the photosynthetic rate. Investigations by Górski (1930, 1931, 1935) consisting of the measurement of emitted oxygen in the form of bubbles (volumetric method) and also of the determination of oxygen content dissolved in water (Winkler's method) established the dependence between the oxygen actually produced in photosynthesis and the volume of oxygen emitted in bubbles. The error of this method is not greater than 10%.

The bubble method is no longer used in serious scientific work as it is inaccurate, does not permit reliable recording and cannot be used for respiration measurements. Another type of volumetric method consists in measurement of the change in the volume of the gas phase which is in equilibrium with a liquid medium containing the biological material. Such methods have recently been used for measurement of respiratory rates of small objects. A description of the construction of capillary micro-respirometers is given by Glick (1949). More recently Zurzycki adapted the capillary microvolumetric method for measurement of photosynthesis. The prototype of his micro-respirometer was constructed in 1954 (Zurzycki 1955a, b). Modifications and improvements in its construction, published in part by Starzecki (1961), were dictated by the need for simultaneous measurements and for simplification in handling the apparatus. More details of this method and apparatus are given below.

6.2 | Micro-respirometric technique

6.2.1 | Principle of the method

The micro-respirometric method is used for the determination of gas exchange (photosynthesis and respiration) in small biological objects and allows the estimation of production or consumption of oxygen at rates varying from 10^{-1} to 10^{-4} μl h^{-1}, with an accuracy of $\pm$ 5%.

Measurements are based upon the volumetric principle, *i.e.* measurement of the change in gas volume under constant pressure. This apparatus is one of the differential capillary respirometers. The main part of the apparatus consists of two chambers each joined to a capillary. The micro-chambers (Fig. 6.1 – *A*, *B*),

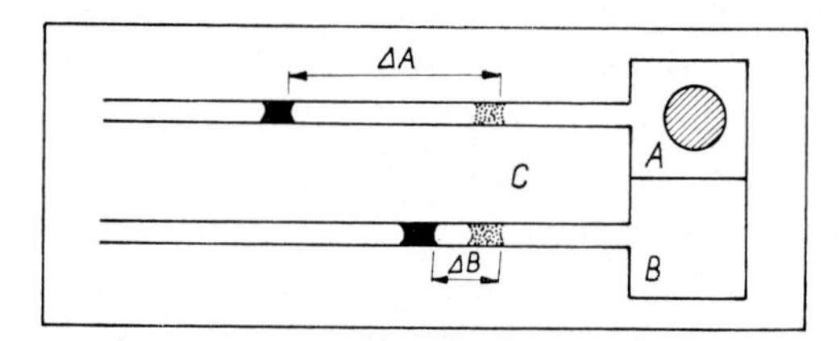

Fig. 6.1 Diagram of respirometer chambers: *A:* micro-chamber, *B:* micro-chamber functioning as a thermobarometer, *C:* compensation chamber. Details given in text.

together with the capillaries, are inside a hermetically sealed main chamber, the so-called compensation chamber (Fig. 6.1 – *C*). Each capillary is closed by a drop of low viscosity index liquid, which is able to move freely along the capillary. Changes in the position of this drop show the changes in the volume of gas inside the associated micro-chambers. The experimental material is placed inside a micro-chamber in which a solution of KOH or carbonate buffer maintains a constant CO_2 concentration, so that changes in the gas volume are caused only by the production or consumption of oxygen.

The assumption is made that the apparatus is at a constant temperature and that chamber *C* is absolutely isolated from the external atmosphere. Under these conditions, any displacement of the meniscus of the liquid inside the capillary (*e.g.* ΔA) is due to production of gas inside the micro-chamber A; its volume is described by the formula of Cunninghan & Kirk (1940):

$$\Delta V = F \cdot \Delta A \left(\frac{V_A + V_C}{V_C} \right) \cdot \frac{V_C}{V_C - F\Delta A} \tag{6.1}$$

where F is the active capillary cross section and V_A and V_C the gas volume in chambers A and C, respectively. If $V_C \gg V_A$ then

$$\frac{V_A + V_C}{V_C} \quad \text{and} \quad \frac{V_C}{V_C - F\Delta A}$$

tends to one and the equation (6.1) takes the form

$$V = F\Delta A \tag{6.2}$$

This condition is fulfilled in the respirometer, as V_C exceeds V_A by several thousand times.

It is difficult to fulfil the condition of maintaining an exactly constant temperature in the system, especially in photosynthetic measurements in which micro-chambers are sometimes irradiated with bright light. If there is a difference in temperature of gas between the micro-chambers and the compensation chamber the difference of gas volume read from the displacement of the index drop is caused not only by gas production by the object but also by thermal expansion. This error is eliminated by using another micro-chamber B, identical to A but containing no object and functioning as a thermobarometer. The reading of the index drop displacement in the capillary B (ΔB) acts as a correction. If both micro-chambers contained the same volume of gas, the corrected production of gas would be expressed by the formula:

$$\Delta V = F(\Delta A - \Delta B) \tag{6.3}$$

Chambers A and B, even if identical in size, may differ in volume of the gas phase. These differences are caused by the presence of the object in one of the chambers, slight lack of precision in the amount of the liquid phase, and slight differences in the way in which individual micro-chambers are closed.

In this situation, the increase in gas volume caused by identical changes of temperature in both micro-chambers causes a greater displacement of the meniscus of the index liquid for a larger volume of the micro-chamber. These differences can be corrected by introducing into the formula a factor incorporating the volume of the micro-chambers:

$$\Delta V = F\left(\Delta A - \Delta B \frac{V_A}{V_B}\right) \tag{6.4}$$

Calculation of the correction does not require knowledge of the absolute volume of the gas phase in both micro-chambers but only of their ratio. This is easily calculated by applying an increased gas pressure in the compensation chamber and measuring the displacements of the menisci in both capillaries:

$$\frac{V_A}{V_B} = \frac{D_A}{D_B} = I \tag{6.5}$$

where D_A and D_B are the index liquid displacements in capillaries A and B caused by the change of gas pressure in the compensation chamber.
The final formula used for calculation of production and consumption of gas by the experimental material is then:

$$\Delta V = F(\Delta A - \Delta B \cdot I) \tag{6.6}$$

6.2.2 | *Description of the apparatus*

A standard micro-respirometer (Fig. 6.2) includes:
a. system of micro-chambers,
b. main container *(1)*,
c. reading microscope *(2)*,
d. illuminating system *(3)*,
e. additional equipment *(4, 5)*.

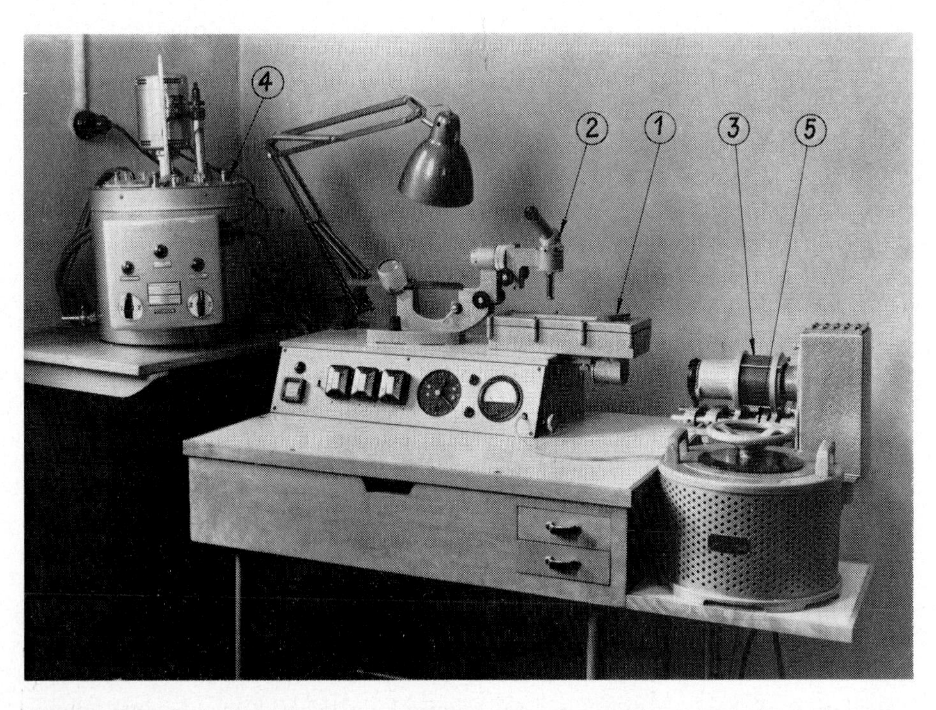

Fig. 6.2 General view of the microrespirometer. *1:* main container, *2:* reading microscope, *3:* irradiating system, *4:* ultrathermostat, *5:* autotransformer.

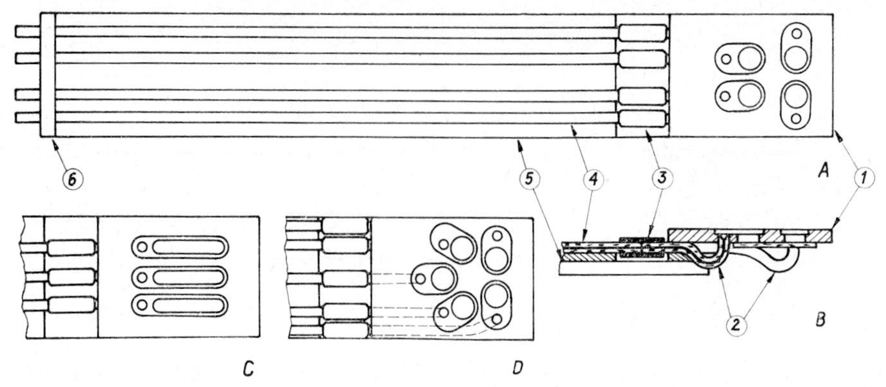

Fig. 6.3 Micro-chamber systems. *A* and *B:* standard micro-chamber system (*A:* view from above, *B:* cross-section), *C:* modification with three elongated micro-chambers, *D:* modification with 5 micro-chambers. *1:* brass plate, *2:* capillaries, *3:* plastic tubes, *4:* measurement capillaries, *5:* mounting base, *6:* combs.

6.2.2.1 | The micro-chamber system

The experimental material is placed in the micro-chambers and changes in oxygen volume are registered in the capillaries joined to them.
The standard micro-chamber system consists of: a brass plate, measurement capillaries and a mounting base (Fig. 6.3 *A*, *B*). There are four apertures in the brass plate *(1)* placed symmetrically and closed from below by a cemented glass plate. The inner metal surfaces of these containers (micro-chambers) are coated with an insulating layer of synthetic resin of the epoxy type. On the upper surface of the plate there are four elliptical incisions for elliptical cover glass plates. Each covers a micro-chamber and the end of one capillary and is sealed by melted vaseline.
Capillaries *(2)* pass vertically through the brass plate, into which they are tightly cemented. Underneath they are bent and project horizontally 6 mm beyond the edge of the plate. The capillary tube outer diameter is about 2.5 mm, the inner diameter is about 0.5 mm. The projecting ends of the capillaries are connected to measurement capillaries *(4)* by tightly fitting plastic tubes *(3)*. Depending on the rate of gas exchange of the material, the diameter of the measurement capillary can be varied from 0.07 to 0.01 mm and is carefully calibrated with mercury. The mounting base *(5)* which is equipped with a millimeter scale, holds the brass plate and protects the measurement capillaries to some extent. The free ends of the measurement capillaries are fastened by means of a comb *(6)* and project about 6 mm from the mounting base.

6.2.2.2 | The main container

This serves as a compensation chamber and also has other functions: it maintains constant temperature, enables the micro-chamber system to be placed in relation to the irradiating system and permits readings of the position of the liquid indices in the capillaries (Fig. 6.4).
In order to maintain constant temperature, a water jacket supplied with circulating

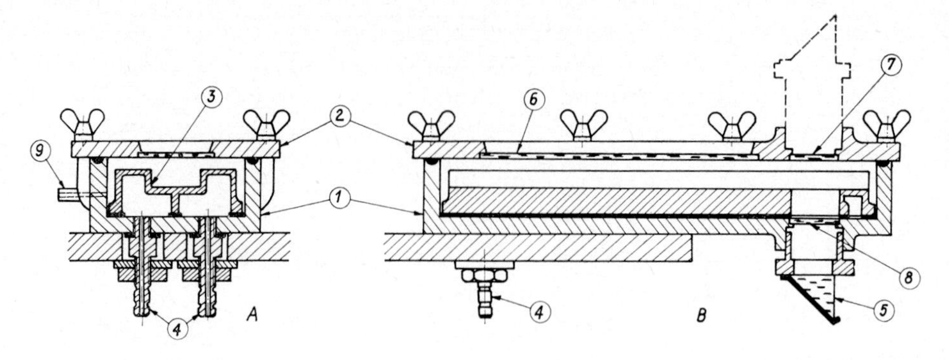

Fig. 6.4 Main container: *A:* cross section, *B:* longitudinal section. *1:* base of the main container, *2:* cover of the main container, *3:* water jacket with a channel for micro-chamber system, *4:* water supply from the ultrathermostat, *5:* prism, *6:* glass window for readings, *7:* round window above the plate, *8:* round window below the plate, *9:* outlet pipe to pressure changes in the compensation chamber. The position of the rubber packing is marked in black.

water from an ultrathermostat is mounted inside the main container. A suitably shaped channel in the water jacket *(3)* holds the micro-chambers in place. A tightly sealed glass window *(6)* in the cover *(2)* of the main container allows readings of the position of the meniscus in the measurement capillaries to be made. Other circular windows (*7, 8*) are sealed in the container walls above and below the plate with the micro-chambers. The lower window *(8)* serves for irradiation of the material, the upper one *(7)* can serve either for observation of the material during the course of measurement or for irradiating the object from the upper side.

The main container is hermetically closed by a cover resting on a rubber gasket, tightened with eight screws. All windows are sealed with epoxy resin. An outlet *(9)* connected with a needle valve permits the pressure to be changed or equalized with the external pressure.

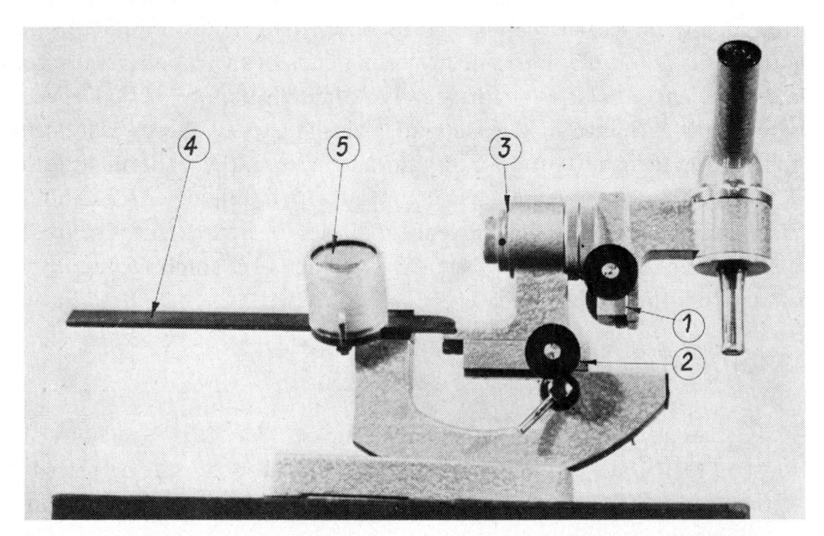

Fig. 6.5 Reading microscope. *1:* vertical rack, *2:* horizontal slide, *3:* rotation axis of the microscope, *4:* ruler with a scale, *5:* magnifying glass for nonius readings.

6.2.2.3 | Reading microscope

A special microscope (Fig. 6.5) is used for reading the meniscus position in the measurement capillaries. The range of the macromovement permits movement of the microscope tubes horizontally through a distance of 80 mm. A slide of 90 mm range was also introduced in order to make readings over a range of 160 mm possible. The microscope is equipped with a ×15 eye-piece. A disc of plexiglass with a thin line perpendicular to the line of measurement capillaries is placed in the focal plane of the eye-piece. The microscope is provided with an objective ×3 (f = 54.04 mm).
A steel ruler with a millimeter scale *(4)* moves in a slideway with a nonius. The line in the eye-piece is set on the meniscus of the index liquid and the position of the meniscus is read on the scale using a magnifying glass with an accuracy of 0.1 or 0.05 mm, depending on the type of nonius.

6.2.2.4 | The irradiating system

The system (Fig. 6.6) consists of: the source *(1)* (incandescent projection lamp of 250–700 W, 110 or 220 V), a condenser *(2)* (f = 4 cm) and collector *(5)* (f = 12 cm) lenses, iris diaphragm *(4)* and liquid filter *(3)*. This optical arrangement gives a uniformly irradiated area of 34 mm diameter on the surface of the plate of the micro-chambers.

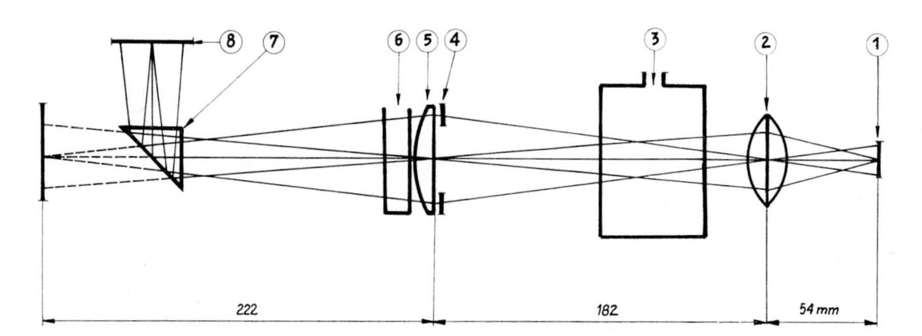

Fig. 6.6 Optical diagram of the irradiation system. *1:* filament of the incandescent projection lamp, *2:* condenser lenses, *3:* liquid filter, *4:* diaphragm, *5:* collector lens, *6:* filter frame, *7:* prism, *8:* plane of the object in the micro-chambers.

Irradiance is changed by the iris diaphragm *(4)* placed in front of the collector lens. Infra-red radiation is absorbed by a 50 mm thick liquid filter *(3)* containing 140 g ferrous ammonium sulphate [$Fe(NH_4)_2(SO_4)_2 \cdot 6H_2O$] in a liter of 2% H_2SO_4.

6.2.2.5 | Additional equipment

The apparatus additional to the micro-respirometer consists of:
a. Ultrathermostat (*4* on Fig. 6.2) connected to the water jacket in the compensation chamber (*4* on Fig. 6.4).

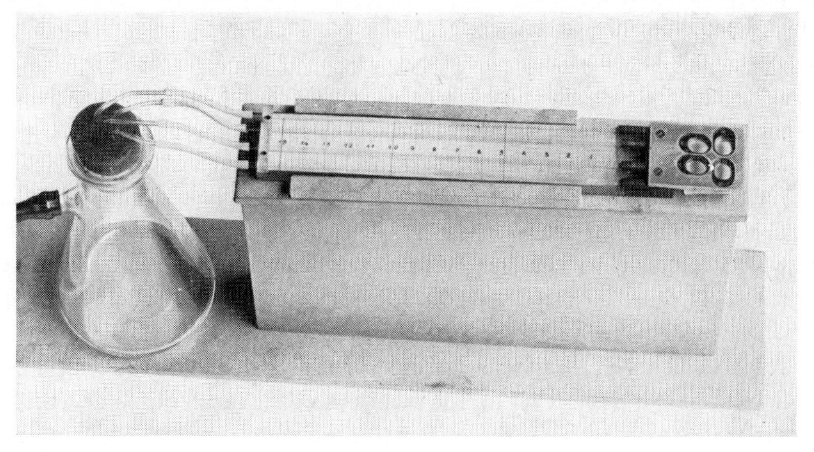

Fig. 6.7 Arrangement for washing capillaries.

b. Stabiliser of voltage supplying the bulb of the irradiating system. The stabiliser is mounted under the micro-respirometer pulpit. The stabilised current is additionally regulated, depending on the type of bulbs, by means of an autotransformer (*5* on Fig. 6.2).
c. Arrangement for washing the capillary system (Fig. 6.7). The washing liquids are sucked through by means of a filter pump connected with a vacuum Erlenmeyer flask which is corked with a stopper with (four) or (five) capillaries coming through it.
Before washing, the ends of these capillaries are joined to the free ends of the measurement capillaries by rubber tubes. For washing, a filter pump is switched on and some drops of 96% ethanol are pipetted into the enlarged ends of the capillaries near the micro-chamber. The capillaries are then dried by passing air through them. From time to time it is advisable to wash the measurement capillaries with 'chromic acid' after taking them off the plate, to rinse them well subsequently with distilled water, and to wash finally with alcohol.
Sometimes the capillary becomes blocked by solid particles, which must be removed with a thin wire. When very thin capillaries are used, replacement of the measurement capillaries may be necessary.

6.3 | Description of procedure

6.3.1 | Temperature control of the system

The circulation of water between ultrathermostat and main container must be switched on 30–60 min before starting the experiment.

6.3.2 | Preparation of micro-chamber system

a. A pipette filled with index liquid (*i.e.* kerosene treated for several days with concentrated sulphuric acid and coloured with Sudan III or Sudan blue) is used to fill the measurement capillaries from their free ends. The kerosene column should be about 40 mm long.

b. In order to moisten the bore of the capillaries with the index liquid the micro-chamber system is tilted and the index liquid flows through. Care must be taken that the kerosene does not come down to the place where the measurement capillaries join those coming out from the brass plate.
c. By changing the angle of tilt the index liquid comes back to the free ends of the measurement capillaries.
d. With a piece of cotton wool the excess of the index liquid is removed until a 5–10 mm long column is left in the capillaries. Columns of the index liquid should be equal in length in all capillaries.
e. Tilting the micro-chamber system correctly brings the columns of liquid to half way along the measurement capillaries. In order finally to equalize the index columns, air is carefully sucked or blown into the capillaries by means of the thin rubber tube.
f. 20–40 μl of carbonate buffer are pipetted into the bottom of the micro-chambers. When the measurements of photosynthesis are to be carried out at CO_2 concentration 0.3%, it is recommended that either 0.1 mol l^{-1} buffer composed of 15 parts/vol. Na_2CO_3 0.1 mol l^{-1} and 95 parts/vol. $NaHCO_3$ 0.1 mol l^{-1}, or 0.2 mol l^{-1} buffer composed of 24 parts/vol. Na_2CO_3 0.2 mol l^{-1} and 76 parts/vol. $NaHCO_3$ 0.2 mol l^{-1} should be used.
The volume of the buffer pipetted into each micro-chamber should depend on the rate of gas exchange and the time of its measurement. The limiting volumes are given below (Zurzycki 1970):

Rate of CO_2 consumption [μl 10 min^{-1}]	Limiting volume of 0.2 mol l^{-1} buffer for	
	1 h measurements	3 h measurements
0.2	12	24
0.37	24	36
0.55	36	—

g. The experimental material is placed in a hanging drop on elliptical cover glasses. In the case of leaves of dicotyledonous plants the upper epidermis is put on the surface of the drop. One glass is left without any experimental material.
h. Cover glasses are placed in the elliptical incisions of the brass plate in such a way that the material is directed towards the middle of the micro-chamber. The contact between the cover glass and brass plate is sealed with hot vaseline pipetted along the edges of the glass, leaving a 2–3 mm long space unsealed. The micro-chamber without any material acts as a thermobarometer.
j. The micro-chamber system is put into the channel of the main container, which is then covered.
k. After 5–10 min (time required for equalization of temperature of the micro-chamber system), the cover is opened and edges of the cover glasses are finally sealed with vaseline.

6.3.3 *Determination of coefficient I*

After sealing the main container by means of screws and after the elapse of 5–10 min, the measurement of the coefficient can be made:
a. The position of the liquid meniscus in individual measurement capillaries is read by means of the millimeter scale on the mounting base, with the needle valve of the compensation chamber open.
b. The pressure inside the compensation chamber must then be increased by blowing in air through the rubber tube connected with the needle valve. The index liquid columns are caused to move along the capillaries in the direction of the micro-chambers. When the displacement reaches about 5 cm (care must be taken that the liquid does not get to the end of the measurement capillaries) the needle valve is closed and the position of the meniscus is read again.
If the index liquid columns do not take up a stable position after closing the needle valve, the compensation chamber has not been properly sealed. If one of the menisci shows no shift after air has been blown into the compensation chamber, the micro-chamber has not been properly sealed.
c. The procedure is repeated using decreased pressure in the compensation chamber.
d. Coefficient I for each micro-chamber is calculated according to equation (6.5); for an example see Table 6.1.

Table 6.1 Example of the determination of coefficient I.

Position of kerosene column in measurement capillaries in mm			Displacement D		
	Chamber with object A	Thermo-barometer B	D_A	D_B	Coefficient I
Initial	77	62			
Under excess pressure	55	36	77−55=22	62−36=26	$\frac{22}{26}=0.846$
Under tension	124	119	124−77=47	119−62=57	$\frac{47}{57}=0.825$
					mean I=0.836

6.3.4 *Measurement of photosynthesis or respiration*

a. The vertical line in the field of the vertical microscope is set on the edge of the meniscus and its position is read by means of the ruler with a nonius. In this way, zero points are determined successively for all measurement capillaries.
b. After 5 min, the positions of the menisci in the measurement capillaries are determined in the same order. Measurements are repeated several times at equal time intervals (*e.g.* every 5 min).

c. An example of the protocol of the experiment for a two capillary micro-chamber system and calculation of data are given in Table 6.2.
Note: Readings must always be taken at the meniscus on the same side of the index drop.

Table 6.2 Example of experimental protocol.
Fragment of *Elodea* leaf of 7.73 mm^2 area. Temperature 22 °C. Monochromatic irradiance of wavelength 642 nm and 1.2 W m^{-2}. Capillaries of true cross-section 0.021; active cross-section $F = 0.0185$ mm^2. Coefficient $I = 0.94$.

Time [min]	Position of meniscus in mm: Chamber A	Thermo-barometer B	Displacement ΔA [mm]	ΔB [mm]	$\Delta B \cdot I$ [mm]	$\Delta A - \Delta BI$ [mm]	$(\Delta A - \Delta BI) \cdot F = \Delta V$ [$\mu l \cdot 10^{-2}$]
0	69.9	41.8	—	—	—	—	0.0
5	71.0	42.0	+1.1	+0.2	+0.2	+0.9	1.7
10	72.4	42.4	+2.5	+0.6	+0.6	+1.9	3.5
15	73.8	42.6	+3.9	+0.8	+0.8	+3.1	5.7
20	74.9	43.2	+5.0	+1.4	+1.3	+3.7	6.9
25	76.2	43.5	+6.3	+1.7	+1.6	+4.7	8.7

6.4 | Application of the micro-respirometer

6.4.1 | *Experimental material*

A micro-respirometer can be used for measurements of photosynthesis and respiration of various biological materials: cell suspensions, whole organs, and organ fragments.
a. Suspensions of spores or microorganisms are placed on the elliptical cover glass of the micro-chamber in a hanging drop. Examples of such measurements are experiments in respiration of germinating *Funaria* spores (Krupa 1964), determination of the gas exchange in *Paramecium bursaria* (Pado 1965) and measurement of oxygen evolution by chloroplast suspensions (Taiıbekov & Stazhetskiï 1970).
b. Because of the size of the micro-chambers, only small whole organs can be placed inside them, *e.g.* leaves of mosses or assimilatory fronds of *Lemna trisulca* (Zurzycki 1955a), small leaves of ferns, such as *Asplenium trichomanes* (Starzecki 1958, 1959), or of higher plants such as *Peleae rotundifolia*, *Muchlenbekia complexa*, *Fuchsia procumbens* (Nakoneczny 1962), turions of *Spirodela polyrrhiza* (Czopek 1964).
c. Use of fragments or discs of organs greatly increases the potential use of the micro-respirometer. Among water plants, investigations on fragments of filaments of *Spirogyra* and *Mougeotia* (Zurzycki 1955c), and leaf fragments of *Elodea canadensis* (Zurzycki & Starzecki 1961) have been carried out. In photosynthesis measurements using land plants, small leaves such as those of *Arabidopsis* (Vele-

mínský, Švachulová & Starzecki 1969) or 4 mm diameter leaf discs are most commonly employed. Discs of 2 to 6 mm diameter can also be used (Kubala 1961; Starzecki 1961; Nakoneczny 1962; Czopek 1967a) for investigation of the basic factors of photosynthesis, and for comparison of photosynthetic and respiratory activity of various parts of the leaf blade (Kubala 1961), or of necrotic areas and adjoining areas of healthy tissue of virus-infected leaf blades of tobacco.

6.4.2 | Variation of environmental factors

The micro-respirometric technique is a relatively simple way of studying the rate of gas exchange in relation to irradiance and temperature, and to some extent to CO_2 concentration.

The construction of the irradiating system allows irradiance to be changed easily by regulation of an iris diaphragm aperture or by use of diaphragms of various diameters and nets or neutral filters. The highest irradiance obtainable with a 750 W/110 V incandescent lamp and the standard optical system shown in Fig. 6.6 is about 60 W m^{-2} (*i.e.* about 12 klx) for white light. By using interference filters, irradiances from 15 W m^{-2} (for blue radiation) up to 40 W m^{-2} (for red) are obtainable. In order to obtain polarized radiation, a polarizer or nicol prism can be inserted instead of a colour filter (Zurzycki 1955c). Higher radiation flux densities may be obtained using a modified system as described in Section 6.5.3.

The micro-respirometer with an ultrathermostat cooled with tap water maintains temperatures between 20 and 40°. An ultrathermostat furnished with a special refrigerating system allows a much greater range of temperatures.

On the other hand, the micro-respirometric technique does not permit change of the atmosphere or liquid medium surrounding the biological material during the course of the measurements. The influence of adding some chemical factors (*i.e.* inhibitors) or changing CO_2 concentration in the micro-chamber atmosphere on photosynthesis and respiration can be studied only in consecutive experiments. After completion of a series of measurements the micro-chambers must be opened, different Warburg carbonate buffer pipetted into the bottom of the chamber, the material treated with the required chemical and placed back into the micro-chambers, which must be sealed before measurements in the new conditions can be made (Zurzycki & Zurzycka 1955; Zurzycki & Starzecki 1961; Zurzycki 1965).

6.5 | Modifications of the micro-respirometer for special measurements

6.5.1 | Simultaneous microscopic observation

The micro-respirometric method allows observations of the material to be made concomitantly with gasometric measurements. With this aim, a microscope from which the microscope table and condenser had been removed was set up so that its objective was situated above the micro-chambers with the material. For observations under low magnification, ordinary objectives, ×5 or ×10, can be used; for higher magnifications long distance working objectives produced by *Cooke-AEI* (×20 or ×40) must be employed. Observations can be made using the standard irradiation system of the micro-respirometer. Because of the low

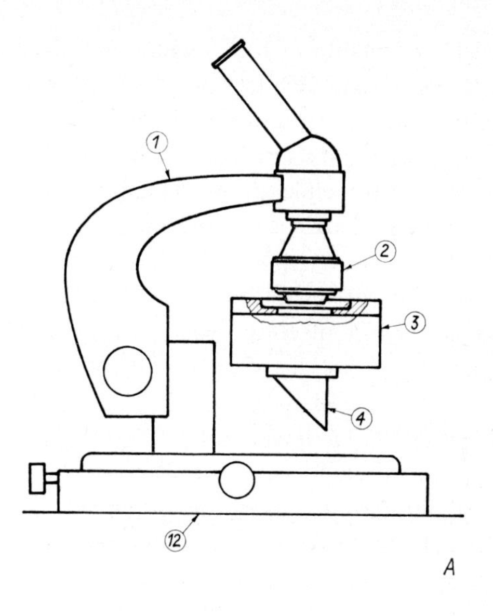

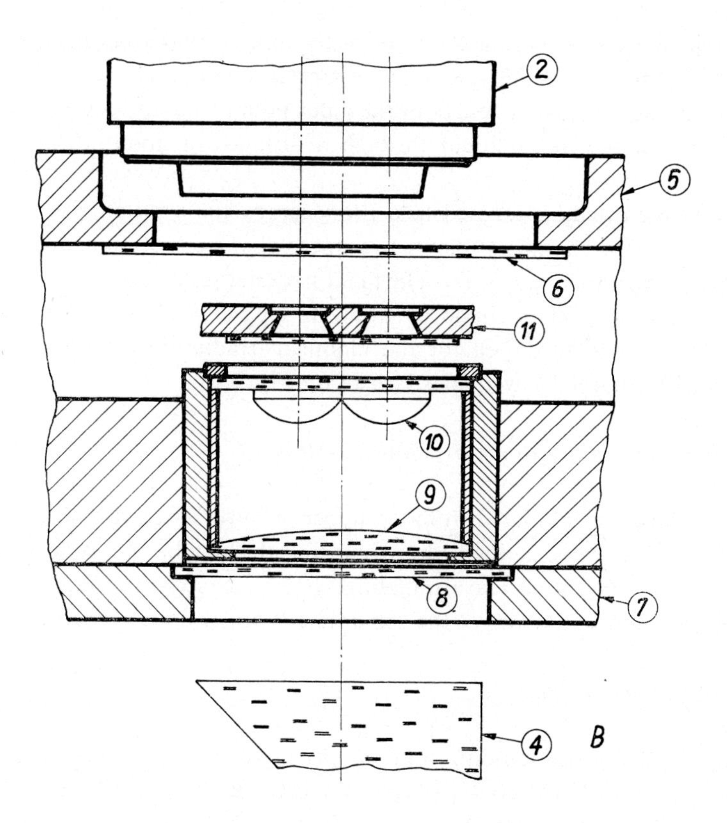

Fig. 6.8 Modification of the micro-respirometer permitting observations of the object during measurements. *A:* general view of situation of the microscope. *B:* cross-section of micro-chambers and a part of the optical system. *1:* microscope, *2:* long distance working objective, *3:* main container, *4:* prism, *5:* cover of the main container, *6:* glass window, *7:* base of the main container, *8:* glass window, *9:* lens, *10:* small lenses, *11:* plate with micro-chambers, *12:* slide base of the microscope.

aperture of this system, however, the quality of the image is not satisfactory. In a recently made modification to the irradiation system, designed especially for microscopic observations (Fig. 6.8), the aperture of the diaphragm was increased to 0.4, thus giving images of higher quality and also higher irradiance at the object. This modification consists in principle of introducing an inset with a correction lens and four small condenser lenses, each irradiating one of the micro-chambers.

Microscopic observations during measurements were made of photosynthetic changes during phototactic displacements of chloroplasts (Zurzycki 1955a), for determination of respiration during plasmolysis of cells, and for other purposes.

6.5.2 | *Modifications to the system of micro-chambers*

More accurate readings can be obtained by using measurement capillaries of smaller bore. In the present system there is no need for a separate system of micro-chambers for each capillary diameter, since it is sufficient to exchange the measurement capillaries.

It should be stressed that in capillaries of small bore the active diameter *(F)* must be determined. This is because the layer of the index liquid moistens the capillary walls and in this way makes the active diameter smaller. This correction is calculated from the decrease in length of the index liquid column occurring after slow displacement of the index liquid through a distance of about 10 cm in a dry capillary.

The area of the evenly irradiated field produced by the irradiating system in the plane of the micro-chambers allows five micro-chambers of standard size to be placed on its surface (Fig. 6.3, *D*). The plant material sometimes requires a micro-chamber shape other than round or elliptical, *e.g.*, considerably elongated (Fig. 6.3, *C*). Micro-chambers used for the modified irradiation system have conoid apertures with enlarged lower sides (see *11* on Fig. 6.8).

6.5.3 | *Modifications to the irradiating system*

The material can be irradiated from the upper or lower side, without changing its position in the micro-chambers, by displacing the irradiating system vertically (Starzecki 1962). By using two irradiating systems the experimental material can be irradiated from both sides at the same time (Czopek 1964, 1967b).

6.5.4 | *Mixing of fluids*

The recently developed modification of micro-chambers enables two drops of liquids to be mixed in the course of gas exchange measurements (Zurzycki 1970). This arrangement extends the application of microrespirometric technique to biochemical and enzymatical measurements.

6.6 | Estimation of the measurement error

 Errors influencing the accuracy of determination of the gas exchange rate in the micro-respirometer can be divided into two groups:

1. Errors associated with the method, causing the gas exchange rate calculated from the readings to differ from the true one;

2. Errors associated with the material, causing differences between the respiration and photosynthetic rates in normal and experimental conditions.

The errors in group *1* can be caused by:

a. Simplification of the calculation formula, consisting of applying equation (6.2) instead of (6.1). For normal volumes of the micro-chambers and compensation chamber, the error caused by this simplification has been calculated as below 0.06 %, and therefore has no significant effect.

b. Local differences of temperature in the measurement system; such differences can occur between micro-chambers and the compensation chamber or between individual micro-chambers. The former is a common phenomenon especially when high irradiances are used. The resultant error is eliminated by introducing a correction from the thermobarometer reading which takes into consideration the volume difference between the micro-chambers (see p. 259). Possible differences of temperature between individual micro-chambers are a likely source of error. The probability of such a difference of temperature is reduced by placing the micro-chambers close to one another in a brass block, which is a good heat conductor.

c. Insufficient diffusion rate of gases in the liquid and gas phases in the micro-chambers. The problems of diffusion rate have been elaborated on the basis of the theory of non-stationary states of Lindestrøm-Lang (1942). Results of calculations for micro-chambers of moderate size are given in Fig. 6.9, *A*. The diffusion rate of CO_2 from the object to the gas phase *(a)*, the diffusion rate of oxygen from the gas phase to the object, *(b)*, and CO_2 absorption by the buffer *(c)*, have been plotted in relation to the ratio of the true partial pressure of the gas in the gas phase, P_t, and the partial pressure which would obtain if differences in

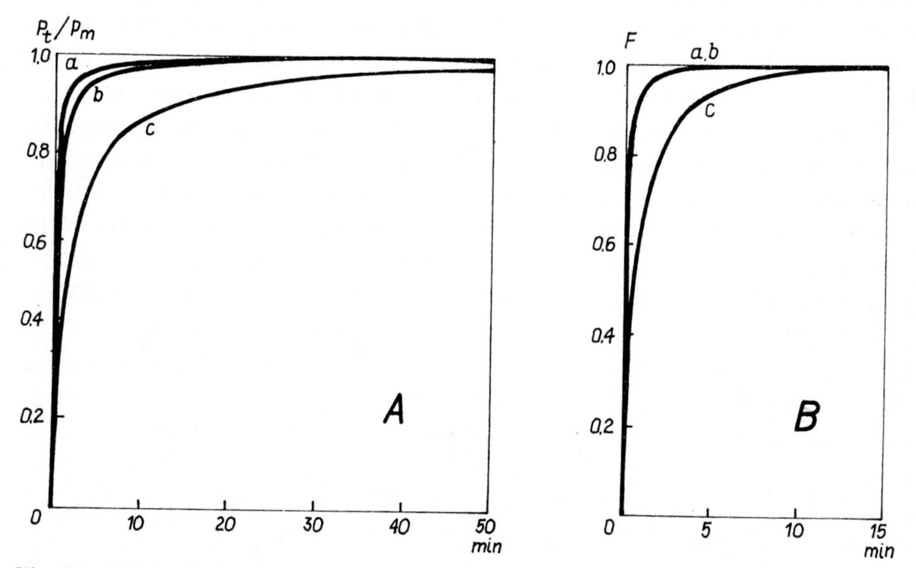

Fig. 6.9 *A:* Dependence of the ratio P_t/P_m on time; *B:* dependence of the value F on time. Details given in the text.

pressure were balanced immediately, P_m. As seen from the graph, the slowest process *(c)* is balanced to the extent of 90% only after 20 min. In the majority of measurements it is in practice not a question of determining absolute amounts of gas production or consumption but the rates of these processes. The ratio *(F)* of the rate of quantitative changes in the gas phase to the rate of production or consumption of gases by the material is essential for estimation of the error of this parameter. Fig. 6.9, *B* indicates that the measured changes represent 90% of the true changes after 5 min, and are equal to the true changes after 10 min. Thus the rate of diffusion is not a factor influencing the accuracy of the determination of the gas exchange rate in fairly long measurements, and can cause an error only within the first 10 min after a change of experimental conditions.

d. Changes in concentration of CO_2 and O_2 occurring during measurements. The concentration of CO_2 in the gas phase in equilibrium with the Warburg buffer No. 10 is 0.45%[1]. If the volume of buffer is 25 μl and 1 μl CO_2 is photosynthesized, there will be a decrease of CO_2 concentration in the gas phase to 0.36%, *i.e.* of about 1/5 of the initial concentration. Such a change, especially at high concentrations of CO_2, should not have any significant influence on photosynthesis. The decrease in CO_2 concentration in the gas phase associated with a decrease in CO_2 dissolved in the liquid phase (in water) is another source of error. This error results in a calculated photosynthetic rate 2% higher than the actual rate. Similar considerations for oxygen show that differences in the quantity of dissolved oxygen are related to a change in its volume in the gas phase and give a reading 3.1% lower than that expected as a result of the actual photosynthetic rate (for more details of calculation see Zurzycki 1955a). Together, changes in O_2 and CO_2 concentration may vary and induce a measurement error of the order of 1%. It should be stressed that these examples are for extremely high photosynthetic rates. In practice, consumption of CO_2 is never so high and measurements of respiration and photosynthesis are made in turn, thus reducing the changes in gas concentration considerably.

e. Resistance of the liquid column. A certain difference in gas pressure on the two sides of the liquid column is necessary in order to move it. The excess pressure necessary to move the column is higher for finer capillaries and longer columns. Experimental measurements of this resistance show that even in the finest of the capillaries used, a 5 mm column moves under excess pressure caused by an increase of 3×10^{-4} μl in the gas phase volume in the micro-chambers. The resistance of the kerosene column is important only if there is a change in direction of the column movement. This is usually connected with a change in experimental conditions and introduces an error in the initial reading in the new conditions. However, its effect on measurements in constant conditions is very small.

f. Decrease of the capillary cross-section by the layer of liquid adhering to the inner wall of the capillary. This phenomenon causes a smaller inner active cross-section of the capillary than that calculated from calibration with mercury. This phenomenon is important only in calculations of the absolute gas exchange rate. The error is eliminated by calculating the active diameter (see Section 6.5.2).

g. Precision of capillaries. It is very important to use only capillaries in which

1. Data from Warburg (1919); but *cf.* Table 5.5.

the differences in diameter at different points do not exceed 0.5%. A capillary can be tested under the microscope by measuring the changes in length of a mercury column 1–2 mm long moving inside the capillary.

h. Precision of reading. The reading of the position of the kerosene meniscus in the capillary is accurate to $\pm$ 0.05 mm; this is associated with an error of 5×10^{-4} to 3×10^{-3} in individual readings, depending on the capillary diameter. This error is random in character and is reduced to a great extent in serial readings.

i. Differences between the time of reading the capillaries. This phenomenon is not the source of a systematic error, because readings are taken in the same order and so with more or less the same retardation for each capillary in relation to the previous reading.

Generally these errors in group *1* result in a total error of not more than 10% for an individual reading, whereas this error calculated as the mean value of several readings (4–6), of the mean oxygen consumption in 10 min, for example, is reduced to below 5%.

Group *2* includes errors connected with the material. It must be stressed that in this micro-respirometric technique the experimental material has no direct contact with the strongly alkaline medium used as carbonate buffer because it is placed in a hanging drop of water on a cover glass and separated spatially from the buffer on the bottom of the micro-chamber.

There can be no serious objection to the use of suspensions and whole organs. They are usually not injured and are in a normal liquid culture medium or in water. In some cases there is slight damage caused by separation of the organ from the parent plant (*e.g.* cutting off a leaf, preparation of the embryo *etc.*) which may change the course of the measured processes in comparison with their level in uninjured material. The effect can be exerted by injury, by lack of contact with the plant or by change in the environment.

In leaf discs and similar fragments of organs the injury to the tissues is more extensive. Investigations by Kubala (1961), Starzecki (1961) and Nakoneczny (1962) showed that in the majority of species the respiration rate of leaf discs decreases within 2–3 h of cutting out. After this time the respiration rate stabilizes and undergoes no major change for three days. In some more sensitive species the respiration rate does not stabilize even after 48 hours after cutting. It has been established that in some cases the respiration rate of discs was twice as high after stabilization as respiration of the same area of an uninjured leaf. Mean values for individual species varied for discs 4 mm in diameter from 132–167% and for discs of 2 mm diameter from 152–196%, as compared with uninjured leaves. The measured apparent photosynthesis in fragments does not reflect its values in uninjured leaves. In discs it is considerably lower. The measurements of respiration and photosynthesis of small leaf discs cannot be generally applied to the whole organ, because the rates for discs differ from the rates for whole leaves more for discs of smaller diameter and for thicker leaf blades.

The micro-respirometric method has already been used in some laboratories for 15 years. Experience has shown its usefulness for measurements of gas exchange of small objects (see examples in Fig. 6.10). It can easily be modified and adapted for investigation of numerous problems. Although it is not applicable to calculation of gas exchange of whole organs from the results from cut parts, it proves useful in solving various problems, *e.g.* the distribution of respiration and photosynthetic activity in an organ or its part, especially when relative results are satisfactory.

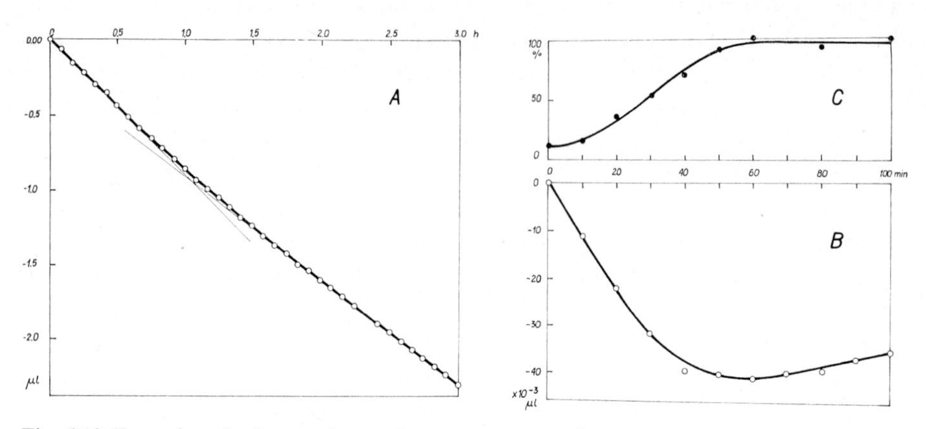

Fig. 6.10 Examples of microrespirometric measurements of gas exchange. *A:* consumption of O_2 in darkness by a leaf disc of *Primula* of 12.5 mm^2 area; cross-section of measurement capillaries 0.07 mm^2. *B:* gas exchange of a *Funaria* leaf of 1.01 mm^2 area in 430 lx; cross-section of capillary 0.0106 mm^2. *C:* % of chloroplasts in flat position, as registered in the course of gasometric measurements.

6.7 | References

Cunninghan, B., Kirk, P. L.: A new form of differential microrespirometer. – J. gen. Physiol. 24: 135-149, 1940.

Czopek, M.: The course of photosynthesis and respiration in germinating turions of *Spirodela polyrrhiza*. – Bull. Acad. Pol. Sci., Sér. Sci. biol. 12: 463-469, 1964.

Czopek, M.: Ecophysiological studies on photosynthesis and respiration of some plant species in meadow ecosystem. – Acta Soc. bot. Pol. 36: 73-86, 1967a.

Czopek, M.: Photosynthesis and respiration of turions and vegetative fronds of *Spirodela polyrrhiza*. – Acta Soc. bot. Pol. 36: 87-96, 1967b.

Dutrochet, R. J. H.: Mémoires pour servir à l'histoire anatomique et physiologique des végétaux et des animaux. – Bruxelles 1837.

Glick, D.: Techniques of Histo- and Cytochemistry. – Intersci. Publ., New York 1949.

Godlewski, E.: De la méthode consistant à déterminer la vitesse de l'assimilation en complant les bulles de gaz qui se dégagent de la plante plongée dans l'eau. – Compt. Rend. Acad. Sci. Cracovie 1: 210-246, 1874.

Górski, F.: Sur la précision de la numération des bulles dans les recherches de photosynthèse. – Bull. Acad. Pol. Sci. Lett. Ser. BI: 1-37, 1930.

Górski, F.: Sur l'action de faible courants électrique sur l'assimilation chlorophylliene chez *Elodea canadensis*. – Bull. Acad. Pol. Sci. Lett. Ser. BI: 85-101, 1931.

Górski, F.: Gas exchange in aquatic plants during photosynthesis. – Bull. Acad. Pol. Sci. Lett. Ser. BI: 177-198, 1935.

Kniep, H., Minder, F.: Über den Einfluss verschiedenfarbigen Lichtes auf die Kohlensäureassimilation. – Z. Bot. 1: 619-650, 1909.

Kohl, F. G.: Die assimilatorische Energie der blauen und violetten Strahlen des Spektrums. – Ber. Deut. bot. Ges. 15: 111-124, 1897.

Krupa, J.: Studies on the physiology of germination of spores of *Funaria hygrometrica*. I. The influence of light on germination with respect to water balance and respiratory processes. – Acta Soc. bot. Pol. 33: 179-192, 1964.

Kubala, A.: Wpływ wielkości zranienia blaszki liściowej na fotosyntezę i oddychanie. [Influence of size of leaf blade injury on photosynthesis and respiration.] – Thesis, Univ. Cracow 1961.
Lindestrøm-Lang, K.: Approximate solution of certain diffusion problems in liquid systems. – Compt. Rend. Trav. Lab. Carlsberg, Ser. chim. 24: 249-279, 1942.
Nakoneczny, M.: Wpływ zranienia blaszki liściowej na oddychanie. [Influence of leaf blade injury on respiration.] – Thesis, Univ. Cracow 1962.
Pado, R.: Mutual relation of protozoans and symbiotic algae in *Paramecium bursaria*. II. Photosynthesis of symbiotic complex. – Folia biol. (Warszawa) 13: 173-182, 1965.
Pfeffer, W.: Die Wirkung farbigen Lichtes auf die Zersetzung der Kohlensäure in den Pflanzen. – Arb. bot. Inst. Würzburg 1: 1-76, 1871.
Sachs, J.: Wirkung des farbigen Lichtes auf Pflanzen. – Bot. Zeit. 22: 353-358, 361-367, 369-372, 1864.
Starzecki, W.: Wpływ mikroklimatu jaskiń na zmiany morfologiczne, anatomiczne i fizjologiczne u *Asplenium trichomanes* L. i *A. ruta-muraria* L. [The influence of the microclimate of the caves on the morphology, anatomy and physiology of *Asplenium trichomanes* L. and *A. ruta-muraria* L.] – Acta Soc. bot. Pol. 27: 221-248, 1958.
Starzecki, W.: Dependence of photosynthesis on light intensity and thickness of the leaf of *Asplenium trichomanes*. – Acta biol. Cracov. Ser. bot. 2: 35-42, 1959.
Starzecki, W.: An improved microrespirometer and extension of its application over plants with big leaves. – Acta Soc. bot. Pol. 30: 327-343, 1961.
Starzecki, W.: The role of the palisade and spongy parenchymas of leaves in photosynthesis. – Acta Soc. bot. Pol. 24: 419-436, 1962.
Tairbekov, M. G., Stazhetskiĭ, V. V.: Dinamika protsessov fotosinteza i dykhaniya v list′yakh duba (*Quercus robur*) v zavisimosti ot usloviĭ osveshcheniya. [Dynamics of photosynthesis and respiration in oak leaves (*Quercus robur*) as related to conditions of illumination.] – Fiziol. Rast. 17: 686-692, 1970.
Uspenskaya, V. P.: Bioelektricheskiĭ potentsial fotosinteza. [Bioelectric potential of photosynthesis.] – Dokl. Akad. Nauk SSSR 78: 259-262, 1951.
Veleminský, J., Švachulová, J., Starzecki, W.: Photosynthesis of two chlorophyll mutants of *Arabidopsis thaliana* growing on a sucrose medium. – Photosynthetica 3: 97-103, 1969.
Warburg, O.: Über die Geschwindigkeit der photochemischen Kohlensäurezersetzung in lebenden Zellen. – Biochem. Z. 100: 230-270, 1919.
Wilmott, A. J.: Experimental research on vegetable assimilation and respiration. XIV. Assimilation by submerged plants in dilute solution of bicarbonates and of acids: an improved bubble counting technique. – Proc. Roy. Soc. B 92: 304-361, 1921.
Zurzycki, J.: Chloroplast arrangement as a factor in photosynthesis. – Acta Soc. bot. Pol. 24: 27-63, 1955a.
Zurzycki, J.: A micromethod for measuring photosynthesis. – Experientia 11: 261-262, 1955b.
Zurzycki, J.: Photosynthesis in polarized light. – Acta Soc. bot. Pol. 24: 539-547, 1955c.
Zurzycki, J.: The energy of chloroplast movements in *Lemna trisulca* L. – Acta Soc. bot. Pol. 34: 637-666, 1965.
Zurzycki, J.: Some improvements of the microrespirometric technique. – Acta Soc. Bot. Polon. 39: (in press), 1970.
Zurzycki, J., Starzecki, W.: Photosynthesis of *Helodea canadensis* after vital staining with rhodamine B. – Protoplasma 53: 57-75, 1961.
Zurzycki, J., Zurzycka, A.: Influence of some catalyst poisons on phototactic movements of chloroplasts. – Acta Soc. bot. Pol. 24: 663-674, 1955.

7 | METHODS OF MEASURING RATES OF PHOTOSYNTHESIS USING CARBON-14 DIOXIDE

7.1 | Introduction

One way of studying photosynthesis is by measurement of radioactive carbon dioxide assimilated by illuminated green cells, and carbon-14 dioxide has been used extensively in such studies during the last thirty years. Carbon-14 has been the most commonly used isotope because it is readily available and cheap, has a long half-life (about 5 700 years: Godwin 1962) and is one of the least hazardous, of the radioactive isotopes in common use. It decays with the emission of beta-particles having a maximum energy of 0.155 MeV (Sullivan 1957). The range of these particles in air is about 22 cm, and in a medium of unit density, 0.2 mm. The low energy of the beta-particles emitted by carbon-14 has required the development of reliable and sensitive equipment for quantitative studies involving this isotope. By the middle 1950's, however, the main principles and techniques for counting low energy beta-particles had been developed (Kamen 1948; Reid 1948; Calvin *et al.* 1949; Bochkarev *et al.* 1953) and the estimation of carbon-14 can now be carried out reliably and routinely using any of the wide range of beta counting equipment now available.

Another radioactive isotope of carbon, with mass 11, has been used in botanical investigations (Moorby, Ebert & Evans 1963) but is of limited value on account of its short half-life of about 20 minutes. The stable isotopes of carbon, of mass 12 and mass 13 respectively, when present in a mixture of the isotopes, can only be determined by mass spectrometry.

Great advances in the study of photosynthesis were made possible by the use of carbon-14 dioxide and much of our knowledge of the biochemical pathways of photosynthetic carbon fixation has come from studies on the kinetics of the incorporation of carbon-14 into organic compounds. In addition, studies of the distribution and movement of carbon-14 labelled products of photosynthesis have contributed greatly to the understanding of rates and pathways of translocation. In comparison with these uses of carbon-14, its use for estimating rates of photosynthesis has received relatively little attention. There are several reasons for this, which will be examined before the carbon-14 methods for estimating photosynthesis are described.

7.2 | Principles and limitations of methods for estimating rates of photosynthesis using carbon-14 dioxide

The methods fall into two groups. In the first, the leaf (or other photosynthetic tissue) is exposed to a gas mixture in which the carbon dioxide consists of a mixture of carbon-12 dioxide and carbon-14 dioxide. For the present purpose the carbon-13 (natural abundance 1.1%) normally present with carbon-12 can be considered as equivalent to carbon-12. After a timed exposure, the leaf is killed and the amount of carbon-14 it has fixed is determined. The rate of photosynthesis may then be estimated if it is assumed that the two isotopes of carbon have been photosynthetically fixed in proportion to their partial pressures in the air surrounding the leaf.

In the second group of methods, the leaf is exposed in a closed space to a gas mixture containing the carbon-12 and carbon-14 isotopes, and the rate of decrease of radioactivity of the gas is measured using a beta-counter built into the closed space. The rate of photosynthetic fixation of carbon-14 can be calculated from the product of the rate of decrease of activity and the volume of the system, and, if the same assumptions about the relative rates of fixation of carbon-12 and carbon-14 are made as for the first group of methods, the total rate of photosynthetic carbon dioxide fixation can be calculated.

Apart from the sources of error arising from instrumental and technical limitations, both groups of methods suffer to an uncertain extent from two inherent kinds of error which may limit their use to semi-quantitative and comparative determinations of photosynthetic rate, rather than to fully quantitative and absolute determinations. These errors are due to:

1. Isotope discrimination. Isotope effects in chemical reactions have been studied intensively, and are of two main kinds, *kinetic* isotope effects and *equilibrium* isotope effects. When the reaction rate constant of a chemical reaction is changed by the substitution of an isotope in a reacting molecule, the change is called a *kinetic*, or rate, isotope effect. In inter-molecular kinetic isotope effects, labelled and unlabelled molecules compete with one another. These effects are greatest where the isotopically substituted atom is at the reaction centre; when the substitution is not at the reaction centre, the isotope effect is generally much smaller. In reversible reactions involving normal and isotopically substituted molecules, *equilibrium* isotope effects occur. They are usually expressed as the ratios of the equilibrium constants for the reactions of the two types of molecule.

The kinetic isotope effect in which ^{14}C–^{12}C bonds are made or broken commonly varies between 5 and 10% (the maximum observed value is 14%: Biegeleisen, Bothner-By & Friedman 1953; for a bibliography see Raaen, Ropp & Raaen 1968). In the degradation of urea by urease *in vitro*, discrimination against carbon-14 has been reported to be 10% (Rabinowitz *et al.* 1956). Discrimination against carbon-14 in the multi-enzyme system of photosynthetic carbon fixation seems likely but results of experiments to investigate such discrimination are difficult to interpret because of the production within the leaf of respiratory carbon dioxide (Weigl & Calvin 1949; Weigl, Warrington & Calvin 1951; van Norman & Brown 1952; Holm-Hansen *et al.* 1958; Sorokin 1959).

Yemm & Bidwell (1969) have used maize leaves, which evolve little or no carbon dioxide during irradiation, to determine the discrimination against carbon-14 dioxide during photosynthesis. Their results show that the discrimination against carbon-14 is only about 2%. Since the relative rates of diffusion of $^{14}CO_2$ and $^{12}CO_2$ are in the ratio approximately 1 : 1.02, this suggests that difference in diffusion rates is the probable cause of discrimination against $^{14}CO_2$, at least with maize. If so, in species showing appreciable photorespiration, the apparent discrimination would be due mainly to dilution of the $^{14}CO_2$ by respiratory $^{12}CO_2$, at least in short term experiments.

2. Dilution of carbon-14 and carbon-12 mixtures by respiratory carbon-12 dioxide. In experiments involving exposure to mixtures of carbon-14 and carbon-12 dioxide for periods of up to a few minutes, it seems likely that the effective concentration of carbon-14 dioxide at the sites of its fixation will be less than that presented to the leaf because of the recycling of carbon-12 dioxide produced by respiration within the leaf. In such short term experiments little or no carbon-14 will be present in the respiratory carbon dioxide, at least at normal concentrations of atmospheric carbon dioxide (Porter & Bird 1962; Goldsworthy 1966b). It can be envisaged that some of this carbon dioxide will be recycled in the cytoplasm and some *via* the intercellular spaces, and that the amount of recycling of carbon dioxide will depend on many factors including temperature, leaf age and irradiance. If it is appreciable in relation to the net flux of carbon dioxide into the leaf it may cause serious errors in the estimation of rates of net carbon dioxide exchange in the leaf, as predicted from measurement of the amount of carbon-14 fixed (see also Chapter 8).

There is not sufficient evidence either on the isotope effect, or on the dilution of carbon-14 dioxide in the leaf by respiratory carbon-12 dioxide, to allow any generalisations about their importance as possible sources of error when measuring rates of photosynthesis using carbon-14 dioxide, and accordingly it is desirable for any carbon-14 method to be checked by an independent method, for example, by infra-red gas analysis.

7.3 Methods for measuring rates of photosynthesis from the amount of carbon-14 assimilated

The methods are of two types: in one, carbon dioxide is applied at a controlled, and usually natural, concentration of 300 $\mu l\ l^{-1}$; in the other, the carbon dioxide is applied at a saturating concentration to determine the potential photosynthetic rate when the limitations normally caused by gaseous diffusion resistance are overcome.

7.3.1 Measurements of photosynthesis in non-saturating concentrations of carbon dioxide

While photosynthesis in most plants is independent of carbon dioxide concentration above 1 000 $\mu l\ l^{-1}$, it is very sensitive to changes in concentration at normal atmospheric levels of about 300 $\mu l\ l^{-1}$. In photosynthesis studies at non-saturating levels of carbon dioxide, therefore, it is usual to arrange that the carbon dioxide concentration in the gas mixture is constant, either by drawing from a reservoir in which the concentration is known and constant, or by generating a gas mixture of known concentration. Where carbon-14 dioxide is being used it is necessary, in addition, to maintain the carbon dioxide at a constant specific activity.

7.3.1.1 Generation of carbon-14 dioxide gas mixtures

Constant concentration and specific activity can be achieved in two ways; by batch generation with storage in a gasholder, and by continuous generation.

Batch generation. Convenient systems have been described by Strebeyko (1967) and Shimshi (1969). As a gasholder Strebeyko used a steel cylinder of 2.6 l capacity. The cylinder was filled with a gas mixture produced according to the method of Voznesenskiĭ, Semikhatova & Saakov (1959), as follows. Air was first evacuated from the cylinder, which was then connected to a flask containing carbon 14-labelled carbonate sufficient to generate the required amount of carbon dioxide of known specific activity. An excess of acid having a low vapour pressure, such as perchloric or lactic, was then added to the carbonate and the gas in the flask then sucked into the cylinder. The cylinder was then pressurised with air of known carbon dioxide content, the air being drawn through the flask to purge it of remaining carbon-14 dioxide. If carbon-14 labelled carbon dioxide were prepared from carbonate of high specific activity the total increase in carbon dioxide concentration in the cylinder was insignificant. Strebeyko (1967) filled the cylinder to a pressure of 101 bar. The carbon dioxide concentration was 300 $\mu l\ l^{-1}$ and the specific activity of the carbon dioxide was 0.11 mCi $mmol^{-1}$, and the cylinder contained sufficient gas for 2 500 determinations of photosynthetic rate each requiring about 100 ml of air for an exposure of one minute.

In Shimshi's (1969) variant of this system (Fig. 7.1), an aliquot of sodium carbonate solution of known specific activity and concentration was enclosed in a reaction vessel *(A)* capable of withstanding at least 10 bar. This was connected to a cylinder *(B)* containing carbon dioxide-free air at atmospheric pressure and also to a source of compressed carbon dioxide-free air (*C* & *D*). Acid placed in a U-tube *(E)* was blown into the reaction vessel and the carbon dioxide generated was forced into the cylinder by compressed carbon dioxide-free air. The compressed air was admitted until the pressure in the cylinder had reached the desired value. Shimshi's system thus enabled the concentration and specific activity of the carbon dioxide to be pre-determined.

Irvine (1967) also used carbon-14 labelled air stored under pressure in a cylinder.

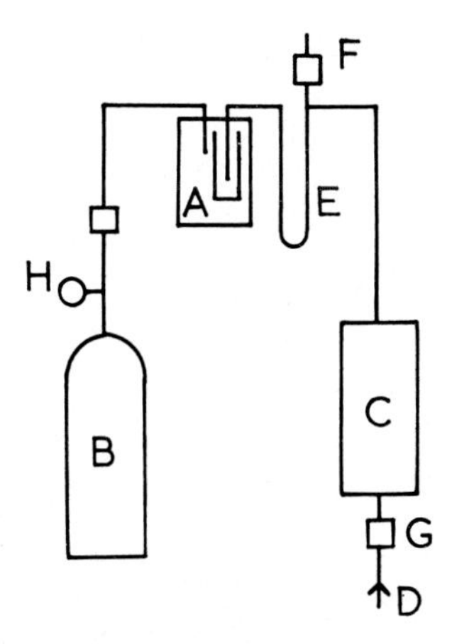

Fig. 7.1 The apparatus used by Shimshi (1969) for the generation of gas mixtures containing carbon-14 labelled carbon dioxide. *A*, reaction vessel into which is placed a vial containing carbon-14 labelled carbonate. *B*, gas storage vessel initially filled at atmospheric pressure with carbon dioxide-free air. *C*, soda lime absorber. *D*, compressed air supply. *E*, 'U' tube containing acid. *F* and *G*, taps. *H*, pressure gauge.

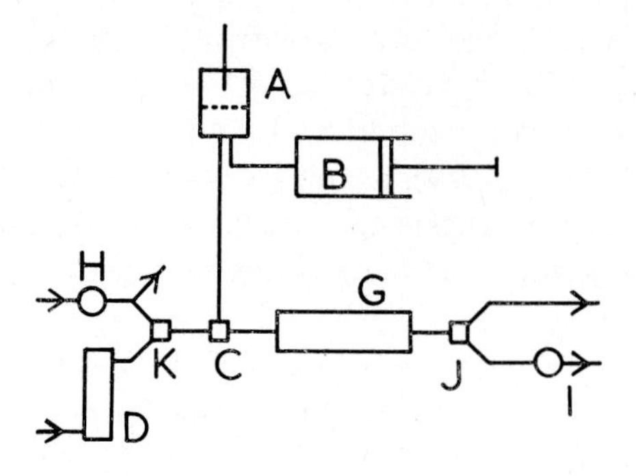

Fig. 7.2 The apparatus used by Austin & Longden (1967) for generating 50 ml aliquots of air containing carbon-14 labelled carbon dioxide. *A*, reaction vessel into which is placed a disc of filter paper having on it carbon-14 labelled carbonate. *B*, 50 ml syringe. *C*, *J* and *K*, 'T' tap. *D* and *I*, soda lime absorbers. *G*, leaf chamber. *H*, air pump for passing air through leaf chamber before and after exposure to labelled gas.

Austin & Longden (1967) devised a method for producing small volumes of air containing known concentrations of carbon dioxide of known specific activity. The apparatus (Fig. 7.2) consisted of a reaction vessel *(A)* closed with a serum cap and connected to a 50 ml medical syringe *(B)* and also to a three-way 'T' tap *(C)* one arm of which was connected to a soda lime absorber *(D)*. A disc of filter paper having on it a known amount of carbon-14 labelled potassium carbonate of known activity was placed in the reaction vessel *(A)*. Using the syringe *(B)* as a pump, air was drawn through the soda lime and into the reaction vessel and syringe until the latter was full. The 'T' tap *(C)* was turned and the air expelled to waste. This procedure was repeated three times. With an hypodermic syringe, sufficient normal perchloric acid was applied to the filter paper in the reaction vessel to liberate the carbon dioxide. One minute was allowed for this reaction to

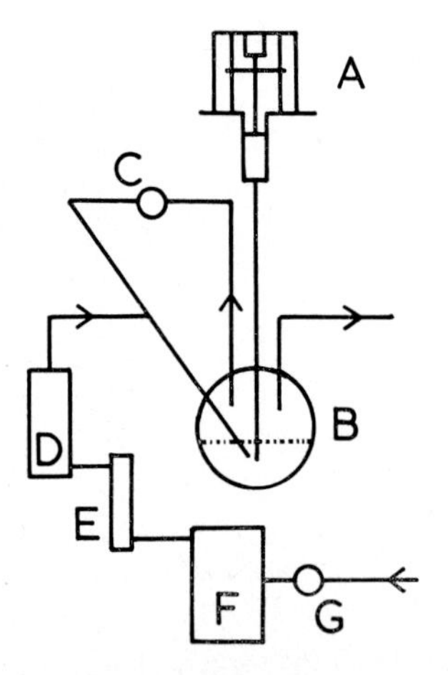

Fig. 7.3 The apparatus used by Goldsworthy (1966a) for the continuous addition of carbon-14 labelled carbon dioxide to a gas stream. *A*, motorised syringe for delivering labelled carbonate solution. *B*, reaction vessel containing lactic acid. *C*, purging pump. *D*, soda lime absorber. *E*, flow meter. *F*, reservoir. *G*, air pump.

proceed to completion. Fifty ml of air were drawn across the soda lime absorbers, through the reaction vessel and into the syringe.
Mokronosov (1966) generated carbon-14 dioxide into air in a gasholder by treating carbon-14 labelled barium carbonate with acid. He used a medical syringe to withdraw aliquots of the air containing carbon-14 labelled carbon dioxide, replacing the gas removed with an equal volume of acidified water.

Continuous generation. A method used by Goldsworthy (1966a) to liberate carbon-14 labelled carbon dioxide at a known rate into a gas stream, has many advantages for laboratory work. A schematic diagram of the apparatus is shown in Fig. 7.3. A solution of carbon-14 labelled Na_2CO_3 contained in a hypodermic syringe *(A)* was expelled at a constant rate into dilute lactic acid contained in a generating flask *(B)*. The nozzle of the syringe dipped into the acid, which was purged of gas by an air stream maintained by a purging pump *(C)*. A constant flow rate of gas, usually carbon dioxide-free air, was passed through the apparatus, and thus the gas leaving it contained carbon dioxide of known concentration and specific activity.

7.3.1.2 | Exposure of leaves to carbon-14 labelled gas mixture

Leaf chambers. Many different kinds of leaf chamber or cuvette have been used for introducing carbon-14 dioxide into leaves (Aronoff *et al.* 1947; Nezgovorova 1953; Belikov 1955; Kuzin 1955; Larsen & Nielsen 1955; Aronoff 1956; Novitskiï 1956; Austin & Longden 1967; Irvine 1967; Strebeyko 1967; Pyarnik & Keerberg 1969; Shimshi 1969, *etc.*).
Many factors should be taken into account in designing a leaf chamber suitable for any particular study, but for quantitative studies on photosynthetic rates, it will generally be necessary to satisfy the following conditions:
1. Air tightness,
2. Uniform irradiation of the leaf,
3. Sufficient turbulent air movement to reduce diffusion gradients to an acceptable level,
4. Sufficient rate of carbon dioxide supply to maintain the concentration to within a few per cent of the desired level,
5. Control of leaf temperature, or at least, prevention of excessive rise in leaf temperature,
6. Control of air humidity,
7. Absence of phytotoxic materials used in the construction.

Most of these features are common to leaf chambers whether designed for use with carbon-14 dioxide or not, and thus are discussed in detail in Chapter 2. As an example, four types of chambers used in recent years for measurements of photosynthesis with $^{14}CO_2$ are mentioned here.
The leaf chamber of Strebeyko (1967) was adapted from a porometer cup used by him, and similar to the cup of Alvim (1965). The chamber consisted of a cylindrical box (*ca.* 2.5 cm in diameter and 0.4 cm high) with holes in the sides for the exhaust gas. It was fixed to one half of a medical clamp, the other half consisting of a

ring, which when the clamp was in position, pressed the leaf against the chamber. During exposure, the chamber was pressed onto the lower part of a leaf. The temperature and irradiation of the upper surface of the leaf were hardly affected by the presence of the clamp. This cell was very convenient to use and the interval of time between exposures could be kept to a minimum. It was not suitable for small leaves or those with stomata on both the upper and lower surfaces.

The leaf chamber used by Austin & Longden (1967) was, like Strebeyko's, clamped onto a leaf, but differed in that two similar halves, each of internal plan area 6 × 1 cm, were clamped on opposite sides of the leaf. Each half had a 1 cm wide washer of non-intercellular plastic foam and these pressed onto the leaf from opposite sides, thus ensuring airtightness. The chamber was thus suitable for amphistomatous leaves.

Shimshi's (1969) leaf chamber consisted of two symmetrical valves made from '*Perspex*' methacrylate polymer and held in modified crucible tongs. The area enclosed by the chamber was 100 mm^2, and the total volume of the chamber was 200 mm^3. The cell was designed so that when clamped on to a leaf a tyre valve was depressed by the clamping action, thus releasing labelled air over both surfaces of the leaf. When the clamp was released, the valve closed. As with Austin and Longden's chamber, the air flowing out of the cell was passed through a soda lime absorber to remove residual carbon-14 dioxide.

Chmora, Semenenko and Karpushkin (see Nichiporovich *et al.* 1961) used a chamber in which were fitted seven neutral-density filters, each transmitting a different fraction of the radiation incident on the chamber. With this chamber, it was possible to expose seven different areas of a leaf simultaneously, each receiving a known fraction of full irradiance, thus enabling the photosynthesis/irradiance curve of the leaf to be characterised. A variant of this principle was used by Austin and Longden (1967) in the design of their chamber.

Time of exposure to carbon-14 dioxide gas mixtures. The times of exposure that have been used vary from one minute (Strebeyko 1967) to 15–20 seconds (Austin & Longden 1967; Shimshi 1969). Chambers will generally cause changes in the condition of the enclosed leaf within seconds, and this makes it desirable to use the shortest exposure that can be timed accurately if it is intended to estimate the rate of photosynthesis under near natural conditions. Too brief an exposure, however, makes 'dead time' an appreciable source of error. 'Dead time' is the interval between the turning on of the labelled gas and its reaching the leaf, and that between the turning off of the labelled gas and the disappearance of all traces of it from the neighbourhood of the leaf. With short exposures, the time that diffusion processes within the leaf and its boundary layer are in a non-steady state might assume importance as a source of error. A theoretical study of this was made by Austin (unpublished) with a model leaf, simulated on a computer. Using typical values of diffusion resistances and leaf geometry, the results indicated that this source of error would generally be quite small, provided that the exposures were of about 15 seconds or more.

During exposures of no more than a few minutes, translocation of carbon-14 labelled products of photosynthesis is likely to be small and so no significant errors are likely to be incurred by sampling only from the part of the leaf which has been exposed to labelled air.

When the time of exposure has been chosen, the specific activity of the carbon dioxide must be adjusted according to the amount that it is expected will be photosynthetically fixed during the exposure, so that sufficient carbon-14 is present in the leaf to enable it to be estimated accurately with the counting equipment available to the experimenter. Thus, the time of exposure, the rate of photosynthesis and the efficiency of the counting system must all be taken into account in adjusting the specific activity to a convenient level.

7.3.1.3 | Preparation of the labelled leaf tissue for beta-counting

As soon as possible after exposure, a sample from the exposed leaf is taken and processed so that loss of carbon-14 by translocation and/or respiration is minimised. Sampling of a disc of tissue of precisely known area can conveniently be achieved by using a laboratory cork borer. The area sampled can be determined by measuring the diameter of a paper disc cut with the cork borer.

Austin & Longden (1967) found that the carbon-14 in leaf discs could be estimated with acceptable accuracy by pressing the fresh disc on to the centre of a flat aluminium planchet, which had been smeared with a mucilaginous glue, drying at 100 °C for ten minutes, and then counting the preparation with an end window Geiger counting system. To estimate the amount of carbon-14 present, the counts recorded were corrected for self-absorption, which is known to be a function only of the thickness (weight per unit area) of the material being counted, if in other respects the geometry of the system is kept constant.

Corrections for self absorption cannot be predicted accurately from theoretical considerations because of self-scattering within the radioactive preparation and back-scattering from the planchet on which the preparation is held, and so it is desirable to prepare a self absorption graph by mixing a carbon-14 labelled compound of high specific activity with inactive leaf powder and plotting counts observed against weight of material per unit area. Useful approximations to the experimentally determined self absorption graph may be obtained using the equation of Herforth & Koch (1962):

$$\frac{I}{I_0} = \frac{1 - e^{\mu d}}{\mu d}$$

where

I is observed count rate

I_0 is count rate with no self absorption

d is sample thickness [mg cm^{-2}]

μ is $0.695/d_{0.5}$

$d_{0.5}$ is $32\ E^{1.33}$ [mg cm^{-2}]

E is maximum energy of beta-particles, *i.e.* 0.155 MeV for carbon-14.

Such corrections are only applicable to material in which the radioactive isotope is uniformly distributed. Considering the structure of the leaves of most plants it is unlikely that photosynthetic fixation of carbon-14 dioxide would take place at an equal rate in all the cells which would give the desired uniform distribution of the isotope. In tests with *Phaseolus* species and *Beta vulgaris*, however, Austin & Longden (1967) found that there was no significant difference between the activity of the discs measured when they were fixed to the planchets by their adaxial or by their abaxial surfaces. This result indicated that, for these species at least, the errors due to unequal distribution of carbon-14 in the leaves were likely to be small.

These uncertainties can be overcome if the exposed leaf is dried, powdered, and a sample of standard weight and geometry placed in a planchet for counting. This method was used by Zalenskiĭ, Semikhatova & Voznesenskiĭ (1955) and by Voznesenskiĭ, Zalenskiĭ & Semikhatova (1965) and has also been used for preparing other samples of plant tissue for beta-counting (O'Brien & Wardlaw 1961).

Shimshi (1969) digested leaf discs in a hot saturated solution of chromium trioxide in concentrated sulphuric acid, absorbing the carbon dioxide produced in a solution of sodium hydroxide. The absorbing solution was mixed with a scintillating liquid (Patterson & Greene 1965) and aliquots of the mixture counted.

An alternative method for estimating the amounts of carbon-14 in plant tissue was described by Dobbs (1963). Dried leaf tissue was burnt in oxygen in a closed flask containing a scintillation liquid capable of absorbing carbon dioxide. Dobbs found that when burnt in this apparatus some materials gave products which were marked quenching agents. It would be necessary, therefore, to determine the counting efficiency after combustion of different types of leaves.

7.3.1.4 | Computation of the rate of photosynthesis

Results can be expressed in relative or absolute terms. At its simplest, the relative uptake of carbon-14 by leaves can be expressed as counts per minute if the time of exposure, sample size and geometry and counting system have been standardised. The absolute rate of fixation of carbon-14 dioxide, P', can be determined from the amount, Q (in micrograms), of carbon dioxide in the sub-sample of W milligrams, as determined by beta-counting (after correction for self-absorption) or scintillation counting from:

$$P' = \frac{Q}{W} \cdot \rho \cdot \frac{60}{t} \times \frac{46}{14} \quad [\mu g\, ^{14}CO_2\, cm^{-2}\, min^{-1}]$$

$$= \frac{197\, Q\, \rho}{Wt}$$

where ρ is the weight in milligrams of one cm^2 of leaf and t the time of the exposure in seconds.

The estimate of the rate of fixation of carbon-14 dioxide can thus be made with a minimum of error. The result obtained will relate only to the environmental conditions during the exposure and to the condition of the leaf during exposure, which may be affected by the cell used. Thus the result cannot be regarded as representative of the rate over longer periods of time and for large leaf areas. To determine this, more than one, and typically many, exposures to labelled gas will be required because rates of photosynthesis are well known to be sensitive to many plant and environmental factors.

Estimates of the rate of photosynthesis from the rate of carbon-14 dioxide fixation are subject to many uncertainties and it is thus desirable to calibrate any radio-isotope method against an independent method, for example, by infra-red gas analysis.

Furthermore, this calibration will be valid only for the range of conditions in which it was established. Thus, if irradiance or leaf temperature are varied, it may be expected that the rate of photorespiration will also vary, so affecting the ratio of photosynthesis as determined by the radio-isotope method, to that determined by gas analysis.

In an attempt to overcome many of the problems of calibration including those of the counting system, Zalenskiĭ, Semikhatova & Filippova (1955) used a standard leaf powder. This was prepared from a leaf exposed to carbon-14 dioxide of known specific activity, the net fixation of carbon dioxide (all isotopes) being determined simultaneously by infra-red gas analysis. It was thus possible to derive, for any counting system, a proportionality constant relating counts per minute to the rate of net fixation of carbon dioxide. However, this proportionality constant will vary if the ratio of fixation of carbon-14 to that of carbon-12 varies.

In the absence of any isotope effect or of interference from photorespiration, computation of the rate of fixation of carbon dioxide, P_N in mg CO_2 cm^{-2} min^{-1}, requires knowledge only of the relative abundance of carbon-14 in comparison with other isotopes. Thus:

$$P_N = \frac{100}{N} \cdot \frac{P'}{1\,000} \quad [\text{mg CO}_2\ \text{cm}^{-2}\ \text{min}^{-1}]$$

$$= \frac{P'}{10N}$$

where N is the percentage of carbon atoms that are of the mass 14 isotope ('isotopic abundance'). This can be calculated from the specific activity of the labelled gas (or that of the carbonate used to generate it, which will usually be known accurately), since the weight of a millicurie of carbon-14 dioxide is 0.738 mg. [In a typical case, Austin & Longden (1967) used carbonate having a specific activity of 10.1 millicuries per millimole (mCi mmol^{-1}), which had an isotopic abundance of 16.1 %.]

7.3.2 *Measurements of photosynthesis at saturating concentrations of carbon dioxide*

Zalenskiĭ and his colleagues at the Komarov Botanical Institute in Leningrad (Zalenskiĭ, Semikhatova & Filippova 1955; Zalenskiĭ, Semikhatova & Voznesenskiĭ 1955; Zalenskiĭ 1959; Voznesenskiĭ, Zalenskiĭ & Semikhatova 1965) have developed an apparatus for measuring the rates of photosynthesis at high carbon dioxide concentrations, when photochemical or biochemical reactions, rather than resistances to gaseous diffusion, limit the rate of photosynthesis. This is termed the potential photosynthetic rate.

In essence, a source of air containing carbon-14 dioxide of known specific activity, at a concentration sufficient to saturate photosynthetic processes, is passed over a leaf for a known time. The leaf chamber and gas holder, together with the pump and tubing, form a closed system and so the 'used' air is returned to the gas holder. After exposure, the leaf is fixed, and the amount of carbon-14 it has assimilated is determined by beta-counting.

7.3.2.1 | Generation of carbon-14 dioxide gas mixture

In the apparatus of Zalenskiĭ *et al.* (Fig. 7.4) a 10 litre white polyethylene bottle *(A)* was used as a gas holder. Within the bottle was a reaction vessel *(B)* containing a known amount of carbon-14 labelled barium or sodium carbonate of known specific activity, sufficient to generate a concentration of one per cent carbon dioxide in the gas holder. Into this reaction vessel acid was admitted from outside through a tube *(C)* which was normally sealed. Two other tubes, both normally sealed, were connected to the tank. The gas in this holder could be used repeatedly until the concentration of carbon dioxide in it only just exceeded that necessary to saturate photosynthesis, which for most plants is between 0.10 and 0.20%. The holder was recharged when the concentration fell to 0.3%. The activity of the gas in the holder was monitored between runs by pumping it through a closed circuit, one part of which contained a mica end-window Geiger-Müller tube.

7.3.2.2 | Exposure of leaves to carbon-14 dioxide gas mixture

A hermetically sealed rectangular chamber *(E)* (10 × 10 × 1.5 cm) was made of clear plastic. Heat-absorbing glass *(F)* placed about 1 cm above the chamber was used to prevent excessive temperature rise within it. The chamber was connected in series with a pump *(D)* and with the gas holder, the entire system being com-

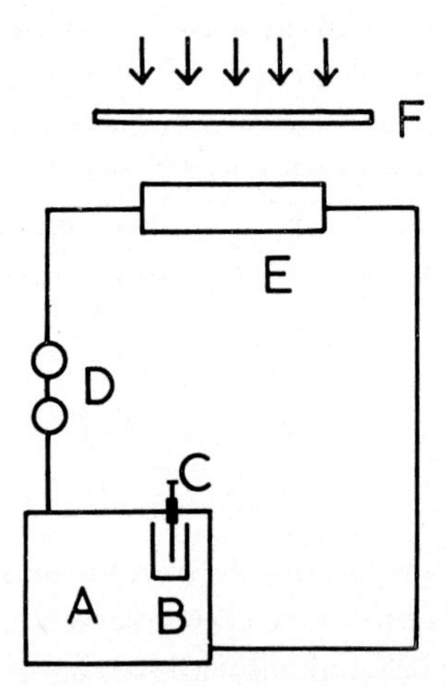

Fig. 7.4 The apparatus of Zalenskiĭ, Semikhatova & Voznesenskiĭ (1955) for measuring photosynthesis at saturating carbon dioxide concentrations. *A*, gas holder. *B*, reaction vessel containing carbon-14 labelled carbonate. *C*, injection port for acid. *D*, adapted insufflator, or, alternatively, a pump, for circulating gas round the system. *E*, leaf chamber. *F*, heat shield.

pletely gas tight. Exposure (3–10 min) was timed from the moment the pump was started, and immediately after exposure the leaf was fixed. When working away from a source of electricity, Zalenskiĭ *et al.* found that a rubber insufflator would serve satisfactorily as a pump.

7.3.2.3 | Preparation of the labelled leaf tissue for beta-counting and computation of the rate of photosynthesis

Boiling alcohol was used to fix exposed leaf tissue. After evaporating to dryness the tissue was powdered, placed on a planchet and the activity determined with a counting system incorporating a mica end-window Geiger-Müller tube. The observed count rate was corrected for self-absorption. For computation of the rate of photosynthesis the same procedure as described in Section 7.3.1.4 is applicable.

7.4 | Methods for measuring rates of photosynthesis from the rate of decrease of radioactivity in the gas mixture surrounding the leaf

Kummer (1948) and Bonner & Turkevich (1951) showed that gaseous carbon-14 dioxide could be counted with end-window Geiger-Müller tubes and this method of estimating carbon-14 dioxide was used by Weigl, Warrington & Calvin (1951) who developed an apparatus for the continuous measurement of the concentrations of carbon-12 dioxide and carbon-14 dioxide in a closed system containing a photosynthesising leaf. The total carbon dioxide concentration was measured with an infra-red gas analyser in the system, while that of the carbon-14 dioxide was measured with an end-window Geiger-Müller tube and counter.
Modified versions of this apparatus have been used by Rachinskiĭ (1955), Voznesenskiĭ (1955), Lister, Krotkov & Nelson (1961), Pyarnik & Keerberg (1966) and Lupton (1967).
In general these authors have used the method for laboratory rather than for field work, unlike the methods based on measurements of carbon-14 absorbed by leaves, which can readily be adapted for use in the field. A general description of the method, with modifications used by some of the above authors is given in the following sections.

7.4.1 | Apparatus

In Voznesenskiĭ's (1955) apparatus (Fig. 7.5), the plant leaf *(A)* was sealed into an assimilation chamber large enough to contain a propeller *(B)* for maintaining air circulation, the window of a Geiger-Müller tube *(C)* and an ante-chamber *(D)* in which the carbon-14 labelled carbon dioxide was generated. Within the chamber there was also a heat exchanger *(E)* to enable the temperature of the air within the apparatus to be controlled. Lupton's (1967) apparatus (Fig. 7.6) consisted of a leaf chamber *(A)*, a beta counter *(B)*, a circulating pump *(C)*, a means of generating carbon-14 dioxide *(D)* and a water vapour condenser *(E)*, all arranged in series in a closed circuit.

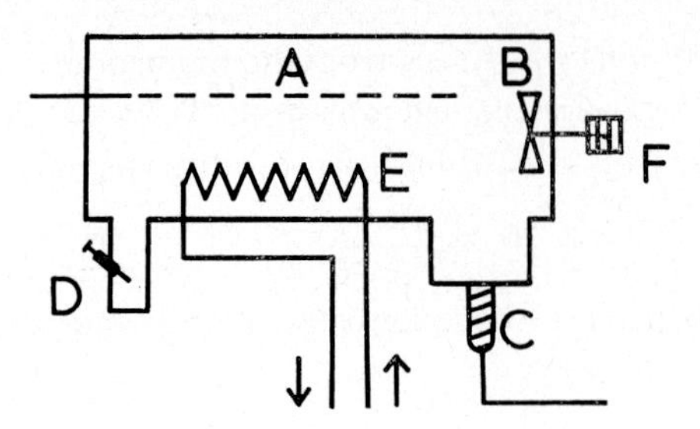

Fig. 7.5 Voznesenskiĭ's (1955) apparatus for measuring photosynthesis from the decrease of radioactivity of gas mixtures surrounding leaves. *A*, leaf contained in chamber. *B*, fan for creating turbulent air movement within apparatus, driven by motor *F*. *C*, end-window Geiger tube. *D*, reaction vessel containing carbon-14 labelled carbonate to which acid is added *via* a normally closed injection port. *E*, heat exchanger for regulating the air temperature within the leaf chamber.

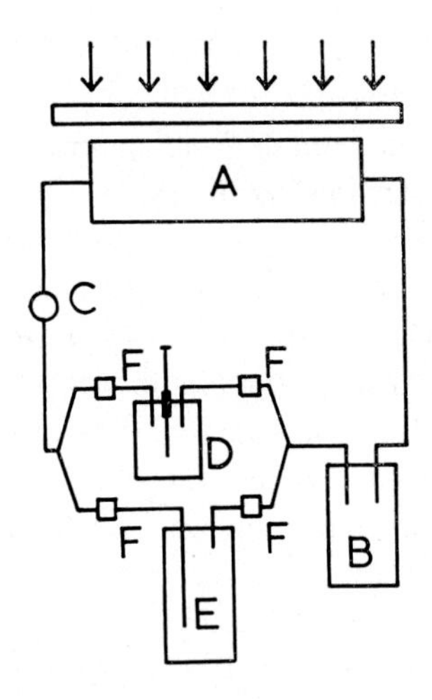

Fig. 7.6 Lupton's (1967) closed circuit apparatus for measuring rates of photosynthesis from the decrease of radioactivity of gas mixtures passed over leaves. *A*, leaf chamber. *B*, gas scintillation counter. *C*, circulating pump. *D*, reaction vessel, containing carbon-14 labelled carbonate, with a normally closed injection port for acid. *E*, water vapour condenser. *F*, taps.

With any system it is essential to use components which do not absorb carbon dioxide and through which gas cannot leak, either in or out.

Leaf chamber. Because of the difficulty of ensuring reliable gas tightness of any washers pressed on to leaves, it is preferable to use a chamber which fully encloses the leaf.

Beta counter. Most thin mica end-window Geiger-Müller tubes will serve as adequate radiation detectors. Lupton (1967) used a gas scintillation counter which had the advantage of greater sensitivity than that of the Geiger tube.

Circulating pump. Piston pumps will generally be unsatisfactory because the vapour and droplets of lubricant from them will become entrained in the gas stream, interfering with leaf function and possibly reducing the sensitivity of the beta counting system. Suitable pumps are of the peristaltic or diaphragm kind, providing they do not contain material which will either absorb carbon dioxide or be permeable to it. Most natural rubbers will absorb carbon dioxide but flexible polyamide polymers such as '*Tygon*'[1] are non-absorbent. The rate of pumping must be adjusted in relation to the volume of the gas circuit and the dimensions of the assimilation chamber so that gradients of CO_2 concentration in the circuit are small, say 10–20 $\mu l\ l^{-1}$, when the average concentration is 300 $\mu l\ l^{-1}$.

Condenser. Lupton (1967) found that water vapour, produced by transpiration, condensed on the cooler surfaces of the gas circuit, and incorporated an ice cooled condenser to remove this water. The condensate should be kept acid, to minimise the loss of carbon dioxide from the gas in the circuit by solution in the condensate.

Carbon dioxide generator. In Voznesenskiĭ's (1955) apparatus (Fig. 7.5) labelled carbonate was put into the ante-chamber *(D)* when the leaf was inserted in the chamber. Carbon dioxide was generated from this carbonate when required by injecting an excess of acid into the ante-chamber. Lupton (1967) (Fig. 7.6) placed labelled carbonate in a flask *(D)* arranged in a by-pass of the condenser. At the start of an experiment, an excess of lactic acid was injected into the flask, the carbon dioxide was generated over a period of 20–30 minutes (generation of the gas was slow because of the viscosity of the lactic acid). This carbon dioxide was released into the main circuit as required.

7.4.2 | *Experimental procedure*

Sufficient labelled carbonate is put into the generator to give a concentration of carbon dioxide (all isotopes) of approximately 0.1%. The leaf or plant is sealed in the chamber and the irradiance, temperature and other factors are adjusted as required.

After checking that the system is air tight, the carbon dioxide is generated by the injection of an excess of acid.

The counter is started and the count rate plotted against time. The tangent to the curve, *i.e.*, the rate of decrease in count rate with time, is proportional to the rate of photosynthesis. With Lupton's (1967) apparatus it is possible to release the carbon dioxide in more than one dose, thus permitting replication of the curves of count rate against time.

7.4.3 | *Computation of the rate of photosynthesis*

The rate of fixation of carbon-14 dioxide, P', in $\mu g\ cm^{-2}\ min^{-1}$, can be computed from the rate of decrease in count rate per minute, ΔC, and a proportionality constant, S, which is the number of counts per minute registered by the counter per millicurie of carbon-14 dioxide generated in the system when no leaf is present, by:

1. Unfortunately, '*Tygon*' tubing is appreciably permeable to CO_2.

$$P' = \frac{738\ S \cdot \Delta C}{A}\ [\mu g\ ^{14}CO_2\ cm^{-2} min^{-1}]$$

when A is the area in cm^2 of leaf in the assimilation chamber.
Because of the dependence of photosynthetic rate on carbon dioxide concentration it will generally be required to calculate the value of P' for a known carbon dioxide concentration, say 300 $\mu l\ l^{-1}$.
The count rate equivalent to 300 $\mu l\ l^{-1}$, C_{300}, can be calculated from:

$$C_{300} = \frac{300\ S \cdot Q}{(10^{-6}\ v/V) + I}$$

where
S is the proportionality constant as defined above
Q is the number of millicuries of activity generated in the test
v is the volume of CO_2 generated in the test in ml
V is the volume of the system in ml
I is the initial concentration of carbon dioxide in the circuit in $\mu l\ l^{-1}$.
The determination of I, the initial concentration of carbon dioxide in the circuit in $\mu l\ l^{-1}$ may present some difficulty unless a suitable method for analysis of this gas is available.
The rate of photosynthetic fixation of carbon dioxide, P_N (all isotopes), can be determined from the product of ΔC, the rate of decrease in count rate per minute, and the count rate per minute equal to 1 $\mu l\ l^{-1}$ of carbon dioxide, and the weight, m, mg CO_2 per 1 $\mu l\ l^{-1}$ of this gas in the circuit, that is:

$$P_N = \frac{C \cdot m \cdot S \cdot Q}{(10^{-6}\ v/V) + I} \cdot \frac{1}{A}\ [mg\ CO_2\ cm^{-2}\ min^{-1}]$$

To evaluate m, the pressure and temperature and volume of the gas in the system must be taken into account, but at N.T.P., it is given by:

$$m = 1.965V \times 10^{-6}\ mg$$

The expression for obtaining P_N, the rate of photosynthetic fixation of all isotopes of carbon dioxide, is subject to uncertainties caused by isotopic discrimination and photorespiration in the same way as when determined by the other methods. These uncertainties become greater as the carbon dioxide concentration in the chamber approaches the compensation point, when its specific activity decreases continually while its concentration remains constant (Krotkov, Runeckles & Thimann 1958; Voznesenskiĭ 1961, 1965). For these reasons, Voznesenskiĭ regarded estimates of photosynthetic rate obtained from closed system experiments with carbon-14 dioxide as valid only at atmospheric concentrations and above.

7.5 | Conclusion

 Under standardised conditions, carefully chosen to minimise possible errors

arising from photorespiration and from isotopic discrimination, carbon-14 methods for measuring rates of photosynthesis have the advantage of being rapid, easy to carry out and cheap. Thus it can be envisaged that they would be valuable for studying the interactions of the many factors that affect photosynthesis and possibly for the appraisal of parental lines and progenies in plant breeding.
The simultaneous measurement of the rates of fixation of carbon-12 and carbon-14 dioxides appears to offer the possibility of determining photorespiration and net photosynthesis concurrently but adequate theory has yet to be developed for this kind of study (see Chapter 8).

7.6 | References

Alvim, P. de T.: A new type of porometer for measuring stomatal opening and its use in irrigation studies. – In: Eckardt, F. E. (ed.): Methodology of Plant Eco-Physiology. Pp. 325-329. Unesco, Paris 1965.
Aronoff, S.: Techniques of Radiobiochemistry. – Iowa, Ill. 1956.
Aronoff, S., Benson, A. A., Hassid, W., Calvin, M.: Distribution of C^{14} in photosynthesizing barley seedlings. – Science 105: 664-665, 1947.
Austin, R. B., Longden, P. C.: A rapid method for the measurement of rates of photosynthesis using $^{14}CO_2$. – Ann. Bot. 31: 245-253, 1967.
Belikov, I. F.: O dvizhenii i raspredelenii produktov fotosinteza u soi v period vegetatsii. [Translocation and distribution of photosynthetic products of soybean during the vegetation period.] – Fiziol. Rastenii̇ 2: 354-357, 1955.
Biegeleisen, J., Bothner-By, A. A., Friedman, L.: Fractionation of the carbon isotopes in decarboxylation reactions. V. The mechanism of the pyrolysis of barium adipate. – J. Amer. chem. Soc. 75: 2908-2910, 1953.
Bochkarev, V., Keirim-Markus, I., L'vova, M., Pruslin, Ya.: Izmerenie Aktivnosti Istochnikov Beta- i Gamma-Izluchenii̇. [Measurement of Beta- and Gamma-Radiation Activity.] – Izd. Akad. Nauk SSSR, Moskva 1953.
Bonner, F., Turkevich, J.: Study of the carbon dioxide-carbon reaction using C^{14} as a tracer. – J. Amer. chem. Soc. 73: 561-564, 1951.
Calvin, M., Heidelberger, C., Reid, J. C., Tolbert, B. M., Hankwich, P. F.: Isotopic Carbon. – John Wiley and Sons, New York 1949.
Dobbs, H. E.: Oxygen flask method for the assay of titrium-, carbon-14-, and sulfur-35-labeled compounds. – Anal. Chem. 35: 783-786, 1963.
Godwin, H.: Half-life of radiocarbon. – Nature 195: 984, 1962.
Goldsworthy, A.: A simple apparatus for generating an air stream containing a constant concentration of $^{14}CO_2$. – J. exp. Bot. 17: 147-150, 1966a.
Goldsworthy, A.: Experiments on the origin of CO_2 released by tobacco leaf segments in the light. – Phytochemistry 5: 1013-1019, 1966b.
Herforth, L., Koch, H.: Radiophysikalisches und radiochemisches Grundpraktikum. – Verlag der Wissenschaften, Berlin 1962.
Holm-Hansen, O., Moses, V., van Sumere, C. F., Calvin, M.: The effect of radiocarbon on the rate of carbon dioxide utilization during photosynthesis. – Biochim. biophys. Acta 28: 587-591, 1958.
Irvine, J. E.: Photosynthesis in sugarcane varieties under field conditions. – Crop Sci. 7: 297-300, 1967.
Kamen, M. D.: Radioactive Tracers in Biology. – Academic Press, New York 1948.
Krotkov, G., Runeckles, V. C., Thimann, K. V.: Effect of light on the CO_2 absorption and evolution by *Kalanchoë*, wheat and pea leaves. – Plant Physiol. 33: 289-292, 1958.
Kummer, J. T.: Counter design for gaseous weak beta emitters. – Nucleonics 3: 27-28, 1948.
Kuzin, A. M.: O putyakh ispol'zovaniya metoda mechenykh atomov v sel'skom khozyaïstve. [Use of labelled atoms method in agriculture.] – In: Trudy nauchnoï Sessii posvyashchennoï Dostizheniyam i Zadacham sovetskoï Biofiziki v sel'skom Khozyaïstve. Pp. 215-226. Izdatel'stvo Akad. Nauk SSSR, Moskva-Leningrad 1955.

Larsen, S., Nielsen, G.: Et transportabelt apparat til måling af relativ fotosyntese ved hjaelp af C^{14}. [A transportable apparatus for measuring relative photosynthesis using ^{14}C.] – Tidsskr. Planteavl. 58: 651-656, 1955.
Lister, G. R., Krotkov, G., Nelson, C. D.: A closed-circuit apparatus with an infrared CO_2 analyzer and a Geiger tube for continuous measurement of CO_2 exchange in photosynthesis and respiration. – Can. J. Bot. 39: 581-591, 1961.
Lupton, F. G. H.: The supply of carbohydrate to the grain in wheat. – In: Isotopes in Plant Nutrition and Physiology. Pp. 575-578. Int. At. Energy Agency, Vienna 1967.
Mokronosov, A. T.: Nekotorye voprosy metodiki primeneniya izotopa ugleroda-14 dlya izucheniya fotosinteza. [Some problems of using carbon-14 isotopic methods for photosynthesis studies.] – Zapiski Sverdlovskogo Otd. Vsesoyuznogo bot. Obshchestva 4: 3-13, 1966.
Moorby, J., Ebert, M., Evans, N. T. S.: The translocation of ^{11}C-labelled photosynthate in the soy bean. – J. exp. Bot. 14: 210-220, 1963.
Nezgovorova, L. A.: Dinamika pogloshcheniya uglekislogo gaza list'yami rasteniï v temnote i na svetu. [Dynamics of CO_2 absorption in the darkness and in the light by plant leaves.] – Dokl. Akad. Nauk SSSR 92: 1085-1088, 1953.
Nichiporovich, A. A., Strogonova, L. E., Chmora, S. N., Vlasova, M. P.: Fotosinteticheskaya Deyatel'nost' Rasteniï v Posevakh. [Photosynthetic Activity of Crop Plants.] – Izd. Akad. Nauk SSSR, Moskva 1961.
van Norman, R. W., Brown, A. H.: The relative rates of photosynthetic assimilation of isotopic forms of carbon dioxide. – Plant Physiol. 27: 691-709, 1952.
Novitskiï, Yu. I.: Pribor dlya izucheniya fotosinteza s pomoshch'yu C^{14} v toke vozdukha. [Apparatus for studying photosynthesis using ^{14}C in air flow.] – Fiziol. Rasteniï 3: 574-578, 1956.
O'Brien, T. P., Wardlaw, I. F.: The direct assay of ^{14}C in dried plant materials. – Aust. J. biol. Sci. 14: 361-367, 1961.
Patterson, M. S., Greene, R. C.: Measurement of low energy beta-emitters in aqueous solution by liquid scintillation counting of emulsions. – Anal. Chem. 37: 854-857, 1965.
Porter, H. K., Bird, I. F.: Assimilation and respiration by tobacco leaf tissue. A quantitative study using ^{14}C. – Indian J. Plant Physiol. 5: 5-32, 1962.
Pyarnik, T., Keerberg, O.: Usovershenstvovannaya kamera dlya kratkovremennykh ekspozitsiï list'ev v atmosfere radioaktivnogo uglekislogo gaza. [An improved chamber for the short exposure of leaves in the atmosphere of radioactive carbon dioxide.] – Izv. Akad. Nauk Est. SSR, Ser. biol. 15(1): 32-37, 1966.
Pyarnik, T. R., Keerberg, O. F.: Mnogokanal'naya ekspozitsionnaya kamera dlya issledovaniya fotosinteza v diskakh list'ev. [A multi-channel exposure chamber for studying photosynthesis of leaf discs.] – Fiziol. Rast. 16: 1098-1103, 1969.
Raaen, V. F., Ropp, G. A., Raaen, H. P.: Carbon-14. – McGraw-Hill Book Co., New York 1968.
Rabinowitz, J. L., Sall, T., Bierly, J. N. Jr., Oleksyshyn, O.: Carbon isotope effects in enzyme systems. I. Biochemical studies with urease. – Arch. Biochem. Biophys. 63: 437-445, 1956.
Rachinskiï, V. V.: Metod opredeleniya pogloshcheniya i vydeleniya mechenoï dvuokisi ugleroda rasteniyami. [A method for determining labelled carbon dioxide absorption and outlet by plants.] – Fiziol. Rast. 2: 182-186, 1955.
Reid, J. C.: Discovery and measurement of isotopic tracers. – In: Wilson, D. W., Nier, A. O. C. (ed.): Preparation and Measurement of Isotopic Tracers. J. W. Edwards, Ann Arbor 1948.
Shimshi, D.: A rapid field method for measuring photosynthesis with labelled carbon dioxide. – J. exp. Bot. 20: 381-401, 1969.
Sorokin, Yu. I.: Opredelenie velichiny izotopicheskogo effekta pri fotosinteze v kul'turakh *Scenedesmus quadricauda*. [Determination of the isotope effect on photosynthesis in *Scenedesmus quadricauda* cultures.] – Byul. Inst. Biol. Vodokhranilishch Akad. Nauk SSSR 4: 7-9, 1959.
Strebeyko, P.: Rapid method for measuring photosynthetic rate using $^{14}CO_2$. – Photosynthetica 1: 45-49, 1967.
Sullivan, W. K.: Trilinear Chart of Nuclides. – U.S. Gov. Printing Office, Washington, D. C. 1957.
Voznesenskiï, V. L.: Kolichestvennye izmereniya intensivnosti fotosinteza pri pomoshchi radioaktivnogo izotopa ugleroda C^{14}. [Quantitative photosynthetic rate measurements with the aid of radioactive carbon isotope ^{14}C.] – Bot. Zh. 40: 402-408, 1955.

Voznesenskiĭ, V. L.: K voprosu ob izuchenii gazoobmena rasteniĭ v zamknutykh sistemakh s $^{14}CO_2$. [To the problem of studying gas exchange in plants in closed systems with $^{14}CO_2$.] – Biofizika 6: 725-733, 1961.

Voznesenskiĭ, V. L.: O vozmozhnosti issledovaniya gazoobmena rasteniĭ v zamknutykh sistemakh pri pomoshchi $C^{14}O_2$. [On the possibility of studying gas exchange in plants in closed systems by means of $^{14}CO_2$.] – Fiziol. Rast. 12: 746-749, 1965.

Voznesenskiĭ, V. L., Semikhatova, O. A., Saakov, V. S.: Eksperimental'naya proverka radiometricheskogo metoda rascheta intensivnosti fotosinteza. [Experimental check up of the radiometric method of photosynthetic rate calculation.] – Fiziol. Rast. 6: 380-384, 1959.

Voznesenskiĭ, V. L., Zalenskiĭ, O. V., Semikhatova, O. A.: Metody Issledovaniya Fotosinteza i Dykhaniya Rasteniĭ. [Methods of Studying Plant Photosynthesis and Respiration.] – Nauka, Moskva–Leningrad 1965.

Weigl, J. W., Calvin, M.: An isotope effect in photosynthesis. – J. chem. Phys. 17: 210, 1949.

Weigl, J. W., Warrington, P. M., Calvin, M.: The relation of photosynthesis to respiration. – J. Amer. chem. Soc. 73: 5058-5063, 1951.

Yemm, E. W., Bidwell, R. G. S.: Carbon dioxide exchanges in leaves. I. Discrimination between $^{14}CO_2$ and $^{12}CO_2$ in photosynthesis. – Plant Physiol. 44: 1328-1334, 1969.

Zalenskiĭ, O. V.: Obzor metodov izucheniya fotosinteza nazemnykh rasteniĭ. [Review of methods for studying photosynthesis of terrestrial plants.] – In: Lavrenko, E. M., Korchagin, A. A. (ed.): Polevaya Geobotanika. Pp. 245-330. Izd. Akad. Nauk SSSR, Moskva–Leningrad 1959.

Zalenskiĭ, O. V., Semikhatova, O. A., Filippova, L. A.: Novyĭ metod izucheniya fotosinteza v estestvennykh usloviyakh. [A new method of studying photosynthesis under natural conditions.] – In: Trudy Nauchnoĭ Sessii, Posvyashchenoĭ Dostizheniyam i Zadacham Sovetskoĭ Biofiziki v Sel'skom Khozyaĭstve. Pp. 263-267. Izd. Akad. Nauk SSSR, Moskva – Leningrad 1955.

Zalenskiĭ, O. V., Semikhatova, O. A., Voznesenskiĭ, V. L.: Metody Primeneniya Radioaktivnogo Ugleroda C^{14} dlya Izucheniya Fotosinteza. [Methods Using Radiocarbon ^{14}C for Photosynthesis Investigations.] – Izd. Akad. Nauk SSSR, Moskva–Leningrad 1955.

8 | METHODS FOR MEASURING PHOTORESPIRATION IN LEAVES

8.1 | Introduction

It is now recognised that the respiratory processes in chlorophyllous leaves are different in light[1] and darkness (Hoch, Owens & Kok 1963; Thomas 1965; Moss 1966, 1968; Tregunna, Krotkov & Nelson 1966; Lake 1967a; Zelitch 1967; Downton & Tregunna 1968b). In this account, respiration is taken as the production of CO_2 at a reaction centre either in the dark (at a rate R_D) or in the light (at a rate R_L), rather than as the metabolic events leading up to CO_2 production. Although the evidence is not unequivocal, it is now thought that dark respiration is inhibited by light and is replaced by a process, photorespiration, which has a different metabolic pathway so that respiration in light and darkness shows different responses to inhibitors and to environment (see Jackson & Volk 1970). Estimates of the rate of photorespiration (together with the rate of net photosynthesis, P_N) are necessary for the calculation of total (or gross) photosynthesis, quantum efficiency (Thomas 1965) and mesophyll resistance to CO_2 transfer (Lake 1967b). Estimates of the photorespiration rate of most Dicotyledons and temperate grasses range between 10 and 20 mg CO_2 dm^{-2} h^{-1} (Hesketh & Baker 1967; Lake 1967a; Begg & Jarvis 1968; Ludlow 1969), whereas some Dicotyledons and many of the highly productive tropical grasses (*e.g.* sugar cane, maize, sorghum) appear to lack photorespiration (Downton & Tregunna 1968a, b). Thus it may be possible to increase net photosynthesis and production of many varieties of economic importance by breeding and selecting for low rates of photorespiration, or by inhibiting the process with chemicals (Zelitch & Day 1968).

The metabolism of photorespiration is not known but the glycolic acid pathway proposed by Zelitch (1964) is the most favoured hypothesis at present (Bidwell 1968). Zelitch proposed that the CO_2 generated in photorespiration arises from the oxidation of glycolic acid in the presence of glycolic acid oxidase. As glycolic acid is thought to be an early product of photosynthesis, a close biochemical linkage between photorespiration and photosynthesis is likely. Such a linkage is supported by evidence from other studies. Photorespiration does not occur in achlorophyllous organs (Hew & Krotkov 1968), and the action spectra of photorespiration and photosynthesis are similar (Bulley & Nelson 1968). In addition, oxygen produced in photosynthesis can be metabolised in photorespiration and CO_2 produced in photorespiration assimilated in photosynthesis. Because photorespiration and photosynthesis occur simultaneously in light, accurate measurements of photorespiration in leaves based on the exchanges of O_2 and CO_2 are extremely difficult and have not yet been made in a normal physiological environment.

1. In view of the lack of information on the action spectrum of photorespiration, in this Chapter, light is taken to mean radiant energy between about 380 and 720 nm (*i.e.* PhAR).

Recently several models have been proposed describing the fluxes of CO_2 within leaves in light and darkness (*e.g.* Moss 1966; Lake 1967a; Bravdo 1968; Samish & Koller 1968a). Here the model presented by Lake is used, slightly modified, to describe the pathways traversed by CO_2 in photorespiration and photosynthesis and to define the components of the exchange processes which must be determined if photorespiration is to be measured accurately (Fig. 8.1). The various methods for measuring photorespiration are assessed in relation to this model.

Carbon dioxide moving from the ambient air to the reaction sites in the chloroplasts in light encounters a number of resistances to transfer. The definition of resistance, the nature of the pathway, the mode of transfer and the magnitude and environmental sensitivity of the resistances are described in Chapter 16. The principal resistances are located in the boundary layer, the stomata, the intercellular spaces and the walls and cytoplasm of mesophyll cells. To provide a unified treatment, to these may be added the so-called excitation and carboxylation

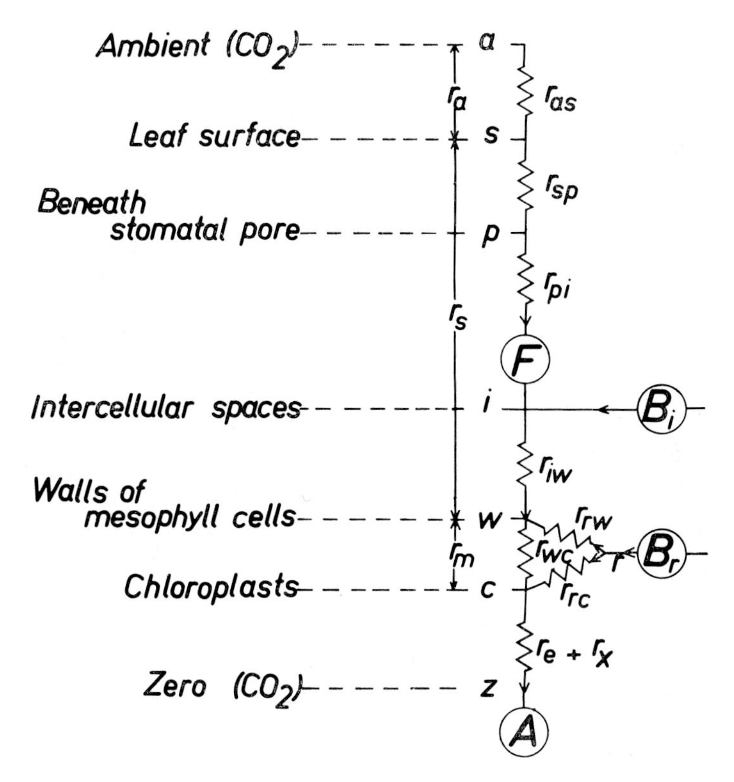

Fig. 8.1 A model of the pathways of CO_2 exchange in a photosynthesising leaf (adapted from Lake 1967a).
Locations along the pathway are indicated by the letters *a*, *s* . . . *c*, *z* and segments of the pathway delimited by the locations at each end; *z* is a hypothetical site at which after carboxylation the CO_2 concentration is zero; F ($= P_N$) is flux of CO_2 taken as positive in the direction shown by the arrows and r is resistance to CO_2 transfer, between both sites shown by the subscripts; C is concentration of CO_2; B_i and B_r are the rates of CO_2 production by non-photosynthetic and photosynthetic cells, respectively: A ($= P_G$) is rate of gross photosynthesis; r_a, r_s, r_m, r_e and r_x are boundary layer, stomatal, mesophyll, excitation and carboxylation resistances as described in Chapter 16.

resistances associated with limitation of photosynthesis by the photochemical and carboxylation processes (see Monteith 1963 and Chapter 16).

In normal photosynthesis (Fig. 8.1) CO_2 produced in respiration by non-photosynthesising cells (B_i) enters the pool of CO_2 in the intercellular spaces from where there is a net movement of CO_2 towards the reaction sites in the chloroplasts. Carbon dioxide produced in respiration within photosynthesising cells (B_r) may either enter the pool of CO_2 within the intercellular spaces or move directly through the cell to the reaction sites in the chloroplasts. Movement within the cell is probably partly by molecular diffusion and partly by mass transfer as a result of cytoplasmic streaming. It may also be facilitated by the enzyme carbonic anhydrase (see Enns 1967 and Chapter 16). At present there are no estimates of the relative magnitudes of the three transfer resistances within the cell: between the intercellular spaces and the sites of respiration (r_{rw}), between the intercellular spaces and the sites of carboxylation (r_{wc}), and between the sites of respiration and carboxylation (r_{rc}). It might be supposed that if transfer of CO_2 is dominated by a mass transfer process, all three resistances would be approximately equal. If, on the other hand, molecular diffusion predominates, the relative sizes of the resistances would be expected to depend on the arrangement and distribution of organelles and enzymes within the cell. For example, if the chloroplasts lie close to cell walls adjacent to the intercellular spaces, r_{wc} is probably small (Rackham 1966). The position of the chloroplasts is readily identified but the location of the sites of photorespiration is not known. Mitochondria (sites of the Krebs cycle) are often closely associated with the chloroplasts in mesophyll cells. However, if the Krebs cycle and dark respiration are inhibited by light (Benson & Calvin 1950; Weigl, Warrington & Calvin 1951; Gibbs 1953; Holmgren & Jarvis 1967), the mitochondria are unlikely to be the source of photorespiratory CO_2. If the glycolic acid pathway is involved in photorespiration (Zelitch 1965), the CO_2 sources may be close to the sinks because glycolate is synthesised by chloroplasts (Kisaki & Tolbert 1968). Its oxidation in the chloroplasts or other organelles such as peroxisomes (Tolbert *et al.* 1968) in the nearby cytoplasm would result in a small r_{rc} compared with r_{rw} and a large flux of CO_2 between r and c. El-Sharkawy, Loomis & Williams (1967) estimated that r_{rc} was lower in tropical grasses than in most Dicotyledons.

At high irradiance and normal (300 $\mu l\ l^{-1}$) ambient CO_2 concentration, the net flux density of CO_2 uptake (F) is usually positive and $R_L = B_i + B_r$. It is not clear whether respiration of the achlorophyllous cells in light (B_i), is metabolically and quantitatively similar to dark respiration or to photorespiration in chlorophyllous cells.

In CO_2-free air in light, respiration raises the concentration of CO_2 in the intercellular spaces above ambient and there is a net flux of CO_2 out of the leaf. This represents only part of the CO_2 produced in respiration, the remainder is absorbed at the sites of carboxylation.

The process by which respired CO_2 enters the intercellular spaces, whether from chlorophyllous or achlorophyllous cells, and then moves to the sites of carboxylation is called intercellular reassimilation. Transfer of CO_2 from a site of respiration to a site of carboxylation within the same cell and its assimilation is called intracellular reassimilation in this Chapter.

8.2 | Requirements of a method to measure photorespiration

For accurate estimates of the rate of photorespiration, R_L, all the components described in Section 8.1 should be measured together with the transfer resistances (r_a, r_s, and r_m), to ensure reproducible and explicable results and to allow calculation of the CO_2 concentration at various points along the pathway. Open and semi-closed systems (Chapter 2) are most suitable for measurements of transfer resistances (Chapter 16).

Both shoots and individual leaves have been used for photorespiration studies so that care must be taken when interpreting results. Stems, petioles and meristematic tissues of shoots have high dark respiration rates in light and darkness (Begg & Jarvis 1968; Ludlow 1969) which can mask the R_L of leaves. This can lead to erroneous comparisons of R_L and R_D for shoots and leaves and of responses of R_L to environmental factors (Audus 1947; Gabrielsen 1949; Nishida 1962; El-Sharkawy, Loomis & Williams 1967; Brix 1968).

Although knowledge of R_L over a range of CO_2 concentrations is desirable, its magnitude near normal ambient concentrations is of practical interest. However, many estimates of R_L are made at or near zero CO_2 concentration. If photorespiration is independent of CO_2 concentration or photosynthesis, as a number of workers have assumed (Decker 1957; Decker & Wien 1958; Forrester, Krotkov & Nelson 1966a, b; Tregunna, Krotkov & Nelson 1966), such estimates of R_L are relevant at 300 $\mu l\ l^{-1}$ CO_2. On the other hand, some workers consider that photorespiration may possibly increase with CO_2 concentration and rate of photosynthesis (Semenenko 1964; Egle & Fock 1967; Lake 1967a; Żelawski 1967; Bidwell 1968; Moss 1968) especially if photorespiration and photosynthesis are closely linked through a common metabolite such as glycolic acid. Until the effect of photosynthesis and CO_2 concentration on R_L has been elucidated it is desirable to measure R_L at normal CO_2 concentrations. The same argument can be applied to estimates of R_L made at concentrations greater than 300 $\mu l\ l^{-1}$, and in comparisons of R_L with R_D, because R_D appears to change with CO_2 concentration (El-Sharkawy, Loomis & Williams 1967; Begg & Jarvis 1968; Ludlow 1969: *cf.* Holmgren & Jarvis 1967; Poskuta, Nelson & Krotkov 1967).

Although the rate of photorespiration cannot yet be measured accurately, it seems to be affected by irradiance (Holmgren & Jarvis 1967; Poskuta, Nelson & Krotkov 1967; Samish & Koller 1968b), temperature (Decker 1959a, b; El-Sharkawy & Hesketh 1965; Holmgren & Jarvis 1967; Begg & Jarvis 1968; Björkman 1968; Zelitch 1968), CO_2 concentration (Bidwell 1968), and oxygen concentration (Forrester, Krotkov & Nelson 1966a, b; Tregunna, Krotkov & Nelson 1966; Holmgren & Jarvis 1967; Zelitch 1968). Therefore, these factors should be accurately controlled and measured when R_L is being estimated. As R_L, P_N (net photosynthetic rate) and R_D respond differently to these environmental factors, a method which allows study of such responses is evidently advantageous.

As indicated above, there is no fully satisfactory method of measuring the three components of R_L, but those methods which have been used to measure some of the components are described. Some attempt has been made to group similar methods together but classification must, by the nature and degree of immaturity of the subject, be arbitrary. Assumptions, advantages and disadvantages of the methods are discussed in relation to the requirements presented here and the model described earlier.

8.2.1 | *Carbon dioxide surge following irradiation*

In 1955, Decker observed that the rate of CO_2 efflux from a leaf immediately following irradiation was higher than the dark respiration rate. From this and later work (Decker & Wien 1958; Decker 1959a; Decker & Tió 1959), he concluded that the CO_2 burst following irradiation was a continuation of photorespiration which was distinct from dark respiration. Decker and others (Tregunna, Krotkov & Nelson 1961, 1964, 1966; Moss 1966; Egle & Fock 1967) used the magnitude of the burst as a measure of R_L. The burst has usually been measured using a closed system consisting of an infra-red gas analyser (IRGA), a leaf chamber and a pump. The IRGA, which is used as a direct reading instrument, records the CO_2 concentration in the system, and the rate of change of concentration with time gives an estimate of the CO_2 exchange rate. R_L is taken as the slope of the tangent to the CO_2 concentration trace at the end of the irradiation period (allowing for the time lag for flow between the chamber and the IRGA; Decker 1955), or as the maximum rate of the burst (Tregunna, Krotkov & Nelson 1961). The burst usually lasts a few minutes or less. In most cases the length of the period used to estimate R_L is less than one minute but in some experiments using open systems, periods of about 30 minutes have been taken (Moss 1966; El-Sharkawy, Loomis & Williams 1967). The high rate of CO_2 efflux during the early part of this period is associated with low stomatal resistance and the subsequent decline in rate with a rise in stomatal resistance (Figs. 8.2a and b). Thus it seems that the variations in rate over these longer periods may be related to stomatal behaviour rather than a continuation of photorespiration.

The technique has the inherent disadvantage that a steady state is not attained and the determination of the maximum rate of efflux is therefore subjective. In addition, no estimate of r_a,r_s or r_m is made, and flow rate and volume of the system affect the magnitude and period of the burst. The basis of the technique has been questioned at various times. Van der Veen (1960) considered that the burst simply represents a sudden physical change in the endogenous CO_2 pool and has little relevance to rates of physiological processes. Björkman (1968) thought that part of the burst may result from an overshoot in oxidation, caused by alleviation of light-inhibited glycolysis. In addition, a number of objections have arisen from experimental work: the magnitude of the burst and its response to external factors do not always agree with other estimates of R_L (Decker 1959a; Tregunna, Krotkov & Nelson 1966; Heath & Orchard 1968); the burst occurs in leaves of some species in which R_P cannot be detected by other techniques (El-Sharkawy, Loomis & Williams 1967; Björkman 1968); and the burst does not always occur in leaves of the same species (Decker & Wien 1958). Furthermore this technique (like many others) only attempts to estimate F (Fig. 8.1) and inter- and intracellular reassimilation are not considered.

However, although the burst may not be an absolute measure of R_L, it appears to bear some relation to R_L because its magnitude varies with oxygen concentration (Björkman 1966; Forrester, Krotkov & Nelson 1966a; Tregunna, Krotkov &

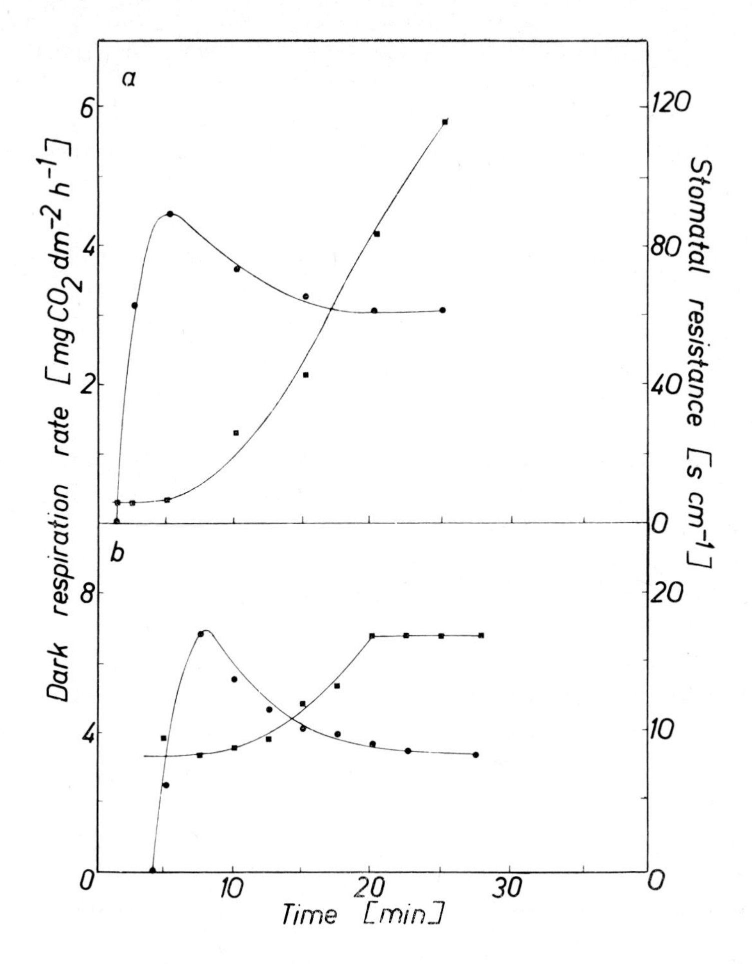

Fig. 8.2 The time course of dark respiration rate (•) and stomatal resistance (▪) following irradiation of leaves of (*a*) a Dicotyledon thought to have photorespiration (*Dolichos biflorus*) and (*b*) a tropical grass thought not to have photorespiration (*Panicum maximum* cv. Petrie). (Leaf temperature 30°C; 312 ± 1 μl l^{-1} ambient CO_2 concentration; 21.3 ± 1.3 mb leaf-air water vapour pressure difference.)

Nelson 1966; *cf.* Björkman 1968), it is absent in tissues lacking chlorophyll and the ability to photosynthesize (Tregunna, Krotkov & Nelson 1964) and some species in which photorespiration cannot be detected by other techniques do not show it (Tregunna, Krotkov & Nelson 1964; Forrester, Krotkov & Nelson 1966b; Moss 1966; El-Sharkawy, Loomis & Williams 1967). An advantage of the method is that it can be used at a wide range of CO_2 concentrations and for studying the effects of other environmental factors (Decker & Wien 1958; Decker 1959a; Tregunna, Krotkov & Nelson 1961, 1966).

8.2.2 | *Carbon dioxide efflux into CO_2-free air*

8.2.2.1 | By extrapolation

After using the burst as an estimate of photorespiration, Decker (1957) attempted to determine R_L from the relationship between net photosynthesis and ambient CO_2 concentration. He argued that if the relationship was linear at low ambient CO_2 concentrations, the CO_2 efflux at zero CO_2 concentration would be a measure of R_L (except for reassimilation within the leaf) since photosynthesis would be inhibited in the absence of CO_2. Thus extrapolation of the linear relationship to zero ambient CO_2 concentration ($C_a = 0$) gives an estimate of R_L as shown by *a* in Fig. 8.3. Furthermore he assumed that R_L was independent of gross photosynthetic rate (P_G) and CO_2 concentration (*cf.* Section 8.2) and this led him to conclude that the relationship between P_G and ambient CO_2 concentration was parallel to the relationship between P_N and ambient CO_2 concentration, and that it passed through the origin (Fig. 8.3).

Decker (1959b) and others (Voznesenskiĭ 1964; Forrester, Krotkov & Nelson 1966a; Tregunna, Krotkov & Nelson 1966; Brix 1968) have used this method to estimate R_L, and others have derived mathematical expressions to describe it (Tregunna, Krotkov & Nelson 1966; Żelawski 1967; Bravdo 1968). P_N can be measured with closed, open or semi-closed systems; open and semi-closed systems being more desirable because steady state values and estimates of r_a, r_s and r_m can be obtained.

Extrapolation to $C_a = 0$ to yield *a* as in Fig. 8.3 neglects both inter- and intracellular reassimilation. Samish & Koller (1968b) point out that intercellular reassimilation must be zero when the intercellular space CO_2 concentration, C_i, is zero. They calculate C_i from a knowledge of the stomatal and boundary layer resistances:

$$C_i = C_a - F(r_a + r_s) \tag{8.1}$$

and extrapolate the relationship between P_N and C_i to zero (broken line in Fig. 8.3).

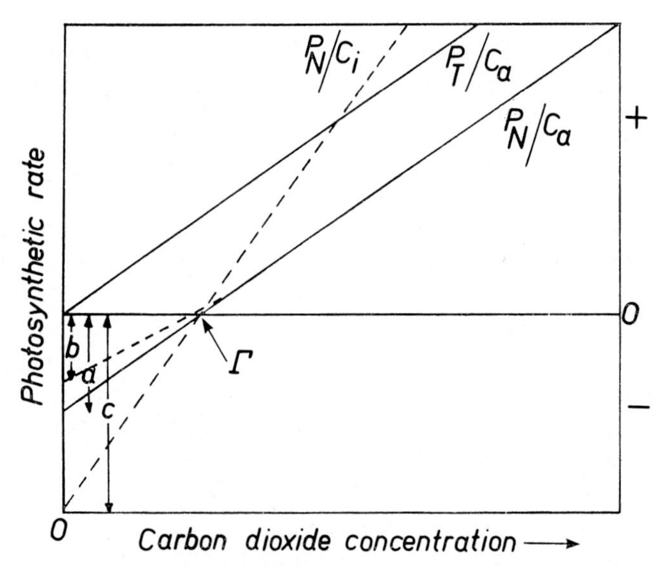

Fig. 8.3 The relationship between net (P_N) and gross [$P_T(=P_G)$] photosynthetic rates, and ambient (C_a) and intercellular space (C_i) carbon dioxide concentration. Γ is the CO_2 compensation concentration. *a*, *b* and *c* are estimates of photorespiration at zero CO_2 concentration, obtained by extrapolation.

This yields an estimate of R_L, as shown by c in Fig. 8.3, which is greater than a by the amount of intercellular reassimilation. Alternatively Lake's model can be used in conjunction with this method to obtain an estimate of R_L which also includes intercellular reassimilation:

$$R_L = F + C_i/r_m$$

Although somewhat different in approach, in practice these two methods yield identical values and represent an advanced form of Decker's original method.
It is noteworthy that irrespective of the slopes of the relationships between P_N and CO_2 concentration (C_i or C_a), which depend upon the values of r_m and $(r_m + r_s + r_a)$, and the corresponding values of c and a, the curves coincide at the CO_2 compensation concentration Γ. It is often suggested that Γ represents a useful measure of R_L although the precise relationship is not explicitly stated. Clearly Γ is related to a or c by the slope dC/dP_N which in turn gives the CO_2 transfer resistance (see Chapter 16).
The main limitations of the technique are its dependence upon a linear relationship which may not occur in practice and the assumption that P_G and ambient CO_2 concentration do not influence R_L. Although linear relationships between P_N and ambient CO_2 are often found (*e.g.* Samish & Koller 1968b), in a number of cases (Voznesenskiĭ 1964; Holmgren & Jarvis 1967; Heath & Orchard 1968; Holmgren 1968; Ludlow & Jarvis, unpublished) significant departure from linearity has been found at CO_2 concentrations near or below the CO_2 compensation concentration (broken line in Fig. 8.3). In Sitka spruce shoots (Ludlow & Jarvis, unpublished) this is associated with increases both in r_s and r_m, as the ambient CO_2 concentration approaches zero, and results in a discrepancy between R_L estimated by extrapolation and from CO_2 efflux at low CO_2 concentration (Section 8.2.3). Holmgren & Jarvis (1967) suggest that the deviation from linearity results from a decrease in the rate of CO_2 production and this would be expected to give an apparent increase in r_m. Data of Brix (1968) and Heath & Orchard (1968) may also be explained by an increase in r_s or r_m.
The usefulness of the method is limited by these disadvantages and the inability to account for intracellular reassimilation.

8.2.2.2 | By measurement

An irradiated leaf is supplied with CO_2-free air and the increase in ambient CO_2 concentration in the chamber, resulting from CO_2 efflux, is measured. In principle this is similar to the extrapolation method (Section 8.2.2.1) but differs in that an attempt is made to measure CO_2 efflux directly. Maximum efflux would be expected at an ambient concentration of zero and a proportionately lower rate at higher concentrations (see Fig. 8.3). The ambient CO_2 concentration at which efflux is measured is determined by the area and activity of the leaf and by the flow rate. It is a compromise between accuracy in the determination of the increase in CO_2 concentration caused by the leaf, and the usual objective to measure efflux at an ambient concentration which is very close to zero.
Efflux of CO_2 has been measured in open systems (El-Sharkawy & Hesketh 1965;

El-Sharkawy, Loomis & Williams 1967; Holmgren & Jarvis 1967; Begg & Jarvis 1968; Hew & Krotkov 1968) and in closed systems (Moss 1966; Poskuta, Nelson & Krotkov 1967; Brix 1968). The method is convenient for studying the influence of both environmental and internal factors.

Application of Lake's model (Fig. 8.1) allows the reduction in efflux at higher CO_2 concentrations to be taken into account and also allows calculation of the flux of CO_2 involved in intercellular reassimilation (Begg & Jarvis 1968). From a knowledge of the stomatal and boundary layer resistances, the average concentration of CO_2 in the intercellular spaces, C_i, can be calculated from equation (8.1). If the mesophyll resistance is also known, the flux from the intercellular spaces into the chloroplasts can be estimated as:

$$F_{wc} = C_i / r_m$$

Thus two of the fluxes of photorespired CO_2, $F + F_{wc}$, are estimated, the intracellular flux, F_{rc}, being neglected.

If the ambient CO_2 concentration rises above zero, F is depressed but F_{wc} increases until at the compensation concentration net F is zero and intercellular reassimilation absorbs all CO_2 entering the intercellular spaces. If F alone is measured, photorespiration is underestimated, but $(F + F_{wc})$ would be expected to be independent of the ambient CO_2 concentration up to the compensation concentration, unless the production of CO_2 in photorespiration is influenced by the concentration in the intercellular spaces. There is no definite evidence on the last question (see Holmgren & Jarvis 1967).

8.2.3 | *The oxygen or Warburg effect*

When the ambient oxygen concentration is reduced from 21 to near 0%, net photosynthesis of most Dicotyledons and temperate grasses measured at high irradiance and normal CO_2 concentrations is increased by 30–45% (Björkman 1966, 1968; Forrester, Krotkov & Nelson 1966a; Hesketh 1967; Downes & Hesketh 1968; Downton & Tregunna 1968b; Jolliffe & Tregunna 1968; Poskuta 1968; Table 8.1). This increase could result from an inhibition of photorespiration, alleviation of an inhibition of photosynthesis, or both. If photorespiration alone is involved, the stimulation of net photosynthesis resulting from the removal of O_2 from the ambient air seems to provide a good estimate of R_L because dark respiration is only slightly affected by oxygen concentration (Björkman 1966, 1968; Forrester, Krotkov & Nelson 1966a; Downton & Tregunna 1968b; Hew & Krotkov 1968; Poskuta 1968, 1969).

Much early work on the influence of O_2 on photosynthesis (see Turner & Brittain 1962) may have been wrongly interpreted because respiration was assumed to be the same in light and in darkness. However, there is some evidence that photosynthesis is affected by O_2 (Björkman 1966). Furthermore, net photosynthesis of maize (a plant which is thought to lack photorespiration) is inhibited by oxygen concentrations between 21 and 100% (Forrester, Krotkov & Nelson 1966a; Poskuta 1969). If the C_4-dicarboxylic acid pathway of CO_2 fixation of maize (Hatch & Slack 1966) and the Calvin pathway have the same sensitivity to O_2

Table 8.1 The effect of oxygen concentration on the net photosynthetic rate of leaves (P_N) and CO_2 transfer resistances (r_a, r_s and r_m) of four tropical grasses and four tropical legumes. Each value is a mean of twelve leaves (4 species × 3 replicates). (85 klx, 300 ± 1 $\mu l\ l^{-1}$ ambient CO_2 concentration; 30 ± 0.1 °C leaf temperature and 22.7 ± 4 mb leaf-air water vapour pressure difference.) (From Ludlow 1969.)

	Oxygen concentration [%]	P_N [mg CO_2 dm^{-2} h^{-1}]	r_a [s cm^{-1}]	r_s [s cm^{-1}]	r_m [s cm^{-1}]	Enhancement*
Tropical grasses	21	50.6	0.89	2.48	0.74	
	0.2	49.7	0.89	2.47	0.93	−0.9
Tropical legumes	21	33.0	0.78	1.43	3.31	
	0.2	47.7	0.72	1.42	2.32	44.7

$$* \frac{P_{N,0.2} - P_{N,21}}{P_{N,21}} \times 100$$

and if maize does lack photorespiration, then this is evidence of a general effect of O_2 on the photosynthetic process.

A number of workers in Canada (Forrester, Krotkov & Nelson 1966a, b; Tregunna, Krotkov & Nelson 1966; Jolliffe & Tregunna 1968; Poskuta 1968) consider that the stimulation of P_N accompanying removal of O_2 from the ambient air is the result of the effect of O_2 on both photorespiration (estimated by the extrapolation method; Section 8.2.2) and photosynthesis. The relationship between P_N and ambient CO_2 concentration, which is more or less linear (Fig. 8.3) at normal ambient oxygen concentrations (21%) and ambient CO_2 concentrations below about 250 $\mu l\ l^{-1}$, is also linear at lower oxygen concentrations although with a different slope (see Fig. 8.4a). Forrester, Krotkov & Nelson (1966a) and Tregunna, Krotkov & Nelson (1966) interpret these linear relationships as an indication that CO_2 concentration does not influence photorespiration, which can be regarded as constant, and that the different slopes of the $P_{G,21}$ and $P_{G,100}$ from that of the $P_{G,1}$ curve is the result of a direct effect of oxygen on the photosynthetic process. However, a linear relationship between P_N and CO_2 concentration does not necessarily mean that R_L remains constant with increasing CO_2 concentration: it might increase linearly with CO_2 concentration and still give a straight line relationship between P_N and CO_2 concentration (Fig. 8.4b). Furthermore, it is possible that P_G is unaffected by O_2 concentration, the depression of P_N by O_2 concentration resulting solely from an increase in R_L. The possibility of R_L increasing with P_G and CO_2 concentration was discussed earlier.

Therefore it is not possible to say whether O_2 affects either photosynthesis or photorespiration or both. However, because the net photosynthesis of tropical grass leaves is largely unaffected by oxygen concentration below 21%, some workers have assumed implicitly that the photosynthetic mechanism of other species is similarly unaffected, and that the stimulation of P_N by O_2 removal is a measure of R_L (Hesketh 1967; Hesketh & Baker 1967; Björkman 1968; Downes & Hesketh 1968; Downton & Tregunna 1968b; Table 8.1).

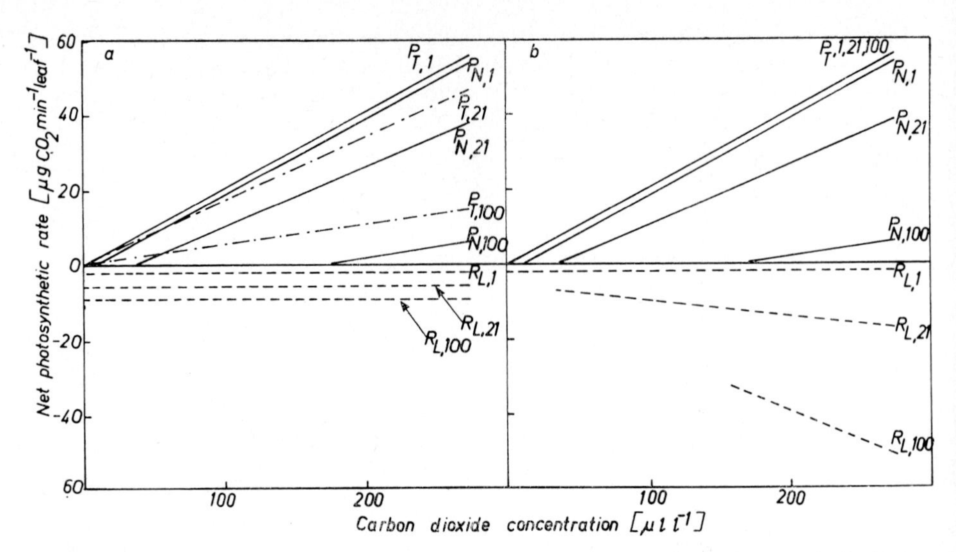

Fig. 8.4 The effect of carbon dioxide and oxygen concentration on net photosynthesis (P_N), photorespiration (R_L) and gross photosynthesis [$P_T(=P_G)$]: *a.* from Forrester, Krotkov & Nelson (1966a), *b.* an alternative interpretation.

Considering Fig. 8.1 on this basis, in the presence of O_2 there are two sources of CO_2 for photosynthesis, the ambient air external to the leaf and the sites of photorespiration within the leaf cells. In the absence of O_2, it is supposed that photorespiration is inhibited completely so that the internal source of CO_2 is eliminated. If this is so, the relevant question is whether the influx of CO_2 into the leaf from the external source, the ambient air, would be expected to increase by an amount equal to the inter- and intracellular fluxes of CO_2 originating from the photorespiratory sites.

In normal air the net flux of CO_2 through the stomata is

$$F_{ai} = \frac{C_a - C_i}{r_s}$$

and the flux through the mesophyll is

$$F_{ai} + B_{r\ inter} = \frac{C_i - C_c}{r_m}$$

where the subscript '*inter*' indicates intercellular flux. In oxygen-free air, the flux through both stomata and mesophyll is, on the above supposition:

$$F_{ac} = F_{ai} + B_{r\ inter} + B_{r\ intra} = \frac{C_a - C_i'}{r_s'} = \frac{C_i' - C_c'}{r_m'}$$

where the subscript '*intra*' indicates intracellular flux and the prime indicates possible new values. Thus for F_{ai} to increase by an amount equal to B_r either the resistance in the pathway or the concentration of CO_2 at the chloroplast must decrease.

 Oxygen concentration does not appear to influence the stomatal resistance (*i.e.*

$r_s = r_s'$, Table 8.1), and consequently C_i would be expected to fall in proportion to $(B_{r\ inter} + B_{r\ intra})$ when O_2 concentration is reduced. If r_m also does not change, the concentration of CO_2 at the chloroplast, C_c, will fall in proportion to the decline in C_i and the increase in flux through r_m, $B_{r\ intra}$. Whether or not the flux of CO_2 into the leaf is increased by an amount proportional to B_r then depends upon the relationship between the carboxylation reaction and the concentration and rate of supply of the substrate (see Chapter 16). If the carboxylation reaction is independent of substrate concentration but strongly dependent on the rate of supply, *i.e.* plenty of active enzyme is present and the resistances are rate-limiting, and r_s and r_m are unaffected, photosynthesis would be expected to increase by an amount equal to B_r. If on the other hand photosynthesis is limited by the activity of the carboxylating enzymes, the increase in rate observed would be somewhat less than B_r. If the mesophyll resistance to CO_2 transfer is affected by O_2, as indicated in Table 8.1, a change in resistance will further affect the expected increase in CO_2 influx by influencing both the rate of transfer and C_c (Fig. 8.1).

In conclusion, varying the ambient oxygen concentration can be expected rarely to give a quantitative estimate of photorespiration rate.

The influence of O_2 removal on P_N can be studied in an open, closed or semi-closed system: open and semi-closed systems give more accurate estimates, but closed systems are more convenient to study the effects of environmental factors on R_L (Jolliffe & Tregunna 1968). This method of estimating R_L has certain advantages: it is simple, rapid and reversible, and it has been used to study the effects of environmental (Björkman 1968; Jolliffe & Tregunna 1968) and internal factors (Downton & Tregunna 1968b; Hew & Krotkov 1968), and in taxonomic studies (Downes & Hesketh 1968).

8.2.4 | *Carbon dioxide compensation concentration*

The carbon dioxide compensation concentration of leaves (Γ in Fig. 8.3; equal to $C_i = C_a$ when $F = 0$ in Fig. 8.1) varies with species, physiological condition, environmental history and current environment. The magnitude of Γ has sometimes been used as an indication of R_L (Tregunna 1966; Meidner 1967; Tregunna & Downton 1967; Downton & Tregunna 1968a) and it is often more or less explicitly stated that a close relationship between the two exists (*e.g.* Heath & Orchard 1968). For example, it has been suggested that tropical grasses of the Panicoid group (*e.g.* maize, sorghum, sugar cane) which have $\Gamma \approx 0\ \mu l\ l^{-1}$ also have little or no photorespiration, whereas in most Dicotyledons and temperate grasses, which are thought to have photorespiration, Γ lies between *ca.* 30 to 130 $\mu l\ l^{-1}$, and is reduced to zero when the ambient oxygen concentration is reduced to zero (Forrester, Krotkov & Nelson 1966a; Tregunna, Krotkov & Nelson 1966; Tregunna & Downton 1967; Downton & Tregunna 1968a). If the relationship between P_N and ambient CO_2 concentration is linear (Fig. 8.3), Γ is related to CO_2 efflux at zero CO_2 concentration:

$$\Gamma = \frac{CO_2\ \text{efflux}}{\Delta P_N / \Delta C}$$

Thus Γ is closely related to R_L as measured by CO_2 efflux methods. It is easily measured and if it is closely related to the rate of photorespiration, it is important that the relationship should be stated as explicitly as possible.

Consider a leaf in bright light at the CO_2 compensation concentration ($F = 0$ and $C_a = C_i$). The supply of CO_2 to the carboxylation sites presumably limits the rate of carboxylation and neither the photochemical nor biochemical processes are limiting. Because the liquid phase transfer resistance is relatively large and because of the rapid moving and mixing of the cytoplasm which occurs in living cells, the following approximations are not likely to be seriously in error:

$$r_{rw} \approx r_{rc} \approx r_{wc}$$

Since

$$\frac{1}{r_m} = \frac{1}{r_{rw} + r_{rc}} + \frac{1}{r_{wc}}, \qquad \text{(Lake 1967a)}$$

$$r_m \approx 2/3\, r_{rw}$$

Neglecting B_i for the moment:

$$C_r - C_w \approx C_w - C_c$$

and

$$C_r \approx 2C_w$$

Since

$$F_{rw} = \frac{C_r - C_w}{r_{rw}},$$

$$F_{rw} \approx \frac{C_w}{r_m} \cdot \frac{2}{3}$$

Since

$$F_{rc} = \frac{C_r - C_c}{r_{rc}},$$

$$F_{rc} \approx \frac{C_w}{r_m} \cdot \frac{4}{3}$$

Thus the total flux of CO_2 produced by photorespiration within the cells is

$$F_{rw} + F_{rc} \approx \frac{2C_w}{r_m}$$

If B_i is negligible $C_w = C_i$ and

$$F_{rw} + F_{rc} = \frac{2C_i}{r_m} = \frac{2\Gamma}{r_m}$$

If B_i is appreciable

$$F_{rw} + F_{rc} = \frac{2\Gamma - (F_{iw} \cdot r_{iw})}{r_m}$$

(if it is assumed that $r_m = r_{wc}$, as might be the case with a simpler model, the coefficient of Γ is 3 rather than 2 as in the above equations).

Thus for a certain tissue with constant mesophyll and carboxylation resistances and constant respiratory flux from the non-photosynthesising cells, Γ is proportional to the rate of CO_2 production in photorespiration. It must be emphasised, however, that changes in the capacity of the photosynthetic mechanism affecting the activity of the carboxylation reaction invalidate the above analysis. Hence Γ should only be used in studies of the effects on R_L of such internal and environmental factors which do not affect P_G.

The CO_2 compensation concentration can be measured in either an open or a closed system. Closed systems have been widely used because of their greater simplicity, but great care must be taken to prevent laboratory air leaking into the system. The leaf either increases or decreases the CO_2 concentration of the air in the system until a constant CO_2 concentration, Γ, is reached when the net CO_2 flux, F, (Fig. 8.1) is zero. Internal and environmental factors affecting Γ can be readily studied with such a system.

In open systems the CO_2 compensation concentration is determined from the relationship between P_N and CO_2 concentration. If the relationship is linear, Γ is the CO_2 concentration at which P_N extrapolates to zero. On the other hand, if the relationship is curvilinear (see Section 8.2.2 and Fig. 8.2) rather more observations are required to characterise it. Alternatively Γ can be determined by adjusting the composition of the air passing through the assimilation chamber so that the net CO_2 flux is zero (*e.g.* Holmgren & Jarvis 1967). This last approach requires very precise control of the preparation of gas mixtures and a rapidly responding system.

8.2.5 | *Isotopes of oxygen and carbon*

Attempts have been made to estimate photorespiration by simultaneously measuring oxygen uptake and release using $^{16}O_2$ and $^{18}O_2$ (Brown 1953; Rabinowitch 1956; Hoch, Owens & Kok 1963; Thomas 1965), and uptake and release of O_2 and CO_2 using $^{16}O_2$, $^{18}O_2$, $^{12}CO_2$ and $^{13}CO_2$ (Brown & Weis 1959; Weis & Brown 1959; Ozbun, Volk & Jackson 1964, 1965; Volk & Jackson 1964) or $^{16}O_2$, $^{12}CO_2$ and $^{14}CO_2$ (Weigl, Warrington & Calvin 1951), or $^{16}O_2$ and $^{12}CO_2$ (Schaub, Hilgenberg & Fock 1968). Generally $^{13}CO_2$ and $^{18}O_2$ are measured with a mass spectrometer, $^{12}CO_2$ with an infra-red gas analyser, $^{16}O_2$ with a paramagnetic oxygen analyser and $^{14}CO_2$ with a Geiger-Müller tube, proportional counter or ionisation chamber.

Superficially it would appear that such methods using three or four isotopes of oxygen and carbon offer the best means of satisfactorily estimating the rate of photorespiration, because only in this way can the simultaneous fluxes of CO_2 in photosynthesis and respiration be separated.

However these methods, too, are not without criticism. The logic of the method utilizing two isotopes of oxygen was questioned by Decker (1958), and subsequently other problems have emerged.

Molecular oxygen seems to participate in biochemical reactions other than photosynthesis and respiration. In particular, it may compete with CO_2 for light-generated reducing power (Bidwell 1968) or there may exist a different terminal oxidase system which only operates in the light (Ozbun, Volk & Jackson 1964). These hypotheses, together with the possibility of O_2 being used in the glycolic acid pathway to produce compounds other than CO_2 (*e.g.* glycine and serine), have been used to explain O_2 uptake in the light which occurs without commensurate release of CO_2 (Ozbun, Volk & Jackson 1964, 1965; Fock, Schaub & Hilgenberg 1968; Jackson & Volk 1969). Jackson & Volk (1969) obtained a large increase in O_2 uptake of maize leaves without release of CO_2. On the basis of the response of CO_2 uptake and O_2 release to varying O_2 and CO_2 concentrations, Fock, Schaub & Hilgenberg (1968) concluded that photorespiration is better characterised by CO_2 exchange than by O_2 exchange.

Another objection to isotopic techniques is that inter- and intracellular reassimilation of both O_2 and CO_2 is not taken into account. Furthermore the mass spectrometric techniques are restricted to relatively high CO_2 and low O_2 concentrations (*e.g.* Hoch, Owens & Kok 1963; Volk & Jackson 1964) which do not normally occur in nature. This probably explains the unusual results obtained by Ozbun, Volk & Jackson (1964). Stomatal behaviour, which was not measured, was probably greatly affected by the high ambient CO_2 concentration, and glycolic acid metabolism is known to be affected by CO_2 and O_2 concentration (Zelitch 1958; Bassham & Kirk 1962; Coombs & Whittingham 1966).

8.2.6 | $^{12}CO_2$ *and* $^{14}CO_2$ *exchange*

Rabinowitch (1956, pp. 1926–29) reviewed early work in which $^{12}CO_2$ and $^{14}CO_2$ were used to investigate the simultaneous occurrence of respiration and photosynthesis. More recently, Lister, Krotkov & Nelson (1961) described a closed system in which the exchange of $^{12}CO_2$ and $^{14}CO_2$ could be followed with a Geiger-Müller tube and an IRGA. Subsequently others used such a method to study respiration in light and darkness (Tregunna, Krotkov & Nelson 1964; Goldsworthy 1966; Kluge 1968). Theoretically, photosynthesis (CO_2 uptake) and respiration (CO_2 release) can be studied under a wide range of environmental conditions. A ^{14}C-containing substrate (*e.g.* CO_2 or glucose) is fed to the tissue. Subsequently P_N is measured by conventional means and respiration by efflux of $^{14}CO_2$. It is difficult to assess how well $^{14}CO_2$ release reflects R_L, because inter- and intracellular reassimilation of CO_2 (irrespective of its origin) is not usually considered (but *cf.* Samish & Koller 1968b) and because it has been shown that recent assimilate is the substrate for photorespiration (Tregunna, Krotkov & Nelson 1964; Goldsworthy 1966; Ludwig & Krotkov 1967; Bidwell 1968; Canvin

1968). If the latter is true, $^{12}CO_2$ from current photosynthesis would be utilized by photorespiration in preference to $^{14}CO_2$ previously assimilated so that the $^{14}CO_2$ release probably underestimates R_L independently of other errors.
In passing, it is worth noting that the infra-red absorption spectra of $^{12}CO_2$ and $^{14}CO_2$ overlap only very slightly if at all. As a result an IRGA, the detector of which is filled with $^{12}CO_2$, measures only $^{12}CO_2$ and not total CO_2 (Weigl, Warrington & Calvin 1951).
Samish & Koller (1968a) have proposed a model, which is essentially similar to Lake's (1967a) model, to calculate R_L from simultaneous measurements of $^{12}CO_2$ uptake, and $^{14}CO_2$ and H_2O efflux:

$$R_L = {}^*F + \frac{{}^*F \cdot r_{aw}}{r_{wz}} + \frac{{}^*C_a}{r_{wz}}$$

where the symbols are the same as those used in Fig. 8.1, and the asterisk indicates isotopically labelled CO_2 released from the respiratory centre and diffusing to the ambient air and the photosynthetic sinks. Although Samish & Koller's model includes reassimilation of CO_2 within the leaf (they do not distinguish between inter- and intracellular reassimilation), it underestimates R_L because of the simplifying assumptions made about the sizes of the intracellular resistances. Furthermore, if recent assimilate is readily available for photorespiration, $^*F$ underestimates the actual flux. The magnitude of this error increases with time as the concentration of non-labelled substrate increases. However, this method is the only one which both includes intracellular reassimilation and which can be used at normal ambient CO_2 concentrations. At the time of writing, no R_L values determined by this method have been published.

8.2.7 | $^{14}CO_2$ *efflux*

A number of workers (Nishida 1962; Semenenko 1964; Zelitch 1968) fed leaves with $^{14}CO_2$ (or other ^{14}C-containing substrate such as glucose or glycolate) in either in light or darkness and used the rate of efflux of $^{14}CO_2$ from the leaf as an indication of respiration rate in light and darkness.
Zelitch (1968) studied this technique in detail, with a view to using it as a method of assaying photorespiration of leaf disks from different varieties and species (Zelitch & Day 1968). The $^{14}CO_2$ released into CO_2-free air was trapped in an ethanolamine solution and its radioactivity determined by scintillation counting.
A serious disadvantage of measuring evolution of $^{14}CO_2$ alone is that it is not possible to distinguish between a change in total CO_2 flux and a change in the concentration of $^{14}CO_2$ in the carbon dioxide exchanged. This is well exemplified by experiments done by Goldsworthy (1966) who measured both $^{14}CO_2$ and total CO_2 exchange.
This method has the disadvantages of the previous one; it does not take into account inter- and intracellular reassimilation, and may also underestimate R_L if recent photosynthate is preferentially respired. Using inhibitors (Section 8.2.8) Zelitch (1968) estimated that 66% of R_L of tobacco leaf discs was recycled within the leaf so that the $^{14}CO_2$ efflux only represented 33% of R_L at 35°C.

Furthermore both Goldsworthy (1966) and Zelitch (1968) found that R_L (measured by $^{14}CO_2$ efflux) was much higher in CO_2-free air than in normal air. This may result from a decrease in R_L as the ambient CO_2 concentration increases or as the stomatal resistance increases (*e.g.* Begg & Jarvis 1968). Alternatively dilution of $^{14}CO_2$ inside the leaf (Zelitch 1968) or stimulation of fixation of respired CO_2 (Goldsworthy 1966) may cause such a result. Support for Zelitch's explanation comes from inhibitor studies (Zelitch 1965, 1968) in which he found that more glycolate accumulated in leaves in air than in CO_2-free air.

8.2.8 | Chemical inhibitors

8.2.8.1 | Chemical inhibitors of photosynthesis

Attempts have been made to study R_L in the absence of photosynthesis by the use of inhibitors (El-Sharkawy, Loomis & Williams 1967; Poskuta, Nelson & Krotkov 1967; Downton & Tregunna 1968b; Moss 1968; Zelitch 1968). However since it appears that photosynthesis and photorespiration are intimately related (Section 8.1), the resulting respiration is probably uncoupled respiration or dark respiration (see data of El-Sharkawy, Loomis & Williams 1967 and Downton & Tregunna 1968b).

8.2.8.2 | Chemical inhibitors of glycolic acid oxidase

Inhibitors of glycolic acid oxidase have been used to study photorespiration and their effect followed by measuring: the accumulation of glycolic acid (Zelitch 1966, 1968; Fock & Egle 1967; Moss 1968); the reduction in CO_2 efflux (Goldsworthy 1966; Moss 1968; Zelitch 1968); the increase in CO_2 uptake (Zelitch 1966, 1968); and the change in the CO_2 compensation concentration, Γ (Meidner 1967).
The accumulation of glycolic acid caused by chemical inhibitors (Zelitch 1966, 1968; Fock & Egle 1967; Moss 1968) and by low oxygen tensions (Björkman 1968) is too small to account for the observed rates of photorespiration, and reported results are variable. However it does seem that there is sufficient glycolic acid oxidase in leaves to account for the observed rates of photorespiration (Bidwell 1968; Fock & Krotkov 1969). The small and variable amounts of accumulated glycolic acid found may result from losses in extraction ($\approx$ 20%) because of its volatile nature (Zelitch 1968) and because the inhibitors used may also affect photosynthesis (Moss 1968). Björkman (1968) could not detect any difference in glycolic acid content in leaves of *Solidago* which had been in 1.5 or 21% O_2, whereas Fock & Egle (1967) showed that if leaf petioles were placed in solutions of inhibitors, accumulation occurred at low oxygen tensions.
Zelitch (1968) used an inhibitor of glycolic acid oxidase to estimate the fraction of R_L which is reassimilated in CO_2-free air. Based on the results of earlier experiments, he assumed that 50% of all refixed CO_2 goes into glycolic acid. Leaf discs were fed with $^{14}CO_2$ and components of R_L calculated from the $^{14}CO_2$ efflux in the presence and absence of inhibitor and the accumulation of ^{14}C-glycolic acid in the presence of inhibitor. At 35 °C, the amount of $^{14}CO_2$ released was only 33% of gross photorespiration (R_L).

Before inhibition of glycolic acid oxidase can be used to provide quantitative evidence about R_L, a number of questions require clarification. When glycolic acid oxidase is inhibited, is photorespiration inhibited, and to what extent is glycolic acid converted into other compounds such as glycine and serine? What other effects on plant metabolism do inhibitors of glycolic acid oxidase have? The latter applies to all inhibitor studies especially if P_G and R_L are linked (Goldsworthy 1966; Meidner 1967; Moss 1968).

The analysis of subsequent uptake of CO_2 when photorespiration is inhibited by lack of oxygen, made in Section 8.2.3, applies equally well to uptake of $^{14}CO_2$ subsequent to inhibition of photorespiration by glycolic acid oxidase. That is to say, it is not to be expected that the increase in $^{14}CO_2$ uptake following inhibition should equal the rate of photorespiration prior to inhibition.

8.3 | Conclusions

All of the methods described here are unsatisfactory from one viewpoint or another and it is difficult to put forward any one as being especially suitable. However, some would seem to provide a better estimate of R_L than others. The CO_2 burst following irradiation (Section 8.2.1) seems to be the least suitable although it may be used to advantage when studying the influence of environmental and internal factors on R_L. Because of the difficulties in interpreting measurements of O_2 exchange, methods utilising isotopes of oxygen and isotopes of carbon in CO_2 have no advantages over those utilising only isotopes of carbon in CO_2 (Section 8.2.5). The usefulness of concurrent estimates of P_N and $^{14}CO_2$ efflux (Section 8.2.6) is limited because recently formed assimilate is preferentially used in photorespiration, and measurement of $^{14}CO_2$ efflux alone does not permit discrimination between changes in efflux and specific activity of the CO_2. The most suitable methods would seem to be those which measure CO_2 efflux into CO_2-free air (Section 8.2.2) and the CO_2 compensation concentration (Section 8.2.4) and to which Lake's model can be applied to calculate intercellular reassimilation. However, if R_L is closely linked to photosynthesis and varies with the ambient CO_2 concentration, these methods do not yield estimates relevant to normal air. A similar criticism can be applied to most applications of the isotope methods in which abnormally high ambient CO_2 and low O_2 concentrations have been used. The remaining two methods, the O_2 effect (Section 8.2.3) and the chemical inhibitor methods (Section 8.2.8), represent a different approach to the problem of measuring R_L and pose other problems. Inadequate knowledge about the influence of oxygen concentration and chemical inhibitors on steps in photosynthesis and photorespiration other than those expected to be affected, makes interpretation of the results conditional.

Although there has been an explosion of interest in photorespiration over the past five years, the lack of definite, incontrovertible information about photorespiration at present is largely a reflection of the inadequacy of the methods being used to measure it. This situation is further exacerbated by the use by most investigators of only one or two of the available methods. Hence it is not possible at present to compare methods because few extensive comparisons have been made on the same material in the same laboratory. Very recently quite good agreement has been found amongst three different methods on the same material by Hew, Krotkov & Canvin (1969a, b). The methods compared were extrapolation (Section 8.2.2.1), CO_2 efflux in the light (Section 8.2.2.2) and decrease in specific activity of $^{14}CO_2$ in a closed system (Weigl, Warrington & Calvin 1951). More comparative studies of this kind are highly desirable.

Before the methods outlined here can be used with confidence, much more information is needed about certain aspects of photorespiration, particularly with regard to its spatial, physiological and biochemical links with photosynthesis. The following points require clarification:

a. definition of the metabolic pathway of photorespiration and its interrelationship with photosynthesis,

b. the importance of the glycolic acid oxidase system,

c. the localisation of the centres of photorespiration in the cell and the distribution of photorespiratory cells,

d. the influence of ambient CO_2 and O_2 concentration on photorespiration and photosynthesis.

8.4 | References

Audus, L. J.: The effects of illumination on the respiration of shoots of the cherry laurel. – Ann. Bot. N.S. 11: 165-201, 1947.

Bassham, J. A., Kirk, M.: The effect of oxygen on the reduction of CO_2 to glycolic acid and other products during photosynthesis by *Chlorella*. – Biochem. biophys. Res. Commun. 9: 376-380, 1962.

Begg, J. E., Jarvis, P. G.: Photosynthesis in Townsville lucerne (*Stylosanthes humilis* H.B.K.). – Agr. Meteorol. 5: 91-109, 1968.

Benson, A. A., Calvin, M.: The path of carbon in photosynthesis VII. Respiration and photosynthesis. – J. exp. Bot. 1: 63-68, 1950.

Bidwell, R. G. S.: Photorespiration. – Science 161: 79-80, 1968.

Björkman, O.: The effect of oxygen concentration on photosynthesis in higher plants. – Physiol. Plant. 19: 618-633, 1966.

Björkman, O.: Further studies of the effect of oxygen concentration on photosynthetic CO_2 uptake in higher plants. – Carnegie Inst. Year Book 66: 220-228, 1968.

Bravdo, Ben-Ami: Decrease in net photosynthesis caused by respiration. – Plant Physiol. 43: 479-483, 1968.

Brix, H.. Influence of light intensity at different temperatures on rate of respiration of Douglas-fir seedlings. – Plant Physiol. 43: 389-393, 1968.

Brown, A. H.: The effects of light on respiration using isotopically enriched oxygen. – Amer. J. Bot. 40: 719-729, 1953.

Brown, A. H., Weis, D.: Relation between respiration and photosynthesis in the green alga, *Ankistrodesmus braunii*. – Plant Physiol. 34: 224-234, 1959.

Bulley, N. R., Nelson, C. D.: Action spectra of photosynthesis and photorespiration in radish leaves.–Plant Physiol. 43: S-20, 1968.

Canvin, D. T.: Photorespiration. International Congress of Photosynthesis Research, Freudenstadt, June 4-8, 1968. – Photosynthetica 2: 318-319, 1968.

Coombs, J., Whittingham, C. P.: The mechanism of inhibition of photosynthesis by high partial pressures of oxygen in *Chlorella*. – Proc. Roy. Soc. B 164: 511-520, 1966.

Decker, J. P.: A rapid, postillumination deceleration of respiration in green leaves. – Plant Physiol. 30: 82-84, 1955.

Decker, J. P.: Further evidence of increased carbon dioxide production accompanying photosynthesis. – J. solar Energy Sci. Eng. 1: 30-33, 1957.

Decker, J. P.: The effects of light on respiration using isotopically enriched oxygen: an objection and alternate interpretation. – Plant Sci. Bull. 4: 3-4, 1958.
Decker, J. P.: Comparative responses of carbon dioxide outburst and uptake in tobacco. – Plant Physiol. 34: 100-102, 1959a.
Decker, J. P.: Some effects of temperature and carbon dioxide concentration on photosynthesis of *Mimulus*. – Plant Physiol. 34: 103-106, 1959b.
Decker, J. P., Tió, M. A.: Photosynthetic surges in coffee seedlings. – J. Agr. Univ. Puerto Rico 43: 50-55, 1959.
Decker, J. P., Wien, J. D.: Carbon dioxide surges in green leaves. – J. solar Energy Sci. Eng. 2: 39-41, 1958.
Downes, R. W., Hesketh, J. D.: Enhanced photosynthesis at low oxygen concentrations: differential response of temperate and tropical grasses. – Planta 78: 79-84, 1968.
Downton, W. J. S., Tregunna, E. B.: Carbon dioxide compensation – its relation to photosynthetic carboxylation reactions, systematics of the *Gramineae*, and leaf anatomy. – Can. J. Bot. 46: 207-215, 1968a.
Downton, W. J. S., Tregunna, E. B.: Photorespiration and glycolate metabolism: A re-examination and correlation of some previous studies. – Plant Physiol. 43: 923-929, 1968b.
Egle, K., Fock, H.: Light respiration – correlations between CO_2 fixation, O_2 pressure, and glycollate concentration. – In: Goodwin, T. W. (ed.): Biochemistry of Chloroplasts. Vol. II. Pp. 79-87. Academic Press, London and New York 1967.
El-Sharkawy, M., Hesketh, J.: Photosynthesis among species in relation to characteristics of leaf anatomy and CO_2 diffusion resistances. – Crop Sci. 5: 517-521, 1965.
El-Sharkawy, M. A., Loomis, R. S., Williams, W. A.: Apparent reassimilation of respiratory carbon dioxide by different plant species. – Physiol. Plant. 20: 171-186, 1967.
Enns, T.: Facilitation by carbonic anhydrase of carbon dioxide transport. – Science 155: 44-47, 1967.
Fock, H., Egle, K.: Über die Beziehungen zwischen dem Glykolsäure-Gehalt und dem Photosynthese-Gaswechsel von Bohnenblättern. – Z. Pflanzenphysiol. 57: 389-397, 1967.
Fock, H., Krotkov, G.: Relation between photorespiration and glycolate oxidase activity in sunflower and red kidney bean leaves. – Can. J. Bot. 47: 237-240, 1969.
Fock, H., Schaub, H., Hilgenberg, W.: Über den Sauerstoff- und Kohlendioxidgaswechsel von *Chlorella* und *Conocephalum* während der Lichtphase. – Z. Pflanzenphysiol. 60: 56-63, 1968.
Forrester, M. L., Krotkov, G., Nelson, C. D.: Effect of oxygen on photosynthesis, photorespiration and respiration in detached leaves. I. Soybean. – Plant Physiol. 41: 422-427, 1966a.
Forrester, M. L., Krotkov, G., Nelson, C. D.: Effect of oxygen on photosynthesis, photorespiration and respiration in detached leaves. II. Corn and other monocotyledons. – Plant Physiol. 41: 428-431, 1966b.
Gabrielsen, E. K.: Photosynthesis in leaves at very low carbon dioxide concentrations. – Nature 163: 359-360, 1949.
Gibbs, M.: Effect of light intensity on the distribution of C^{14} in sunflower leaf metabolites during photosynthesis. – Arch. Biochem. Biophys. 45: 156-160, 1953.
Goldsworthy, A.: Experiments on the origin of CO_2 released by tobacco leaf segments in the light. – Phytochemistry 5: 1013-1019, 1966.
Hatch, M. D., Slack, C. R.: Photosynthesis by sugar-cane leaves. A new carboxylation reaction and the pathway of sugar formation. – Biochem. J. 101: 103-111, 1966.
Heath, O. V. S., Orchard, B.: Carbon assimilation at low carbon dioxide levels. II. The processes of apparent assimilation. – J. exp. Bot. 19: 176-192, 1968.
Hesketh, J. D.: Enhancement of photosynthetic CO_2 assimilation in the absence of oxygen, as dependent upon species and temperature. – Planta 76: 371-374, 1967.
Hesketh, J., Baker, D.: Light and carbon assimilation by plant communities. – Crop Sci. 7: 285-293, 1967.
Hew, C.-S., Krotkov, G.: Effect of oxygen on the rates of CO_2 evolution in light and in darkness by photosynthesizing and non-photosynthesizing leaves. – Plant Physiol. 43: 464-466, 1968.
Hew, C.-S., Krotkov, G., Canvin, D. T.: Determination of the rate of CO_2 evolution by green leaves in light. – Plant Physiol. 44: 662-670, 1969a.

Hew, C.-S., Krotkov, G., Canvin, D. T.: Effects of temperature on photosynthesis and CO_2 evolution in light and darkness by green leaves. – Plant Physiol. 44: 671-677, 1969b.

Hoch, G., Owens, O. H., Kok, B.: Photosynthesis and respiration. – Arch. Biochem. Biophys. 101: 171-180, 1963.

Holmgren, P.: Leaf factors affecting light-saturated photosynthesis in ecotypes of *Solidago virgaurea* from exposed and shaded habitats. – Physiol. Plant. 21: 676-698, 1968.

Holmgren, P., Jarvis, P. G.: Carbon dioxide efflux from leaves in light and darkness. – Physiol. Plant. 20: 1045-1051, 1967.

Jackson, W. A., Volk, R. J.: Oxygen uptake by illuminated maize leaves.– Nature 222: 269-271, 1969.

Jackson, W. A., Volk, R. J.: Photorespiration. – Annu. Rev. Plant Physiol. 21: 385-432, 1970.

Jolliffe, P. A., Tregunna, E. B.: Effect of temperature, CO_2 concentration, and light intensity on oxygen inhibition of photosynthesis in wheat leaves. – Plant Physiol. 43: 902-906, 1968.

Kisaki, T., Tolbert, N. E.: Metabolism of glycolate and glyoxylate by microbodies. – Plant Physiol. 43: S-38, 1968.

Kluge, M.: Untersuchungen über den Gaswechsel von *Bryophylllum* während der Lichtperiode. I. Zum Problem der CO_2-Abgabe. – Planta 80: 255-263, 1968.

Lake, J. V.: Respiration of leaves during photosynthesis. I. Estimates from an electrical analogue. – Austr. J. biol. Sci. 20: 487-493, 1967a.

Lake, J. V.: Respiration of leaves during photosynthesis. II. Effects on the estimation of mesophyll resistance. – Austr. J. biol. Sci. 20: 495-499, 1967b.

Lister, G. R., Krotkov, G., Nelson, C. D.: A closed-circuit apparatus with an infrared CO_2 analyzer and a Geiger tube for continuous measurement of CO_2 exchange in photosynthesis and respiration. – Can. J. Bot. 39: 581-591, 1961.

Ludlow, M. M.: Growth and photosynthesis of tropical pasture plants. – Ph.D. Thesis, Univ. of Queensland, Australia 1969.

Ludwig, L. J., Krotkov, G.: The kinetics of labeling of the substrates of CO_2 evolution by sunflower leaves in the light. – Plant Physiol. 42: S-47, 1967.

Meidner, H.: Further observations on the minimum intracellular space carbon-dioxide concentration (Γ) of maize leaves and the postulated roles of 'photo-respiration' and glycollate metabolism. – J. exp. Bot. 18: 177-185, 1967.

Monteith, J. L.: Gas exchange in plant communities. – In: Evans, L. T. (ed.): Environmental Control of Plant Growth. Pp. 95-112. Academic Press, New York 1963.

Moss, D. N.: Respiration of leaves in light and darkness. – Crop Sci. 6: 351-354, 1966.

Moss, D. N.: Photorespiration and glycolate metabolism in tobacco leaves. – Crop Sci. 8: 71-76, 1968.

Nishida, K.: Studies on the re-assimilation of respiratory CO_2 in illuminated leaves. – Plant Cell Physiol. 3: 111-124, 1962.

Ozbun, J. L., Volk, R. J., Jackson, W. A.: Effects of light and darkness on gaseous exchange of bean leaves. – Plant Physiol. 39: 523-527, 1964.

Ozbun, J. L., Volk, R. J., Jackson, W. A.: Effect of potassium deficiency on photosynthesis, respiration and the utilization of photosynthetic reductant by immature bean leaves. – Crop Sci. 5: 69-75, 1965.

Poskuta, J.: Photosynthesis, photorespiration and respiration of detached spruce twigs as influenced by oxygen concentration and light intensity. – Physiol. Plant. 21: 1129-1136, 1968.

Poskuta, J.: Photosynthesis, respiration and post-illumination fixation of CO_2 by corn leaves as influenced by light and oxygen concentration. – Physiol. Plant. 22: 76-85, 1969.

Poskuta, J., Nelson, C. D., Krotkov, G.: Effects of metabolic inhibitors on the rates of CO_2 evolution in light and in darkness by detached spruce twigs, wheat and soybean leaves. – Plant Physiol. 42: 1187-1190, 1967.

Rabinowitch, E. I.: Photosynthesis and related processes. Vol. II, part 2. – Interscience Pub. Inc., New York 1956.

Rackham, O.: Radiation, transpiration, and growth in a woodland annual. – In: Bainbridge, R., Evans, G. C., Rackham, O. (ed.): Light as an Ecological Factor. Pp. 167-185. Blackwell Sci. Pub., Oxford 1966.

Samish, Y., Koller, D.: Photorespiration in green plants during photosynthesis estimated by use of isotopic CO_2. – Plant Physiol. 43: 1129-1132, 1968a.

Samish, Y., Koller, D.: Estimation of photorespiration of green plants and of their mesophyll resistance to CO_2 uptake. – Ann. Bot. N.S. 32: 687-694, 1968b.
Schaub, H., Hilgenberg, W., Fock, H.: Eine neue Messanordnung zur gleichzeitigen Messung von Sauerstoff und Kohlendioxid im offenen Gasstrom. – Z. Pflanzenphysiol. 60: 64-71, 1968.
Semenenko, V. E.: Osobennosti uglekislogo gazoobmena v perekhodnykh sostoyaniyakh fotosinteza pri perekhode ot osveshcheniya ob'ekta k temnote. Indutsirovannoe svetom vydelenie CO_2. [Characteristics of carbon dioxide gas exchange in the transition states of photosynthesis upon changing from light to darkness. Light induced evolution of CO_2.] – Fiziol. Rastenii̇̆ 11: 375-384, 1964.
Thomas, M. D.: Photosynthesis (carbon assimilation): Environmental and metabolic relationships. – In: Steward, F. C. (ed.): Plant Physiology. Vol. IVA. Pp. 9-202. Academic Press, New York–London 1965.
Tolbert, N. E., Oeser, A., Kisaki, T., Hageman, R. H., Yamazaki, R. K.: Peroxisomes from spinach leaves containing enzymes related to glycolate metabolism. – J. biol. Chem. 243: 5179-5184, 1968.
Tregunna, B.: Flavin mononucleotide control of glycolic acid oxidase and photorespiration in corn leaves. – Science 151: 1239-1241, 1966.
Tregunna, E. B., Downton, J.: Carbon dioxide compensation in members of the *Amaranthaceae* and some related families. – Can. J. Bot. 45: 2385-2387, 1967.
Tregunna, E. B., Krotkov, G., Nelson, C. D.: Evolution of carbon dioxide by tobacco leaves during the dark period following illumination with light of different intensities. – Can. J. Bot. 39: 1045-1056, 1961.
Tregunna, E. B., Krotkov, G., Nelson, C. D.: Further evidence on the effects of light on respiration during photosynthesis. – Can. J. Bot. 42: 989-997, 1964.
Tregunna, E. B., Krotkov, G., Nelson, C. D.: Effect of oxygen on the rate of photorespiration in detached tobacco leaves. – Physiol. Plant. 19: 723-733, 1966.
Turner, J. S., Brittain, E. G.: Oxygen as a factor in photosynthesis. – Biol. Rev. 37: 130-170, 1962.
van der Veen, R.: Induction phenomena. – In: Ruhland, W. (ed.): Handbuch der Pflanzenphysiologie 5/1: 675-688. Springer-Verlag, Berlin–Göttingen–Heidelberg 1960.
Volk, R. J., Jackson, W. A.: Mass spectrometric measurement of photosynthesis and respiration in leaves. – Crop Sci. 4: 45-48, 1964.
Voznesenskiĭ, V. L.: Issledovanie uglekislotnykh krivykh gazoobmena rasteniĭ v oblasti nizkikh kontsentratsiĭ CO_2. [Investigation of the carbon dioxide gas exchange curves in plants in the region of low CO_2 concentrations.] – Fiziol. Rast. 11: 974-977, 1964.
Weigl, J. W., Warrington, P. M., Calvin, M.: The relation of photosynthesis to respiration. – J. Amer. chem. Soc. 73: 5058-5063, 1951.
Weis, D., Brown, A. H.: Kinetic relationships between photosynthesis and respiration in the algal flagellate, *Ochromonas malhamensis*. – Plant Physiol. 34: 235-239, 1959.
Żelawski, W.: A contribution to the question of the CO_2-evolution during photosynthesis in dependence on light intensity. – Bull. Acad. Pol. Sci. Cl. II 15: 565-570, 1967.
Zelitch, I.: The role of glycolic acid oxidase in the respiration of leaves. – J. biol. Chem. 233: 1299-1303, 1958.
Zelitch, I.: Organic acids and respiration in photosynthetic tissues. – Annu. Rev. Plant Physiol. 15: 121-142, 1964.
Zelitch, I.: The relation of glycolic acid synthesis to the primary photosynthetic carboxylation reaction in leaves. – J. biol. Chem. 240: 1869-1876, 1965.
Zelitch, I.: Increased rate of net photosynthetic carbon dioxide uptake caused by the inhibition of glycolate oxidase. – Plant Physiol. 41: 1623-1631, 1966.
Zelitch, I.: Water and CO_2 transport in the photosynthetic process. – In: San Pietro, A., Greer, F. A., Army, T. J. (ed.): Harvesting the Sun – Photosynthesis in Plant Life. Pp. 231-248. Academic Press, New York–London 1967.
Zelitch, I.: Investigations on photorespiration with a sensitive ^{14}C-assay. – Plant Physiol. 43: 1829–1837, 1968.
Zelitch, I., Day, P. R.: Variation in photorespiration. The effect of genetic differences in photorespiration on net photosynthesis in tobacco. – Plant Physiol. 43: 1838-1844, 1968.

9 | USE OF LEAF TISSUE SAMPLES IN VENTILATED CHAMBERS FOR LONG TERM MEASUREMENTS OF PHOTOSYNTHESIS

9.1 | Leaf tissue samples as an object of photosynthesis measurements

9.1.1 | Introduction

The first papers dealing with long term photosynthesis measurements of leaf tissue samples in ventilated chambers appeared in the early sixties (Bartoš, Kubín & Šetlík 1960; Šetlík, Bartoš & Kubín 1960). Before that time, samples of leaf tissue had not acquired much popularity in photosynthesis research. In general they were only used for the investigation of certain biochemical or biophysical problems (*e.g.* quantum yields, $^{14}CO_2$ fixation intermediates and products, photophosphorylation – see Wassink 1946; Porter, Martin & Bird 1959; Kalberer, Buchanan & Arnon 1967; Forti & Parisi 1963 *etc.*). A notable exception represents the work in laboratories of Zalenskiï and Zurzycki, where physiological problems were also attacked and where manometric and volumetric methods for short term measurements with leaf discs were very thoroughly developed (see Chapters 5 and 6). The lack of enthusiasm for a more systematic use of leaf tissue samples for investigating the photosynthetic characteristics of leaves remains: one cannot avoid the impression that their potential value in solving a good many problems is not often properly appreciated. In Section 9.1.2 we try to point out some of the advantages of leaf tissue samples. Another important factor may be the widespread prejudice that normal functioning of the photosynthetic apparatus is likely to be impaired to a variable and unpredictable extent, both by injury to the leaf tissue caused by cutting out the samples from leaf laminae, and by various consequences of isolating the piece of assimilatory tissue from the continuity of the whole leaf. Evidence showing that these apprehensions are largely unjustified is presented in Section 9.1.4. Finally, the successful use of leaf samples for long runs of photosynthesis measurements requires solution of several specific problems of technique and calls for instrumental facilities not available commercially. The principles of creating favourable conditions for photosynthesis of leaf tissue samples are discussed in Section 9.1.3 and various details of procedures and apparatus design are described in the rest of the Chapter.

9.1.2 | Advantages of leaf tissue samples in photosynthesis measurements

Several lines of reasoning point to samples of leaf tissue as an extremely useful and versatile experimental material the use of which can substantially contribute to our knowledge of overall kinetics, physiology and genetics of leaf photosynthesis. First, samples of leaf tissue represent an intermediary stage between the whole leaf and the chloroplasts. The knowledge of leaf tissue behaviour provides a convenient and often badly missing link between photosynthetic characteristics of whole leaves and evidence collected at the cellular level. If it is sometimes difficult to compare directly the properties of chloroplasts or activities of enzymes with photosynthetic rates of leaves from which they have been isolated, this may be less so with leaf samples. The latter may be more easily kept in well defined physiological conditions (*e.g.* with respect to water saturation) and they may be also readily subjected to various chemical influences (absorption of nutrients, inhibitors, intermediates).

Secondly, leaf discs or segments provide a convenient, and in several respects unique, opportunity for comparing the photosynthetic characteristics of assimilatory tissue in leaves of different species or genotypes. Subjected, as they are, to conspicuous variation of both genetic and environmental origin, genotype-specific values of photosynthetic rate can be reliably assessed only on condition that leaves from a satisfactory number of individuals in each population are examined under strictly comparable conditions. If leaves from all the variants are examined simultaneously their previous history in the field is as similar as possible and the weather-dependent noise becomes substantially reduced. The developmental changes in photosynthetic rate also make it essential to complete one experimental series within a few days.

In a reasonably sized irradiation chamber, 180 samples of 6 discs each may be accommodated simultaneously. If each set of six discs represents one leaf, then one three hour run of the chamber is equal to 180 simultaneous measurements for which the leaves may be harvested at a definite time of day (say early in the morning) within a short time (half an hour). Pretreatment of all the leaves can be similar and the net labour requirement (including weighing of the samples) amounts to seven hours work for two technicians. Clearly, in the accomplishment of a similar task with gasometric equipment, pretreatment of the leaves will be less uniform and more labour will be involved.

When attempting comparative gasometric measurements on rather dissimilar leaves (*e.g.* sugar beet and clover, or maize and wheat), it may sometimes be rather difficult to arrive at unequivocally comparable conditions of leaf surface ventilation, leaf irradiation or water balance. Problems of interpretation may emerge whether the same chamber is used throughout the measurements or different, specially designed chambers are applied to each category of leaf size and shape. All these doubts can be dismissed when working with leaf samples of identical size and shape accommodated in a chamber with unchanging geometry and aerodynamic characteristics which are not affected by the character of the leaves from which the samples originate.

When exposing variants simultaneously in one chamber, a measure of photosynthetic rate must be adopted which allows evaluation of the activity of each sample in the chamber separately. The quantity of organic matter produced by the sample during an exposure period of an appropriate length satisfies this requirement. Determination of the dry weight increase in leaf discs and segments has been in fact most widely and successfully used to this end. This technique has become important because of its simplicity and because a satisfactory, sensitive balance is available in almost every laboratory. As discussed in Section 9.2.1, other criteria of photosynthetic activity of leaf tissue samples, *e.g.* the amount of absorbed $^{14}CO_2$, might prove equally suitable or, perhaps, preferable to sample weighing.

9.1.3 | *Environmental conditions during exposure*

The methods described in this chapter emphasise the need to create favourable and strictly controllable combinations of environmental conditions for photosynthesis of leaf tissue samples. There are two major methodological problems:

a. Adequate supply of water to the photosynthesising tissue. Placing the samples on the surface of water or on a wetted filter paper is a poor method for maintaining their water balance. Firstly, because water transfer through the epidermis is slow, water supply is not sufficient with higher irradiation densities unless the cut edge of the sample is also wetted. Discs from leaves whose surface is rather hydrophobic (due to cuticular layers or to hairs) may be literally dried by irradiation while floating on water. Secondly, if good contact of the sample with water is secured, the stomata in the lower epidermis are blocked and the conditions for normal CO_2 exchange are impaired (Glinka & Meidner 1968).
It has been shown by Bartoš, Kubín & Šetlík (1960) that the water demand of leaf samples may be fully satisfied merely by providing a reliable contact between the cut edges of the sample and water. With leaf discs this can be conveniently achieved by placing them in circular openings in a flat matrix made of a porous material (polyurethane foam) soaked with water. This technique opened the way to photosynthesis measurements on leaf samples under high irradiation densities and with stomatal resistance near to the normal values. Efficient ventilation must be provided to compensate for the increased boundary layer resistances at the sample surfaces, which are sunk in the holes of the matrix (*cf.* Section 9.3.1).
With segments of gramineous leaves a procedure similar to that devised for leaf discs can be employed, in establishing contact of the cut edges with strips of water soaked foam (Nátr & Špidla 1961; Rychnovská & Bartoš 1962). Alternatively, by squeezing the two ends of the segment between narrow strips of a suitable sealing material, the cut edges can protrude into a trough filled with water. This arrangement introduced by Nátr & Gloser (1967) has the drawback of confining the portion of the segment within and outside the seal, to conditions differing from those of the exposed part. It is advantageous, however, in that it allows precise gasometric measurements to be performed with leaf samples (*cf.* Section 9.3.2.2) in an open system arrangement.

b. Another important technical problem raised by the use of tissue samples for comparative measurements is the design of the irradiation chamber, in which the conditions of irradiation, air movement and temperature must be extremely homogeneous. The design of irradiation chambers is discussed in Section 9.3.

9.1.4 | *The behaviour of leaf tissue samples*

The objections most often raised against the use of leaf tissue samples in photosynthesis measurements centre on the contention that photosynthetic characteristics of whole leaves attached to the plants cannot be derived from measurements on isolated samples of leaf tissue. It should be made clear, however, that the aim of measurements on leaf tissue samples is to provide a reliable characteristic of their photosynthetic behaviour under well defined conditions, whatever be the relation of their photosynthetic behaviour to that of intact leaves. The only decisive question in this respect is whether the behaviour of leaf tissue samples, examined with methods discussed here, reveals constant and characteristic properties of the leaf tissue, which are not subjected to unpredictable variation induced by the treatment of the samples and affecting samples from leaves of different origin in various ways.

The early experiments with leaf discs in ventilated chambers have shown that photosynthesis in the discs can proceed at an even and reproducible rate for several hours of exposure to a rather high irradiance (Šetlík, Bartoš & Kubín 1960). After six to nine hours of irradiation the curve of increasing amount of photosynthate starts to decline from linearity, thus revealing an influence either of some damage to the leaf tissue or of the large quantity of photosynthates accumulated (more than 50% of the original dry weight of the sample).

Later, Nátr (1967) showed with segments of barley leaves that at a low rate of photosynthesis, induced by low irradiance, dry weight increase continued for remarkably long periods of time (up to 100 h). It can be further concluded from these experiments that, at least under the conditions examined, the decline in the rate of photosynthesis is linked with some deterioration processes in the samples

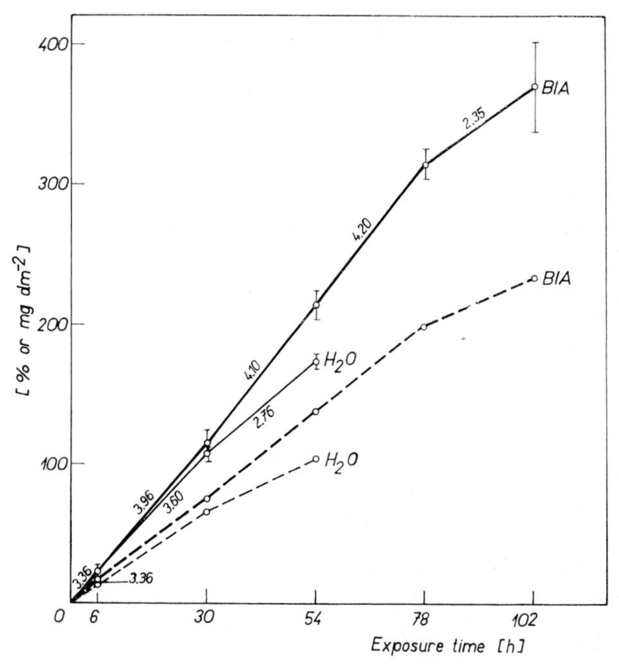

Fig. 9.1 The time course of dry weight increase in segments from 11 day old barley leaves under continuous irradiance of 45 W m^{-2} (400–700 nm) at 25 °C. The leaf segments were supplied during the exposure either with distilled water (H_2O) or with benzimidazole solution (BIA). Average values are given for weight increase expressed as mg synthetized organic matter per dm^2 of segment surface (full lines) and as per cent increase of the dry weight of samples (dashed lines). The figures on the individual sections of the curves give the mean rates of dry weight increase for the appropriate time interval expressed in mg dry weight dm^{-2} h^{-1}. The vertical lines represent the significance limits for $P = 0.05$. (From Nátr 1967.)

(*e.g.*, chlorophyll degradation, denaturation of enzymes *etc.*) which make themselves apparent after 30 h of sample exposure in the chamber. When the ageing of the tissue samples was retarded by benzimidazole the rate of photosynthesis remained stable for a much longer period of time (78 h) than without this treatment (see Fig. 9.1). Similarly, a comparison of sample behaviour from young and mature leaves showed that a steady rate of photosynthesis is maintained longer in the former than in the latter (Nátr 1969). This again points to a close interconnection between the photosynthetic rate and the overall physiological condition of the tissue which is much more pronounced than the immediate influence of the amount of accumulated assimilates (for a review see Neales & Incoll 1968). Moreover, the effect of different organic substances accumulated in the tissue may be very different. Nátr & Ludlow (1970a) found that glucose taken up from the external solution lowered the photosynthetic rate by *ca.* 50%, while assimilates formed in photosynthesis had no influence. Externally applied glucose also lowered transpiration rates and increased stomatal and mesophyll resistances to CO_2 diffusion. The most detailed information on leaf segment behaviour comes from Nátr's gasometric measurements (Nátr 1967, 1969, 1970; Nátr & Gloser 1967). These provide to date the most relevant evidence for interpretation of results obtained with leaf tissue samples and it is to be regretted that more data of this kind are not available for leaf discs as well. The course of photosynthesis in leaf segments is characterized, in general, by a curve having the shape *a* shown in Fig. 9.2. As can be seen the photosynthetic rate gradually increases from the start of irradiation

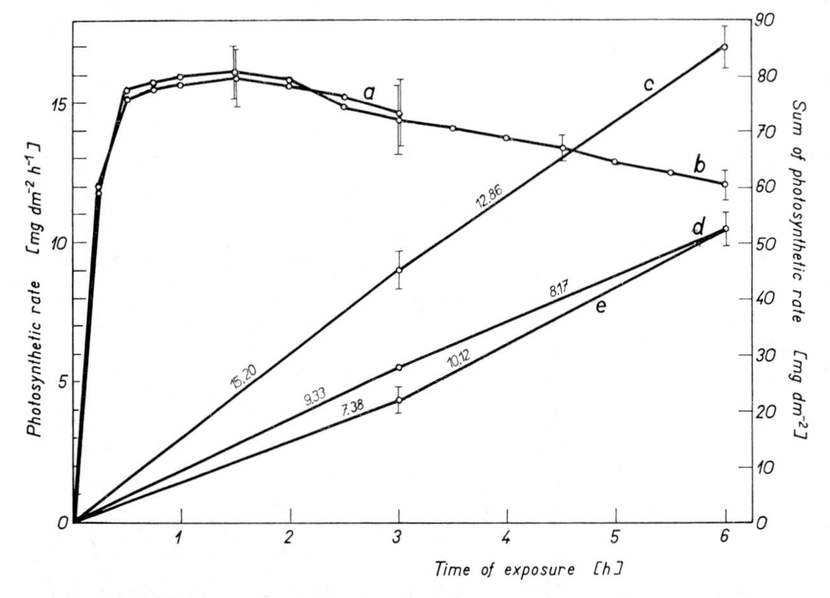

Fig. 9.2 Time course of CO_2 absorption and the dry weight increment in segments of barley leaves. From the curves for CO_2 absorption (two replications *a*, *b*) total CO_2 absorption for 3 h intervals were summed (*c*). From these values theoretical dry weight increments were calculated by multiplying by the coefficient 0.62 (*d*) and compared with recorded dry weight increments obtained after 3 and 6 h of irradiation (*e*). The vertical lines on the curves indicate the interval $\pm s_{\bar{x}}$, the numbers close to the lines indicate rates of photosynthesis [mg CO_2 or dry weight dm^{-2} h^{-1}]. (From Nátr & Gloser 1967.)

and reaches its maximum in about 0.5–1 h. Then a very slow and relatively uniform decline in the photosynthetic rate sets in and continues for many hours. The initial rise in the CO_2 absorption rate can be most probably attributed to the opening of stomata. The cause of the slow decline in later phases of the experiment cannot be unequivocally explained so far. Also lacking are simultaneous gasometric measurements of the time course of photosynthesis on leaf tissue samples and whole attached leaves performed with the same method on the same material. Indirect evidence can be provided by comparing the gasometric measurements on whole leaves provided by other authors (Milner, Hiesey & Nobs 1962; Hopkinson 1964) with those on leaf segments described above. It seems that their character is, in general, similar and that none of the parts of the time response curve is specific to the leaf samples. Indirect evidence of normal photosynthetic behaviour of leaf portions was presented by Wilson *et al.* (1969) who found highly significant similarity of photosynthetic rates of attached leaves of *Lolium perenne* measured by infra-red gas analysis with photosynthetic rates of leaf segments measured manometrically under similar conditions.
Considering the time response curve first of all from the viewpoint of gasometric measurements or measurements of $^{14}CO_2$ fixation, the question arises as to what rate is to be taken as the representative value. If it is the maximum then the representative value is higher than any real average production of the leaf. Therefore some average value is equally suitable or even preferable. This is just what is provided by the estimations of dry weight increase which integrate the photosynthetic rate for say three or six hours. The shape of the curve in Fig. 9.2 explains also the peculiar circumstance that although the detailed time course of photosynthetic rate is far from constant, the time course of dry weight accumulation, reconstructed from weight increments of samples exposed for three and six hours, very often approaches linearity. The lag at the start is compensated by a maximum consistently occurring within the first three hour period so that the sum becomes equal to the average of the slowly declining rate in the second period.
Comparative long term gasometric measurements on whole leaves and leaf tissue samples from the same plant are lacking, unfortunately, as they might help to answer the often debated problem of the significance of injury to leaf tissue accompanying sampling. Some authors think that cutting the tissue induces a shock which is transmitted to neighbouring cells and to the whole leaf and may be irreversible. It is also suggested that in response to the injury the rate of respiration may be increased up to 50% and thus reduced rates of net photosynthesis are measured (see also Section 6.6). Until now, measurements of injury-induced leaf respiration have been made only in darkness (*e.g.* Roberts 1951 in wheat; Eberhardt 1954 in *Saxifraga crassifolia*); measurements of photorespiration are lacking. On the other hand, some authors found a stimulation of photosynthesis from cutting injury to the leaf (Lubimenko & Stscheglova 1932). Measurements of net photosynthesis with leaf discs of various diameters seem to indicate that the direct consequence of cutting is rather local. A decline in the rate of photosynthetic dry matter accumulation per unit area was observed in a series of discs 8, 5 and 3 mm in diameter, while the discs of 8 mm and larger diameter showed the same rates per unit area (Šetlík *et al.* 1966). The practical use of discs of a diameter larger than 8 to 12 mm is limited by the difficulty of cutting such discs from most leaves without

including the larger veins, which increase the variability of initial dry weight of the irradiated and control samples.

A transient effect induced by disc sampling and transmitted over greater distances might be the closure of stomata. Heath & Russell (1954) described transmission of the effect of light on wheat leaf stomata over a distance up to 2 cm. The reactions of stomata to physical influences may be almost immediate (Stålfelt 1956); they close more rapidly than they open. Having transferred plants from strong to weak light, Kuiper (1961) found a closing reaction as rapid as 6 min, while the full opening of stomata of intact leaves of *Xanthium pennsylvanicum* after transfer from darkness to light requires almost 2 h (Glinka & Meidner 1968). These authors found that the rate of stomatal opening was even slower (up to 3.5 h) in leaf discs, but the final steady state aperture was slightly increased as the discs were more turgid. Very slow opening of stomata ('irreversible closure' for the 3–6 h exposure time) may be the reason why, with some plant species (*e.g.* banana and *Pelargonium* leaves), the disc method fails to produce the expected results.

These effects which induce the initial slow rate of dry matter accumulation and gradual slowing up after reaching the maximum value may lead to an estimate of photosynthetic rate up to 20% lower than that obtained from the maximum rate of CO_2 uptake measured gasometrically (Nátr 1970). To decrease the initial period of stomatal opening, Nátr recommends an appropriate (*e.g.* 1 h) pre-exposure of both control and experimental sets of leaf samples to light. Last but not least, the average rates of photosynthesis determined as dry matter increase during a 3 to 6 h exposure time are usually comparable with average photosynthetic rates measured as CO_2 uptake in leaf segments (Nátr & Gloser 1967), as well as in whole leaves (Nátr & Kousalová 1965). The coefficient found experimentally for the multiplication of dry weight increase to obtain the CO_2 uptake value – 1.56 – was similar to that given in Table 1.3 (1.543). The only exceptionally conspicuous differences between these two measures of photosynthetic activity were found: at a low irradiance (Nátr & Kousalová 1965) or with old leaves (Cartwright & Papenfus 1967).

In any case, it is desirable to test the behaviour of stomata in each plant species or variety prior to starting the actual experiments, *e.g.* by a rapid direct microscopic observation of the lower epidermis of discs immediately after cutting and during the exposure. It is also recommended that the time course of dry matter accumulation should be determined for each new plant type under study. Another possibility of error may be the growth of tissue, mainly of young leaves, during prolonged light exposure (see Dale 1967). Such increase in irradiated area and tissue thickness, as well as possible increase (or decrease) in chlorophyll content and changes in the optical properties, might significantly change the photosynthetic rate of the samples. These problems deserve further study.

9.2 Procedures used for measuring the amount of photosynthates formed in leaf tissue samples

9.2.1 Measures of photosynthetic rate

As discussed in Section 9.1.2 the most useful advantage of leaf tissue samples is that they provide a simultaneous assessment of the photosynthetic rate of samples from a large number of variants. With the most frequently used method, the dry weight method, the requirements imposed on pretreatment of the leaves and on the sampling operation are very rigorous. In what follows, the procedures will be described from the point of view of this, the most practical variant.

However, it must be emphasized that other measures of the amount of photosynthates accumulated in leaf tissue samples might help to improve the method in both precision and efficiency. It is to be regretted that the amount of $^{14}CO_2$ fixed in leaf samples, as indicative of photosynthetic rate, has not so far been tried extensively. If the activity of leaf tissue samples that have been photosynthesizing $^{14}CO_2$ is counted, the measured value is directly proportional to the rate of photosynthesis during the exposure period without the complexities of measuring small dry weight increments against a large background dry weight. Thus, even if the error of radiometric determination was much greater than that of weighing, the estimate of photosynthetic rate can still be more precise. Furthermore, only one set of samples is needed for each variant (excluding replication) and the number of individual leaf discs or segments necessary to produce a representative sample might well be lower compared with dry weight increase measurements, thus reducing the labour requirements and, simultaneously, increasing the possible number of experiments per day since shorter exposures will give sufficient accuracy. However, the rate of $^{14}CO_2$ fixation in whole leaves has already been measured in several cases by counting radioactivity of leaf discs punched from leaves previously exposed to radioactive carbon dioxide (*e.g.* Strebeyko 1967; Shimshi 1969). Experience gained in experiments of this type may provide a useful guide to the choice of the necessary activity levels, exposure times and counting procedures, if elaboration of the leaf disc method using $^{14}CO_2$ comes about. The greatest problem with the use of $^{14}CO_2$ lies in the attainment of appropriate concentrations of CO_2. In much of the work done previously, high (*e.g.* 1 %) concentrations of little or no physiological or environmental relevance have been used for convenience (for a detailed account of $^{14}CO_2$ methods, see Chapter 7).

Leaf discs have also been successfully used for calorimetric determination of the amount of energy fixed during the exposure period (Nátr 1968). This may be a very valuable method for several types of specific questions. Since calorimetry is substantially more time-consuming than weighing it is of little value for routine work.

There are two disadvantages inherent in methods estimating the accumulated photosynthate, carbon or energy:

a. they either destroy the sample or, at least, as a result of drying decompose some substances which cannot then be further analysed (pigments, vitamins, *etc.*);

b. the determination requires knowledge of the status of the material before the exposure, and thus a second control sample has to be taken simultaneously with the exposed one.

9.2.2 | *Sampling and sampling pattern*

The schedule adopted for taking samples from the various parts of a leaf, from various leaves on one plant, and from the plants in the population, depends entirely on the purpose of the experiment In addition, the sampling pattern must take into account the natural heterogeneity amongst the leaves on a plant as well as within one leaf blade. This heterogeneity is determined by the development of the plant and the leaf: it is reflected in the changes in its area, thickness, dimensions of cells and cell layers, numbers of stomata and their dimensions, amount of photosynthetic pigments and concentration of components of the photosynthetic apparatus, *etc.* (*cf.* Section 1.3.1; for a review see Šesták & Čatský 1967).

When using discs, the method is only suitable for plants with the dicotyledonous leaf type with a large, flat and uniform leaf blade which permits sampling of paired discs close together without touching the larger veins. From narrow monocotyledonous leaves, segments can always be sampled conveniently. For wide-leaf monocotyledons, *e.g.* maize, discs are recommended. Whole needles and segments of conifer needles can also be used (Nátr & Ludlow 1970b).

Unlike the Sachs' (1884) method, in which leaf samples are punched out symmetrically with respect to the main vein from each half of the leaf, Bartoš, Kubín & Šetlík (1960) found that the conjugate sets of exposed and control discs are more comparable if two paired samples are taken in close proximity on different parts of the leaf blade. In all compared leaves or plants, the samples should be taken from identical parts of the blade. The discs are usually taken alternately closer to the top or base and to the centre or margin of the leaf blade. The segments are sampled alternately nearer to the top or base of the leaf. The tissue samples are never chosen at random, but so as to represent a mean value of the leaf, plant, population, *etc.*

In addition to this general question, a method based on determination of dry weight increment in samples of leaf tissue must include appropriate sampling procedures to yield significant differences between the two sets (exposed and control) of discs or segments, whose initial dry weight difference should not exceed 0.5%. Such an initial dry weight difference would give $\pm$ 5% accuracy of determination with an assumed 10% increment of the initial dry matter. Such representative samples of reasonable similarity are usually obtained with sets of 6–8 discs or

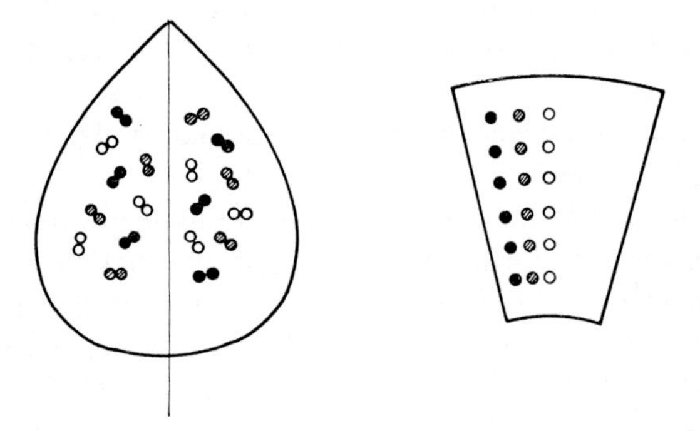

Fig. 9.3 Diagram of the sampling pattern for one leaf. Open, shaded and full circles represent three replications of pairs of control and treatment discs cut out of the leaf (left) and put into radial rows of the polyurethane matrix (right). If a leaf with representative photosynthetic activity is chosen, this sampling pattern may be sufficient for characterization of the whole plant. (After Avratovščuková 1967.)

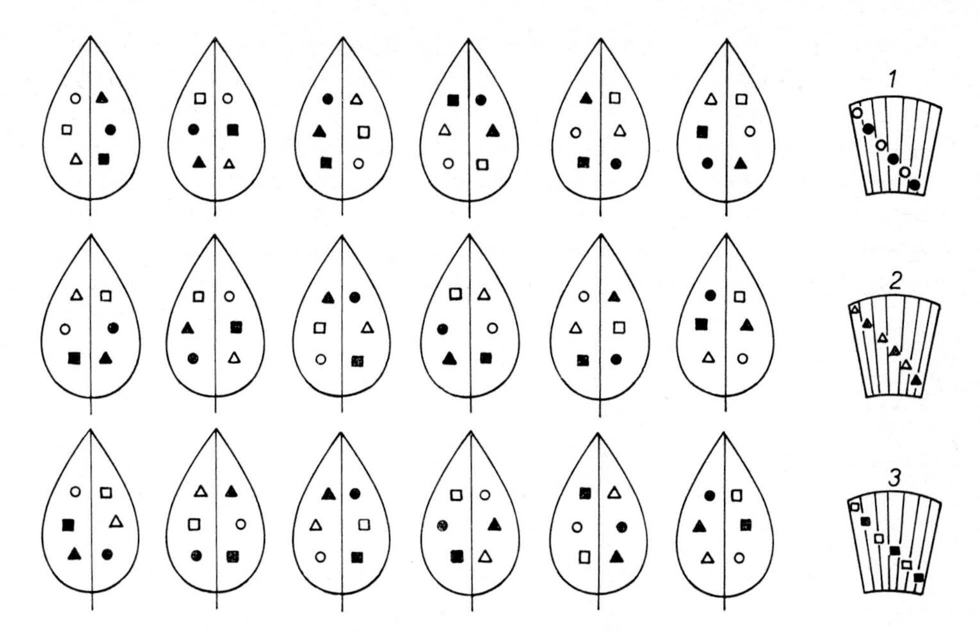

Fig. 9.4 Diagram of the sampling pattern for a plant population. Each leaf belongs to the same insertion level on a different plant. Open or full circles, triangles and squares represent discs of one replication which are put into radial rows of the polyurethane matrices. In close proximity to these discs, sets of control discs are sampled. (From Avratovščuková 1968).

segments each of an area 0.5 to 1 cm^2. Sets of this size can also be easily weighed in contrast to individual discs or segments whose dry weight may be as low as 1 mg. The necessary sample size is determined from the standard deviation. Sets of 6 to 18 discs of 8 mm in diameter are recommended for standard measurements. Avratovščuková (1967) found that it is necessary to use 3 to 6 sets of 6 discs of 8 mm in diameter to characterise the photosynthetic rate of a given leaf or plant, and 9 to 18 samples to represent a plant population. An example of the sampling pattern used for the characterisation of one plant is given in Fig. 9.3, and for the characterisation of a plant population in Fig. 9.4. Naturally each experiment requires the use of a special sampling pattern. The control and exposed sets should be paired before exposure so that confidence limits or a standard error can be assigned to the mean rate of photosynthesis estimated from the difference between several pairs of control and exposed sets of samples.

9.2.3 | Selection of leaves and their pretreatment

In some research problems it is necessary to take individual samples from leaf blades attached to a plant. In this case the turgor of individual plants and leaves may be very different and the discs may have different areas when subsequently saturated with water. This difference, of 5 (Thoday 1909) to 18% (Montemartini 1930), may introduce a big experimental error. In addition to this, sampling from attached leaves directly in the field or experimental plot is more tedious and requires special care.

In most cases leaves are detached from the plant and saturated with water prior to sampling. Thus it is necessary to decide which leaves have to be removed from the plant and how to mark them. This depends on the type of experiment, *e.g.* characterization of a compound leaf requires sampling to include all parts of the blade, and therefore the whole leaf is detached. If mean assimilation of the plant is to be characterized, samples are taken from all leaves of the plant. To characterize maximum values for a plant, one to three leaves just reaching the state of 'photosynthetic maturity', usually the 3rd to 6th leaf from the top of the plant, are

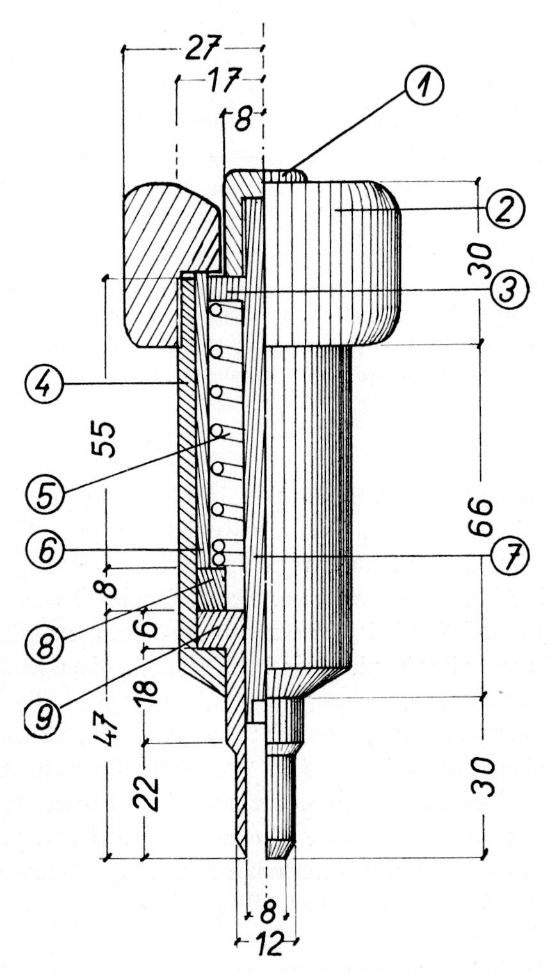

Fig. 9.5 Schematic section through a manual punch showing its construction. The handle (*2*) is connected with the mantle (*4*) by means of a screw so that on turning the flange the handle presses the inner mantle (*6*) onto a ring (*8*) which holds the knife (*9*) firmly on the opening at the lower end of the mantle (*4*). The piston (*7*) moves at its lower end through the knife cavity and at its upper end with its extended part (*3*) through the cavity of the inner mantle (*6*). The extended part (*3*) supports a spring (*5*) which holds the piston in its upper position. The piston is pressed with the thumb which rests on a push-button (*1*). The piston and the knife are exchangeable so that knives of internal diameter 8 or 12 mm can be used. Dimensions in mm. (After Bartoš, Kubín & Šetlík 1960.)

taken as suitable samples. To characterize the plant population, one photosynthetically mature leaf from 15–20 plants in the population is taken for the average sample. After the detachment of leaves, the petioles are immediately immersed in water, the blades are washed free of soil residues and air pollution particles and taken to a shaded place in the laboratory.
For some plants detachment of leaves in the evening and storage in the dark overnight is recommended, but this procedure can cause irreversible physiological changes in susceptible plant species (Šetlík, Bartoš & Kubín 1960). Sampling of leaves at different times of day causes variable results (Nátr 1965; Avratovščuková 1967). Therefore to obtain uniform results the leaves should always be detached from the plant at the same, early morning hour (*e.g.* 7.00) to ensure high leaf turgor, and the discs then cut from the leaves after 30 or 60 min with the petioles immersed in water; this procedure increases the water saturation of leaves. The best way of marking leaves is at the tip of the blade with Indian ink and a fine brush; the water-resistant filling of felt tipped pens or markers always contains organic solvents which may induce stomatal closure. Leaves are usually numbered from the oldest one or from the lowest scar of the abscissed leaves. If the number of the youngest expanded leaf on the shoot or branch is also given (*e.g.* as a denominator of a fraction, 8/13 = eighth leaf from the base in a total of thirteen leaves, *i.e.* sixth leaf from the top of the plant), the position of a particular

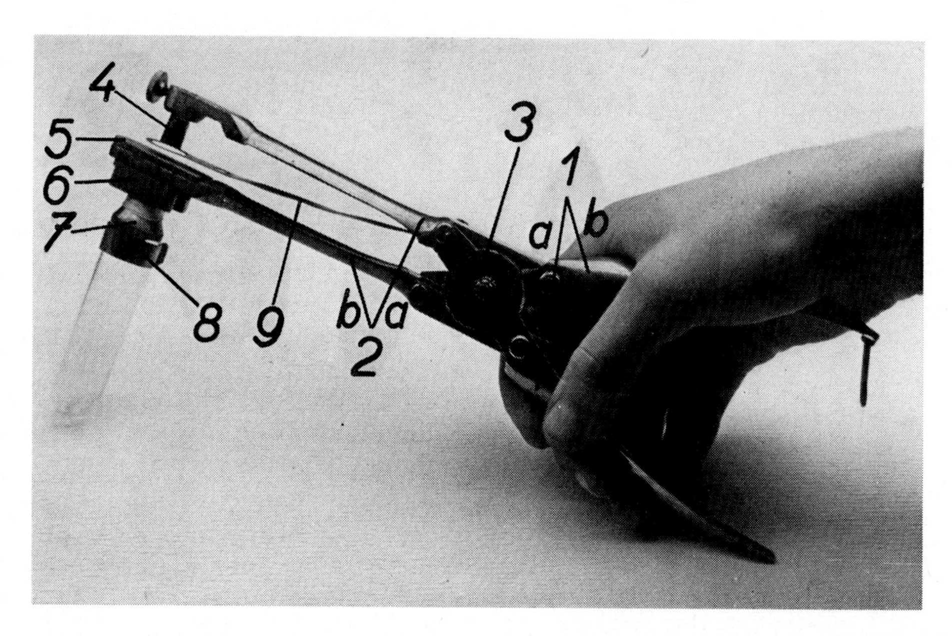

Fig. 9.6 Tongs punch. The joint mechanism (*3*) which connects the arms of the tongs (*2a*, *b*) with the handles (*1a*, *b*) is made so that on closing the tongs the arms move in parallel. The knife (*4*) cuts out the discs against a steel matrix (*5*) which contains a hole corresponding to the knife diameter. Both the knife and the matrix are exchangeable. Into the block (*6*) on the lower arm a hollow conical shaft (*7*) is introduced, carrying a holder (*8*) for a test-tube in which the samples are collected. In order to prevent the leaf blade from adhering to the knife after cutting out the disc, it is pressed back by a spring (*9*). (From Bartoš, Kubín & Šetlík 1960.)

leaf from the base or top may be easily compared during the ontogenesis of the plant. In shrubs, trees or branched shoots, the branch position must also be recorded.

9.2.4 | *Cutting of leaf discs or segments*

Leaf discs can be sampled with simple cork borers of a diameter 8 to 12 mm. The cutting edge must be kept sharp in order to give an exact area of samples and also to minimise the injury. To speed up the sampling procedure with larger experimental series, use of a special punch is recommended. Construction of a manual punch for working with detached leaves is shown in Fig. 9.5. The leaf is laid on a support made of softened polyethylene plate and the disc is cut out by a mild perpendicular pressure on the knife. The discs rest in the hollow of the circular knife and the whole series is pushed out by pressing down the push-button of the piston.
For working in the field with leaves attached to the plant, tongs and lever punches are recommended (Figs. 9.6 and 9.7). These punches collect the discs into a test-tube or a small box.

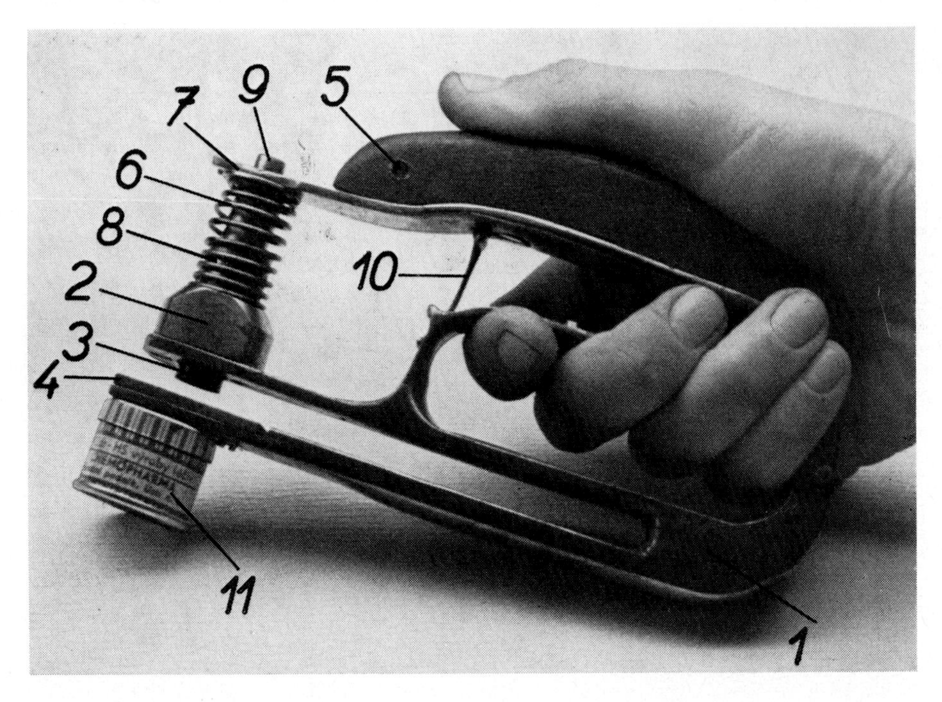

Fig. 9.7 Lever punch. The punch base (*1*) has the form of a U lying on its side. On its upper arm the groove (*2*) for the knife (*3*) can be seen; on its lower arm the matrix (*4*) is placed. Both the knife and the matrix are exchangeable. On compressing the lever (*5*) the knife is forced into the opening in the matrix. The lever returns to its original position, activated by a spring (*6*) which is supported on the extended part (*7*) of the knife groove (*8*). The pin (*9*) in the knife groove then moves in a forked notch at the end of the lever. The upper extreme position of the lever is controlled by an arrester catch (*10*). The discs are collected in a box (*11*) fixed to the lower arm. (From Bartoš, Kubín & Šetlík 1960.)

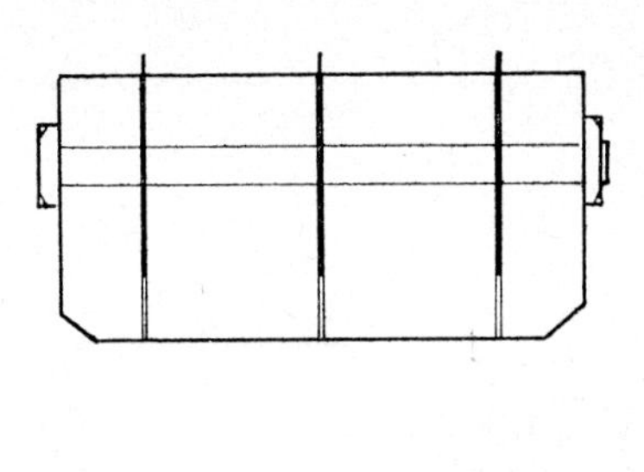

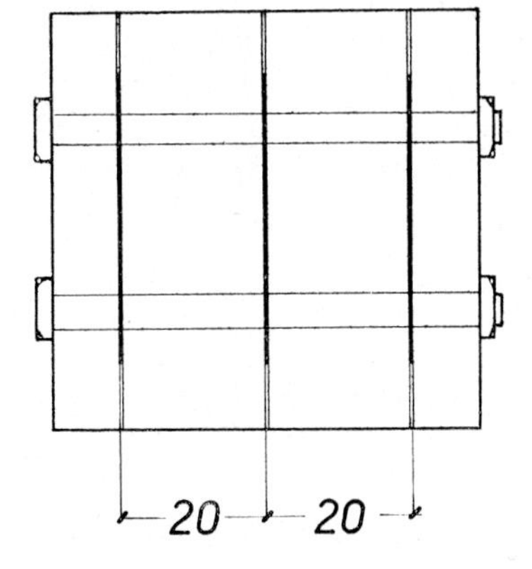

Fig. 9.8 Diagram of the punch for cutting leaf segments. Razor blades are fixed between the perspex blocks by means of screws. Dimensions in mm. (After Šetlík *et al.* 1966.)

From narrow leaves, segments are cut with the simple device shown in Fig. 9.8. It consists of razor blades fixed *e.g.* 20 mm apart by perspex blocks and screws. The device cuts both the control and experimental segments simultaneously. A modification recommended by Paulech & Gašparík (1968) for measurements on fruit tree leaves uses square samples 20 × 20 mm cut from the leaves by a special device. They found better results with samples of this shape than with the standard discs.

9.2.5 | Drying and weighing of samples

The control samples are dried immediately after sampling, the exposed samples just after the exposure period (see Section 9.3). Discs or segments are pinned and the pins with sets of discs or segments are pushed into the support plate of cork or polystyrene. The standard drying period is 12 h at the temperature 85 °C, the minimum sufficient time being 4 h. After drying, the supports with samples are transferred into a small (100 mm diameter) desiccator with $CaCl_2$.
Another procedure (Nátr 1971) is to dry the samples in small baskets of wire netting for 20 min at 105 °C and then for at least 8 h at 60 °C. Each dry sample is then put into a special desiccator (Fig. 9.9). Open desiccators with samples are exposed to 100 °C for 20 min, and then closed.
After temperature equilibration (30–60 min), the samples are weighed on a balance.

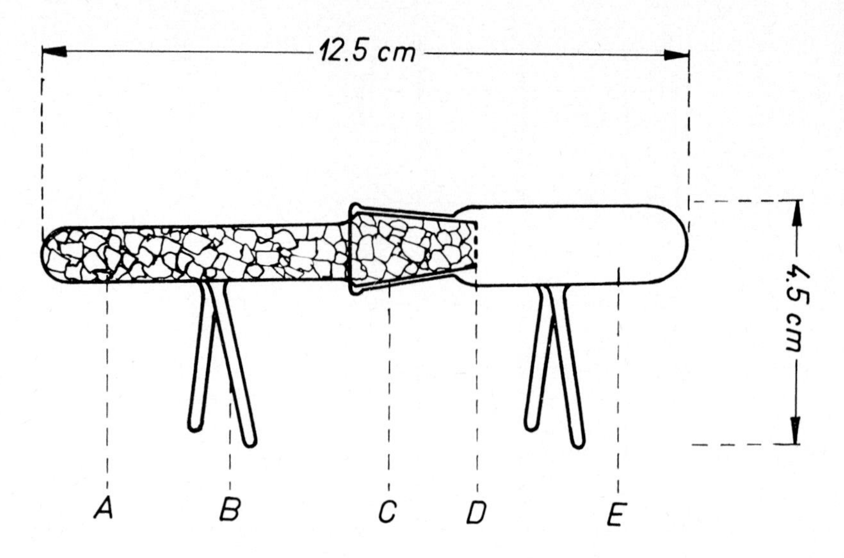

Fig. 9.9 Small glass desiccator for individual samples. Its two halves (*A*, *E*) standing on supports (*B*) are tightly connected by a joint (*C*). Part *A* is filled with coloured silica gel which is kept in place by a mesh of wire or nylon (*D*). Leaf samples are put into part *E*. (From Nátr 1971.)

A torsion balance or appropriate semi-automatic analytical balance (*e.g.* '*Sartorius 2604*', capacity 100 g, sensitivity 10^{-5} g, scale 10^{-1} g) is recommended. The dry samples absorb water vapour from the atmosphere very rapidly and thus the weighing should take the same time for all compared samples.

9.3 | Exposure and exposure chambers

9.3.1 | Sample positioning and water saturation

Immediately after sampling, the leaf discs are inserted into circular holes in a water-saturated matrix of polyurethane foam. They are fixed at half the depth of the matrix, resting on thin-walled 1 mm thick rings cut from polythene tube. The edges of the discs are gently pressed against the matrix. The polyurethane matrices are fixed on supports made either of a metal mesh or of perspex plate with drilled holes to ensure the supply of CO_2 to the lower side of the leaf discs. Leaf segments are usually held on a support by means of a nylon string and their cut edges are gently pressed against two strips of the polyurethane foam saturated with water. Another modification places the segments between the top and bottom parts of a chamber (see Fig. 9.11) submerged in water (Nátr & Gloser 1967).
The perfect contact of sample cut edges with water during the whole exposure period is essential; it ensures undisturbed water supply to the sample, which is a question of vital importance at high irradiances, which result in enhanced rates of transpiration.
Putting the leaf disc lower side upwards decreases its photosynthetic rate by up to 25% in sunflower and kale; accidental doubling of leaf discs lowers photosynthetic

rate of both discs (Šesták & Vodová 1965). Hence positioning of leaf samples in the matrix must be done very carefully.

9.3.2 | *The exposure chambers*

Exposure of leaf samples to photosynthetically active radiation for 3–6 h may take place either in natural (field) conditions or in highly controlled conditions in the laboratory.
Exposure directly in the field ensures a semi-natural combination of physical factors influencing the leaf samples. However, field exposure cannot be used for the determination of photosynthetic capacity, because of the variability and inadequate stability of the environmental factors in the field.
Devices for field exposure may be quite simple, and open as much as possible so as not to disturb movement of air round the samples. They may consist of a simple holder made of a thin perspex sheet with drilled holes upon which the polyurethane matrix is placed. Two edges of the matrix are immersed in water in attached troughs. The disturbance to the microclimate induced by putting the samples in a much thicker polyurethane foam plate may be reduced by moderate ventilation (a fan directed to move the air both under and over the samples). In these experiments the only environmental factor which is kept constant is the water supply to the tissue.

The design of a suitable chamber for laboratory measurements must ensure uniform and stable environmental conditions throughout the exposure period, when measuring the photosynthetic rate, and keep them as near optimum as possible when measuring the photosynthetic capacity of the leaf tissue. From the laboratory equipment already designed three types have frequently been used with success:
1. Chamber with the square, stable sample holder;
2. Chamber for simultaneous measurement of dry weight increase and CO_2 consumption in leaf segments;
3. Annular chamber with the rotating sample holder.

9.3.2.1 | Chamber with the square, stable sample holder

The general scheme of the equipment is shown in Fig. 9.10. It is based on a square exposure chamber of dimensions 20 × 20 × 3 cm made of perspex or of non-rusting metal with the upper side of glass glued on. The chamber contains a drawer which bears troughs of water and a wire mesh support for the polyurethane foam matrix holding the leaf samples. Two edges of this matrix are immersed in the water troughs. Normal or CO_2-enriched air is circulated by means of a fan through the chamber and through a heat exchanger supplied with thermostated water, the temperature of which is controlled by a contact thermometer measuring the temperature of the air after passage through the chamber. Uniform irradiance of all the exposed samples (up to 18 rows of 18 discs of 8 mm diameter) is improved by a mirror surrounding a high output light bulb. The bulb is continuously cooled by immersion in flowing water.

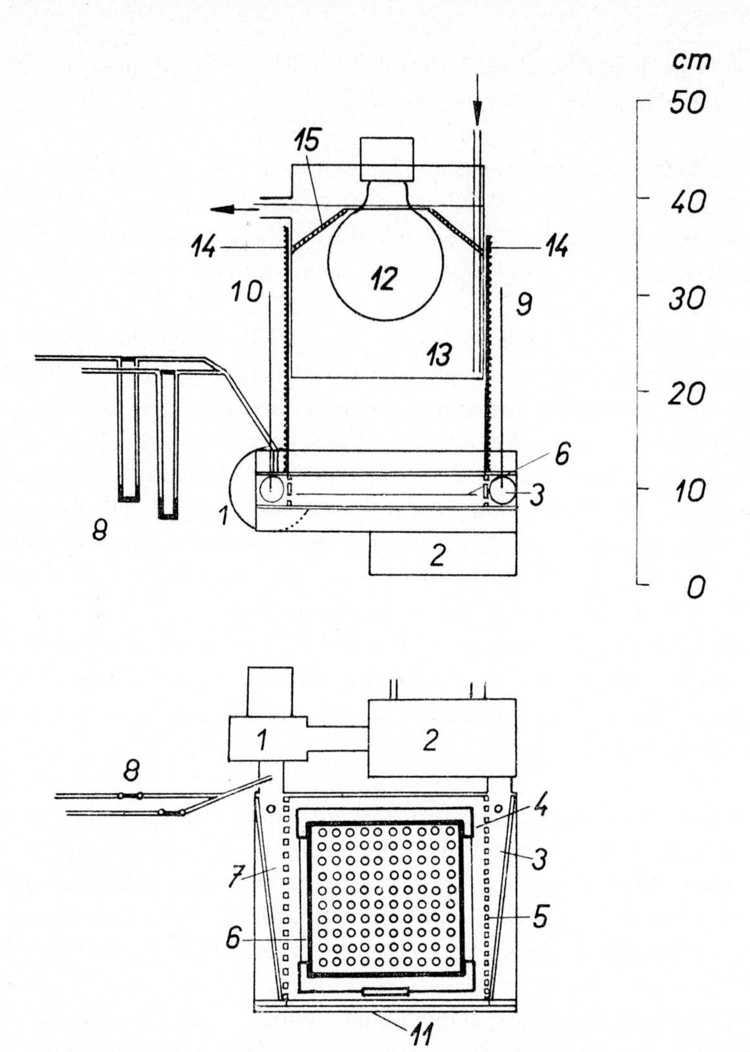

Fig. 9.10 Diagram of the exposure chamber with the square, stable sample holder. A fan (*1*) forces the air through the thermostated heat exchanger (*2*) into the distribution channel (*3*) separated from the exposure space (*4*) by a perforated septum (*5*). It divides the air into flows over and under the leaf samples placed on a drawer (*6*). The air is sucked from the outlet channel (*7*) and recirculated by the fan (*1*). New air and/or CO_2 is supplied through the inlet provided with control flow meters (*8*); surplus air escapes through the slightly leaky perspex door (*11*) to the exposure space. Air temperature is controlled by the thermometer (*10*) which regulates the temperature of water entering the heat exchanger (*2*); the other thermometer (*9*) has a precise scale for reading. The light bulb (*12*) is immersed in water steadily flowing through the cuvette made of perspex (*13*). The cuvette is placed inside the mirror cavity (*14*) which with supplementary mirrors (*15*) homogenises the radiation field. (After Šetlík *et al.* 1966.)

9.3.2.2 Chamber for simultaneous measurement of dry weight increase and CO_2 consumption in leaf segments

Segments of longish leaves (mainly of monocotyledonous plants) are suitable for simultaneous measurement as their two straight cut edges are easily saturated with

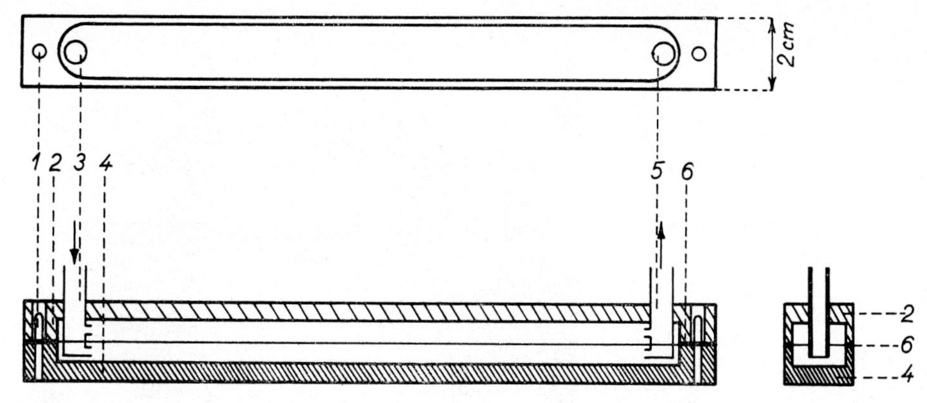

Fig. 9.11 Diagram of the assimilation chamber used in the simultaneous measurements of CO_2 uptake and dry matter increment of leaf segments. A plug (*1*) in the lower part (*4*) of the chamber, made of hardened PVC, fits the hole in the perspex upper part (*2*). Both parts are sealed together by means of terostat strips (*6*). The leaf segments are placed on one level between the two parts of the chamber. Air is led through the inlet (*3*) and outlet (*5*). (From Nátr & Gloser 1967.)

water from outside the chamber. Twelve to 24 leaf segments 20 mm long are placed in the chamber designed by Nátr & Gloser (1967) – see Fig. 9.11. They are fixed between the perspex upper part and hardened PVC lower part of the chamber; air-tight sealing of the chamber is ensured by terostat or silicon rubber strips. The cut edges of the segments are in continuous contact with water in the water bath into which the chamber is submerged. Circulating water ensures uniform temperature of the air passing through the chamber the CO_2 content of which is monitored by an infra-red gas analyser. For irradiation, strip quartz-iodine lamps are suitable. An arrangement of this kind is preferable when using an open system because the retention of CO_2 in the water contained in the polyurethane foam may distort the measurements. On the other hand, in a semi-closed circuit in which the CO_2 concentration is kept at a constant value, retention of CO_2 cannot cause much trouble since CO_2 present in water in a closed system soon becomes equilibrated with pCO_2 of the gas phase. With such a system, inclusion of foam matrices within the chamber may be satisfactory.

9.3.2.3 | Annular chamber with the rotating sample holder

The problems of ensuring satisfactory uniformity of environmental factors (irradiance, temperature and CO_2 supply) have been most successfully solved by Šetlík, Avratovščuková & Křítek (1967) who made an apparatus in which leaf samples are placed radially in exposure carriers on an annular holder, which rotates slowly under a circle of irradiation lamps. Radial gradients of factors over the samples are small since the annular surface is comparatively narrow. Moving regularly through all possible positions along the circumference of the chamber, all samples are exposed to the same average conditions during the irradiation period. The circular shape of the chamber also allows a simple design of an efficient air circulation and heat exchange system installed within the chamber. The total number of samples (90 samples, each including 6 discs, in the standard

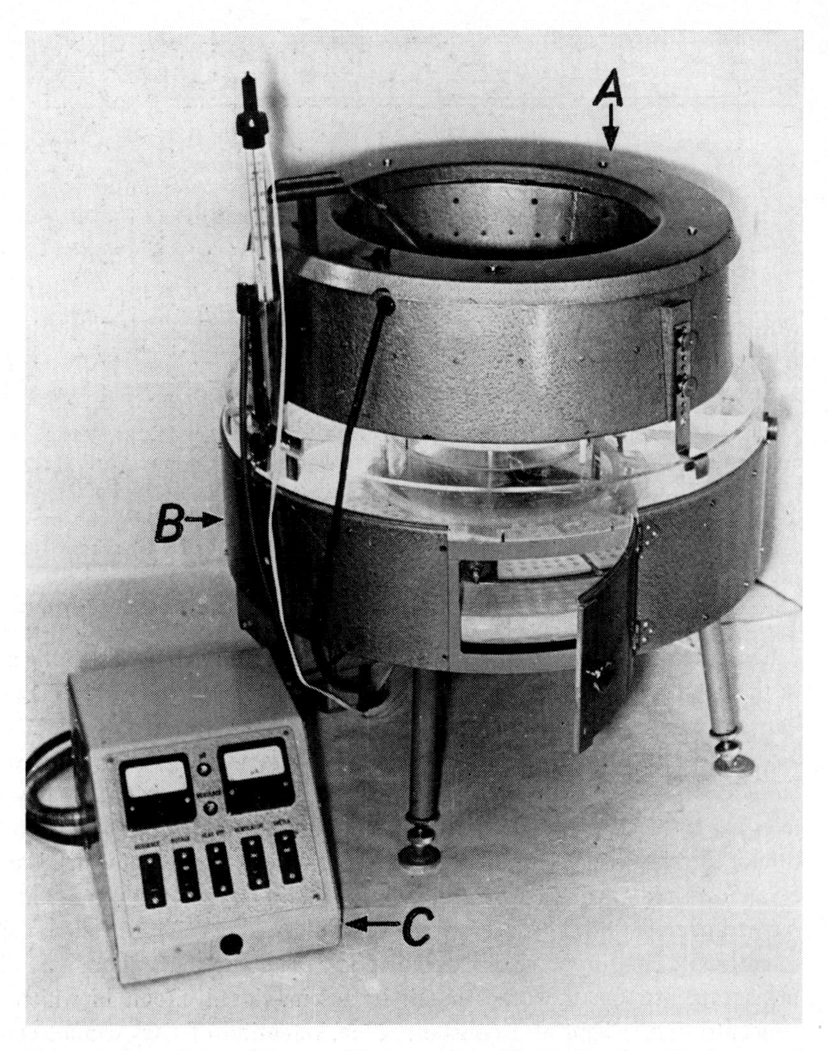

Fig. 9.12 General view of the assembled annular irradiation chamber with the control box. *A:* Lamp housing in its working position. *B:* Irradiation chamber. The door used for transferring the leaf sample carriers in and out of the chamber is left open. A section of the white enamelled upper surface of the heat exchanger and border parts of two polyurethane matrices resting on the rotating holder can be seen through the door opening. *C:* Control box. (From Šetlík, Avratovščuková & Křítek 1967.)

apparatus, 180 samples of the same size in the new model) is divided into smaller subgroups (of six samples) arranged in individual carriers, each of which can be independently inserted or taken out of the chamber. This substantially shortens the manipulation time intervals for individual samples.

The apparatus has three main construction units: the lamp housing, the irradiation chamber, and the control box. The overall view of the assembled apparatus is shown in Fig. 9.12, more details of the chamber and the lamp housing are shown in Fig. 9.13. An axial section of the chamber and the lamp housing is shown in Fig. 9.14.

 The lamp housing (*A* in Figs. 9.12 and 9.13) is designed so as to house a circle of

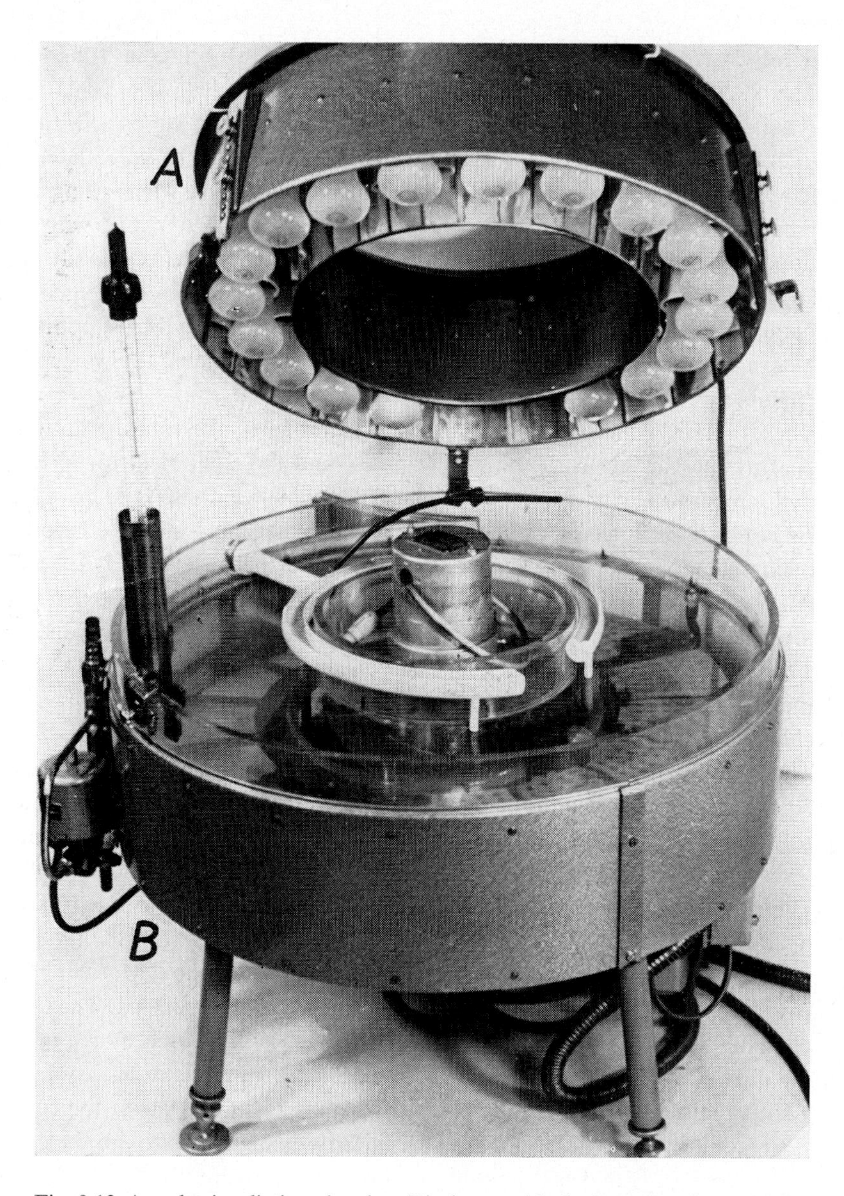

Fig. 9.13 Annular irradiation chamber (*B*) shown with the lamp housing (*A*) lifted and inclined. The lamp housing is equipped with 100 W lamps in this case, two of them (in the remote lower part of the body) being removed from their sockets. The mirror facets lining the reflector walls can be seen. The cover of the chamber with the trough for the water filter, the annular overflow channel and the casing of the fan motor are seen on the top of the chamber. The annular rotating holder is seen within the chamber fitted with leaf disc carriers in the right half of the chamber. In the background on the right side the photocell housing is fixed to one of the spokes of the annular holder. The water flow regulating unit is attached to the side wall at the left hand side of the chamber. (From Šetlík, Avratovščuková & Křítek 1967.)

evenly spaced incandescent lamps. The housing is an annular trough (*1* to *4* in Fig. 9.14) made of enamelled sheet steel and provided with 20 lamp sockets. It can be equipped either with twenty 100 W krypton-filled lamps or with ten 250 W internal reflector photoflood lamps. The mean value of adequately uniform irradiance within the 400 to 700 nm waveband reached when using the 100 W lamps was 56 W m^{-2} in the plane of the samples, and 209 W m^{-2} with the photoflood lamps. The sidewalls of the housing are lined with reflecting silvered mirror strips. The lamps in the housing are sufficiently cooled by a spontaneous draught of air. The lamp housing is provided with three adjustable supports *(19)* by means of which it can be fixed at the desired distance above the water filter of the chamber.

The irradiation chamber consists of: the water filter, the rotating annular holder bearing the carriers with the leaf samples, and the equipment for air circulation and temperature control. The frame of the chamber consists of two *L*-sectional rings *(9, 14)* interconnected by flats, both of hard aluminium. The outer jacket of the chamber *(12)* is made of sheet steel and the bottom *(15)* of brass sheet. All the iron and aluminium parts are enamelled. The jacket of the chamber is provided with a door (clearly seen in Fig. 9.12) for insertion of the sample carriers. The bottom of the chamber is slightly conical so that the condensed water from the surface of the heat exchanger is drained to the centre, where it can be discharged through an outlet valve.

The cover of the chamber is made of 10 mm thick perspex sheet and supports a 50 mm high perspex annular trough for a water filter. Water is supplied to the trough by twelve inlets *(27)* arranged along the circumference on the bottom, and is discharged by overflow to an U-shaped annulus *(6)* at the inner rim of the water filter. The effective depth of the water layer maintained by the overflow during operation of the apparatus is about 45 mm. The motor *(26)* of the fan *(29)* which provides air circulation within the chamber, is fixed to the dry central part of the cover; the shaft of the fan is provided with a seal in the perspex. The cover of the chamber with the water filter trough and the fan is supported by the upper rim of the chamber *(9)*, the bearing surface being fitted with the necessary sealing ring. To lift the cover from the chamber it is necessary to pull down the rubber tubes *(10)* from the water inlet nozzles. A capillary tube going through the cover in the water space *(25)* makes it possible to supply the polyurethane matrices with water during the irradiation period.

The driving shaft of the rotating annular holder *(11)* goes through the centre of the bottom and rests in a ball-bearing *(32)* under the chamber. The upper end of the shaft has the form of a hexagonal head. Six L-shaped beams *(31)* which bear the rotating annular holder *(11)* are attached to it. Their vertical arms pass between the propeller of the fan and the inner circumference of the heat exchanger. The rotating annular holder of the sample carriers *(11)* is made of one piece of hard aluminium sheet cut as an annular ring (270 mm inner diameter and 560 mm outer diameter) with trapezoidal openings. The sample carriers with leaf discs are placed just above these openings so that the circulating air has free access to the discs from both sides. The sample carriers are thus separated by the spokes of the holder, which are 15 mm wide. One of these spokes is fitted with a rectangular selenium photocell *(28)* provided with filters, which allows continuous measurement of the radiant flux density at different positions in the chamber. The connecting wires to the photocell *(16)* pass through one of the beams bearing the annular holder and then through the hollow shaft down to friction contacts *(34)* situated under the bearing of the shaft. The lower end of the shaft is fitted with a driving pulley *(33)* for a round sectional belt *(35)* which connects it with the pulley *(17)* of a small D.C. motor *(18)* fitted with a reduction gear. The motor speed is controlled by the voltage supplied so that the sample holder rotates at 30 r.p.m.

The sample carriers (Fig. 9.15) consist of a 1 mm thick perspex base plate *(A)* provided with drilled holes (7 mm in diameter) above which the leaf discs (8 mm in diameter) rest on 1 mm thick rings cut from an 8 mm polythene tube.

The forced air circulation in the chamber is produced by an axial or centrifugal fan with a nominal output of *ca.* 250 m^3 h^{-1}. Under the usual conditions in the chamber the observed air flow velocity is 2 m s^{-1}. The propeller of the fan (Fig. 9.14, *33*) is adjusted on the vertical shaft to such a height that the air stream passes under the body of the heat exchanger *(14)* from the centre of the chamber to its

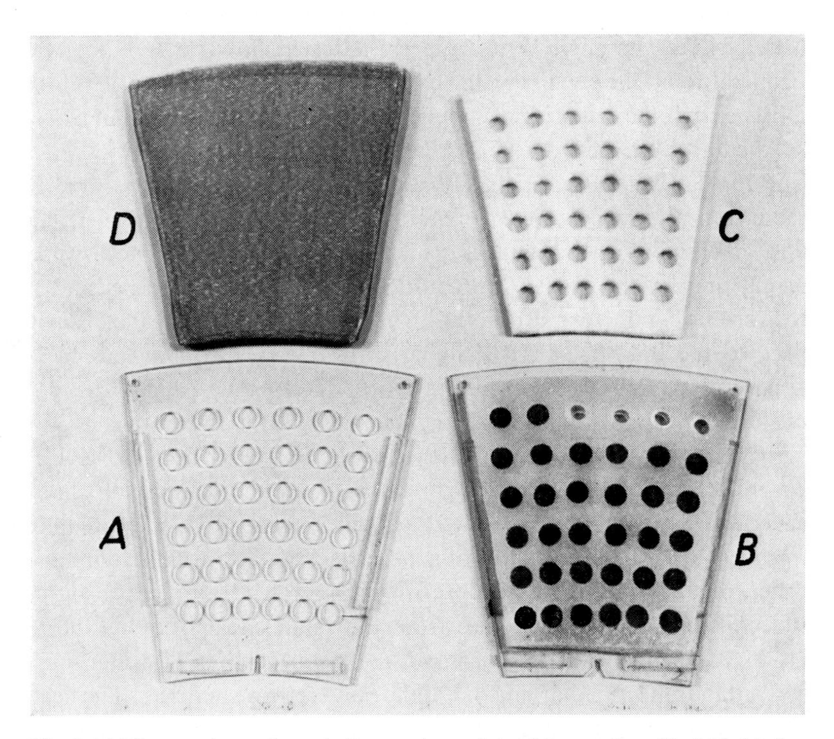

Fig. 9.15 The sample carriers. *A:* Perspex base plate of the carrier with drilled holes. The perspex bars stuck on the plate at the side edges and near the lower edge keep the polyurethane matrix in correct position. The tiny holes drilled in the upper corners of the plate and the slit in the middle of the lower edge fit corresponding pins on the rotating holder and fix the carrier in the right position. *B:* The sample carrier with the water soaked polyurethane matrix fitted by leaf discs; four openings in the upper right corner of the matrix are left free. *C:* Dry polyurethane matrix with circular openings for discs. *D:* Neutral filter of wire gauze which can be used to screen one carrier and its leaf samples when examining the influence of irradiance on the dry weight increase of leaf discs. (From Šetlík, Avratovščuková & Křítek 1967.)

circumference and returns above the heat exchanger, flushing from both sides the rotating holder with the leaf samples.

Air temperature in the chamber is controlled solely by cooling, since radiation entering the chamber always ensures adequate heating. The annular heat exchanger *(13)* is made of brass sheet, and is situated under the rotating annular ring of the sample holder. Cooling water enters first into a circular manifold tube situated under the bottom of the chamber. From the twelve manifold outlets the water flows through rubber tubes *(36)* to inlet nozzles which are inserted into the wall of the heat exchanger near its inner circumference. The nozzles support the whole body of the heat exchanger. From the heat exchanger cooling water is discharged to the water filter of the chamber as indicated above.

The cooling water for the equipment flows through a regulating element consisting of a manually controlled valve *(22)* and a solenoid valve *(21)* connected in parallel. The basic flow rate of the cooling water through the heat exchanger is regulated by the hand valve to give an equilibrium air temperature in the chamber at a value somewhat higher (*ca.* 0.2 °C) than that desired. The flow of water through the solenoid valve is then sufficient to bring the temperature to the preset value. The solenoid valve is actuated by a relay which in turn is energised by a control thermometer in the chamber. With properly adjusted flow rates of the water the air temperature in the chamber can be held constant within $\pm$ 0.2 °C. This is achieved most easily if the water is not supplied directly from the mains but from a reservoir situated above the apparatus at a height of 1.5 to 2 m.

The control box (Fig. 9.12, *C*) contains the following: switches and fuses for all the electrical circuits of the apparatus, control lights, a voltmeter indicating the voltage supplied to the lamps, a meter indicating the photocell signal, and the supply unit for the small *D.C.* motor consisting of a transformer and rectifier. All the various conductors are led through an armoured hose to the distribution panel fixed to the bottom of the chamber. It is always advantageous to connect the apparatus to a stabilized voltage supply, since this extends the possibility of comparing results obtained in individual runs of the apparatus.

There are two weak points in the construction described above. First, the tap water introduces light-absorbing sediments on the bottom of the water filter cuvette which has to be cleaned at short intervals. This shortcoming may be removed by filtering the tap water or replacing it by a closed circuit of distilled water, pumped through a heat exchanger in a refrigerator and through a thermostat. A second difficulty comes from the small capacity of the heat exchanger inside the irradiation chamber, causing condensation of water vapour on its surface and thus rapid drying out of the polyurethane matrices. The heat exchanger should have a larger surface and be separated from the sample holder by a circular collar.

9.4 | Use of the method

The method described in this Chapter is a modification of Sachs' (1884) well-known method. Unlike the previous modifications, Bartoš, Kubín & Šetlík (1960) minimised all its major inherent errors, *i.e.* translocation of assimilates, uncontrolled growth of leaf area and irregularly varying exposure conditions, and especially the influence of water deficit. In its present form the method can be used to compare the photosynthetic response of leaf tissue to a standard set of conditions for a large number of variants. It is therefore useful for comparative studies of a wide range of experimental material, *e.g.* for genetics and selection. Although the results are comparable to data from gasometric measurements of photosynthetic rate, it cannot replace the infra-red gas analysers at present used as a standard method for photosynthetic studies. Nevertheless the measurements on discs and segments are complementary to gasometric methods and may be indispensible for large scale studies.

The method has up till now been used for the study of interactions between nutrition and photosynthesis (Bezděk, Nátr & Zemánek 1964; Kousalová 1964; Nátr & Purš 1969, 1970), for the determination of varietal differences in photosynthetic rate (Nátr 1964; 1966; Nováková & Kutáček 1965) as well as their genetic basis (Frydrych 1961, 1965, 1966, 1970; Fousová & Avratovščuková 1967; Avratovščuková 1968; Cukrová & Avratovščuková 1968), for studies of the relationship between chlorophyll and photosynthesis and influence of leaf ageing on photosynthetic rate (Avratovščuková, Bartoš & Šesták 1962; Šesták & Bartoš 1962, 1963; Šesták & Čatský 1962; Šesták 1963a, b, 1966a, b; Šesták & Václavík 1965) and seasonal changes in the photosynthetic rate of trees and shrubs (Steinhübel & Halás 1969), and for determination of photosynthesis under field conditions (Nátr 1965; Cartwright & Papenfus 1967; Rychnovská 1967).

9.5 | References

Avratovščuková, N.: Genetická analysa fotosynthetické aktivity vzorků listové čepele některých kulturních rostlin. [Genetic analysis of photosynthetic activity of leaf blade samples of some cultural plants.] – CSc. Thesis, Biol. Fac. Charles Univ., Praha 1967.

Avratovščuková, N.: Differences in photosynthetic rate of leaf disks in five tobacco varieties. – Photosynthetica 2: 149-160, 1968.

Avratovščuková, N., Bartoš, J., Šesták, Z.: Závislost mezi intenzitou fotosyntézy, množstvím chlorofylu a kresbou listů u jetele lučního (*Trifolium pratense* L.). [Relationship between photosynthetic rate, chlorophyll content and leaf pattern in clover (*Trifolium pratense* L.)]. – Rostlinná Výroba 8: 1225-1234, 1962.

Bartoš, J., Kubín, Š., Šetlík, I.: Dry weight increase of leaf disks as a measure of photosynthesis. – Biol. Plant. 2: 201-215, 1960.

Bezděk, V., Nátr, L., Zemánek, M.: Některé morfologicko-anatomické a fyziologické studie jarního ječmene s ohledem na výnos a jakost při zvýšených dávkách dusíkatých hnojiv. [Some morphologico-anatomical and physiological studies of summer barley with regard to yield and quality in the case of increased doses of nitrogenous fertilizers.] – Vědecké Práce Výzkumného Ústavu obilnářského (Kroměříž) 3: 87-106, 1964.

Cartwright, P. M., Papenfus, H. D.: The contribution of leaves of different ages to the total assimilation of a crop canopy: Methods for measuring the daily net photosynthesis of individual leaves and some data from an experimental tobacco crop. – In: Book of Abstracts. Pp.5-7. European Photobiology Symposium, Hvar 1967.

Cukrová, V., Avratovščuková, N.: Photosynthetic activity, chlorophyll content and stomata characteristics in diploid and polyploid types of *Datura stramonium* L. – Photosynthetica 2: 227-237, 1968.

Dale, J. E.: Growth changes in disks cut from young leaves of *Phaseolus*. – J. exp. Bot. 18: 660-671, 1967.

Eberhardt, F.: Über die Beziehungen zwischen Atmung und Anthocyansynthese. – Planta 43: 253-287, 1954.

Forti, G., Parisi, B.: Evidence for the occurrence of cyclic photophosphorylation *in vivo*. – Biochim. biophys. Acta 71: 1-6, 1963.
Fousová, S., Avratovščuková, N.: Hybrid vigour and photosynthetic rate of leaf disks in *Zea mays* L. – Photosynthetica 1: 3-12, 1967.
Frydrych, J.: Růstové projevy C_0-C_2 generace autotetraploidní ředkvičky Saxa k rychlení. [Growth of C_0-C_2 generation of autotetraploid radish Saxa for forcing.] – Vědecké Práce Výzkumného Ústavu zelinářského (Olomouc) 1961: 217-225, 1961.
Frydrych, J.: Studium fotosyntetické asimilace diploidní a autotetraploidní ředkvičky (*Raphanus sativus* L.). [Studying photosynthetic assimilation in diploid and autotetraploid radish (*Raphanus sativus* L.)]. – Genetika Šlechtění 1: 25-30, 1965.
Frydrych, J.: Fotosyntetická aktivita a produkční schopnost di-, tri- a tetraploidního zelí. [Photosynthetic activity and production ability of diploid, triploid and tetraploid cabbage.] – Vědecké Práce Výzkumného Ústavu zelinářského (Olomouc) 1966: 69-75, 1966.
Frydrych, J.: Photosynthetic characteristics of diploid and tetraploid forms of *Brassica oleracea* var. *gongylodes* grown under differerent irradiance. – Photosynthetica 4: 139-145, 1970.
Glinka, Z., Meidner, H.: The measurement of stomatal responses to stimuli in leaves and leaf discs. – J. exp. Bot. 19: 152-166, 1968.
Heath, O. V. S., Russell, J.: Studies in stomatal behaviour. VI. An investigation of the light responses of wheat stomata with the attempted elimination of control by the mesophyll. Part I. Effects of light independent of carbon dioxide and their transmission from one part of the leaf to another. – J. exp. Bot. 5: 1-15, 1954.
Hopkinson, J. M.: Studies on the expansion of the leaf surface. IV. The carbon and phosphorus economy of a leaf. – J. exp. Bot. 15: 125-137, 1964.
Kalberer, P. P., Buchanan, B. B., Arnon, D. I.: Rates of photosynthesis by isolated chloroplasts. – Proc. Nat. Acad. Sci. 57: 1542-1549, 1967.
Kousalová, I.: Sledování vztahu mezi fotosyntézou a výživou u ozimé pšenice. [Investigation of the relationship between photosynthesis and nutrition in winter wheat.] – Rostlinná Výroba 10: 11-16, 1964.
Kuiper, P. J. C.: The effects of environmental factors in the transpiration of leaves, with special reference to stomatal light response. – Mededel. Landbouwhogeschool Wageningen 61: 1-49, 1961.
Lubimenko, V. N., Stscheglova, O. A.: Über den Einfluß des Protoplasmareizes auf die Photosynthese. – Planta 18: 383-404, 1932.
Milner, H. W., Hiesey, W. M., Nobs, M. A.: Physiology of climatic races. – Carnegie Inst. Wash. Year Book 61: 313-317, 1962.
Montemartini, L.: Materiali per uno studio del sistema assimilatore delle piante. – Ann. Bot. (Roma) 18: 38-91, 1930.
Nátr, L.: Studium tvorby výnosu zrna u obilovin. I. Odrůdové rozdíly ve fotosyntéze ozimé pšenice. [Study of the formation of grain yields produced by cereal crops. I. Varietal differences in winter wheat photosynthesis.] – Rostlinná Výroba 10: 5-10, 1964.
Nátr, L.: Studium tvorby výnosu zrna u obilnin. II. Účinnost využití slunečního záření listovou čepelí ozimé pšenice. [Study of the formation of grain yields produced by cereal crops. II. Efficiency of utilization of the solar radiation by the leaf blade of winter wheat.] – Vědecké Práce Výzkumného Ústavu obilnářského (Kroměříž) 4: 149-164, 1965.
Nátr, L.: Odrůdové rozdíly v intenzitě fotosyntézy. [Varietal differences in photosynthetic rate.] – Rostlinná Výroba 12: 163-178, 1966.
Nátr, L.: Time-course of photosynthesis and maximum figures for the accumulation of assimilates in barley leaf segments. – Photosynthetica 1: 29-36, 1967.
Nátr, L.: La mesure de l'intensité de la photosynthèse dans les conditions naturelles par une méthode gravimétrique. – In: Eckardt, F. E. (ed.): Functioning of Terrestrial Ecosystems at the Primary Production Level. Proc. Copenhagen Symp. Pp. 345-348. Unesco, Paris 1968.
Nátr, L.: Influence of assimilate accumulation on rate of photosynthesis of barley leaf segments. – Photosynthetica 3: 120-126, 1969.
Nátr, L.: The use of leaf tissue samples for studying the characteristics of the photosynthetic apparatus. – In: Prediction and Measurement of Photosynthetic Productivity. Pp. 331-337. PUDOC, Wageningen 1970.

Nátr, L.: Akumulace produktů fotosyntézy v asimilačním pletivu. [Accumulation of photosynthates in assimilatory tissue.] – Vědecké Práce Výzkumného Ústavu obilnářského (Kroměříž) 8: (in press), 1971.
Nátr, L., Gloser, J.: Carbon dioxide absorption and dry weight increase in barley leaf segments. – Photosynthetica 1: 19-27, 1967.
Nátr, L., Kousalová, I.: Comparison of results of photosynthetic intensity measurements in cereal leaves as determined by the dry weight increase or by the gazometric method. – Biol. Plant. 7: 98-108, 1965.
Nátr, L., Ludlow, M. M.: Influence of glucose absorption and photosynthate accumulation on gas exchange of barley leaf segments. – Photosynthetica 4: 288-294, 1970a.
Nátr, L., Ludlow, M. M.: The use of the leaf-disc gravimetric method for measuring the photosynthetic rate of Sitka spruce needles. – Photosynthetica 4: 156-157, 1970b.
Nátr, L., Purš, J.: The relation between rate of photosynthesis and N, P, K concentration in barley leaves. I. Nitrogen absent from the nutrient solution. – Photosynthetica 3: 320-325, 1969.
Nátr, L., Purš, J.: The relation between rate of photosynthesis and N, P, K concentration in barley leaves. II. Phosphorus absent from the nutrient solution. – Photosynthetica 4: 31-37, 1970.
Nátr, L., Špidla, J.: Application of the leaf-disk method to the determination of photosynthesis in cereals. – Biol. Plant. 3: 245-251, 1961.
Neales, T. F., Incoll, L. D.: The control of leaf photosynthesis rate by the level of assimilate concentration in the leaf: A review of the hypothesis. – Bot. Rev. 34: 107-125, 1968.
Nováková, J., Kutáček, M.: Váhové stanovení intenzity fotosyntézy terčíku listového pletiva u dvou odrůd cukrovky a čekanky. [The gravimetric estimation of the photosynthetic rate in leaf discs in two varieties of sugar beet and chicory.] – Rostlinná Výroba 11: 171-180, 1965.
Paulech, C., Gašparík, J.: A modification of dry weight increase method for photosynthesis measurements in leaf tissue samples employing rectangular segments. – Photosynthetica 2: 68-74, 1968.
Porter, H. K., Martin, R. V., Bird, I. F.: Synthesis and dissolution of starch labelled with ^{14}carbon in tobacco leaf tissue. – J. exp. Bot. 10: 264-276, 1959.
Roberts, D. W. A.: Physiological and biochemical studies in plant metabolism. III. The effects of starvation and mechanical stimulation on the respiratory metabolism of the first leaf of the wheat plant. – Can. J. Bot. 29: 383-402, 1951.
Rychnovská, M.: A contribution to the autecology of *Phragmites communis* Trin. I. Physiological heterogeneity of leaves. – Folia geobot. phytotax. 2: 179-188, 1967.
Rychnovská, M., Bartoš, J.: Measurement of photosynthesis by dry weight increment of samples composed of leaf segments. – Biol. Plant. 4: 91-97, 1962.
Sachs, J.: Ein Beitrag zur Kenntnis der Ernährungstätigkeit der Blätter. – Arb. Bot. Inst. Würzburg 3: 1-33, 1884.
Šesták, Z.: Changes in the chlorophyll content as related to photosynthetic activity and age of leaves. – Photochem. Photobiol. 2: 101-110, 1963a.
Šesták, Z.: On the question of the quantitative relation between the amount of chlorophyll, its forms, and the photosynthetic rate. – In: Colloques int. C.N.R.S. No. 119: La Photosynthèse. Pp. 343-356. Édit. C.N.R.S., Paris 1963b.
Šesták, Z.: Leaf ageing, chlorophyll content and photosynthetic rate. – Acta Univ. Carolinae – Biol. Suppl. 1966: 115-118, 1966a.
Šesták, Z.: Limitations for finding a linear relationship between chlorophyll content and photosynthetic activity. – Biol. Plant. 8: 336-346, 1966b.
Šesták, Z., Bartoš, J.: Photosynthesis and chlorophyll content in different areas of fodder cabbage leaves. – Biol. Plant. 4: 47-53, 1962.
Šesták, Z., Bartoš, J.: Vliv snížení obsahu chlorofylu na intenzitu fotosyntézy u kukuřice. [Influence of declined chlorophyll content on photosynthetic rate in maize.] – Rostlinná Výroba 9: 119-134, 1963.
Šesták, Z., Čatský, J.: Intensity of photosynthesis and chlorophyll content as related to leaf age in *Nicotiana sanderae* hort. – Biol. Plant. 4: 131-140, 1962.
Šesták, Z., Čatský, J.: Sur les relations entre le contenu en chlorophylle et l'activité photosynthétique pendant la croissance et le vieillissement des feuilles. – In: Sironval, C. (ed.): Le

Chloroplaste, Croissance et Vieillissement. Pp. 213-262. Masson et Cie, Paris 1967.
Šesták, Z., Václavík, J.: Relationship between chlorophyll content and photosynthetic rate during the vegetation season in maize grown at different constant soil water levels. – In: Slavík, B. (ed.): Water Stress in Plants. Pp. 210-218. Publ. House Czechoslov. Acad. Sci., Praha, and Dr. W. Junk N.V. – Publ., The Hague 1965.
Šesták, Z., Vodová, J.: The effect of reversion and duplication of leaf disks on the accuracy of photosynthesis determination by the dry weight method. – Biol. Plant. 7: 109-115, 1965.
Šetlík, I., Avratovščuková, N., Křítek, J.: An annular irradiation chamber for photosynthesis measurements in leaf disks. – Photosynthetica 1: 89-95, 1967.
Šetlík, I., Bartoš, J., Kubín, Š.: Photosynthesis in leaf disks as a measure of photosynthetic capacity in crop plants. – Biol. Plant. 2: 292-307, 1960.
Šetlík, I., Bartoš, J., Avratovščuková, N., Šesták, Z.: Měření fotosynthesy na terčících a úsecích z listů v konstantních podmínkách. [Photosynthesis measurements on leaf discs and segments under constant conditions.] – In: Šesták, Z., Čatský, J. (ed.): Metody Studia Fotosynthetické Produkce Rostlin. Pp. 279-314. Academia, Praha 1966.
Shimshi, D.: A rapid field method for measuring photosynthesis with labelled carbon dioxide. – J. exp. Bot. 20: 381-401, 1969.
Stålfelt, M. G.: Die stomatäre Transpiration und die Physiologie der Spaltöffnungen. – In: Ruhland, W. (ed.): Handbuch der Pflanzenphysiologie III. Pp. 351-426. Springer-Verlag, Berlin–Göttingen–Heidelberg 1956.
Steinhübel, G., Halás, L.: Seasonal trends in rates of dry-matter production in the evergreen and winter green broadleaf woody plants. – Photosynthetica 3: 244-254, 1969.
Strebeyko, P.: Rapid method for measuring photosynthetic rate using $^{14}CO_2$. – Photosynthetica 1: 45-49, 1967.
Thoday, D.: Experimental researches on vegetable assimilation and respiration. V. A critical examination of Sachs' method for using increase in dry weight as a measure of carbon dioxide assimilation in leaves. – Proc. Roy. Soc. B82: 1-55, 1909.
Wassink, E. C.: Experiments on photosynthesis of horticultural plants, with the aid of the Warburg method. – Enzymologia 12: 33-55, 1946.
Wilson, D., Treharne, K. J., Eagles, C. F., de Jager, J. M.: A manometric technique for determination of apparent photosynthesis of *Lolium*. – J. exp. Bot. 20: 373–380, 1969.

10 | METHODS OF GROWTH ANALYSIS

10.1 | General principles

Growth analysis, as it has been worked out by the British school (Blackman 1919; Briggs, Kidd & West 1920; Williams 1946; Watson 1952; Coombe 1960; Blackman 1968) or with only slight modifications (Nichiporovich *et al.* 1961; Birke 1965; Nečas 1965), has become established as a standard method of estimating net photosynthetic production of plants and plant stands in many parts of the world. Although the methods of growth analysis seemed nearly complete some time ago, new stimuli have brought about further development, especially in mathematical techniques, in the elaboration of indirect methods for estimating the primary values on which growth analysis is based, and in the analysis of canopy structure (see also Chapter 11). This Chapter will deal with 'classical' growth analysis using the technique of direct harvesting, with the mathematical techniques and with the application of this kind of growth analysis to investigations of photosynthetic production of single plants as well as of plant stands.

Growth analysis represents the first step in the analysis of primary production, being a link between merely recording plant production and analysing it by means of physiological methods. The need to analyse plant production was stressed by Boysen-Jensen in 1932. In growth analysis, growth is defined as increase in dry weight of the plants or stand investigated.

An advantage of growth analysis is that the primary values, on which it is based, are relatively easy to obtain without great demands on laboratory equipment. These primary values are usually the dry weight of whole plants and/or of their parts (stems, leaves, whole shoots, *etc.*), and the dimensions of the assimilatory apparatus (leaf area, leaf and stem area, chlorophyll content, *etc.*). The primary values are assessed in growing plant material at certain time intervals; from them, various indexes and characteristics are calculated that describe the growth of the plants and of their various parts as well as the relationship between the assimilatory apparatus and dry matter production. These indexes and characteristics are called growth characteristics and their correct calculation as well as interpretation are at the core of growth analysis. In 'classical' growth analysis, sampling for the primary values consists of harvesting destructively, representative sets of plants or plots, and it is impossible to follow the same plants or plots throughout the whole experiment. This is the main drawback of this approach and various techniques (pairing, *etc.*) have been suggested to diminish its importance as a source of error. In any case, however, it is statistical sets rather than individual plants or plots that are measured and weighed. Hence follows the importance of statistically correct design as well as evaluation of growth analytical observations and experiments.

10.2 | Basic concepts

Growth analysis can be regarded as a useful approach to analysing net photosynthetic production by plants, net production being defined as the net result of the assimilatory work taking place in a plant or plant stand during a certain period. In photosynthetic terminology, this means that net production is equal to net assimilation (gross assimilation minus respiration) minus the losses of dead plant parts (or of a certain proportion of whole plants – in a stand) over a certain period of time. This concept implies that one day (24 h) is the shortest period that can be used in growth analysis. It is, indeed, used as the time unit in most calculations of growth characteristics. The amount of actually functioning tissues present in a plant or plant stand at any one time is called *biomass* and is usually measured by the dry weight, organic matter or energy content of the plant material (symbol W). (Strictly speaking, biomass should involve only living tissues but their separation from non-living but functioning tissues, *e.g.*, parts of the xylem or bark, is often impossible.) If the biomass is harvested at relatively short time intervals (weekly, fortnightly, monthly, according to the material investigated and the purpose pursued), the rate of production can be estimated from the increase in biomass, but a certain correction usually has to be introduced for the amount of material that has died or has been otherwise lost during that interval. In ecosystems, the rate of plant production is defined as the primary production over a certain period, this value being also called *primary productivity* by certain authors, *e.g.* Lieth (1962, 1965) defines primary productivity (= rate of production) as all material formed in a plant community per unit ground area per unit time. *Rate of production* can be measured in terms of increase in dry weight, organic matter, carbon, carbon dioxide, or solar energy fixed, *etc.* These measures can be transformed by the following approximations: 1 g plant dry matter $\approx$ 17 kJ $\approx$ 0.4 g C $\approx$ 1.5 g CO_2. In more detailed investigations, these equivalents must be established separately for each type of plant material. The ratio of the energy fixed in plant dry weight to the incident solar energy, both over the same time period, is a measure of solar energy utilization. Lieth's (1965) definition of primary productivity nearly coincides with those of the rate of dry matter production and of *crop growth rate* (C, CGR) (Watson 1952), which are used in growth analysis. The most appropriate measure of growth, which is independent of the amount of growing material, is then *the relative growth rate* (R, RGR) (Briggs, Kidd & West 1920), or efficiency index (Blackman 1919). While relative growth rate is a differential value, being proportional to the slope of the growth curve at any one point, biomass duration (Květ & Ondok, not published) is an integral value, which is proportional to the area under the growth curve or under a part of it. Both relative growth rate and biomass duration can be applied without knowing the size of the assimilatory apparatus. The same applies to the ratios of dry weight (organic matter, *etc.*) of different plant organs to total dry weight, describing the biomass distribution within the plants. A special case of such a ratio is called the harvest index or coefficient of economic yield (see, *e.g.* Nichiporovich 1967), *i.e.*, the ratio of dry weight of economically important plant parts (*e.g.*, grain in cereals, tubers in potatoes) to total dry weight.

Calculations of other characteristics used in growth analysis require knowledge of the size of the assimilatory apparatus, which is usually measured in terms of leaf area or otherwise defined *assimilatory surface area*, per plant or sample of several plants (symbol A or often also L), or per unit area of ground. The leaf area per unit of ground area is of great importance in plant stands and is called *the leaf area index (L, LAI)*, (Watson 1952). A time integral of leaf area index over a certain period is called *leaf area duration (D, LAD)* (Watson 1952). The surface area of other organs than leaves (*e.g.* stems, petioles, flower bracts) should be added to the leaf area if these organs are assumed to contribute substantially to the overall photosynthesis of the plants investigated. Other attributes sometimes used to describe the size of the assimilatory apparatus will be discussed later.

All attributes of the size of the assimilatory apparatus used in standard 'classical' growth analysis and all growth characteristics calculated from them, neglect the fact that different leaves, or even parts of leaves, play different rôles in the overall photosynthetic production of a plant or stand, according to their age, position on the plant, position in the canopy, *etc.* Whilst knowledge of the stratification of photosynthetic capability is still very scanty, this problem has stimulated investigations of the vertical structure of stand canopies, and of the light distribution within stands (see Chapter 12).

One of the most important growth characteristics, describing the net production efficiency of the assimilatory apparatus, is the unit leaf rate or *net assimilation rate (E, NAR)* (Briggs, Kidd & West 1920; Gregory 1926; Williams 1946; Coombe 1960). Another important characteristic, describing the relative size of the assimilatory apparatus, is *the leaf area ratio (F, LAR)* (Gregory 1926), which is the ratio between leaf area (A) and total dry weight (W). Leaf area ratio can be split into two components, namely *the leaf weight ratio* (leaf dry weight (W_L)/total dry weight (W)) and *specific leaf area* (leaf area (A)/leaf dry weight (W_L)). Specific leaf area *(SLA)* usually reflects leaf thickness and the relative proportions of assimilatory and conductive or mechanical tissues in leaves.

Relative growth rate of the assimilatory apparatus (and of other plant parts) is defined analogously to the relative growth rate of biomass. Changes in the ratio between the two relative growth rates indicate changes taking place in the relative proportions of assimilatory organs in the biomass (Whitehead & Myerscough 1962).

Most growth characteristics are mutually dependent. The basic relationships are those between relative growth rate (R), net assimilation rate (E) and leaf area ratio (F), and – in stands – those between crop growth rate (C), net assimilation rate (E) and leaf area index (L):

$$R = E \cdot F \quad \text{and} \quad C = E \cdot L$$

Hence R or C can be affected by any factor primarily affecting either the net efficiency or the size of the assimilatory apparatus, or both. The equations also demonstrate that optimum combinations exist in each type of plant or stand, of E and F, and of E and L, at which highest production rates, measured as R or C, respectively, will be attained. Methods of estimating the primary values and formulae for calculating the different growth characteristics will now be presented in more detail.

10.3 | Primary values

Growth analysis is based on the following primary values describing the morphological status of the plants at each sampling occasion: total dry weight and separate dry weight values of various plant parts (shoots, roots, leaves, stems, *etc.*), shoot size, sizes and numbers of different plant parts (leaves, stems, branches, tillers, *etc.*) per plant or per sample, size of the assimilatory apparatus, usually in terms of assimilatory surface area (leaf area, perhaps plus the surface area of other organs – stems, petioles, *etc.*) but sometimes also in terms of leaf dry weight, leaf protein, chlorophyll content, *etc.* In stands, the number of shoots per unit ground area (stand density) is yet another important primary value. The techniques of assessing the primary values are presented in Section 10.10.

10.4 | Meaning of growth characteristics

It follows from the introductory remarks that growth analysis is a method of following the dynamics of photosynthetic production measured by the production of dry matter, growth being defined as increase in plant dry weight. Apart from this primary purpose, growth analysis can also be used to investigate ecological phenomena such as the success of species in various habitats, or competition amongst species, or genetic differences in yielding capacity, and effects of agricultural treatments on crop growth, *etc.* In general, all applications of growth analysis may be regarded as investigations of one or both of the following:

a. The dependence of the productive capacity of a plant genotype on internal factors, *e.g.* in comparative investigations of production and growth amongst varieties, species, populations or communities; this covers both genotypic and phenotypic differences.

b. Production and growth as affected by environmental factors, *e.g.* in ecological and agronomic investigations of the influence of climate, weather, and edaphic factors on the rate of dry matter production and its components.

Internal factors affecting growth characteristics are usually connected with basic physiological processes such as photosynthesis, respiration and assimilate transport, nitrogen metabolism, morphogenetic processes, *etc.* The distribution of matter within the plant and the form of the plant are the products of complex developmental processes which depend on, among other things, the supply of assimilate and the distribution of active growth hormones, as well as on previous environmental history. Of the environmental factors, radiation, temperature, water and nutrient supply have been investigated most intensively and their effects are relatively easy to demonstrate. More complex factors, such as stand density, have also been frequently investigated, because of their practical significance.

Growth characteristics are most frequently calculated over certain finite time intervals. The time course of growth is divided into a series of intervals, and growth characteristics are calculated for each of these intervals separately. Correlations between environmental (especially weather) factors and various growth characteristics are easier to follow if the intervals are short; longer intervals obscure

the effects of fluctuating environmental conditions and allow the ontogenetic trend to stand out more clearly.
Alternatively, growth characteristics can be calculated from growth curves fitted through all the primary values. Such an approach offers great advantages if general tendencies rather than actual values depending on variable circumstances are investigated. It also allows an entirely different design of experiment in which the requirement for labour is spread evenly through the experiment instead of being concentrated at peak periods (Hughes & Freeman 1967; Radford 1967).

10.5 | Time interval calculation of growth characteristics

This paragraph deals with the calculation of growth characteristics for intervals between two consecutive recordings of the primary values. This is usually accomplished by harvesting the plant material and by estimating the appropriate values of dry weight, assimilatory surface area, *etc.*, but the primary values can also be calculated from measurements recorded on intact plants making use of different, indirect methods of estimation (see also Chapter 11).
In all the following equations, the symbols W_1, W_2 and A_1, A_2 represent biomass (W, usually measured as dry weight) and assimilatory surface area (A, usually measured as leaf area), recorded at two sequential harvests, made at times t_1 and t_2.

10.5.1 | Biomass increment, rate of dry matter production, crop growth rate and coefficient of solar energy utilization

Increment in biomass, ΔW, expressed in terms of dry weight, is the simplest growth characteristic, which is used mainly with separate plants or samples of several plants.

$$\Delta W = W_2 - W_1 \qquad (10.1)$$

where the subscripts 1 and 2 indicate values of W on two occasions. During the growth of a plant, ΔW shows a pronounced ontogenetic trend which must be taken into account if environmental effects on plant growth are to be distinguished. This trend in ΔW is more pronounced with longer intervals between harvests, and is shown in Fig. 10.1.
The mean rate of dry matter production, or mean growth rate, G, over an interval of time from t_1 to t_2 is given by

$$G = \int_{t_1}^{t_2} G' \mathrm{d}t = \frac{1}{t_2 - t_1} \int_{t_1}^{t_2} \frac{\mathrm{d}W}{\mathrm{d}t} \cdot \mathrm{d}t = \frac{W_2 - W_1}{t_2 - t_1} \, [\text{weight.time}^{-1}] \qquad (10.2)$$

where G' is the instantaneous growth rate and W_1 and W_2 are values of W at two consecutive harvests carried out at times t_1 and t_2, respectively. The only assumption necessary to carry out this integration is that W varies without discontinuity throughout the interval t_1 to t_2.
Biomass increments in plant stands are usually expressed on a ground area basis.

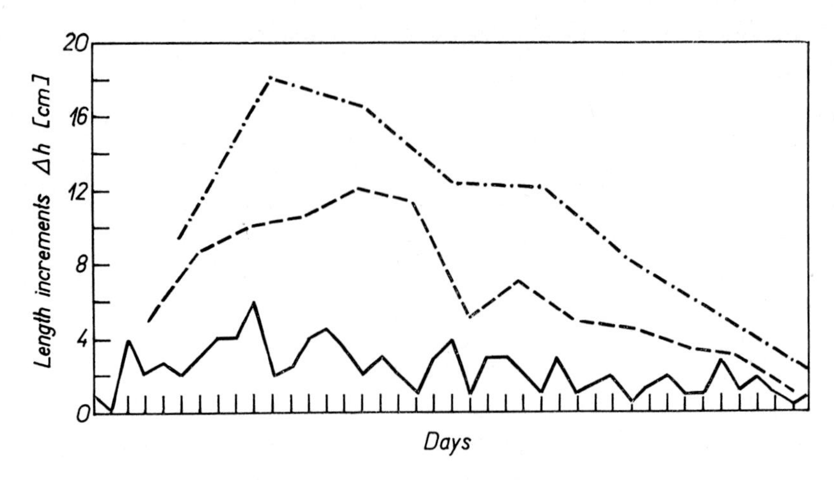

Fig. 10.1 Length increments (Δh) which were correlated with those in dry weight (ΔW), of shoots of *Scirpus lacustris* in glasshouse culture. ——— daily, – – – – 3 days', –.–.–. 5 days' increments. (From Dykyjová & Ondok, unpublished.)

The average daily increment of stand biomass, C, is an important characteristic called either rate of dry matter production (*e.g.* Blackman 1968) or crop growth rate (*e.g.* Watson 1952), or productivity (*e.g.* Lieth 1962, 1965) and is given by

$$C = \int_{t_1}^{t_2} C'\mathrm{d}t = \frac{1}{P(t_2 - t_1)} \int_{t_1}^{t_2} \frac{\mathrm{d}W}{\mathrm{d}t} \cdot \mathrm{d}t \tag{10.3}$$

$$= \frac{W_2 - W_1}{P(t_2 - t_1)} [\text{weight.ground area}^{-1}.\text{time}^{-1}] \tag{10.4}$$

where C' is the instantaneous crop growth rate and P is the ground area on which W_1 and W_2 have been estimated. Again the only assumption necessary to carry out this integration is that W varies without discontinuity from t_1 to t_2.

Crop growth rate (*CGR*) is a widely used characteristic of production efficiency of plant stands, and enables comparisons to be made between stands, and communities of different types, in different habitats *etc.*

If *CGR* is expressed in energy units as a percentage of the daily mean total of incident solar radiation, it is transformed into a coefficient of solar energy utilization, η. This coefficient indicates how economically a stand uses the solar radiation available during an interval between two harvests and provides a useful, practical comparison of production efficiencies among communities, species, varieties, techniques *etc.* (Nichiporovich 1967, 1968; Ustenko & Yagnova 1967; Wassink 1968, *etc.*).

Absolute values of the rate of dry matter production depend on the amount of growing plant material present. This feature gives them great ecological value – especially with respect to stands and communities – but diminishes their value in comparisons of growth rate between individual plants of different sizes. The next growth characteristic does not possess this drawback.

10.5.2 | *Relative growth rate, RGR, R*

The basic idea of modelling growth and dry matter production as augmentation of capital led to the concept of the 'efficiency index' (Blackman 1919) in which the rate of growth is expressed as the rate of interest on the capital. This is identical with the present concept of relative growth rate, *RGR*, *R*. The relative growth rate at any instant, R', is defined as the rate of increase in biomass per unit of biomass present:

$$R' = \frac{1}{W} \cdot \frac{dW}{dt} \tag{10.5}$$

The mean relative growth rate, R, over a time interval from t_1 to t_2 is derived from R' as follows (Fisher 1921):

$$R = \frac{1}{t_2 - t_1} \int_{t_1}^{t_2} R' \mathrm{d}t = \frac{1}{t_2 - t_1} \int_{W_1}^{W_2} \frac{\mathrm{d}W}{W} = \frac{\ln W_2 - \ln W_1}{t_2 - t_1}$$

$$[\text{weight} \cdot \text{weight}^{-1} \cdot \text{time}^{-1}] \tag{10.6}$$

where W_1 and W_2 are the biomass at times t_1 and t_2 respectively. The only assumption necessary to carry out this integration is that W varies without discontinuity during the time interval. As Fisher (1921) showed, it is not necessary to assume exponential growth, although the solution in that case is the same (Blackman 1919). If exponential growth does occur, the above expression not only gives the mean relative growth rate for the period t_1 to t_2, but it also gives the relative growth rate throughout the interval.

The mean relative growth rate of different plant parts, such as shoots (R_s), roots (R_r), leaves (R_l) and leaf area (R_A) can also be estimated in this way. The sum of the relative growth rates of the component parts of a plant equals the relative growth rate of the whole. Partitioning of the assimilate during growth can be assessed by calculating the relative growth rate of the parts, and those parts of the plant likely to be most sensitive to environmental charges ascertained.

For example, the mean relative growth rate of leaf area, R_A, over the interval $(t_2 - t_1)$ is given by

$$R_A = \frac{\ln A_2 - \ln A_1}{t_2 - t_1} [\text{area} \cdot \text{area}^{-1} \cdot \text{time}^{-1}] \tag{10.7}$$

where A_1 and A_2 are the leaf areas at times t_1 and t_2 respectively. Leaf area (A) and biomass (W) may be linearly related, or the relationship may be more complex. For example W may be related to the square of A or to some other power such as 1.25 in other circumstances (*e.g.* Evans & Hughes 1962). The general relationship between W and A takes the form

$$W = a + bA^{\alpha} \tag{10.8}$$

where a and b are constants (Williams 1946; Evans & Hughes 1962; Radford 1967). If a is negligible, α is the ratio between the relative growth rates of total biomass and leaf area ($\alpha = R/R_A$) (Whitehead & Myerscough 1962). The ratio R/R_A describes the allometric relationship between A and W, and shows how the relative proportion of assimilatory tissues changes during growth and development. It is relevant to the calculation of net assimilation rate and will be further discussed in Section 10.5.3.

Seasonal changes in relative growth rate can be used in comparisons of production efficiency among different plant genotypes or among plants given different treatments. Seasonal changes can be also correlated with weather and climatic factors such as radiation and temperature (Blackman, Black & Kemp 1955; Warren Wilson 1966, 1967; Hodgson 1967; Bínová & Ondok 1971). However unless experiments are carried out with young plants, such correlations are likely to be obscured by the decrease in *RGR* with age, resulting at least in part from the gradually increasing proportion of non-assimilatory tissues (Williams 1946; Thorne 1960, 1961). This problem can be largely avoided by serial sowings through the growing season (*e.g.* Stern 1965).

In certain crops, environmentally caused changes in *RGR* stand out more clearly if *RGR* is calculated for the weight of whole plants minus the weight of organs that participate to only a small extent in the overall production process. In potatoes, for instance, environmental effects on *RGR* are better seen and the ontogenetic drift in *RGR* is decreased when *RGR* of whole plant minus tuber weight is calculated (Nečas 1965, 1968). This may apply also to other plants with bulky storage organs, or with other relatively inactive assimilate sinks, *e.g.* to sugar beet or certain perennial herbs or woody plants.

10.5 3 | Net assimilation rate or unit leaf rate (E, NAR)

Net assimilation rate and unit leaf rate are synonymous terms used for a growth characteristic whose original purpose was to remove, to a certain extent, the drawback of a large ontogenetic drift inherent in the concept of relative growth rate (Briggs, Kidd & West 1920; Gregory 1926; Coombe 1960). This was accomplished by expressing the rate of dry weight increase at any instant on a leaf area basis, with leaf area *(A)* representing an estimate of the size of the assimilatory apparatus:

$$E' = \frac{1}{A} \cdot \frac{\mathrm{d}W}{\mathrm{d}t} \qquad (10.9)$$

where E' is the instantaneous net assimilation rate.

Nowadays, A in this equation may be the value of any measure of the size of the assimilatory apparatus, *i.e.* leaf area, leaf and stem surface area, leaf weight, leaf nitrogen or protein, amount of chlorophyll present in the plants, *etc.* Leaf area, however, is still the most commonly used attribute. The advantages and disadvantages of various measures of the size of assimilatory apparatus are discussed by Williams (1946), Watson (1952), Thorne (1959, 1960, 1961) and Nečas (1965).

Thorne (1960, 1961) has demonstrated that the ontogenetic drift, *i.e.* decrease of

NAR values with plant age, though generally smaller than that of *RGR*, cannot be fully removed by employing any of these attributes. *NAR*, like *CGR* and *RGR*, has photosynthetic and respiratory components, the relative importance of the latter usually increases with plant age. Attempts to split *NAR* into those two components in growth analytical experiments have been made (Watson & Hayashi 1965; Watson *et al.* 1966; Ludlow & Wilson 1970; Ondok 1970).

In the literature, much discussion has been devoted to ways of calculating *NAR*, because there is no simple unique solution to the above equation (Williams 1946; Coombe 1960; Evans & Hughes 1962; Whitehead & Myerscough 1962; Radford 1967). It follows from equation (10.9) that the mean net assimilation rate, E, over a time interval from t_1 to t_2 is given by

$$E = \frac{1}{t_2 - t_1} \int_{t_1}^{t_2} E' \mathrm{d}t = \frac{1}{t_2 - t_1} \int_{W_1}^{W_2} \frac{\mathrm{d}W}{A} \tag{10.10}$$

This expression can only be integrated if either the relationship between W and A is known, or the relationships between W and t, and A and t are known.

The type of formula used to calculate E depends on the value of α. It is usual either to assume an arbitrary relationship between W and A, or to determine the relationship graphically (*e.g.* Williams 1946; Evans & Hughes 1961). For the latter, either several harvests are needed so that the relationship between W and A can be established, or else non-destructive estimates of A between harvests are needed. In the two equations most frequently used, α is taken as 1 and as 2, respectively.

a. Linear relationship between W and A, and consequently also between R_W and R_A, *i.e.* $\alpha = 1$.

If $1/A \cdot \mathrm{d}A/\mathrm{d}t = R_A$, as defined by equation (10.7), and if on the basis of values established in two consecutive harvests $\mathrm{d}W/\mathrm{d}A = (W_2 - W_1)/(A_2 - A_1)$, then:

$$E = \frac{1}{t_2 - t_1} \int_{t_1}^{t_2} \frac{1}{A} \cdot \frac{\mathrm{d}A}{\mathrm{d}t} \cdot \frac{\mathrm{d}W}{\mathrm{d}A} \cdot \mathrm{d}t \tag{10.11}$$

$$= \frac{W_2 - W_1}{A_2 - A_1} \cdot \frac{1}{t_2 - t_1} \int_{A_1}^{A_2} \frac{\mathrm{d}A}{A}$$

$$= \frac{W_2 - W_1}{A_2 - A_1} \cdot \frac{\ln A_2 - \ln A_1}{t_2 - t_1} \text{ [weight} \cdot \text{area}^{-1} \cdot \text{time}^{-1}\text{]} \tag{10.12}$$

As Williams (1946) points out, if either W or A are increasing exponentially, *e.g.* $W = a_1 e^{b_1 t}$, $A = a_2 e^{b_2 t}$, then this equation can only be used if both are increasing exponentially with the same exponent, *i.e.* $b_1 = b_2$.

b. Quadratic relationship between W and A, *i.e.* $\alpha = 2$.

A curve relating A to W will pass through the points $A_1 W_1$ and $A_2 W_2$. From equation (10.8) it follows that the equation of the curve will have the form

$$W = k + \frac{W_2 - W_1}{A_2^2 - A_1^2} \cdot A^2$$

where k is a constant. Hence

$$\frac{dW}{dA} = \frac{2A(W_2 - W_1)}{(A_2 + A_1)(A_2 - A_1)}$$

Substituting into equation (10.11)

$$E = \frac{1}{t_2 - t_1} \cdot \frac{2A}{A} \cdot \frac{W_2 - W_1}{(A_2 + A_1)(A_2 - A_1)} \int_{t_1}^{t_2} \frac{dA}{dt} \cdot dt$$

$$= \frac{2(W_2 - W_1)}{(A_2 + A_1)(t_2 - t_1)} \text{ [weight} \cdot \text{area}^{-1} \cdot \text{time}^{-1}] \qquad (10.13)$$

which is the formula presented by Briggs (from Coombe 1960). This formula is often used because of its simplicity, but should not be applied if α deviates substantially from 2.

Equations (10.12) and (10.13) are used in most calculations of net assimilation rate.

Equation (10.12), can be used for α ranging from 0.5 to 1.5 and equation (10.13) for α ranging from 1.5 to 2.5 without the introduction of large errors. According to Coombe (1960), either formula may be used – the differences between the resulting values of E being small and non-significant – if A does not increase by a factor of more than two between consecutive harvests, *i.e.* $A_2 / A_1 \leq 2$. Hence individual harvests should be timed according to the increments of A.

Equations (10.12) and (10.13) are particular solutions for special cases. However, net assimilation rate can be calculated for any value of α if it is known. From equations (10.8) and (10.10), a general expression for E is given by the following (Whitehead & Myerscough 1962):

$$E = \frac{(W_2 - W_1)}{(t_2 - t_1)} \cdot \frac{(A_2^{\alpha-1} - A_1^{\alpha-1})}{(A_2^{\alpha} - A_1^{\alpha})} \cdot \frac{\alpha}{(\alpha - 1)} \text{ [weight} \cdot \text{area}^{-1} \cdot \text{time}^{-1}] \qquad (10.14)$$

A similar expression is given by Evans & Hughes (1962).

Effectively the sets of terms containing α provide a means of calculating the mean leaf area between t_1 and t_2. A further alternative general expression for E can be obtained in terms of the leaf area ratio, F ($= A/W$). At any instant $\alpha = R/R_A = A/W \cdot dW/dA$. From equation (10.8) $dW/dA = b\alpha A^{\alpha-1}$ and hence $W/A = bA^{\alpha-1}$. Substituting F into equation (10.14) and simplifying it with the aid of equation (10.8) yields:

$$E = \frac{1}{t_2 - t_1} \cdot \left(\frac{1}{F_2} - \frac{1}{F_1}\right) \cdot \frac{\alpha}{\alpha - 1} \text{ [weight} \cdot \text{area}^{-1} \cdot \text{time}^{-1}] \qquad (10.15)$$

in which F_1 and F_2 are the values of leaf area ratio found in two consecutive harvests.

For $\alpha = 2$, both equations (10.14) and (10.15) reduce to equation (10.13). The general formula (10.15) is relatively simple and applicable in all situations in which α can be estimated with sufficient reliability.

In the derivation of α from equation (10.8), as $\alpha = R/R_A$, it has been assumed that the constant a in equation (10.8) is negligible. This is true for young plants but as Evans & Hughes (1962) demonstrate, a may be too large to be ignored for mature plants. In this case at least three values of both W and A are needed to calculate E, as the calculation involves three constants. The result is a transcendental equation, the solution to which is empirical. Evans & Hughes (1962) give three methods for determining α when a is not negligible. However, when the growth functions of both W and A are to be approximated in one time interval only, as is often the case, the value of a must be neglected.

Evans & Hughes (1962) present a useful table (see Table 10.1) showing the percentage differences between mean values of E calculated on the assumption that $W = a + bA^\alpha$ (equation 10.8) and the corresponding value for the assumption that $W = a + bA^2$ (equation 10.13) as a function of A_2/A_1 and α. Besides showing the size of the errors resulting from the use of equation (10.13) in unjustified circumstances, this table can be used to correct values of E determined from equation (10.13), which is extremely simple to calculate, to the appropriate real values if α and A_2/A_1 are known.

Table 10.1 Percentage differences between mean values of net assimilation rate (unit leaf rate) calculated on the assumption that $W = a + bL^a$ and the corresponding value for the assumption that $W = a + bL^2$, as a function of $p = A_2/A_1$, *i.e.* the ratio of total leaf area at the second harvest to that at the first. (From Evans & Hughes 1962.)

$a\backslash p$	1.0	1.5	2.0	2.5	3.0	4.0	5.0	7.5	10.0	∞
0.5	0	+2.04	+6.08	+10.69	+15.47	+25.0	+34.2	+55.2	+73.9	—
1.0	0	+1.38	+3.95	+ 6.90	+ 9.89	+15.50	+20.7	+31.7	+40.8	—
1.5	0	+0.68	+1.91	+ 3.33	+ 4.67	+ 7.14	+ 9.27	+13.46	+16.50	+50.0
2.0	0	0	0	0	0	0	0	0	0	0
2.5	0	−0.58	−1.85	− 3.05	− 4.12	− 5.91	− 7.29	− 9.57	−10.95	−16.6
3.0	0	−1.32	−3.58	− 5.77	− 7.69	−10.71	−12.90	−16.31	−18.24	−25.0
3.5	0	−1.95	−5.18	− 8.20	−10.75	−14.57	−17.21	−21.1	−23.2	−30.0
4.0	0	−2.55	−6.67	−10.34	−13.33	−17.65	−20.5	−24.6	−26.7	−33.3

The calculation of *NAR* by means of any of the above formulae is invalidated if W or A vary discontinuously during the time interval between two harvests (Radford 1967). This may be caused, *e.g.* by the loss of leaves due to drought or some pest, followed by the restitution of leaf area. Such phenomena, when occurring repeatedly during the growing season, are reflected in wide fluctuations of α. In these circumstances it is advantageous to employ the graphical method of estimating *NAR*.

In this method, mean values of A, $\bar{A}$, between harvests are estimated from a

smooth curve of time changes of A. The corresponding values of W_1 and W_2 occurring, respectively, at the beginning and end of each interval, are estimated similarly, from a curve showing changes of W with time.
Mean NAR (E) is then calculated by the formula

$$E = \frac{W_2 - W_1}{t_2 - t_1} \cdot \frac{1}{\bar{A}} \tag{10.16}$$

The accuracy of such an estimate will, of course, increase with the accuracy and frequency of the measured values of A and of W. To obtain these values, non-destructive indirect methods of estimating A (Chapter 14) and W (Chapter 11) can be employed. This method is extremely useful when the effect of experimental treatment is to cause variations in the relationship between W and A.
The estimation of NAR and of other growth characteristics from fitted smooth curves is described and discussed in Section 10.6.
The most frequently used measure of the size of the assimilatory apparatus, A, is the leaf area or otherwise defined assimilatory surface area, *e.g.* leaf area plus stem surface area. Difficulties arise in defining this for plants having narrow or thread-like leaves (*e.g* many grasses and sedges), for sclerophyllous plants and for plants whose inflorescences contribute substantially to total photosynthesis, *e.g.* ears in some cereals (Thorne 1959, 1965), panicles in some other grasses.
Some of these difficulties can be avoided if NAR is calculated on a leaf weight basis. However, a great disadvantage of such estimates of NAR is their larger ontogenetic drift (decrease of NAR) than that of NAR values estimated on a leaf area basis (Williams 1946; Thorne 1960). The reason for this drift is often the decrease in leaf area ratio (A/W) with plant age (see Section 10.5.4). In general, therefore, leaf weight is regarded as a less suitable attribute than leaf area. Williams (1939), Petrie & Arthur (1943) and others suggested leaf protein as the most suitable measure of the size of the assimilatory apparatus, thus excluding the non-protoplasmic components of the leaf tissues. Fig. 10.2 shows the changes of

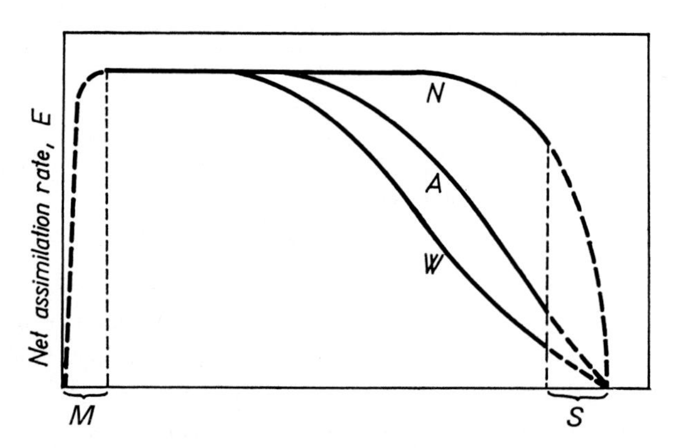

Fig. 10.2 Schematic representation of the ontogenetic drift in values of net assimilation rate (E) calculated on the basis of leaf weight (W), leaf area (A) and leaf nitrogen content (N), respectively, in plants grown under constant environmental conditions, including nitrogen supply. M – seedling stage; S – senescent stage. (From Williams 1946.)

NAR with plant age, when calculated on the basis of leaf area, leaf weight and leaf protein, respectively. The ontogenetic drift appears to be most conspicuous with *NAR* values calculated on a leaf weight basis, while with leaf protein the drift is small. These relationships will, however, be different in different species.
Only relatively recently, increasing attention has been paid to the amount of chlorophyll present in whole plants or in leaves, as a measure of the size of the assimilatory apparatus. In principle, there are no obstacles to calculating *NAR* either on a leaf or total chlorophyll basis. Section 10.5.6 is devoted to this problem.

NAR depends more closely on incoming radiation than on other environmental factors. Shading experiments (*e.g.* Blackman & Black 1959a, b; Wassink 1961, 1965; Huxley 1967), and investigations of seasonal changes of *NAR* (Blackman, Black & Kemp 1955; Warren Wilson 1966, 1967; Hodgson 1967) have confirmed the existence of positive correlations between *NAR* and incoming radiation. With respect to temperature, the kind of correlation obtained depends on the plant or stand in question (Blackman 1961). *NAR* decreases as a result of water stress (see, *e.g.* Václavík 1967, 1969). Some evidence exists for positive effects of mineral nutrient supply, especially of potassium on *NAR* (Watson 1952; Ruck & Bolas 1956; Delap & Ford 1958; Blackman 1968). Because of increased mutual shading of leaves, *NAR* is negatively correlated with leaf area index *(LAI)* and, consequently, with all factors bringing about an increase in *LAI* (nitrogen supply, density, shading, high levels of water supply, *etc.*). Hence *NAR* usually decreases during the growth and development of a plant stand.

10.5.4 Leaf area ratio (F, LAR), specific leaf area (A/W_L, SLA) and leaf weight ratio (W_L/W, LWR)

Leaf area ratio is defined as the ratio between leaf area and total plant dry weight, and can be interpreted as a product of two simpler ratios, namely of the specific leaf area, which is the leaf area (A): leaf dry weight (W_L) ratio, and of the leaf weight ratio, which is the ratio of leaf dry weight (W_L) to total dry weight (W).

$$F = \frac{A}{W} = \frac{A}{W_L} \cdot \frac{W_L}{W} \tag{10.17}$$

In these equations, A can stand for any measure of the size of the assimilatory apparatus, but leaf area is again the one most commonly used.
LAR characterizes the relative size of the assimilatory apparatus, thus being a useful measure of differences between plants or stands, resulting from genetic factors, environment, or different treatments. Seasonal changes in *LAR* usually reflect the interaction of ontogenetic factors (average leaf age and position with respect to leaf area) with environmental effects (increase of *LAR* with shading, high levels of nitrogen and water supply, *etc.*). For reasons explained in Section 10.5.2, with respect to *RGR*, it may sometimes be useful to calculate *LAR* as the ratio of A to total biomass less that of storage organs or other slightly active plant parts. When only shoot production is estimated, *LAR* is the ratio of A to W_s (shoot dry weight).

The mutual relationships between leaf area ratio *(F)*, net assimilation rate *(E)* and relative growth rate *(R)*, at any instant, are described by:

$$R' = E' \cdot F'$$

$$\frac{1}{W} \cdot \frac{dW}{dt} = \frac{1}{A} \cdot \frac{dW}{dt} \cdot \frac{A}{W} \qquad (10.18)$$

where the prime denotes instantaneous values. Hence any effects on growth rate can be interpreted in terms of effects either on the net efficiency, or on the relative size of the assimilatory apparatus, or on both. Usually, both components are affected. Since many factors have opposite effects on *NAR* and on *LAR*, the final effect on *RGR* reflects the interaction of the two effects. This interaction is most conspicuous with respect to shading or stand density (see Blackman 1961; MacColl & Cooper 1967 and others).

Leaf area ratio is usually calculated separately for each harvest as F_1, F_2 *etc.* These values can then be used in equation (10.15) to estimate *E*. It may be noted that average *F* between harvests cannot be calculated from $F = R/E$ where *R*, *E* and *F* are mean values over an interval, unless *A* and *W* are both increasing exponentially with the same exponent (Radford 1967).

Mean *LAR (F)* may be obtained from:

$$F = \frac{1}{t_2 - t_1} \int_{t_1}^{t_2} \frac{A}{W}\, dt \qquad (10.19)$$

This can only be integrated if either the relationship between A/W and *t* is known or if the relationships between *A* and *t* and *W* and *t* are known. Clearly then in calculating *F* by this formula the same value of α relating *W* to *A* must be employed as used in calculating the corresponding value of *E*.

Of the two components of *LAR*, specific leaf area *(SLA)* is much more plastic, especially with respect to environmental factors, than the leaf weight ratio *(LWR)* (see, *e.g.* Květ 1962, 1966). *LWR* is a rather 'conservative' characteristic, with environmental conditions affecting the number and size of individual leaves rather than the relative proportion of leaf dry weight to total dry weight. *LAR* thus often seems to buffer the effects of environment on *SLA*, which is perhaps the most plastic growth characteristic of all. The extent to which *SLA*, as well as *LWR* and *LAR*, is affected by environment is different in different species (Geyger 1964; Květ 1966). *SLA* also varies with position in a single leaf or shoot (Rychnovská 1967) and within a stand canopy (Květ, Svoboda & Fiala 1969). The relationship between *LAR* and *NAR*, as described by equation (10.18), implies, in principle, the same kind of relationship between *SLA* and *NAR*. Its existence has been confirmed experimentally by Hayashi (1966, 1968) but its exact form has to be investigated individually in each case.

10.5.5 | Leaf area index (LAI, L)

 Leaf area index (Watson 1947, 1952) describes the size of the assimilatory apparatus of a plant stand, and serves as a primary value for the calculation of other growth characteristics. *LAI (L)* is defined as leaf area, A, (or otherwise defined assimilatory surface) over a certain ground area P:

$$L = \frac{A}{P} \text{ [area} \cdot \text{area}^{-1}\text{]} \qquad (10.20)$$

The rate of dry matter production in a stand (the crop growth rate, C) depends on *LAI (L)* as well as on *NAR (E)*; this relationship may be described by the equation:

$$C' = L' \cdot E', \quad i.e. \quad \frac{dW}{dt} \cdot \frac{1}{P} = \frac{dW}{dt} \cdot \frac{1}{A} \cdot \frac{A}{P} \qquad (10.21)$$

where the prime indicates instantaneous rates.

Because of the effect of *LAI* on *NAR*, mentioned in Section 10.5.4, *LAI* is the primary factor that determines the rate of dry matter production *(CGR)* in closed stands. *LAI* usually increases during the growth and development of a stand, until most plants reach the reproductive phase. In crops, the maximum *LAI* can be controlled by stand density, fertilization and other treatments. In natural stands, both pure and mixed, *LAI* usually increases during the growing season, up to a certain value, depending on the water balance, nutrient supply, light relations, and other environmental factors.

LAI thus reflects the actual productive capacity of a stand. From the point of view of overall net photosynthetic production, the *LAI* values at which a stand or community attains the highest *CGR* values at a given phase of development can be regarded as optimal, the product of *LAI* and *NAR* (equation (10.21)) being then maximum (*e.g.* Blackman 1968). Such optimal *LAI* values usually differ from *LAI* values required to attain the highest economic yield, when this is different from total biomass (grain, tubers, fruits, *etc.* – see, *e.g.* Nichiporovich *et al.* 1961; Hodáňová 1967).

Theoretically, with optimum *LAI* the lowest situated leaves in the canopy should have a slightly positive carbon balance on average over 24 h (Brougham 1960; Donald 1961, and other authors).

In most stands, knowledge of the changes in *LAI* is the key to understanding the changes in other growth characteristics, especially *NAR* (see, *e.g.* Watson 1958). *LAI*, leaf arrangement and shoot height are usually the most important factors in competition for light. Differences in productive efficiency between plant populations or crop varieties may depend on the rate at which a closed canopy develops, leading to high *LAI* values and better use of the incoming solar radiation.

For greatest efficiency, maximum *LAI* should occur when radiation is maximal. Unfortunately, this is not the case in a great many crops.

In temperate environments, optimal *LAI* values for economic yield lie between 3 and 6 for most arable crops. In grass and fodder crops, where the yield is total shoot biomass, the optimum *LAI* values are usually 6 to 11. Rather higher values are obtained in mediterranean and tropical climates. An unusually high optimum *LAI* value of 13 was found by Blackman (1962) in *Scilla hispanica*, in which *CGR* and *RGR* were still positive at a *LAI* of 30.

10.5.6 | *Chlorophyll index (CI, L_c)*

Methods of investigating the kinds and amounts of chlorophyll in plants are described in Chapter 18. In the context of growth analysis, the amount of chlorophyll present in plants represents a measure of the size of the assimilatory apparatus, which can be correlated with the rate of dry matter production and with other growth characteristics.

Sprague & Curtis (1933) found that the amount of chlorophyll present in leaves or whole plants of maize was correlated with both leaf area and growth rate. The existence of such correlations was confirmed by Bray (1960) in 13 different stands. Brougham (1960), working with clover, maize and kale, found a significant correlation between *CGR* and the amount of chlorophyll present in the leaves that received more than 95% of full daylight. Medina (1964), Medina & Lieth (1964) and Pilát (1967), working mainly in meadow communities, found a linear relationship between the amount of biomass produced in a certain period after shoot emergence and an integral – over the same period – of the chlorophyll weight present per unit ground area (chlorophyll duration, analogous to leaf area duration, see Section 10.5.7). In white mustard, Lieth (1965) found the same kind of relationship between chlorophyll present in the plants and *CGR* as there was between *LAI* and *CGR*. Aruga & Monsi (1963) arrived at a similar conclusion (their paper reviews other data found in the literature). Ōkubo, Hoshino & Nishimura (1964) and Ōkubo *et al.* (1968) use the term chlorophyll index *(CI)*, which is defined, analogously with *LAI*, as grams of chlorophyll present in a stand per unit ground area. In the stands investigated, the relationship between *CGR* and *CI* is similar to that between *CGR* and *LAI* (see Medina 1964; Pilát 1967).

The chlorophyll index *(CI)* is similar to *LAI* in that neither all the chlorophyll present in the plants nor the total leaf area appears to be fully employed in overall stand photosynthesis. It seems therefore quite justified to use *CI* instead of *LAI*, as well as for *A*, in calculations of *NAR*, as a measure of the size of the assimilatory apparatus. It may be more appropriate to use *CI*, which is also easier to determine than *LAI*, in stands in which plant parts other than leaves (*e.g.* inflorescences, stems) play a significant role in photosynthesis. However, it should be borne in mind that leaf area is likely to be a better basis on which to express photosynthesis in high radiation conditions when CO_2 is limiting, whereas chlorophyll is likely to be more suitable in low radiation environments where photosynthesis is largely limited by the photochemical reactions.

10.5.7 | *Leaf area duration (LAD, D) and biomass duration (BMD, Z)*

These two characteristics take into account the time factor, since it is clear that growth is influenced by the period over which plants maintain their leaf area and biomass.

Leaf area duration (*LAD*, *D*; Watson 1952) is defined by the equation:

$$D = \int_{t_1}^{t_2} A \, dt, \quad \text{or, in stands} \quad D = \int_{t_1}^{t_2} L \, dt \qquad (10.22)$$

To evaluate these equations numerically, the relationships between A and t or L and t must be known. However since A and L can be measured quite frequently, the simplest possible solution is to integrate them graphically by measuring the area under the curve of their changes with time. The relationship between A and time is given by the relative growth rate of leaf area.
From equations (10.6) and (10.7)

$$D = \frac{1}{R_A} \int_{t_1}^{t_2} \frac{dA}{dt} dt = \frac{A_2 - A_1}{R_A} = \frac{A_2 - A_1}{\ln A_2 - \ln A_1} (t_2 - t_1) \text{ [area} \cdot \text{time]} \quad (10.23)$$

Some authors (*e.g.* Nichiporovich *et al.* 1961; Ross & Vlasova 1967) call D 'photosynthetic potential' and relate its value to mean *NAR (E)*, especially over longer intervals, in the following way:

$$D = \frac{W_2 - W_1}{E} \quad (10.24)$$

or

$$E = \frac{W_2 - W_1}{\int_{t_1}^{t_2} A \, dt} \quad (10.25)$$

In the definition of *NAR* by equation (10.9), the expression $A\,dt$ in the denominator is a derivation of *LAD*.
Calculation of mean *NAR* values by equations (10.24) or (10.25) is therefore mathematically not quite correct, especially when *LAD* is estimated as the area of a trapezium (Fig. 10.3) which can be done only when A is measured frequently and/or changes only slightly within an interval (Květ, Svoboda & Fiala 1969):

$$D = \frac{A_1 + A_2}{2} (t_2 - t_1) \quad (10.26)$$

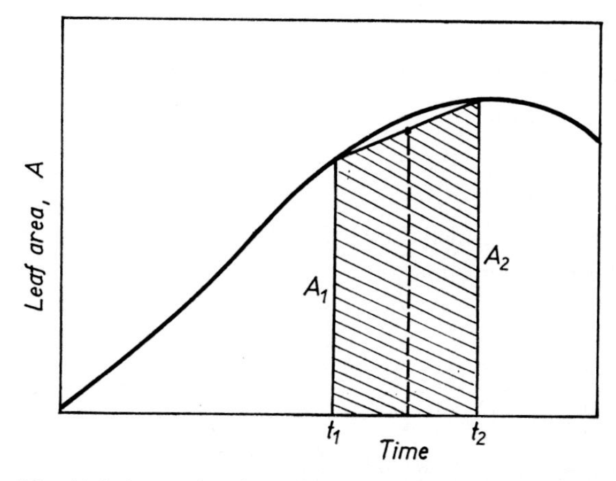

Fig. 10.3 Approximation of leaf area duration (D, shaded area) by the area of a trapezium: $D = 1/2 \cdot (A_1 + A_2) \cdot (t_2 - t_1)$.

LAD expresses in quantitative terms how long a plant or stand maintains its active assimilatory surface. Plants or stands with the same *A* or *LAI* but longer *LAD* are usually the more effective producers (Nichiporovich 1967, 1968).
LAD is sometimes used to estimate the mean *NAR (E)* from the start of the growing season t_0 to the time t of maximum biomass (W_{max}):

$$E = \frac{W_{max}}{D} = \frac{W_{max}}{\int_{t_0}^{t} A \, dt} \qquad (10.27)$$

(see Nichiporovich *et al.* 1961; Květ 1962; Stoy 1965). Birke (1965) correlated the yield of sugar beet with *LAD* and found a closer correlation than with other growth characteristics. Watson (1956) and Walter (1963) have concluded similarly that the size of the assimilatory apparatus and its duration are of primary importance for the productive efficiency of most standard crops. Watson (1956) has also stressed the importance of the coincidence of the development of the assimilatory apparatus *(LAI)* with seasonal changes in radiation. Agronomic treatments should try to ensure such a coincidence. [Chlorophyll duration is analogous to *LAD* and its significance for production is mentioned in Section 10.5.6.]
Biomass duration (*BMD*, *Z* – Květ 1962; Květ, Svoboda & Fiala 1969; Květ & Ondok, not published) is defined and calculated for *W* in the same way as *LAD* is for *A* or *LAI*:

$$Z = \int_{t_1}^{t_2} W \, dt \qquad (10.28)$$

$$Z = \frac{W_2 - W_1}{R} \quad \text{or} \quad Z = \frac{W_2 - W_1}{\ln W_2 - \ln W_1} \cdot (t_2 - t_1) \text{ [weight} \cdot \text{time]} \qquad (10.29)$$

The limitation of this equation with respect to *RGR (R)* is much the same as that of equation (10.23) with respect to R_A. Alternatively, *BMD* can be estimated from graphical integration of the time course of *W*.
The sum of biomass present during the period of *BMD*, approximating the overall net production W_i, is defined by the equation

$$W_i = Z \cdot R \qquad (10.30)$$

The ratio of *LAD (D)* to *BMD (Z)* is, in fact, the mean value of *LAR* ($\bar{F}$), which can be estimated for any period, including the whole growing season or the whole period of increasing biomass, in this way:

$$\bar{F} = \frac{\int_{t_1}^{t_2} A \, dt}{\int_{t_1}^{t_2} W \, dt} \qquad (10.31)$$

BMD can also be employed in estimating the respiratory components of *CGR*, *RGR* and *NAR*. The dry weight losses in a plant or stand due to respiration, *U*, are proportional to total biomass:

$$U = r \cdot Z \tag{10.32}$$

where r is a respiration coefficient representing the weight of dry matter respired per unit dry weight and unit time (Ondok 1970).

10.6 | Estimation of growth characteristics from fitted growth curves

The accuracy of the time-interval calculation of *CGR*, *RGR*, *NAR*, *etc.*, as presented in the previous Section 10.5, renders meaningful data only if the sampling errors of the primary values of W and A are smaller than the changes in them resulting from the effects of the factors being investigated.
The variance of a mathematical function f, s_f^2, depends on the variances of the primary values $x_1, x_2 \dots x_n$, s_{x_i}; $\partial f / \partial x_i$ standing for partial derivations,

$$s_f^2 = \left(\frac{\partial f}{\partial x_1}\right)^2 \cdot s_{x_1}^2 + \left(\frac{\partial f}{\partial x_2}\right)^2 \cdot s_{x_2}^2 + \dots + \left(\frac{\partial f}{\partial x_n}\right)^2 \cdot s_{x_n}^2 \tag{10.33}$$

The variance of *RGR*, which is based on two primary values of W_1 and W_2, is calculated from the formula:

$$s_R^2 = \frac{1}{(t_2 - t_1)^2} \cdot \left(\frac{s_{W_1}^2}{W_1^2} + \frac{s_{W_2}^2}{W_2^2}\right), \tag{10.34}$$

in which s_R^2 is the variance of *RGR*, and $s_{W_1}^2$ and $s_{W_2}^2$ are the variances of the two dry weight data.
Clearly, the variance of values of characteristics based on 4 variable primary values, such as *NAR*, may be very large. Without harvesting intolerably large samples or without employing some techniques that reduce the natural variation artificially, such as pairing of plants, large sampling errors cannot be avoided in the growth analysis of many kinds of plant material, and especially in rather heterogeneous crop and other plant stands. In many comparative experiments carried out under varying climatic conditions (between species, populations, treatments, habitats, *etc.*), it is the general trend of the growth characteristics that is followed rather than their short term fluctuations. Estimation of the growth characteristics from fitted growth curves of W and A may serve this purpose better than estimation over definite time intervals.
The principle of this procedure consists in the choice of a suitable mathematical function, represented by a smooth curve which is fitted through the recorded values of W or A, so that it approximates the real growth curve. The growth characteristics *(CGR, RGR, NAR, etc.)* are then calculated and their time course is constructed from values given by the fitted curve. This can be done directly from the fitted function by means of the general definitions of the growth characteristics given in Section 10.5.

Let the fitted curves of changes in biomass (W) and leaf area (A) with time (t) be represented in a general form by equations:

$$W = f_1(t) \tag{10.35}$$

and

$$A = f_2(t) \tag{10.36}$$

RGR (R) is then calculated from Eq. (10.35):

$$R = \frac{\mathrm{d}f_1(t)}{\mathrm{d}t} \cdot \frac{1}{f_1(t)}, \tag{10.37}$$

and NAR (E) is calculated similarly from Eqs. (10.35) and (10.36):

$$E = \frac{\mathrm{d}f_1(t)}{\mathrm{d}t} \cdot \frac{1}{f_2(t)} \tag{10.38}$$

The other growth characteristics such as CGR, mean LAR, LAD and BMD are calculated analogously.

If smooth curves are to be fitted through the primary values, less rigid criteria and looser confidence limits are acceptable in sampling for representative average values of both W and A, and frequent harvesting, every two or three days, of relatively small samples is preferable to harvesting large samples at longer time-intervals of every week or so (Hughes & Freeman 1967). This is a practical advantage of great significance as it allows the work load to be spread out evenly through the growing period.

The fitted curves should represent the best approximation to the real growth curves of W and A. The complexity of the function describing the curves depends on the data and on the required degree of accuracy. Vernon & Allison (1963) used parabolic functions for both W and A:

$$W = a + bt + ct^2 \tag{10.39}$$

$$A = a' + b't + c't^2 \tag{10.40}$$

where a, b, c and a', b', c' are equation parameters to be determined.

RGR (R) and NAR (E), respectively, are then estimated as

$$R = \frac{b + 2\,ct}{a + bt + ct^2} \tag{10.41}$$

$$E = \frac{b + 2\,ct}{a' + b't + c't^2} \tag{10.42}$$

This approach may be generalized by considering f_1 (t) and f_2 (t), in equations (10.35) and (10.36), as polynomes of any chosen degree.

Radford (1967) fitted exponential curves of the following kind:

$$W = \alpha + \beta\, e^{\gamma t} \tag{10.43}$$

$$A = \alpha' + \beta'\, e^{\gamma' t} \tag{10.44}$$

where α, β, γ and α', β', γ' are equation parameters. Hughes & Freeman (1967) have also used exponential functions:

$$W = \exp\,(a + bt + ct^2 + dt^3) \tag{10.45}$$

$$A = \exp\,(e + ft + gt^2 + ht^3) \tag{10.46}$$

where a to h are equation parameters. In general the cubic expression does not contribute significantly to the accuracy of the fit. Ondok (unpublished) suggested the possibilities of applying other fitted curves, such as the sigmoid and cumulative frequency curves. The technique of curve fitting is demonstrated by a simple example later in this Chapter: further details can be found in textbooks of statistics, *e.g.* Snedecor (1957), Weber (1957), Fisher (1963), *etc.* Some details can be found also in Chapter 11. *CGR*, *RGR*, *NAR etc.* are calculated on the basis of these fitted functions analogously to the first case.

The decision to estimate growth characteristics from fitted growth curves of W and A, and the selection of a suitable function should be made after a preliminary statistical analysis of the following kind:

a. The variances of the recorded primary values of W and A are established and the variances of the respective growth characteristics are estimated from equation (10.33).

b. Suitable functions are selected to fit the changes of W and A with time. The variances describing the dispersion of the recorded primary values of W or A along the fitted curves are calculated from:

$$s^2 = \Sigma \frac{(y_i - y_i^*)^2}{n - 1} \tag{10.47}$$

where y_i and y_i^* represent the recorded and fitted primary values, respectively, and n is the number of values recorded. Finally, the variances of the growth characteristics (*RGR*, *NAR*, *etc.*) as derived from the fitted curves are estimated using equation (10.33).

c. The method of calculation resulting in the smallest variance of the growth characteristics is selected.

An alternative way of comparing the two kinds of methods has been put forward by Hughes & Freeman (1967) (see Figs. 10.4 and 10.5).

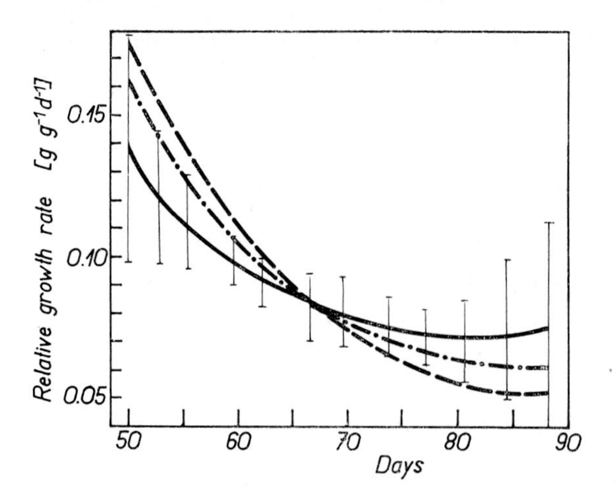

Fig. 10.4 Time course of *RGR* derived from fitted cubic curves. Bars are the fiducial limits for means of three plants per sample (95% probability). CO_2 concentrations: ——— 900 vpm, ------ 600 vpm, –.–.–.–. 325 vpm. (From Hughes & Freeman 1967.)

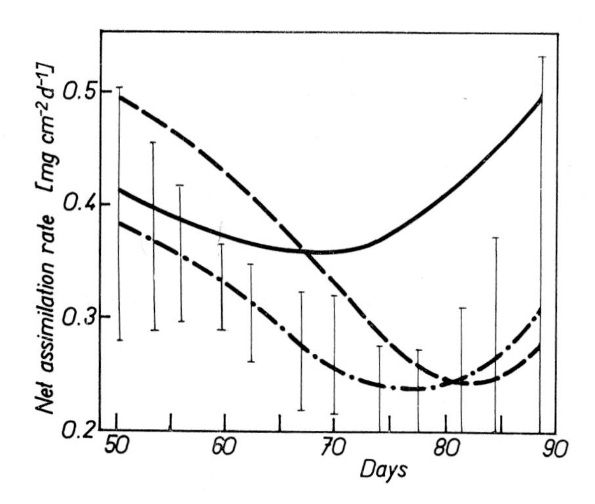

Fig. 10.5 Time course of *NAR* derived from fitted cubics of ln *W* and ln *A*. Bars are the fiducial limits for means of three plants per sample (95% probability). CO_2 concentrations: ——— 900 vpm, ------- 600 vpm, –.–.–.– 325 vpm. (From Hughes & Freeman 1967.)

10.7 | Use of allometric relationships in growth analysis

For a detailed growth analysis, it is often important to know how the newly produced dry matter is distributed into various plant organs (Brouwer 1962a, b; van Dobben 1962; Sonneveld 1962; Milthorpe 1963; Nösberger & Humphries 1965; Nösberger & Thorne 1965). This can be achieved by the calculation of the relative growth rates of different parts of the plant or by means of allometric relationships to compare the growth rates of different parts of an organism with one another or with the growth of the whole organism.

The general form of an allometric relationship is described by the equation (Huxley & Teissier 1936),

$$y = b\,x^a \tag{10.48}$$

in which x and y are the growth rates to be compared, and a and b are equation parameters.

An example of such an allometric relationship is the root : shoot ratio, *i.e.* the ratio of the dry weight of underground plant parts to that of the above-ground parts. Storage organs may be excluded from this ratio when the relations between shoots and physiologically active roots are to be described. The ratio possesses a high ecological as well as morphogenetic value and is of interest especially in perennial herbaceous plants whose shoots sometimes grow at the expense of materials stored in the underground organs.

Allometric relationships between above-ground and underground parts have been followed, *e.g.* by Troughton (1955) and by Brouwer (1963). Engel & Raeuber (1962) and Raeuber & Engel (1966) have applied allometric relationships to the analysis of growth and yield formation in potatoes. The growth of various plant organs seems to follow allometric lines of different directions in different periods of plant development, the changes of direction corresponding to changes in assimilate distribution within the plant. Transformation of an allometric relationship into a linear one requires, of course, the choice of a suitable system of coordinates: semilogarithmic, hologarithmic, *etc.*

The relative growth of individual plant organs may also be described by simple regression equations, in which the dry weight changes in individual plant organs are described in terms of percentages of total dry weight. Analogous correlations also exist between leaf and total assimilatory surface (*e.g.*, leaf area + stem surface). Examples of such correlation graphs are shown in Figs. 10.6 and 10.7.

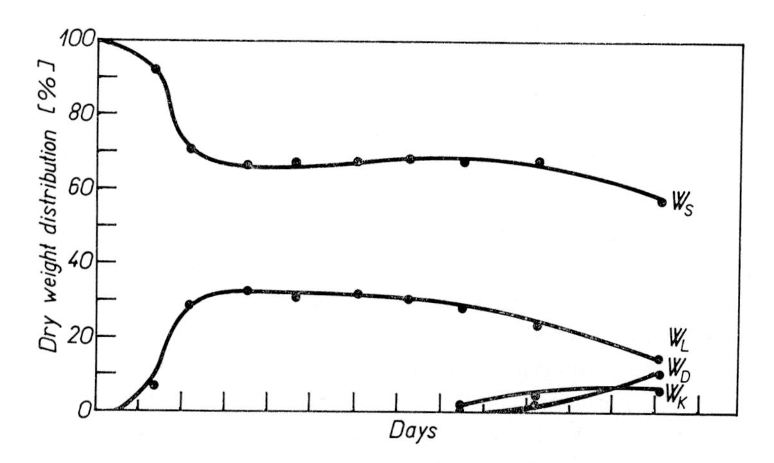

Fig. 10.6 Time course of dry weight distribution (in per cent) in shoots of *Phragmites communis* Trin. W_S – stems; W_L – leaves; W_D – dead leaf laminae; W_K – inflorescences. (From Dykyjová, Ondok & Přibáň 1970.)

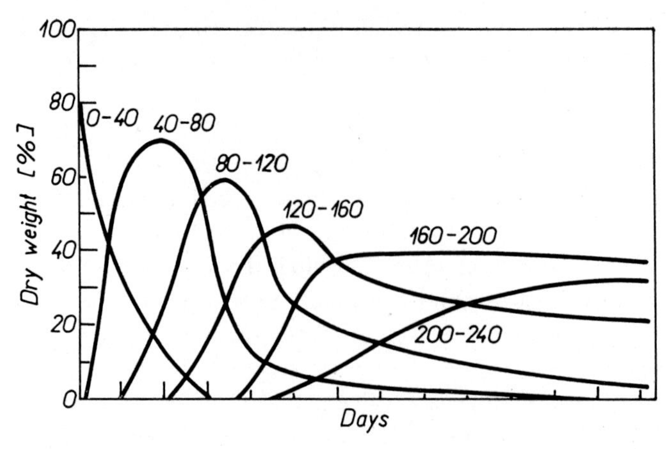

Fig. 10.7 Changes of leaf dry weight (*W*) distribution (in per cent) in separate 40 cm canopy layers (figures at the curves, in cm) during the development of a stand of *Phragmites communis* Trin. (From Dykyjová, Ondok & Přibáň 1970.)

10.8 | Application of growth analysis

Growth analysis makes it possible to follow the formation and accumulation of plant biomass as determined by either environmental or internal factors or both. The dependence of plant growth on both kinds of factors is usually specific, *i.e.* determined by genotype. Growth characteristics have been primarily designed to describe, in quantitative terms, the plants and stands as productive systems. From the practical point of view, growth characteristics are also useful as indices of yield capacity. The purpose of certain agricultural or experimental treatments may be to increase the harvest index (Nichiporovich *et al.* 1961) without necessarily increasing total production. In such cases, growth characteristics may serve as morphogenetic indices.

Destructive harvesting, which is usual in standard growth analysis, forces the investigators to follow the growth of statistically homogeneous sets of plants or sample plots. The resulting primary values and growth characteristics are average values representative of these sets, but differences between individual plants cannot be detected. Therefore, growth analysis has been applied far more to ecological and physiological problems than to genetic investigations and breeding.

Most environmental factors affect different growth characteristics in different ways. Irradiance, as a rule, has a positive effect on net assimilation rate, and a negative effect on leaf area ratio, and, particularly, on specific leaf area (Blackman & Rutter 1950; Blackman & Black 1959a, b; Wassink 1961, 1965; Blackman 1961, and others). The resulting effect of radiation on relative growth rate and hence the shade tolerance of the plants, are determined by the combined effects of radiation on the two major components of relative growth rate, as shown in Fig. 10.8. Temperature, water supply and nitrogen supply usually have a positive effect on leaf expansion (*e.g.* Václavík 1967, 1969). The specific leaf area, leaf area ratio and leaf area index are thus increased while net assimilation rate decreases due to increased mutual shading of the leaves (Watson 1958). The crop growth rate, therefore, decreases when the optimum leaf area index is surpassed. These com-

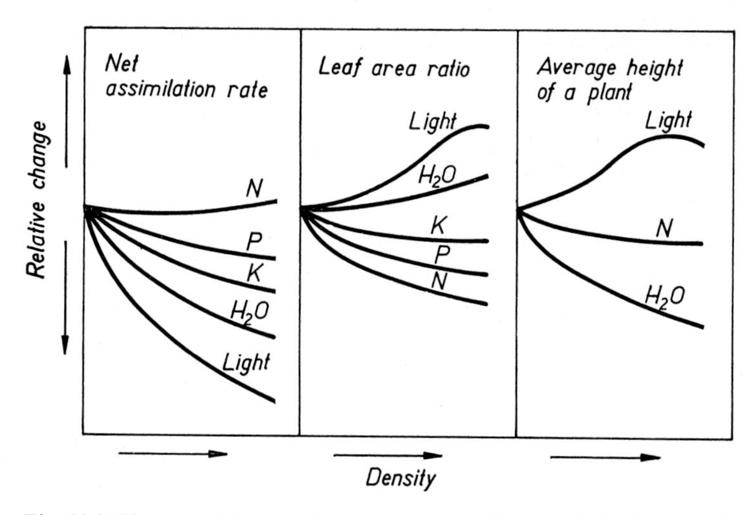

Fig. 10.8 Changes with increasing stand density, in net assimilation rate, leaf area ratio, and average height of an individual plant, assuming that the change is largely determined by competition for a single factor – that is, light or water (H_2O), or supplies of nitrogen (N), phosphorus (P) or potassium (K). (From Blackman 1968.)

plex interactions are best demonstrated in density experiments, designed to follow interactions and competition for various factors between plants either of the same species or of different species (see, *e.g.*, Iwaki 1959; Kamel 1959; Kuroiwa 1960; Donald 1961; Harper 1961; Milthorpe 1961; Blackman 1962, 1968; Hodáňová 1967). Plant communities tend to be dominated by their most productive component species. As a rule, a plant can thrive in a certain habitat only if its long term dry matter balance is positive (Boysen-Jensen 1949). Growth characteristics of individual species in a community are useful indicators of the actual equilibrium between the plant community and its habitat. These examples have illustrated how growth analysis can be applied to ecological problems.

Various growth characteristics can be used as common denominators in comparisons of productivity between different types of plant communities, both natural and managed. Ecological aspects of growth analysis have been reviewed or discussed by Filzer (1951), Zalenskiï (1956), Blackman (1961, 1962, 1968), Květ (1962), Lieth (1962, 1965), Ovington (1962), Newbould (1963), Westlake (1963, 1965a, b), Nichiporovich (1967, 1968), PP Photosynthesis ... (1967, 1969), Cowan & Milthorpe (1968), Wassink (1968), *etc.*

Relatively little use has been made of growth analysis in genetic investigations of crops and in plant breeding. However, growth analysis represents a promising experimental approach in the initial stages of analysing the complex character of yield capacity. Specific or varietal differences in various growth characteristics have been described, *e.g.* by Watson (1947), Begishev (1953), Watson, Thorne & French (1958), Nečas (1962), Huxley (1967), and Nečas, Zrůst & Partyková (1967). Schwarze (1956) describes the use of growth analysis in breeding. Nečas (1965, 1968) employed growth analysis to analyse the phenotypic structure of yield capacity in several potato varieties. Differences between three spring wheat varieties were examined by Stoy (1965). Ecotype differences have been examined, *e.g.* by Enyi (1962), Cooper (1964) and MacColl & Cooper (1967).

Growth analysis is more suitable for some types of plants than others. Ideal plants for growth analysis are relatively fast-growing, with regularly shaped leaves which persist for a long time.

Sunflower, tobacco, maize (see Kostková 1968) and *Sorghum* seem to fulfill most of these requirements. However, drying large samples of these bulky plants may present difficulties. Smaller terrestrial plants, such as *Gladiolus* (Wassink 1961, 1965; Blackman 1968) and flax or linseed (Blackman 1968) or aquatic plants such as *Lemna* or *Salvinia* (Blackman 1961, 1962) have also proved very suitable. Plants with bulky roots, tubers, corms, *etc.* show large variation in their underground dry weight so that pairing of individuals based on shoot parameters is ineffective. Potato plants may be taken as an example (see, *e.g.* Nečas 1965 or Nösberger & Humphries 1965). Harvesting sufficiently large samples seems to be the only reliable technique. For comparative purposes (Nečas 1968), the dry weight of the tubers may be regarded as metabolically inactive and need not be included in calculations of growth characteristics such as *RGR*. This consideration may apply also to other plants having large storage organs or fruits acting as assimilate sinks. Many of these plants also show large variation in leaf area and tend to be highly susceptible to damage to the leaves by pests (*e.g.*, sugar beet, *e.g.*, Schultz 1962; Birke 1965). This risk is reduced by chemical treatment. Last (1962) described the effects of a fungus disease on growth characteristics in barley.

Growth analysis of forage crops and grassland is often confined to shoots only. The inclusion of root biomass in the growth analysis is, however, highly desirable (see also Section 10.10). It can be only partly replaced, in studies on the effects of different treatments, by phenological observations, measurements of *LAI* and investigations of stand pattern and vertical structure.

Growth analysis of perennial herbs should take into account the translocation of assimilates between the storage organs and the growing shoots (Blackman & Rutter 1950; Zalenskiĭ 1956; Smetánková 1959; Lieth 1965; Iwaki, Monsi & Midorikawa 1966; Květ 1966; MacColl & Cooper 1967; Mutoh *et al.* 1968a, b; Dykyjová, Ondok & Přibáň 1970). The seasonal rhythm of growth and development of the plants should be known in detail beforehand as certain modifications of the method may be required (Diels 1918; Wassink 1965; Dykyjová 1969; Ondok 1969, *etc.*).

Standard growth analysis can be applied satisfactorily to seedlings and small plants, raised from grafts or cuttings, of trees and shrubs (Monselise 1953; Barua 1956; Ruck & Bolas 1956; Rutter 1957; Delap & Ford 1958; Coombe 1960; Cunningham & Burridge 1960; Coombe & Hadfield 1962; Rees 1963; Jarvis & Jarvis 1964; Huxley 1967). However, once young trees get beyond a certain size, standard growth analysis becomes difficult to apply. Maggs (1960) tried to apply growth analysis to young fruit trees, but with complicated results. Methods for analysing the growth of large trees and shrubs differ from standard growth analysis (*e.g.*, Ovington 1957, 1962; Mayer 1958; Magin 1959; Kramer 1962; Newbould 1967; Ovington, Forrest & Armstrong 1967; Pardé 1968; Popescu-Zeletin 1968; Vinš 1968) to such an extent that they fall outside the scope of this Chapter. Accounts of productivity of whole tree stands have been presented, *e.g.* by Möller, Müller & Nielsen (1954) and Müller & Nielsen (1965).

 The use of young crop plants as phytometers is an old idea (Clements & Gold-

smith 1924), but the application of growth analysis to the evaluation of phytometers was first suggested by Blackman, Black & Kemp (1955) and has been further developed by Warren Wilson (1966, 1967) and Hodgson (1967). Leach & Watson (1968) and Leach (1969) used young plants as phytometers exposed in stand canopies. Rychnovská (1967) and Květ (1971) have applied certain growth characteristics to the morphological description of plant indicators.
Of more interest physiologically is the growth analysis of plants grown under controlled conditions (*e.g.* Thorne 1961; Thorne, Ford & Watson 1968). This enables the environmental and internal effects on both the primary values and the growth characteristics to be separated.

10.9 Estimation of the efficiency of solar energy conversion in growth analytical investigations

In growth analysis, the attention is concentrated on the overall matter and energy balance attained by a plant or plant stand over a period of several days to several weeks. The solar energy fixed by photosynthesis is accumulated in the plants. All growth characteristics can therefore also be expressed in energy units. The ratio between the energy contained in the biomass of a stand and the integrated flux density of solar radiation energy incident on the stand, whilst the biomass was being formed, characterizes the efficiency of conversion of solar energy into potential chemical energy contained in the plant dry matter. This approach can be refined by considering only the conversion of the energy that is intercepted by the stand canopy. This requires knowledge not only of the overall *LAI* but also of the vertical structure of the stand canopy and of the optical properties of the leaves. Methods employed in assessing canopy structure are described in Chapter 12.
Estimates of the efficiency of solar energy conversion can be based either on the total incoming solar radiation or only on its photosynthetically active part (PhAR). Problems of measuring radiation are discussed in Chapters 12 and 19. The calorie (cal, or kcal = 10^3 cal) has been most commonly used for estimating the energy content of both the incoming radiation and the plant biomass but with the adoption of SI units the joule or watt should now be used (1 cal = 4.186 J, see Chapter 1). The energy content of most plant tissues fluctuates between 3.5 and 4.8 kcal (14 650 and 20 100 J) per 1 g dry matter. Tissues containing storage fat show appreciably higher values, from 5 to 7 kcal g^{-1} (20 930 to 29 300 J g^{-1}). Ideally, one should know the energy content of one's own experimental material (*e.g.*, Golley 1960). However, since calorimetric measurements are time-consuming, it may be justifiable to employ, after careful consideration, data from the literature on the energy content of a similar plant material. Table 10.2 shows several values of energy content of plant biomass, taken from Lieth (1968b). The value of about 4 kcal g^{-1} (16 744 J g^{-1}) seems to be characteristic of many herbaceous plants, while about 4.7 kcal g^{-1} (19 674 J g^{-1}) seems to be applicable to many woody plants (see also Ovington & Heitcamp 1960). The energy content of organic matter found in aquatic plants is discussed by Westlake (1965a, b) and Straškraba (1968). The energy content of plant organic material, *i.e.* ash-free dry matter, is less variable than that of dry matter. Comparisons between both the

Table 10.2 Energy content of different plant stands averaged for the total yield. (From Lieth 1968b.)

Country (or region)	Author	Vegetation type	Energy content per g dry matter [kcal]	[kJ]
1. Herbaceous plants				
Japan:	Kaishio, Hoshizume & Morimoto (1961)	Grassland community	4.0–4.3	16.8–18.0
		Phleum pratense stand	4.2	17.6
		Rice straw	3.6–3.9	15.1–16.3
North America:	Long (1934)	*Solanum tuberosum*	3.4–3.8	14.2–15.9
		Helianthus annuus	4.3	18.0
North America:	Golley (1961)	*Andropogon virginicus* stand	4.2–4.3	17.6–18.0
North America:	Bliss (1962)	Various herbs	4.4	18.4
		Mosses and lichens	4.1–4.2	17.2–17.6
Germany:	Pflanz (1964)	*Phaseolus vulgaris*	3.8–4.0	15.9–16.8
Germany:	Lieth (1968b)	*Helianthus annuus*	4.3	18.0
		Zea mays	4.2	17.6
2. Woody plants				
North America:	Bliss (1962)	Evergreen shrubs	4.8	20.1
		Deciduous shrubs	4.7	19.7
France and Spain:	Lieth (1968b)	*Quercus ilex* and *Quercus pubescens* mixed forest	4.7–4.9	19.7–20.5
Germany:	Pflanz (1964)	*Populus* plantation	4.6	19.3
Great Britain:	Ovington (1961)	*Pinus sylvestris* stand	4.8	20.1

primary values and growth characteristics found in plants having different ash contents should be based on ash-free dry weight or on the energy content.

Knowledge of the time course of the efficiency of solar energy conversion or of the limitations of this efficiency by environmental factors may serve as a useful guideline in crop management (Nichiporovich 1967; Ustenko & Yagnova 1967; Wassink 1968). Fig. 10.9 demonstrates how the efficiency of solar energy conver-

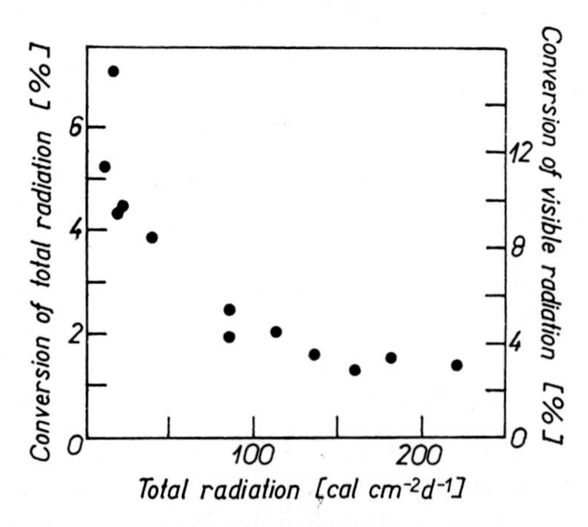

Fig. 10.9 Dependence of the efficiency of energy conversion in spaced seedlings of forage grasses (mean of all varieties) on incident total radiation. (From MacColl & Cooper 1967.)

sion in widely spaced grass seedlings decreases with increasing flux density of the incoming radiation (MacColl & Cooper 1967). This kind of relationship is found in all photosynthetic systems.

10.10 Design of growth analytical investigations and techniques of assessing the primary values

The design of growth analytical experiments and observations should follow, as far as possible, the same principles as that of other field or pot experiments. Both the timing of harvests and the number of replicates should be adjusted to the growth rate of the experimental plants, to prevent the dry weight increments or losses from being obscured by the sampling variation. Calculation of *NAR* is easier when the assimilatory area increases by a factor of less than two between consecutive harvests (see p. 352). If this is exceeded, the changes in the assimilatory area should be estimated by non-destructive methods during the interval between harvests (see Chapter 14). The environmental factors which should be recorded depend on the purpose of the experiment. Monteith (1967) describes a recommended minimum of meteorological measurements accompanying growth analytical investigations.

Estimation of plant dry weight is not a simple matter. It is usually desirable to know the distribution of total dry weight amongst individual plant organs, in both investigations of single plants and of stands. The harvested plants should be killed rapidly by high temperature (80° to 105°C, depending on further use of the dry matter, *e.g.* for chemical analysis). Drying of the whole sample is preferable wherever possible. However, even with large drying ovens, in many cases only representative subsamples can be dried: the dry weight of the rest is then calculated from the fresh to dry weight ratio found in the subsample. The fresh weight of both the subsample and the rest must be recorded simultaneously and in a strictly comparable way, otherwise large errors can arise. Hence, representative subsampling of plants or plant parts deserves attention. Table 10.3 shows that even after careful preparation of subsamples such as taking quarters of each plant organ, the overall variation in dry weight data may be seriously affected.

Leaf area or total assimilatory surface is the most commonly used attribute of the size of the assimilatory apparatus, but chlorophyll content (see Section 10.5.6) is being used with increasing frequency. Methods of measuring leaf area are described in Chapter 14 while methods suitable for estimating the chlorophyll content in plants are presented in Chapter 18. Alternatively, leaf nitrogen or protein content can be estimated, if required, by the usual chemical analytical procedures. In most growth analytical investigations, the size of the assimilatory apparatus is assessed only in a representative subsample and related to the subsample dry weight. The dry weight of the whole sample is then multiplied by the resulting ratio (*e.g.* the leaf area: leaf weight ratio, *i.e.* the specific leaf area) in order to estimate the total size of the assimilatory apparatus. A representative subsample of leaves is best obtained when the leaves are stripped off the stems in a representative subsample of shoots. This is obtained, *e.g.* by arranging all shoots in the sample in ascending order and by taking every *n*-th (usually 5th to 10th) shoot to form the subsample. It is often desirable to reduce the excessively large variation in the investigated

Table 10.3 Analysis of variance to check the method of assessing the dry weight of potato plants. (From Nečas, not published.)

Variation component	N	$\Sigma(x - \bar{x})^2$	V	F	s
Individual	29	41.635 8	1.435	4.73**	
Preparation of samples	3	4.844 2	1.614	5.32**	
Replicates	2	2.337 2	1.168	3.85*	
Sample prep. × replicates	6	4.992 8	0.832	2.75*	
Residual	79	24.284 8	0.303		0.551
Total	119	78.094 8			

Dry weight values were estimated on whole, glasshouse-grown potato plants, about 30 cm high. Each replicate consisted of 30 plants. Each shoot was divided in quarters which were dried separately. From the resulting dry weight values, total dry weights were calculated for the individual plants, on which the analysis of variance is based. Variation due to sample preparation exceeds the individual variation, which is large in potato plants.
N – degrees of freedom; $\Sigma(x - \bar{x})^2$ – sum of squares of deviations from the arithmetic mean $\bar{x}$; V – variance; F – ratio of V for each component to the residual V; s – overall standard deviation; * and **, respectively, denote the 95 and 99% levels of significance of F.

plant material. Sampling of comparable (usually either average or maximum size) plants, batches of them or plots is a relatively simple technique. More effective are the various techniques of pairing individual replicates (plants or plots) to be harvested on two or more subsequent occasions. The replicates to be paired are selected for similarity, either visually (which requires great experience) or according to certain non-destructive measurements from which the plants' initial dry weight and assimilatory surface may be estimated (see Chapter 11). Goodall (1945) and Evans & Hughes (1961) elaborated the pairing technique to great precision. Another modification of this technique consists in selecting the plants or plots to be harvested and matching them with standard plants or plots that are left intact throughout the whole experiment. Further development of the pairing technique leads to indirect sampling for growth analysis, which is described in Chapter 11.

The amount of storage material contained in the seeds, tubers, *etc.* from which the experimental plants are started greatly affects their growth rate (see, *e.g.*, Bremner & El Saeed 1963). Variation amongst the experimental plants is appreciably reduced when all the starting material is of the same size and weight. Nečas (1965) harvested potato plants by fours started from average-size tubers (4 plants per 1 replicate), while the guard-row plants were started from tubers taken indiscriminately.

Ideally, growth analysis should be applied to whole plants including the underground organs (roots, rhizomes, tubers, *etc.*). It is often difficult to do this, especially in field experiments or in observations of natural vegetation. Estimates of underground biomass are then based on a smaller number of samples, on less frequent harvests, on sampling only the larger parts of the root systems (reaching a certain depth in the soil), *etc.* Sometimes, only small parallel samples are taken to estimate the shoot : root dry weight ratio which is then applied to the whole

experimental material. The error of sampling for the underground dry weight should be always stated, as well as the share of this error in the overall variation of sampling for total dry weight. In some cases, especially in the field, growth analysis has been applied only to shoots and the underground biomass has not been assessed at all. This over-simplification should be avoided wherever possible. The most recent surveys of methods applicable to productivity studies in underground plant organs have been published by Lieth (1968a), Troughton (1968) and other contributors to the symposium volume Methods of Productivity Studies (1968), in which further literature may be found. Useful technical guidelines are presented by Schuurman & Goedewaagen (1965).
Growth analysis of spontaneously growing vegetation, especially of mixed stands, is complicated by the great variation in density, pattern, vertical structure, age structure and often also specific composition. (See, *e.g.* the assessment of this problem by Ondok 1969.) Nevertheless, the sampling design for growth analysis in natural vegetation should follow, as far as possible, that used in field experiments with crops, though entirely random sampling can be applied effectively only in exceptionally simple situations such as monospecific even-aged stands having a nearly regular pattern. Purely subjective sampling gives rise to large errors that cannot be assessed in quantitative terms. A feasible compromise, therefore, seems to be random sampling within comparable and exactly defined (for density, pattern, *etc.*) parts of a stand. The handbooks by Newbould (1967) and by Milner & Hughes (1968) contain some recommendations for biomass sampling in woodlands and grasslands, respectively. Some methods applicable to aquatic macrophytes have been described by Westlake (1965a), and the problems of growth analysis in stands of tall grasses and grass-like plants are apparent from the papers by Mutoh *et al.* (1968a, b), Květ, Svoboda & Fiala (1969), Ondok (1969), and others.

10.11 | Statistical treatment of growth analytical data

Most growth analytical investigations are conducted with statistically homogeneous sets of plants or plots. Statistical methods are consequently applied to the evaluation of results of these investigations. Suitable statistical procedures are found in various handbooks of statistics, *e.g.* those by Fisher (1963), Snedecor (1957) and Weber (1957). This Chapter contains only a brief survey of the most common applications of statistical treatment to growth analytical data:
a. Estimates of the variation of the mean primary values of dry weight, leaf area, *etc.*, as well as of the growth characteristics by means of their variance, standard deviation or variation coefficient. Methods of calculating these values for the growth characteristics are shown in Section 10.6.
b. Calculation of the fiducial limits of the estimates of primary values and of the growth characteristics. The fiducial limits indicate the accuracy of the estimates as well as the possibility of discrimination between two estimates, *e.g.*, in two consecutive harvests or in two 'neighbouring' treatments.
c. Testing of differences between primary values or growth characteristics, which result from different treatments, genetic differences, methods used, *etc.* – usually by means of Student's t-test.

d. Testing of differences between variances of data obtained by different methods, formulae, *etc.*, in order to find those rendering the least variable data.
e. Analysis of variance in complex comparisons. As opposed to *c*, more than two treatments, varieties, *etc.*, may be compared at once. The relative contribution of different components of the overall variance of individual growth analytical data can thus be estimated.
f. Selection of an appropriate sampling design and technique, *e.g.* of the number and size of replicates, by various statistical procedures.
g. Correlation analysis, to test the degree of correlation between the growth characteristics and various environmental factors, treatments, varieties, *etc.*, or to define allometric relationships.
h. Construction of regression equations and fitted curves describing, in analytic terms, the course of a certain primary value or growth characteristics as derived from empirical data. The choice of each fitted curve can be tested, *e.g.* by means of the analysis of variance, the closest fit resulting in the smallest variance. Regression equations may be employed also in indirect estimates of those primary values that cannot be assessed directly. More details of this procedure are given in Chapter 11.

10.12 | Prospects for growth analysis

Growth analysis is based on relatively simple principles and permits only a limited degree of accuracy; though all its possibilities have not yet been fully put to use. The main advantage of growth analysis is its technical simplicity, and the possibility of assessing an integrated balance of the production process over certain time intervals as well as over the whole growing season. Growth analysis is best suited to following the effects on net photosynthetic production of relatively long-lasting treatments or conditions such as fertilization, irrigation and other agronomic treatments, or the effects of genotypic differences. The effects of the ever-changing climatic factors are far less easy to follow (Watson 1963), because they tend to be obscured by both the sampling variation and the averaging of the weather over the intervals between harvests. A rather elaborate approach to this problem is based on the principles outlined by Blackman, Black & Kemp (1955). The effects of radiation and temperature on the growth characteristics are examined by multiple regression analysis. Another way of avoiding the drawbacks of assessing weather effects on growth by standard growth analysis is the introduction of daily phenometric measurements on intact plants (see Chapter 11), calibrated, occasionally, by parallel destructive harvesting and assessment of growth characteristics (Engel, Raeuber & Meinl 1968). As compared with gasometric measurements of instantaneous photosynthetic rates, growth analysis appears clumsy; yet it is at present the most practical method of assessing net photosynthetic production (Iwaki, Monsi & Midorikawa 1966).
Further development of growth analysis is desirable in several respects. Recently improvements in the mathematical approach have been outlined (Radford 1967) and further developments may be looked for. Calculation of growth characteristics from fitted growth curves is a relatively new approach, in many situations sounder than mechanical employment of the traditional formulae.
Sound interpretation must be based on reliable basic data. The accuracy of the

assessment of the primary values of dry weight, leaf area, *etc.*, is increased if the data are sampled in a qualified way, *e.g.* by organs of different age, by canopy layers or by shoots of different sizes – according to the purpose of the investigation. Combination of growth analysis with stratified harvesting, described in Chapter 12, has made it possible to link up gasometric measurements of photosynthetic rates with long term estimates of net photosynthetic production in stands (Saeki 1960). The standard growth analytical 'leaf' characteristics *(LAI, LAD, LAR, etc.)*, together with data on leaf age and developments (Saeki 1959, 1961; Šesták & Čatský 1967) and on plastochrones (Ondok 1968; Václavík 1969) are also employed in studies of potential production (*e.g.* Alberda 1962; Monteith 1965; de Wit 1965; Ross & Vlasova 1967; Monsi 1968).
Another application deserving further development is the use of long term growth characteristics such as leaf area duration and biomass duration. Attempts are being made to use these long term characteristics in estimates of total assimilation or respiration over long periods. Watson & Hayashi (1965) and Watson *et al.* (1966) split *NAR (E)* into its two components: total assimilation *(P)* and total respiration (R_s) over a period of n days:

$$E = nP - R_s \tag{10.49}$$

The experimental plants were kept under controlled conditions so that the daily values of both P (per unit leaf area) and R_s (per unit dry weight) could be regarded as constants. Selective shading of the plants for different numbers of days resulted in a whole range of values of E, and both P and R_s were calculated as constants of a regression equation between E and n. Ondok's (1970) calculation is based on the assumption that total assimilation and total respiration are correlated with total assimilatory area and total biomass, respectively. This assumption is described by the equation:

$$dW = \lambda A \, \mathrm{d}t - \varkappa W \mathrm{d}t \tag{10.50}$$

in which $\mathrm{d}W$ is the dry weight increment during time $\mathrm{d}t$, while λ and $\varkappa$ are the coefficients of daily mean assimilation and respiration, respectively. After integration, for a time interval $(t_2 - t_1)$:

$$W_2 - W_1 = \lambda \int_{t_1}^{t_2} A \, \mathrm{d}t - \varkappa \int_{t_1}^{t_2} W \mathrm{d}t \tag{10.51}$$

i.e.,

$$W \approx \lambda M - \varkappa Z \tag{10.52}$$

in which W is the total dry matter production, and M and Z are the leaf area duration and biomass duration, respectively. However, in making calculations of this kind, care should be taken to avoid making assumptions which are unwarranted physiologically about, for example, the character of respiration.

Table 10.4 Growth analysis of a *Sinapsis alba* star

Harvest no. and date	Biomass [dry weight, g m^{-2}] Shoots W_S	Roots W_R	W_S/W_R	Total W	LAI	Chloroph ($a + b$) [g m^{-2}]
1 1962 11.12.	—	—	3.5	—	—	—
2 (*a*) 27.12.	5.46	2.31	2.56	7.8	0.29	—
(*b*) 27.12.	5.46	2.50	—	7.96	—	—
(*c*) 27.12.	8.49	3.96	2.3	12.45	0.46	0.08
3 1963 (*a*) 14.1.	28.5	4.96	5.74	33.5	1.38	—
(*b*) 14.1.	29.8	5.21	—	35.0	—	—
(*c*) 17.1.	31.5	5.42	5.8	36.9	1.44	0.34
4 (*a*) 31.1.	90.2	16.4	5.5	106.6	3.75	—
(*b*) 31.1.	90.3	16.4	—	106.7	—	—
(*c*) 4.2.	118.9	44.0	2.5	162.9	4.56	1.09
5 (*a*) 14.2.	166.0	41.8	3.95	206.8	4.49	—
(*b*) 14.2.	165.2	41.8	—	207.0	—	—
(*c*) 20.2.	206.3	93.8	2.2	300.1	5.47	1.27

10.13 | Examples of growth analytical investigations

A few examples have been selected from the literature to demonstrate different types of growth analytical investigations with respect to purpose pursued or methods employed.

10.13.1 | *Growth analysis using simple dry weight increments. Calculation of the efficiency of solar energy conversion in Sinapis alba.* (Authors: Oswald & Martens, Pflanz, Medina; from Lieth 1965)

This example shows the use of primary values and of simple characteristics such as shoot: root ratio and leaf area index, and the estimation of the energy budget of plant growth. Table 10.4 presents the results of three parallel pot experiments done in the glasshouse by different students: *a.* (Oswald & Martens), *b.* (Pflanz), *c.* (Medina). The mustard seeds were sown on November 1962, the plants were grown in fertilized sand culture. The resulting values are means of values recorded on 6 individual plants. The plants were dried at 105 °C, leaf area was measured with an optical photoelectric planimeter. Chlorophyll ($a + b$) content in the plants was estimated with a spectrophotometer. The maximum coefficient of variation of the recorded values was 15%.

From Lieth 1965.)

iomass icrements g m^{-2}]		Energy [kJ m^{-2}]				Efficiency of PhAR conversion [%]
		contained in plants			Incident PhAR (mean daily total)	
otal between arvests	Daily mean	Total content	Increase between harvests	Mean daily increase		
–	—	—	—	—	—	—
–	—					
5.94	0.22	124.7	74.1	4.6	1 617.1	0.17
10.4	0.38					
–	—					
25.0	1.39	580.2	404.8	25.1	1 216.5	1.85
24.5	—					
–	—					
59.6	4.09	1 840.2	1 210.2	71.6	2 575.6	2.76
26.1	—					
–	—					
98.3	7.02	3 647.3	1 832.6	134.4	1 987.9	4.18
37.1	—					

10.13.2 *Growth analysis of three spring wheat varieties grown at different levels of nitrogen and soil moisture* (from Stoy 1965)

The varieties compared were Dala, Diamant II and Sv 01200, and the experiments were conducted in 5 consecutive years, 1958–62.
1958–59: Field experiments, each variety was sown on the area of 2×10 m^2, in a block arrangement. Harvest dates: 6.6., 12.6., 26.6., 10.7., 24.7., 21.8., each harvest consisting of 20 shoots. The assimilatory area of each shoot was estimated as the sum of total lamina area, half stem (with leaf sheaths) surface and ear surface (projected areas of 4 sides of the ear). Dry weight of the leaves, stems and ears was estimated separately at 105 °C. Mean values per plant were obtained as averages of the 20 measurements recorded, and their time courses were presented as smooth curves. *NAR (E)* was calculated for individual intervals between harvests using Eq. (10.12). Root dry weight was not estimated. The field experiment was repeated in 1959, and additional measurements involved the assessment of tillering, leaf area ratio, *etc.*
In the subsequent years, the experiments were carried out in pots placed in growth cabinets. The temperature regime, photoperiod and soil moisture conditions were set up so as to follow the mean values recorded during the previous 2 years' field experiments. Illuminance was 30 to 35 klx. Harvests were taken at weekly intervals,

and root dry weight was also recorded. In 1962, the effects of two levels of soil moisture were compared. At each harvest, five plants (selected for uniformity) were taken from two pots. The following primary values and growth characteristics were calculated as averages for the five plants:

a. Assimilatory surface, in the same way as in the field experiments. Varietal differences were found in leaf area, not in stem surface. Nitrogen levels had a

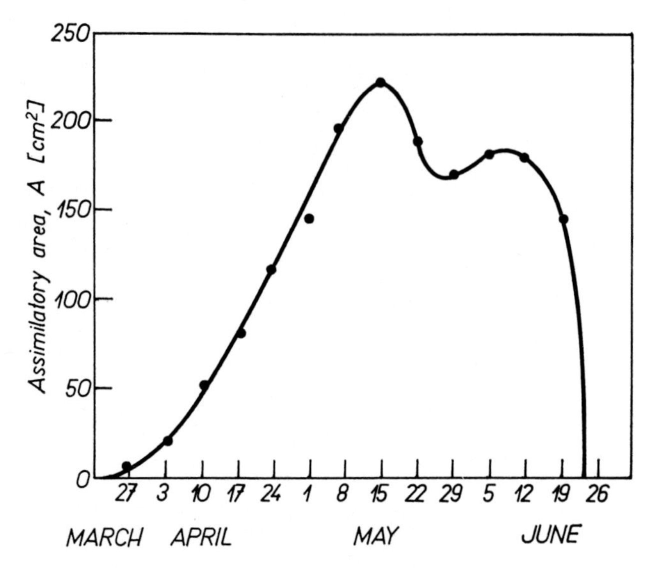

Fig. 10.10 Development of plant assimilatory area (A) in spring wheat (var. Dala) at a high (80%) level of soil moisture. (From Stoy 1965.)

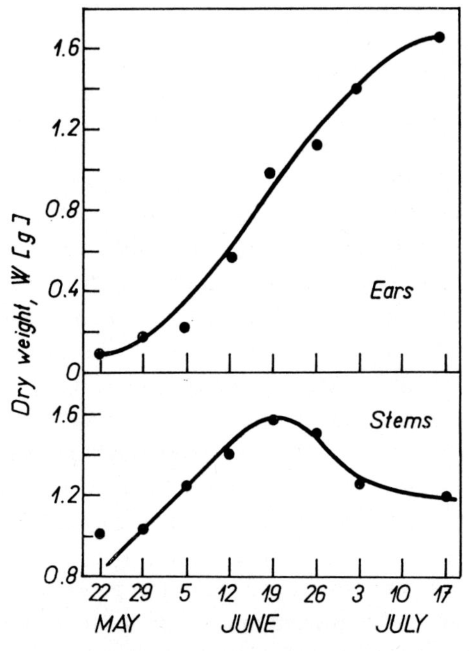

Fig. 10.11 Changes in dry weight of ears and stems in spring wheat (var. Diamant) during the period from ear emergence to maturity. (From Stoy 1965.)

Table 10.5 Average values of net assimilation rate (*NAR*) [g m^{-2} $week^{-1}$] recorded in growth analysis experiments with 3 spring wheat varieties given different treatments (N = nitrogen) in 4 successive years. (From Stoy 1965.)

Variety & treatment			*NAR*
Dala			
1958	Low	N	37.7
	High	N	40.1
1959	Low	N	40.0
	High	N	38.5
1960	—		38.6
1962	Low	moisture	37.2
	High	moisture	37.3
Mean			38.5
Diamant			
1958	Low	N	42.2
	High	N	42.5
1959	Low	N	44.7
	High	N	38.4
1960	—		37.7
1961	Low	moisture	38.0
	High	moisture	37.9
Mean			40.2
Sv 01200			
1958	Low	N	45.9
	High	N	48.1
1959	Low	N	44.8
	High	N	41.6
1960	—		40.8
1962	Low	moisture	39.8
	High	moisture	38.4
Mean			42.8

significant effect while the effect of soil moisture was negligible. The seasonal changes of the assimilatory surface had two peaks, associated with tiller growth (see Fig. 10.10).

b. Dry weight. The dry weight increments were found to depend on leaf area ratio. Greater varietal differences were found in the field experiments than in the growth cabinets. The seasonal changes of ear and stem dry weight, respectively, are shown in Fig. 10.11. The decrease in stem dry weight after ear emergence seemed to be connected with assimilate translocation from the stems to the ears.

c. Net assimilation rate *(NAR, E)*. Individual *NAR* values differed according to the plants' phase of development, but the average *NAR* values were much the same in all varieties and treatments. Differences between the field and growth cabinet experiments were not found either. Table 10.5 shows all the mean *NAR* values found. The relationship between *NAR* and *LAI*, and *CGR* and *LAI*, in the growth cabinet and the field experiments, respectively, is non-linear, as shown in Fig. 10.12.

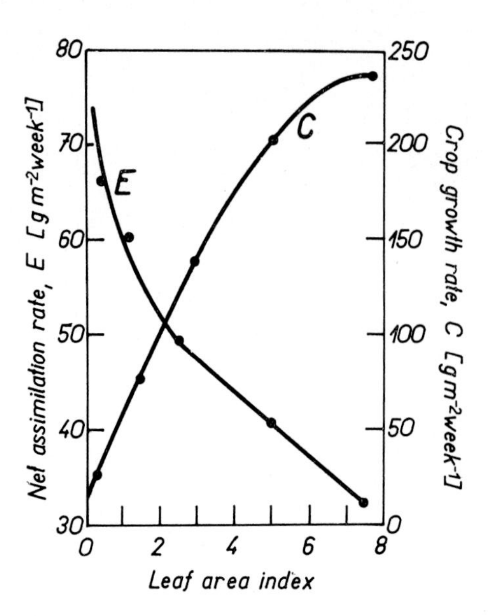

Fig. 10.12 The dependence of net assimilation rate E (per unit green area) and crop growth rate C on leaf area index in spring wheat. (From Stoy 1965.)

The main factors determining the net photosynthetic production seemed to be the size and arrangement of leaf area, as well as the time over which the leaves were photosynthetically active (*i.e.*, the leaf area duration).

10.13.3 *Establishment of correlations between growth characteristics and climatic factors and the effect of variation in the values of R and E on these correlations (*from Bínová & Ondok 1971)

Tests of photosynthetic productivity were done according to the recommendations for the so-called sowing date experiments in the Initial Programme of the Photosynthesis Sub-section (IBP/PP) of the International Biological Programme. Experiments were done with young plants of sunflower (*Helianthus annuus* var. Pole Star) grown in hydroponic sand culture, in boxes 25 cm × 25 cm × 25 cm. In each experiment, four plants were selected for uniformity out of a larger number of seedlings in each box. The first harvest was taken when two pairs of true leaves had fully developed. This harvest consisted of 8 boxes, i.e. 32 plants, one box representing one replicate. Another 8 boxes were paired to match those selected for the first harvest and harvested a week later. In the two successive harvests, the respective primary values of dry weight (W_1, W_2) and leaf area (A_1, A_2) per box were established. The values of relative growth rate (R) and net assimilation rate (E) were then calculated from these initial values. The correlations between R and E and incident solar radiation were found to be relatively small ($r_R = 0.388$ and $r_E = 0.382$, respectively). One of the main reasons for this appears to be the great variation in both R and E. The effect of this variation was tested in the following way:

a. The coefficients of variation of the primary values of W and A were established (see Table 10.6).

Table 10.6 Mean total dry weight (W) and mean leaf area (A) and the coefficients of variation (V, %) of these values recorded in 14 successive experiments with young plants of *Helianthus annuus* var. Pole Star in sand culture with standard irrigation and mineral nutrition at Třeboň (Czechoslovakia) in 1968. W_1, A_1 and W_2, A_2 are values recorded at the beginning and end, respectively, of each weekly experimental interval. (From Bínová & Ondok 1971.)

Exp. no.	W_2[g]	V[%]	W_1[g]	V[%]	A_1[cm^2]	V[%]	A_2[cm^2]	V[%]
1	7.78	8.24	2.83	6.72	441	5.49	1019	11.10
2	6.06	5.37	2.57	6.15	324	4.63	813	7.10
3	7.16	9.31	3.26	9.26	420	10.88	1004	11.65
4	10.65	10.59	2.30	8.37	402	9.99	1504	10.24
5	8.21	9.06	2.16	7.67	314	5.85	1016	8.79
6	8.79	4.10	2.94	5.24	458	5.18	1156	5.49
7	8.10	6.26	3.18	6.48	478	5.06	960	5.57
8	7.73	7.80	2.73	7.98	397	6.54	929	7.53
9	7.88	4.93	2.77	5.10	405	6.42	1067	4.47
10	8.99	5.32	2.44	5.42	372	7.10	985	5.01
11	8.21	4.06	4.88	7.49	663	8.16	1015	4.11
12	5.11	7.76	2.88	4.07	374	2.97	590	5.29
13	6.88	4.24	2.76	6.89	445	6.59	825	3.45
14	3.49	4.64	2.14	3.50	299	3.76	516	5.22

Table 10.7 Mean values of relative growth rate (R) and their fiducial limits as recorded in the experiments presented in Table 10.6.

Exp. no.	R[g g^{-1} d^{-1}]	Fiducial limits ($P = 0.05$)
4	0.236	0.192–0.280
5	0.191	0.165–0.217
6	0.157	0.117–0.197
9	0.149	0.128–0.171
8	0.149	0.128–0.170
1	0.144	0.141–0.148
7	0.134	0.120–0.148
13	0.131	0.122–0.139
10	0.130	0.125–0.136
11	0.130	0.089–0.171
2	0.123	0.114–0.132
3	0.112	0.083–0.142
12	0.082	0.070–0.094
14	0.070	0.067–0.073

b. The variances of the values of both R and E were calculated from equation (10.34). The variation was expressed in terms of fiducial limits of the respective R and E values ($P = 0.05$) (see Tables 10.7 and 10.8).

c. It is apparent that adjacent values of both R and E overlap so that the variation in R and E (larger than that of the corresponding primary values of W and A),

Table 10.8 Mean values of net assimilation rate (E) and their fiducial limits, as recorded in the experiments presented in Table 10.6.

Exp. no.	E[g m^{-2} d^{-1}]	Fiducial limits (P = 0.05)
5	13.00	12.97–13.03
4	12.52	12.48–12.56
8	10.77	10.08–10.79
6	10.36	10.32–10.40
9	9.93	9.91– 9.95
11	9.93	9.89– 9.97
7	9.77	9.76– 9.79
1	9.69	9.69– 9.69
10	9.65	9.65– 9.65
13	9.29	9.28– 9.30
2	8.77	8.76– 8.78
3	7.83	7.80– 7.86
12	6.62	6.61– 6.63
14	4.73	4.73– 4.73

may reduce the significance of the correlations between R and E and the climatic factors.

The relative variation of R exceeds that of E. Many of the recorded weekly values of both radiation and temperature overlapped, which shows that shorter experimental intervals (with a larger number of replicate plant samples to keep the variation of the plant material at the same level) would have resulted in closer correlations.

10.13.4 *Correlation between growth characteristics and climatic factors in pot experiments with young plants of Vicia faba and Helianthus annuus* (from Hodgson 1967)

Excess seed of both sunflower (var. Pole Star) and field bean was sown to a standard pattern in a 1 : 1 mixture of soil and sand. The seedlings were thinned prior to the experimental period, to leave the required number of uniform plants in each pot. All the pots received a standard nutrient solution at the time of emergence and again 6 days prior to the experimental period, and were watered whenever necessary. For each experiment, over one week, plants were selected in which the third pair of leaves could just be seen. At the beginning of each experiment, matched pairs of pots, containing six plants each, were selected to form one block. Replication of blocks was sixfold. For the initial sampling, one randomly selected pot was taken from each pair, and the remaining pot provided the final sample. At each harvest, the mean dry weights of the leaf laminae, stems with petioles, and roots were estimated for each pot. The stems were cut at ground level, the roots were obtained by washing away the soil and sand mixture through a 0.6 cm sieve. To estimate the leaf area, a blueprint was made of a subsample of the leaf laminae, and the leaf area : leaf weight ratio was estimated after the copies had been planimetered. In *Vicia faba*, the area of the stipules was included with that of leaves. The harvested plant material was dried at 95 °C for 24 h before weighing.

Daily amounts of light were measured with an integrating photometer which was calibrated against a radiometer. The daily mean temperatures were calculated from the daily minima and maxima, and the result of this simple procedure did not differ significantly from mean temperatures determined by planimetering the area below a thermograph trace (the experiments were done in Scotland, where the climate is temperate oceanic).

RGR and *NAR* were calculated using equations (10.7) and (10.12), respectively. Neither linear nor quadratic regressions between *RGR* or *NAR* and the weather factors gave the best fit. The introduction of the initial *LAR* values (F_i) in the regression equations between irradiance (I) and mean temperature (T) on the one hand, and *NAR* (E) or *RGR* (R) on the other, improved the fit by reducing and sometimes eliminating the time trends. Examples of such regression equations, for R, E and F_f (final *LAR*), in sunflower in 1956, are given:

$E\,[\mathrm{g\ dm^{-2}\ d^{-1}}] = -0.117 + 0.000\,182\,I + 0.007\,4\,T + 0.036\,1\,F_i$

(variation accounted for: 92%; residual $SD = 0.10$)

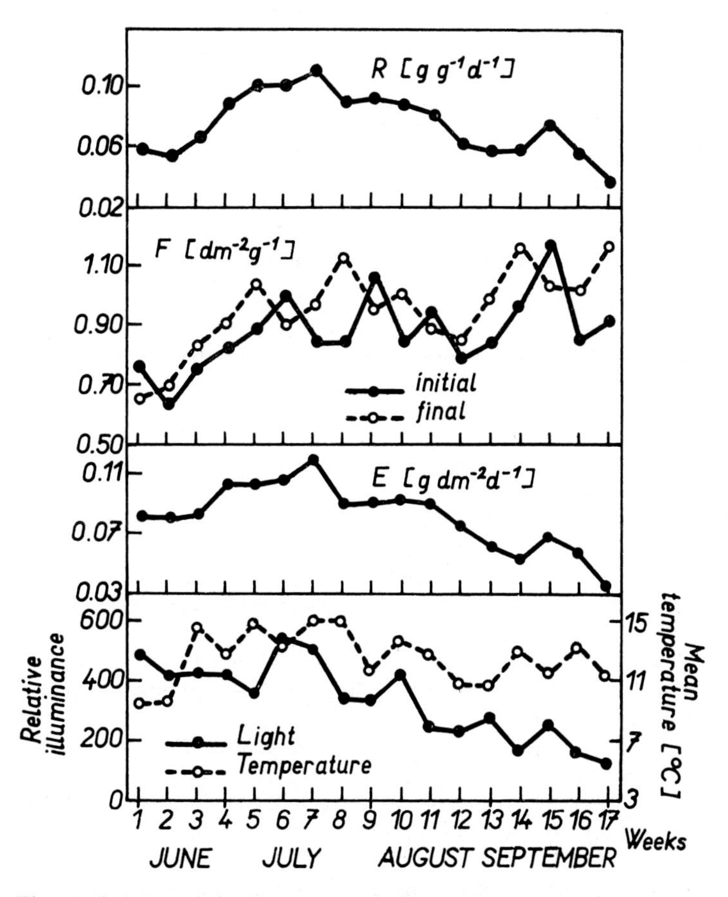

Fig. 10.13 Seasonal changes over successive weekly periods in mean diurnal illuminance and temperature, together with net assimilation rate (E), initial and final leaf area ratios (F), and relative growth rate (R) in *Vicia faba*. (From Hodgson 1967.)

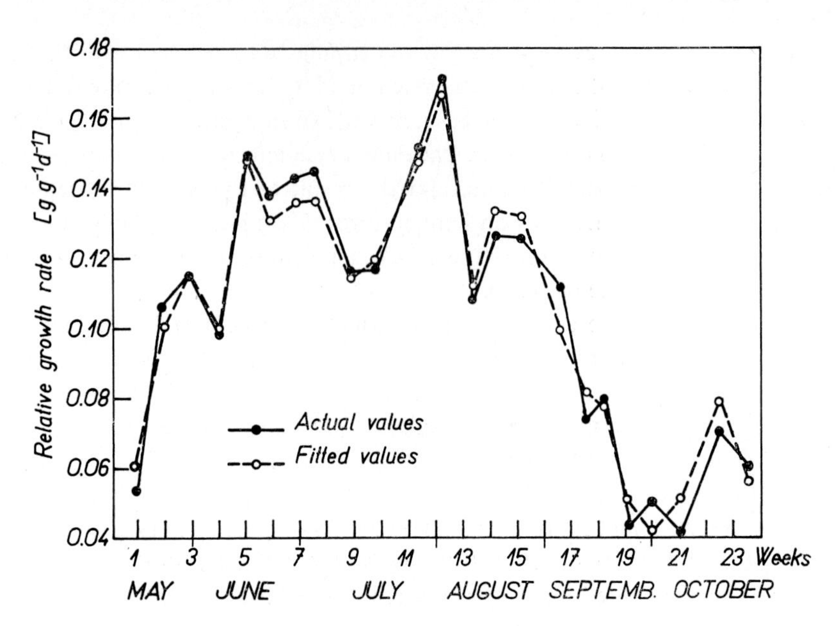

Fig. 10.14 The weekly observed actual values of relative growth rate (R) compared with the corresponding values calculated from a fitted regression (*Helianthus annuus*, 1957). (From Hodgson 1967.)

R [g g^{-1} d^{-1}] = $-$ 0.198 + 0.000 244 I + 0.008 2 T + 0.092 F_i
(variation accounted for: 94%)
F_f [dm^2 g^{-1}] = 1.279 $-$ 0.001 007 I + 0.256 F_i
(variation accounted for: 76%).
Figs. 10.13 and 10.14 show some results of these experiments.

10.14 | References

Alberda, Th.: Actual and potential production of agricultural crops. – Neth. J. agr. Sci. 10: 325-333, 1962.

Aruga, Y., Monsi, M.: Chlorophyll amount as an indicator of matter productivity in bio-communities. – Plant Cell Physiol. 4: 29-39, 1963.

Barua, D. N.: Light intensity, assimilation rate and yield of young tea plants. – Ann. Rep. Tocklai exp. Sta. Ind. Tea Assoc. 1956: 34-46, 1956.

Begishev, A. N.: Rabota list'ev raznykh sel'skokhozyaĭstvennykh rasteniĭ v polevykh usloviyakh. [Activity of leaves of different agricultural plants in field conditions.] – Trudy Inst. Fiziol. Rast. K.A. Timiryazeva 8: 229-263, 1953.

Bínová, J., Ondok, J. P.: Testy fotosynthetické produktivity mladých rostlin slunečnice v roce 1967. [Tests of photosynthetic productivity in young sunflower plants in 1967.] – Rostlinná Výroba (Praha) 17: in press, 1971.

Birke, J.: Über die Abhängigkeit des Zuckerrübenertrages von der Entwicklung des Assimilationsapparates. – Albrecht-Thaer-Arch. 9: 715-729, 1965.

Blackman, G. E.: Responses to environmental factors by plants in the vegetative phase. – In: Zarrow, M. X. (ed.): Growth in Living Systems. Pp. 525-556. Basic Books Inc., New York 1961.

Blackman, G. E.: The limit of plant productivity. – Ann. Rep. East Malling Res. Sta. 1961: 39-50, 1962.

Blackman, G. E.: The application of the concepts of growth analysis to the assessment of productivity. – In: Eckardt, F. E. (ed.): Functioning of Terrestrial Ecosystems at the Primary Production Level. Pp. 243-259. UNESCO, Paris 1968.

Blackman, G. E., Black, J. N.: Physiological and ecological studies in the analysis of plant environment. XI. A further assessment of the influence of shading on the growth of different species in the vegetative phase. – Ann. Bot. N.S. 23: 51-63, 1959a.

Blackman, G. E., Black, J. N.: Physiological and ecological studies in the analysis of plant environment. XII. The role of the light factor in limiting growth. – Ann. Bot. N.S. 23: 131-145, 1959b.

Blackman, G. E., Rutter, A. J.: Physiological and ecological studies in the analysis of plant environment. V. An assessment of the factors controlling the distribution of the bluebell *(Scilla non-scripta)* in different communities. – Ann. Bot. N.S. 14: 487-520, 1950.

Blackman, G. E., Black, J. N., Kemp, A. W.: Physiological and ecological studies in the analysis of plant environment. X. An analysis of the effects of seasonal variation in daylight and temperature on the growth of *Helianthus annuus* in the vegetative phase. – Ann. Bot. N.S. 19: 527-548, 1955.

Blackman, V. H.: The compound interest law and plant growth. – Ann. Bot. 33: 353-360, 1919.

Bliss, L. C.: Caloric and lipid content in alpine tundra plants. – Ecology 43: 753-757, 1962.

Boysen-Jensen, P.: Die Stoffproduktion der Pflanzen. – G. Fischer, Jena 1932.

Boysen-Jensen, P.: Causal plant geography. – Kgl. Danske Vid. Selskab, Biol. Medd. 21(3): 1-19, 1949.

Bray, J. R.: The chlorophyll content of some native and managed plant communities in Central Minnesota. – Can. J. Bot. 38: 313-333, 1960.

Bremner, P. M., El Saeed, A. K.: The significance of seed size and spacing. – In: Ivins, J. D., Milthorpe, F. L. (ed.): The Growth of Potato. Pp. 267-280. Butterworths, London 1963.

Briggs, G. E., Kidd, R., West, C.: Quantitative analysis of plant growth. – Ann. appl. Biol. 7: 103-123, 202-223, 1920.

Brougham, R. W.: The relationship between the critical leaf area, total chlorophyll content, and maximum growth-rate of some pasture and crop plants. – Ann. Bot. N.S. 24: 463-474, 1960.

Brouwer, R.: Distribution of dry matter in the plant. – Neth. J. agr. Sci. 10: 361-376, 1962a.

Brouwer, R.: Nutritive influences on the distribution of dry matter in the plant. – Neth. J. agr. Sci. 10: 399-408, 1962b.

Brouwer, R.: Some aspects of the equilibrium between overground and underground plant parts. – Jaarb. I.B.S.: 31-39, 1963.

Clements, F. E., Goldsmith, G. W.: The Phytometer Method in Ecology. – Carnegie Inst. Washington Publ. 356, Washington 1924.

Coombe, D. E.: An analysis of the growth of *Trema guineensis*. – J. Ecol. 48: 219-231, 1960.

Coombe, D. E., Hadfield, W.: An analysis of the growth of *Musanga cecropiodes*. – J. Ecol. 50: 221-234, 1962.

Cooper, J. P.: Climatic variation in forage grasses. I. Leaf development in climatic races of *Lolium* and *Dactylis*. – J. appl. Ecol. 1: 45-61, 1964.

Cowan, I. R., Milthorpe, F. L.: Physiological responses in relation to the environment within the plant cover. – In: Eckardt, F. E. (ed.): Functioning of Terrestrial Ecosystems at the Primary Production Level. Pp. 107-130. UNESCO, Paris 1968.

Cunningham, R. K., Burridge, J. C.: The growth of cacao *(Theobroma cacao)* with and without shade. – Ann. Bot. N.S. 24: 458-462, 1960.

Delap, A. V., Ford, E. M.: Studies in the nutrition of apple root stocks. 1. Effects of deficiencies of iron and magnesium on growth. – Ann. Bot. N.S. 22: 137-158, 1958.

Diels, L.: Das Verhältnis von Rhytmik und Verbreitung bei den Perennen des europäischen Sommerwaldes. – Ber. deut. bot. Ges. 36: 337-351, 1918.

Dobben, W. H. van: Influence of temperature and light conditions on dry-matter distribution, development rate and yield in arable crops. – Neth. J. agr. Sci. 10: 377-389, 1962.

Donald, C. M.: Competition for light in crops and pastures. – In: Milthorpe, F. L. (ed.): Mechanisms of Biological Competition. Symp. Soc. exp. Biol. 15: 282-313, 1961.

Dykyjová, D.: Kontaktdiagramme als Hilfsmethode für vergleichende Biometrie, Allometrie und Produktionsanalyse von *Phragmites*–Ökotypen. – Rev. roum. Biol. Zool. (București) 14: 107-119, 1969.

Dykyjová, D., Ondok, J. P., Přibáň, K.: Seasonal changes in productivity and vertical structure of reed-stands (*Phragmites communis* Trin.). – Photosynthetica 4: 280-287, 1970.

Engel, K. H., Raeuber, A.: Das allometrische Wachstum der Kartoffel. Ein Beitrag zur Festlegung von Wachstumsabschnitten. – Z. Pflanzenzüchtung 47: 114-119, 1962.

Engel, K. H., Raeuber, A., Meinl, G.: Phenometric studies on cultivated plants. (Proposal for PP/IBP.) – Photosynthetica 2: 298-302, 1968.

Enyi, B. A. C.: Comparative growth-rates of upland and swamp rice varieties. – Ann. Bot. N.S. 26: 467-487, 1962.

Evans, G. C., Hughes, A. P.: Plant growth and the aerial environment. I. Effect of artificial shading on *Impatiens parviflora*. – New Phytol. 60: 150-180, 1961.

Evans, G. C., Hughes, A. P.: Plant growth and the aerial environment. III. On the computation of unit leaf rate. – New Phytol. 61: 322-327, 1962.

Filzer, P.: Die natürlichen Grundlagen des Pflanzenertrags in Mitteleuropa. – 198 S.E. Schweizerbart Verlag, Stuttgart 1951.

Fisher, R. A.: Some remarks on the methods formulated in a recent article on the quantitative analysis of plant growth. – Ann. appl. Biol. 7: 367-372, 1921.

Fisher, R. A.: Statistical Methods for Research Workers. – 13th Ed. Oliver & Boyd, London 1963.

Geyger, E.: Methodische Untersuchungen zur Erfassung der assimilierenden Gesamtoberflächen von Wiesen. – Ber. geobot. Forsch.-Inst. Rübel 35: 41-112, 1964.

Golley, F. B.: Energy dynamics of a food chain of an old field community. – Ecol. Monogr. 30: 187-206, 1960.

Golley, F. B.: Energy values of ecological materials. – Ecology 42: 581-584, 1961.

Goodall, D. W.: The distribution of weight change in the young tomato plant. Dry-weight changes of the various organs. – Ann. Bot. N.S. 9: 101-139, 1945.

Gregory, F. G.: The effect of climatic conditions on the growth of barley. – Ann. Bot. 40: 1-26, 1926.

Harper, J. L.: Approaches to the study of plant competition. – In: Milthorpe, F. L. (ed.): Mechanisms of Biological Competition. Symp. Soc. exp. Biol. 15: 1-39, 1961.

Hayashi, K.: Efficiencies of solar energy conversion in rice varieties as affected by planting density. – Proc. Crop Sci. Soc. Japan 35: 205-211, 1966.

Hayashi, K.: Efficiencies of solar energy conversion in rice varieties. – In: Photosynthesis and Utilization of Solar Energy. Level III Experiments 1966-1967. Pp. 39-42. Tokyo 1968.

Hodáňová, D.: Development and structure of foliage in wheat stands of different density. – Biol. Plant. 9: 424-438, 1967.

Hodgson, G. L.: Physiological and ecological studies in the analysis of plant environment. XIII. A comparison of the effects of seasonal variations in light energy and temperature on the growth of *Helianthus annuus* and *Vicia faba* in the vegetative phase. – Ann. Bot. N.S. 31: 291-308, 1967.

Hughes, A. P., Freeman, P. R.: Growth analysis using frequent small harvests. – J. appl. Ecol. 4: 553-560, 1967.

Huxley, J. S., Teissier, G.: Zur Terminologie des relativen Grössenwachstums. – Biol. Zentralbl. 56: 381-383, 1936.

Huxley, P. A.: The effects of artificial shading on some growth characteristics of *Arabica* and *Robusta* coffee seedlings. I. The effects of shading on dry weight, leaf area and derived growth data. – J. appl. Ecol. 4: 291-308, 1967.

Iwaki, H.: Ecological studies on interspecific competition in a plant community. I. An analysis of growth of competing plants in mixed stands of buckwheat and green grams. – Jap. J. Bot. 17: 120-138, 1959.

Iwaki, H., Monsi, M., Midorikawa, B.: Dry matter production of some herb communities in Japan. – The Eleventh Pacific Science Congress, Tokyo, August–September 1966. Mimeographed paper.

Jarvis, P. G., Jarvis, M. S.: Growth rates of woody plants. – Physiol. Plant. 17: 654-666, 1964.

Kaishio, Y., Hashizume, T., Morimoto, H.: Energy values of wild grass hay and rice straw for maintenance. – In: Second Symposium on Energy Metabolism, Vol. 10. Pp. 165-176. EAAP, Wageningen 1961.

Kamel, M. S.: A physiological study of shading and density effects on the growth and the efficiency

of solar energy conversion in some field crops. – Meded. Landbouwhogeschool (Wageningen) 59(5): 1-101, 1959.
Kostková, H.: Remarks on the use of maize in comparative growth analytical investigations of photosynthetic production. – Photosynthetica 2: 212-214, 1968.
Kramer, H.: Kronenaufbau und Kronenentwicklung gleichalter Fichtenpflanzenbestände. – Allg. Forst- Jagdzeit. 133: 249-256, 1962.
Kuroiwa, S.: Intraspecific competition in artificial sunflower communities. – Bot. Mag. (Tokyo) 73: 300-309, 1960.
Květ, J.: Produkční ekologie bylinného patra lesních společenstev. [Production ecology of the herbaceous layer in woodlands.] – CSc. Thesis. Inst. Bot., Czechosl. Acad. Sci., Průhonice and Brno 1962.
Květ, J.: Productivity studies in the woodland herbacious vegetation. – Acta Univ. Carolinae – Biologica 1966 (Suppl. 1/2): 123-125, 1966.
Květ, J.: Reaction of woodland herbaceous plants to the removal of tree canopy. – Folia geobot. phytotax. (Praha) 6: in press, 1971.
Květ, J., Svoboda, J., Fiala, K.: Canopy development in stands of *Typha latifolia* L. and *Phragmites communis* Trin. in South Moravia. – Hidrobiologia (Bucureşti) 10: 63-75, 1969.
Last, F. T.: Analysis of the effects of *Erypsiphe graminis* D.C. on the growth of barley. – Ann. Bot. N.S. 26: 279-289, 1962.
Leach, G. J.: The relation of photosynthesis by phytometers in the profiles of kale crops to leaf area index above them. – J. appl. Ecol. 6: 499-505, 1969.
Leach, G. J., Watson, D. J.: Photosynthesis in crop profiles, measured by phytometers. – J. appl. Ecol. 5: 381-408, 1968.
Lieth, H. (ed.): Die Stoffproduktion der Pflanzendecke. – G. Fischer, Stuttgart 1962.
Lieth, H.: Ökologische Fragestellungen bei der Untersuchung der biologischen Stoffproduktion I. – Qualitas Plant. Materiae vegetabiles 12: 241-261, 1965.
Lieth, H.: The determination of plant dry-matter production with special emphasis on the underground parts. – In: Eckardt, F. E. (ed.): Functioning of Terrestrial Ecosystems at the Primary Production Level. Pp. 179-186. UNESCO, Paris 1968a.
Lieth, H.: The measurement of calorific values of biological material and the determination of ecological efficiency. – In: Eckardt, F. E. (ed.): Functioning of Terrestrial Ecosystems at the Primary Production Level. Pp. 233-242. UNESCO, Paris 1968b.
Long, F. L.: Application of calorimetric methods to ecological research. – Plant Physiol. 9: 323-338, 1934.
Ludlow, M. M., Wilson, G. L.: Studies on the productivity of tropical pasture plants. II. Growth analysis, photosynthesis, and respiration of 20 species of grasses and legumes in a controlled environment. – Aust. J. agric. Res. 21: 183-194, 1970.
MacColl, D., Cooper, J. P.: Climatic variation in forage grasses III. Seasonal changes in growth and assimilation in climatic races of *Lolium*, *Dactylis* and *Festuca*. – J. appl. Ecol. 4: 113-127, 1967.
Maggs, D. H.: The effect of number of shoots on the quantity and distribution of increment in young apple-trees. – Ann. Bot. N.S. 24: 345-355, 1960.
Magin, R.: Struktur und Leistung mehrschichtiger Mischwälder in den bayerischen Alpen. – Mitt. Staatsforstverwaltung Bayerns 30: 1-161, 1959.
Mayer, R.: Kronengrösse und Zuwachsleistung der Traubeneiche auf süddeutschen Standorten. – Allg. Forst- Jagdztg. 129: 151-163, 1958.
Medina, E.: Über die Beziehungen zwischen Chlorophyllgehalt, assimilierender Fläche und Trockensubstanzproduktion einiger Pflanzengemeinschaften. – Thesis, Inst. Bot. Landw. Hochschule, Stuttgart-Hohenheim 1964.
Medina, E., Lieth, H.: Die Beziehungen zwischen Chlorophyllgehalt, assimilierender Fläche und Trockensubstanzproduktion in einigen Pflanzengemeinschaften. – Beitr. Biol. Pflanzen 40: 451-494, 1964.
Methods of Productivity Studies in Root Systems and Rhizosphere Organisms. – Nauka, Leningrad 1968.
Milner, C., Hughes R. E.: Methods for the Measurement of the Primary Production of Grassland. – IBP Handbook No. 6. Blackwell Sci. Publ., Oxford 1968.

Milthorpe, F. L.: The nature and analysis of competition between plants of different species. – In: Milthorpe, F. L. (ed.): Mechanisms of Biological Competition. – Symp. Soc. exp. Biol. 15: 330-335, 1961.

Milthorpe, F. L.: Some aspects of plant growth. An introductory survey. – In: Ivins, J. D., Milthorpe, F. L. (ed.): The Growth of Potato. Pp. 3-16. Butterworths, London 1963.

Möller, C. M., Müller, D., Nielsen, J.: Graphic presentation of dry matter production of European beech. – Forstlige Forsøgsvaesen i Danmark 21: 327-335, 1954.

Monselise, S. P.: Growth analysis of *Citrus* seedlings. II. A comparison between sweet lime, rough lemon and sour orange. – Palest. J. Bot. 8: 125-132, 1953.

Monsi, M.: Mathematical models of plant communities. – In: Eckardt, F. E. (ed.): Functioning of Terrestrial Ecosystems at the Primary Production Level. Pp. 131-149. UNESCO, Paris 1968.

Monteith, J. L.: Light distribution and photosynthesis in field crops. – Ann. Bot. N.S. 29: 17-37, 1965.

Monteith, J. L.: Climatological measurements. – Photosynthetica 1: 129-132, 1967.

Müller, D., Nielsen, J.: Production brute, pertes par respiration et production nette dans la forêt ombrophile tropicale. – Forstlige Forsøgsvaesen i Danmark 29: 69-160, 1965.

Mutoh, N., Yoshida, K. H., Yokoi, Y., Kimura, M., Hogetsu, K.: Studies on the production processes and net production of *Miscanthus sacchariflorus* community. – Jap. J. Bot. 20: 67-92, 1968 a.

Mutoh, N., Yoshida, K. H., Yokoi, Y., Kimura, M., Midorikawa, B.: Studies on the production processes and net production of the *Miscanthus sacchariflorus* community. – In: Photosynthesis and Utilization of Solar Energy. Level III Experiments 1966-1967. Pp. 47-54. Tokyo 1968.

Nečas, J.: Die Beziehungen von Blattfläche und Trockensubstanzproduktion bei Kartoffeln. – In: Fragen der Pflanzenzüchtung und Pflanzenphysiologie. Tagungsberichte Deut. Akad. Landwirtschaftswiss. (Berlin) 48: 79-93, 1962.

Nečas, J.: Application of growth analysis to potatoes in field culture and some specific features of potato growth. – Biol. Plant. 7: 180-193, 1965.

Nečas, J.: Growth analytical approach to the analysis of yielding capacity of potato varieties. – Photosynthetica 2: 85-100, 1968.

Nečas, J., Zrůst, J., Partyková, E.: Determination of the leaf area of potato plants. – Photosynthetica 1: 97-111, 1967.

Newbould, P. J.: Production ecology. – Sci. Prog. twent. Cent. 51: 91-104, 1963.

Newbould, P. J.: Methods for Estimating the Primary Production of Forests. – IBP Handbook No. 2. Blackwell Sci. Publ., Oxford-Edinburgh 1967.

Nichiporovich, A. A.: Aims of research on the photosynthesis of plants as a factor of productivity. – In: Nichiporovich, A. A. (ed.): Photosynthesis of Productive Systems. Pp. 3-36. Israel Program for sci. Translations. Jerusalem 1967.

Ničiporovič, A. A.: Evaluation of productivity by study of photosynthesis as a function of illumination. – In: Eckardt, F. E. (ed.): Functioning of Terrestrial Ecosystems at the Primary Production Level. Pp. 261-270. UNESCO, Paris 1968.

Nichiporovich, A. A., Strogonova, L. E., Chmora, S. N., Vlasova, M. P.: Fotosinteticheskaya Deyatel'nost' Rasteniĭ v Posevakh. [Photosynthetic Activity of Plants in Crops.] – Izdat. Akad. Nauk SSSR, Moskva 1961.

Nösberger, J., Humphries, E. C.: The influence of removing tubers on dry-matter production and net assimilation rate of potato plants. – Ann. Bot. N.S. 29: 579-588, 1965.

Nösberger, J., Thorne, G. N.: The effect of removing florets or shading the ear of barley on production and distribution of dry matter. – Ann. Bot. N.S. 29: 635-644, 1965.

Ōkubo, T., Hoshino, M., Nishimura, S.: Chlorophyll amount for analysis of matter production in forage crops. I. Changes in leaf area index and chlorophyll amount with the regrowth of ladino clover sward. – Proc. Crop Sci. Soc. Jap. 33: 125-129, 1964.

Ōkubo, T., Ōizumi, H., Hoshino, M., Nishimura, S.: Chlorophyll amount for analysis of matter production in forage crops. – In: Photosynthesis and Utilization of Solar Energy. Level III Experiments 1966-1967. Pp. 43-46. Tokyo 1968.

Ondok, J. P.: Analyse des Blattwachstums als Methode zur Bestimmung des Massstabes der ontogenetischen Entwicklung. – Studia biophysica (Berlin) 11: 161-168, 1968.

Ondok, J. P.: Die Probleme der Anwendung der Wachstumsanalyse auf Forschungen von *Phragmites communis* Trin. – Hidrobiologia (Bucureşti) 10: 87-95, 1969.

Ondok, J. P.: Growth analysis applied to the estimation of gross assimilation and respiration rate. – Photosynthetica 4: 214-222, 1970.

Ovington, J. D.: Dry-matter production by *Pinus silvestris* L. – Ann. Bot. N.S. 21: 287-314, 1957.

Ovington, J. D.: Some aspects of energy flow in plantations of *Pinus silvestris* L. – Ann. Bot. N.S. 25: 12-20, 1961.

Ovington, J. D.: Quantitative ecology and the woodland ecosystem concept. – Adv. ecol. Res. 1: 103-192, 1962.

Ovington, J. D., Heitkamp, D.: The accumulation of energy in forest plantations in Britain. – J. Ecol. 48: 639-646, 1960.

Ovington, J. D., Forrest, W. G., Armstrong, J. S.: Tree biomass estimation. – In: Primary Productivity and Mineral Cycling in Natural Ecosystems. Univ. of Maine Press, December 27, 1967.

Pardé, J.: Bases et méthodes d'évaluation de la productivité ligneuse stationelle n'impliquant pas la coupe des arbres. – In: Eckardt, F. E. (ed.): Functioning of Terrestrial Ecosystems at the Primary Production Level. Pp. 203-209. UNESCO, Paris 1968.

Petrie, A. H. K., Arthur, J. I.: Physiological ontogeny in the tobacco plant. – Aust. J. exp. Biol. med. Sci. 191-200, 1943.

Pflanz, B.: Der Energiegehalt und die ökologische Energieausbeute verschiedener Pflanzen und Pflanzenbestände. – Thesis, Techn. Hochschule, Stuttgart 1964.

Pilát, A.: Chlorophyll content and dry matter production in five meadow communities. – Photosynthetica 1: 253-257, 1967.

Popescu-Zeletin, I.: Méthode et appareils pour déterminer la dynamique de l'accroissement radial des arbres pendant la période de végétation. – In: Eckardt, F. E. (ed.): Functioning of Terrestrial Ecosystems at the Primary Production Level. Pp. 211-217. UNESCO, Paris 1968.

PP Photosynthesis and Utilization of Solar Energy; Level I Experiments. Report I. Technical Problems and Data Collected in 1966. – Tokyo 1967.

PP Photosynthesis and Utilization of Solar Energy; Level I Experiments. Report II. Data Collected in 1967. – Tokyo 1969.

Radford, P. J.: Growth analysis formulae, their use and abuse. – Crop Sci. 7: 171-174, 1967.

Raeuber, A., Engel, K.-H.: Untersuchungen über den Verlauf der Massenzunahme bei Kartoffeln (*Solanum tuberosum* L.) in Abhängigkeit von Umwelt- und Erbguteinflüssen. – Abhandl. meteorol. Dienstes DDR (Berlin) 10 (76): 1-117, 1966.

Rees, A. R.: An analysis of growth of oil palm seedlings in full daylight and in shade. – Ann. Bot. N.S. 27: 325-337, 1963.

Ross, Yu. K., Vlasova, M. P.: Biometric characteristics of a maize stand and the dynamics of its development. – In: Nichiporovich, A. A. (ed.): Photosynthesis of Productive Systems. Pp. 60-74. Israel Program for sci. Translations, Jerusalem 1967.

Ruck, H. C., Bolas, B. D.: Studies in the comparative physiology of apple rootstocks. I. The effect of nitrogen on the growth and assimilation of Malling apple rootstocks. – Ann. Bot. N.S. 20: 57-68, 1956.

Rutter, A. J.: Studies in the growth of young plants of *Pinus sylvestris* L. I. The annual cycle of assimilation and growth. – Ann. Bot. N.S. 21: 399-426, 1957.

Rychnovská, M.: A contribution to the autecology of *Phragmites communis* Trin. I. Physiological heterogeneity of leaves. – Folia geobot. phytotax. (Praha) 2: 179-188, 1967.

Saeki, T.: Variation of photosynthetic activity with ageing of leaves and total photosynthesis in a plant community. – Bot. Mag. (Tokyo) 72: 404-408, 1959.

Saeki, T.: Interrelationships between leaf amount, light distribution and total photosynthesis in a plant community. – Bot. Mag. (Tokyo) 73: 55-63, 1960.

Saeki, T.: Analytical studies on the development of foliage of a plant community. – Bot. Mag. (Tokyo) 74: 342-348, 1961.

Schultz, G.: Blattfläche und Assimilationsleistung in Beziehung zur Stoffproduktion. Untersuchungen an Zuckerrüben. – Ber. deut. bot. Ges. 75: 261-267, 1962.

Schuurman, J. J., Goedewaagen, M. A. J.: Methods for the Examination of Root Systems and Roots. – PUDOC, Wageningen 1965.

Schwarze, P.: Stoffproduktion und Pflanzenzüchtung. – In: Handbuch der Pflanzenzüchtung 1: 307-335, 1956.
Šesták, Z., Čatský, J.: Sur les relations entre le contenu en chlorophylle et l'activité photosynthétique pendant la croissance et le vieillissement des feuilles. – In: Sironval, C. (ed.): Le Chloroplaste, Croissance et Vieillissement. Pp. 213-262. Masson et Cie, Paris 1967.
Smetánková, M.: Dry matter production and growth in length of overground parts of *Carex humilis* Leyss. – Biol. Plant. 1: 235-247, 1959.
Snedecor, G. W.: Statistical Methods. – 6th Ed., Iowa State College Press, Ames, Iowa 1957.
Sonneveld, A.: Distribution and re-distribution of dry matter in perennial fodder crops. – Neth. J. agr. Sci. 10: 427-444, 1962.
Sprague, H. B., Curtis, N.: Chlorophyll content as an index of the productive capacity of selfed lines of corn and their hybrids. – J. Amer. Soc. Agron. 25: 709-724, 1933.
Stern, W. R.: The seasonal growth characteristics of irrigated cotton in a dry monsoonal environment. – Aust. J. agr. Res. 16: 347-366, 1965.
Stoy, V.: Photosynthesis, respiration and carbohydrate accumulation in spring wheat in relation to yield. – Physiol. Plant. 18 (Suppl. IV): 1-125, 1965.
Straškraba, M.: Der Anteil der höheren Pflanzen an der Produktion der stehenden Gewässer. – Mitt. int. Verein. Limnol. (Stuttgart) 14: 212-230, 1968.
Thorne, G. N.: Photosynthesis of lamina and sheaths of barley leaves. – Ann. Bot. N.S. 23: 365-370, 1959.
Thorne, G. N.: Variations with age in net assimilation rate and other growth attributes of sugar-beet, potato, and barley in a controlled environment. – Ann. Bot. N.S. 24: 356-371, 1960.
Thorne, G. N.: Effect of age and environment on net assimilation rate of barley. – Ann. Bot. N.S. 25: 29-38, 1961.
Thorne, G. N.: Physiological aspects of grain yield in cereals. – In: Milthorpe, F. L., Ivins, J. D. (ed.): The Growth of Cereals and Grasses. Pp. 88-105. Butterworths sci. Publ., London 1965.
Thorne, G. N., Ford, M. A., Watson, D. J.: Growth, development and yield of spring wheat in artificial climates. – Ann. Bot. N.S. 32: 425-446, 1968.
Troughton, A.: The application of the allometric formula to the study of the relationship between the roots and shoots of young grass plant. – Agr. Progress 30: 1-7, 1955.
Troughton, A.: Grass roots, their morphology and relationship with the shoot system. – In: Methods of Productivity Studies in Root Systems and Rhizosphere Organisms. Pp. 213-220. Nauka, Leningrad 1968.
Ustenko, G. P., Yagnova, S. N.: Planning high maize yields based on the use of solar radiation at a chosen efficiency. – In: Nichiporovich, A. A. (ed.): Photosynthesis of Productive Systems. Pp. 144-156. Israel Program for sci. Translations, Jerusalem 1967.
Václavík, J.: Growth response to different constant soil moisture levels in maize (*Zea mays* L.) during the vegetative phase. – Biol. Plant. 9: 462-472, 1967.
Václavík, J.: Effect of different constant soil moisture levels on foliage development in maize. – Biol. Plant. 11: 68-78, 1969.
Vernon, A. J., Allison, J. C. S.: A method of calculating net assimilation rate. – Nature 200: 814, 1963.
Vinš, B.: Foundations, methods and use of tree-ring analyses on cores extracted by an increment borer. – In: Eckardt, F. E. (ed.): Functioning of Terrestrial Ecosystems at the Primary Production Level. Pp. 219-227. UNESCO, Paris 1968.
Walter, H.: La productivité du tapis végetal. – Lejeunia 22: 1-13, 1963.
Warren Wilson, J.: High net assimilation rates of sunflower plants in an arid climate. – Ann. Bot. N.S. 30: 745-751, 1966.
Warren Wilson, J.: Effects of seasonal variation in radiation and temperature on net assimilation and growth rates in an arid climate. – Ann. Bot. N.S. 31: 41-57, 1967.
Wassink, E. C.: The effect of light intensity on growth and development of *Gladiolus*. – In: Christensen, B. C., Buchmann, B. (ed.): Progress in Photobiology. Pp. 371-378. Elsevier Publ. Co., Amsterdam–London–New York–Princeton 1961.
Wassink, E. C.: Light intensity effects in growth and development of tulips, in comparison with those in *Gladiolus*. – Meded. Landbouwhogeschool Wageningen 65(15): 1-21, 1965.
Wassink, E. C.: Light energy conversion in photosynthesis and growth of plants. – In: Eckardt,

F. E. (ed.): Functioning of Terrestrial Ecosystems at the Primary Production Level. Pp. 53-66. UNESCO, Paris 1968.
Watson, D. J.: Comparative physiological studies on the growth of field crops. II. The effect of varying nutrient supply on net assimilation rate and leaf area. – Ann. Bot. N.S. 11: 375-407, 1947.
Watson, D. J.: The physiological basis of variation in yield. – Adv. Agron. 4: 101-145, 1952.
Watson, D. J.: Leaf growth in relation to crop yield. – In: Milthorpe, F. L. (ed.): The Growth of Leaves. Pp. 178-191. Butterworths, London 1956.
Watson, D. J.: The dependence of net assimilation rate on leaf-area index. – Ann. Bot. N.S. 22: 37-54, 1958.
Watson, D. J.: Climate, weather and plant yield. – In: Evans, L. T. (ed.): Environmental Control of Plant Growth. Pp. 337-350. Academic Press, New York–London 1963.
Watson, D. J., Hayashi, K.: Photosynthetic and respiratory components of the net assimilation rates of sugar beet and barley. – New Phytol. 64: 38-47, 1965.
Watson, D. J., Thorne, G. N., French, S. A. W.: Physiological causes of differences in grain yield between varieties of barley. – Ann. Bot. N.S. 22: 321-352, 1958.
Watson, D. J., Wilson, J. H., Ford, M. A., French, S. A. W.: Changes with age in the photosynthetic and respiratory components of the net assimilation rates of sugar beet and wheat. – New Phytol. 65: 500-508, 1966.
Weber, E.: Grundriss der biologischen Statistik für Naturwissenschaftler, Landwirte und Mediziner. – 3. Aufl. VEB G. Fischer, Jena 1957.
Westlake, D. F.: Comparisons of plant productivity. – Biol. Rev. (Cambridge) 38: 385-425, 1963.
Westlake, D. F.: Some basic data for investigations of the productivity of aquatic macrophytes. – Mem. Ist. ital. Idrobiol. 18 (Suppl.). 229-248, 1965a.
Westlake, D. F.: Theoretical aspects of the comparability of productivity data. – Mem. Ist. ital. Idrobiol. 18 (Suppl.): 313-321, 1965b.
Whitehead, F. H., Myerscough, P. J.: Growth analysis of plants. The ratio of mean relative growth rate to mean relative rate of leaf area increase. – New Phytol. 61: 314-321, 1962.
Williams, R. F.: Physiological ontogeny in plants and its relations to nutrition. 6. Analysis of the unit leaf rate. – Austr. J. exp. Biol. med. Sci. 17: 123-132, 1939.
Williams, R. F.: The physiology of plant growth with special reference to the concept of net assimilation rate. – Ann. Bot. N.S. 10: 41-72, 1946.
de Wit, C. T.: Photosynthesis of leaf canopies. – Agric. Res. Rep. (Wageningen) 663: 1-57, 1965.
Zalenskiĭ, O. V.: Ob ekologo-fiziologicheskom izuchenii faktorov produktivnosti dikorastushchikh mnogoletnikh rasteniĭ. [Ecophysiological investigations on factors affecting the productivity of wild-growing perennial plants.] – In: Akademiku Sukachevu k 75-letiyu so Dnya Rozhdenya. – Pp. 217-238. Izdat. Akad. Nauk SSSR, Moskva–Leningrad 1956.

11 | INDIRECT ESTIMATION OF PRIMARY VALUES USED IN GROWTH ANALYSIS

11.1 | Definition and use of the indirect methods

Ideally, in growth analysis the same plants should be followed throughout the experiment. We can only approach this ideal situation by estimating indirectly the primary values (dry weight, leaf area, *etc.*) for growth analysis. Indirect methods are usually less time-consuming than other similar techniques used in destructive harvesting, *e.g.* matching pairs of the plants, plots, *etc.* Indirect sampling implies non-destructive recording of certain parameters on intact plants, *e.g.* the numbers and dimensions of whole shoots and other plant parts. The primary values used for further calculations of growth characteristics are derived from these parameters by various statistical procedures. Choice of the parameters and of the statistical procedures depends mainly on the kind of plant investigated and on the information required. Indirect methods of estimating leaf area are presented in Chapter 14. This chapter will therefore deal mainly with methods of indirect estimations of dry weight and rate of dry matter production.

Indirect non-destructive methods of assessment of timber production have been developed to a high degree in forestry. With plants other than trees, direct destructive harvesting of large samples is also often impracticable or too time-consuming. Application of indirect methods is thus of advantage even with herbaceous plants and their stands. In communities of wild plants, with their generally large variation in specific composition, density, vertical structure and pattern, indirect estimations enable growth analytical investigations to be carried out without harvesting very large samples. This avoids severe damage to the stand and saves labour, time, drying-ovens, *etc.*

Effects of short term fluctuations in climatic factors on crop growth rate and other growth characteristics are easiest to follow if short term biomass increments are estimated indirectly from non-destructive measurements. In Unger's (1962) experiments with peas, an area of 100 m^2 would have to be harvested every day to assess a statistically significant increase in crop growth rate corresponding to an increase of 3 °C in daily mean temperature. Apart from being extremely time-consuming, harvesting the samples from such a large area would increase the error caused by variation in soil conditions.

The same plant or stand cannot be harvested more than once but can be measured many times. Growth curves based on data obtained by indirect estimations will therefore be smoother than those based on destructive harvests. This difference is shown in Fig. 11.1. The shape of any growth curve, as we record it, is determined by factors of ontogenesis, environment and sampling. Fig. 11.2 shows the superposition of these three effects. Curve *a* is a theoretical curve of growth under optimal environmental conditions (which will be, of course, different in different stages of development). Such a curve will reflect the ontogenetic drift of growth rate during the growing period. Curve *b* illustrates the course of actual growth during that period. Deviations of *b* from *a*, brought about by sub-optimal growth

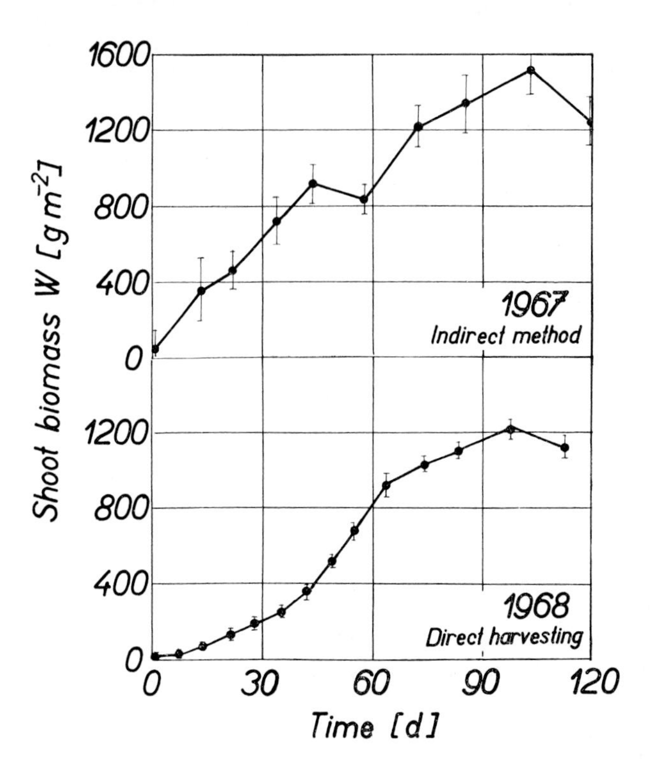

Fig. 11.1 Seasonal changes in shoot biomass W [g dry weight m^{-2}] in a stand of common reed *(Phragmites communis)*. Top: The biomass values were obtained by the indirect method of non-destructive measurements with 4 harvested, parallel samples chosen to be similar to the stand growing in the standard plot (50 cm × 100 cm). Bottom: Values obtained by direct destructive harvesting of four 0.5 m^2 plots on each sampling occasion.

rate, are proportional to the differences between the optimal and actual environmental conditions at any one time. Curve c is based on measured dry weight data. Deviations of c from b result from the sampling error.
Usually, we wish to assess either the ontogenetic component of growth and production or the modifying effects of environment. In either case, we should try to reduce the sampling error to a minimum. For this, indirect methods are often useful.

11.2 | Technique of indirect estimation

11.2.1 | Apparatus for recording growth of stands in situ

The apparatus of Unger (1962, 1968) measures the absorption and scattering of ionizing radiation, which are proportional to the fresh weight of the stand. Measurement is continuous or at frequent intervals, so that daily fluctuations in the fresh weight of the plants are recorded. The dry weight of the plants is assessed from parallel destructive samples. Electronic apparatuses with similar properties, suitable for recording above-ground biomass of pastures, have been devised by Campbell, Phillips & O'Reilly (1962), Alcock & Lovett (1967), and Alcock,

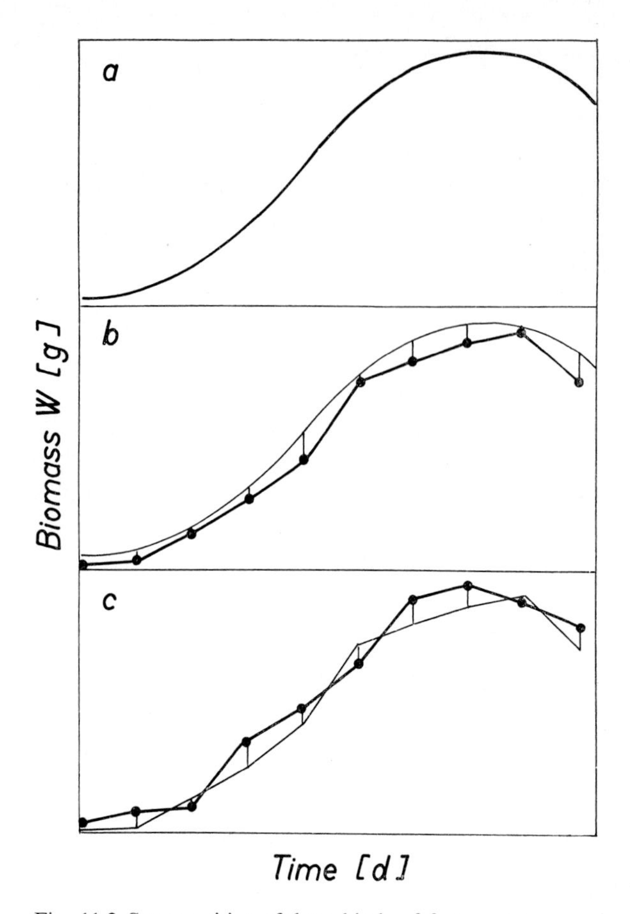

Fig. 11.2 Superposition of three kinds of factors, ontogenesis (*a*), environment (*b*) and measurement (*c*) affecting the shape of a growth curve. For further explanation see text.

Lovett & Machin (1968). Mechanical devices for measuring increments in trunk diameter of trees are called dendrographs – if the output appears directly on a drum (*e.g.* Fritts & Fritts 1955; Kozlowski & Winget 1964), or dendrometers – if the output is in the form of an electrical analogue (*e.g.* Impens & Schalck 1965; Daum 1967; Popescu-Zeletin 1968).

11.2.2 Non-destructive measurements of standard plants or plots with parallel destructive sampling

Growth of a selected part of the stand, *e.g.* on a standard permanent quadrat of 1 m^2 area, is followed by means of non-destructive measurements throughout the experiment. The measurements include some parameters which characterize the growth of plants (height of individual plants, number of leaves on individual plants, number of plants in the permanent quadrat *etc.*) and are taken at certain suitably selected intervals during the whole season. At the same intervals several destructive parallel samples are taken, chosen to resemble, as far as possible, the stand growing on the standard plot. This may be done, *e.g.*, by harvesting the same number of plants as that in the permanent quadrat, from a suitable site in the stand with approximately the same density and plant characteristics as those on the standard quadrat. Success and accuracy in obtaining the values required – dry weight of the biomass, leaf area, *etc.* – depend on the choice and number of suitable criteria of similarity between the standard and parallel plots and on the frequency of both non-destructive measurements and destructive harvesting. The criteria of similarity are usually the number of shoots per plot, shoot lengths, dimensions and numbers of leaves, stem diameters, *etc.* The accuracy of the method will increase with increasing number of parallel samples harvested. Harvesting more parallel samples will often be simpler and will disturb the permanent standard plot less than measuring a larger number of parameters. In a stand of *Phragmites communis* L., for example, satisfactory accuracy of sampling was achieved by taking two criteria of similarity, namely stand density and shoot length, and by harvesting four parallel samples at weekly intervals. Variation of mean values recorded in the parallel destructive harvests (expressed in terms of standard deviation, variation coefficient, *etc.*) will indicate whether or not enough criteria of similarity and a sufficient number of replicates have been introduced. The sampling technique may then be modified during the experiment.

Parallel destructive harvesting can be accomplished either by selecting individual shoots from different parts of the stand and making up 'synthetic' parallel samples or by harvesting all shoots growing on parallel plots. The first of these two techniques is usually easier and more accurate, especially in wild communities. However, attention must be paid to the effect of stand density on shoot size and other shoot properties; the shoots constituting the parallel 'synthetic' samples should preferably be harvested at places where the stand density is much the same as in the permanent plot.

Although this technique has been designed primarily for wild communities, its application to field and pot experiments with crops can also be of advantage.

11.2.3 | Non-destructive measurements of standard plants or plots with calibration by means of regression equations

This method resembles the previous one described in Section 11.2.2. The non-destructive measurements of selected parameters on the plants growing in permanent standard quadrats at certain suitably selected intervals are again made during the whole growing season, but at the date of each measurement no parallel destructive samples of similar size are taken. The parameters recorded on the intact plants are not used as criteria of similarity with parallel harvests but are used as input data for regression equations, by means of which primary values for further growth analysis are calculated. The number of regression equations is equal to the number of primary values required. For constructing the regressions between the parameters measured on the intact plants and the primary values required, individual plants (or only shoots) are sampled in parallel, to cover the whole range of variation of parameters found in shoots growing in the standard plot(s). By means of this sampling of individual plants the coefficients of regression equations are determined. The number of plants (shoots) in the parallel samples will depend on the fiducial limits set up by the investigator.

The variables in the regression equations are the parameters measured on the growing stand in the permanent quadrat, *e.g.* for calculating the dry matter of the total biomass, the parameters are the height of individual plants, the diameter of their stems, the number of leaves, *etc.* The choice of the parameters measured on the intact plants depends on the morphological character of these plants and on the required accuracy of estimates of the primary values. It is advisable to have more than one standard plot. Later in the experiment, only the most representative plot may be retained. Frequent measurements must not damage the plants or alter the environment in the standard plot. As a rule, the more parameters that are measured, the more reliable the regression equations obtained. It is useful to estimate beforehand the importance of individual parameters for the regressions. If, however, the investigator has already recorded several parameters he can test statistically the importance of each of them and decide on its inclusion in a regression equation.

The parameters recorded are usually of the same kind as those discussed in Section 11.2.2. Let us take a few examples. For calculating total leaf and stem dry weights and total leaf area in a maize stand, Ross & Vlasova (1966) used the following parameters: shoot height, stem length, number of leaves per shoot, stem diameter, and stand density. (For details see Section 11.2.3.1.) In a stand of *Carex physodes*, Gringov & Alimzhanov (1962) calculated total biomass from the number of stems per m^2 and from stem lengths. Evans *et al.* (1961) calculated the total dry weight of grasses in glasshouse pot experiments from the lengths of the longest green leaves and from the numbers of leaves per shoot. Svoboda, Květ, Ondok & Fiala (unpublished) calculated total shoot dry weight and total leaf area in *Typha latifolia* from stem length, inflorescence length, number of leaves per shoot, and length and width of the longest leaf.

Various types of regression equations can be used, *e.g.* linear functions, polynomes and various exponential functions. Selection of an appropriate type of equation is connected with statistical problems which are discussed in Section 11.3.2.

In what respect do the methods described in Sections 11.2.2 and 11.2.3 differ? Both are based on non-destructive measurement. But in the first case the parallel harvesting is much larger than in the second, in which only individual plants are harvested to construct the regression equations. Thus the first method is more time-consuming, while the second procedure involves more calculation and may therefore be used with advantage where computer facilities are available. It is also important that the stand is not damaged by frequent harvesting in such an extent as with the first method. The second method seems to be more accurate as it allows estimation of the confidence interval for the values which are used to estimate the real values in the stand by means of regression equations. An estimation of reliability may be realized by considering the error connected with each of the regression equations and its influence on the final error of the derived values. Such an estimation cannot be made for the first method.

11.2.3.1 Example: indirect estimation of growth and dry matter production in a maize stand (from Ross & Vlasova 1966)

The maize plants were grown in rows 50 cm apart, with 154 000 plants per

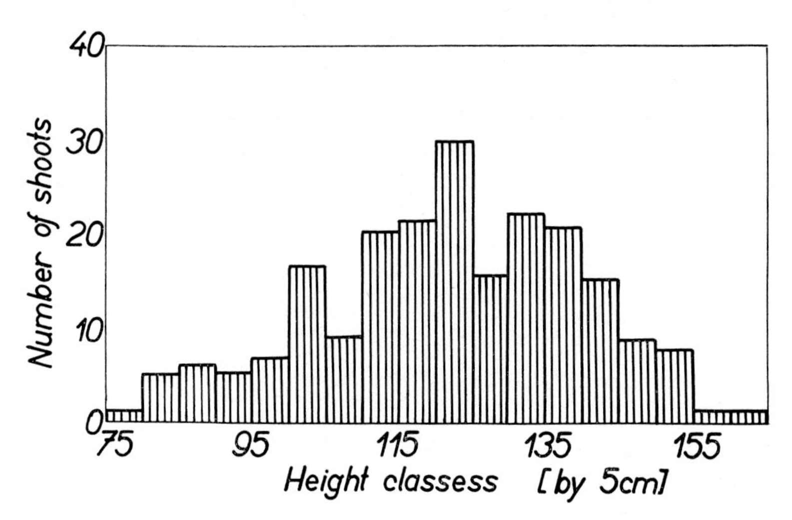

Fig. 11.3 Distribution of shoot height in a maize stand. (From Ross & Vlasova 1966.)

hectare. The large variation in shoot lengths in the stand is shown in Fig. 11.3. In a sample of 200 shoots, the following parameters were recorded every 10 days: h_1: shoot height from soil surface to the uppermost leaf in its natural position [cm]; h_c: stem length (in later stages stem and panicle length) [cm]; n_L: number of leaves per shoot; d: maximum stem diameter [mm]; n_t: stand density, *i.e.* number of shoots per m^2. For each set of measurements recorded (*i.e.*, every 10 days), the distribution of each parameter in the set of 200 shoots was assessed, and the corresponding values of the arithmetic mean, standard deviation, and variation coefficient were calculated. All the parameters were normally distributed. Calculation showed that at least 150 plants must be measured to keep the standard error of the mean within 5% limits. Analysis showed correlations between the individual parameters recorded.
First, correlation graphs were plotted for finding total leaf area (*i.e.*, leaf area index), $\bar{L}(t)$, and total shoot dry weight, $\overline{W}_s(t)$, of the stand. For this purpose, mean values obtained from measurements recorded on 15 to 20 shoots at 7 to 10 day intervals were sufficient. The following regression equations were used to calculate leaf area, L, and dry weight, W_s, respectively, of individual shoots:

$$L = 1.32\, h_l n_L \tag{11.1}$$

$$W_s = 1.25\, h_l h_c + 3.4;\ W_s > 6 \tag{11.2}$$

(h_l and h_c [cm], L [cm^2], W_s [g])

The leaf area index, $\bar{L}(t)$, and total shoot dry weight, $\overline{W}_s(t)$, were calculated from equations similar to (11.1) and (11.2), respectively, introducing the appropriate mean values of h_l, h_c and n_L and the number of shoots per hectare, N_p:

$$\bar{L}(t) = 1.32\, N_p\, \bar{h}_l(t)\, \bar{n}_L(t) \tag{11.3}$$

$$\overline{W}_s(t) = 1.25\, N_p\, \bar{h}_l(t)\, \bar{h}_c(t)\, \bar{n}_L(t) + 3.4\, N_p \tag{11.4}$$

(t) indicates that the mean values were determined for each date of measurement separately.
Values needed for subsequent growth analysis were calculated from values obtained by means of equations (11.1) to (11.4). They are, *e.g.* the mean daily increase of leaf area $\Delta L/\Delta t$, crop growth rate $C = \Delta W_s/\Delta t$, photosynthetic potential (*i.e.* leaf area duration), D, and net assimilation rate, E. The last two values were calculated in the following way:

$$D = \int_0^t \bar{L}(t')\mathrm{d}t' \qquad (11.5)$$

$$E = \frac{W_s(t_2) - W_s(t_1)}{D(t_2) - D(t_1)} \qquad (11.6)$$

Individual values are presented in Table 11.1. They were correlated with fluctuations in weather conditions.

Table 11.1 Growth characteristics of maize obtained indirectly from regression equations (from Ross & Vlasova 1966).

Date	$\bar{L}(t)$	$\frac{\Delta\bar{L}}{\Delta t}$	$W_s(t)$	$\frac{\Delta W_s}{\Delta t}$	E	D
		[$\times 10^4$ m^2 ha^{-1} d^{-1}]	[$\times 10^2$ kg ha^{-1}]	[$\times 10^2$ kg ha^{-1}d^{-1}]	[g m^{-2} d^{-1}]	[$\times 10^6$ m^2 ha^{-1} d^{-1}]
5-6	0	0.002	0	0.02	0	0
10-6	0.01	0.014	0.1	0.06	6	0
15-6	0.08	0.018	0.3	0.06	7	0.004
20-6	0.17	0.024	0.6	0.13	3	0.011
25-6	0.29	0.028	1.2	0.18	2	0.024
30-6	0.43	0.030	2.1	0.14	2.6	0.043
5-7	0.58	0.032	2.8	0.16	2.4	0.070
10-7	0.74	0.088	3.6	0.51	5.8	0.104
15-7	1.20	0.116	6.2	1.02	6.8	0.148
20-7	1.78	0.082	11.3	0.74	3.6	0.229
25-7	2.19	0.188	15.0	0.83	2.5	0.333
31-7	3.13	0.283	19.2	3.01	8.5	0.499
5-8	4.83	0.228	37.2	2.22	3.9	0.713
10-8	5.97	0.202	48.3	2.85	4.3	0.997
15-8	6.98	0.254	62.5	4.00	5.1	1.330
20-8	8.25	—	82.5	—	—	1.720

$\bar{L}(t)$ is the leaf area index at time t; W_s is shoot dry weight at time t; E is net assimilation rate; D is leaf area duration.

11.2.4 *Indirect estimation of growth of underground parts in individual plants and stands*

Indirect methods are of great value in the application of growth analysis to whole plants, including roots, rhizomes, *etc.*, though they are not without technical difficulties.

11.2.4.1 Direct observations of growing roots

Various devices have been constructed to enable direct measurements or photography of growing roots. These devices are usually modifications to Sachs' 'boxes' and have been described by Griffith & Howland (1961), Larson (1962), Wilcox (1962), Rogers & Head (1963, 1968) and others. Root lengths and diameters can be used to calculate root biomass from regression equations. Devices for direct observation are, however, better suited for observing the rhythm and rate of growth in length or volume of roots, rhizomes and tubers than for estimating their dry weight. The root environment is usually modified to such an extent that the results of these observations are hardly applicable to normal conditions.

11.2.4.2 Use of regression equations

Several authors have estimated root biomass by means of regression equations. Karizumi (1968) has applied this method to the tree species *Cryptomeria japonica* (see Section 11.2.4.3). Kira and Ogawa (1968) have modelled the growth of underground organs using allometric relations between the weights of trunk, branches, leaves and roots in different tree species. The basic relation:

$$W_R = a\,W_s^h \tag{11.7}$$

describes the allometric relation between root and trunk weight (W_R is root weight; W_S stem weight; h and a constants specific for the stand concerned). The same authors give another allometric relation between root biomass, W_R, and the breast-height diameter of stem, d:

$$W_R = cd^2 \tag{11.8}$$

in which c is an empirical constant.

The empirical constants of these equations are determined by destructive sampling of specimen individuals. Estimation of increments of root biomass in a stand is possible by simply recording Δd if c is known and remains constant, *i.e.* increments of d over a period of one or a few years. Both allometric relations, (11.7) and (11.8) give similar estimates so that either can be used. Losses of root biomass due to root mortality and decay must be estimated separately, *e.g.* by the method of Dahlmann (1968).

Allometric relations between shoot and root biomass in certain grasses, and their dependence on environmental conditions, were investigated by Troughton (1955,

1960, 1961). These papers show the extent to which the root biomass can be estimated from root : shoot ratios found in parallel small samples. Data on rhizome growth in certain reedswamp species, presented by Fiala *et al.* (1968) and by Westlake (1968), indicate that rhizome biomass may be estimated from the rate and pattern of vegetative spread of colonies of these species.

Raeuber & Engel (1966) have worked out a combined method of estimating the biomass of potato tubers and their growth. The method consists in periodically recording photographically or cinematographically the growth of the tubers in special cultivation boxes. The tubers are regarded as ellipsoids: the two diameters of each ellipsoid are related to tuber dry weight. A regression equation describing this relationship is based on parallel destructive harvesting of tubers of all the sizes found in the experimental material. Effectiveness as well as errors of this method are checked in the same way as in the methods described in Section 11.2.3.

11.2.4.3 | Example: choice of a suitable regression equation for estimating dry weight of various organs in *Cryptomeria japonica* (from Karizumi 1968)

This example illustrates the procedure of selecting a suitable form of regression equation. Biomass of individual plant organs y_{ij} was calculated from different types of regression equations in which the independent variables were d: breast height diameter [cm]; h: height from soil surface [m]; V: above-ground stem volume [cm^3]. Biomass y_{ij} was expressed as dry weight [g]. The following forms of equation were considered:

1. $y = a + b \log d + c \log h$
2. $y = a + b \log d$
3. $y = a + b \log (d^2h)$
4. $y = a + b\ (\pi d^2/4)$
5. $y = \log a + b \log (d^2h)$
6. $y = a + bV$
7. $y = a_0 + a_1d + a_2h + a_3d^2 + a_4dh + a_5h^2 + a_6d^3 + a_7d^2h + a_8dh^2 + a_9h^3$

Table 11.2 presents coefficients of variation ($c_V[\%] = s \cdot 100/\bar{x}$; s = standard deviation, $\bar{x}$ = mean value) for each regression equation and each y_{ij} value or combinations of these values. The complex regression equation (7) has not reduced the coefficient of variation appreciably in comparison with simpler types of equations. For estimating most y_{ij} values, (5) and (6) appear to be the most suitable regression equations. Total root biomass y_{11} can thus be estimated relatively easily from the simple equation (6):

$$y = a + bV \tag{11.9}$$

V, however, is a complex value that must be estimated separately. In fact, the somewhat more complicated equation (5), using directly measurable values of d and h, may therefore be easier to apply.

11.2.5 | Phenometric measurements

These measurements may also be considered under the heading of indirect methods,

Table 11.2 Comparison of the accuracy of estimation of tree biomass by 7 different forms of equation given in the text, in terms of the coefficient of the differences between calculated and observed values of y. (From Karizumi 1968.)

Dependent variables (y)	Coefficient of variation for equation						
	1	2	3	4	5	6	7
y_1 – stem weight	19	19	19	10	11	6	7
y_2 – branch weight	28	27	27	21	23	22	21
y_3 – leaf weight	20	19	19	23	22	22	18
y_4 – total shoot weight	16	16	15	10	9	6	8
y_5 – weight of fine roots	5	5	5	3	5	4	2
y_6 – weight of small roots	8	8	8	5	8	6	4
y_7 – weight of medium roots	13	13	13	7	9	6	6
y_8 – weight of large roots	23	23	22	18	22	15	16
y_9 – weight of very large roots	15	17	15	14	—	9	13
y_{10} – weight of root stock	14	17	16	16	11	14	8
y_{11} – total root weight	15	14	15	8	7	7	7
y_{12} – total tree weight	15	15	15	9	8	6	8
y_{13} – annual stem growth	20	20	19	14	16	7	10
y_{14} – annual leaf growth	20	19	19	23	22	22	18
y_{15} – annual branch growth	20	20	19	14	16	7	10
y_{16} – weight of above-ground woody organs ($y_1 + y_2$)	19	19	18	10	10	6	7
y_{17} – weight of active roots ($y_5 + y_6$)	7	6	7	4	6	5	2
y_{18} – weight of inactive roots ($y_7 + y_8 + y_9 + y_{10}$)	16	15	16	8	7	7	8
y_{19} – weight of total woody organs ($y_1 + y_2 + y_{11}$)	18	18	17	9	8	6	7
y_{20} – total annual growth ($y_{13} + y_{14} + y_{15} + y_{13} \cdot y_{11}/y_1$)	14	15	14	13	13	9	10
y_{21} – maximum depth of root	3	3	3	4	3	4	2

although biomass estimation is not their primary purpose. Phenometry is the measurement, on intact plants, of growth and development as affected by soil and climatic factors. One or several simple parameters are recorded, such as plant height, leaf length and width, leaf number, usually at daily intervals. Direct estimation of daily dry weight increments in a plant stand is impracticable, as has been stated before. Daily phenometric measurements replace the direct dry weight estimations when changes of growth rate are related to soil and weather conditions, which often change substantially and rapidly from day to day. However, as dry matter is not considered in phenometric measurements, we must be aware of the effects of radiation on growth in length: in extreme conditions, elongation of the plant stem, for example, does not correspond to growth of the plant as measured by increment of dry biomass. This may in practice represent a rather important limitation of phenometric methods. Phenometric measurements tend to be most reliable in those phases of development in which the morphological and anatomical structure of the plants does not change rapidly, *e.g.* in the linear phase of vegetative growth.

Phenometric measurements can be extremely useful for looking at response to environment, *e.g.* leaf elongation is a very sensitive measure of water stress (Perrier, McKell & Davidson 1961; Jarvis 1963). Phenometric measurements have been applied to the growth and development of cereal crops (*e.g.* Kretschmer 1949; Mayr 1953) and of maize (Raeuber *et al.* 1961; Raeuber & Bellmann 1968). Raeuber & Engel (1966) and Engel, Raeuber & Meinl (1968) regarded phenometry as a most useful tool for following the effect of climatic factors on plant production and growth.

11.3 | Certain statistical procedures applicable to indirect measurements

Most of these procedures are described in various handbooks of biological statistics, *e.g.* by Snedecor (1957), Weber (1957), Fisher (1963) and others. Therefore only those procedures which may be important for the needs of non-destructive methods are reviewed here.

11.3.1 | Selection of regression equations and of the fitting procedure

Different growth analytical primary values (total dry weight, leaf dry weight, leaf area, *etc.*) may change in different ways during the growing season. Hence the growth curves of these values will acquire different shapes. The general shape of a growth function (ascending or descending course, maxima and minima, repetition of extreme values, *etc.*) is evident if the data recorded in the experiment are plotted against time.

Fig. 11.4 shows the shapes of certain functions for various parameters and primary values that occur in regression equations used in indirect growth analysis. Comparison of the time course of experimental data with the functions shown in Fig. 11.4 will indicate which function could be used for fitting the regression equation. Statistical criteria are, of course, more refined. The following paragraphs

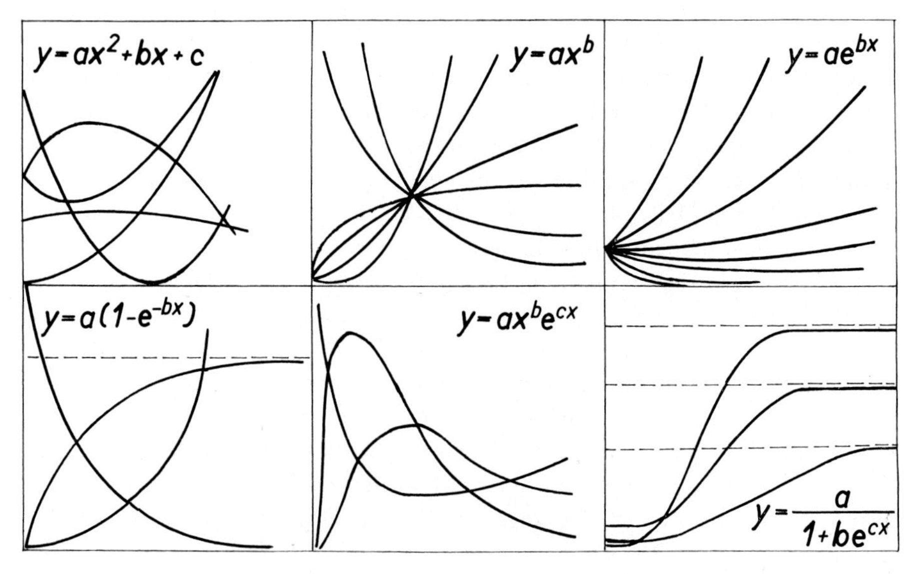

 Fig. 11.4 Examples of 6 different kinds of functions used for fitting the growth curves.

Table 11.3 Fitted regression functions; several common types.

Fitted function	Equation	Course	Fitting procedure	Remarks
Linear (with one variable)	$y = a_0 + a_1 x$	ascending or descending; no maximum	least squares, graphical, group, *etc.*	—
Linear (with several variables)	$y = a_0 + a_1 x + a_2 x + \ldots + a_n x_n$	ascending or descending, no maximum	least squares, graphical	suitable for: Gauss-Doolittle method, Gaussian multiphers, computer
Polynomes (with one variable)	$y = a_0 + a_1 x + + a_2 x^2 + \ldots + a_n x^n$	$(n - 1)$ extreme values (maxima or minima)	least squares, orthogonal polynomes	suitable for computer
Parabolic	$y = a_0 x^{a_1}$	unevenly ascending or descending; no maximum	transfer to logarithms, treat as linear functions	graphical solution possible
Exponential	$y = a_0 e^{a_1 x}$	so-called natural growth; no maximum	transfer to logarithms, treat as linear functions	graphical solution possible
Exponential (with an absolute expression)	$y = a_0 + e^{a_1 x}$	so-called natural growth (with a maximum or minimum)	approximative methods (see text)	—
Exponential (with a quadratic exponent)	$y = \exp(a_0 + a_1 x + + a_2 x^2)$	one maximum or minimum	transfer to logarithms, treat as quadratic functions	suitable for computer
Exponential (with a cubic exponent)	$y = \exp(a_0 + a_1 x + + a_2 x^2 + a_3 x^3)$	two extreme values	transfer to logarithms, treat as cubic functions	suitable for computer
Probability curve	$y = b \int_{-\infty}^{\infty} e^{\frac{(x - a_0)^2}{a_1}} \mathrm{d}x$	one maximum	graphical probability paper	—

illustrate several commonly occurring cases; a survey of regression functions is given in Table 11.3.

11.3.1.1 | Linear regressions with one independent variable

This type of function is often used for the sake of its simplicity. Its general shape is

$$y = a_0 + a_1 x \tag{11.10}$$

Calculation of these functions makes use of the method of least squares by means of the so-called normal equations. Graphical solutions may also be used: they are quicker but only approximate the mathematical solution. This degree of accuracy is nevertheless sufficient in many cases. One such solution consists in fitting a straight line through the experimentally obtained points in such way that the sums of their distances from the line on either side are minimal and cancel each other. The methods of orthogonal regression line and of principal axes (Dagnelie 1964) are other possible ways finding the regression functions. The degree of correlation and effectiveness of the regressions can be estimated from the correlation coefficients and from the coefficients of determination, respectively. The coefficient of determination c_d is given by the expression:

$$c_d = \frac{\sum_{i=1}^{n} (y_i^* - \bar{y})^2}{\sum_{i=1}^{n} (y_i - \bar{y})^2} \tag{11.11}$$

where y^* is a fitted value of y and $\bar{y}$ is mean. c_d is therefore a measure of the share of variance y which may be explained by the regression function and may be used for all sorts of these functions. To test the effectiveness of the regression or the importance of individual parameters in the regression function, the analysis of variance must be used.

11.3.1.2 | Quadratic function and functions of higher degrees for one independent variable

These functions, of which the quadratic function is most commonly used, can be presented in the following form

$$y = a_0 + a_1 x + a_2 x^2 + \dots + a_n x^n \tag{11.12}$$

The method of least squares would be rather time-consuming in these cases. Fisher's (1963) method of orthogonal polynomes is much more effective but yet more complicated than the previous method. Computer calculations are advisable. By this method the importance of each expression in the polynome is tested, enabling a decision to be made on the degree of polynome needed for fitting the function. The effectiveness of fitting can again be tested by means of the coefficient of determination or by the analysis of variance.

11.3.1.3 | General parabolic function

The general form of a parabolic function is:

$$y = ax^b \tag{11.13}$$

Fitting a general parabolic function is not difficult in the absence of an absolute expression in the equation. By taking logarithms, a parabola is transformed into a straight line:

$$\log y = \log a + b \log x \tag{11.14}$$

$\log y$ and $\log x$ represent, in fact, new variables of the fitted line. The parameters a and b are determined by the method of least squares.

11.3.1.4 | Linear functions with several independent variables

The general form of these functions is

$$y = a_0 + a_1x_1 + a_2x_2 + \dots + a_nx_n \tag{11.15}$$

Of these functions, those with two independent variables are used most frequently. The method of least squares is again used to calculate the parameters but the calculation tends to be time-consuming. Various advantageous procedures known as 'Gauss-Doolittle Method' or the method of Gaussian multipliers are therefore used. An approximate solution is fairly easy to find by means of group comparison. In this method, values which are represented by the dependent variable in a regression equation are arranged in ascending order. The whole set of values of the dependent variable, with their corresponding values of independent variables, is then divided into as many groups as there are parameters in the regression equation. Group mean values are calculated for all variables in each group and the group means are afterwards substituted in the regression equation whose parameters we wish to find. In this way, a total of n equations with n unknown parameters are obtained, and the parameters are found by solving these equations. Further precision is introduced if the numbers of expressions in individual groups are modified so as to be proportional to the corresponding average deviations of group means, *i.e.* $n_1 : n_2 : n_3 : \dots = d_1 : d_2 : d_3 \dots$. d is found by means of the approximate relation

$$d = \frac{5\Sigma\,(\Delta +)_i}{n_i - 1} \tag{11.16}$$

in which $\Sigma\,(\Delta +)_i$ stands for the sum of positive deviations from the group mean and n_i stands for the number of expressions in the group.

11.3.1.5 | Exponential functions

Exponential functions usually describe growth of living objects; consequently they will often arise in our regressions. Relatively simple exponential functions are easily transformed into linear functions but with more complicated exponentials this procedure is rather difficult or is possible only under certain conditions. For example:

$$(a) \quad y = a\, e^{bx} \tag{11.17}$$

This function is easily transformed into a linear function:

$$\ln y = \ln a + bx \tag{11.18}$$

and can be fitted afterwards by the method of least squares.

$$(b) \quad y = a + b\, e^{cx} \tag{11.19}$$

An exponential equation with a constant can be fitted by the methods of Pontier (1965), and of Rash & Stammberger (1967). This calculation is rather complicated. However, if we can estimate parameter a, the expression can be simply transformed to a linear function as in the previous example.

$$(c) \quad y = e^{a+bx+cx^2} \tag{11.20}$$

This function is fitted relatively easily. By taking logarithms, a linear equation is obtained, which can be fitted by the method of least squares. An analogous procedure can also be applied if the polynome in the exponent is of higher degree as in (d):

$$(d) \quad y = e^{a+bx+cx^2+dx^3} \tag{11.21}$$

(*e*) It is also possible to fit a cumulative frequency curve (of a normal distribution) which has a sigmoid shape similar to that of the logistic curve. This function is given by the expression

$$y = a \int_{-\infty}^{x} e^{-(bx^2+cx+d)}\, dx \tag{11.22}$$

Fitting can be accomplished graphically by simply plotting adjusted experimental data onto probability paper, the fitted curve being thus transformed into a straight line. The procedure is described *e.g.* in Weber (1957).

11.3.2 | Testing the effectiveness of indirect methods

Indirect methods offer great advantages with highly variable and heterogeneous plant material, as in plant communities under natural conditions. Another advantage is that a relatively large amount of data can be recorded during the growing season, as most of the evaluation can be postponed to a later date. However, objective criteria of the suitability and effectiveness of these methods are statistical. Two basic statistical tests, corresponding to the two main types of indirect estimations of growth and production presented in Sections 11.2.2 and 11.2.3, can be used.

11.3.2.1 Testing the effectiveness of the method of parallel samples (see also Section 11.2.2)

This test is relatively easy. The variation in the values obtained by the indirect method is compared with that in the values obtained by direct destructive harvesting. Suitable parameters for statistical comparison of both methods are the variances or coefficients of variation; significance can be easily tested by the F-test or t-test. The following is an example.

In a stand of common reed *(Phragmites communis)*, variation of biomass per m^2 within the stand was assessed by harvesting a row of 1 m^2 plots in a transect 28 m long and 1 m wide. The coefficient of variation of biomass, expressed as g dry weight per m^2, was 25%. Coefficients of variation of individual biomass data, obtained at different times during the growing season by the indirect method of non-destructive measurements with parallel destructive harvests, were much smaller, varying only from 2.3 to 6.0% (Table 11.4). Parallel destructive harvests were taken from four 0.5 m^2 parallel plots of about the same shoot density as the standard plot at weekly intervals. (From Dykyjová, Ondok & Přibáň 1970.)

Table 11.4 Coefficients of variation (c_V) of dry weights (W) recorded in a stand of common reed *(Phragmites communis)* during the growing season.

Sampling No.:	1	2	3	4	5	6	7	8	9	10	11	12	13
c_V [%]	5.1	2.3	3.6	2.7	4.6	4.4	5.4	4.3	4.2	2.4	4.0	6.0	6.0

However, it must again be pointed out that the non-destructive methods approximate the real growth of the plants in the actual stand. They cannot provide average values valid for the whole crop. If we do not distinguish between these two points of view the variability of values obtained by these methods can hardly be compared.

11.3.2.2 Testing the effectiveness of the method of regression equations (see also Section 11.2.3)

This test is analogous to the previous one: variation of the data obtained by means of regression equations is compared with that of the data obtained by direct destructive harvesting. If the former variation is significantly smaller, the indirect method of regression equations will give more reliable data. For fitting the regression line or any other regression function successfully, it is of paramount importance that the parallel destructive samples from which the original data for calculation of regression equation are derived include the whole range of variation in plant (shoot) sizes and other morphological features occurring in the standard plot. An example of this procedure follows.

Seasonal changes of biomass, expressed in terms of g dry weight per m^2 were estimated in a stand of *Typha angustifolia* L. This stand showed great local and seasonal variation in stand density, relative proportion of flowering or fruiting shoots, shoot height, *etc.* Ten standard 0.5 m^2 quadrats were selected in the stand. At fortnightly intervals, the following parameters were recorded in these standard quadrats: shoot length, length and width of the longest leaf on all shoots, inflorescence length in fertile shoots, the numbers of flowering or fruiting and vegetative shoots and total shoot number in each quadrat. Each time, 10 parallel shoots were harvested. In each of these shoots, the same parameters were recorded as in the shoots growing in the standard quadrats. Afterwards, total leaf area and total dry weight were determined in each shoot separately. These parallel samples were used for fitting the regression equations. Both leaf area and biomass were calculated from linear regression equations with a general form

$$y = a + bx \tag{11.23}$$

For calculating the leaf area, $x = l \; w \; n$, *i.e.* the product of length and width of the longest leaf multiplied by the number of leaves per shoot. For calculating shoot dry weight, $x = h$, *i.e.* shoot length, in vegetative shoots; or $x = h \; f$, *i.e.* shoot length multiplied by inflorescence length, in flowering or fruiting shoots. Stand densities recorded in the ten standard quadrats were used for transforming these data into leaf area index and biomass data representative of the whole stand. Biomass data obtained in this way were compared with biomass data recorded in the same stand, by direct destructive harvesting in a row of 1 m^2 quadrats forming a transect 24 m long and 1 m wide. The mean shoot biomass found in this way was 870 g m^{-2} and the coefficient of variation was 27.6%. Calculations have proved that 138 quadrats of 1 m^2 would have to be harvested to reduce the value of the variation coefficient to 10%. For this reason, indirect methods must be introduced, or the selection of plots for harvesting must be done subjectively, not randomly.
Residual variance of dry weight values predicted from the regression equation was calculated by

$$s_0^2 = \frac{1}{n\text{-}2} \left[\Sigma y_i^2 - a\Sigma(x_i y_i) \right] \tag{11.24}$$

in which s_0^2 is the residual variance, proportional to the sum of deviations from the regression line, and b is a parameter of the regression equation. In our case, the residual variance was found to be equal to 3.9 g per shoot. With the maximum stand density of 35 shoots per m^2, the greatest residual variance of total biomass in the stand was 35×3.9 g m^{-2} = 136.5 g m^{-2}, which is 5.6 times less than the variance of the value obtained by direct harvesting. The F-test shows the difference to be significant at $P = 0.05$. The effectiveness of the indirect estimation of leaf area was tested in a similar way.

11.4 | Choice of indirect method

To present a rapid information on various indirect methods of biomass estimation, a survey of their types, applicability, advantages and disadvantages is given in Table 11.5.

Table 11.5 Survey of indirect methods of biomass estimation.

Type of method	Applicability to		Advantages	Disadvantages	Application to growth analysis
	experiments or observations	plants or stands			
In situ apparatus recordings (11.2.1)	Following of growth and production rates	Field experiments Natural vegetation	Automatic recording, continuous or frequent measurements	Costly, dry weight percentage in fresh weight must often be estimated	possible
Standard plants with parallel destructive sampling (11.2.2)	Ditto in individual plants	Water cultures Pot experiments	Small number of replicates required	Results cannot be expressed on unit ground area basis	possible
Standard plots with parallel destructive sampling (11.2.2)	Ditto in stands	Field experiments, crops Natural vegetation	Ditto, possible to follow rather heterogeneous stands	Results valid only for a certain part of stand	possible
Standard plants, calibration by regression equations (11.2.3)	Ditto in individual plants	Water cultures, pot experiments, small-scale field experiments	Small number of replicates required	Results cannot be expressed on unit ground area basis	possible
Standard plots, calibration by regression equations (11.2.3)	Ditto in stands	Field experiments, crops Natural vegetation	Ditto, possible to follow rather heterogeneous stands	Results valid only for a certain part of stand	possible
One-term biomass estimation from regressions	Estimation of biomass or (with correction) of annual production	Mostly trees and shrubs and their stands Underground organs Some perennial herbs	Application possible where other methods would fail	Mathematical treatment sometimes complicated	impossible
Phenometric methods (11.2.5)	Following growth rate as affected by weather	Pot experiments, field experiments, crops, natural vegetation	Easy measurements, possibility of correlation with climatic factors	Transformation of measurements into dry weight values difficult	difficult

11.5 | References

Alcock, M. B., Lovett, J. V.: The electronic measurement of the yield of growing pasture. – J. agr. Sci. 68: 27-38, 1967.

Alcock, M. B., Lovett, J. V., Machin, D.: Techniques used in the study of the influence of environment on primary pasture production in hill and lowland habitats. – In: Wadsworth, R. M. *et al.* (ed.): The Measurement of Environmental Factors in Terrestrial Ecology. – Pp. 191-203. Blackwell, Oxford–Edinburgh 1968.

Campbell, A. G., Phillips, D. S. M., O'Reilly, E. D.: An electronic instrument for pasture yield estimation. – Brit. Grassland Soc. J. 17: 89-100, 1962.

Dagnelie, P.: Cours de statistique mathématique, 1. Pp. 70-74. – Gembloux 1964.

Dahlmann, R. C.: Root production and turnover of carbon in the root-soil matrix of a grassland ecosystem. – In: Methods of Productivity Studies in Root Systems and Rhizosphere Organisms. Pp. 11-21. Nauka, Leningrad 1968.

Daum, C. R.: A method for determining water transport in trees. – Ecology 48: 425-431, 1967.

Dykyjová, D., Ondok, J. P., Přibáň, K.: Seasonal changes in productivity and vertical structure of reed-stands (*Phragmites communis* Trin.). – Photosynthetica 4: 280-287, 1970.

Engel, K. H., Raeuber, A., Meinl, G.: Phenometric studies on cultivated plants (Proposal for PP/IBP). – Photosynthetica 2: 298-302, 1968.

Evans, G. C., Raymond, A., Eckert, R. E., Kinsinger, F. E.: A technique for estimating grass yields in greenhouse experiments. – J. Range Manage. 14: 41-42, 1961.

Fiala, K., Dykyjová, D., Květ, J., Svoboda, J.: Methods of assessing rhizome and root production in reed-bed stands. – In: Methods of Productivity Studies in Root Systems and Rhizosphere Organisms. Pp. 36-47. Nauka, Leningrad 1968.

Fisher, R. A.: Statistical Methods for Research Workers. – 13th Ed. Oliver & Boyd, London 1963.

Fritts, H. C., Fritts, E. C.: A new dendrograph for recording radial changes of a tree. – Forest Sci. 1: 271-276, 1955.

Griffith, A. L., Howland, P.: Silviculture research rate of growth of new roots and new mycorrhiza immediately after planting. – Rep. East. agr. Forest Res. Organ. Pp. 84-85. 1961.

Gringov, I. G., Alimzhanov, A. G.: Metodika polevogo opredeleniya urozhaya osoki vzdutoï na pastbishchakh. [A method for the field determination of the yield of *Carex physodes* in pastures.] – Bot. Zh. 47: 1170-1176, 1962.

Impens, I. I., Schalck, J. M.: A very sensitive electric dendrograph for recording radial changes of a tree. – Ecology 46: 183-184, 1965.

Jarvis, M. S.: A comparison between the water relations of species with contrasting types of geographical distribution in the British isles. – In: Rutter, A. J., Whitehead, F. H. (ed.): The Water Relations of Plants. Pp. 289-312. Blackwell, London 1963.

Karizumi, N.: Estimation of root biomass in forests by the soil block sampling. – In: Methods of Productivity Studies in Root Systems and Rhizosphere Organisms. Pp. 79-86. Nauka, Leningrad 1968.

Kira, T., Ogawa, H.: Indirect estimation of root biomass increment in trees. – In: Methods of Productivity Studies in Root Systems and Rhizosphere Organisms. Pp. 96-102. Nauka, Leningrad 1968.

Kozlowski, T. T., Winget, C. H.: Diurnal and seasonal variation in radii of tree stems. – Ecology 45: 149-155, 1964.

Kretschmer, G.: Wachstums-Messungen an Pflanzen auf dem Acker. – Z. Pflanzenernährung Düngung Bodenkunde 47: 213-226, 1949.

Larson, M. M.: Construction and use of glass-faced boxes to study root development of tree seedlings. – Res. Note Rocky Mt. For. Range exp. Sta. 73: 1-4, 1962.

Mayr, E.: Einfluss der Bodentemperatur auf das Halmlängenwachstum bei Getreide. – Schlern Schriften (Innsbruck) 145: 76, 1953.

Perrier, E. R., McKell, C. M., Davidson, J. M.: Plant-soil-water relations of two subspecies of orchard grass. – Soil Sci. 92: 413-420, 1961.

Pontier, J.: Calcul des paramètres d'un model en type $x = x_m + C\,e^{kt}$. Application à l'étude de l'hypercalcemie par perfusion. – Biometrie-Praximetrie 6: 153-164, 1965.

Popescu-Zeletin, I.: Méthode et appareils pour déterminer la dynamique de l'accroissement radial des arbres pendant la période de végetation. – In: Eckardt, F. E. (ed.): Functioning of Terrestrial Ecosystems at the Primary Production Level. Pp. 211-217. UNESCO, Paris 1968.
Raeuber, A., Bellmann, K.: Zur Umweltabhängigkeit von Regressionsparametern bei phänometrischen Untersuchungen an Mais. – Z. angew. Meteorol. 5: 261-266, 1968.
Raeuber, A., Engel, K.-H.: Untersuchungen über den Verlauf der Massenzunahme bei Kartoffeln (*Solanum tuberosum* L.) in Abhängigkeit von Umwelt- und Erbguteinflüssen. – Abhandl. meteorol. Dienstes DDR 10 (76): 1-117, 1966.
Raeuber, A., Bellmann, K., Meinl, G., Mrázek, O., Pfeffer, Ch., Winkel, A.: Anwendung nichtlinearer Korrelationen bei phänometrischen Arbeiten bei Mais. – Z. Pflanzenzüchtung 46: 433-442, 1961.
Rash, D., Stammberger, A.: Verschiedene Schätzverfahren für die Parameter der Funktion $\eta = a + be^{c\xi}$. – Biometrische Z. 9: 34-49, 1967.
Rogers, W. S., Head, G. C.: A new root-observation laboratory. – Rep. East Malling Res. Sta. 1962: 55-57, 1963.
Rogers, W. S., Head, G. C.: Studies of roots of fruit plants by observation panels and time-lapse photography. – In: Methods of Productivity Studies in Root Systems and Rhizosphere Organisms. Pp. 176-185. Nauka, Leningrad 1968.
Ross, Yu. K., Vlasova, M. P.: Biometricheskaya kharakteristika i dinamika razvitiya poseva kukuruzy. [The biometric characteristics and dynamics of the growth of maize stands.] – In: Nichiporovich, A. A. (ed.): Fotosinteziruyushchie Sistemy Vysokoï Produktivnosti. Pp. 78-95. Nauka, Moskva 1966.
Snedecor, G. W.: Statistical Methods. – 6th Ed. Iowa State College Press, Ames, Iowa 1957.
Troughton, A.: The application of the allometric formula to the study of the relationship between the roots and shoots of young grass plants. – Agr. Progress 30: 1-7, 1955.
Troughton, A.: Further studies on the relationship between shoot and root systems of grasses. – J. Brit. Grassland Soc. 15: 41-47, 1960.
Troughton, A.: The effect of period and temperature on the relationship between the root and shoot systems of *Lolium perenne*. – J. British Grassland Soc. 16: 291-295, 1961.
Unger, K.: Die Bestimmung der Pflanzenmasse von Einzelpflanzen und Pflanzenbeständen mit Hilfe ionisierender Strahlen zur Ermittlung des Wachstumsverlaufes unter natürlichen Bedingungen. – In: Fragen der Pflanzenzüchtung und Pflanzenphysiologie. Tagungsberichte DALW 48: 31-33, 1962.
Unger, K.: The use of gamma rays for the determination of change in biomass with time. – In: Eckardt, F. E. (ed.): Functioning of Terrestrial Ecosystems at the Primary Production Level. Pp. 229-231. UNESCO, Paris 1968.
Weber, E.: Grundriss der biologischen Statistik für Naturwissenschaftler, Landwirte und Mediziner. – 3. Aufl. VEB G. Fischer, Jena 1957.
Westlake, D. F.: Methods used to determine the annual production of reedswamp plants with extensive rhizomes. – In: Methods of Productivity Studies in Root Systems and Rhizosphere Organisms. Pp. 36-47. Nauka, Leningrad 1968.
Wilcox, H.: Growth studies of the root of Incense Cedar, *Libocedrus decurrens*. I. The origin and development of primary tissues. II. Morphological features of the root system and growth behavior. – Amer. J. Bot. 49: 221-236; 237-245, 1962.

12 | RADIATION AND CROP STRUCTURE

12.1 | Introduction

At best, only about a quarter of the photosynthetically active radiation in the 400–700 nm waveband could be converted into chemical energy by photosynthesis after absorption by the plant. So far, measurements in the field suggest that normal efficiencies of conversion are much lower (Lemon 1966, 1967). Radiant energy of longer wavelengths is also absorbed by the plant, and, together with the 400–700 nm waveband, affects other energy transformations, such as the evaporation of water, which interact with each other.

Much of the absorbed radiation is dissipated by latent heat transfer through transpiration and by sensible heat transfer along gradients of temperature. Carbon dioxide transfer, transpiration and sensible heat transfer are all spatially coupled through common pathways of exchange with bulk air around the leaf, and a change in the environmental conditions affecting one process will also affect the others. The diffusion resistance external to the leaf affects all three transfer processes, and the stomatal resistance both CO_2 and water exchange. Indirectly, there is a feedback process over a period of time between physiological processes: for instance, a change in radiation spectral quality can affect stomatal aperture (Mansfield & Meidner 1966), this in turn affects the stomatal diffusion resistance, which then affects the intercellular CO_2 concentration, which can act on stomatal aperture (Chapter 16; Allaway & Mansfield 1967). There is an elaborate interaction between the water vapour and CO_2 exchanges by the leaf: both are radiation dependent processes, partly under stomatal control, but able also to affect some diffusive resistances (Bierhuizen & Slatyer 1964, 1965; Slatyer & Bierhuizen 1964; Rackham 1966). The total past history of the radiation environment of the plant affects its present response to radiation conditions (Hughes 1966). Therefore, if we hope to understand the effect of environment on photosynthesis, rather than just seeking local correlations between photosynthetic production and solar radiation, we must, as a first step, measure other radiation components besides photosynthetically active radiation.

The radiation climate within a plant stand is closely related to stand structure, since the gaps in the canopy determine how much radiation can penetrate in a given direction. The frequency of gaps is a function of the foliage (leaf, stem, flower, fruit *etc.*) area index (leaf area index) and the foliage inclination, as was first demonstrated by Monsi & Saeki (1953). Later, Kasanaga & Monsi (1954) outlined the effects of multiple reflection and transmission by the spectrally selective foliage. Isobe (1962a, b, 1969), Ross & Nil'son (1963, 1965, 1967), Ross (1967) and Cowan (1968) developed independently a similar theory of radiation extinction on the spectral composition of radiation in the stand. Warren Wilson (1959a, b, 1960, 1963a) developed an inclined point quadrat technique for estimating foliage area and foliage inclination non-destructively. Anderson M. C. (1966a) showed that she and Monsi & Saeki (1953) were using effectively the same mathematical model of randomly arranged foliage. Anderson M. C. (1964b, 1966a) showed that gap frequency could be related to radiation penetration, using an empirical distribution for diffuse sky radiation.

Meanwhile, various models of foliage and radiation distribution in relation to photosynthesis have been proposed (Monsi & Saeki 1953; de Wit 1959, 1965; Saeki 1960; Verhagen, Wilson & Britten 1963; Budyko & Gandin 1965; Laïsk 1965a; Monteith 1965; Chartier 1966a, 1967; Idso, Baker & Gates 1966; Duncan *et al.* 1967; Loomis, Williams & Duncan 1967; Tooming 1967b, 1968; Nil'son 1968b; Ross & Bichele 1968; Williams *et al.* 1968). None of these models combine all possible plant and environmental factors: many, for instance, take a single average flux of radiation in the stand at any given level, not accounting for sunflecks. With the increasing availability of large, high speed computers and multichannel automatic recording equipment, it has become much easier to measure and model such complex interactions.

Instruments used to measure radiation must be carefully calibrated and maintained. Particularly when working with plants, there are considerable problems of spectral sensitivity of instruments in relation to the spectral quality of the measured radiation to be taken into account when assessing the results (see also Chapter 19). There are also considerable sampling problems when measuring radiation in stands directly, and the relevance of any proposed measurements to the purpose of the investigation should be carefully considered at the outset. Further details of all these problems may be found in Withrow & Withrow (1956), Gaastra (1959), Sauberer & Härtel (1959), Vershinin *et al.* (1959), Kleschnin (1960), Slatyer & McIlroy (1961), Gates (1962), Evans L. T. (1963), Tanner (1963), van Wijk (1963), Anderson M. C. (1964a), Dirmhirn (1964), Reifsnyder & Lull (1965), Bainbridge, Evans G. C. & Rackham (1966), Businger (1966), Griffiths & Griffiths (1966), Munn (1966), Robinson (1966), Lemon (1967), Reifsnyder (1967), Shul'gin (1967), and Poldmaa (1968), which provide extensive bibliographies on instrumentation.

12.2 | Radiation measurement

12.2.1 | Terminology and units in radiation measurement

'Light' strictly refers to the sensations produced by electromagnetic radiation on the human eye. The eye is highly spectrally selective, with a peak sensitivity in the green region around 555 nm. A whole system of photometric measuring units based on this spectral sensitivity has been devised, including such units as the lux and foot candle. Since plants have totally different spectral properties, the continued use of photometric units in some botanical work is deplored (Norris 1968). Every effort should be made to express measurements in radiometric units, accounting for the total energy received over a chosen waveband. A large number of different radiometric units are used for particular purposes: conversion factors are given in Tables 1.4 and 12.1 and in Figs. 19.3 and 19.4. At present, the use of the calorie as unit of measurement is often preferred, although these are being succeeded by SI measurements in J or W ($= J\ s^{-1}$). In the U.S.A., 1 langley $\equiv$ 1 cal cm^{-2}. Measurements of radiant flux density (often referred to as intensity, which is incorrect – see Tabs. 12.3 and 19.2) are usually of the most interest. The radiant flux density is the total energy flux received or emitted per unit area per unit time. The undesirability of using photometric units, because of the effects of changed spectral composition, is illustrated by Table 12.2, where various conversion factors for natural and artificial sources are given. In Table 12.3 a glossary of terms and abbreviations used in the literature on solar radiation is given. There is some difference in usage between countries. There is an extensive literature on radiation in the open and on methods of measurement, and further information may be found in Linke (1942), Handbook of Meteorological Instruments, Pt. I (1956), Withrow & Withrow (1956), Annals of IGY V (1957), U.S. Air Force Handbook of Geophysics (1960), Drummond (1961), Goody (1964), Kondrat'ev (1965a), Robinson (1966) and Poldmaa (1968) and in Meteorological and Geo-astrophysical Abstracts.

12.2.2 | *Scope and purpose of radiation measurements*

When concerning the conversion of photosynthetically active radiation of the 400–700 nm waveband into chemical energy, several points should be emphasised. First, this waveband is a remarkably constant proportion of the total short-wave solar radiation, about 45%, under different weather conditions (Blackwell 1953; Drummond 1960). Second, the properties of instruments measuring total solar radiation have been far more thoroughly investigated than those designed to measure only the 400–700 nm band. Third, in most parts of the world, coverage of radiation measuring networks is still very poor despite recent increases (see map in Berliand 1966), and additional measurements would benefit meteorological and hydrological work, such as the International Hydrological Decade. Fourth, in some research problems measurements of total solar radiation would be of value. Therefore, in the interests of maintaining intercomparability, all scientists studying photosynthetic production in plants should try to maintain at least one of the common pyranometers under conditions acceptable to local meteorological practice. Where any estimates are being made of water use or energy balance, net radiation should also be measured.

12.2.3 | *General principles of radiation measurement*

Two major types of instrument may be distinguished: radiometric instruments in which the heat produced when a black surface absorbs radiation is measured, usually by a thermocouple; and photometric instruments, which are usually much more highly spectrally selective and include such devices as photoemissive and photoconductive cells. The latter are also dealt with in Chapter 19, while Walsh (1961) provides great detail on general principles of photometric instruments.

The spectral selectivity of radiometric instruments, which include the common pyranometers and net radiometers, is determined by:

a. The spectral properties of the black absorbing surface;
b. the spectral properties of the reflecting surface covering cold reference junctions, if present;
c. the spectral transmissivity of the protective dome.

Table 12.1 Interconversion of units of radiant energy and flux density (*cf.* also Table 1.4 and Figs. 19.3 and 19.4).

A: Energy [dimensions: mass length^2 time^{-2}]

	erg	cal	kcal	J(=W s)	W h	kW h	Btu
erg	1	2.39×10^{-8}	2.39×10^{-11}	10^{-7}	2.78×10^{-11}	2.78×10^{-14}	9.48×10^{-11}
cal	4.19×10^{7}	1	10^{-3}	4.19	1.16×10^{-3}	1.16×10^{-6}	3.97×10^{-3}
kcal	4.19×10^{10}	10^{3}	1	4.19×10^{3}	1.16	1.16×10^{-3}	3.97
J(=Ws)	10^{7}	0.239	2.39×10^{-4}	1	2.78×10^{-4}	2.78×10^{-7}	9.48×10^{-4}
W h	3.6×10^{10}	8.60×10^{2}	8.60×10^{-1}	3.6×10^{3}	1	10^{-3}	3.41
kW h	3.6×10^{13}	8.60×10^{5}	8.60×10^{2}	3.6×10^{6}	10^{3}	1	3.41×10^{3}
Btu*	1.06×10^{10}	2.52×10^{2}	2.52×10^{-1}	1.06×10^{3}	2.93×10^{-1}	2.93×10^{-4}	1

B: Power (energy per unit time) [dimensions: mass length^2 time^{-3}]

	erg s^{-1}	cal s^{-1}	cal min^{-1}	W(=J s^{-1})	Btu* min^{-1}	Btu* h^{-1}
erg s^{-1}	1	2.39×10^{-8}	1.43×10^{-6}	1.00×10^{-7}	5.69×10^{-9}	9.48×10^{-11}
cal s^{-1}	4.19×10^{7}	1	60	4.19	2.38×10^{-1}	3.97×10^{-3}
cal min^{-1}	6.97×10^{5}	1.67×10^{-2}	1	6.97×10^{-2}	3.97×10^{-3}	6.62×10^{-5}
W(=J s^{-1})	1.00×10^{7}	2.39×10^{-1}	14.3	1	5.69×10^{-2}	9.48×10^{-4}
Btu* min^{-1}	1.76×10^{8}	4.20	2.52×10^{2}	17.6	1	1.67×10^{-2}
Btu* h^{-1}	1.06×10^{10}	2.52×10^{2}	1.52×10^{4}	1.06×10^{3}	60	1

* British thermal unit

a. The most uniformly black surface at all wavelengths (absorptivity > 0.985) is *Parson's Optical Black Lacquer*, whose manufacture has unfortunately ceased, although some laboratories still have stocks. Other manufacturers' efforts to make optical black lacquer to the same 'recipe' do not seem to have produced quite so satisfactory a product, and other formulations, such as *3M Matt Black Aerosol*, are also not so satisfactory. The spectral properties of the matt black surface change slightly with age, particularly at first, and are readily altered by moisture. The way in which the lacquer is applied is also important: there is no substitute for practical experience in achieving a uniformly matt surface. Only one coat should be applied over undercoat.

b. The reflecting surface in many short-wave pyranometers is provided by some form of white paint, or pure MgO *(Eppley)*. Details of the spectral properties vary with substrate and chemical composition (Strain 1961; Voïtikova 1965). Although 'white' paints reflect fairly uniformly in the 0.4–1.0 μm, their reflectivity declines gradually at longer wavelengths and most absorb UV radiation quite strongly. They are more susceptible to ageing effects than black paint.

A few long wave pyranometers use polished metal surfaces to reflect infrared radiation.

Table 12.1 Continued

C: Radiant flux density and irradiance units [dimensions: mass time^{-3}] [λ in cm].

	quantum cm^{-2} s^{-1}	einstein cm^{-2} s^{-1}	erg cm^{-2} s^{-1}	cal cm^{-2} s^{-1}	cal cm^{-2} min^{-1}	cal cm^{-2} h^{-1}
quantum cm^{-2} s^{-1}	1	1.66×10^{-24}	$1.99 \times 10^{-16}\ \lambda^{-1}$	$4.75 \times 10^{-24}\ \lambda^{-1}$	$2.85 \times 10^{-22}\ \lambda^{-1}$	$1.71 \times 10^{-20}\ \lambda^{-1}$
einstein cm^{-2} s^{-1}	6.02×10^{23}	1	$1.20 \times 10^{8}\ \lambda^{-1}$	$2.86\ \lambda^{-1}$	$1.72 \times 10^{2}\ \lambda^{-1}$	$1.03 \times 10^{4}\ \lambda^{-1}$
erg cm^{-2} s^{-1}	$5.03 \times 10^{15}\ \lambda$	$8.35 \times 10^{-9}\ \lambda$	1	2.39×10^{-8}	1.43×10^{-6}	8.6×10^{-5}
cal cm^{-2} s^{-1}	$2.11 \times 10^{23}\ \lambda$	$3.50 \times 10^{-1}\ \lambda$	4.19×10^{7}	1	60	3.6×10^{3}
cal cm^{-2} min^{-1}	$3.51 \times 10^{21}\ \lambda$	$5.83 \times 10^{-3}\ \lambda$	6.98×10^{5}	1.67×10^{-2}	1	60
cal cm^{-2} h^{-1}	$5.85 \times 10^{19}\ \lambda$	$9.71 \times 10^{-5}\ \lambda$	1.16×10^{4}	2.78×10^{-4}	1.67×10^{-2}	1
cal dm^{-2} h^{-1}	$5.85 \times 10^{17}\ \lambda$	$9.71 \times 10^{-7}\ \lambda$	1.16×10^{2}	2.78×10^{-6}	1.67×10^{-4}	10^{-2}
kcal m^{-2} h^{-1}	$5.85 \times 10^{18}\ \lambda$	$9.71 \times 10^{-6}\ \lambda$	1.16×10^{3}	2.78×10^{-5}	1.67×10^{-3}	10^{-1}
μW cm^{-2}	$5.03 \times 10^{16}\ \lambda$	$8.35 \times 10^{-8}\ \lambda$	10	2.39×10^{-7}	1.43×10^{-5}	8.6×10^{-4}
W cm^{-2}	$5.03 \times 10^{22}\ \lambda$	$8.35 \times 10^{-2}\ \lambda$	10^{7}	2.39×10^{-1}	14.33	8.6×10^{2}
W m^{-2}	$5.03 \times 10^{18}\ \lambda$	$8.35 \times 10^{-6}\ \lambda$	10^{3}	2.39×10^{-5}	1.43×10^{-3}	8.6×10^{-2}
Btu ft^{-2} min^{-1}	$0.95 \times 10^{21}\ \lambda$	$1.58 \times 10^{-3}\ \lambda$	1.89×10^{5}	4.53×10^{-3}	0.27	16.2

Table 12.1 Continued

	cal dm^{-2} h^{-1}	kcal m^{-2} h^{-1}	μW cm^{-2}	W cm^{-2}	W m^{-2}	Btu ft^{-2} min^{-1}
quantum cm^{-2} s^{-1}	1.71×10^{-18} λ^{-1}	1.71×10^{-19} λ^{-1}	1.99×10^{-17} λ^{-1}	1.99×10^{-23} λ^{-1}	1.99×10^{-19} λ^{-1}	1.05×10^{-21} λ^{-1}
einstein cm^{-2} s^{-1}	1.03×10^{6} λ^{-1}	1.03×10^{5} λ^{-1}	1.20×10^{7} λ^{-1}	12.0 λ^{-1}	1.20×10^{5} λ^{-1}	6.34×10^{2} λ^{-1}
erg cm^{-2} s^{-1}	8.6×10^{-3}	8.6×10^{-4}	10^{-1}	10^{-7}	10^{-3}	5.28×10^{-6}
cal cm^{-2} s^{-1}	3.6×10^{5}	3.6×10^{4}	4.19×10^{6}	4.19	4.19×10^{4}	2.21×10^{2}
cal cm^{-2} min^{-1}	6×10^{3}	6×10^{2}	6.98×10^{4}	6.98×10^{-2}	6.98×10^{2}	3.69
cal cm^{-2} h^{-1}	10^{2}	10	1.16×10^{3}	1.16×10^{-3}	11.63	6.17×10^{-2}
cal dm^{-2} h^{-1}	1	10^{-1}	11.63	1.16×10^{-5}	1.16×10^{-1}	6.17×10^{-4}
kcal m^{-2} h^{-1}	10	1	1.16×10^{2}	1.16×10^{-4}	1.163	6.17×10^{-3}
μW cm^{-2}	8.6×10^{-2}	8.6×10^{-3}	1	10^{-6}	10^{-2}	5.28×10^{-5}
W cm^{-2}	8.6×10^{4}	8.6×10^{3}	10^{6}	1	10^{4}	5.28×10
W m^{-2}	8.6	8.6×10^{-1}	10^{2}	10^{-4}	1	5.28×10^{-3}
Btu ft^{-2} min^{-1}	1.62×10^{3}	1.62×10^{2}	1.89×10^{4}	1.89×10^{-2}	1.89×10^{2}	1

Table 12.2 Deviation from ideal photon response of common types of photocell (from Federer & Tanner 1966a and McPherson 1969).

Radiation source		Sensors								
		1	2	3	4	5	6	7	8	9
Xenon arc lamps	XBF6000	0.96	1.03	0.98	0.98	1.22	1.00	1.02	1.05	1.08
	XBO900	1.03	1.03	1.01	0.99	1.16	1.01	1.02	1.09	1.06
Tungsten lamps at various colour temperatures	2854 K	1.36	0.95	1.17	0.99	0.88	0.95	0.96	1.28	0.96
	3025 K	1.29	0.96	1.14	0.99	0.89	0.96	0.97	1.23	0.97
	3475 K	1.00	1.01	1.00	1.01	0.99	0.99	1.01	0.98	0.99
Fluorescent lamps	'daylight'	0.33	1.23	0.71	1.11	1.41	1.18	1.20	0.51	1.10
	'cool white'	0.36	1.26	0.72	1.16	1.33	1.20	1.25	0.49	1.06
	'warm white'	0.39	—	0.74	—	1.26	—	—	0.47	0.01
Undercorn crop on clear *(C)* and overcast *(O)* day (Yocum, Allen & Lemon 1964)	*C*	3.24	1.04	2.30	1.09	1.20	1.05	1.05	2.96	1.07
	O	1.50	1.05	1.33	1.03	1.15	1.01	1.04	1.43	1.04
Federer & Tanner's experimental sites, with clear *(C)*, dark cloud *(DC)*, white cloud *(WC)* and overcast *(O)* sky	Pine *(C)*	1.38	1.00	1.27	0.98	1.28	1.02	1.00	1.42	1.11
	Pine *(DC)*	1.11	1.04	1.11	1.01	1.20	1.03	1.03	1.14	1.07
	Oak *(C)*	2.54	0.98	1.92	1.03	1.16	0.98	0.98	2.35	1.06
	Oak *(WC)*	1.55	1.06	1.36	1.05	1.17	1.03	1.05	1.50	1.05
	Maple *(C)*	3.56	0.91	2.48	1.06	0.91	0.92	0.91	3.14	0.98
	Maple *(O)*	2.20	1.04	1.74	1.07	1.15	1.03	1.04	2.04	1.05
Federer & Tanner, blue sky		0.39	0.99	0.70	0.89	1.43	1.01	0.99	0.63	1.17

Sensors:
1. Silicon photovoltaic cell (*Int. Rect. Corp.*, USA).
2. The same with 4 mm *Schott BG38* and a double layer of *Kodak Wratten 81B* filters.
3. Silicon blue photovoltaic cell (*Hayakawa Electric Co.*, Japan).
4. The same with *Kodak Wratten 86B* and 4 mm *Schott KG3* filters.
5. Selenium photovoltaic cell (*Int. Rect. Corp.*, USA).
6. The same with 2 mm *Schott UG3* and 4 mm *GG4* filters.
7. The same with 2 layers *Kodak Wratten 81EF* filters.
8. Standard pyrheliometer.
9. Standard pyrheliometer over 400–700 nm band.

c. Optical glasses transmit 90–95% of the radiation in the 0.4–2.5 μm waveband, and cut off fairly sharply above and below those limits, providing a convenient selective filter for short-wave solar radiation against a background of long-wave thermal radiation. Some of these glasses are soft, and easily damaged by careless polishing. Films of oil and dirt invisible to the naked eye can reduce transmission by as much as 10%, so domes on instruments in use should be cleaned daily with fresh soft paper tissue. Wash leathers should not be used, since they can leave an oil film.

Common symbols	Term	Definition and comments	Units
Q, R	Radiant energy	Energy in the form of electromagnetic radiation.	J (erg, cal)
Φ	Radiant flux	Radiant energy emitted, received or transformed per unit time (*i.e.* power).	J s^{-1}, W (erg s^{-1}, cal min^{-1})
H, I, F	Radiant flux density	Radiant flux per unit area of surface, $d\Phi/dA$. This is strictly the irradiant flux density when the radiation is directed towards the surface of observation. Flux density is generally meant when people speak about intensity in biological literature.	J $m^{-2}s^{-1}$, W m^{-2}, μW cm^{-2}, W cm^{-2} (erg $cm^{-2}s^{-1}$, cal cm^{-2} min^{-1})
M, ε	Emittance	Radiant flux density emitted by a source.	
I, J	Radiant intensity	Radiant flux per unit solid angle, $d\Phi/d\omega$. If I is identical in all directions, $H = \pi I$.	W $steradian^{-1}$
λ	Wavelength	Nanometres preferable to millimicrons or Ångstrom units.	nm ($= 10^{-9}$m) ($\equiv m\mu = 10$Å)
$\nu = c/\lambda$	Frequency	Speed of light divided by wavelength.	Hz
$1/\lambda$	Wavenumber	If spectral flux density is plotted as a function of frequency, the area under the curve is proportional to the available energy.	m^{-1}, cm^{-1}
X_λ	Spectral flux density, *etc.*	The term used with respect to a particular wavelength.	
	Short-wave	Generally 300 $\langle\lambda\rangle$ 3 000 nm.	
	Long-wave	Generally $\lambda >$ 3 000 nm. ($\equiv$ far infra-red).	
NIRR	Near infra-red	700 $\langle\lambda\rangle$ 3 000 nm.	
	Visible	400 $\langle\lambda\rangle$ 750 nm, *i.e.* approximately the photosynthetic region also.	
PhAR	Photosynthetically active radiation	All radiation in the 400–700 nm waveband. The term 'plant watts' is sometimes used for watts of power in this waveband (McCree 1966).	
UV	Ultraviolet	290 $\langle\lambda\rangle$ 400 nm.	
	Solar radiation	That received by the earth from the sun, sometimes used for the direct component alone.	
S, I	Direct radiation	That part of the solar beam that passes through the earth's atmosphere without absorption or scattering. (Watch the distinction between flux density at normal incidence and on a horizontal surface.)	
D	{Diffuse radiation / Sky radiation}	The scattered component of solar radiation received from the sky.	
T, G	{Global radiation / Total radiation}	Direct and diffuse radiation at the earth's surface: $T = D + S$.	
	Extraterrestrial	Radiation received at the outer limit of the earth's atmosphere. Solar constant ≈ 2.0 cal $cm^{-2}min^{-1}$.	
	Terrestrial	Long-wave radiation emitted by the earth.	
	Atmospheric	Long-wave radiation emitted by the atmosphere.	
R_n, R, H	Net radiation	The downward minus the upward flux, usually of both short and longwave radiation.	
	Allwave	Short- and long-wave radiation taken together.	
a, α, ρ, r	Albedo	The fraction of light reflected by a surface (remember to state over what waveband).	
t, τ	Transmissivity	The fraction of radiation passing through a semiopaque body.	
a, k, K	Extinction coefficient	The fraction of radiation absorbed per unit path length in the medium.	
m	Air mass	A measure of the effective path length for solar radiation through the atmosphere, depending largely on solar altitude and atmospheric content of water vapour, ozone, *etc.*	

Clear polythene film transmits 75–85% of both short- and long-wave radiation, with a few absorption bands produced largely by other chemicals used in manufacture. There is therefore a variation in spectral properties with manufacturer and batch (Bolle & Fleischer 1953/4; Schulze 1962), and the most suitable polythene domes for non-ventilated net radiometers are generally made from special batches, manufactured without plasticiser. Reduction in transmission of 6–10% over a period of 3–5 months has been observed for Schulze radiometer domes, while that of comparably exposed domes on Funk radiometers increased very slightly (Palland & Wartena 1968). A number of substances, mostly halides of rare earths (*Kodak Irtran* and others) provide broad band selective filters for long-wave radiation and are used in some infra-red detectors, such as *Irtran 5*, transmitting over 8–13 μm, in infra-red thermometers.
The sensitivity of a radiometer depends on the temperature difference produced between the black and reference sites. The radiant energy absorbed by the black surface will partly be dissipated by conduction, convection and reradiation. The magnitude of these processes depend in a complex way on the exact dimensions and ambient conditions (Bener 1950; Anderson M. C. 1967), so that no instrument is perfectly linear or insensitive to changing ambient temperatures. Individual instruments will vary slightly in their properties, while apparently trivial changes in dimensions between manufacturers, or even just batches, may affect instrument performance substantially. The following comments on particular makes of instrument are given as general guides, individual instruments can vary.

12.2.4 | Standard short-wave pyranometers

These instruments are normally used to measure total short-wave solar energy incident on a horizontal surface, though they may occasionally be covered by coloured glass filters to reduce the waveband range. They can also be fitted with shade rings, to measure diffuse sky radiation. The advice of the local meteorological service should be sought if this is intended. Robinson (1966) discusses most of the instruments in great detail; Hornbaker & Rall (1966) review their performance. The properties of the four most widely used commercial instruments are summarised in Table 12.4. Of these, the Moll-Gorczynski pyranometer is often called the *Kipp*, after *Kipp & Zonen*, Delft, Holland, the most long standing manufacturers. Fairly similar instruments are now manufactured by *Middleton*, by *Swissteco* and by *Solar Radiation Instruments* in Melbourne, Australia, and in the *Eppley Laboratories* in the U.S.A., where they are superseding the classic bulb type '*Eppley*' pyranometer. The *Kipp* version needs a lot of attention to keep thoroughly dry, but its properties are well known (*e.g.* Bener 1950; Anderson M. C. 1967), and it is already very widely used, which makes it a very suitable reference instrument. The *Eppley* elements are sealed inside a glass bulb, which makes it weatherproof, but it is a costly instrument, relatively easily broken, and its cosine response is not particularly good (Woertz & Hand 1941; MacDonald 1951; Fuquay & Buettner 1957). The Stern or star pyranometer is made by a number of manufacturers in different forms, most of which appear to perform well (Dirmhirn 1958a, b), but it has not been so widely used in meteorological networks as the two preceeding instruments. The Soviet Yanishevskiĭ pyranometer is generally used in the U.S.S.R.

(Ross 1957a, b; Vershinin *et al.* 1959), but is little known elsewhere. It is generally held that, when instruments of these types are properly calibrated and maintained, daily totals of radiation can be measured to an accuracy of ± 2–3%. During the I.G.Y., at Cuidad Universitaria in Mexico City, a Moll-Gorczynski, *Eppley* and Yanishevskiĭ were maintained beside each other, and sometimes showed rather greater discrepancies. Poldmaa (1968) Part III contains much comparative data on performance of Russian and other instruments.

Two other instruments are also used in some meteorological networks, and have the advantage of being independent of an electrical recorder; the Robitzsch bimetallic actinograph and the Bellani distillation pyranometer. Neither instrument is suitable for measuring radiation totals over periods of less than a day. Most of the Bellani pyranometers have a spherical, not horizontal receiving surface, whose records cannot be compared at all easily (Thams & Wierzejewski 1963) with those on horizontal surfaces, and the use of this type of instrument as a reference standard is not desirable although under some circumstances it is the most convenient way of measuring an assymetrical flux. Most Bellani pyranometers are rather temperature sensitive, while the Robitzsch actinograph needs careful mechanical adjustment, and its sensitivity varies appreciably with solar altitude and azimuth, casing temperature and incident flux. Robinson (1966) gives further details and McCulloch & Wangati (1967) described an ice filled Bellani. Where possible, the use of one of the pyranometers previously described is preferable.

12.2.5 | Alternative cheap pyranometers

Where wide scale sampling is needed, the cost of all the instruments already described prevents their use. Cheap thermopile elements can now be made by photoelectric plating of copper and constantan on a fibreglass base. Alternatively, and still cheaper, copper can be plated locally on clean constantan wire, partly protected by wax, to produce a series of thermocouples (Monteith 1959). Trickett (1963) describes a method of producing thermal junctions by depositing evaporated metal film. If the electrolytic method is tried, current density while plating must be carefully controlled, and, even where satisfactory plating has apparently been achieved, a sudden change in the properties of the thermopile may occur after a time, apparently due to flaking of some of the copper plate. A version of the Monteith (1959) thermopile, with casing, and elements of another design, plated on fibreglass (Anderson M. C. 1967) are made by *Lintronic Ltd.*, London EC2, for about US $ 50 and 10, respectively. The complete Monteith instrument, as made commercially, is difficult to keep dry, and the large area of unsupported fibre glass is liable to warp: this, with the cheap glass dome directly above, can produce appreciable errors of cosine and azimuth response. This is also a problem in a number of other 'home made' instruments of this type. The instrument designed by Blackwell and Anderson (Anderson M. C. 1967) attempts to overcome these disadvantages, and is specifically designed to sample two wavebands at the same point under a crop (Section 12.4). Kozyrev (1968) describes a small, high sensitivity pyranometer which sounds very suitable for much crop work.

Table 12.4 Properties of widely used short-wave pyranometers.

Instrument property	Moll-Gorczynski	*Eppley*
Number of junctions	Generally 14	'10' actually 16 or 50
Thermocouple type	Constantan/manganin	0.9 Pt + 1 Rh/0.6 Au + 0.4 Pt
Cold junctions	Large copper plate below black surface	Outer white MgO surface on silve film, 29 mm diam. surroundin black circle
Azimuth sensitivity	Appreciable at high solar altitude	Small
Thermocouple layout	Rectangular 10 × 14 mm	Radial
Diameter of glass dome	Inner 28 mm Outer 46 mm	Globe 7.8 cm diameter
Output in mV per cal cm^{-2} min^{-1} (μV per W m^{-2})	7.5–8.5 (11–12)	2 or 7–8 (3 or 10–11)
Internal impedance	About 10 ohm	35 or 100 ohm
Temperature coefficient $°C^{-1}$	−0.15 to 0.25%	−0.05 to −0.15%
Wind sensitivity	Noticeable	Slight
Cosine correction	Reasonable, good above 15° altitude	Tolerable above 20°
Linearity with flux density	Good in most versions	Reasonable
Zero flux output	Small, fairly stable	Noticeable, can drift
Cost in country of manufacture (US $)	$100–200	$500
Response to 99% in s	15	30
Pros and *cons: pro*	Widely used, well known, good overall performance, high output v. resistance	Good weather sealing, low azimu sensitivity, little sensitivity to changes in wave flux
con	Easily affected by humidity wind effects	Price of instrument and repairs poor linearity, easily broken

12.2.6 | Photometric instruments and measurement of PhAR

Selenium and silicon photovoltaic cells are widely used in biological work and can be very useful, if due attention is paid to problems of spectral sensitivity (Chapter 19). Both types give linear plots of daily totals of short-wave radiation in the open against standard pyranometers with a few percent (Blackwell 1953; Kerr, Thurtell & Tanner 1967). Under plant cover their use is more complicated (Coombe 1957; Inoue & Ota 1957; Anderson M. C. 1964a; Federer & Tanner 1966a, b; Norman, Tanner & Thurtell 1969). Table 12.2 gives the approximate deviations from photon response in the 400–700 nm waveband (equality of response under all conditions to the total photon flux in the 400–700 nm band) for various cells and filter combinations, from Federer & Tanner (1966a) and McPherson (1969).

·w model *Eppley*	Stern	Yanishevskiĭ
	32 or 36 on most models	80–100
·pper/constantan	Manganin, nichrome or copper/constantan	Constantan/manganin
$_{.}SO_4$ coating ·on hygroscopic)	Alternate black and white Cu plates above thermocouple junctions	White MgO surfaces in black/white checker-board
·) effect of orientation on ·trument performance	Small	−2 to −10%
·dial	Radial	3 × 3 or 4 × checker-board
	3–5 cm in most instruments	8 cm
5 (11) (standard model)) (3)(lower sensitivity model) to 30 (36–43) (high sensitivity model)	About 2 (3) in smaller models	7–11 (10–16)
0 ohm	About 5 ohm	25–35 ohm (higher in earlier models)
mpensated, ± 1.5% constancy ·om −20 to +40°C	Within limits of experimental accuracy	−0.01 to −0.02%
	Very slight	Slight
2% from normalization	Good to 15°, reasonable below in specially treated models	Rather poor below 20° altitude
1% from 0 to 2.0 cal cm^{-2} min^{-1}		Good
	Small	Small
00 (higher sensitivity model $600)	$150–200	n.a.
·to 4	15–20	less than 40 s
	Generally good performance, but models need further testing, low resistance	Widely used, robust
	Insufficiently investigated	Apparent sensitivity to spectral changes in total radiation (Ross 1957a, b), but has been unusually thoroughly investigated. Poor cosine response

Filtered photometric sensors are often recommended for the measurement of photosynthetically active radiation (PhAR); but it is extremely difficult to limit their response entirely to the 400–700 nm band. Above the crop, this is not a serious disadvantage: as Blackwell (1953) and Drummond (1960) emphasise, despite substantial changes in spectral composition the proportion of radiation (0.4–0.7)/(0.7–3.0) μm is almost constant. Various Estonian and Russian authors since Ross & Nil'son (1963) point out that photosynthetically active radiation can be adequately estimated from measurements of total short-wave radiation: using data from the entire Soviet Union, Efimova (1965, 1967) suggests that

$$R_{PhAR} = 0.43\ I + 0.57\ D$$

where R_{PhAR} is the PhAR, I the direct solar and D the diffuse radiation. Within the crop, even a slight residual instrumental sensitivity to wavelengths longer than

0.7 μm can produce appreciable errors. Instruments such as McCree's (1966) thermopile fitted with a *Chance ON8* filter are entirely inadequate, and even specially designed instruments are suspect. Some sensors can be fitted interchangeably with different filters, such as the *EKO* tube solarimeters used by Allen & Brown (1965) and that described in Anderson M. C. (1967). It is much easier to obtain filters which cut off wavelengths below 700 nm. Using this, PhAR can be estimated more satisfactorily by a difference technique.

Selenium cells have the advantage that their chief sensitivity lies in the 400–730 nm region (this varies somewhat with type), and, with appropriate filters, such as the *Kodak Wratten 86C*, respond largely to photosynthetic wavelengths (Federer & Tanner 1966b). Conversely, their output is low, may drift under rapidly fluctuating radiation, they are damp sensitive ('potting' in acrylic resins has much reduced this problem), and are damaged by high flux densities and heavy (> 100 μA) current drain (heavy neutral filters minimise this). Using heavily filtered *Megatron* selenium cells in a special cosine corrected casing, Anderson M. C. has found little decline in sensitivity when the cells were exposed for long periods under temperate woodland canopy. Huxley (1964) using the same cells in the open in the tropics, found a greater sensitivity loss and temperature sensitivity a problem. Like other types of photocell, their response becomes more and more non-linear as the impedance of the circuit is increased, when operated in the resistance across sensor or reversed biased modes, which limits the types of recording equipment with which they can be used (Section 12.2.8). When used in the short circuit current mode, silicon cells have an excellent linear response, and no dark current. Silicon cells have a much higher output and are more robust, but are largely sensitive to the near infra-red, with a peak sensitivity around 0.8–0.9 μm. Although they also are non-linear in high impedance circuits, the high output means that they can be used with relatively simple integrating devices in the open, or that the very small, high output cells used in computer paper tape readers (Fig. 12.3) can be used in cramped situations where no other instrument will fit, but their spectral sensitivity makes them unsuitable for measurements with many biological systems (Federer & Tanner 1966b; Dirmhirm 1967) although useful in the open (Yellot, Chamnes & Selcuk 1962). Cadmium sulphide cells are sometimes used, they share with silicon cells the problems of spectral response to the near IR, some types are definitely highly nonlinear and require an external bias, and the ways in which they are potted give them peculiar directional responses. In general, photometric cells or emission tubes are unsuitable for direct exposure to measure radiant flux on a horizontal surface, and some sort of diffusing head to improve cosine response is needed.

Kerr, Thurtell & Tanner (1967) have described an excellent example of a self contained sensing, integrating and recording system built in the laboratory for about US $ 35. A silicon cell is mounted under a diffuser, set in a moulded plastic weatherproof case, which contains a compact transistorised amplifier and print out. These devices have been used to maintain a secondary radiation network in the open in the State of Wisconsin (Kerr, Thurtell & Tanner 1968). A number of commercial instruments of this type are made, generally with a whole battery of cells exposed under a glass dome. In most, the cosine correction and temperature sensitivity of the integrator compare unfavourably with Kerr *et al.*'s instrument

e.g. Dirmhirm (1967) in the *Sol-a-Meter*, although the version made by *Rauchfuss* in Melbourne has performed satisfactorily in a number of tests. Trickett & Moulsley (1955) (see also McCree & Morris 1967) originally described another self contained sensor plus integrator, the sensor being a selenium cell in a weatherproofed, cosine corrected head. The integrator, a *Siemens* electrolytic one (Section 12.2.8), is no longer available, but the cells remain one of the most satisfactory forms of mounting of selenium cells (*Megatron*, London, complete about US $ 35, cell alone US $ 7). Bell (1955) and Federer & Tanner (1966a, b) describe means of filtering the output of selenium cells to respond to the 400–700 nm waveband only. Kubín & Hládek (1963) and Šetlík (1968) describe a self contained system based on a photoemission tube with response filtered to 400–700 nm, and Niïlisk (1963) also describes a similar system, with less elaborate filters.
The use of photosensitive solution in transparent vials and of stacks of photosensitive paper is still sometimes proposed, but is not recommended. These photosensitive devices are highly UV/blue sensitive. As their spectral properties change with exposure the duration of exposure can affect the result and their spatial sampling properties are extremely difficult to define. (The shape of the containers of solutions can produce very peculiar directional responses.) Allen, Yocum & Lemon (1964), Laïsk (1964), Niïlisk (1965) and Brach & Wiggins (1967) describe spectroradiometers for use in crops, and a commercial instrument is available from *Instrumentation Specialties Corporation* in Nebraska for US $ 2000.

12.2.7 | *Auxiliary measurements of sunshine duration and cloud cover*

A knowledge of the periods during which the sun was shining is useful in interpreting radiation measurements under crops. Besides, for many parts of the world useful empirical relations between sunshine duration or cloud cover and total short-wave (occasionally all wave) radiation have been established (Ångström 1924; Kimball 1928; Haurwitz 1945, 1946, 1948; Black, Bonython & Prescott 1954; Albrecht 1955; Black 1956; Budyko 1956; Glover & McCulloch 1958; Berliand 1960; Laevastu 1960; Liu & Jordan 1960; Lumb 1964; Grunow 1966; Robinson 1966; Anderson E. A. & Baker 1967; Khelkhovski 1967; Kondo 1967). Measurements of sunshine duration with a Campbell-Stokes or other recorder can therefore provide a useful check on the accuracy of radiation records, and a means of estimating local variation in radiation income (Section 12.3.2) where the cost of standard pyrheliometers is prohibitive.
The Campbell-Stokes recorder consists of a large clear glass sphere, which focusses the direct solar beam onto a card, along which a trace is burnt when the sun is shining. Full details of installation, operation and maintenance are given in Handbook of Meteorological Instruments (1956). As WMO-RA-1 (1961) point out, there are local differences in convention for determining sunshine duration from the trace, which should be allowed for. The Campbell-Stokes is the most robust, and, in principle, one of the most simple sunshine recorders and is to be preferred to the Marvin recorder used in the U.S.A., which is fragile and difficult to standardise. The Jordan recorder, made by *Negretti and Zambra*, London, is very cheap, and uses UV sensitive paper exposed through a slit in the sensitive cylinder. It is not widely used and there are few accounts of its performance versus a Campbell-

Stokes, though Sekihara & Suzuki (1967) discuss differences in empirical prediction formulae using data from the two instruments. Summer (1966) describes a type of recorder which can be left unattended for six months.
Records of the extent and nature of cloud cover are also useful (for empirical relations, see above references, also Haurwitz (1945, 1946, 1948); Lumb (1964); Tabata (1964); Pochop, Shanklin & Horner (1968); Quinn & Burt (1968). Such records can be made automatically through a fish eye lens (180° lens: Hill 1924, Pochop & Shanklin 1966), or visually, recording cloud cover in 8ths or 10ths through the day, and cloud type, following an official observer's handbook or cloud atlas.

12.2.8 | Net (all wave) radiometers

Three types of instrument are available to measure radiation in the 0.3 μm waveband. All normally measure the downward minus the upward (net) flux, by comparing the temperatures of the upper and lower sides of a horizontal black surface, although some can also be adapted to make unidirectional measurements. Of the three types, the non-ventilated shielded surface instruments are generally the most suitable for agricultural investigations, and the easiest for persons unfamiliar with them to handle. Barashkova, Lebedeva & Yastrova (1966) and Sulev (1966) provide Russian language reviews of types available in the Soviet Union.

a. Non-ventilated, shielded surface instruments. The black surfaces of these instruments are protected by polythene (or *Lupolen*), usually inflated by bleeding nitrogen or dry air into the instrument. Bolle & Fleischer (1953/4) and Schulze (1962) discuss the transmissivity of these polythene materials to radiation.
The Funk (1959, 1960, 1961, 1962a, b) net radiometer, now manufactured in Melbourne, Australia by *Middleton Pty* and by *Swissteco* for about US $ 270, is a suitable instrument for work with crops, being robust and of fairly high sensitivity, about 30 mV per cal cm^{-2} min^{-1}. It is not so bulky and heavy as the others described here, although still too large for use in some crops. A miniature version which is difficult to level and has a lower sensitivity, and several sizes of linear net radiometers (Denmead 1966), which may produce appreciable azimuth errors, are also available. Heating rings to prevent dew deposition are also manufactured. A similar instrument to the standard Funk described by Fritschen & van Wijk (1959) and Fritschen (1963) has a far lower sensitivity.
Lange Ges. (Berlin) also make a similar instrument, designed by Schulze (1953). This originally contained two Moll (1923) thermopiles, later replaced by ones designed by Fleischer (1959), but still leaving the instrument much heavier and bulkier than the Funk. A rather simpler version was described by Georgi (1956). At the Davos Observatory, a version designed by Courvoisier (1950) has been made, which is also rather bulky. Like the later Funk and Schulze instruments, it can be used to record a unidirectional flux.
Suomi & Kuhn (1958) and Suomi, Staley & Kuhn (1958) designed a 'poor man's' radiometer, made of a wooden box with polythene windows top and bottom. The sensor inside is a flake thermistor or thermocouples sandwiched between

blackened aluminium foil. The high output from the thermistor is readily measured. The cube design produces poor cosine correction and the polythene sheets are difficult to keep clean (Swan, Federer & Tanner 1961), while the wooden box is liable to warp and makes it difficult to keep the sensor dry.
A fair approximation to the Funk type of instrument can be made very cheaply in the laboratory by threading a fibreglass disc with constantan wire and plating (Monteith 1959; Funk 1962c; Tanner 1963 (*M3-3*); Jensen & Åslyng 1967) with copper appropriately. Two polythene domes can be moulded from a thin polythene sheet over a 25 W light bulb.
Polythene thick enough to be self-supporting absorbs too much radiation for accurate measurements, so that the domes of these instruments must be kept inflated with dry air or nitrogen bled from a cylinder through a needle valve. A simple bubbler through a 10 cm long boiling tube filled with water placed in series after the instrument enables the flow rate to be monitored. One bubble a minute is normally adequate.

b. Ventilated, exposed surface radiometers. In these instruments convective heat losses from the upper and lower surfaces of a flat, black plate are equalised as far as possible by blowing air over both surfaces. This makes the instruments fairly bulky and unsuitable for use inside crops, particularly as the blower motor needs to be mounted at some distance from the sensitive surface. The Gier & Dunkle (1951) version, manufactured by *Beckman and Whitely*, San Carlos, Cal., has been criticised for the obstruction to air flow from the plate supports, and from the ventilator housing. The ventilation speed is low, so that the instrument is sensitive to changes of wind speed. The sensitivity is in the range of 5 mV per cal cm^{-2} min^{-1}. Franssila (1953) and Suomi, Franssila & Islitzer (1954) describe modifications reducing the obstruction and providing a vane to regulate the proportion of air flowing over the two surfaces. The sensitivity is about half that of the original instrument. A similar instrument has been developed in Britain by MacDowall (1954, 1955), later versions using a heat flow unit of *Joyce, Loebl and Co.*, Newcastle. Similar instruments are also made in Germany and Switzerland (Falckenburg 1947; Courvoisier 1950), where careful attention has been given to ventilation design (see also Möriköfer 1953 for discussion).

c. Non ventilated, exposed surface radiometers. Instruments of this type vary in response with wind speed and ambient temperature, and either elaborate compensating devices are required or corrections must be applied for wind speed *etc.* as in the case of the Russian Yanishevskiĭ radiometer (Kondrat'ev 1965b; Sulev 1966; Poldmaa 1968). The difficulties and potential inaccuracies of their use are such that they cannot be recommended to provide a routine supporting measurement in any biological work.

12.2.9 | Measuring and recording equipment

For radiation measurements in relation to plant growth studies, integrated totals are usually required. Any current or potential measuring device should therefore provide some permanent record on strip chart or computer tape, or integrate automatically. As other environmental measurements will probably also be made at the same time, a multichannel potentiometric data logging system is extremely useful, if it can be afforded. With increasing demand, the price of logging systems has fallen substantially over the past few years. Otherwise, the pros and cons of buying a number of integrators at a constant price per channel or a multichannel recording potentiometer, at a lower cost per channel, but requiring manual integration of records until such time as a logging system is fitted to it, must be considered.

a. Potentiometric instruments. Two types are available: null balance, D.C. potentiometric recorders and digital voltmeters. The latter can only be used in conjunction with a logging system.
Potentiometric recorders are widely used industrially, are generally reliable and relatively cheap, can be bought as multichannel instruments, and many can be fitted with integrators. Their recording charts provide a most valuable permanent record. Two types are made: the more common and robust types use a chopper stabilised D.C. amplifier to detect the error signal and drive the potentiometer to the balance point, but types using sensitive reflecting galvanometers are also available. The latter reject mains frequency pick up very satisfactorily, and may be useful where this is a problem (an asynchronous chopper on the amplifier can also be used). The galvanometer type instruments tend to have a rather low input impedance. This is particularly true of some small, sensitive and cheap ones, some of which can be left to operate on batteries in the field, where a sensitivity of 10 mV full scale is achieved with an input impedance of 10 Ω. When using this type of instrument, the whole sensor-recorder circuit must be carefully considered, since the system response will depend on the impedances of all the components.
Digital voltmeters would normally be purchased as part of a commercial logging system. Compared with a recording potentiometer logging system, the DVM system has several advantages. Except where very high accuracy is required, the speed of scanning the channels is much higher, automatic ranging is available on many systems, it is generally cheap and simple to add more channels, and the system is more compact. There are two serious disadvantages. No analogue chart record of the signals is obtained, which, in the field, makes it very difficult to detect sensor malfunction on the spot. DVM's capable of measuring to 1 μV, and resolving to 2–5 μV in conjunction with a logging system, are very much more expensive than recording potentiometers of equivalent sensitivity, and the balance time of both instrument types is comparable. In some commercial DVM logging systems, the input impedance of the DVM drops far below the manufacturer's quoted value on switching between channels, and, at relatively high scan speeds, does not rise before the measurement is made.

b. Recording current meters. These are generally galvanometer type instruments of low input impedance. Some of the higher output thermopile type instruments, *e.g.* a Funk net radiometer, could successfully be used, but their sensitivity is generally too low to handle such instruments as the 10 junction *Eppley*. Alternatively, they provide a convenient low resistance component to insert direct in a circuit using a photocell. In either case, the impedances of all components must be considered when determining system response, which will rarely be linear. These impedances should also be checked at least once a year.

c. Integrators:

I. Strip chart recorders. Ball and disc or switch adder integrators are available commercially from the manufacturers of many chart recorders. Some recorders are fitted with transmitting slide wires, which can be used with coulometers (see below). King & Graham (1959) describe a non-commercial switch adder system for multichannel recorders.

Methods of tabulating chart records are dealt with in detail in the Annals of IGY V Instruction Manual (1957) on radiation. It is generally necessary to use this method for non-linear or multichannel records. For single channels linear records, weighing or planimetering the area under the curve are better solutions. Russell (1960) describes a means of cutting paper while recording a single trace.

II. Integrating D.C. motors. The revolutions of a low friction, D.C. motor can be totalised, the speed of the motor being proportional to the input voltage. There are problems with the friction of motor and counter, as discussed by Trickett, Moulsley & Edwards (1957). Tanner (1963) recommends mounting miniature magnets on the motor gear chain to drive a reed switch. Schoffer & Suomi (1961) use a circuit with feed-back proportional to motor speed to reduce friction errors, which Tanner (1963) suggests can be simplified by using an auxiliary generator winding to give a speed sensitive feed-back voltage, which can be used directly. The main advantage of integrating motors is ease of reading: for reasonable precision the electrical circuitry becomes complicated and quite expensive.

III. Coulometers. In these, the time integral of current is measured by electrodeposition of metals or electrical dissociation of a fluid to a gas. When operated at low current densities, so that the electrical efficiency is high, the method can be exceedingly accurate and reliable. The impedance of coulometers varies appreciably with temperature, current density and electrolyte composition: therefore they should not be operated from voltage sources, but from high impedance current sources such as photocells. A good discussion of the problems can be found in Tanner, Thurtell & Swan (1963).

Tanner, Thurtell & Swan also describe a circuit based on an inexpensive mercury coulometer (*Curtis Instruments Inc.*, Mount Kisco, N.Y.), operating on currents of 5 mA or less. The meter (various types are made) can be damaged if the gap between the mercury electrodes is driven past the end of the glass capillary, so it cannot be left unattended for long periods. The circuit also requires a stable amplifier to provide current feed back.

Siemens used to manufacture a D.C. liquid/gas coulometer for domestic current metering, as described by Trickett & Moulsley (1955). Some of the domestic versions can still be found second-hand in Continental Europe, although most versions are of inconveniently low sensitivity for radiation work. An English firm has manufactured a slightly modified version, but these have not proved very satisfactory in use. The instruments are fragile and rather difficult to reset.

IV. Resistance-capacitance integrators. With these common analogue integrators either current or voltage can be integrated over time. A capacitor is charged by the feed-back current of an operational amplifier, the charge being proportional to the time integral of the feed-back current, which, in turn, is proportional to the input signal to the amplifier. Details may be found in Gray (1948) and Thurtell & Tanner (1964). A variety of instruments are commercially available.

V. Relaxation oscillator integrators. The signal is integrated by storing current in a capacitor placed in parallel with a cold cathode tube, biased thyratron or unijunction transistor, which periodically become conducting and discharge the capacitor as it reaches firing voltage. The discharges are used to operate a counter. Ives (1962), Kubín & Hládek (1963), Turner (1966) and Kerr, Thurtell & Tanner (1967) discuss the construction of these circuits in detail, meeting the criteria of reasonably low cost, good linearity and zero drift and temperature stability. Many commercial integrators of this type are available, and their threshold sensitivity, temperature stability and linearity should be considered critically before purchase.

VI. Galvanometer digitisation. Rider & Bradley (1962) and Bradley & Wall (1965) have described low cost integrating systems in which deflections of a galvanometer are directly digitised and counted. The system performs well over an hour or so, but its long term stability has not been closely investigated.

VII. Counters in integrating circuits. Although counters can be photographed by an automatic time lapse camera, it is cheaper in the long run to buy or make a machine using a printing counter.

d. Scale and sensitivity requirements in recording instruments. The majority of thermopile instruments discussed in Sections 12.2.6 and 12.2.8 produce 5–20 mV per cal cm^{-2} min^{-1}. The maximum short-wave downward flux density is usually around 1.5 cal cm^{-2} min^{-1}, though for short periods the solar constant of 2.0 cal cm^{-2} min^{-1} may be exceeded. Daily totals of short-wave radiation may be as high as 750 cal cm^{-2} in arid subtropical areas, or, on heavily overcast days in high latitudes, fall below 10 cal cm^{-2} even in months when plants are growing. Recording instruments for short-wave radiation in the open would therefore normally require a full scale of 10–20 mV, and a sensitivity to a flux of 0.01 cal cm^{-2} min^{-1}, *i.e.* 50–200 μV. When working with instruments under crops, a much higher sensitivity is needed, prevailing flux densities throughout the day may well be 1% of that in the open, and an instrument sensitive to 1 μV and capable of measuring to 2–5 μV accurately may be needed. Except in automatic ranging digital voltmeters, such sensitivity will probably only be found with an instrument measuring to 1 mV full scale. It is relatively simple to reduce a signal, and difficult to amplify microvolt signals from under the crop satisfactorily. Where resistors are used to reduce an input voltage, their sensitivity to temperature changes should be checked. It is wise to calibrate the sensor/resistor combination as a unit. Many digital voltmeters and recording potentiometers can be bought with several ranges for a slight extra cost. Digital voltmeters accept signals of either polarity automatically. In many chart recorders zero suppression is either infinitely adjustable or can be ranged. When

working with radiation it is generally desirable not to have zero on the far left hand side of the chart, since many sensors show some zero drift at night, which must be allowed for when evaluating the daytime record. For net radiometers, the maximum negative flux is generally about 25% of the maximum positive flux, and a recorder with 20–50% zero suppression is suitable. In a recorder with 50% suppression (central zero), it is often convenient to connect successive signals with opposite polarity, which simplifies evaluating a chart record.
Low impedance, current measuring chart recorders can only be used with the higher output thermopiles, since the current they produce, even in a low impedance circuit, is small. An instrument producing 10 mV will only produce 0.1 mA in an 100 Ω circuit. Generally, current measuring recorders are more suitable for use with photocells, where they provide a convenient low impedance component in the circuit. With suitable shunts, photocells can equally well be used with potentiometers.

e. Frequency of sampling. Since Shannon & Weaver (1949) published their classical work on the mathematical theory of communication, a very extensive literature on optimum sampling times for retrieval of information has developed, which is outside the scope of this article. Anyone wishing to investigate the variation of radiation fluxes with time should consult Shannon & Weaver and such works as Blackman & Tukey (1958) and Karbowiak (1967). When measuring daily integrated totals above the crop, it is generally adequate to record once every five minutes. In the crop, no hard and fast rules can be made, since so much depends on the size of the sensor relative to the gaps in the canopy, as discussed in Section 12.4. As Norman & Tanner (1969) show, the frequency with maximum spectral density varies greatly with the crop, being around 3 Hz for a bromegrass-alfalfa mixture and greater than 20 Hz for soy bean.

12.2.10 | Setting up and maintenance

12.2.10.1 | Positioning sensors

All radiation sensors should be mounted horizontally on a rigid, non-obstructing support. Those instruments with an asymmetric sensing area *e.g.* Moll-Gorczynski, Robitzsch, should be mounted with the long axis running E.-W. (remember to correct for the difference between geographic and magnetic north). The minimum of obstructions, particularly along the solar track, should be present for instruments mounted in the open. Hemispherical photographs (Section 12.6.1) are useful in assessing the extent of any obstruction. When instruments are mounted on a roof, they should be kept as far as possible from any chimneys or vents from fume cupboards. The geographical coordinates and height above mean sea level of the site should be recorded.
The use of shade rings or occulting discs, so that the sensor receives diffuse sky radiation only, is outside the scope of this article. If diffuse radiation is to be measured separately, which is highly desirable when interpreting measurements in crops, the local meteorological service and IGY Annals (1957) should be consulted. Sensors used within the crop should similarly be mounted rigidly and horizontally.

When measuring at several levels within the crop, care should be taken that the upper instruments do not shade the lower. There is a serious problem in maintaining instruments in the crop without damaging the crop by trampling. It is often desirable to mount the instrument on the end of a long rod for insertion. Other solutions are a miniature railway and trolley, or a bridge that will go over the crop, on which a person can stand. Obviously, as little disturbance as possible of plant parts should take place when inserting instruments.
All sensors should be fitted with adequate means of dehydration. A polythene wash bottle filled with self indicating silica gel and attached to the instrument by tubing is suitable, as squeezing the bottle produces air circulation.
The problem of the number of sensors needed for adequate sampling in the crop is discussed in Section 12.4.

12.2.10.2 | Electrical connections

When measuring the low level D.C. signals produced by most radiation sensors, two sources of noise in the electrical circuits must be kept as low as possible: pick up, particularly from A.C. sources or adjacent transmitters, and spurious thermal e.m.f.'s from connections in the circuit.
Pick up can be minimised by adequate shielding, grounding and avoidance of ground loops. Details of particular requirements depend on local conditions, but in general, signal leads should be shielded and grounded at one end only, usually at that of the recorder. Generally several leads can be run through a single shield, and a common neutral wire used for several instruments. Recording and auxiliary equipment such as mains voltage stabilisers should be tied to the common ground also, avoiding ground loops between instruments. The manufacturer's recommended polarity should be preserved on all power plugs. The neutral wire of A.C. power supplies and the ground wire may be at different A.C. grounds and either wire may be at a different potential compared to that of the earthing stake. This may produce A.C. ground loops, which can be avoided by using a well earthed isolation transformer.
Thermal e.m.f.'s will obviously be reduced by minimising the number of connections and screening them from temperature changes. It is desirable, wherever possible, to use the same type of metal in all connecting circuits and often to solder the junctions. Where the circuit is liable to need changing, terminal blocks or junction boxes with the connections insulated with self curing silicon rubber can be used. Where a patch board type connection into a multichannel recorder is needed, mercury pool slip rings or large banana plugs, giving an appreciable area of contact, may be used. All connections should be tested with a portable meter, to make sure that the resistance is neglible. People are always liable to fall over cables in the field, so it is advisable to strap all connections so that no mechanical strain is taken by them.
Lead resistance can become an appreciable part of the total circuit resistance, and where measuring devices are used that are likely to be affected, a record of lead resistance should be kept. As low a resistance lead as can be afforded should be used, and calibration checked with the lead when a long one is in use. The various plastic insulations put on the outside of cables sometimes prove palatable to

rodents, and cables left lying around in the field for any length of time should be inspected periodically. When stripping the insulation on fine multistranded leads it is very easy to cut through most of the wires. The bare wires should be well tinned before connection to a terminal block *etc.*
It is always desirable to use pyranometers with a temperature compensating device such as that described by Rodskjer (1964) or Collins & Walton (1967). The new *Eppley* pyranometer is sold with a built-in compensator.

12.2.10.3 | Daily maintenance

A log book should be kept recording daily instrument readings, weather conditions, any changes or adjustments to instruments, failure of power supply *etc.* Details of cloud cover (Section 12.2.7) should be noted.
The protective covers of radiation sensors should be cleaned daily with a lint free cloth or tissue. If much dust has accumulated, it should be wiped off lightly first, before polishing with a clean tissue, to avoid scratching the dome. Rime or frost on the dome can sometimes be moved by gentle warming with the hand, but this may upset instrument performance for a while, and a cloth moistened with alcohol is more suitable. The condition of the desiccant should be noted, and changed before exhaustion. Any condensation inside the domes, or frost *etc.* on the outside, should be noted. The surfaces of exposed net radiometers require very gentle cleaning with a fine clean paint brush or equivalent. The Australian manufacturers provide a cleaning, water repellent solution of silicone oil in an organic solvent. After cleaning, the levelling of all instruments should be checked.
Recorder charts should be clearly marked at least once a day, with station, date, instrument identification and a time (Section 12.3.1) mark. Paper tape from loggers should be labelled with felt tip pen or pencil at both ends. Where recorders are turned off at night, a check on zero position should be carried out by covering the sensor until a steady record is obtained. Should a power failure occur, mark the position on any recorder charts at the time.
Completed charts and paper tape should be stored in a dry clean place. Rolls of paper tape should be stored flat to avoid distortion.

12.2.10.4 | Long term maintenance

Manufacturers' recommended servicing should be carried out on all instruments and the service noted in the log book. Excessive oiling of moving parts defeats its own object by encouraging dust accumulation. Paper tape punches should be cleaned regularly to remove chads and paper frass. A small vacuum cleaner is very useful. The resistance of electrical connections to the sensors should be checked periodically, particularly those exposed in the field.
Recording systems and sensors require periodic recalibration. When records of solar radiation are being made within the crop for several weeks or months, it is advisable to run all the sensors against each other in the open periodically, in case any are changing in sensitivity. With instruments above crops, which are much easier to service properly, such frequent checks are unnecessary, but it is usually advisable to check any permanently exposed sensor once every six months,

particularly those based on photocells. A properly maintained standard thermopile should only require checking annually. On most net radiometers, a rapid spot check for any change of performance can be made by comparing the readings under steady conditions with the instrument turned with one and then the other side up. The polythene domes of shielded net radiometers require periodic renewal, particularly if they show obvious signs of weathering or scratching. A few small scratches on glass domes do not generally affect response greatly, but if a glass dome becomes appreciably scratched, it should be replaced and the instrument recalibrated. Where filters are used in sensors, their transmissivity should be checked occasionally, preferably with a spectrophotometer.

Recording potentiometers incorporate a standard cell against which they normally check automatically about once an hour. Periodic checks against a standard voltmeter should be made, and any necessary scale and mechanical adjustments made. Slide wires should be cleaned regularly. Where a shaft encoder is fitted, it should be protected from dust as far as possible and its mechanical setting checked periodically. Digital voltmeters normally incorporate a manually operated calibration setting, which should be operated regularly. In any logging system, it is advisable to check the performance of the system as a whole by feeding in a series of known voltages, even if no trouble is apparent. Recording microammeters require periodic recalibration. Details of the procedure can be found in the I.G.Y. Annals (1957).

12.3 | Radiation in the open

To predict and understand the relation between crop structure and radiation penetration, we need to know the distribution of radiation in the open in space and time. Several definitive works are available in various languages (Linke 1942; Kondrat'ev 1965a; Robinson 1966) and only an outline is given here.

12.3.1 | Defining and calculating solar position

A diagram of the position S of the sun relative to a point P on the earth's surface is given in Fig. 12.1. To define the position of S relative to P, two angles must be known, the *altitude* $\beta = \angle SPR$ and the *azimuth* $\xi = \angle NPR$, which is the angular distance in the horizontal plane between the sun and the north point N of the meridian plane NMZ. Altitude and azimuth can be calculated from the *latitude* λ of P on the earth's surface; the *declination* δ of P, which is the difference between the sun's altitude when it crosses the meridian plane near noon and the co-latitude $(\pi/2 - \lambda)$; and the *hour angle* h, proportional to the time elapsed since the sun crossed the meridan plane. h is measured along the circle of the solar track $S_R S$ S_S (S_R position at sunrise, S_S position at sunset), while PQ is the line joining P with the celestial north pole. Since the sun apparently moves through 2π in a day, it appears to move 15° in one hour. Altitude and azimuth are given by:

$$\sin \beta = \sin \lambda \sin \delta + \cos \lambda \cos \delta \cos h \qquad (12.1)$$

$$\sin \xi = \sin h \cos \delta \sec \beta. \qquad (12.2)$$

 At the crossing of the meridian plane, $h = 0$, and (12.1) reduces to

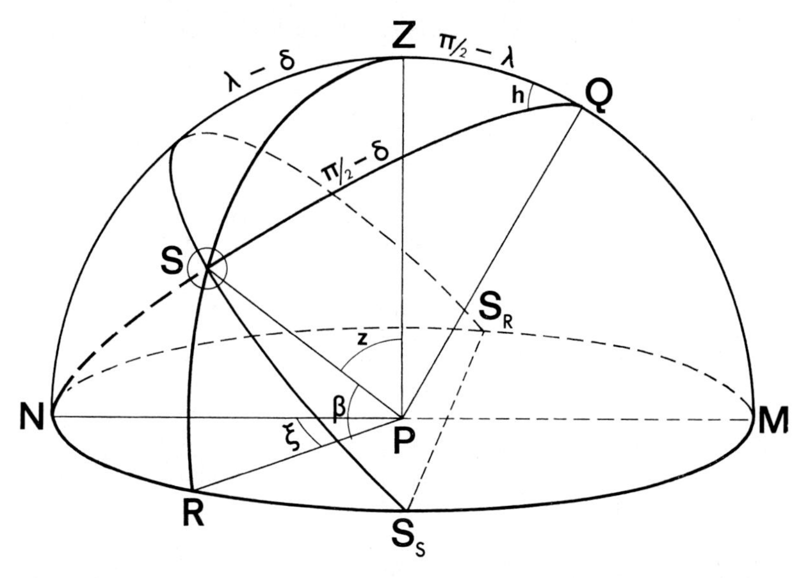

Fig. 12.1 Diagram to illustrate terms describing solar position. *S* sun; *Z* zenith; *NMZ* meridian plane; *P* observer; β altitude; ξ azimuth; δ declination; λ latitude; for further symbols see text.

$$\beta = \lambda - \delta. \tag{12.3}$$

Calculations are often made using the complement of altitude $\angle SPZ$, called the *zenith distance* z.

Three time bases must be distinguished: *local apparent time* LAT, *local mean time* LMT and *zone mean time* ZMT. LAT is the time observed directly from solar position, *i.e.* it is 12.00 LAT when the sun is due south in the northern hemisphere. The earth wobbles slightly on its axis, and there is some variation ($\pm c$ 15 min) in the time at which the sun crosses the meridian, which is averaged out in LMT for that meridian. The difference between LAT and LMT is given by the *equation of time*. ZMT is that normally shown by clocks throughout a region, and generally changes one hour at each 15° of longitude east or west of the Greenwich Meridian 0°. Within a zone, clock time is the LMT on a standard meridian. To convert to LMT 4 min must be added or subtracted for each degree west or east the observation point lies of the standard meridian.

When taking compass bearings, *e.g.* to fix due south of a fish eye photograph, remember to correct for the difference between magnetic and true north. Most Ordnance maps give this correction and its annual variation.

Mean values for declination and the equation of time are given in Table 12.5. These vary very slightly from year to year, and for really accurate work a precise value must be found from the current Nautical Almanac.

12.3.2 | *The solar constant and extraterrestrial radiation*

The sun emits an almost constant radiant flux. The mean flux density on a surface normal to the sun's rays above the earth's atmosphere is known as the *solar constant* I_0. A recent determination gives a value of 1.95 cal cm^{-2} min^{-1} (Drum-

Table 12.5 The sun's declination and equation of time.

Date		Declination		Eq. of time		Date		Declination		Eq. of time	
		°	′	m.	s.			°	′	m.	s.
Jan	1	−23	4	− 3	14	July	1	23	10	− 3	31
	13	−21	37	− 8	27		13	21	57	− 5	30
	21	−20	5	−11	10		21	20	38	− 6	15
Feb.	1	−17	19	−13	34	Aug.	1	18	14	− 6	17
	13	−13	37	−14	20		13	14	55	− 4	57
	21	−10	50	−13	50		21	12	23	− 3	19
Mar.	1	− 7	53	−12	38	Sep.	1	8	35	− 0	15
	13	− 3	14	− 9	49		13	4	6	3	45
	21	− 0	5	− 7	32		21	1	1	6	35
Apr.	1	4	14	− 4	12	Oct.	1	− 2	53	10	1
	13	8	46	− 0	47		13	− 7	29	13	30
	21	11	35	1	6		21	−10	25	15	10
May	1	14	50	2	50	Nov.	1	−14	11	16	21
	13	18	11	3	44		13	−17	45	15	47
	21	20	2	3	34		21	−19	45	14	18
June	1	21	57	2	27	Dec.	1	−21	41	11	16
	13	23	10	0	18		13	−23	6	6	12
	21	23	27	− 1	25		21	−23	26	2	19

mond *et al.* 1968): for the previous decade a value of 2.00 cal cm^{-2} min^{-1} was used. The earth's orbit is slightly eccentric, with a mean radius r_0 of 149.5 × 10^6 km, the astronomical unit, and an actual radius r (which is given in the Nautical Almanac or Ephemeris). The correction term $(r_0/r)^2$ gives the seasonal variation in solar constant, and should be introduced in accurate work. McCullough (1968) describes a mean of calculating the extraterrestrial flux density on a horizontal surface as a harmonic of the day of the year.

12.3.3 | Depletion of solar radiation by the earth's atmosphere

As solar radiation passes through the earth's atmosphere, some is absorbed and the spectral composition is changed by wavelength dependent processes. These processes are:

I. Rayleigh scattering by molecules of air and other particles less than one tenth diameter compared with the wavelength of the radiation. Scattering is inversely proportional to the fourth power of the wavelength, hence blue light is scattered much more than red, and makes a relatively greater contribution to sky compared to sun radiation.

II. Mie scattering and diffuse reflection from larger particles, such as dust and smoke.

III. Selective absorption by gases, *e.g.* ozone in the ultraviolet; water vapour around 0.9, 1.1, 1.4, 1.9 μm *etc.*

IV. Scattering and absorption by cloud masses.

 Analytical solutions for processes I–III may be calculated for a particular wave-

length, but solutions for broad wavebands and for effects of cloud are largely empirical.
To calculate the extinction of the direct solar beam, it is necessary to know the path length of the beam through the atmosphere, the *optical air mass m*. For solar altitudes greater than 10°, this can be taken as

$$m = \csc \beta \qquad (12.4)$$

but at low altitudes corrections must be applied for refraction, *etc*. A standard text should be consulted.
The spectral intensity I_λ of the direct beam on a surface normal to the beam at the earth's surface is often given by

$$I_\lambda = I_{0\lambda} \exp(-\alpha_\lambda m) \qquad (12.5)$$

where α_λ is the extinction coefficient for wavelength λ.
Prediction of the diffuse solar radiation from the sky is more complex. Robinson (1966) gives a detailed account.
Frequently the only records of solar radiation available are of global (or total) T (sun S + sky D) flux density on a horizontal surface. For most calculations on penetration into crops S and D must be known separately. Extinction formulae of the type (12.5) are difficult to use for partly cloudy skies. Anderson M.C. (1970, 1971) has shown that a general empirical relation exists between T and S:

$$S = a\, T^b \qquad (12.6)$$

for both hourly and daily totals.

12.3.4 | *Spatial distribution of diffuse solar radiation*

Several theoretical treatments of this problem exist for clear skies, which emit far more in the region near the sun than elsewhere. There are also many measurements recorded in the literature.
When even a little cloud is present, variation of emittance with altitude is far less pronounced. It is much more convenient where possible to work with a model in which it is assumed that emittance is constant with azimuth. The simplest model, the *Uniform Overcast Sky* UOC assumes that emittance is constant all over the sky, the isotropic sky of some authors. The total flux density I_β on a horizontal surface received from the sky at an altitude β is then:

$$I_\beta = \sin 2\beta \qquad (12.7)$$

In 1942 Moon & Spencer suggested that the variation of luminance with altitude of completely overcast skies could be described by the formula:

$$L_\beta = (L_z/3) \cdot (1 + 2 \sin \beta) \qquad (12.8)$$

where L_β is the luminance at altitude β, and L_z that at the zenith. Equation (12.8) was adopted in 1955 by the Commission Internationale de l'Éclairage to describe the *Standard Overcast Sky* SOC. Radiant emittance in the short-wave region is closely similar to luminance. For a SOC the expression analogous to (12.7) is:

$$I_\beta = (2 \cos \beta)/3 \cdot (\sin \beta + 2 \sin^2 \beta) \tag{12.9}$$

The total flux density I on a horizontal surface received from a sky below the altitude of β is then for a UOC:

$$I = \int_0^\beta \sin 2\beta \cdot d\beta = (1 - \cos 2\beta) \tag{12.10}$$

and for a SOC

$$I = \frac{2}{3} \int_0^\beta (\sin \beta + 2 \sin^2 \beta) \cos \beta \cdot d\beta = \frac{1}{3} \sin^2 \beta + \frac{4}{9} \sin^3 \beta. \tag{12.11}$$

For (12.11), when $\beta = \pi/2$, $I = 7/9$. It follows that the radiant flux density on a horizontal surface completely exposed to a SOC is 7/9 of the zenith radiance. The SOC formulae can be used satisfactorily to predict penetration of diffuse radiation into forest over daily or monthly periods as shown by Anderson (1964b). Obviously, these empirical descriptions of radiation distribution over an overcast sky do not adequately describe most instantaneous conditions. These, however, change rapidly, and the average over a time period often comes close to the standard conditions.
Pokrowski (1929) produced a semi-empirical equation to describe emittance from a perfectly clear sky. This is nearly 200 times brighter near the sun than close to the horizon 180° from the sun. The presence of even a few clouds profoundly modifies this distribution, and the variation is usually only about 10 : 1 (see diagrams in Walsh 1961).

12.4 Theories of stand structure

The only general treatments of stand structure assume that the 'foliage' is randomly distributed in space. This model foliage consists of infinitely thin planes of indeterminate size and shape. To define the properties of the foliage, its inclination α to the horizontal, the angle of the penetrating ray or probe β above the horizon, and the foliage area index F, the total one sided foliage area per unit area of ground[1], must be known. F is defined cumulatively from the top of the foliage. The angles are sometimes defined from the vertical, rather than the horizontal, in some of the papers cited here, hence apparent discrepancies. For foliage inclined at a constant

1. The Russian 'relative leaf area' is normally expressed in square metres per hectare of field, and is equal to 10^4 times leaf area index [see translation editor's note to Nichiporovich (1966)].

angle to the horizontal, or with a random distribution of inclination [a spherical distribution in the sense of Nichiporovich (1961) or de Wit (1965), since the distribution of angles is proportional to the slope of surfaces over a sphere] the frequency of 0, 1, 2, *etc.* contacts with a probe is a Poisson distribution of mean *KF*, the projection of the foliage area onto a horizontal plane. For the various cases:

$$K = \cos\alpha \qquad \beta \geqq \alpha \qquad (12.12)$$
$$K = \cos\alpha \cdot (1 + 2(\tan\theta - \theta)/\pi) \qquad \beta < \alpha < \pi/2 \qquad (12.13)$$
$$K = (2\cot\beta/\pi) \qquad \alpha = \pi/2 \qquad (12.14)$$
$$K = 1/(2\sin\beta) \qquad \text{random } \alpha \qquad (12.15)$$

In (12.13)

$$\theta = \cos^{-1}(\tan\beta/\tan\alpha) \qquad (12.16)$$

K is plotted in Fig. 12.2. Isobe (1969) gives a detailed table for equations (12.12) to (12.14). Parts of this theory have been produced independently by a number of authors working on radiation: Monsi & Saeki (1953) first dealt with constant α, and Ross and co-workers described the spherical solution as well, but Isobe (1962 a, b, c, 1969), Chartier (1966 a, b, c) and Cowan (1968) reached the same conclusions, while Reeve in an appendix to Warren Wilson (1960) developed the same theory for inclined point quadrats. As Isobe (1969) points out, Monteith's (1965) 'discrete' method is not essentially different from the normal continuous approach. A good

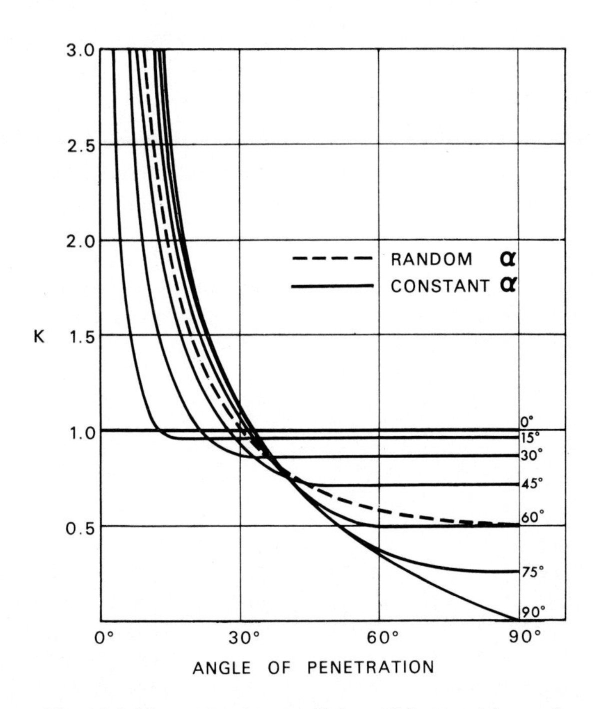

Fig. 12.2 The extinction coefficient *K* for model stands as a function of the angle of penetration.

deal of tidying up, comparison and extension is given in Kuroiwa & Monsi (1963), Philip (1965a, 1966), Anderson M. C. (1966a), Kuroiwa (1968) and Anderson M. C. & Denmead (1969).

The zero term of the Poisson distribution defined by KF will be

$$p(0) = \exp(-KF) \tag{12.17}$$

which gives the probability of a ray of light or a probe passing through the foliage without touching it, the 'gap frequency'. K is a function of both α and β, so, except for strictly horizontal foliage, the extinction or radiation from all angles of the sky will not follow a simple exponential process. In most cases, however, it is not far from this, and Monsi & Saeki's (1953) original proposition, later also put forward by Davidson & Philip (1958), that

$$I = I_0 \exp(-KF) \tag{12.18}$$

holds approximately, where I_0 is the flux density on a horizontal surface above the stand and I the flux density on a horizontal surface within the stand, at a depth F. K, however, will be smaller than that calculated for an isotropic sky. For further discussion see Anderson M.C. (1966a).

Two very important limitations to the practical usefulness of equation (12.18) must be remembered. First, since the extinction coefficient K will depend on solar elevation in part, the extinction profile for direct radiation will vary with time of day, and need never necessarily follow that for the diffuse sky radiation. That means, that at any given depth in the crop the fractions of direct solar and diffuse sky radiation penetrating are not generally the same, and to talk of a single percentage transmission figure is meaningless (Anderson M. C. 1964a, b). There will also be substantial seasonal differences in the transmission of direct radiation (Anderson M. C. 1964c gives examples from continuous measurements at three sites for several years). Second, when calculating photosynthesis, it is not the flux density on a horizontal surface that is required, but that on the inclined foliage

Table 12.6 The average relative flux density of radiation on randomly oriented, unshaded foliage surfaces for various foliage inclinations α and angles of solar elevation β (from Anderson M.C. & Denmead 1969).

β	α						
	0°	15°	30°	45°	60°	75°	90°
0°	1.000	∞	∞	∞	∞	∞	∞
15°	1.000	0.983	1.394	1.951	2.537	3.133	3.732
30°	1.000	0.983	0.929	1.051	1.259	1.491	1.732
45°	1.000	0.983	0.929	0.835	0.843	0.913	1.000
60°	1.000	0.983	0.929	0.835	0.686	0.609	0.577
75°	1.000	0.983	0.929	0.835	0.686	0.456	0.286
90°	1.000	0.983	0.929	0.835	0.686	0.456	0.000

surface. This adds considerably to the calculations, as discussed by Kuroiwa (1968), Uchijima *et al.* (1968) and Anderson M. C. & Denmead (1969). The latter show that for F less than 4 and an overcast sky, the extinction profiles are largely independent of foliage inclination and have $K \approx 1$. The pattern of distribution of direct radiation, however, is very different from that on a horizontal surface, as Table 12.6 shows. The majority of models of photosynthesis in plant communities neglect this difference.

Recently, there has been a considerable interest in using theories for scattering light through multiple layers in plant canopies. This has received a particular impetus from studies of albedo of crops by remote sensing (Allen & Richardson 1968; Allen, Gayle & Richardson 1970). The mathematics of the earlier treatment is effectively identical with the solutions provided by Cowan (1968) and Verhagen & Wilson (1969). The great disadvantage of these treatments is that interactions between sun and leaf inclination are not taken into account.

12.4.1 | *Sunlit foliage area*

At a depth F in the crop, the gap frequency is $\exp(-KF)$. This is also the proportion of the total foliage that is sunlit at that depth. The total foliage area that is sunlit down to a depth F in the stand is:

$$\int_0^F \exp(-KF) \cdot dF = \{1 - \exp(-KF)\}/K = S \qquad (12.19)$$

This is the 'sunlit foliage area index' of Warren Wilson (1967), and is also derived by Isobe (1969). For large F, $\exp(-KF)$ tends to zero and $S \approx 1/K$. This means that, at low solar altitudes, the sunlit foliage area index will be very small, as might be expected.

The shaded foliage area index is $F - S$, and the ratio of sunlit to shaded foliage at any given depth is $\exp(-KF)/\{1 - \exp(-KF)\}$, while for the whole crop above F it is $\{KF - 1 + \exp(-KF)\}/K$. Isobe (1969) shows that the variance σ^2 (not the standard deviation, as stated) of the flux density of direct radiation on a horizontal surface among random foliage is $I_0^2 \exp(-KF)\{1 - \exp(-KF)\}$. σ^2 is maximum when $\exp(-KF) = 0.5$, and then

$$\sigma^2 = 0.25\, I_0^2 \qquad (12.20)$$

This theoretical distribution of direct radiation might be, but has not been, compared with sunfleck frequency.

12.4.2 | *Limitations of the simple model*

Apart from the omission of scattering in this model, discussed below in Section 12.4.3, the model has considerable practical limitations in describing real plants with determinate growth. It does, however, provide an important insight into the very different fates of diffuse and direct radiation within the stand.

It is immediately apparent that most foliage is not randomly distributed. As Warren Wilson (1959a, 1965) shows, the distribution of contact frequency along a probe rarely follows a Poisson distribution: there is either less than the predicted frequency of gaps (underdispersion), found mostly in woodland herbs growing in shade; or an excess of gaps (overdispersion), found in most field crops. If the model is refined to include the effects of variation of foliage angle within the crop (Nichiporovich 1961; Philip 1965a; de Wit 1965), underdispersion can be partly accounted for. Summing the gap frequencies for all α gives

$$\sum_{\alpha=0}^{\alpha=\pi/2} \exp(-K_\alpha F_\alpha) = \exp\left(-\prod_{\alpha=0}^{\alpha=\pi/2} K_\alpha F_\alpha\right) \tag{12.21}$$

which gives a multiple, rather than simple Poisson distribution (Feller 1957) with larger zero term than that predicted for a constant α by the simple distribution. Leaves are not necessarily randomly oriented, even in crops such as maize with no pronounced phyllotactic pattern (Ross & Nil'son 1967; Udagawa *et al.* 1968). Actual measurement is extremely tedious. A mathematical treatment which takes into account non-random distribution in both vertical and horizontal directions is badly needed, but at present only numerical solutions for particular situations have been attempted (Duncan *et al.* 1967; Loomis, Williams & Duncan 1967; and see de Wit 1965 for a numerical treatment of random α foliage).

There is no doubt that stand structure and leaf position affect crop productivity (Hayashi & Ito 1962; Pearce, Brown & Blaser 1967; Williams *et al.* 1968), but adequate quantitative description of crop structure on top of other measurements is tedious. Before embarking on actual measurement the hypothesis to be tested and the suitability of the proposed measurement should be critically examined.

12.4.3 | Scattering and transmission of radiation in crops

Simple theory neglects the radiation reflected from and transmitted through foliage. In the photosynthetically active region this fraction is small, rarely more than 0.1 for the individual leaf, but in the near infra-red leaves transmit and reflect freely, thus reducing the total heat load on the plant (Billings & Morris 1951; Gates 1962; Gates *et al.* 1965). There are a number of theoretical treatments of scattering in stands, but those which attempt generality (Cowan 1968; Isobe 1969) require knowledge of a large number of more or less unmeasurable parameters, and are therefore extremely difficult to test. The original treatment of Kasanaga & Monsi (1954) introduced the term m, the fraction of the radiation transmitted by a leaf. Then:

$$I = I_0 \exp(-KF)/(1 - m) \tag{12.22}$$

Saeki (1963) pointed out that this was an oversimplification for a problem of multiple scattering, but did not propose an alternative. Ross (1964) and Ross & Nil'son (1963, 1965, 1968) treated the crop by an extension of theory used for radiation propagation in stellar atmospheres and found analytic solutions for horizontal, vertical and randomly oriented foliage. Introducing a scattering function f(ω):

$$I = I_0\{\exp(-KF) + f(\omega)\} \quad (12.23)$$

For the individual cases:

$$f(\omega) = \omega/8 \qquad \alpha = 0 \quad (12.24)$$

$$f(\omega) = \pi^2\omega/32 \qquad \alpha = \pi/2 \quad (12.25)$$

$$f(\omega) = \frac{\omega}{3}\left[\frac{1}{1 + 2\sin\beta}\right] \qquad \text{random } \alpha \quad (12.26)$$

where ω is the scattering coefficient for the foliage.
Later, Ross & Nil'son (1968) produced revised expressions for the scattering function, assuming first order scattering only and equal transmission and reflexion coefficients ($\omega/2$) and an infinite total foliage area index. Their assumption of first order scattering is based on experimental work of Laïsk (1968a). The revised expressions are

$$f(\omega) = \frac{\omega F}{2} \cdot \exp(-F) \qquad \alpha = 0 \quad (12.27)$$

$$f(\omega) = \frac{\omega/2}{2\sin\beta - 1} \cdot \left\{\exp\left(-\frac{F}{2\sin\beta}\right) - \exp(-F)\right\} \qquad \alpha = \pi/2 \quad (12.28)$$

$$f(\omega) = \frac{\omega/2}{\pi/2 \cdot \cot\beta - 1} \cdot \left\{\exp\left(-\frac{2F}{\pi} \cdot \cot\beta\right) - \exp(-F)\right\} \qquad \text{random } \alpha \quad (12.29)$$

Nil'son (1968a) extends this treatment further for multiple scattering, and separates upward and downward fluxes.
Isobe predicts that the scattering function analogous to that of Ross will be:

$$f(\omega) = \omega\,|\,n\,|\,K_i\{\exp(-K_sF - \exp(-K_iF)\}/(K_i - K_s) \qquad K_i \neq K_s \quad (12.30)$$
$$f(\omega) = \omega\,|\,n\,|\,KF\exp(-KF) \qquad K_i = K_s \quad (12.31)$$

where K_i and K_s are extinction coefficients for direct and scattered radiation respectively. The matrix $|n|$ describes three dimensional transfer functions for both unscattered and scattered radiation. Although we know that scattering for leaves is not isotropic (Moldau 1965), actual definition of these parameters is difficult. Cowan's and Nil'son's treatments are too lengthy for summary here. They only provide analytic solutions for limited cases, including that of $\omega \leqq 0.2$.
Partly because of instrumental problems, these theories of scattering have not been adequately tested. They predict differently the ratio between the percentage transmission of photosynthetically active and that of near infra-red radiation. Kasanaga & Monsi's and Isobe's treatment imply that this ratio should be in-

dependent of F, those of Ross and of Cowan that the ratio decreases with increasing F, or decreases with a decrease of F in wheat and sunflowers (Anderson M. C. 1969). Niïlisk (1964), Tooming & Ross (1964) and Tooming (1967a, b) also obtained reasonable agreement for maize, although they did not consider alternative theories. It is to be hoped that the rapid increase in availability of spectrophotometric instruments for work in crops may encourage more critical examination of this problem.

12.5 | Radiation measurements in plant communities

This is a subject full of pitfalls: apart from the reviews of Tranquillini (1960), Stern (1962) and Anderson M. C. (1964a), the discussion in Atkins, Poole & Stanbury (1937), Evans (1956) and Isobe (1969) might be consulted. The problem lies in adequate sampling of the sunflecks of direct solar radiation superimposed on a background of diffuse and scattered radiation. This consists of the unaltered diffuse radiation from the sky, coming through canopy gaps, and diffuse and direct radiation scattered by the foliage. The diffuse radiation is changed in spectral composition (Coombe 1957; Inoue & Ota 1957; Laïsk 1964, 1968a; Yocum, Allen & Lemon 1964; Tooming 1967a; Nil'son 1968a). As Federer & Tanner (1966a, b) show, this severely complicates choice of sensors. Although for mathematical theory it is convenient to treat the solar disc as a point source, it actually subtends 0.5° arc. The penumbra that develops round shadows of plant parts, due to the size of the sun's disc, can be particularly clearly seen on the floor of a deciduous forest when the trees are leafless. Under dense canopy small gaps can sometimes form a pinhole image of the sun (Guillemin 1882; Evans G. C. 1956; Reid 1962). Both these phenomena complicate measurement of the sunlit foliage area.

When relating measurements made in plant communities to photosynthetic models, there is the serious problem of relating the horizontal flux received on the instrument with that on inclined foliage (Anderson M. C. 1966b). If the leaves are really oriented and inclined at random, a spherical receiver would be an appropriate instrument (Wassink & van der Scheer 1951; Giovanelli 1953; Middleton 1953; Logan 1955; Ambach 1958; Richardson 1959; Powell & Heath 1964), though some of these instruments are not very accurate in the directional response, where it has been tested at all. As already discussed (Anderson M. C. 1964a), the use of a spherical receiver has other disadvantages, particularly that of the lack of correlation with standard measurements on a horizontal surface.

Under most sunny conditions the frequency of various flux densities over an area at any one time is far from normal (Anderson M. C. 1964a, 1966b; Laïsk 1965a, 1968b; Isobe 1969). There is usually a bimodal distribution, with one peak representing the flecks of direct solar radiation and another at a much lower level for the diffuse and scattered radiation. Laïsk (1968a, Figs. 1 and 2) gives normalised statistics of the duration of different flux densities as a function of leaf area index at two wavelengths and three solar altitudes. These figures bring out clearly the difficulties of interpreting measurements made with instruments with a large sensing area, such as tube solarimeters. Particularly with leaf area indices in the range 1–3, there is a pronounced bimodal distribution, with frequent low and high flux densities. Averaging these to give a single figure between the two extremes gives a highly misleading representation of conditions prevailing in the plant community. Sunflecks can vary in intensity across their area (Reid 1962). There are two approaches to measurements to meet these problems. Either average measurements representing mean conditions at the time of measurement may be made, or the separate transmission of diffuse and direct radiation may be estimated, directly or indirectly. In either case, it cannot be too strongly emphasised that spot measurements on clear days to obtain an 'average transmission' of radiation through the canopy, from which estimates are projected for other times, are quite valueless. Vézina (1964) reported a greater scatter of readings on cloudy than on clear days, but his apparent scatter on the cloudy days can largely be attributed to instrumental error when attempting to measure very low flux densities (Anderson M. C. 1970). A great deal of potentially useful information is lost by taking averaged measurements over an area, though for some experiments this mean may be all that is required. Special tube solarimeters (Szeicz, Monteith & dos Santos 1964) and net radiometers (Denmead 1966) have been designed to obtain an average over a strip in the crop. When used in row crops, care should be taken that such instruments sample row and inter-row spaces adequately. Since, by their shape, they are somewhat azimuth sensitive, it is generally advisable to use two placed at right angles. An alternative approach is to pull a sensor through the crop on a miniature railway or tight rope *e.g.* Kornher & Rodskjer (1967), Rodskjer & Kornher (1967). Again, there are problems in representative sampling without getting tied up in the plants. In many crops, such as the cereals, the size of any normal sensor is such that some spatial averaging occurs, since the surface area of the sensor is far larger than the usual size of sunflecks. This is illustrated in Fig. 12.3, which compares the traces from two sensors recorded on a high speed chart recorder, for a crop of wheat (*Triticum aestivum* var. Robin). This was made with a completely clear sky, solar altitude 54°, light wind of 5–8 m s^{-1} above the crop, which had a leaf area index

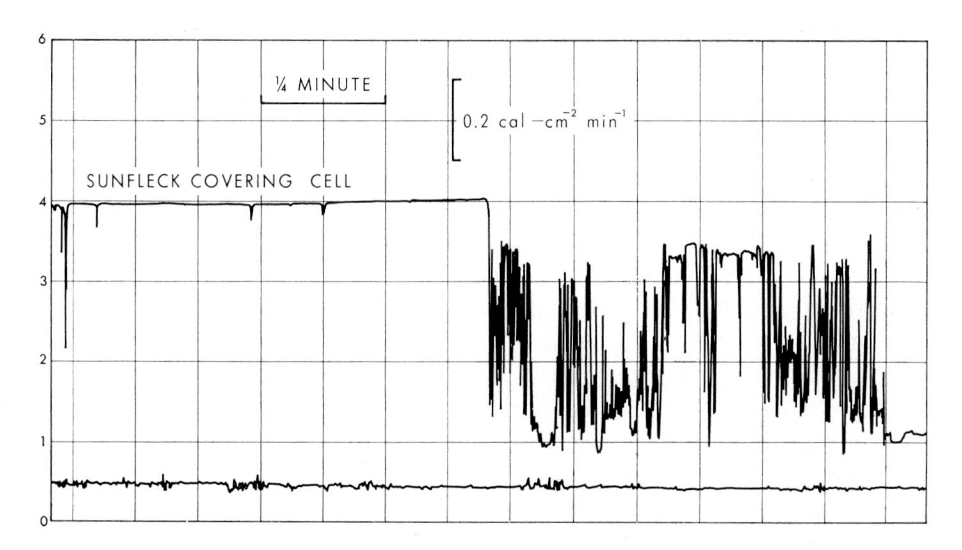

Fig. 12.3 Tracings of high speed chart records of output from: above, 1 mm × 1.5 mm silicon photovoltaic cell; below, *Megatron* selenium photocell under 5 cm diameter diffusing glass. Both sensors at the bottom of a wheat crop of LAI about 2.5, with a completely clear sky. The zero positions are displaced relative to each other.

of about 2.5. The two sensors were immediately adjacent at the bottom of the crop. The upper trace is from a silicon photovoltaic cell, with a sensitive area 1.0 × 1.5 mm, the lower from a *Megatron* selenium cell with a cosine corrected diffusing glass cover, circular, of diameter 5 cm. The effect of leaf flutter on the small sensor is very clear: variations of 0.4 cal cm^{-2} min^{-1} may occur 10 to 20 times in quarter of a minute, though when a larger sunfleck moves across the cell these fluctuations become less frequent. The large area of the selenium cell averages out most of these fluctuations, and shows a more or less steady reading throughout. (The zeros of the two instruments are displaced relative to each other, the mean level for the selenium cell was around 0.25 cal cm^{-2} min^{-1}.)

When attempting to measure the percentage transmission of direct and diffuse radiation separately sampling problems are much more severe. Generally, the quickest method of obtaining some idea of the spatial variation and the probable transmissions is to take a series of fish eye photographs under the canopy. The evaluation of these is discussed in Section 12.6. For direct measurement, the simplest strategy, but the most expensive in equipment and time, is to sample at a very large number of sites over a period of time. The number of samples needed varies widely, depending on the uniformity of crop structure, and conflicting reports will be found in the literature (Anderson M. C. 1964a, 1966b). Provided diffuse and direct radiation above the crop are estimated separately at the same time, a multiple regression can be used to estimate the percentage transmission of the two types of radiation. Transmission of diffuse radiation alone on an overcast day will provide a check on the accuracy of these estimations.

Alternatively, provided there is some overcast weather, the percentage transmission of diffuse radiation, which varies little with weather conditions, may be determined directly, and then the sunlit area examined throughout the day on a clear day. These methods involve visual estimation of sunlit areas, and consequently pose problems of estimating boundaries with the penumbra. G. C. Evans' (1956) apparatus, which measures flux density on a large area of white paper, viewed from above by a photocell, is too bulky for use except in forest. Evans himself, Whitmore & Wong (1959) and Evans, Whitmore & Wong (1960) do not seem to have experienced too much difficulty in estimating sunfleck area in Nigerian and Malayan rain forest with clear skies, but Grubb & Whitmore (1967) found this a problem under hazy conditions in Ecuador. For slightly hazy skies, Evans, Whitmore & Wong could not detect sunflecks adequately, and suggest that readings be treated as diffuse radiation from a clear sky. Trying to use Evans' apparatus in temperate deciduous forest in winter, with bare trees and low solar altitude, Anderson M. C. found the sunfleck boundaries almost indistinguishable. As designed at present, the equipment is difficult to manage single handed and unstable in a wind. Alone, under these conditions, it was impossible to obtain enough data for valid statistical treatment. Reid (1962) describes a rather similar technique for following sunfleck distribution through the day. Horie (1966) describes a purely visual method of estimating sunfleck area in low-growing crops, estimating sunfleck area on a 10 × 10 grid. All these methods are tedious, but much less expensive in equipment than direct measurement.

Long term maintenance of sensors in a crop is difficult, because of damp, animal life and dirt falling from above. The sensors must be thoroughly sealed and desiccant changed regularly. In many crops it is necessary to clean the surface of the sensor several times a day. This often poses problems of access without damage to the crop, and a bridge of planks over the crop may be useful. In a permanent installation, mounting the sensor at the end of a rod or rail, by which it may be withdrawn for servicing is an advantage.

12.6 | Indirect estimates of radiation and stand structure

From the theory discussed in Section 12.4 it is clear that an estimate of vertical gap frequency ('crown closure' in forestry terms) cannot generally be directly related to radiation. Measurements of gap frequency at all angles above the horizon are required. The simplest method of doing this is to take a fish eye photograph, but if a suitable camera is not available, some of the foresters' devices for measuring crown closure could be used, such as those of Wright (1943) and Lemmon (1956, 1957). Various devices have also been produced for estimating closure along the solar track (Berger 1953; Matusz 1953; Roussel 1953; Graniczny 1959; Korel'skiï 1960; Wagar 1965). Inclined point quadrats (Section 12.7.1) can also be used to provide an estimate for low growing crops, though this is a tedious method.

12.6.1 | 'Fish eye' photographs

Hill (1924) first published an account of a lens producing a spherical image of a view covering 180°, and suggested its use for cloud studies. This lens was available commercially for some time, but is no longer. Meteorological use of such fish eye lens in cloud and auroral studies is common (Elvey & Stoffregen 1957/8; Koldovský 1960; Pochop, Shanklin & Horner 1968), but many of these cameras photograph the image on a concave or convex mirror from above. Such cameras are difficult to use in crops, although this has been attempted (Monsi & Saeki 1953; Suzuki & Satoo 1954). Brown (1962) and Pontin (1962) describe other lenses for studies of forest canopy. Two commercial fish eye lenses for 35 mm cameras are available, covering 180° and giving an equiangular projection, *i.e.* one in which radial distance is directly proportional to angular altitude, which greatly simplifies grid construction. The *Nikon* lens can only be used on the most expensive *Nikon* body, and the cost of the entire set up is around US $ 700. The *Cosmos* fish eye lens is fitted as an auxiliary to other 35 mm lenses, and only costs about US $ 60. The size of the image it produces increases with the focal length of the lens with which it is used: in the example in Fig. 12.4 it was fitted to an 85 mm lens and part of the scene near the horizon was lost. With a 50 mm lens a complete circular image is produced on the film. Unlike the *Nikon*, in which the mirror of the reflex viewing system has to be locked out of the way when using the lens, the *Cosmos* does not interfere with the normal operation of the viewing system of the camera body. Image quality with both lenses does not compare well with that produced by the Hill camera. The 35 mm cameras fitted with these lenses are quite bulky, with a height of at least 12 cm when the lens is pointing upwards, which makes them difficult to use in low crops.

When photographing canopies, a long (10 m) pneumatic cable release to keep the operator out of the picture is almost essential, unless the camera has a delayed

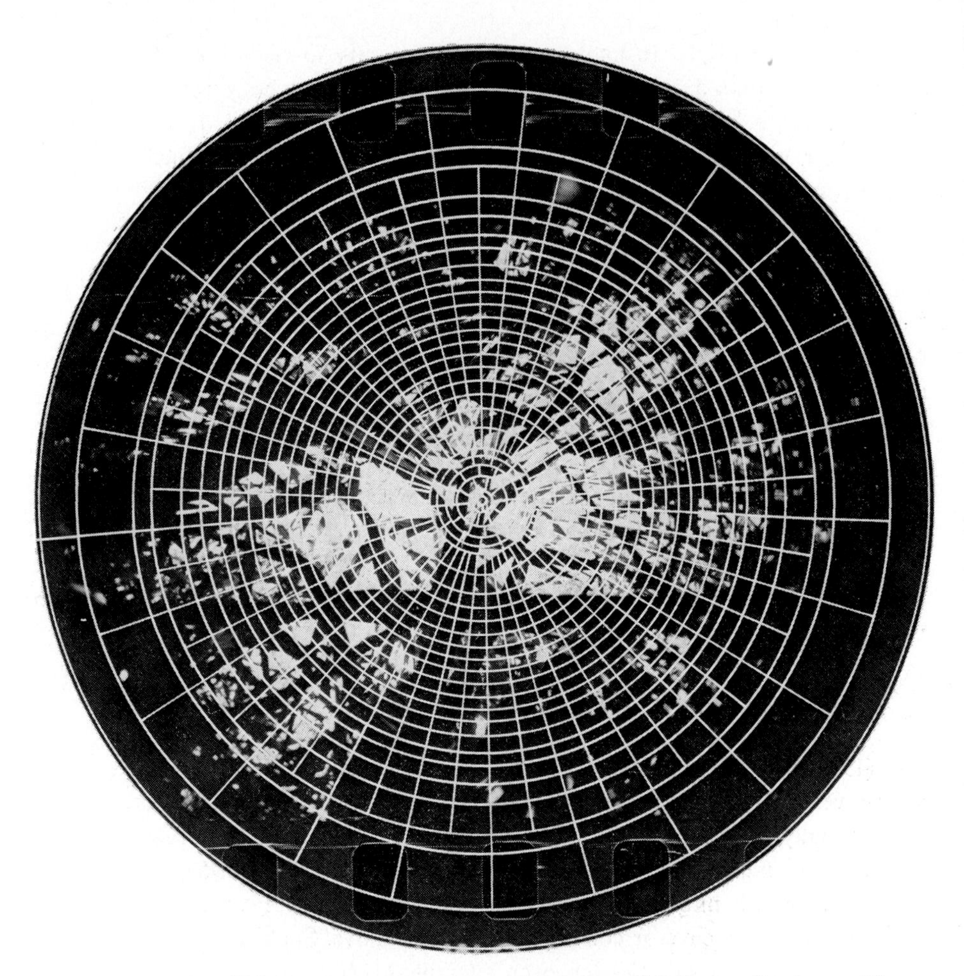

Fig. 12.4 Examples of fish eye photographs taken with a *Cosmos Fish Eye* lens fitted on an 85 mm lens on a 35 mm single lens reflex camera. The crop is dryland wheat (*Triticum aestivum* var. Robin) at Deniliquin, N.S.W. The lens was 15 cm above the soil surface. The leaf area index of the part of the crop above the lens was about 1.8.
a. Overlaid with the 'spider's web' grid, designed so that each segment contributes 0.001 of the total radiant flux on a horizontal surface from a Standard Overcast Sky. This grid is scored in Fig. 12.5.

release shutter and the operator is agile! A panchromatic, fine grain film is desirable, whose effective speed can be increased by use of Farber or other phenidone based two stage developers. According to sky conditions a blue (clear sky) or red (overcast) filter is needed to increase contrast. Exposure times vary considerably, but it is rarely possible to use anything faster than 1/25 s, so leaf flutter is often a problem. Working in the calm of early morning can often overcome this. It is rarely advisable to use a greater aperture than f.11, or serious loss of image quality occurs. A negative with reasonable total gradation is required, which is then enlarged onto a contrast paper, where, by local manipulation of exposure time, a good overall contrast is achieved.

When taking the photograph, the camera is carefully levelled, site and height of the base of the lens above ground recorded, together with compass bearings to the nearest degree with a prismatic compass on to two, or preferably three, readily

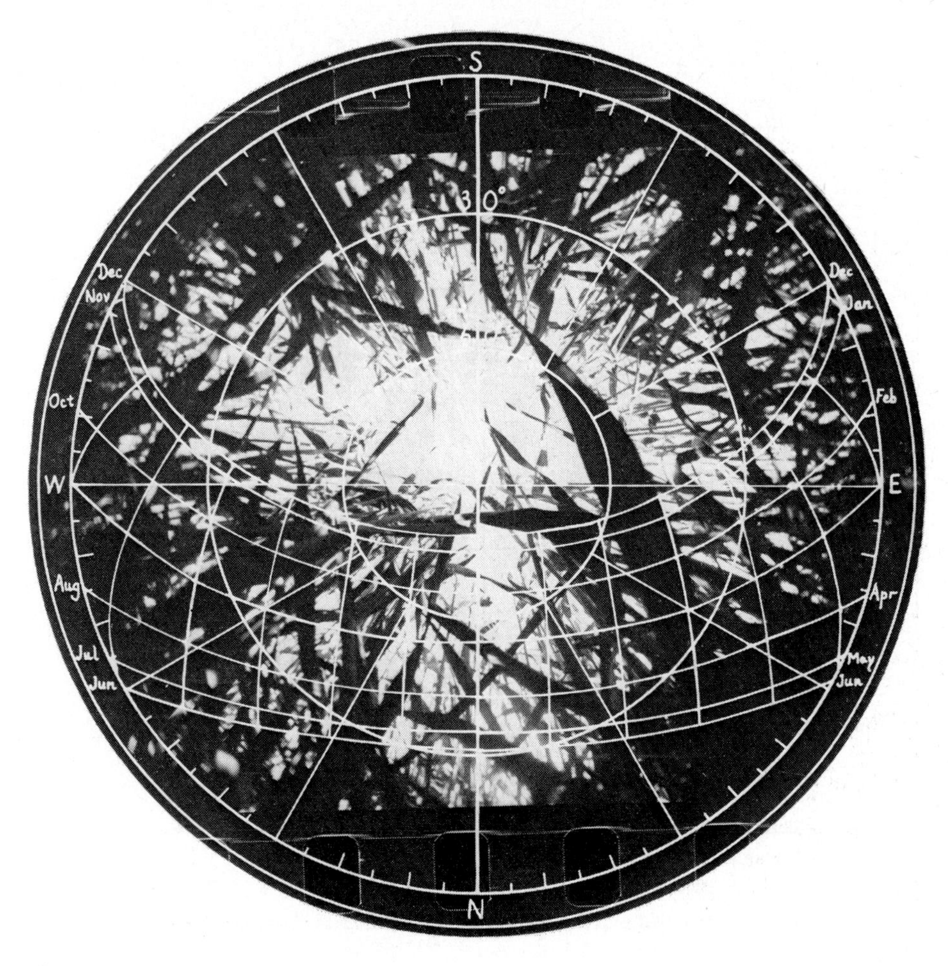

Fig. 12.4
b. Overlaid with a solar track diagram for 35°17′ S. The solar track is calculated for the 22nd of each month.

recognisable objects (such as stakes) by which the solar track can afterwards be correctly located on the photograph.

By comparison with some three years records of daily totals of radiation at several sites under a forest canopy, Anderson M. C. (1964b) showed that fish eye photographs can be used to predict the mean percentage transmission of diffuse and direct radiation (diffuse and direct site factors). This is done by superimposing grids and estimating the amount of obstruction. The 'spider's web' grid (Fig. 12.4*a*) for diffuse radiation is calculated so that each of the 1 000 segments cover an area contributing 0.001 of the radiation from a Standard Overcast Sky (Eq. 12.11), and its construction is described in Anderson M. C. (1964b). The design has now been slightly modified to improve the shape of the segments at the zenith: the angular heights of the annuli are listed on the right hand side of Fig. 12.5, which is a sample form for scoring a photograph. Working round each annulus in turn,

Photograph no. Deni. 5. Site Dryland. Height 15 cm Date 30/8/1968

Camera Edixa + 85 mm Plate Pan X. Exposure f.11. 1/100. Filter None. Developer Microphen

Prints on Ilfobrom 5 /developer Dektol Weather Fine, 1/10 cloud, calm

Bearings n.a., camera E-W long axis

	100	75	50	25	0	100	75	50	25	0	Total	Max.	Percent	Height
1	(only 16)				16					16	0	2500	0	12.5°
2	(only 18)			1	17				1	17	18	2500	0.7	17.0°
3				卌||	43				7	43	175	5000	3.5	23.3°
4			|	卌|	43			1	6	43	200	5000	4.0	27.8°
5			||	卌||	41			2	7	41	275	5000	5.5	31.8°
6		|	||||	卌||	38		1	4	7	38	450	5000	9.0	35.3°
7			||	卌||||	39			2	9	39	325	5000	6.5	38.6°
8		||	|||	卌|||| 卌卌	26		2	3	19	26	775	5000	15.5	41.8°
9		|	||||	卌卌| 卌卌	24		1	4	21	24	800	5000	16.0	44.1°
10			卌	卌	40			5	5	40	375	5000	7.5	46.8°
11		||||	卌	卌|	35		4	5	6	35	675	5000	13.5	49.5°
12	|	卌|	卌|	卌|	32	1	6	6	6	32	1000	5000	20.0	52.2°
13	||	卌|	|||	卌卌	29	2	6	3	10	29	1050	5000	21.0	54.9°
14	|	卌	||||	卌||	33	1	5	4	7	33	850	5000	17.0	57.7°
15	||	卌	|||	卌卌|	29	2	5	3	11	29	1000	5000	20.0	60.5°
16	||||	卌|	卌||	卌|||	卌卌卌卌卌	4	6	7	8	25	1400	5000	28.0	63.3°
17	|||	卌|||	卌卌||	卌||	卌卌卌卌	3	8	12	7	20	1675	5000	33.5	66.6°
18	||||	卌||||	卌||	|| 卌卌	卌||| 卌卌	4	9	7	12	18	1725	5000	34.5	69.8°
19	|||	卌||||	卌卌 卌|	卌||	卌 卌卌	3	9	16	7	15	1950	5000	39.0	73.8°
20	|||	卌|||	|| 卌卌	卌卌	卌卌|| 卌卌	3	8	12	10	17	1750	5000	35.0	78.3°
21		||	|||	卌|	||		2	3	6	2	450	1300	34.6	80.0°
22	|	||	|	||	卌	1	2	1	2	5	275	1300	21.2	81.8°
23	|	||	||	|||	||||	1	2	2	3	4	425	1200	35.4	83.7°
24	|		卌	||||		1		5	4		450	1000	45.0	87.2°
25			||					2			100	200	50.0	88.4°
26				|					1		25	100	25.0	90.0°
Total						26	76	109	181	591	18.093			

Analyst M.C.A. Date 14/5/1969

Fig. 12.5 Form for scoring gap frequency and penetration of diffuse radiation from a Standard Overcast Sky, using an equiangular fish eye photograph. The example concerns the situation from Fig. 12.4. For the two outermost circles a correction has been applied for the missing segments. The term 'plate' for film dates back to the period before 35 mm fish eye lenses were available.

from horizon to zenith, the number of segments which are completely, 75 %, 50 %, 25 % and 0 % clear are scored, and this summed to give the diffuse site factor. The percentage clear in each annulus gives the gap frequency at that altitude. This visual scoring is fairly tedious, and a computerized method would be desirable. The problem is that the range of intensities represented on the photograph is far outside the range of linear response in density of any film, while in photographs of sunlit canopies, such as those in Fig. 12.4, some foliage appears darker, and some lighter than the sky behind.

Solar tracks (Fig. 12.4*b*) are calculated for the periods of interest from Eqs. (12.1) and (12.2). Further details are given by Evans & Coombe (1959). For studies through the year the tracks for the 22nd day of each month are calculated, 7 in all, since the tracks are then symmetric about the summer and winter solstices. The percentage transmission for the month can then be determined by examining obstruction along a band around the track. For a particular day the obstruction along a line is taken. A better estimate of the average transmission for the whole community is obtained by taking the average gap frequency at the appropriate solar altitude from the diffuse spider's web estimates.
The number of replicates needed for a community varies considerably and can only be determined by trial and error. A trial run of 10 at a given level will give an indication of the variability. Estimates near the top of most crops show considerable variation. On the other hand, distant, fine structured crops, such as pine forest viewed from the floor, show remarkably little variation in diffuse transmission, although the chance presence or absence of a branch in a particular spot can produce great local variation in the direct site factor (Anderson M. C. 1966b). This method does not take into account the contribution of scattered radiation, but gives a good estimate of the average transmission of photosynthetically active radiation, which is little scattered. It will not predict penetration of the sun on a particular partly cloudy day unless the times when the sun is covered are known. In climates with a marked diurnal variation in cloudiness (*e.g.* some montane and monsoon climates in the wet season) a correction must be applied to allow for this variation in calculating the mean transmission (Grubb & Whitmore 1967).
Apart from providing an estimate of radiation transmission, fish eye photographs provide a quick and convenient record of crop structure, and are a useful check on the accuracy of point quadrat records (Warren Wilson 1965). Where a suitable camera is available, it is recommended that photographs be taken as a routine measure for record purposes.

12.7 | Measurements of crop structure

The crop parameters that can already be treated theoretically are foliage area index and its distribution with height, foliage inclination, and, in advanced work, foliage orientation. Spacing between plant parts and their sizes has so far only been treated numerically. Destructive or non-destructive measurements can be made, the latter generally being more laborious. The most comprehensive method is also non-destructive: the use of inclined point quadrats, but this is undeniably laborious, and can only be used in vegetation less than 2 m high. In any case, it is desirable to check the accuracy of the quadrat measurements by taking stratified clips as well. These, of course, may be required anyhow for growth analysis.

12.7.1 | Stratified foliage clips

Methods of determining foliage area after sampling are dealt with in Chapter 14. For stratified sampling, a number of horizontal layers are cut from a rectangular or circular sampling area, and the foliage area in each layer determined separately. With a row crop drilled at a known spacing, a length of row can be sampled.

The strategy depends very much on the plants. Large sharp scissors will deal with most herbs, secateurs and a pruning saw may be needed for woody vegetation. It is generally advisable to have a light steel wire frame welded together, which encloses the whole sampling area and delimits each layer: if working single-handed such equipment is essential. Before starting to harvest, prepare a series of clearly labelled bags to hold each layer and cut away contiguous vegetation so that the limits of the sample volume can be clearly seen. Polythene bags are generally suitable, but they are so permeable to gas, including water vapour, that separate samples must be taken for any foliage water status studies. (If there is a wind, a screen may be necessary to keep the vegetation still.) After harvesting, the bags should be taken to the laboratory as quickly as possible, and each layer sorted into stems, leaves *etc.* as necessary before making area and dry weight determinations. The number of layers into which the crop is divided depends on the experiment. When radiation, CO_2 *etc.* are being measured at various heights in the crop, boundaries of the layers for harvesting are usually set at these heights. With most vegetation, it is very difficult to cut quickly and accurately layers less than 5 cm deep. The sample area depends on the growth habit; with pasture, 0.25 m^2 will generally be adequate, with large herbs a minimum of 1 m^2 is more appropriate. In tall stands, 0.5 m^2 quadrats (0.5 m $\times$ 1.0 m) are advantageous in that the shoots are within easy reach by hand from outside the plot. Even in an apparently uniform crop, at least 4 replicates should be taken: in most natural vegetation a larger number will be essential because of the variability. Sometimes, especially in tall crops, a compromise cannot be avoided; the sample is first harvested as a whole and divided into layers afterwards. When doing this, the foliage should be kept in or returned to its natural or nearly natural position. Otherwise, if the stems and leaves are packed tightly together, an undesirable 'upward shift' of foliage area index takes place. In any case, the exact way of accomplishing stratified clipping should be indicated. It is clear, that a programme of stratified harvesting involves considerable labour, and cannot generally be managed single handed when other measurements have also to be made.

12.7.2 | Direct measurement of foliage inclination and orientation

Foliage inclination can be measured directly by holding a protractor, fitted with a levelling device, against the foliage (Nichiporovich 1961; de Wit 1965). It is often desirable to cut off each piece of foliage as it is measured. Though in theory simple, this method has considerable disadvantages. It is extremely difficult to design a suitable sampling programme, unless the whole of a large sample area is measured. In many leaves, the lamina is set at an angle to the midrib, and it can be difficult to place the protractor against the steepest part of the leaf. Many long leaves droop at their tips. If this method is adopted, it is recommended that a sample area be measured completely; as the inclination of each straight piece of foliage, which may only be a small part of a whole leaf, is measured, it is cut off and placed in a bag for foliage in that grade of inclination, taking 6 or 9 frequency classes with a range of inclination of 15° or 10°. At the end, the area of foliage in each frequency class is determined.

 Laïsk (1965b) (see Ross & Nil'son 1967 for discussion of theory) also included a compass with his protractor, and then classed the foliage in eight groups with respect to azimuth and six for inclination. Uchijima *et al.* (1968) used this method in a detailed study of solar radiation penetration. For thin canopies, orientation alone can be estimated from fish eye photographs or normal photographs taken above the crop. Trigonometric principles can be usefully applied with plants having long and rather firm leaves (Květ, Svoboda & Fiala 1967).

12.7.3 | Inclined point quadrats

This method was developed by Warren Wilson (1959b, 1960, 1963a, b, 1965) for non destructive sampling of foliage area index and foliage inclination. It is particularly useful in estimating the area contribution of such solid objects as stems. It is difficult to design a quadrat stable enough to use on tall vegetation. Warren Wilson's own (1963b) design is shown in Fig. 12.6. Experience of constructing other quadrats shows that the square aluminium rod (often difficult to obtain) of the frame cannot be replaced with round without seriously reducing rigidity. The screw clamping the probe carrying boss onto the protractor is too small, and shears off. For convenience in the field, it is worth engraving centimetre scales on legs, cross bar and probe. The sharpened steel knitting needle that makes the top of the probe should be removable for safety and repair, and held in position with a small grub screw. A spare needle should always be carried: if kept sharp enough to avoid errors due to thickness (Warren Wilson 1963b), the point is easily damaged. A level should be mounted permanently on the head carrying the protractor and probe.

For use in the field, two operators and a wind screen are required. The recording operator needs plenty of graph paper, a sharp pencil and a rubber. For most crops (row and single plant, see Warren Wilson 1965, Philip 1965b, 1966) the frame is set up with the head level and the probe in turn pointing N, E, S, and W. This will detect any azimuthal variation in properties. The angle of the probe is adjusted and the boss clamped firmly in position, and the height of the tip of the probe adjusted to an arbitary level above the top of the crop. The probe is then passed slowly through the vegetation, and each time the point touches foliage, this is recorded, together with a sign for leaf, stem *etc.* on the graph paper, which is graduated so that the position of the probe can also be recorded. Finally, except for zero inclination of the probe, the position of the ground surface is also recorded. If the probe is not sufficiently long to reach from top to bottom of the crop in one go, it must be repositioned with the head lower, and the tip of the probe at the level reached at the end of the upper sample. In these circumstances it is wise to mount the head on one of the legs of the frame. Ten probes are generally made in each direction. When the head is mounted on the cross bar, they can be randomised by using a table of random numbers to determine the position of the head along the cross bar. If the head is on the leg, the frame will have to be moved.

Afterwards, the number of contacts with foliage of each type is recorded at the bottom of the line on the graph paper representing each probe, and the mean number of contacts f_β for a given probe inclination β is calculated. If stratified samples are required, the score sheet is divided into layers of length proportional to $x/\sin\beta$, where x is the vertical depth of the sample.

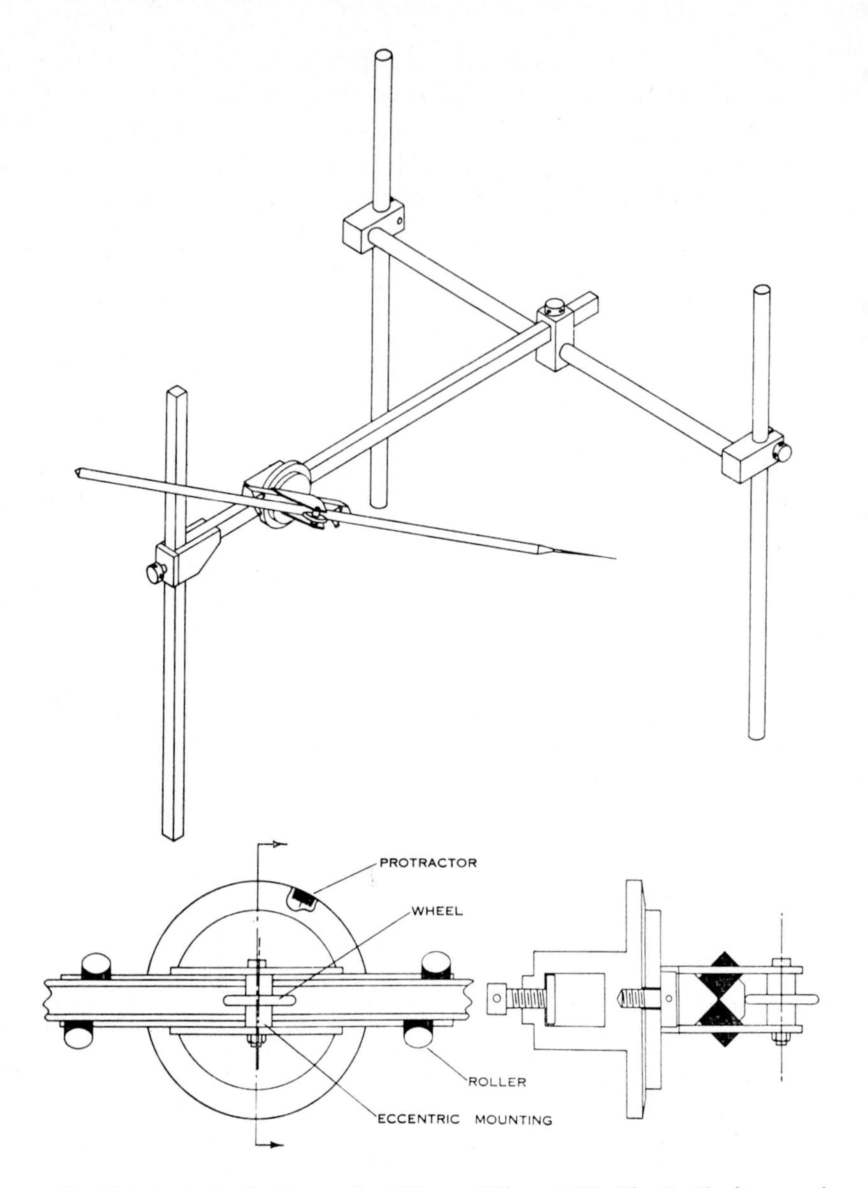

Fig. 12.6 An inclined point quadrat (Warren Wilson 1963b, Fig. 7). The framework is constructed from aluminium alloy, and is 70 cm high. Larger stands require extra bracing. Pressure on the probe is maintained by the rubber tyre on the eccentrically mounted wheel.

The choice of angle for sampling depends on the purpose of the investigation. From Section 12.4, if the foliage is randomly distributed, contact frequency is a Poisson series of mean $KF = f_\beta$. If K is known, F can be determined. Warren Wilson (1963a) showed that K varied little with α when $\beta = 32.5°$ and the formula

$$F \approx 1.1 f_{32.5} \tag{12.32}$$

 could be used with an error of $+10\%$ when $\alpha = 0°$ or $90°$ and nearly -10%

when $\alpha = 36°$. When the probe was inserted at two or three angles, errors were reduced for the formulae:

$$F \approx 0.23f_{13} + 0.78f_{52} \tag{12.33}$$

and

$$F \approx 0.089f_{8} + 0.462f_{32.5} + 0.453f_{65} \tag{12.34}$$

Miller (1967), after a critical mathematical analysis, suggested the use of:

$$F \approx 0.393f_{0} + 1.020f_{30} + 0.589f_{60} \tag{12.35}$$

$$F \approx 0.244f_{0} + 1.032f_{27.5} + 0.296f_{45} + 0.427f_{67.5} \tag{12.36}$$

$$F \approx 0.175f_{0} + 0.674f_{15} + 0.302f_{30} + 0.494f_{45} + 0.175f_{60} + 0.181f_{75} \tag{12.37}$$

Probing at 15° intervals, as required by Eq. (12.37), is tedious, but gives a useful cross check on the accuracy of gap frequency determinations from fish eye photographs. It can also be used to estimate the distribution of foliage inclination (Philip 1965a), if there is plenty of good and consistent data; for as Miller points out, the method involves taking a third derivative of a curve fitted to empirical data. Warren Wilson (1959b) originally estimated mean foliage angle from the ratio of f_0 to f_{90}:

$$\alpha = \tan^{-1}(\pi f_0/2f_{90}) \tag{12.38}$$

In his 1963a paper he lists values of f_0/f_{90}, f_{13}/f_{52} and f_8/f_{65} as a function of α at 5° intervals. Of these various ratios, f_0/f_{90} varies most widely with α and therefore provides the most sensitive indicator. Where foliage area index is independently estimated, α can be determined from the formula $K = f_\beta/F$ and Fig. 12.2. Since, for random foliage, gap frequency $p(0)$ is $\exp(-KF)$, estimates of $p(0)$ from fish eye photographs and stratified foliage clips could be used to determine mean α:

$$K = \ln p(0)/F \tag{12.39}$$

Use of the equations such as (12.39), rests on the assumption of random foliage distribution. When using inclined point quadrats, this assumption should be tested by calculating the variance/mean ratio for contact frequency, and recording the result. When the ratio is 1, it is justifiable to assume a random Poisson distribution; but with the ratio greater than 1 the foliage is underdispersed, and with the ratio less than 1 it is overdispersed.

Point quadrats can be used to examine foliage distribution of single plants or rows. In this case (Philip 1965b, 1966; Warren Wilson 1965), the probe is inserted from the side over a grid pattern. The comments about choice of angle in relation to information yield still apply.

12.8 | Conclusion

In the past few years a number of elaborate models of crop photosynthesis in relation to structure and radiation climate have been produced. Few of them have been adequately tested against field data. The reasons may be clear from this article: such measurements take a good deal of time and labour, and often also need expensive equipment. A single research worker will find it very difficult to handle such measurements alone. Unfortunately, there are still a large number of valueless measurements being published, in which little or no attention has been given to sampling problems or spectral sensitivities. Unless adequate instrumental and labour forces are available, it would be wiser to work on other problems.

12.9 | References

Albrecht, F. H. W.: Methods of computing global radiation. – Geofis. pura applic. 32: 131-138, 1955.

Allaway, W. G., Mansfield, T. A.: Stomatal responses to changes in carbon dioxide concentration in leaves treated with 3-(4-chlorophenyl)-1,1-dimethylurea. – New Phytol. 66: 57-63, 1967.

Allen, L. H., Brown, K. W.: Shortwave radiation in a corn crop. – Agron. J. 57: 575-580, 1965.

Allen, L. H., Yocum, C. S., Lemon, E. R.: Photosynthesis under field conditions. VII. Radiant energy exchanges within a corn crop canopy and implications in water use efficiency. – Agron. J. 56: 253-259, 1964.

Allen, W. A., Richardson, A. J.: Interaction of light with a plant canopy. – J. opt. Soc. Amer. 58: 1023-1028, 1968.

Allen, W. A., Gayle, T. V., Richardson, A. J.: Plant-canopy irradiance specified by the Duntley equations. – J. opt. Soc. Amer. 60: 372-376, 1970.

Ambach, W.: Ein Strahlungsempfänger mit kugelförmiger Empfängerfläche zur Bestimmung des Extinktionscoeffizienten in Gletschern. – Arch. Meteorol. Bioklim. B 8: 433-441, 1958.

Anderson, E. A., Baker, R. D.: Estimating incident terrestrial radiation under all atmospheric conditions. – Water Resources Res. 3: 975-988, 1967.

Anderson, M. C.: Light relations of terrestrial plant communities and their measurement. – Biol. Rev. 39: 425-486, 1964a.

Anderson, M. C.: Studies of the woodland light climate. I. The photographic computation of light conditions. – J. Ecol. 52: 27-41, 1964b.

Anderson, M. C.: Studies of the woodland light climate. II. Seasonal variation in the light climate. – J. Ecol. 52: 643-663, 1964c.

Anderson, M. C.: Stand structure and light penetration. II. A theoretical analysis. – J. appl. Ecol. 3: 41-54, 1966a.

Anderson, M. C.: Some problems of simple characterization of the light climate in plant communities. – In: Bainbridge, R., Evans, G. C., Rackham, O. (ed.): Light as an Ecological Factor. Pp. 77-90. Blackwell sci. Publ., Oxford 1966b.

Anderson, M. C.: The role of heat transfer in the design and performance of solarimeters. – J. appl. Meteorol. 6: 941-947, 1967.

Anderson, M. C.: A comparison of two theories of scattering of radiation in crops. – Agr. Meteorol. 6: 399-405, 1969.

Anderson, M. C.: Interpreting the fraction of solar radiation available in forest. – Agr. Meteorol. 7: 19-28, 1970.

Anderson, M. C.: An empirical relation between global and direct solar radiation. – Quart. J. roy. meteorol. Soc. (in press), 1971.

Anderson, M. C., Denmead, O. T.: Short wave radiation on inclined surfaces in model plant communities. – Agr. J. 61: 867-872, 1969.

Ångström, A.: Report to the International Commission for Solar Research on actinometric

observations of solar and atmospheric radiation. I. Continuous registrations of direct and reflected solar radiation. – Quart. J. roy. meteorol. Soc. 50: 121-125, 1924.
Annals of the I.G.Y.: Radiation instruments and measurements. – 5(VI): 365-466, 1957.
Atkins, W. R. G., Poole, H. H., Stanbury, F. A.: The measurement of the intensity and the colour of the light in woods by means of emission and rectifier photoelectric cells. – Proc. roy. Soc. B 121: 427-450, 1937.
Bainbridge, R., Evans, G. C., Rackham, O. (ed.): Light as an Ecological Factor. – Symp. Brit. ecol. Soc. 6. Blackwell sci. Publ., Oxford 1966.
Barashkova, E. P., Lebedeva, K. V., Yastrova, T. K.: Sravnenie potokov dlinnovolnovoï radiatsii izmerenykh razlichnymi priborami. [Comparison of long wavelength radiation fluxes measured by different devices.] – Akad. Nauk SSSR, Mezhved. geofiz. Komitet, Met. Issledov.: Sb. Stat. 15: 44-49, 1966.
Bell, L. N.: Fotoelektricheskiï pribor dlya izmereniya fotosinteticheski aktivnoï radiatsii. (fotoelektricheskiï fitoaktinometr). [A photoelectric equipment for measuring photosynthetically active radiation.] – Trudy Inst. Fiziol. Rast. K.A. Timiryazeva 10: 257-264, 1955.
Bener, P.: Untersuchung über die Wirkungsweise des Solarigraphen Moll-Gorczynski. – Arch. Meteorol. Bioklim. B 2. 188-249, 1950.
Berger, P.: Radiation in forest at Williamette Basin Snow Laboratory. – U.S. Corps Engineers, Snow Investig., Res. Note 12, 1953.
Berliand, T. G.: Metodika klimatologicheskikh raschetov summarnoï radiatsii. [Method of climatological calculation of the sum of radiation.] – Met. Gidrol. 6: 2-12, 1960.
Berliand, T. G.: Sovremennoe sostoyanie issledovaniya radiatsionnogo klimata. [Present state of studying radiation climate.] – In: Budyko, M. I. (ed.): Sovremennye Problemy Klimatologii. Pp. 28-40. Gidrometizdat, Leningrad 1966.
Bierhuizen, J. F., Slatyer, R. O.: Photosynthesis of cotton leaves under a range of environmental conditions in relation to internal and external diffusive resistances. – Aust. J. biol. Sci. 17: 348-359, 1964.
Bierhuizen, J. F., Slatyer, R. O.: Effect of atmospheric concentration of water vapour and CO_2 in determining transpiration-photosynthesis relationships of cotton leaves. – Agr. Meteorol. 2: 259-270, 1965.
Billings, W. D., Morris, R. J.: Reflection of visible and infrared radiation from leaves of different ecological groups. – Amer. J. Bot. 38: 327-331, 1951.
Black, J. N.: The distribution of solar radiation over the earth's surface. – Arch. Meteorol. Bioklim. B 7: 165-189, 1956.
Black, J. N., Bonython, C. W., Prescott, J. A.: Solar radiation and the duration of sunshine. – Quart. J. roy. meteorol. Soc. 80: 231-235, 1954.
Blackman, R. B., Tukey, J. W.: The Measurement of Power Spectra.-Dover, New York 1958.
Blackwell, M. J.: Five years' continuous recording of daylight illumination at Kew Observatory. – Meteorol. Res. Comm., Air Min., Lond. Meteorol. Res. Pamphl. 791: 1-10, 1953.
Bolle, H. J., Fleischer, R.: Der Einfluss der Lupolen-Absorption auf die Messung und Registrierung der Ultrarot-Strahlungsströme. – Ann. Meteorol. (Hamburg) 6: 380, 1953/4.
Brach, E. J., Wiggins, B. W. E.: A portable spectrophotometer for environmental studies of plants. – Lab. Pract. 16: 302-309, 1967.
Bradley, E. F., Wall, B. H.: Digitization and integration of low-level fluctuating signals. – Rev. sci. Instrum. 36: 691-693, 1965.
Brown, H. E.: The canopy camera. – Rocky Mtn Forest. Range exp. Sta., Station Paper 72: 1-22, 1962.
Budyko, M. I.: The heat balance of the earth's surface. – Transl. Offic. Tech. Serv., U.S. Dept. Com., Washington 1956.
Budyko, M. I., Gandin, L. S.: K teorii fotosinteza v sloe rastitel'nogo pokrova. [On the theory of photosynthesis in the layer of the plant covering.] – Dokl. Akad. Nauk SSSR 164: 454-457, 1965.
Businger, J. A.: Properties of the radiation environment of plants. – In: Conference on Instrumentation for Plant Environment Measurements, Aspendale. Aust. J. Soc. instrum. Technol. 7-10, 1966.
Chartier, P.: Étude du microclimat lumineux dans la végétation. – Ann. agr. 17: 571-602, 1966a.

Chartier, P.: Étude théorique de la photosynthèse globale de la feuille. – C. R. Acad. Sci. (Paris) 263 D: 44-47, 1966b.
Chartier, P.: Étude théorique de l'assimilation brute de la feuille. – Ann. Physiol. vég. 8: 167-195, 1966c.
Chartier, P.: Lumière, eau et production de matière sèche du couvert végétal. – Ann. agr. 18: 301-331, 1967.
Collins, B. G., Walton, E. W.: Temperature compensation of the Moll-Gorczynski pyranometer. – Meteorol. Mag. 96: 225-228, 1967.
Coombe, D. E.: The spectral composition of shade light in woodlands. – J. Ecol. 45: 823-830, 1957.
Courvoisier, P.: Über einen neuen Strahlungsbilanzmesser. – Verh. schweiz. Naturforsch. Ges. 130: 152, 1950.
Cowan, I. R.: The interception and absorption of radiation in plant stands. – J. appl. Ecol. 5: 367-379, 1968.
Davidson, J. L., Philip, J. R.: Light and pasture growth. – In: Climatology and Microclimatology. Arid Zone Res. 11: 181-187, 1958.
Denmead, O. T.: A strip net radiometer. – In: Conference on Instrumentation for Plant Environment Measurements, Aspendale. Aust. J. Soc. instrum. Technol., 1966.
Dirmhirn, I.: Untersuchungen an Sternpyranometern. – Arch. Meteorol. Bioklim. B 9: 124-148, 1958a.
Dirmhirn, I.: Die Weitwinkel-Himmelsaufnahme als Hilfsmittel für die Strahlungforschung. – Arch. Meteorol. Bioklim. B 8: 336-351, 1958b.
Dirmhirn, I.: Das Strahlungsfeld im Lebensraum. – Akad. Verlag, Frankfurt/M. 1964.
Dirmhirn, I.: On the applicability of silicon cells in atmospheric radiation studies. – Atmos. Sci. Pap., Colorado State Univ., Fort Collins 113, 1967.
Drummond, A. J.: Notes on the measurement of natural illumination. II. Daylight and skylight at Pretoria; the luminous efficiency of daylight. – Arch. Meteorol. Bioklim. B 9: 149-163, 1960.
Drummond, A. J.: Instrumentation for the measurement of solar radiation – a survey of modern techniques and recent developments. Solar energy availability and instruments for measurements. – U.N. Rep. E/3577, pp. 335-340. U.N. Conf. New Sources of Energy, Rome 1961.
Drummond, A. J., Hickey, J. R., Scholes, W. J., Lane, E. G.: New value for the solar constant of radiation. – Nature 218: 259-261, 1968.
Duncan, W. G., Loomis, R. S., Williams, W. A., Hanau, R.: A model for simulating photosynthesis in plant communities. – Hilgardia 38: 181-205, 1967.
Efimova, N. A.: Raspredelenie fotosinteticheski aktivnoï radiatsii na territorii Sovetskogo Soyuza. [The distribution of photosynthetically active radiation on the Soviet Union territory.] – Trudy glav. geofiz. Observat. (Leningrad) 179: 118-130, 1965.
Efimova, N. A.: Photosynthetically active radiation over the USSR. – In: Nichiporovich, A. A. (ed.): Photosynthesis of Productive Systems. Pp. 53-59. IPST, Jerusalem 1967.
Elvey, C. T., Stoffregen, W.: Auroral photography by all-sky camera. – Ann. int. Geophys. Year 5: 121-151, 1957/8.
Evans, G. C.: An area survey method of investigating the distribution of light intensity in woodland, with particular reference to sunflecks. – J. Ecol. 44: 391-428, 1956.
Evans, G. C., Coombe, D. E.: Hemispherical and woodland canopy photography and the light climate. – J. Ecol. 47: 103-113, 1959.
Evans, G. C., Whitmore, T. C., Wong, Y. K.: The distribution of light reaching the ground vegetation in a tropical rain forest. – J. Ecol. 48: 193-204, 1960.
Evans, L. T. (ed.): Environmental Control of Plant Growth. – Acad. Press, New York 1963.
Falckenburg, G.: Ein Vibrationspyranometer. – Z. Meteorol. 1: 372, 1947.
Federer, C. A., Tanner, C. B.: Sensors for measuring light available for photosynthesis. – Ecology 47: 654-657, 1966a.
Federer, C. A., Tanner, C. B.: Spectral distribution of shade light in the forest. – Ecology 47: 555-560, 1966b.
Feller, W.: An Introduction to Probability Theory and Its Applications. – 2nd Ed. J. Wiley, New York 1957.
Fleischer, R.: Vier Jahre Strahlungsbilanz-Registrierungen am Meteorologischen Observatorium Hamburg. – Ber. Deut. Wetterdienst. 7: 9-13, 1959.

Franssila, M.: A net radiation instrument with constant ventilation. – Geophysica (Helsinki) 4: 131, 1953.
Fritschen, L. J.: Construction and evaluation of a miniature net radiometer. – J. appl. Meteorol. 2: 165-172, 1963.
Fritschen, L. J., van Wijk, W. R.: Use of an economical thermal transducer as a net radiometer. – Bull. Amer. meteorol. Soc. 40: 291-294, 1959.
Funk, J. P.: Improved polythene-shielded net radiometer. – J. sci. Instrum. 36: 267-270, 1959.
Funk, J. P.: Transient response of net radiometers. – Arch. Meteorol. Bioklim. B 10: 228-231, 1960.
Funk, J. P.: A note on the long-wave calibration of convectively shielded net radiometers. – Arch. Meteorol. Bioklim. B 11: 70-74, 1961.
Funk, J. P.: A net radiometer designed for optimum sensitivity and a ribbon thermopile used in a miniaturized version. – J. geophys. Res. 67: 2753-2760, 1962a.
Funk, J. P.: Improvements in polythene-shielded net radiometers. – C.S.I.R.O., Div. Met. Phys., Aspendale, Vic. Australia (mimeo), 1962b.
Funk, J. P.: Ribbon thermopile. – J. sci. Instrum. 39: 32, 1962c.
Fuquay, D., Buettner, K.: Laboratory investigation of some characteristics of the Eppley pyrheliometer. – Trans. amer. geophys. Union 38: 238-243, 1957.
Gaastra, P.: Photosynthesis of crop plants as influenced by light, carbon dioxide, temperature, and stomatal diffusion resistance. – Meded. Landbouwhogesch. (Wageningen) 59(13): 1-68, 1959.
Gates, D. M.: Energy Exchange in the Biosphere. Harper and Row, New York 1962.
Gates, D. M., Keegan, H. J., Schleter, J. C., Weidner, V. R.: Spectral properties of plants. – Appl. Optics 4: 11-20, 1965.
Georgi, J.: Meteorologische Universal-Strahlungsmesser. – Meteorol. Rundschau 9: 89, 1956.
Gier, J. T., Dunkle, R. V.: Total hemispherical radiometers. – Trans. amer. Inst. elect. Eng. 70: 339-343, 1951.
Giovanelli, R. G.: An omnidirectional photometer of small dimensions. – J. sci. Instrum. 30: 326-328, 1953.
Glover, J., McCulloch, J. S. G.: The empirical relation between solar radiation and hours of bright sunshine in the high altitude tropics. – Quart. J. roy. meteorol. Soc. 84: 56-60, 1958.
Goody, R. M.: Atmospheric Radiation. I. Theoretical Basis. – Univ. Press, Oxford 1964.
Graniczny, S.: Prosta methoda określania warunków usłonecnienia jednego z podstawowych czynników ekologicznych w hodowli lasu. [A simple method of assessing solar irradiation, one of the basic ecological factors of forest production.] – Sylwan 103: 31-38, 1959.
Gray, J. W.: Calculus in electronic instruments. – M.I.T. Radiation Lab. Ser. 21: 64-89, 1948.
Griffiths, J. F., Griffiths, M. J.: A bibliography of meso- and micro-environmental instrumentation. – U.S. Weather Bureau, Tech. Note 43-EDS: 1-352, 1966.
Grubb, P. J., Whitmore, T. C.: A comparison of montane and lowland forest in Ecuador. III. The light reaching the ground vegetation. – J. Ecol. 55: 33-57, 1967.
Grunow, H.: Bemerkungen zur Rechnung von Relativwerten und Tagessummen der Globalstrahlung. – Meteorol. Rundschau 19: 50-54, 1966.
Guillemin, A.: La Lumière. – Hachette, Paris 1882.
Handbook of Meteorological Instruments. Part I. Instruments for Surface Observations. – H.M.S.O., London 1956.
Haurwitz, B.: Insolation in relation to cloudiness and cloud density. – J. Meteorol. 2: 154-166, 1945.
Haurwitz, B.: Insolation in relation to cloud type. – J. Meteorol. 3: 123-124, 1946.
Haurwitz, B.: Insolation in relation to cloud type. – J. Meteorol. 5: 110-113, 1948.
Hayashi, K., Ito, H.: Studies of the form of plant in rice varieties with particular reference to the efficiency in utilizing sunlight. I. The significance of extinction coefficient in rice plant communities. – Proc. Crop Sci. Soc. Japan 30: 329-333, 1962.
Hill, R.: A lens for whole sky photographs. – Quart. J. roy. meteorol. Soc. 50: 227-235, 1924.
Horie, T.: Preliminary report of a method for estimating sunlit leaf area within a corn canopy. – J. agr. Meteorol. (Tokyo) 22: 45-49, 1966.
Hornbaker, D. R., Rall, D. L.: Pyrheliometers: a discussion of performance characteristics and a rational standard for calibration. – Proc. annu. tech. Meeting, Inst. environm. Sci., San Diego, Cal., pp. 639-645, 1966.

Hughes, A. P.: The importance of light compared with other factors affecting plant growth. – In: Bainbridge, R., Evans, G. C., Rackham, O. (ed.): Light as an Ecological Factor. Pp. 121-146. Blackwell sci. Publ., Oxford 1966.

Huxley, P. A.: Performance of the Megatron-Siemens integrating photometer in an equatorial climate. – J. agr. eng. Res. 9: 225-229, 1964.

Idso, S. B., Baker, D. G., Gates, D. M.: The energy environment of plants. – Adv. Agr. 18: 171-218, 1966.

Inoue, M., Ota, I.: [Wavelength of sunshine in the forest.] – Spec. Rep. Forest Res. Sta. Hokkaido, 8: 128-157, 1957.

Isobe, S.: [An analytical approach to the expression of light intensity in plant communities.] – J. agr. Meteorol. (Tokyo) 17: 143-150, 1962a.

Isobe, S.: [An analytical approach to the expression of light intensity in plant communities (continued).] – J. agr. Meteorol. (Tokyo) 18: 19-21, 1962b.

Isobe, S.: Preliminary studies on physical properties of plant communities. – Bull. Nat. Inst. agr. Sci. (Tokyo) A 9: 29-67, 1962c.

Isobe, S.: Theory of the light distribution and photosynthesis in canopies of randomly dispersed foliage area. – Bull. Nat. Inst. agr. Sci. (Tokyo) A 16: 1-25, 1969.

Ives, R. L.: Minimum current drain sequential switches for meteorological fieldwork. – J. appl. Meteorol. 1: 60-65, 1962.

Jensen, S. E., Åslyng, H. C.: Net radiation and net long-wave radiation at Copenhagen: 1962–1964. – Arch. Meteorol. Bioklim. B 15: 127-140, 1967.

Karbowiak, A. E.: Elements of information theory. – In: Bradley, E. F., Denmead, O. T. (ed.): The Collection and Processing of Field Data. Pp. 329-372. J. Wiley, New York 1967.

Kasanaga, H., Monsi, M.: On the light-transmission of leaves, and its meaning for the production of matter in plant communities. – Jap. J. Bot. 14: 304-324, 1954.

Kerr, J. P., Thurtell, G. W., Tanner, C. B.: An integrating pyranometer for climatological observer stations and mesoscale networks. – J. appl. Meteorol. 6: 688-694, 1967.

Kerr, J. P., Thurtell, G. W., Tanner, C. B.: Mesoscale sampling of global radiation: analysis of data from Wisconsin. – Monthly Weath. Rev. 96: 237-241, 1968.

Khelkhovski, V.: Summarnaya i rasseyannaya radiatsiya v Mirnom pri nekotorykh formakh oblachnosti (osen' i vesna 1965 g.). [Total and scattered radiation at Mirny during certain cloud types (autumn and spring of 1965).] – Inform. Byull. Sovet. antarkt. Ekspeditsii 61: 43-50, 1967.

Kimball, H. H.: Amount of solar radiation that reaches the surface of the earth on the land and on the sea, and methods by which it is measured. – Monthly Weath. Rev. 56: 393-398, 1928.

King, K. M., Graham, W. G.: Note on a multichannel integrator for use with a recording potentiometer. – Canad. J. Plant Sci. 40: 443-446, 1959.

Kleschnin, A. F.: Die Pflanze und das Licht. – Akademie-Verlag, Berlin 1960.

Koldovský, M.: Fotografie in der Meteorologie. – Fotokinoverlag, Halle 1960.

Kondo, J.: Analysis of solar radiation and downward long-wave radiation in Japan. – Sci. Rep. Tohoku Univ. 5th. Ser. 18: 91-124, 1967.

Kondrat'ev, K. Ya.: Aktinometriya. [Actinometry.] – Gidrometizdat, Leningrad 1965a.

Kondrat'ev, K. Ya.: Radiative Heat Exchange in the Atmosphere. – Pergamon Press, Oxford 1965b.

Korel'skiĭ, G. N.: K raschetu osveshchennosti pryamymi solnechnymi luchami kron derev'ev i pochvy v drevostoe. [Calculation of direct solar irradiation of tree canopies and soil in a forest.] – Lesn. Zh. (Archangelsk) 3: 164-165, 1960.

Kornher, A., Rodskjer, N.: Über die Bestimmung der Globalstrahlung in Pflanzenbeständen. – Flora B 157: 149-164, 1967.

Kozyrev, B. P.: Vysokochuvstvitel'nyĭ neselektivnyĭ piranometr s chernoĭ priemnoĭ poverkhnost'yu i s ksenonovym napolneniem. [High-sensitive non-selective xenon-filled pyranometer with black receiving surface.] – In: Poldmaa, V. K. (ed.): Aktinometriya i Optika Atmosfery. Pp. 170-177. Valgus, Tallin 1968.

Kubín, Š., Hládek, L.: An integrating recorder for photosynthetically active radiant energy with improved resolution. – Plant Cell Physiol. 4: 153-168, 1963.

Kuroiwa, S.: [Theoretical analysis of light factor and photosynthesis in plant communities. (3).

Total photosynthesis of a foliage under parallel light in comparison with that under isotropic light condition.] – J. agr. Meteorol. (Tokyo) 24: 23-38, 1968.

Kuroiwa, S., Monsi, M.: Theoretical analysis of light factor and photosynthesis in plant communities. (1). Relationship between foliage structure and direct, diffuse and total solar radiations. – J. agr. Meteorol. (Tokyo) 18: 143-151, 1963.

Květ, J., Svoboda, J., Fiala, K.: A simple device for measuring leaf inclinations. – Photosynthetica 1: 127-128, 1967.

Laevastu, T.: Factors affecting the temperature of the surface layer of the sea. – Comment. phys. math. Soc. sci. Fenn. 25: 1-135, 1960.

Laïsk, A.: Spektrofotometr dlya detal'nogo issledovaniya radiatsionnogo polya v posevakh. [A spectrophotometer for detailed study of radiation field in crops.] – Issled. Fiz. Atmosf., Akad. Nauk Eston. SSR 6: 73–88, 1964.

Laïsk, A.: Vliyanie struktury radiatsionnogo polya na fotosintez poseva. [Influence of structure of radiation field on crop photosynthesis.] – In: Voprosy Radiatsionnogo Rezhima Rastitel'nogo Pokrova. – Issled. Fiz. Atmosf., Akad. Nauk Eston. SSR 7: 73-88, 1965a.

Laïsk, A.: Usovershenstvovannyĭ fotoplanimetr i prisposoblenie dlya opredeleniya orientatsii list'ev. [An improved photoplanimeter and a device for estimating leaf inclinations.] – In: Voprosy Radiatsionnogo Rezhima Rastitel'nogo Pokrova. Issled. Fiz. Atmosf., Akad. Nauk Eston, SSR 7: 102-113, 1965b.

Laïsk, A.: Perspektivy matematicheskogo modelirovaniya funktsii fotosinteza lista. [Prospects of mathematical modelling of leaf photosynthesis function.] – In: Fotosintez i Produktivnost' Rastitel'nogo Pokrova. Pp. 5-45. Akad. Nauk Eston. SSR, Tartu 1968a.

Laïsk, A.: Statisticheskiĭ kharakter oslableniya radiatsii v rastitel'nom pokrove. [Statistical character of light extinction in plant communities.] – In: Rezhim Solnechnoĭ Radiatsii v Rastitel'nom Pokrove. Pp. 81-111. Akad. Nauk Eston. SSR, Tartu 1968b.

Lemon, E. R.: Energy conversion and water use efficiency in plants. – In: Pierre, W. H. *et al.* (ed.): Plant Environment and Efficient Water Use. Pp. 28-48. Amer. Soc. Agron., Madison 1966.

Lemon, E.: Aerodynamic studies of CO_2 exchange between the atmosphere and the plant. – In: San Pietro, A., Greer, F. A., Army, T. J. (ed.): Harvesting the Sun. Pp. 263-290. Academic Press, New York – London 1967.

Lemmon, P. E.: A spherical densiometer for estimating forest overstory density. – Forest Sci. 2: 314-320, 1956.

Lemmon, P. E.: A new instrument for measuring forest overstory density. – J. Forest. 55: 667-669, 1957.

Linke, F.: Die kurzwellige Himmelstrahlung. Handbuch der Geophysik, Bd. VIII: Physik der Atmosphäre, Absch. I: Atmosph. Strahlungsforschung. – Borntraeger, Berlin 1942.

Liu, D. Y. H., Jordan, R. C.: The inter-relationship and characteristic distribution of direct, diffuse and total solar radiation. – Solar Energy 4(3): 1-19, 1960.

Logan, K. T.: An integrating light meter for ecological research. – Tech. Note Forest. Branch Canada, No. 13. Pp. 1-4. 1955.

Loomis, R. S., Williams, W. A., Duncan, W. G.: Community architecture and the productivity of terrestrial plant communities. – In: San Pietro, A., Greer, F. A., Army, T. J. (ed.): Harvesting the Sun. Pp. 290-308. Academic Press, New York – London 1967.

Lumb, F. E.: The influence of cloud on hourly amounts of total solar radiation at the sea surface. – Quart. J. roy. meteorol. Soc. 90: 43-56, 1964.

MacDonald, T. H.: Some characteristics of the Eppley pyrheliometer. – Monthly Weath. Rev. 79: 153-159, 1951.

MacDowall, J.: A total radiation fluxmeter. – Meteorol. Res. Com., Air. Min., London, Meteorol. Res. Pamphl. 858, 1954.

MacDowall, J.: Total radiation fluxmeter. – Meteorol. Mag. 84: 65, 1955.

Mansfield, T. A., Meidner, H.: Stomatal opening in light of different wavelengths: effects of blue light independent of carbon dioxide concentration. – J. exp. Bot. 17: 510-521, 1966.

Matusz, S.: Swiatłomierz do pomiaru przepuszczalności świetlnej koron drzew leśnych. [Light meter for measuring transmission of forest tree canopies.] – Sylwan 97: 367-372, 1953.

McCree, K. J.: A solarimeter for measuring photosynthetically active radiation. – Agr. Meteorol. 3: 353-366, 1966.

McCree, K. J., Morris, R. A.: A transmission meter for photosynthetically active radiation. – J. agr. eng. Res. 12: 246-248, 1967.

McCulloch, J. S. G., Wangati, F. J.: Notes on the use of the Gunn-Bellani radiometer. - Agr. Meteorol. 4: 63-70, 1967.

McCullough, E. C.: Total daily radiant energy available extraterrestrially as a harmonic series in the day of the year. – Arch. Meteorol. Bioklim. B 16: 129-143, 1968.

McPherson, H. G.: Photocell-filter combinations for measuring photosynthetically active radiation. – Agr. Meteorol. 6: 347-356, 1969.

Middleton, W. E. K.: Spherical illumination as an ecological parameter and an improved integrator. – Ecology 34: 416-421, 1953.

Miller, J. B.: A formula for average foliage density. – Aust. J. Bot. 15: 141-144, 1967.

Moldau, Kh.: Ob ispol'zovanii polyarizovannogo izlucheniya dlya analiza indikatris otrazheniya list'ev rasteniï. [Use of polarized radiation to the analysis of reflection index of plant leaves.] – – In: Voprosy Radiatsionnogo Rezhima Rastitel'nogo Pokrova. Pp. 96-101. Izd. Akad. Nauk Eston. SSR, Tartu 1965.

Moll, W. J. M.: A thermopile measuring radiation. – Proc. phys. Soc. (London) 35: 257-260, 1923.

Monsi, M., Saeki, T.: Über den Lichtfaktor in den Pflanzengesellschaften und seine Bedeutung für die Stoffproduktion. – Jap. J. Bot. 14: 22-52, 1953.

Monteith, J. L.: Solarimeter for field use. – J. sci. Instrum. 36: 341-346, 1959.

Monteith, J. L.: Light distribution and photosynthesis in field crops. – Ann. Bot., N.S. 29: 17-37, 1965.

Moon, P., Spencer, D. E.: Illumination from a non-uniform sky. – Trans. Illum. Eng. Soc. 37: 707-712, 1942.

Möriköfer, W.: The determination of the radiation balance of the earth. – U.G.G.I. 9 Ass. Gen., Brussels. Assoc. Met. Mem. Pp. 207. 1953.

Munn, R. E.: Descriptive Micrometeorology. Suppl. 1, Adv. Geophys. Academic Press, New York 1966.

Nichiporovich, A. A.: O svoïstvakh posevov rasteniï kak opticheskoï sistemy. [Properties of plant crops as an optical system.] – Fiziol. Rast. 8: 536-546, 1961.

Nichiporovich, A. A. (ed.): Fotosinteziruyushchie Sistemy Vysokoï Produktivnosti. [Photosynthesis of Productive Systems.] – Nauka, Moskva 1966.

Niïlisk, K. I.: Svetoizmeritel'naya reïka dlya opredeleniya pryamoï radiatsii vnutri posevov i rastitel'nosti. [Device for determining direct radiation in stands and plant communities.] – Issled. Fiz. Atmos. 4: 119-124, 1963.

Niïlisk, K. I.: Spektral'nyï radiatsionnyï rezhim poseva kukuruzy i raschet fotosinteticheski aktivnoï radiatsii (FAR). [Spectral radiation regime in a maize stand and calculation of photosynthetically active radiation.] – Izv. Akad. Nauk Eston. SSR, Ser. fiz.-mat. tech. Nauk 13(3): 177-191, 1964.

Niïlisk, K. I.: Spektrofotometr dlya izmereniya spektral'nykh potokov vnutri poseva. [Spectrophotometer for measuring spectral flux inside the plant stand.] – Izv. Akad. Nauk Eston. SSR, Ser. fiz.-mat. tech. Nauk 4: 40, 1965.

Nil'son, T.: Raschet spektral'nykh potokov korotkovolnovoï radiatsii v rastitel'nom pokrove. [Calculation of spectral flux of short-wave radiation in the plant cover.] – In: Rezhim Solnechnoï Radiatsii v Rastitel'nom Pokrove. Pp. 55-80. Akad. Nauk Eston. SSR, Tartu 1968a.

Nil'son, T.: Ob optimal'noï geometricheskoï strukture rastitel'nogo pokrova. [On the optimum geometrical structure of plant cover.] – In: Rezhim Solnechnoï Radiatsii v Rastitel'nom Pokrove. Pp. 112-146. Akad. Nauk Eston. SSR, Tartu 1968b.

Norman, J. M., Tanner, C. B.: Transient light measurements in plant canopies. – Agron. J. 61: 647-649, 1969.

Norman, J. M., Tanner, C. B., Thurtell, G. W.: Photosynthetic light sensor for measurements in plants canopies. – Agron. J. 61: 840-843, 1969.

Norris, K. H.: Evaluation of visible radiation for plant growth. – Annu. Rev. Plant Physiol. 19: 490-499, 1968.

Palland, C. L., Wartena, L.: Investigations on the calibration factor of the Schulze and the Funk radiation balance meters and comparison of some measured results. – Arch. Meteorol. Bioklim. B 16: 95-104, 1968.

Pearce, R. B., Brown, R. H., Blaser, R. E.: Photosynthesis in plant communities as influenced by leaf angle. – Crop Sci. 7: 321-324, 1967.
Philip, J. R.: The distribution of foliage density with foliage angle estimated from inclined point quadrat observations. – Aust. J. Bot. 13: 357-366, 1965a.
Philip, J. R.: The distribution of foliage density on single plants. – Aust. J. Bot. 13: 411-418, 1965b.
Philip, J. R.: The use of point quadrats, with special reference to stem-like organs. – Aust. J. Bot. 14: 105-125, 1966.
Pochop, L. O., Shanklin, M. D.: Sky cover photograms; a new technique. – Weatherwise 19: 198-203, 1966.
Pochop, L. O., Shanklin, M. D., Horner, D. A.: Sky cover influence on total hemispheric radiation during daylight hours. – J. appl. Meteorol. 7: 484-489, 1968.
Pokrowski, G. I.: Über einen scheinbaren Mie-Effekt und seine mögliche Rolle in der Atmosphärenoptik. – Z. Phys. 53: 67-71, 1929.
Poldmaa, V. K. (ed.): Aktinometriya i Optika Atmosfery. [Actinometry and Atmosphere Optics.] – Valgus, Tallin 1968.
Pontin, A. J.: A method for quick comparison of the total solar radiation incident on different microhabitats. – Ecology 43: 740-741, 1962.
Powell, M. C., Heath, O. V. S.: A simple and inexpensive integrating photometer. – J. exp. Bot. 15: 187-191, 1964.
Quinn, W. H., Burt, W. V.: Computation of incoming solar radiation over the equatorial Pacific. – J. appl. Meteorol. 7: 490-498, 1968.
Rackham, O.: Radiation, transpiration, and growth in a woodland annual. – In: Bainbridge, R., Evans, G. C., Rackham, O. (ed.): Light as an Ecological Factor. Pp. 167-185. Blackwell sci. Publ. Oxford 1966.
Reid, A.: Light relationships in the white oak forests of southern Wisconsin. – Ph. D. Thesis. Univ. Wisconsin 1962.
Reifsnyder, W. A.: Forest meteorology: the forest energy balance. - Int. Rev. Forest Res. 2: 127-179, 1967.
Reifsnyder, W. E., Lull, H. W.: Radiant energy in relation to forests. – Tech. Bull., U.S. Dept. Agr. 1344: 1-111, 1965.
Richardson, S. D.: The use of a spherical radiation meter in woodlands. – Forestry 32: 126-137, 1959.
Rider, N. E., Bradley, E. F.: Digitization and integration of reflecting galvanometer signals. – Rev. sci. Instrum. 33: 25-26, 1962.
Robinson, N. (ed.): Solar Radiation. – Elsevier, Amsterdam 1966.
Rodskjer, N.: A method to reduce the temperature influence on measurements with thermoelectric pyranometers. – Arch. Meteorol. Geophijs. Bioklim. B 13: 261-269, 1964.
Rodskjer, N., Kornher, A.: Eine Methode zur Registrierung der räumlichen Verteilung der Globalstrahlung in einem Pflanzenbestand. – Arch. Meteorol. Geophys. Bioklim. B 15: 186-190, 1967.
Ross, Yu. K.: Ob izmerenii radiatsii piranometrami Yanishevskogo. [Radiation measurement with Yanishevskiĭ pyranometer.] – Izv. Akad. Nauk Eston. SSR 6: 3-18, 1957a.
Ross, Yu. K.: O zavisimosti perevodnogo mnozhitelya otnositel'nykh aktinometrov ot temperatury. [Relation of actinometer coefficient to temperature.] – Trudy glav. geofiz. Observat. (Leningrad) 68: 204-208, 1957b.
Ross, Yu.: K matematicheskoĭ teorii fotosinteza rastitel'nogo pokrova. [On the mathematical theory of plant cover photosynthesis.] – Dokl. Akad. Nauk S.S.S.R. 157: 1239-1242, 1964.
Ross, Yu. K.: Role of solar radiation in the photosynthesis of crops. – In: Nichiporovich, A. A. (ed.): Photosynthesis of Productive Systems. Pp. 44-52. IPST, Jerusalem 1967.
Ross, Yu., Bikhele, Z.: Raschet fotosinteza rastitel'nogo pokrova I. [Calculation of photosynthesis of plant cover I.] – In: Fotosintez i Produktivnost' Rastitel'nogo Pokrova. Pp. 75-110. Akad. Nauk Eston. SSR, Tartu 1968.
Ross, Yu. K., Nil'son, T.: K teorii radiatsionnogo rezhima rastitel'nogo pokrova. [On the theory of radiation regime of plant cover.] – Issled. Fiz. Atmos. 4: 42-64, 1963.
Ross, Yu., Nil'son, T.: Propuskanie pryamoï radiatsii solntsa sel'skokhozyaïstvennymi posevami. [Transmission of direct solar radiation in agricultural crops.] – In: Voprosy

Radiatsionnogo Rezhima Rastitel'nogo Pokrova. Issled. Fiz. Atmos. 7: 25-64, 1965.
Ross, Yu. K., Nil'son, T.: The spatial orientation of leaves in crop stands and its determination. – In: Nichiporovich, A. A. (ed.): Photosynthesis of Productive Systems. Pp. 86-99. IPST, Jerusalem 1967.
Ross, Yu., Nil'son, T.: Raschet fotosinteticheski aktivnoï radiatsii v rastitel'nom pokrove. [Calculation of photosynthetically active radiation in the plant cover.] – In: Rezhim Solnechnoï Radiatsii v Rastitel'nom Pokrove. Issled. Fiz. Atmos. 11: 5-54, 1968.
Roussel, L.: Recherches théoriques et practiques sur la répartition en quantité et en qualité de la lumière dans le milieu forestier; influence sur la végétation. – Ann. Ec. Eaux For. Nancy 13: 293-400, 1953.
Russell, B. R.: Cutting chart records for integration by weighing. – Rev. sci. Instrum. 31: 216-217, 1960.
Saeki, T.: Interrelationships between leaf amount, light distribution and total photosynthesis in a plant community. – Bot. Mag. (Tokyo) 73: 55-63, 1960.
Saeki, T.: Light relations in plant communities. – In: Evans, L. T. (ed.): Environmental Control of Plant Growth. Pp. 79-94. Academic Press, New York – London, 1963.
Sauberer, F., Härtel, O.: Pflanze und Strahlung. Probleme der Bioklimatologie. Bd. V. – Geest u. Portig, Leipzig 1959.
Schoffer, P., Suomi, V. E.: A direct current motor integrator for radiation measurements. – Solar Energy 5: 29-32, 1961.
Schulze, R.: Über ein Strahlungsmessgerät mit ultrarotdurchlässigen Windschutzhaube am Meteorologischen Observatorium Hamburg. – Geofis. pura applic. 24: 107-114, 1953.
Schulze, R.: Über die Verwendung von Polyäthylen für Strahlungsmessungen. – Arch. Meteorol. Bioklim. B 11: 211-223, 1962.
Sekihara, Y., Suzuki, M.: Solar radiation and duration of sunshine in Japan. – Pap. Meteorol. Geophys. (Tokyo) 17: 190-199, 1967.
Šetlík, I.: The use of integrating photoelectrical radiation recorders for the measurement of photosynthetically active radiation. – In: Eckardt, F. E. (ed.): Functioning of Terrestrial Ecosystems at the Primary Production Level. Pp. 457-462. UNESCO, Paris 1968.
Shannon, C. F., Weaver, W.: The Mathematical Theory of Communication. – Illinois Univ. Press 1949.
Shul'gin, I. A.: K voprosu ob adaptatsii zelenykh rasteniï k spektral'nomu sostavu solnechnoï radiatsii. [Adaptation of green plants to the spectral composition of solar radiation.] – Fiziol. Rast. 14: 592-602, 1967.
Slatyer, R. O., Bierhuizen, J. F.: Transpiration from cotton leaves under a range of environmental conditions in relation to internal and external diffusive resistances. – Aust. J. biol. Sci. 17: 115-130, 1964.
Slatyer, R. O., McIlroy, I. C.: Practical Microclimatology. – UNESCO, Paris 1961.
Stern, W. R.: Light measurements in pastures. – Herb. Abstr. 32: 91-96, 1962.
Strain, R. N. C.: Solar reflectivity of paints. – J. Oil Colour Chemists Assoc. 44: 689-712, 1961.
Sulev, M. A.: O nekotorykh rezul'tatakh sravneniï priemnikov dlinnovolnovoï radiatsii. [Some results of comparison of receptors of long wavelength radiation.] – Sb. Stat. Met. Issled. Akad. Nauk SSSR 15: 7-20, 1966.
Summer, C. J.: A sunshine sensing device for long period recording. – Quart. J. roy. meteorol. Soc. 92: 567-569, 1966.
Suomi, V. E., Kuhn, P. M.: An economical net radiometer. – Tellus 10: 160-163, 1958.
Suomi, V. E., Franssila, M., Islitzer, N. F.: An improved net radiation instrument. – J. Meteorol. 11: 276-282, 1954.
Suomi, V. E., Staley, D. O., Kuhn, P. M.: A direct measurement of infrared radiation divergence to 160 mb. – Quart. J. roy. meteorol. Soc. 84: 134-141, 1958.
Suzuki, T., Satoo, T.: [An attempt to measure the daylight factor under the crown canopy using a solid angle projecting camera.] – Bull. Tokyo Univ. Forest. 40: 160-180, 1954.
Swan, J. B., Federer, C. A., Tanner, C. B.: Economical radiometer performance, construction and theory. – Univ. Wisconsin Soils Dept. Bull. 4, 1961.
Szeicz, G., Monteith, J. L., dos Santos, J. M.: Tube solarimeter to measure radiation among plants. – J. appl. Ecol. 1: 169-174, 1964.

Tabata, S.: Insolation in relation to cloud amount and sun's altitude. – Geophys. Notes, Univ. Tokyo 17: 202-210, 1964.
Tanner, C. B.: Basic instrumentation and measurements for plant environment and micrometeorology. – Univ. Wisconsin Soils Dept. Bull. 6, 1963.
Tanner, C. B., Thurtell, G. W., Swan, J. B.: Integration systems using a commercial coulometer. – Proc. Soil Sci. Soc. Amer. 27: 478-481, 1963.
Thams, J. C., Wierzejewski, H.: Die Grösse der diffusen Zirkumglobalstrahlung. – Arch. Meteorol. Geophys. Bioklimatol. (Ser. B) 12: 47-63, 1963.
Thurtell, G. W., Tanner, C. B.: Electronic integrator for micrometeorological data. – J. appl. Meteorol. 3: 198-202, 1964.
Tooming, Kh.: An approximate method for determining the attenuation and reflection of PHAR and of the near infrared radiation in a maize stand from the measurements of total radiation. – In: Nichiporovich, A. A. (ed.): Photosynthesis of Productive Systems. Pp. 100-113. IPST, Jerusalem 1967a.
Tooming, Kh.: Svyaz' fotosinteza, rosta rasteniï i geometricheskoï struktury listvy rastitel'nogo pokrova s rezhimom solnechnoï radiatsii na raznykh shirotakh. [Relation between photosynthesis, plant growth, geometric structure of plant covers, foliage and regime of solar radiation in different latitudes.] – Bot. Zh. 52: 601-616, 1967b.
Tooming, Kh.: Nekotorye cherty vzaimootnosheniï rasteniï v rastitel'nom soobshchestve v svyazi s ikh fotosintezom. [Some characteristics of plant interrelations in a plant community related to their photosynthesis.] – In: Fotosintez i Produktivnost' Rastitel'nogo Pokrova. Pp. 46–74. Akad. Nauk Eston. SSR, Tartu 1968.
Tooming, Kh., Ross, Yu. K.: Radiatsionnyï rezhim poseva kukuruzy po yarusam i opisyvayushchie ego priblizhennye formuly. [Radiation regime of different leaf insertion levels in a maize crop and its characterization by means of approximate formulas.] – Issled. Fiz. Atmos. 6: 63-80, 1964.
Tranquillini, W.: Das Lichtklima wichtiger Pflanzengesellschaften. – In: Ruhland, W. (ed.): Handbuch der Pflanzenphysiologie. Bd. V/2. Pp. 304-338. Springer, Berlin-Göttingen-Heidelberg 1960.
Trickett, E. S.: An evaporated film thermopile. – J. agr. eng. Res. 8: 147-155, 1963.
Trickett, E. S., Moulsley, L. J.: An integrating photometer. – J. agr. eng. Res. 1: 1-11, 1956.
Trickett, E. S., Moulsley, L. J., Edwards, R. I.: Measurement of solar and artificial radiation with particular reference to agriculture and horticulture. – J. agr. eng. Res. 2: 86-110, 1957.
Turner, D. H.: Highly stable electronic integrator for solar radiation measurements. – J. appl. Meteorol. 5: 895-896, 1966.
U.S. Air Force: Handbook of Geophysics. Rev. Ed. Sect. 16, Thermal Radiation. – Macmillan, New York 1960.
Uchijima, Z., Udagawa, T., Horie, T., Kobayashi, K.: [Studies of energy and gas exchange within crop canopies. (4). The penetration of direct solar radiation into corn canopy and the intensity of direct radiation on the foliage surface.] – J. agr. Meteorol. (Tokyo) 24: 33-43, 1968.
Udagawa, T., Uchijima, Z., Horie, T., Kobayashi, K.: Canopy structure of corn plant. – In: Photosynthesis and Utilization of Solar Energy. Level III Experiments. Pp. 20-22. Jap. Nat. Subcomm. PP/IBP, Tokyo 1968.
Verhagen, A. M. W., Wilson, J. H.: The propagation and effectiveness of light in leaf canopies with horizontal foliage. – Ann. Bot. N.S. 33: 711-727, 1969.
Verhagen, A. M. W., Wilson, J. H., Britten, E. J.: Plant production in relation to foliage illumination. – Ann. Bot. N.S. 27: 627-640, 1963.
Vershinin, P. V., Mel'nikova, M. K., Michurin, B. N., Moshkov, B. S., Povasov, N. P., Chudnovskiï, A. F.: Fundamentals of Agrophysics. IPST, Jerusalem 1959.
Vézina, P. E.: Solar radiation available over snow pack in a dense pine forest. – Agr. Meteorol. 1: 54-65, 1964.
Voïtikova, T. D.: Nekotorye dannye o diffuznom otrazhenii pokrytiï priemnikov aktinometricheskikh priborov. [Some data of diffuse reflexion from paints for receptors of actinometric devices.] – Trud. glav. geofiz. Observat. (Leningrad) 170: 167-169, 1965.
Wagar, J. W.: The insolation grid. – Ecology 45: 636-638, 1965.
Walsh, J. W. T.: The Science of Daylight. – MacDonald, London 1961.

Warren Wilson, J.: Analysis of the distribution of foliage area in grassland. – In: Ivins, J. D. (ed.): The Measurement of Grassland Productivity. Pp. 51-61. Butterworth, London 1959a.

Warren Wilson, J.: Analysis of the spatial distribution of foliage by two-dimensional point quadrats. – New Phytol. 58: 92-101, 1959b.

Warren Wilson, J.: Inclined point quadrats. – New Phytol. 59: 1-8, 1960.

Warren Wilson, J.: Estimation of foliage denseness and foliage angle by inclined point quadrats. – Aust. J. Bot. 11: 95-105, 1963a.

Warren Wilson, J.: Errors resulting from thickness of point quadrats. – Aust. J. Bot. 11: 178-188, 1963b.

Warren Wilson, J.: Stand structure and light penetration. I. Analysis by point quadrats. – J. appl. Ecol. 2: 383–390, 1965.

Warren Wilson, J.: Stand structure and light penetration. III. Sunlet foliage area. – J. appl. Ecol. 4: 159-165, 1967.

Wassink, E. C., van der Scheer, C.: A spherical radiation meter. – Meded. Landbouwhogesch. (Wageningen) 51: 175-183, 1951.

Whitmore, T. C., Wong, Y. K.: Patterns of sunfleck and shade light in tropical rain forest. – Malay. Forester 22: 50-62, 1959.

van Wijk, W. R. (ed.): Physics of Plant Environment. – North-Holland Publ. Co., Amsterdam 1963.

Williams, W. A., Loomis, R. S., Duncan, W. G., Dovrat, A., Nunez A., F.: Canopy architecture at various population densities and the growth and grain yield of corn. – Crop Sci. 8: 303-308, 1968.

de Wit, C. T.: Potential photosynthesis of crop surfaces. – Neth. J. agr. Sci. 7: 141-149, 1959.

de Wit, C. T.: Photosynthesis of leaf canopies. – Agr. Res. Rep. (Wageningen) 663: 1-57, 1965.

Withrow, R. B., Withrow, A. P.: Generation, control, and measurement of visible and near visible radiant energy. – In: Hollaender, A. (ed.): Radiation Biology. Vol. III. Pp. 125-258. McGraw-Hill, New York 1956.

WMO-RA-1: Report on the fourth session of WGR-RA-1 at Tunis, January 10-21, 1961. – Meteorol. Office, Tunis 1961.

Woertz, B. B., Hand, I. F.: The characteristics of the Eppley pyrheliometer. – Monthly Weath. Rev. 69: 146-148, 1941.

Wright, J. G.: Measurement of the degree of shading or crown canopy density on forest sites. – Forest Chron. 19: 183-185, 1943.

Yellot, J. I., Chamnes, L., Selcuk, K.: Measurement of direct, diffuse and total solar radiation with silicon photovoltaic cells. – Solar Energy 6: 155-163, 1962.

Yocum, C. S., Allen, L. H., Lemon, E. R.: Photosynthesis under field conditions. VI. Solar radiation balance and photosynthetic efficiency. – Agron. J. 56: 249-253, 1964.

13 | MEASUREMENT OF CARBON DIOXIDE EXCHANGE IN THE FIELD

13.1 | Introduction

13.1.1 | CO_2 exchange in the field

Photosynthesis by plants involves the uptake of CO_2; respiration by soil[1] and plant parts results in its release. Some of the CO_2 used in photosynthesis may be supplied by respiratory processes internal to the plant, but the net gain of carbon requires uptake of CO_2 from air around the foliage. In a community of plants, this CO_2 is supplied from two sources – the atmosphere above and the soil below.

For most of the daylight hours, photosynthesis in a growing plant community will normally exceed soil and plant respiration, so that there will be transport of CO_2 in two directions: downwards from the air layers above, and, in the lower part of the canopy, upwards from the soil and perhaps lower leaves. A typical daytime situation is depicted in Fig. 13.4. At night, respiration by plants and soil results in an entirely upward transport of CO_2 as it diffuses back into the atmosphere.

Although the atmosphere normally supplies most of the CO_2 taken up by field crops, the soil contribution can still be important – as much as 20–30% of the total CO_2 requirement (*e.g.* Fig. 13.4; Monteith, Szeicz & Yabuki 1964; Denmead 1968). Presumably, for some undisturbed natural communities whose biomass is more or less steady in time, there is little or no net demand for CO_2 from the atmosphere.

Thus, to calculate the actual uptake or loss of CO_2 by a crop, the CO_2 exchange at both crop and soil surfaces must be known. Measurement of the first of these will be discussed in Sections 13.2 and 13.3, and that of the latter in Section 13.4.

13.1.2 | The micrometeorological approach

Measurement of the exchanges of momentum, heat and water vapour between natural surfaces and the atmosphere has been a long-standing pursuit of micrometeorology. Recent years have seen an extension of methods developed in this field to the measurement of the vertical exchange of CO_2 above vegetated surfaces. This provides a non-destructive means for studying the carbon dioxide uptake of plants in the field over periods as short as, say, 20 min. For this purpose, micrometeorological methods have a number of advantages over other approaches to measurement of the assimilation rates of plant stands, such as measurement of weight changes over sampling periods of several days, or use of field enclosures which necessarily create artificial microclimates. There are, however, restrictions

1. Soil respiration is taken to include respiration by living roots, release of CO_2 through the decomposition of roots and other organic debris in the soil, and respiration by micro-organisms.

to the field situations in which they can be used successfully, and limitations to their accuracy. It is our aim to describe the most suitable of these methods and to discuss some of their restrictions and limitations.

Although instrumental errors are important in any consideration of physical methodology, there is not space here to consider instruments *per se*. Details of the design, construction and principles of operation of instruments appropriate for the various measurements described in this paper are contained in many publications. Some general reviews and sources of reference to the literature are Slatyer & McIlroy (1961), Tanner (1963), Wadsworth *et al.* (1968) and several papers in W.M.O. (1968). Measurement of the concentration of carbon dioxide itself is discussed in Chapters 3 and 4.

It is also beyond the scope of this chapter to present a detailed discussion of transfer processes between the earth's surface and the atmosphere. This has been the subject of many texts and reviews, *e.g.* Sutton (1953), Priestley (1959), Slatyer & McIlroy (1961), Tanner (1963), Lumley & Panofsky (1964), Webb (1965), and W.M.O. (1968), and the reader is referred to these works for the micrometeorological background to our discussion. Our particular topic of measurement of CO_2 exchange in the field has also been the subject of a number of publications. Some overlap with these papers has been both unavoidable and necessary. They will be referred to at appropriate places in the text. Recent reviews are contained in Lemon (1969) and Denmead (1970).

Finally, to ensure adequate coverage while avoiding excessive detail in the main text, certain aspects of our topic have been dealt with in Appendices (Sections 13.6 and 13.7), to which reference is made where appropriate.

13.2 | The eddy correlation, or instantaneous fluctuation, technique

13.2.1 | General description of method

Before proceeding to a detailed examination of the main methods currently in use for measurement of CO_2 exchange, we should briefly consider eddy correlation techniques. While not yet representing a practical tool for CO_2 flux determination, with further development these should become of considerable importance, probably within the next few years.

The name derives from the eddying nature of turbulent transport in the atmosphere. Superimposed on the mean air flow at any time or place, there is a continual random movement in all directions of more or less discrete 'parcels' of air. At all times these 'eddies' tend to mix with their immediate surroundings, ultimately losing their identity and being replaced by new ones. Where there is a gradient of concentration of any atmospheric substance or property, parcels moving away from a region of high concentration will tend on the average to have a greater content of the substance concerned than those moving towards it – and *vice versa* for a region of low concentration.

The result is a transfer down the concentration gradient, with an efficiency which is generally far greater than that of the somewhat analogous process, also present, of molecular diffusion. However, unlike the more or less constant efficiency of molecular diffusion, that of eddy transfer varies widely with local atmospheric conditions, also with characteristics of the underlying surface, and with distance from it – *i.e.* in the free atmosphere, with height above the effective surface of the vegetation or soil.

The eddy flux thus arising of a substance Φ, say, is given directly by the covariance of the instantaneous concentration of Φ at the measuring point and the corresponding rate of air flow in the direction being considered (Swinbank 1951; Slatyer & McIlroy 1961; Webb 1965). This is a fundamental approach, and has many advantages over the less direct relationships which will be described later. However, it requires the use of very compact and rapidly responding sensors for both the concentration of Φ and the component of windspeed in the chosen direction – otherwise that part of the covariance due to small or rapid fluctuations will be lost.

13.2.2 | Important restrictions on use

Although instruments have been devised and used successfully for measurement of the eddy fluxes of momentum, heat and water vapour, under favourable conditions, none has yet been found adequate for operation close to the surface where the eddies become smaller and faster, and hence harder to detect. So far, their satisfactory use has been restricted to heights of a metre or so above the surface, and hence to large uniform areas where the fluxes at such heights will not differ appreciably from the corresponding zero height or surface values, which are generally the quantities of real interest. (The effects of advection due to non-uniformity of surface type are discussed in Sections 13.3.3.10 and 13.6.8.)

A further difficulty arises in the presence of a significant *mean* air flow (as distinct from the momentary flows due to eddy motion), in the direction of transfer under consideration. The eddy flux then represents only one component of the total transport, and the other, or mass flux (*cf.* Swinbank 1955; Slatyer & McIlroy 1961), is extremely difficult to determine. For long enough periods and above a reasonably large quasi-horizontal surface, the mean air flow in the vertical will generally be small, and it is customary to neglect it. However, this becomes less justifiable over sloping or heterogeneous surfaces; or at low heights over any but smooth surfaces; and still less so when working right inside a plant community. The answer may lie merely in sufficient replication of sampling points, but the practical range of application of the technique must remain uncertain until more investigatory work has been carried out. For determining CO_2 flux directly in this way, suitable compact rapid-response sensors still remain to be developed, although recent work such as that of Desjardins (cited by Lemon 1969), suggests that general use of this method may become possible before long.

In the meantime, however, there are several other approaches already in use for determining CO_2 transfer. These are mainly based on the assumption that in the fully turbulent atmosphere the eddying process has the same effectiveness in the transport of CO_2 as of other entities: momentum, heat, water vapour and so on. The ratio of the mean flux of any of these to its mean concentration gradient, measured simultaneously, is thus considered to be the same as the corresponding ratio for CO_2. This permits calculation of the CO_2 flux from measurements of the CO_2 gradient. (Inoue *et al.* 1969 have recently reported the indirect determination

of CO_2 flux in this way, using eddy correlation to determine momentum and heat fluxes as a first step.)
In the next Section, we discuss this similarity approach, first in general, then separately for momentum, water vapour and energy, within the air layers above the crop. In Section 13.4 we consider the extension of these techniques to CO_2 exchange within the canopy.

13.3 | Flux versus gradient, or mean value, techniques

The discussion here will be along general lines. Most of the formulae involved will be derived and appropriate units specified, in Section 13.6 (Appendix A). For ease of cross-reference and to avoid ambiguity, the numbers given to equations in Section 13.6 will be adopted also for such equations as are introduced here – in spite of their resulting lack of numerical sequence in the main text.

13.3.1 | Turbulent transport and the similarity approach

13.3.1.1 | General

In turbulent transfer, the vertical transport of a substance or property Φ, whose mean concentration at height z is ϕ (in any chosen units of Φ per unit volume of air), can be represented by the equation

$$F = -K_{\Phi} \frac{\partial \phi}{\partial z} \qquad (13.1a)$$

in which F is the mean vertical flux of the transported entity[1], in the same units of Φ, per unit horizontal area per unit time, and positive when in the same direction as z, while K is a transport coefficient known as the turbulent or eddy diffusivity – the subscript denoting that, in principle at least, its value in given circumstances may be different for different diffusing entities.
The negative sign is included in equation (13.1a) because transport always takes place down the concentration gradient, and therefore flux and gradient must have opposite signs if, as is usual, their positive direction is taken to be the same – generally upwards in the atmospheric case (but see Section 13.3.2 below). The association between flux and concentration gradient can be seen in Figs. 13.3 and 13.4.
Each of the three terms in Eq. (13.1a) will be a function of the height considered (see Figs. 13.3 and 13.4), although *above the canopy* the flux itself will often vary so little over the height range we are normally concerned with that it can be regarded as independent of z. This is an important but sometimes overlooked requirement in using above-crop determinations of K and ϕ in Eq. (13.1a) to infer

1. Strictly what is referred to here is the flux density (*i.e.* flux per unit area), sometimes called the flux intensity, rather than the flux itself; but for ease of reading we have continued the practice already common in the literature of treating the qualifier 'per unit area' as implicit where the context of 'flux' requires it.

values of a flux at the crop surface (or at any height other than that of the measurements involved) – and in the opposite process of inferring K at a particular height, as discussed later. Except in Section 13.4 and where the effects of advection[1] are under discussion (*e.g.* Sections 13.3.10 and 13.6.8), the assumption will be implicit throughout this Chapter that fluxes are constant with height.

In the c.g.s. system[2], K will have the dimensions [$cm^2\ s^{-1}$], and it clearly plays a similar role to the analogous coefficient used in describing molecular diffusion. However, as already pointed out, the nature of the turbulent transfer mechanism is quite different from that of molecular transfer; eddy diffusivities are relatively large and highly variable, typically of order 10^2–10^4 versus 0.15, 0.22 and 0.26 for the molecular diffusivities of momentum, heat and water vapour respectively, in air at usual temperatures and pressures.

In fact, K is a function of height and of wind strength, increasing more or less linearly both with distance above the effective surface, and with windspeed as measured at a standard reference level. For given values of height and windspeed, moreover, K will also vary somewhat with the aerodynamic roughness of the underlying surface, and with the thermal instability or otherwise of the air layer concerned (see later).

Thus, with $\partial\phi/\partial z$ generally determinable (although not without difficulty – *cf.* various reviews cited previously, and those Chapters of the present Manual which deal with measurement of CO_2 concentration), the central problem in the practical use of equation (13.1a) is the reliable determination of K. Unfortunately, except in the case of momentum, which will be discussed further in Section 13.3.2, it is not yet possible to derive values for K solely from properties of the atmosphere which do not include the flux itself.

13.3.1.2 | Carbon dioxide transport

This is certainly true for K_C in that form of equation (13.1a) which specifically describes CO_2 exchange, *viz.*,

$$C = -K_C \frac{\partial \rho_c}{\partial z} \tag{13.3a}$$

where C is the net upward flux of CO_2 between a vegetated surface and the atmos-

1. In the present context, advection can be described as the process of transfer by horizontal motion (Meteorological Office 1957). It occurs where two areas of different surface type adjoin each other in the line of the wind. The properties of air at or near equilibrium with the two surfaces will differ according to the degree of contrast between them. If this is severe, an effective adjustment from the upwind towards the downwind equilibrium condition up to heights of only a few metres may require horizontal distances of several hundred metres. In the adjustment region, downwind of the boundary, there will be horizontal as well as vertical exchange of advected entities such as heat, water vapour, CO_2, and momentum. Thus vertical fluxes will vary both with height from the surface and distance from the upwind boundary, and concentrations will change with height in a manner atypical of near equilibrium profiles, and at any height will vary with distance downwind.
2. c.g.s. system is used throughout this Chapter, but see Tables 1.3. and 1.4.

phere, and ρ_c is the density of CO_2 in the atmosphere at height z. As with water, or any other material substance, density (*i.e.* mass of substance actually present in unit volume of air) is the appropriate way to specify concentration in transfer equations analogous to Eq. (13.1a), and this will be done in most of the illustrative formulae introduced below. Specification in some other way, which is often more convenient in practice, requires the introduction of an additional factor to take account of conversion of units (*cf.* equation (13.3c) of Section 13.6)[1].

In its finite difference form (see Section 13.6.2), equation (13.3a) becomes

$$C = \hat{K}_C \, \Delta\rho_c \tag{13.3b}$$

where the symbols $\hat{}$ and Δ denote, respectively, a value applicable over an air layer rather than at a particular height, and a difference across the same air layer. The dimensions of $\hat{K}$ are [cm s^{-1}], and consistency with a positive sign in equation (13.3b) requires that the difference $\Delta\rho_c$ be taken as the lower concentration minus the upper.

13.3.1.3 | Similarity and the use of tracers

At present K_C and $\hat{K}_C$ can be determined only by assuming them equal to the analogous coefficients for transfer of some 'tracer' entity, whose effectiveness of transport at a given time and place can then be used as a measure of that of CO_2 itself.

The inability to determine a transfer coefficient independently of the associated flux also applies to K_W or $\hat{K}_W$, and to a lesser extent to K_H or $\hat{K}_H$, in the analogues of equations (13.3a) or (13.3b) for water vapour and sensible heat, whose use as tracers is considered later in this Chapter. However, in these cases, and certain others, the relevant coefficient can be determined *in situ* from the ratio of a measured flux, *e.g.* of water vapour or heat, to the corresponding concentration gradient or difference, in effect that of humidity or temperature. On the aforementioned similarity assumption, namely that the effectiveness of turbulent transfer is the same for CO_2 as for momentum, heat or water vapour, for instance, it becomes possible to apply this measured ratio to the corresponding measured value of $\partial\rho_c/\partial z$ or $\Delta\rho_c$, giving what should be a very good estimate of C. *via* equations (13.16a) or (13.17) below.

As an alternative to deriving $\partial\rho_c/\partial z$ and $\partial\phi/\partial z$ separately, from vertical profiles of the respective concentrations, the variation in ρ_c can be related directly to that in ϕ, usually graphically. This involves the fitting of a line to data points $((\rho_c)_{z_1}, (\phi)_{z_1}; \ldots; (\rho_c)_{z_n}, \phi_{z_n})$, for a number of heights $z_1, \ldots, z_n$. The slope of the line of best fit then gives a smoothed value of $\partial\rho_c/\partial\phi$ for use in equation (13.16b). The extent to which the data points depart from linearity also provides a check[2]

1. A list of symbols, dimensions and conversion factors is given in Section 13.7.
2. Constancy with height of $\partial\rho_c/\partial\phi$ does not in itself establish that $K_C = K_\Phi$, of course, but merely that the product $(C/F)\ (K_\Phi/K_C)$ remains constant. However enough is known about turbulent diffusion in general to give confidence that if the latter statement is true, then the former is unlikely to be wrong to a significant extent.

on possible variations in C or F with height, or differences between the height dependence of K_C and that of K_Φ, any of which could cause differences in shape between the respective concentration profiles – and any of which could invalidate the use of the similarity assumption.

A similar check can be obtained for the separate-gradient approach of Eq. (13.16a), although with considerably more effort, by comparing values of the ratio $(\partial \rho_c/\partial z)/(\partial \phi/\partial z)$ at two or more heights.

It should be noted that incorrect placement of instruments such that the *effective* heights are not the same for ρ_c and ϕ can lead to spurious anomalies in the height-dependence of $\partial \rho_c/\partial \phi$ or of $(\partial \rho_c/\partial z)/(\partial \phi/\partial z)$. This can be difficult to avoid unless the sampling points for ρ_c and ϕ are as close alongside each other as possible at each height. Their proximity should be limited only by mutual interference of the sensors. (Ideally, where aspirated sensors are used for ϕ, they should share joint intakes with the air streams to the CO_2 analyser, *e.g.* the equipment shown in Fig. 13.5). These anomalies become particularly important when working heights are low. Then unavoidable errors in estimating the effective local crop height (strictly the height of the profile zero-plane – see Sections 13.6.7 and 13.6.8) can become highly significant.

On balance, the gradient approach is probably worthwhile for above-canopy work only when the gradients themselves are required for other purposes, or when different heights of measurement for ρ_c and ϕ are unavoidable. In this case the heights concerned must be known reasonably accurately, at least relative to each other, to permit matching of gradients derived by interpolation within one or both of the profiles involved. However, if ρ_c and ϕ are determined at the same heights, spread over a suitable range, only an approximate knowledge is required of what these heights are, for use in equation (13.16a), and no knowledge whatsoever for equation (13.16b) or the even simpler finite difference approach of equation (13.17).

The latter's only drawback relative to equations (13.16) would seem to lie in the inability to introduce smoothing, or to detect interfering effects such as mentioned above. This disadvantage could be quite important where the relevant characteristics of the experimental methods or of the site are not known to be satisfactory – see Section 13.3.3.9. Then it will usually be worthwhile to replicate the difference measurements in equation (13.17), or to temporarily employ equations (13.16), in order to establish the reliability of subsequent use of equation (13.17) with just two measuring heights.

The three possible types of relationship described above are expressed in general form (*cf.* Section 13.6.6) by:

$$C = \pm \frac{F}{\partial \phi/\partial z} \frac{\partial \rho_c}{\partial z}; \qquad (13.16a)$$

$$C = \pm F \frac{\partial \rho_c}{\partial \phi}; \qquad (13.16b)$$

$$C = F \frac{\Delta \rho_c}{\Delta \phi}. \qquad (13.17)$$

Note that in Eq. (13.16) the sign will generally be positive, and in equation (13.17) the sense with respect to height will generally be the same for $\Delta\rho_c$ and $\Delta\phi$. However, the reverse will apply where F is defined as positive downwards, as in the case of momentum, dealt with below.
The specific analogues of equation (13.17) which are best used in practice are given, with appropriate allowance for units and sign, as equations (13.18)–(13.21) of Section 13.6; while their practical application and the probable effects of the assumptions involved are outlined for the main cases of importance in the following subsections. The use of corresponding analogues of equations (13.16), where desired, involves very similar considerations, and will not be discussed specifically here.

13.3.2 | Momentum transport and the windspeed profile

13.3.2.1 | Momentum as a tracer

Where the tracer flux is that of momentum, $-F = \tau$, the atmospheric shearing stress, and $\phi = \rho_a u$, *i.e.* the tracer concentration is the product of air density and horizontal velocity (*cf.* equation (13.8) of Section 13.6.4). The appropriate form of equation (13.17) for momentum then becomes

$$C = \tau \frac{\Delta\rho_c}{\rho_a \Delta u} = 1.5 \times 10^{-6}\, \tau \frac{\Delta c}{\Delta u} \qquad (13.18)$$

where C is in [g cm^{-2} s^{-1}], τ in [dyn cm^{-2} = 10^{-1} N m^{-2}], ρ_c and ρ_a in [g cm^{-3}], c in [vpm] (= ppm by volume) of CO_2, and u in [cm s^{-1}]. Δu and $\Delta\rho_c$ or Δc are measured over the same height interval (not necessarily known), but in the opposite sense because of the reversal of the normal sign convention for flux – gradient relationships when dealing with momentum. This is both convenient and by now well-established, its justification lying in the fact that with a normal system of axes stationary with respect to the earth itself, the flow of momentum is *always* downwards from the moving air[1].
Wherever possible it would seem desirable to measure τ independently of Δu, whether by the eddy correlation method (*cf.* Hicks 1969; Inoue *et al.* 1969), or by an instrument which senses directly the drag of the wind on the ground, known variously as a shear stress meter (Brooks & Pruitt 1965) or a drag plate (*e.g.*

1. Although the same can usually be said of CO_2 exchange above the canopy in most of the daylight hours, just the reverse occurs at night, or in the lower canopy by both day and night (see Fig. 13.4 for example). However, for a community as a whole, the 24 h mean flow of CO_2 as well as the net flow during the important daylight hours, will usually be downwards – unlike the flows of water vapour (virtually always upwards) or heat (under most circumstances upwards) – see again Fig. 13.4. Thus under some circumstances it may be deemed worthwhile to define C also as a downward flux. Then the negative sign will be omitted from equations such as (13.3a), and the difference in (13.3b) will be taken as the upper value minus the lower. In any case, the convention chosen should always be stated clearly and unambiguously.

Bradley 1968). Although no application of these techniques to CO_2 flux determination has been reported as yet, their use is to be encouraged, even if only to check the methods described below.

In the practical application of equation (13.18), the use of a common height interval for CO_2 and windspeed differences is a considerable advantage, as this does not demand any particular profile shape as long as the shape is the same in both cases over the range $z_1 - z_2$. Except well within an extremely homogeneous area, the two difference measurements should also be made at locations as close together horizontally as possible, without mutual interference between the sensors concerned. To obtain representative values may also require replication of measuring points, or the rotation or traversing of instrument booms at a single well-chosen location. (Of course, such remarks apply as well to the use of other tracers than momentum.)

13.3.2.2 | Determining τ or K_M from windspeed measurements

Till now the use of momentum as a CO_2 tracer has relied on calculation of τ or $\hat{K}_M$ from wind profile measurements. In either case one arrives at the same expression for C, which, under neutral or near-neutral conditions (see Section 13.6.7), has the generalised form,

$$C = \frac{\mathrm{k}^2 \, \Delta u}{\ln(z_2/z_1)\ln(z_4/z_3)} \, \Delta\rho_c$$

where k ($\approx$ 0.4) is the von Kármán constant (see Section 13.6.7), and Δu and $\Delta\rho_c$ are measured (in opposite senses) over height intervals $z_1 - z_2$ and $z_3 - z_4$ respectively. When, as is most usual, $z_3 = z_1$ and $z_4 = z_2$, this becomes

$$C = \left\{\frac{\mathrm{k}}{\ln\,(z_2/z_1)}\right\}^2 \Delta u \, \Delta\rho_c$$

$$= 1.5 \times 10^{-6} \, \rho_a \left\{\frac{\mathrm{k}}{\ln\,(z_2/z_1)}\right\}^2 \Delta u \, \Delta c \qquad (13.24)$$

Equation (13.24), with z replaced by $z - d$ to give the effective rather than the actual height (z itself being measured from the soil surface and d being the zero-plane displacement due to relatively still air entrapped by the lower foliage – see Section 13.6.7), was used by Inoue (1957) to calculate CO_2 exchange over a rice field, in the first micrometeorological studies of this kind. It has been used subsequently by Inoue *et al.* (1958), Lemon (1960, 1963) and Baumgartner (1969) in studies over wheat, corn and forest, respectively, and in modified forms by Monteith & Szeicz (1960) over sugar beet and Monteith (1962) over grass and beans.

An even better-known equivalent of this equation, formulated for determining evaporation rate, was first introduced by Thornthwaite & Holzman (1939). Its use presents much the same difficulties as those involved in use of equation (13.24), or other formulae based on it. These have been discussed in a number of places, *e.g.* Priestley (1959), Slatyer & McIlroy (1961), Webb (1965), and need not be detailed here.

One important problem, however, is the almost universal one of advection which can invalidate calculations of the surface flux from vertical concentration gradients, as pointed out in Section 13.3.1.1. This applies to calculations of fluxes of any kind, including those of heat, water vapour and CO_2, as well as momentum. Effects of advection in the context of energy transport are discussed in Section 13.3.3.10 and in regard to distortion of windspeed profiles in Section 13.6.8.

13.3.2.3 | Non-neutral atmospheric conditions

Another major problem is that a truly logarithmic change of windspeed with height, on which all these equations are premised, occurs only in an air layer of neutral stability, *i.e.* one in which the change of temperature with height is very small (see again Section 13.6.8). Except under cloudy skies or for short periods around sunrise and sunset, neutral stability is usually approached only very close to the ground, or in strong winds. During the day, in most circumstances, a temperature lapse develops above the radiatively heated crop or ground surface (*i.e.* temperature decreases significantly with height, as in Figs. 13.2 and 13.3), while the reverse, or a temperature inversion, occurs by night.

In these non-neutral conditions, corrections have to be made, or a different approach adopted, to account for thermal effects on the shape of the wind profile. The more important theories which have been developed for this purpose are discussed in reviews such as Slatyer & McIlroy (1961), Webb (1965) and others. So far, however, none has avoided some degree of arbitrariness or empiricism, and in all cases the necessary determination of the exact shape of the profile requires very accurate measurement of windspeed differences which are often quite small. The problem can be overcome to some extent by making measurements very close to the surface, where thermal effects are small relative to those due to wind-shear, as suggested by Pasquill (1949). This procedure brings its own difficulties, however, because small-scale surface heterogeneities can pose increasingly difficult sampling problems at lower heights; and where the formulae in use involve height itself, the necessarily more accurate determination of the zero-plane displacement can be extremely difficult.

In practice, the lowest measuring height cannot be below some limit set by the characteristics of the vegetation (Section 13.6.8). Any marked reduction in the uppermost height then cannot be accompanied by a corresponding reduction in the lowest, so that there is a shrinkage of the overall height ratio within which measurements are to be made. Satisfactory resolution of the smaller differences thus arising, both in windspeed and in CO_2 concentration, requires greater instrumental accuracy and care in mounting and exposure of instruments.

13.3.2.4 | Use of a low-level drag coefficient

Deacon & Swinbank (1958) proposed a compromise procedure which probably represents the best of the approaches *via* momentum. First of all the value of τ is determined from wind observations at reasonable heights, as described in Sections 13.6.7 and 13.6.8, during periods when neutral stability prevails up to these levels. This is then used, along with simultaneous observations of windspeed at a small reference height, z_1, to determine a drag coefficient $(C_D)_1$ defined (for the height z_1) by

$$\tau = (C_D)_1 \, \rho_a \, u_1^2.$$

Provided z_1 is low enough to lie always within the neutral region close to the surface, it can be shown that

$$(C_D)_1 = \left[k/\ln\left\{\frac{z_1 - d}{z_o}\right\}\right]^2 = f(z_1, d, z_o).$$

It should therefore be a constant for that particular height over a surface of constant characteristics. Subsequent to the empirical determination of $(C_D)_1$ (whether *via* τ and u_1 or *via* z_1, z_o and d – see Section 13.6.8), measurement of u_1 alone will then suffice to determine τ even when conditions above z_1 are far from neutral. Substitution for τ in equation (13.18) gives an equation used by Denmead (1968) for calculations of CO_2 exchange over a cornfield:

$$C = 1.5 \times 10^{-6} (C_D)_1 \, \rho_a \, u_1^2 \, \frac{\Delta c}{\Delta u}.$$

Here, for convenience, Δc and Δu are measured (again in opposite senses) between the same z_1 and another height which can be much greater, thus lessening the need

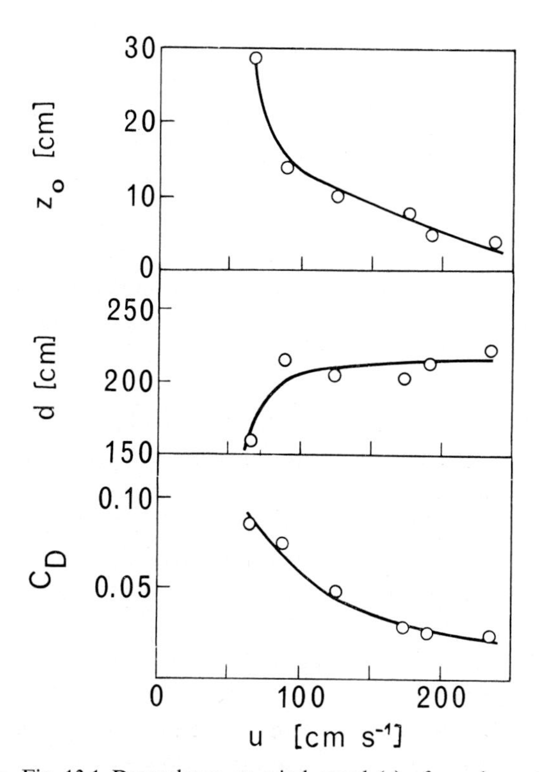

Fig. 13.1 Dependence on wind speed (u) of roughness height (z_o), zero-plane displacement (d) and drag coefficient C_D, for a corn crop 280 cm high. u and C_D measured at 310 cm. (From Denmead 1968.)

for instrumental accuracy in difference measurements. Neither height need be known, although z_1 (or strictly $z_1 - d$) must remain the same at all times.

The whole problem is aggravated when dealing with flexible vegetation that bends with the wind. Then d and z_o both change with windspeed, as demonstrated for a rice crop by Inoue (1963), and shown for a corn crop in Fig. 13.1. A fast-growing crop can also require the regular updating of these parameters, sometimes as frequently as several times a week (*e.g.* Rider 1954; Udagawa 1966).

Any of the above difficulties will invalidate all simple procedures for regularly deriving τ, $\hat{K}$ or C_D from a few low-level windspeed observations alone; and the further sharpening of already stringent accuracy requirements will often rule out the derivation of satisfactory corrections from periodic analyses of overall profile shape. Where suitable conditions do not occur frequently enough or over long enough periods for good neutral profiles to be recorded up to several metres height, the application of the profile method over a surface with changing d and z_o is virtually impossible.

In such cases, and wherever inadequate upwind fetch prevents the full establishment of a representative profile up to the highest measuring point (*cf.* Section 13.6.8), it is better to turn to independent methods of determining τ such as those mentioned earlier – or to the use of other tracers such as water vapour or energy, as discussed in the next section.

13.3.3 | Water vapour and energy transport

13.3.3.1 | General

Because of their connection *via* the energy balance, water vapour and energy exchanges are conveniently dealt with together.

For any CO_2 tracer other than momentum, the recommended procedure is the same as that outlined earlier for use of equations (13.17) or (13.16b) with F directly determined. Simultaneous measurements are made of the chosen flux, the corresponding concentration difference (or profile) over a suitable height interval, and the CO_2 concentration difference (or profile) over the same height interval. The measurements should be made well inside the crop area of interest and as close together as possible without mutual interference.

The obvious features which differ from one tracer to another are the types of sensing devices required for F and ϕ and their particular exposure requirements, and the most appropriate means of data handling. The susceptibility of each approach to breakdown in the underlying assumptions (such as flux constancy and transport-similarity) can also be important in many circumstances. All of these aspects must be looked at in assessing the relative merits of the various methods available.

Little needs to be said here about measuring techniques in themselves, since by now they are mostly well-known and details can be found in the literature. As well as the general references in Section 13.1, some more specific ones will be given in connection with the particular techniques mentioned below. Otherwise discussion will be limited mainly to a few features common to all methods, such as site, exposure and sampling problems, interpretation of results, *etc.*

13.3.3.2 | Water vapour as a tracer

The most obvious and readily employed tracer for CO_2 is water vapour. The flux concerned, the surface evaporation rate, E (or the associated latent heat flux LE, where L is the latent heat of vaporisation), is often of considerable interest and importance in the studies for which the CO_2 flux is required. It can also be determined in a number of ways, some of which have been in reliable use for many years. With methods such as lysimetry and eddy correlation, which are independent in themselves of gradients or differences, the vapour form of equation (13.17) is best utilised:

$$C = E \frac{\Delta \rho_c}{\rho_a \Delta q} = 1.5 \times 10^{-6} E \frac{\Delta c}{\Delta q} \tag{13.20a}$$

where C and E are in [g cm^{-2} s^{-1}], ρ_c and ρ_a in [g cm^{-3}], c in [vpm] and q in [g/g] – *cf.* Section 13.6.6.

As with the other equations below, units can be readily converted by means of factors in Section 13.7.2. Measurement of ρ_c or c is discussed in Chapters 3 and 4, and that of q (or related quantities such as vapour pressure, *etc.*) by Tanner (1963), Wexler (1965), Angus (1968b) and Slavík *et al.* (1972). Probably the method most used for q, and still the most reliable when properly carried out, is that employing fully ventilated and shielded dry- and wet-bulb thermometers (*e.g.* Collins 1965).

Apart from the more direct means mentioned earlier, E (or strictly LE) can also be arrived at by several indirect methods, involving measurements of energy exchange with or without gradients or differences of temperature and humidity (or wet-bulb temperature). The same is true for the sensible heat flux, H, which is itself usable as a CO_2 tracer (*cf.* Section 13.3.3.6).

Where the measurements required for the calculation of LE (or H) include or are capable of yielding Δq (or ΔT), they can be used immediately for determining C, without passing through the intermediate step of calculating an energy flux. However, because of the importance of evaporation as a factor in plant productivity, whenever such data are obtained it will generally be desirable to use them to determine E as well as C.

For this reason, and because the uses of water vapour, sensible heat and total energy as tracers of CO_2 transport involve very similar considerations, we discuss briefly the more important of the energy-based evaporation formulae in Sections 13.3.3.3 to 13.3.3.5. First, however, we have attempted to evaluate, in a pragmatic way, the many methods of all kinds available for measurement of E. Since these present a wide range of possibilities in design and construction of sensors, circuitry, recording requirements, exposure and sampling arrangements, and so on, we have tried to rate the methods with respect to the degree of accuracy and reliability in field operation which can be obtained for a reasonable expenditure of money and effort. On this basis, our broad assessment would be: weighed lysimetry (*e.g.* Pruitt & Angus 1960; Tanner 1960; McIlroy & Angus 1963; Denmead & McIlroy 1970), EPER (McIlroy 1971), energy-balance or Bowen-ratio (*e.g.* Tanner 1960; Fritschen 1966; Denmead & McIlroy 1970), eddy correlation (Section 13.2) or the combination methods of McIlroy & Angus (1964) or van Bavel (1966). Where longer term averages and a low level of accuracy can be tolerated, it is sometimes possible to estimate evaporation with pans or atmometers *via* a carefully established and locally relevant correlation (*e.g.* McIlroy & Angus 1964).

13.3.3.3 | Energy balance

When evaporation has been measured through energy considerations, the proportional form for latent heat can be used,

$$C = 6.2 \times 10^{-13} LE \frac{\Delta c}{\Delta q}. \tag{13.20b}$$

Here, as in equation (13.20a), with both C and E defined as positive upwards, Δc and Δq are measured in the same sense. LE [mW cm^{-2}] can be obtained as a residual *via* the fundamental equation of surface energy balance (*cf.* equation (13.13a) of Section 13.6.5), written for present purposes as

$$LE = R - G - H + \epsilon C. \tag{13.13b}$$

Here, R, G and H are respectively the net radiation absorbed by the surface, the ground heat flux or rate of heat storage in the soil and vegetation, and the sensible heat flux into the atmosphere (always in the same units as LE). They should be measured independently of each other, preferably R by net radiometer (Suomi, Franssila & Islitzer 1954; Möriköfer 1958; Funk 1959; Angus 1968a) and G by soil heat-flux plates (*e.g.* Deacon 1950; Monteith 1958; Fuchs & Tanner 1967) plus a correction where necessary for the usually small amount of heat taken up by the vegetation and top layer of soil, above the depth of installation of the heat-flux plates, *e.g.* by forming the product of an average thermal capacity for the depth of soil or vegetation involved and the rate of change of its average temperature. At the moment, H can be measured independently only by eddy correlation (*e.g.* Dyer, Hicks & King 1967; Inoue *et al.* 1969), subject even then to the serious limitations described in Section 13.2. Further development of devices such as infra-red radiation thermometers might open up the possibility of determining H in some circumstances *via* simple air and surface temperature measurements, combined with transfer coefficients empirically related to windspeed at a single reference height. Such an approach has been used successfully by Fuchs *et al.* (1969) to measure H over a drying soil surface. The extension to vegetation is likely to prove more difficult, particularly with tall crops, because then the sources and sinks of heat are distributed throughout the canopy, as seen in Fig. 13.4, and there is no clearly defined surface of exchange between the vegetation and the free atmosphere.

The minor term ϵC [with $\epsilon(\approx 10^7$ mW s g^{-1}) the average energy requirement for photosynthetic fixation of CO_2] is often neglected, but for crops with high rates of CO_2 fixation (a value of $|\epsilon C|$ of as much as $0.14R$ has been reported for corn by Lemon 1960, for instance) a correction should be made – even if only through an estimate of C[1] (Section 13.3.3.8). Note that C will generally be negative in the daylight hours.

13.3.3.4 | Bowen-ratio

Where conditions are such that the similarity assumption can safely be made (*i.e.* that $K_H = K_W$, see discussion later), it is no longer necessary to undertake the generally difficult separate measurement of H or LE. Instead a measurement of $R - G$, corrected for ϵC when necessary, gives their sum, $H + LE$, which is then divided between the two components according to their ratio, $B (= H/LE)$. Known as the Bowen-ratio, B is taken as equal to the ratio of the corresponding concentration differences. In effect

$$B = \frac{c_p}{L} \frac{\Delta T}{\Delta q} \approx \gamma \frac{\Delta T}{\Delta q}$$

where γ ($\approx 4.2 \times 10^{-4}$ g/g per °C $\approx c_p/L$) is the psychrometric constant in terms of specific humidity. We can then say

$$LE = \frac{R - G}{1 + B}$$

or

$$H = \frac{B(R - G)}{1 + B}$$

The former of these is well-known as the energy balance or heat budget approach, but is probably better described as the Bowen-ratio method, to avoid confusion with direct use of Eq. (13.13). It has been employed successfully for evaporation measurement by many workers, and as a step towards determining CO_2 flux by Denmead (1968) and Inoue *et al.* (1968).

13.3.3.5 | EPER

Alternative formulations for sensible and latent heat exchange can be made in terms of the wet-bulb temperature, T_w, rather than specific humidity, q (Slatyer & McIlroy 1961; McIlroy 1968). These lead to expressions analogous to equation (13.21) of Section 13.3.3.7 below, *i.e.* they use total energy as a tracer for sensible or latent heat and modified wet-bulb temperature as an index of energy concentration – *cf.* Section 13.6.5. Like equation (13.21), they involve quantities which can be measured with relative ease.

1. In principle ϵC could itself be found from Eq.(13.13) with all other quantities measured, and could then be used to give C; but in practice this would require excessive precision in the values used for the other fluxes.

$$H = (R - G)\left\{\frac{\gamma}{s + \gamma}\right\}\frac{\Delta T}{\Delta T_w}.$$

$$LE = (R - G)\left[1 - \left\{\frac{\gamma}{s + \gamma}\right\}\frac{\Delta T}{\Delta T_w}\right].$$

(The factor s is defined on p.502, and $\frac{\gamma}{s + \gamma}$ tabulated on p.513.).

Where wet-bulb thermometry is employed as the means of arriving at humidity, these formulae permit simpler calculations than those of the Bowen-ratio approach. The second of them forms the basis of an Energy Partition Evaporation Recorder (EPER), recently developed to give a continuous automatic record of evaporation (McIlroy 1971). A pilot model of EPER has recently been used with some success in evaluating the evaporation rate, and thence, *via* Eq. (13.20a), the CO_2 flux, from a barley crop (McIlroy *et al.*, unpublished). EPER is now undergoing further development, leading, if a suitable type of CO_2 sensor can be found, to the automation of equation (13.21) below.

13.3.3.6 | Sensible heat as a tracer

Of course, H itself can be used as a tracer flux by means of the sensible heat form of Eq. (13.17),

$$C = \frac{H}{\rho_a c_p}\frac{\Delta\rho_c}{\Delta T} = 1.5 \times 10^{-9} H \frac{\Delta c}{\Delta T} \qquad (13.19)$$

with H in [mW cm^{-2}], $c_p = 10^3$ mW s g^{-1} (°C)$^{-1}$, T in [°C], and other units as for Eqs. (13.20a or b) earlier. In this case, the rather simpler determination of ΔT replaces that of Δq. H can be derived either directly by eddy correlation as mentioned in Section 13.3.3.3, or indirectly as a residual in the energy balance equation or *via* the Bowen-ratio or EPER methods.

13.3.3.7 | Total energy as a tracer

If suitable equipment is available to provide simultaneous measurements of H and LE, their sum can be used as a tracer flux. However, as noted in Section 13.3.3.4, this same flux of total energy can generally be measured more easily and reliably as the difference between R and G (strictly, corrected for ϵC). The appropriate 'concentration' difference will be either ΔT_w alone, or ΔT and Δq combined to give ΔT_e (where T_e is equivalent temperature – see Section 13.6.5). Equation (13.17) then becomes:

$$C = \frac{\dfrac{H + LE}{\rho_a c_p} \text{ or } \dfrac{R - G}{\rho_a c_p}}{\Delta T_e \text{ or } \dfrac{s + \gamma}{\gamma}\Delta T_w} \times (\Delta\rho_c \text{ or } 1.5 \times 10^{-6}\,\rho_a\,\Delta c). \qquad (13.21)$$

 The preferred form of Eq. (13.21), viz.

$$C = 1.5 \times 10^{-9} (R - G) \left\{ \frac{\gamma}{s + \gamma} \right\} \frac{\Delta c}{\Delta T_w}, \tag{13.21b}$$

with a rough correction for net photosynthetic energy as outlined below, has been used recently to calculate CO_2 exchange over barley (Attiwill *et al.*, unpublished). It gave good results by comparison with equation (13.20a) involving Δq measured by dry- and wet-bulbpsychrometry and E by both a sensitive weighed lysimeter and the EPER approach of Section 13.3.3.5. Other variants of equation (13.21), differing mainly in the units employed, have been used by Denmead (1968) over wheat and Inoue *et al.* (1968) over corn.

13.3.3.8 | Correcting for energy of assimilation

A similar formulation incorporating a complete correction for ϵC has been developed by Denmead (1969a), who used it in studies over a pine forest and wheat. In our present terminology, this becomes:

$$C = \frac{(R - G)\Delta\rho_c}{\rho_a c_p \Delta T_e - \epsilon\Delta\rho_c} = \frac{1.5 \times 10^{-9}(R - G)\Delta c}{\Delta T_e - 1.5 \times 10^{-2} \Delta c} \tag{13.21c}$$

or

$$C = \frac{(R - G)\Delta\rho_c}{\rho_a c_p \Delta T_w \left\{ \frac{s + \gamma}{\gamma} \right\} - \epsilon\Delta\rho_c} = \frac{1.5 \times 10^{-9} (R - G) \Delta c}{\left\{ \frac{s + \gamma}{\gamma} \right\} \Delta T_w - 1.5 \times 10^{-2} \Delta c}. \tag{13.21d}$$

The value calculated by equations (13.21a) or (13.21b) will overestimate the true C given by Eqs. (13.21c) or (13.21d). The true value can be obtained by multiplying the former by the factor $[1 + \epsilon C/(R - G)]$. The correction will rarely exceed 10%. If equation (13.21a) or (13.21b) is used, a rounded average of the correction factor can be found for a few typical occasions during the period of measurement. A single correction factor may suffice for lengthy periods, as found by Attiwill *et al.* (unpublished), or it may be necessary to vary the factor throughout.

13.3.3.9 | Multiple method checking

It is evident that if any two of the fluxes H, LE or $(R - G)$ are measured *independently*, C can be calculated by any pair of equations from (13.19), (13.20) and (13.21) - with appropriate measurements of Δc, ΔT and either ΔT_w or Δq over the same height interval. This permits checks of both the quality of the primary measurements, and the similarity assumption, since one can compare $\hat{K}_H$ and $\hat{K}_W$ over the same air layer. If these latter agree with one another, then it is probable that they will agree with $\hat{K}_C$ also.
Of course, measurement of Δc is unnecessary to test equality between $\hat{K}_H$ and $\hat{K}_W$. Denmead & McIlroy (1970), for instance, were able to make such a test by comparing E measured both by lysimetry and the Bowen-ratio method. The agreement found in this case gave some confidence in concurrent measurements of CO_2 exchange over wheat, reported by Denmead (1968, 1969a), which used total energy as a tracer. Likewise, McIlroy *et al.* (unpublished) established good agree-

ment between measurements of E by lysimetry and by the EPER method in conjunction with the studies of CO_2 exchange over barley by Attiwill *et al.* mentioned earlier. As described in Section 13.3.1.3, a partial test of the similarity assumption can also be made, without knowledge of fluxes themselves, if measurements of c, T, *etc.* have been made at more than two heights. Then one can compare ratios of the type $(c_1 - c_2)/(c_1 - c_3)$, $(T_1 - T_2)/(T_1 - T_3)$ and so on, for the entities of interest. Departure from equality will indicate either non-constancy with height of the fluxes, or disparity between the various transport coefficients. Denmead (1969b), for instance, has used such a test as partial evidence for equality between K_C and K_H, K_W and K_M over a grass sward.

Unfortunately, experiments where the scope of the measurements is sufficient for such self-checking are all too rare. Apart from the recent work just referred to, Monteith & Szeicz (1960) used measurements of both evaporation and total energy to infer certain parameters of the wind profile for use of the momentum transfer method of Section 13.3.2.2. Wright & Brown (1967) on the other hand, found quite large discrepancies between K_M calculated from an assumption of a logarithmic wind profile and K calculated from energy balance measurements. In fact, similar anomalies, apparently in K_M, were found by McIlroy *et al.* (unpublished).

13.3.3.10 | Advection error

Where $\hat{K}_H$ and $\hat{K}_W$ are found to differ, the reason may lie in a breakdown under non-neutral conditions of the assumption of equal effectiveness of turbulent transfer for heat and water vapour. On the other hand, at reasonable measuring heights it is more likely that the similarity assumption remains valid, but that advection from upwind surfaces differing from the one underlying the instruments is invalidating our other main assumption of flux-constancy with height (Section 13.3.1.1).[1]

The usual problem here is one of external advection from regions outside the particular area under study, which arises when the latter's upwind edge is too close to the measuring point. Air passing this point may not yet have become modified sufficiently, from an original state characteristic of the upwind region towards a new state corresponding to the surface being studied.

The resulting distortion in profile shape is more easily detected than the associated variation in flux. Particularly marked examples can be seen in the observations of Fig. 13.2, although these were taken at a point 350 m inside a uniform field. Even when not as obvious as this, such distortions can make nonsense of quantities derived from gradients or differences measured wholly or partially within the disturbed region. This applies also to τ, $\hat{K}_M$ or C_D, of Section 13.3.2.

It should be noted that advective distortions in the profile of one quantity do not necessarily resemble those of another. In general, non-neutral conditions would be expected to distort profiles of c and q from logarithmic shapes in about the same way, and measuring Δc and Δq over the same height interval would normally

1. Unless any variation with height is the same for H and LE, which is generally unlikely, it will contribute differently to the weighting of the respective average transfer coefficients for an air layer, even though the similarity assumption applies at any particular height within the layer – *cf.* Section 13.6.2.

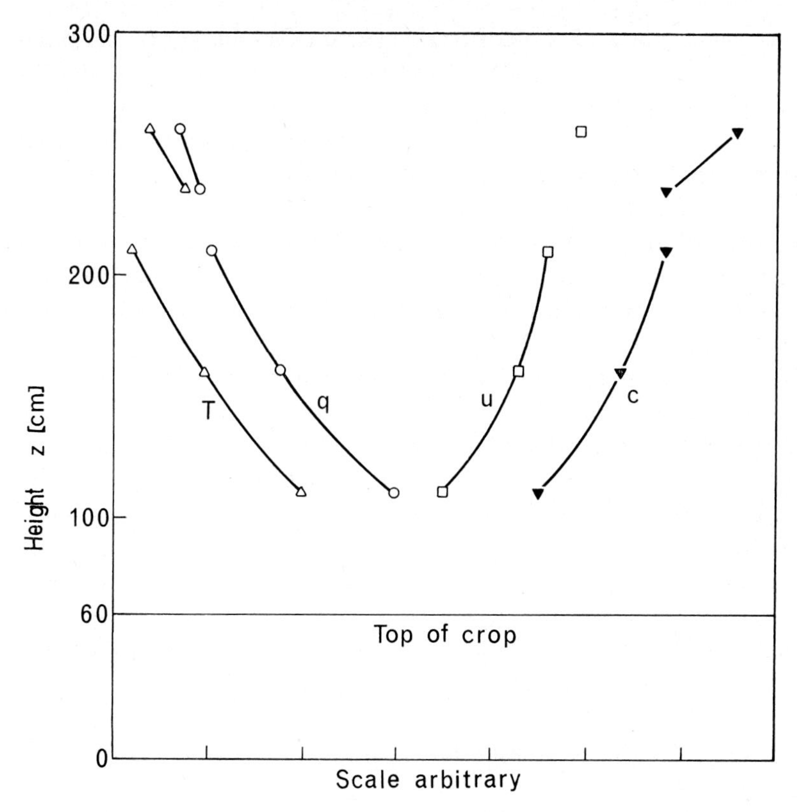

Fig. 13.2 Profiles of temperature (T), specific humidity (q), wind speed (u), and CO_2 concentration (c) over a wheat field at 350 m downwind of the edge of the field. Vegetation at upwind edge consisted of trees up to 15 m high.

ensure reasonable freedom in equations (13.20) from these effects; but this precaution will usually not overcome the effects of distortions due to non-uniform fetch.

To avoid these, at least the upper of the measuring heights must be reduced[1].

1. The steady-state transfer of an entity in the adjustment region downwind of a change in surface types is simply described by the two-dimensional equation:

$$u \frac{\partial \phi}{\partial x} = - \frac{\partial F}{\partial z} = \frac{\partial}{\partial z} \left[K_{\Phi} \frac{\partial \phi}{\partial z} \right],$$

where x is distance downwind from the boundary between the surfaces and the other symbols are as before. Solutions of this equation for the concentration ϕ and the flux F at points (x, z) downwind are given by a number of authors including Philip (1959) and Rider, Philip & Bradley (1963). Profile adjustment of both concentrations and fluxes is most rapid near the surface, and the height of the modified layer increases with distance downwind. At large downwind distances, changes in ϕ with x become very small up to heights of several metres, so that in the normal range of measuring heights, the term $\partial F/\partial z$ approaches zero and to a good enough approximation F can be regarded as constant with height.

Dyer (1963) has used Philip's solutions to establish criteria for the extent of profile distortion due to advective modification, and some practical means for reducing errors due to advective effects are discussed in this Section and Section 13.6.8.

This will also help to reduce occasional anomalies due to extreme effects of buoyancy, arising in conditions of strong atmospheric stability or instability – as these always diminish close to the ground.
Irrespective of its surroundings, where the surface of interest is itself heterogeneous or of irregular height, a smaller-scale internal advection can arise. To overcome this the remedy is just the opposite, in so far as the instruments must be high enough to avoid any strong local influences just upwind of them. Thus a compromise will often be necessary. It is not always easy to distinguish between the three types of anomaly, due to external or internal advection, or to excessive departures from neutral stability. Nevertheless, changing instrument height by trial-and-error, or relating the strength of the anomaly at various times to the corresponding wind direction and/or atmospheric stability, will usually indicate where the remedy lies. Where satisfactory agreement between the transport coefficients cannot be achieved by suitable selection of sampling height, the measuring site should be changed or replicated, or else the instruments should be automatically traversed or repeatedly moved around. In many cases it will be found that an instrumental accuracy which is adequate for greater heights may fail to resolve the smaller concentration differences encountered if the measuring height ratio has to be reduced. The only solution then is to improve the instrumentation itself, and/or the standard of its calibration and maintenance.

13.4 | Measurements inside the canopy

13.4.1 | General

13.4.1.1 | Rationale

While the net exchanges of CO_2 and other entities between the atmosphere and an entire community of plants are useful indications of crop activity, a full appreciation of community behaviour requires knowledge of the distribution of exchange rates through the depth of the canopy. Such detailed information is necessary, for instance, in reconciling field behaviour with the results of experiments on the physiology of individual plant parts in controlled environments, and in many facets of modelling gas and energy exchange in the field, *e.g.* in relating photosynthesis and transpiration to theories of radiation penetration.
Here the aim is to establish the flux as a function of height in the canopy, *i.e.* the flux profile $F(z)$ – see, for instance, Fig. 13.4, and the source- or sink-strengths at height z, *i.e.* the flux divergence $\partial F/\partial z$. The flux at $z = 0$, is, of course, the soil contribution, F_o. In the case of CO_2 exchange, this value C_o must be added to or subtracted from the gain or loss of CO_2 at the top of the canopy, determined by the methods of earlier Sections, in order to obtain the total photosynthesis or respiration of the foliage. An indication of the relative amounts of CO_2 supplied by atmosphere and soil in a field crop is provided by Fig. 13.4. In this case, C_o was about a third of the total uptake of CO_2. Estimation of C_o is discussed in Section 13.4.5. The flux divergence, when divided by the foliage area density α, defined as half the total area of foliage surface per unit volume of space, yields the local foliage exchange rate at height z.

13.4.1.2 | Height–dependence of flux

The very fact that the flux changes with height makes the measurement problem much more difficult than that of forming above-canopy estimates of the flux. Whereas above the canopy, one can work with finite difference equations of the form of equation (13.17), or use several paired observations to form a smoothed average of $\partial \rho_c / \partial \phi$, measurements of the CO_2 flux profile inside the canopy require that either $\partial \rho_c / \partial \phi$ itself, or alternatively $\partial \rho_c / \partial z$ and $\partial \phi / \partial z$ separately, be well-defined at each point at which a flux estimate is needed. This requires many sampling points and accurate measurements of the concentration profiles.
As with similarity approaches above the canopy, it is assumed of necessity that the flux-gradient relationship of equation (13.1a) still applies at any particular height within the crop. Although the fluxes and transport coefficients that have been inferred in this way have generally been consistent with those derived from simultaneous observations above the canopy, as in Figs. 13.3 and 13.4, for instance, it must be acknowledged that there are still many unanswered questions about the mechanisms of transfer in the air layers occupied by vegetation, particularly in respect to the role of mass flow (discussed briefly in Section 13.2.2 and more fully by Lemon 1969).

13.4.1.3 | Sources and sinks

Assessing source- and sink-strengths, *i.e.* forming $\partial F / \partial z$, involves differentiating the concentration profiles a second time. The first differentiation (to establish F) is already an error-prone procedure, and another differentiation of the derived data presents even more problems. The final step, forming the local foliage exchange rates, requires a knowledge of foliage area density as a function of height. This measurement, discussed in Chapter 10, is subject to considerable sampling error and so introduces further uncertainty into the calculations. Thus, within-canopy estimates are inherently more unreliable than those above the canopy. An attempt is made later to assess likely errors.

13.4.1.4 | Crop heterogeneity

Yet another complication is that the only analytical approach available so far has been one-dimensional (vertical). It is assumed that the foliage area density, and the corresponding concentrations and fluxes, are uniform in the horizontal. Obviously this is far from true in any field crop, the more so as the spacing between plants increases. Even within dense crops of nearly uniform height and foliage distribution, the sampling problem is large and special efforts must be made to overcome problems associated with horizontal heterogeneity.
So far only momentum and total energy have been used as natural CO_2 tracers. These approaches are discussed in Sections 13.4.2 and 13.4.3 and their main limitations in 13.4.4. Problems of flux estimation at the ground surface are considered in Section 13.4.5. Currently there is interest in the feasibility of using other tracers, and some recent developments in this field are mentioned briefly in Section 13.4.6.

13.4.2 | Momentum transport

13.4.2.1 | Direct determination of τ

The differential form of equation (13.18) for measurements at a given point inside the canopy is

$$C = -\frac{\tau}{\rho_a(\partial u/\partial z)}\frac{\partial \rho_c}{\partial z} = -1.5 \times 10^{-6}\,\tau\,\frac{\partial c/\partial z}{\partial u/\partial z}. \tag{13.18a}$$

Direct determination of τ is difficult. Whereas above the canopy it can often be inferred without excessive error from an assumed functional form for the wind profile, no simple assumptions about profile shape can be made inside the canopy. Wright & Lemon (1966a, b) used an approximate eddy-correlation technique but found that their within-canopy estimates, although consistent within themselves, appeared to be an order of magnitude too large. The discrepancy appeared to be due to unsuitable instrumentation, incorrect assumptions about the isotropy of the turbulence, and perhaps to the effects of a significant mass-flow.
Successful application of eddy correlation techniques inside the canopy poses a difficult problem. Not only do the instruments have to be of small size to avoid disturbance to the foliage, but also their readings will depend very much on positioning with respect to gaps, foliage elements, inter-row spaces and so on. There is also the possibility of large vertical mean air flows existing in gaps between individual plants, as surmised by Allen (1968a) in his observations of turbulence in a tree plantation. The contributions of these air flows to momentum transport will not be accounted for by eddy correlation techniques, as noted in Section 13.2.2. Other problems which may invalidate the use of eddy correlation techniques, or indeed the use of equation (13.18a) or (13.21a), can arise when there is lateral, rather than vertical, transport within the canopy. This situation is likely to occur when foliage does not extend all the way to the ground, as in many forests, or where there are wide inter-row spaces. The reader is referred to Lemon (1969) for a fuller discussion.

13.4.2.2 | Indirect estimation of τ

Lemon (1967, 1969), Perrier (1967), Wright & Brown (1967) and Lemon & Wright (1969) describe an indirect approach in which the momentum flux at the top of the canopy is related to the loss of momentum at foliage surfaces *via* a foliage drag coefficient. It is assumed that the change in the momentum flux with height (*i.e.* the momentum sink-strength) is given by:

$$\partial\tau/\partial z = \rho_a\, C_f\, \alpha\, u^2,$$

in which C_f is the drag coefficient of the foliage elements and α, as before, is the foliage area density. Assuming that C_f is independent of height and wind speed, and the canopy is so dense that momentum transfer at the ground surface is negligible,

$$C_f = \tau_h / \rho_a \int_0^h \alpha\, u^2 \, dz$$

in which h is the height of the canopy top. These equations then lead to

$$\tau_z = \tau_h \left\{ 1 - \int_z^h \alpha\, u^2 \, dz \Big/ \int_0^h \alpha\, u^2 \, dz \right\}.$$

Lemon (1969) discusses the assumptions underlying the technique. The measurements necessary for its application are: an estimate of τ_h from appropriate measurements above the canopy; the within-canopy wind profile; and the vertical distribution of foliage area density, as well as the CO_2 concentration profile. Obviously measurement of representative wind profiles in the canopy presents a difficult sampling problem, both in terms of the numbers of instruments required and their physical size. Most of the other difficulties mentioned in the previous section in connection with the determination of τ by eddy correlation techniques apply to this approach also.

13.4.3 | Energy transport

13.4.3.1 | General

The differential form of equation (13.21a) is:

$$C = \frac{R - G}{\rho_a \, c_p (\partial T_e / \partial z)} \frac{\partial \rho_c}{\partial z} = 1.5 \times 10^{-9} (R - G) \frac{\partial c / \partial z}{\partial T_e / \partial z}. \qquad (13.21e)$$

As shown in Section 13.3.3, a similar formulation involving the wet-bulb temperature can also be made. Equation (13.21e) has been used by Denmead (1968, 1970) in studies of CO_2 exchange in a wheat crop, by Inoue *et al.* (1968) in a corn crop and Baumgartner (1969) in a forest.
Examples of the primary measurements necessary for application of the equation are contained in Figs. 13.3 and 13.4. Values of the transport coefficients inferred from these measurements are also shown in Fig. 13.3. Here,

$$K = -(R - G) \Big/ \left[\rho_a \, c_p \frac{\partial T_e}{\partial z} \right].$$

The flux profile of CO_2 calculated from the measurements of Fig. 13.3 by equations (13.21e) within the canopy and (13.21a) above it, and those of sensible and latent heat by the appropriate analogues of these equations, are shown in Fig. 13.4.
The main problems in measurement are those associated with obtaining proper spatial averages, at a sufficient number of heights, of the CO_2 concentration, the net radiation and the equivalent or wet-bulb temperature. This requires an elaborate distribution of instruments, generally of special design (see below for

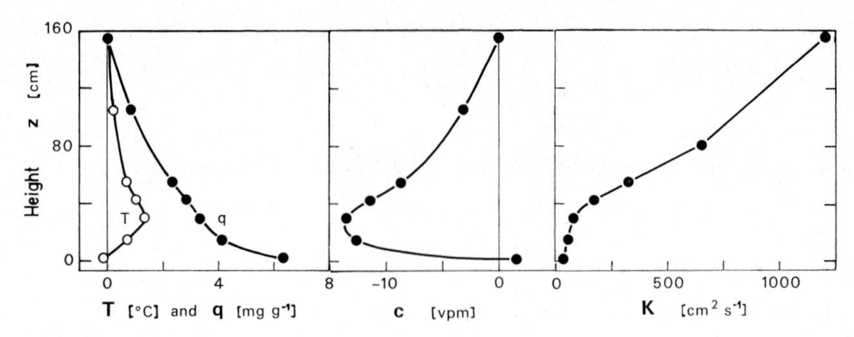

Fig. 13.3 Distribution with height z of temperature T, specific humidity q, CO_2 concentration c, and transport coefficients K in and above a wheat crop 81 cm high. Measurements are means for the period 12.00–12.30 on October 14, 1968 at Deniliquin, Australia. Leaf area index of the crop was 3.2. T, q and c at 155 cm were respectively: 22.6°C, 5.7 mg g^{-1} and 266 vpm.

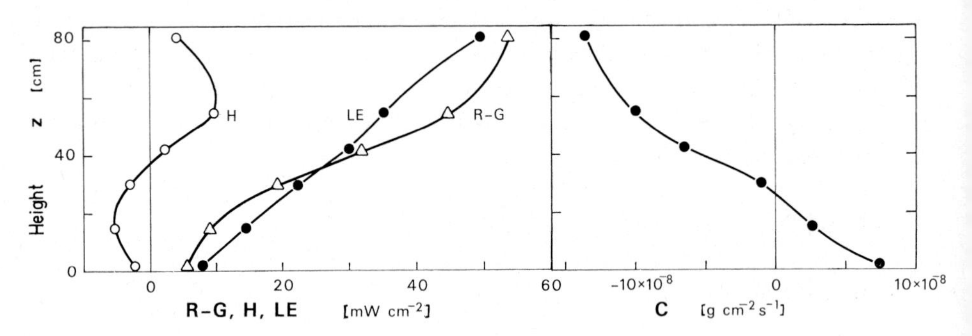

Fig. 13.4 Distribution with height z of net radiation less soil heat flux $R - G$, and fluxes of sensible heat H, latent heat LE and carbon dioxide C calculated from the observations of Fig. 13.3. Fluxes at the top of the canopy were calculated by equation (13.21a) and its analogues for sensible and latent heat; those within it by equation (13.21e) and its analogues.

examples). On the other hand, the data thus obtained provide a useful background for explaining or modelling the details of other exchange processes, in addition to those involving CO_2, which are intimately related to plant production in the field. A concrete illustration is provided by studies of the simultaneous exchanges of heat, water vapour and CO_2 in a wheat crop by Denmead (1970).

13.4.3.2 | Spatial sampling

To overcome point-to-point variation in the radiation climate various devices such as traversing net radiometers (*e.g.* Brown & Covey 1966; Wright & Brown 1967) and strip net radiometers (*e.g.* Denmead 1967) have been used. Radiation measurement inside a crop is discussed in Chapter 12.

Measurements of temperature, humidity and CO_2 concentration in the canopy also require suitable averaging techniques. A convenient arrangement is to employ extended sampling arms along which air temperature is measured with aspirated thermometers at a number of points. The bulked air stream from each level is drawn by tube to a central measuring point where its humidity and CO_2 concentration are determined. When condensation is likely to be a problem, heating devices, such as wires or tapes along the tube, may be necessary. The system not only permits economies in the numbers of humidity and CO_2 sensors required but also provides a useful smoothing of the record since the local fluctuations in water vapour and CO_2 concentration are not only averaged along the length of each sampling arm but also damped by the passage of the air stream along the tube (Philip 1963). Figure 13.5 shows equipment designed for this purpose.

Fig. 13.5 Sampling array used to obtain spatial averages of temperature, humidity and CO_2 concentration. Air is drawn into each sampling arm over radiation-shielded thermometers (5 platinum resistance thermometers at each level) which measure its dry-bulb temperature, and thence by tube to mobile laboratory for measurement of humidity and CO_2 concentration by psychrometry and infra-red analysis. In this array there are eight sampling arms, three above and five within the crop. The most common fetch is to the left foreground.

A difficulty with any aspirated system is that it introduces into the canopy an artificial sink for air. Errors in measurement associated with the withdrawal of air are difficult to determine. Towards the top of the canopy, where windspeeds are several times the aspiration rates normally employed, the effects of withdrawal are probably small; but they undoubtedly become larger near the ground, where aspiration rates may be of the same magnitude as the natural air movement.

13.4.3.3 | Time sampling

A further complication arises from the flow system usually employed in CO_2 measurement by infra-red gas analysis (the most common method used to date). To obtain the resolution required in profile analysis, most such instruments are operated 'differentially' so as to compare air from the sampling level directly with air from a reference level, and absorption tubes of large volume are employed. At typical flow rates, a time of about a minute is required to flush the sample cell and obtain a steady difference signal after each change of sample. Thus, it may take several minutes to scan a profile, during which time the CO_2 concentration of air at any level may not remain constant. This may be due to low frequency eddies in the canopy (*e.g.* Lemon 1969; Lemon, Wright & Drake 1969), or to rapid changes in ambient CO_2 concentrations in the early morning or late afternoon (*e.g.* Allen 1968b; Denmead 1968). In these circumstances it may be desirable to store the air from all levels during a 'run' of say 20 or 30 min and perform the CO_2 analyses while air from the next 'run' is being collected and stored. A flow system employing this principle has been described by Lourence & Pruitt (1967).
With other instruments, such as the conductimetric gas analyser described in Section 4.1, such difficulties may not arise, because measurements of concentrations at all levels are available continuously and the profile can be scanned as rapidly as electrical switching will allow.

13.4.4 | Limitations and errors

13.4.4.1 | General

To assess the relative merits of approaches relying on momentum or energy transfer is difficult. The momentum transfer approach, as it has been applied to date, requires a number of assumptions about the relation between drag coefficients, foliage geometry and wind speed. No such assumptions are necessary for the energy balance approach. However, both methods rely on similarity assumptions. Since wind speeds are lower and lapses and inversions usually very much steeper than in the air layers above the stand, departures from neutrality may be much more extreme and similarity may not always hold. In addition, as discussed previously, both approaches assume one dimensional (*i.e.* only vertical) transport, which may not always apply. Further, non-constancy of flux with height invalidates finite-difference approximations to the true local values required for the concentration gradients (*cf.* Section 13.6.2), unless the height intervals concerned are kept very small.

In the only direct comparison which has been made of the two methods, that of

Wright & Brown (1967), estimates of transport coefficients at the same levels in the canopy differed by a factor of about 2 (the energy balance estimates being higher). However, the normalised profiles of the transport coefficients, *i.e.* $(K_\Phi)_z/(K_\Phi)_h$ for both momentum and total energy, were quite similar.

13.4.4.2 | Finite-difference approximations

Very often, limitations of space and equipment will make it difficult to obtain sufficient observations in the canopy to determine *local* concentration gradients accurately. Denmead (1968) has attempted an analysis of errors in energy balance estimates of C, which would be introduced by approximating the gradients of temperature, humidity and CO_2 concentration at the mid-point of a layer of depth Δz by the ratios $\Delta T/\Delta z$, $\Delta q/\Delta z$ and $\Delta c/\Delta z$. (ΔT, Δq and Δc are the differences in T, q and c between top and bottom of the layer.) The analysis indicated that the finite-difference estimate of C was likely to be within 10% of the true value at the mid-point of a layer across which the fluxes and the transport coefficient changed by a factor of less than 2. Based on most published data, these criteria would usually be met in practice by restricting the height interval to one in which leaf area index changed by about 0.5.

13.4.4.3 | Overall error estimates

More recently, M. G. Groom and E. R. Lemon (unpublished data 1968) have taken into account both instrumental and computational errors in the application of the energy balance method. They examined a number of typical 30-min 'runs' in a corn crop 220 cm high.

Estimates were made of uncertainties arising from instrumental limitations, the loss of accuracy in transposing data from field records to drawings and computer cards, fitting the observed profiles with smooth curves, and differentiating the fitted curves. The resulting uncertainties in the estimate of the CO_2 flux were then calculated for different runs. The absolute errors varied from level to level, but at any one level were about the same at all times of day. Typical errors at 60 cm were about $\pm$ 50% of the maximum flux calculated for that level; at 120 cm, about $\pm$ 20%; and at 180 cm, about $\pm$ 12%.

In assessing the present state of the art, it seems fair to assert that instrumental and computational errors can easily be about 20% of the calculated flux value in the best of circumstances. Departures from the basic assumptions underlying the techniques will of course inflate the overall errors. We have pointed out previously that estimates of the local exchange rates of CO_2 per unit area of foliage involve still more uncertainty. It is difficult to set a figure here, but a reasonable expectation would be for errors of at least 30% and usually more.

13.4.5 | Flux of CO_2 at the ground surface

The possible magnitude of soil respiration has already been indicated in Section 13.1.1. Obviously, the accuracy of its determination can have an important bearing on the overall accuracy of estimates of the total uptake or release of CO_2 by the crop. Unfortunately, its measurement is one of the weaker points in the determination of CO_2 exchange in the field.

13.4.5.1 | Micrometeorological measurements

The structure of some crops may be such that there is an air-layer next to the ground, in which the foliage is so sparse that the fluxes of radiation, heat, water vapour and CO_2 can be considered almost constant with height. If the layer is deep enough to mount within it two sets of sensors at different heights, the finite difference methods of Section 13.3.3 can be applied to the data from the layer to give a reasonable estimate of CO_2 flux at the soil surface.
In other situations, there may be a zone of dead foliage next to the ground, in which the fluxes of CO_2 and water vapour are virtually constant with height, but not those of radiation or sensible heat. Then, provided the layer is deep enough, the differential approach described in Section 13.4.3 can be applied, with some confidence that the flux of CO_2 calculated within the layer represents that from the soil surface. However, because transport coefficients will normally be small in such a zone, concentrations will usually change rapidly with height and gradients will be difficult to define with precision. Therefore these estimates will usually be less reliable than those obtained in the situation described in the preceding paragraph.
Often, the presence of live foliage close to the ground and the physical size of the sensors required will preclude the possibility of obtaining sufficient measurements to apply either of the procedures described above. Then, one is obliged to extrapolate the flux profile to the ground surface or the bottom of the vegetation. This has generally proved to be unsatisfactory.

13.4.5.2 | Other approaches

Unfortunately, alternative methods of measurement leave something to be desired. Monteith, Szeicz & Yabuki (1964) describe a variant of a method employed by Lundegårdh (1927) in which CO_2 is allowed to diffuse from the soil into a closed container placed on the surface. Lundegårdh measured the change in the concentration of CO_2 within the container over periods of 10–20 min, from which he calculated the rate of evolution from the soil. The method assumes that the surface flux is not affected by changes in CO_2 concentration in the container and that the mechanism of transport of CO_2 away from the surface does not affect the rate of CO_2 evolution, *i.e.* that the rate of CO_2 evolution is controlled only by the rates of CO_2 production and molecular diffusion in the soil. However, the work of Farrell, Greacen & Gurr (1966) suggests that this technique could reduce gaseous diffusion considerably below that occurring in the natural field situation. They estimated that fluctuations in atmospheric pressure at the soil surface, induced by turbulence, could increase the effective diffusion coefficient for gases within the surface layers of the soil by as much as 100 times molecular diffusion. In addition, the presence of the container at the surface can be expected to change the temperature and water status of the soil below it, and through them, the rate of CO_2 production. The effects of an excessively high concentration of CO_2 in the container on the CO_2 flux were overcome by Monteith, Szeicz & Yabuki (1964) who kept the concentration low through continuous chemical absorption. The flux was calculated from the changes in weight or chemical composition of the absorbent. Without considering the other problems discussed in the previous paragraph, a difficulty with the method for present purposes is that it gives only an average of the flux over periods of several hours. Since soil respiration can be expected to vary with soil temperature and perhaps with the current rate of CO_2 assimilation in the plants, both of which undergo a diurnal change, such a measurement is not applicable to periods as short as an hour or less, although it may be useful for estimating daily totals of CO_2 exchange.

Yet another possibility is measurement of the flux of CO_2 at the soil surface from considerations of gas diffusion in the soil. This would require measurement of the CO_2 concentration gradient in the soil and calculation of an average soil diffusion coefficient. There are, however, several difficulties involved, including: the possibility of transport of CO_2 in solution as well as by gaseous diffusion; the non-constancy of the CO_2 flux with depth due to the distribution of CO_2 sources in the soil; changes in the diffusion coefficient with changes in soil moisture content; and the possibility of pressure fluctuations at the surface inducing a mass flow of CO_2 as described by Farrell, Greacen & Gurr (1966).

In summary, current methods for measuring soil respiration in the crop are generally unsatisfactory. Because this flux may contribute importantly to the total uptake or release of CO_2 by the community, the development of improved methods for its measurement is to be encouraged strongly.

13.4.6 | *Other tracers*

13.4.6.1. | Radioactive emissions

It is possible to use natural radioactive gases emitted from the soil, such as radon and thoron, as tracers of air movement (e.g. Fontan *et al.* 1966). There are problems in this approach, however, including those of concentration measurement, resolution in space and time, measurement of the surface flux, and advection.

13.4.6.2. | Artificial tracers

A recent development has been the use of artificial tracers to infer transport coefficients in the canopy.

Millington & Peters (1969) describe a technique in which propane gas was released from a point source at a known rate and collected by ring samplers concentric about the source and in the same horizontal plane as it. Their treatment of the problem involves a number of simplifying assumptions both in the physics of turbulent diffusion from a point source and in the mathematics of the solution. Although some of these assumptions are questionable, it is nevertheless an interesting approach which has the theoretical advantage that it purports to measure a mass-transport coefficient, and CO_2 exchange is, of course, a process of mass transfer.

A less arguable approach is one employed by B. J. Legg (unpublished work, but referred to briefly in Rothamsted Experiment Station Report for 1968, Part 1, pp. 31–32), who used an extensive plane-source of nitrous oxide gas at ground level along with measurements of concentration profiles in the canopy to infer distributions of mass-transport coefficients from the flux-gradient relation of equation (13.1a). It seems unlikely that either method will receive routine use in the near future, but they could provide valuable checks on transport coefficients derived from considerations of momentum and energy transfer, whose applicability to mass transfer cannot be tested in the air layers within the canopy by simpler means.

13.5 | Concluding remarks

This Chapter has reviewed various aspects of the use of micrometeorological techniques to obtain short-term, non-disturbing measurements of the exchange of CO_2 by plant communities in the field. We have dealt with three stages in the description of CO_2 exchange. These are:

1. calculation of the net rate of exchange of CO_2 between the community and the atmosphere by means of measurements in the unobstructed air layers above the surface (Sections 13.2 and 13.3);
2. estimation of the contribution of the soil to the overall CO_2 exchange by measurements at or near the ground surface (Section 13.4.5);
3. determination of the distributions and magnitudes of sources and sinks of CO_2 throughout the community by measurements inside the canopy (Section 13.4).

Although satisfactory measurement of CO_2 fluxes by direct means is not yet possible, this may be achieved through eddy correlation methods in the near future. It seems probable, however, that many problems of interpretation will remain for years to come (*cf.* Section 13.2). Meanwhile indirect estimates, of varying degrees of accuracy, can be obtained *via* the similarity principle, *i.e.* by assuming the same effectiveness of turbulent transfer for CO_2 and some other substance or atmospheric property used as a tracer. The flux and the concentration difference (or gradient) of such a substance are measured, and their ratio applied to a simultaneous measurement of the concentration difference (or gradient) of CO_2 itself.

Of the various possible tracers, water vapour (or latent heat) and total energy (sensible plus latent heat) appear the most reliable for use above the crop (Section 13.3), then momentum (Section 13.2) and sensible heat (although the latter may well become more generally useful in the future – Section 13.3.3.6).

All approaches involve considerable difficulties in instrumentation and the location and exposure of sensors (Sections 13.3.3.11 and 13.6.8). In fact, the bearing on these latter of advection, or, under extreme conditions, convection, may often be more decisive than instrumental aspects in selecting both a particular tracer and a particular method for determination of its flux or concentration.

The evolution of CO_2 from the soil can sometimes be estimated from micrometeorological measurements close to the ground, but often the presence of live foliage near the ground will preclude this possibility. Alternative methods of measurement are generally unsatisfactory and there is much scope for improved methodology in this area (*cf.* Section 13.4.5).

Measurements of CO_2 exchange within the canopy present many additional difficulties. In particular, the sampling problem becomes formidable. So far, total energy and momentum appear to be the only practical natural tracers, and for both of these the errors to be expected with any feasible array of sensors are of the order of some tens of per cent *at the best*. Part of the difficulty is that within the canopy, the fluxes of these tracers are not constant with height. New developments in the use of inert, artificial tracer gases, whose fluxes do not change with height, may help reduce the errors (*cf.* Section 13.4.6.)

Micrometeorology is a field outside the usual biologist's training. Therefore at the risk of pedantry (a certain amount of which is perhaps inevitable in a Manual of this kind), we make the following suggestions.

Although a rough order of merit amongst the various possible approaches has been indicated, there will be many factors influencing the choice of a particular method. Hence it is recommended that persons venturing into this field seek expert advice on the alternative methods potentially available to them.

In addition, it would seem highly desirable at the early stages of an investigation to gain practical experience with at least two methods (preferably operated simultaneously and over periods long enough to provide comparative checks of their performance under a wide range of conditions). Even after a particular method is selected, it is recommended that, where resources permit, the measurements be replicated. In all cases, great care is needed in choice of instruments and in their siting, maintenance and calibration. In the absence of direct and independent confirmation of the results, caution must be exercised in their interpretation.

It is emphasized strongly that the field environment is not a simple one to work in. Each facet of the problem must receive proper treatment if the overall result is not to represent a waste of money and effort. These studies can not be undertaken lightly. In fact it is better not to attempt them at all if the considerable resources and attention they require are not available.

The comments in this and preceding Sections may perhaps give an unduly pessimistic view of the usefulness of micrometeorological techniques for studying CO_2 exchange. We conclude on a more optimistic note. Potentially, such methods are extremely useful for studying plant production in the field over short periods, and in a non-disturbing way. They provide an excellent means for pinpointing important environmental influences on plant performance; for studying crop physiology; and for providing a quantitative basis for the development and testing of models of plant growth. Their successful use, however, requires that their limitations, as well as their strengths, be fully recognised.

13.6 | Appendix A: Derivation and application of CO_2 flux formulae

13.6.1 | Introduction

In order to appreciate the relevance and utility of the many and varied formulae employed in this Chapter, it is desirable to set down in some detail the more important of the definitions, sign conventions, derivations and transformations involved. This exercise will also help in understanding the relationships between various expressions encountered in the literature. Many of these differ essentially only in the units employed, although the latter are often specified inadequately or improperly.

In what follows, therefore, a number of key formulae will be derived, in terms of recommended units (including where appropriate the two main ways of expressing CO_2 concentration). Careful attention will be given throughout to specification of units and numerical values of constants, *etc.* The conversion factors listed in Section 13.7.2 will then make it easy to substitute other units where desired. In addition, certain aspects of the determination of atmospheric transfer coefficients, such as the effects of advection, will be discussed in more detail.

13.6.2 | General

Let F be the mean flux of a diffusing substance or property, Φ, through a reference plane or surface usually parallel to a nearby bounding surface (*i.e.* in the present case, the reference plane is generally horizontal), and at a distance from it of z (*i.e.* in general at a height z above ground or the effective surface level of a crop). Let $\partial\phi/\partial z$ be the mean vertical gradient of concentration of Φ at the same point. As is the normal convention, z will be taken as positive upwards, and F likewise unless otherwise specified. (In the latter case the negative sign must be omitted from equation (13.1a).)
The mean flux-gradient relationship can then be expressed in terms of a transfer coefficient for that substance, K_Φ, defined by the equation

$$F = -K_\Phi \times \frac{\partial\phi}{\partial z}. \tag{13.1a}$$

(Quantity of Φ transported per second through a square centimetre of horizontal reference plane) (Transfer coefficient, $cm^2\ s^{-1}$) (Change in quantity of Φ per cubic cm of air mixture, per cm of height)

Alternatively, we may integrate Eq. (13.1a) between two heights, z_1 and z_2 ($z_1 < z_2$), to give

$$\phi_1 - \phi_2 = \int_{z_1}^{z_2} \frac{F}{K_\Phi}\, dz. \tag{13.2}$$

For turbulent transport in the atmosphere, F, K and $\partial\phi/\partial z$ will all vary with height. However, under many circumstances F can be taken as constant over the working height range. This assumption will be made here, but see Section 13.6.8 for the limitations involved. Equation (13.2) can then be transformed into a finite difference form of (13.1a),

$$F = \frac{\phi_1 - \phi_2}{\int_{z_1}^{z_2} \frac{dz}{K_\Phi}} = \hat{K}_\Phi\, \Delta\phi \tag{13.1b}$$

where the symbols $\wedge$ and Δ denote, respectively, a suitably weighted average value for the whole air layer from z_1 to z_2, and a difference across the same layer. As shown in Eq. (13.1b) the difference is taken as the lower value minus the upper where F is positive upwards, otherwise the reverse, thus maintaining a positive sign in the equation in all cases.

13.6.3 | *Specific units involved in CO_2 transport*

In the particular case of carbon dioxide exchange, we may say that the upward flux of CO_2 is given by

$$C = -K_C \times \frac{\partial \rho_c}{\partial z} \tag{13.3a}$$

[g CO_2 cm^{-2} s^{-1}] [cm^2 s^{-1}] [(g CO_2 cm^{-3}) cm^{-1}]

$$= \hat{K}_C \times \Delta\rho_c \tag{13.3b}$$

[cm s^{-1}] [g CO_2 cm^{-3}]

where ρ_c is the local concentration of CO_2 (*i.e.* its density – *cf.* Section 13.3.1.2). If K_C or $\hat{K}_C$ and $\partial\rho_c/\partial z$ or $\Delta\rho_c$ could be measured directly, there would be no further problem. In practice, however, K_C or $\hat{K}_C$ must be found indirectly, by methods outlined below. Furthermore, although ρ_c is essentially the quantity measured by an infra-red gas analyser, the commonest tool used to determine CO_2 concentration, such instruments are usually calibrated in terms of volumetric concentration – parts of CO_2 per million parts of air. Before examining methods for finding K_C or $\hat{K}_C$, therefore, we must transform the basic equations above into their counterparts in more commonly used units.

For gases in general (neglecting departures from the ideal gas laws),

$$pv = n\mathrm{R}T \tag{13.4a}$$

where p, v and T are the partial pressure, volume and absolute temperature of a sample of the gas comprising n moles, and R is the universal gas constant (whose value will depend solely on the units used). Alternatively we may say,

$$pv = \frac{m}{M}\mathrm{R}T \tag{13.4b}$$

or

$$p = \frac{\rho}{M}\mathrm{R}T \tag{13.4c}$$

where m and ρ are respectively the mass and density of the sample, and M is the molar mass of the species concerned.

In the case of a CO_2 – air mixture, for the CO_2 component

$$p_c = \frac{\rho_c}{M_c}\mathrm{R}T, \tag{13.5a}$$

and for the air component

$$p_a = P - p_c \approx P = \frac{\rho_a}{M_a}\mathrm{R}T, \tag{13.5b}$$

where P is total ambient pressure. Thus

$$\rho_c = \frac{M_c}{M_a} \frac{p_c}{p_a} \rho_a = 1.52 \frac{p_c}{p_a} \rho_a \tag{13.6}$$

since $M_a \approx 29$ g mol^{-1} and $M_c = 44$ g mol^{-1}.
The true volumetric concentration can be expressed as the volume of CO_2 per unit volume of air in the mixture, with the former compressed to the same pressure as the air, but with both at the same temperature. In units of parts of CO_2 per million parts of air, this becomes

$$c[\text{vpm}] = 10^6 \frac{p_c}{p_a} = \frac{10^6 \times \rho_c}{\rho_a} \frac{M_a}{M_c}$$

$$= 6.6 \times 10^5 \frac{\rho_c}{\rho_a}. \tag{13.7}$$

Variations in the factor $1/\rho_a$ should always be allowed for when calibrating or reading a gas analyser in volumetric units, particularly when operating at temperatures or pressures above or below ambient.
From equations (13.3) and (13.7), with the reasonable assumption that air density is near enough constant in the atmosphere over the small height ranges considered here, we arrive at working formulae,

$$\underset{[\text{g cm}^{-2}\,\text{s}^{-1}]}{C} = -1.5 \times 10^{-6} \underset{[\text{g cm}^{-1}\,\text{s}^{-1}]}{\rho_a K_C} \times \underset{[\text{vpm cm}^{-1}]}{\frac{\partial c}{\partial z}} \tag{13.3c}$$

$$= 1.5 \times 10^{-6} \underset{[\text{g cm}^{-2}\,\text{s}^{-1}]}{\rho_a \hat{K}_C} \times \underset{[\text{vpm}]}{\Delta c} \tag{13.3d}$$

where ρ_a can be taken under most circumstances as 1.2×10^{-3} g cm^{-3}, but should be corrected for altitude or extremes of weather where necessary. Variations in ρ_a with temperature are given in Table 1.8. (Note that in some subsequent formulae involving another difference as well as Δc, *e.g.* equations (13.18) to (13.21), ρ_a cancels out.)

13.6.4 | Other atmospheric fluxes

Similarly we may say, for the transfer of momentum, sensible heat, water vapour and latent heat, respectively (again paying attention to units),

$$\underset{[\text{g cm}^{-1}\,\text{s}^{-2}]}{\tau} = \underset{[\text{cm}^2\,\text{s}^{-1}]}{K_M} \times \underset{[(\text{g cm}^{-3}) \times (\text{cm s}^{-1})/\text{cm},\ i.e.\ \text{g cm}^{-3}\,\text{s}^{-1}]}{\frac{\partial(\rho_a u)}{\partial z}} \tag{13.8a}$$

$$= \underset{[\text{g cm}^{-1}\,\text{s}^{-1}]}{\rho_a K_M} \times \underset{[\text{s}^{-1}]}{\frac{\partial u}{\partial z}} \tag{13.8b}$$

where τ [dyn cm^{-2}] is the shearing stress or *downward* flux of momentum in the atmosphere[1], and u [cm s^{-1}] is the mean horizontal windspeed;

$$H = -K_H \times \frac{\partial(\rho_a c_p T)}{\partial z} \qquad (13.9a)$$

[mW cm^{-2}] [cm^2 s^{-1}] [(g cm^{-3}) × (mW s g^{-1}(°C)$^{-1}$) × °C cm^{-1}, *i.e.* mW s cm^{-4}]

$$= -\rho_a c_p K_H \times \frac{\partial T}{\partial z} \qquad (13.9b)$$

[mW(°C)$^{-1}$ cm^{-1}] [°C cm^{-1}]

where H is the sensible heat flux into the atmosphere, c_p [= 1.01×10^3 mW s g^{-1}(°C)$^{-1}$] is the specific heat of air at constant pressure, and T[°C] is the dry bulb temperature of the air, strictly potential temperature if large heights are concerned; and

$$E = -K_W \times \frac{\partial \rho_w}{\partial z} \qquad (13.10a)$$

[g H_2O cm^{-2} s^{-1}] [cm^2 s^{-1}] [(g H_2O cm^{-3}) cm^{-1}, *i.e.* g cm^{-4}]

$$= -\rho_a K_W \times \frac{\partial q}{\partial z} \qquad (13.10b)$$

[g cm^{-1} s^{-1}] [cm^{-1}]

where E is the evaporation rate, and q [gH_2O/g air] is the specific humidity; or

$$LE = -K_W \times L\frac{\partial \rho_w}{\partial z} \qquad (13.11a)$$

[mW cm^{-2}] [cm^2 s^{-1}] [mW s cm^{-4}]

$$= -L\rho_a K_M \times \frac{\partial q}{\partial z} \qquad (13.11b)$$

[mW cm^{-1}] [cm^{-1}]

where L [$\approx 2.4 \times 10^6$ mW s g^{-1}] is the latent heat of vaporization of water, and hence LE is the flux of latent heat associated with the flux of evaporated water.

13.6.5 | *Compound flux of sensible and latent heat*

Furthermore, on the again very reasonable assumption of similarity of transfer coefficients at low heights, *i.e.* that $K_H \approx K_W \approx K$, say, we may combine (13.9b) with (13.11b) to give

1. The customary negative sign (*cf.* equation (13.1a)) is dropped from (13.8) because of the well-established practice of defining τ as positive downwards, which is invariably the case in a system of earth-fixed axes (Section 13.3.2.1).

$$H + LE \approx -\rho_a c_p K \times \left\{ \frac{\partial T}{\partial z} + \left(\frac{L}{c_p} \right) \frac{\partial q}{\partial z} \right\} \tag{13.12a}$$

$[\text{mW cm}^{-2}]$ $[\text{mW}(^\circ\text{C})^{-1}\ \text{cm}^{-1}]$ $[^\circ\text{C cm}^{-1}]$

$$= -\rho_a c_p K \frac{\partial T_e}{\partial z} \tag{13.12b}$$

where $T_e \{= T + Lq/c_p\}$ is the equivalent temperature of the air mixture concerned. Although both the flux and the gradient in Eq. (13.12b) cannot be measured directly in themselves, they are readily expressed in terms of related quantities which can. Firstly, the principle of energy balance at the bounding surface between earth and atmosphere requires that the total flux of sensible plus latent heat entering the atmosphere must equal the net flux of energy available at the surface from other sources, *i.e.*

$$H + LE = R - G + \epsilon C \tag{13.13a}$$

where R is the net radiation absorbed at the surface (all wavelengths), G is the ground heat flux, or heat taken up by the soil and vegetation, and $|\epsilon C|$ is a minor term, often neglected, representing the net energy utilisation in photosynthesis. Secondly, a specific humidity gradient can readily be expressed in terms of the corresponding gradients of dry- and wet-bulb temperature, T and T_w (*e.g.* Slatyer & McIlroy 1961; McIlroy 1968). Hence it can be shown that

$$\frac{\partial T_e}{\partial z} = \left\{ \frac{s + \gamma}{\gamma} \right\} \frac{\partial T_w}{\partial z} \tag{13.14}$$

where $(s + \gamma)/\gamma$ is a non-dimensional ratio, slowly varying with temperature, values of which are given at 1 °C intervals in Section 13.7.3. Here s is the slope of the curve relating saturation specific humidity to temperature, at the average of the wet bulb temperatures concerned, and $\gamma\ [\approx 4.2 \times 10^{-4}\ (^\circ\text{C})^{-1}]$ is the psychrometric constant in terms of specific humidity rather than the more usual vapour pressure. To a close approximation, $\gamma = c_p/L$.
By substitution from equations (13.13a) and (13.14) in (13.12b), with neglect of ϵC[1], we thus obtain yet another expression useful for determining a transfer coefficient:

$$R - G = -\rho_a c_p K \left\{ \frac{s + \gamma}{\gamma} \right\} \frac{\partial T_w}{\partial z}. \tag{13.15}$$

For simplicity we have not listed finite difference versions of the foregoing flux equations, which are easily written by analogy with Eq. (13.3b) or (13.3d).

1. As mentioned in Section 13.3.3.8 earlier, the net consumption of energy associated with CO_2 uptake can be estimated well enough for correction purposes where required, by allowing for a heat of formation typical of long chain carbohydrate compounds of 10^7 mW s per g of CO_2 fixed.

13.6.6 | *Determining K or $\hat{K}$ from 'tracer' fluxes*

Extending the similarity assumption by taking K_C to be near enough equal to any of its various analogues above, we may use the corresponding flux as, in effect, a tracer for the transport of carbon dioxide. The flux of CO_2 can then be expressed in terms of one or other of the more readily measured atmospheric fluxes and the appropriate gradient ratio. This latter is obtained from concentration measurements at several known heights, preferably (but not necessarily) the same for CO_2 and the tracer entity.

Alternatively, we may prefer to plot CO_2 concentration directly against that of the chosen tracer, when measurements of both are available at the same heights (not necessarily known). The various approaches possible are typified by the following general relationships:

$$C = \frac{\pm F}{\partial\phi/\partial z}\frac{\partial\rho_c}{\partial z} = \pm\, 1.5 \times 10^{-6}\,\rho_a F \frac{\partial c/\partial z}{\partial\phi/\partial z}; \tag{13.16a}$$

or

$$C = \pm\, F\frac{\partial\rho_c}{\partial\phi} = \pm\, 1.5 \times 10^{-6}\,\rho_a F \frac{\partial c}{\partial\phi}; \tag{13.16b}$$

where F and ϕ are in properly matched units, *e.g.* as used in equations (13.8) to (13.12) and (13.15) above. The sign in Eqs. (13.16) should be positive except when F represents shearing stress.

In practice, it is often most convenient to use merely the concentration differences between two particular heights (which again need not be known, provided they are the same for both CO_2 and ϕ), rather than complete gradients which require at least three measurements at accurately known heights. By equating the various analogues of $\hat{K}_C$ in equation (13.3d), we obtain the following simple general expression:

$$C = F\frac{\Delta\rho_c}{\Delta\phi} = 1.5 \times 10^{-6}\,\rho_a F\frac{\Delta c}{\Delta\phi}. \tag{13.17}$$

Note that where F is specified as positive downwards, as in the case of momentum, the difference $\Delta\phi$ (in this case $\Delta\rho_a\, u$) will be the upper value minus the lower – *cf.* earlier remarks on the non-standard sign convention for momentum flux.

In the most important practical cases, again using the same units as in equations (13.8)–(13.12) and (13.15), we obtain the key formulae:

$$C = \tau\frac{\Delta\rho_c}{\rho_a\,\Delta u} = 1.5 \times 10^{-6}\,\tau\frac{\Delta c}{\Delta u} \tag{13.18}$$

$$C = H\frac{\Delta\rho_c}{\rho_a\,c_p\,\Delta T} = 1.5 \times 10^{-6}\,\frac{H}{c_p}\frac{\Delta c}{\Delta T} \tag{13.19a}$$

$$= 1.5 \times 10^{-9}\,H\frac{\Delta c}{\Delta T} \tag{13.19b}$$

$$C = E \frac{\Delta \rho_c}{\rho_a \Delta q} \qquad = 1.5 \times 10^{-6} E \frac{\Delta c}{\Delta q} \qquad (13.20a)$$

$$C = LE \frac{\Delta \rho_c}{\rho_a L \Delta q} \qquad = 6.2 \times 10^{-13} LE \frac{\Delta c}{\Delta q} \qquad (13.20b)$$

$$C = (R - G) \frac{\Delta \rho_c}{\rho_a c_p \Delta T_e} = 1.5 \times 10^{-6} \frac{R - G}{c_p} \left\{ \frac{\gamma}{s + \gamma} \right\} \frac{\Delta c}{\Delta T_w} \qquad (13.21a)$$

$$= 1.5 \times 10^{-9} (R - G) \left\{ \frac{\gamma}{s + \gamma} \right\} \frac{\Delta c}{\Delta T_w} \qquad (13.21b)$$

These may be converted into whatever units are desired, by means of the factors given in Section 13.7.2. The ratio $\frac{\gamma}{s + \gamma}$ is tabulated in Section 13.7.3.

13.6.7 | Determining K and $\hat{K}$ from the windspeed profile

Since concentrations are generally easier to measure than fluxes, it is desirable wherever conditions permit to obtain values of K or $\hat{K}$ from concentration measurements alone. Unfortunately, this can be done only in the case of momentum transport – and even then only under favourable site and atmospheric conditions – *cf.* Section 13.6.8.
Momentum exchange between the moving atmosphere and the stationary ground is itself the basic cause of the forced or frictional turbulence which usually dominates the transfer process for some distance above the surface. As a result, the theory of such turbulence (see, for instance, Sutton 1953; Slatyer & McIlroy 1961; Webb 1965) is able to provide expressions for the momentum transfer coefficient in terms of windspeeds and heights only, such as

$$K_M = k^2 z^2 \frac{\partial u}{\partial z} = f(z, u) \qquad (13.22a)$$

$$= \frac{k^2 z u_1}{\ln (z_1/z_o)} = f(z_1, z_o, z, u_1) \qquad (13.22b)$$

$$= \frac{k^2 z \Delta u}{\ln (z_2/z_1)} = f(z_1, z_2, z, \Delta u) \qquad (13.22c)$$

where k and z_o are constants, with k ($\approx$ 0.4) an empirically determined turbulence constant due to von Kármán; while z_o, the so-called roughness height (determined by the intercept with the height axis when plotting u_z against ln z for a range of heights), is characteristic of the aerodynamic roughness of the underlying surface, and hence constant only for that surface or very similar ones. Even then this applies only as long as the relevant properties do not change with growth of vegetation, or flexing of stems or leaves (see later).

A further complication is that, over a vegetated surface, the turbulent regime to

which these and subsequent equations apply rarely extends right to the ground. This arises from the entrapping of more or less calm air in the lower layers of the foliage. As a result, height, although normally measured from the ground surface, should really be determined from a zero-plane at some level within the vegetation. Thus in all expressions involving a specified height (such as equations 13.22 to 13.24), z should strictly be replaced by the effective height, $(z - d)$, where d is the zero-plane displacement, usually a substantial fraction of the average canopy height. Like z_o, it varies with growth or bending of the plants, and needs to be determined from time to time from the measured windspeed profile (see later).
In equations (13.22), z (or strictly $z - d$) denotes the height at which the calculated value of K_M applies, *i.e.* for the present application, taking K_C as given by K_M, z would be the height of determination of $\partial \rho_c / \partial z$ in equation (13.3a) or $\partial c / \partial z$ in Eq. (13.3c); while z_1 and z_2 (again corrected for d) are the heights of measurement for u_1 and u_2 respectively, with $\Delta u = u_2 - u_1$.
In the generalised finite difference form, Eq. (13.22b) becomes

$$\hat{K}_M = \frac{k^2 \, \Delta u}{\ln(z_2/z_1)\ln(z_4/z_3)} = f(z_1, \ldots, z_4, \Delta u). \tag{13.23a}$$

Here z_3, z_4 would be the measuring heights for $\Delta \rho_c$ in Eq. (13.3b) or Δc in Eq. (13.3d), not necessarily the same as for Δu. In the particular case where $z_3 = z_1$ and $z_4 = z_2$, this reduces to

$$\hat{K}_M = \left\{ \frac{k}{\ln(z_2/z_1)} \right\}^2 \Delta u = f(z_1, z_2, \Delta u). \tag{13.23b}$$

Substituting Eq. (13.23b) into Eq. (13.3d) gives the well-known aerodynamic formula for CO_2 flux

$$C = 1.5 \times 10^{-6} \rho_a \left\{ \frac{k}{\ln(z_2/z_1)} \right\}^2 \Delta u \, \Delta c. \tag{13.24}$$

This equation is also obtained by substitution into Eq. (13.18) of a well-established expression for the shearing stress,

$$\tau = \rho_a \left\{ \frac{k \Delta u}{\ln(z_2/z_1)} \right\}^2,$$

which can itself be derived from Eq. (13.23b) and the finite difference form of Eq. (13.8).

13.6.8 | Advection, non-neutrality and the zero-plane displacement

All the above transport formulae apply only to the forced turbulence occurring under neutral conditions, and to fully developed boundary layers free from advective distortion due to upwind obstacles or insufficient fetch over a uniform surface. To ensure the fully logarithmic profile of windspeed on which equations (13.22),

(13.23) and others based on them depend, they should only be applied over large regular surfaces, and the maximum height of observation must always be kept as low as possible. Practical limits to this are set on the one hand by increased sampling variability, as the lower instruments begin to be influenced by small-scale surface irregularities; and on the other hand by the smaller windspeed differences encountered over small height ratios, which must be kept within the limits of resolution of the available instrumentation.

A rough rule of thumb for site or exposure requirements would be that upwind obstacles (trees, buildings, *etc.*) should be distant more than 20–50 times their maximum height, depending on the horizontal angle they subtend at the instrument mast; and upwind changes in surface type (crop or field boundaries, *etc.*) should be distant more than 20–50 times the maximum observing height, depending on the severity of the contrast at the boundary. In addition, to keep below a level where departures from neutrality can become important, the upper measuring height should never exceed 1–2 m over grass, cereal crops or other relatively smooth surfaces, 2–4 m over vegetable crops or similar surface-types, and 4–6 m over orchards and the like. The lower ends of these latter ranges would apply on calm sunny days or calm clear nights, but may still be too high during extremes of such conditions, when departures from neutrality become significant down to very small heights.

Limits are even harder to set for the minimum practical measuring height. However, a rough guide here would be a distance above the level of the top of the canopy equal to the typical deviation from the mean in canopy height when averaged over an area of radius around the instrument not less than the greatest measuring height. In concrete terms, this could mean from about 10 cm above mown grass to 25 cm above cereal crops, and so on to about 1 m above a dense orchard. In this connection, it is most important to avoid trampling or otherwise damaging the vegetation in the vicinity of the instruments, whether in installing or servicing them. Where the nature of the crop warrants it, it is worthwhile expending considerable time and effort on special measures or devices to prevent upsetting the effective height of the lower instruments (such as rotary or sliding catwalks, for instance, giving temporary access at or above canopy level for the last few metres of approach to instrument masts).

Where it is impossible to operate consistently within the neutral layer (*e.g.* by use of a low-level drag coefficient, as outlined in Section 13.3.2.4), various theories have been advanced to account for the shape of the non-neutral wind profile. Most of these are discussed in the reviews mentioned earlier. However, the determination of a profile with an accuracy sufficient to properly distinguish departures from a true logarithmic shape, and hence the utilisation of such theories in calculating the correct value of K or $\hat{K}$, requires extremely accurate measurement of both windspeed and effective height.

Even with smooth regular surfaces, height evaluation is difficult. As pointed out previously, the zero-plane for the fully turbulent atmosphere above a vegetated surface is displaced a distance d from the ground. The magnitude of the displacement varies with the leaf density and structure of the vegetation. It can only be determined by analysis of the windspeed profile itself, *e.g.* by trial and error plotting of u (for a given run or set of runs under similar neutral or near neutral conditions) versus the corresponding ln $(z - \delta)$, with δ being given various values initially centred on a first estimate of d. This is repeated until the best fit to a straight line is achieved; whereupon the corresponding value of δ is taken to be the zero-plane displacement on that particular occasion. At the same time, the intercept of the line with the z-δ axis gives z_o. (If facilities permit, a similar but more objective analysis by computer is preferable).

When the appropriate value of d has been found for any given crop or surface-type, it can be taken into account in all height-dependent formulae applied to the same or an equivalent surface, simply by replacing z with $(z - d)$. However, if the structure of the vegetation alters significantly, due for instance to flexing, or growth or defoliation, both d and z_o will be changed thereby, and new values will have to be determined for them or other parameters based on them (K, C_D, *etc.*).

For satisfactory resolution of d and z_o, the exact profile must be found each time, requiring accurate measurements at several heights, preferably widely spaced to reduce the effects of instrumental error. Occasions of true neutrality and freedom from advection, up to several metres height at least, are required to avoid spurious departures from a logarithmic height-dependence of u, *i.e.* departures from a straight line fit in the procedure outlined above, due to causes other than an incorrect choice of δ. In many situations of interest, such occasions will be rare and it will be difficult, if not impossible, to keep up with changes in d or z_o, and hence errors will arise in the use of formulae dependent on them.

If these formulae are to be used with confidence for anything but large open areas of a low uniform crop there is a pressing need for comparative experiments in which K, $\hat{K}$ or C are determined simultaneously by the aerodynamic method and by other more reliable approaches, *e.g.* lysimetry or energy-balance determinations of E in Eq. (13.10) or (13.20). Although these too can be subject to influences of advection or non-neutrality (*cf.* Section 13.3.3.10), they are generally much less affected thereby. Moreover, their use does not normally require that the measuring heights be known, so they can therefore be operated relatively close to the surface. (A lysimeter, of course, measures the surface value of E directly.)

13.7 | Appendix B: Symbols, dimensions, conversion factors and constants

13.7.1 | List of symbols and dimensions

c	volumetric concentration of CO_2 in air [vpm]
c_p	specific heat of air at constant pressure [$= 1.01 \times 10^3$ mW s g^{-1} (°C)$^{-1}$]
d	zero-plane displacement [cm]
f	general function
h	height from ground to top of canopy [cm]
k	von Kármán constant [$\simeq 0.4$]
m	mass of gas sample [g]
n	number of moles of gas
p	partial pressure of gas [mb]
p_a	partial pressure of air excluding water vapour or CO_2 ($\simeq P$) [mb]
p_c	partial pressure of CO_2 in air [mb]

q	specific humidity of air [g water vapour/g air]
s	slope of curve relating saturation specific humidity of air to temperature [$(°C)^{-1}$]
u	horizontal wind speed [$cm\ s^{-1}$]
v	volume of air or gas sample [cm^3]
v_v	volume of gas or vapour initially in v when compressed to air pressure and at air temperature [cm^3]
x	horizontal distance [cm]
z	height above ground [cm]
z_o	roughness height [cm]
B	Bowen-ratio ($= H/LE$)
C	flux (density) of CO_2 [$g\ cm^{-2}\ s^{-1}$]
C_o	flux (density) of CO_2 at ground surface [$g\ cm^{-2}\ s^{-1}$]
E	evaporation rate [$g\ cm^{-2}\ s^{-1}$, or $cm\ s^{-1}$]
F	generalised flux, strictly flux density, see footnote in Section 13.3.1.1
F_o	generalised flux (density) at ground surface
G	ground heat flux or rate of change in heat storage in ground (and air and vegetation in canopy) [$mW\ cm^{-2}$]
H	flux (density) of sensible heat [$mW\ cm^{-2}$]
K	generalised transport coefficient at a particular height [$cm^2\ s^{-1}$]
$K_C, K_H, K_M, K_W, K_\Phi$	transport coefficients for CO_2, heat, momentum, water vapour, and the entity Φ [$cm^2\ s^{-1}$]
$\hat{K}$	weighted average transport coefficient for a layer of air [$cm\ s^{-1}$]
$\hat{K}_C, \hat{K}_H, \hat{K}_M, \hat{K}_W, \hat{K}_\Phi$	weighted average transport coefficients for CO_2, heat, momentum, water vapour, and the entity Φ [$cm\ s^{-1}$]
L	latent heat of vapourisation of water [$\approx 2.4 \times 10^6\ mW\ s\ g^{-1}$]
M	molar mass [$g\ mol^{-1}$]
M_a, M_c	molar mass of air ($= 29\ g\ mol^{-1}$) and CO_2 ($= 44\ g\ mol^{-1}$)
P	total atmospheric pressure [mb]
R	universal gas constant [$= 8.3 \times 10^4\ mb\ cm^3\ K^{-1}$]
R	net radiation [$mW\ cm^{-2}$]
T	air temperature [°C or K]
T_e	equivalent temperature of air ($= T + Lq/c_p$) [°C]
T_w	wet-bulb temperature of air [°C]
α	foliage area density [cm^{-1}]
γ	psychrometric constant ($\approx c_p/L$) [$\approx 4.2 \times 10^{-4}\ (°C)^{-1}$]
δ	estimate of zero-plane displacement [cm]
$\in$	average energy requirement for the photosynthetic fixation of CO_2 [$\approx 10^7\ mW\ s\ g^{-1}$]
ϕ	concentration in air of the entity Φ
ρ	density of gas or vapour in air [g gas or vapour cm^{-3} air]
ρ_a	density of air [$\approx 1.2 \times 10^{-3}\ g\ cm^{-3}$ under usual conditions]
ρ_c	density of CO_2 in air [$g\ cm^{-3}$]
ρ_w	density of water vapour in air [$g\ cm^{-3}$]
τ	shearing stress or *downward* flux of momentum [$dyn\ cm^{-2}$]
Δ	a difference across an air layer
Φ	any transported entity

13.7.2 | Conversion factors

13.7.2.1 | Basic relationships for gas mixtures

For any vapour or gas to which the ideal gas laws can be applied:

$$pv = \frac{m}{M} RT \tag{13.4b}$$

or

$$p = \rho \frac{R}{M} T \tag{13.4c}$$

where the symbols are as defined in Section 13.7.1, and the equation numbers derive from their use in Section 13.6.3.
Then the specific concentration of such a substance in air is given by

$$\text{g vapour/g air} = \frac{\rho}{\rho_a}$$

$$= \frac{1}{\rho_a}, \text{ when } \rho = 1 \text{ g cm}^{-3}.$$

Conversely, $\rho = \rho_a$ when its specific concentration is 1 g/g air.
Also, from equation (13.4c), when $\rho = 1$, its partial pressure will be

$$p = \frac{R}{M} T.$$

Thus, for $\rho = 1$ and T in K we obtain

$$p = \begin{cases} 1\,890\, T \text{ mb for } CO_2 \\ 4\,610\, T \text{ mb for } H_2O, \end{cases}$$

and when $\rho = \rho_a$,

$$p = \frac{M_a}{M} p_a$$

$$= \begin{cases} 0.66\, p_a \text{ for } CO_2 \\ 1.6\ \ p_a \text{ for } H_2O \end{cases}$$

The ratio of the partial pressure of the vapour or gas to the air pressure is given by

$$\frac{p}{p_a} = \frac{\rho M_a}{\rho_a M}$$

$$= \left\{ \begin{array}{l} \dfrac{0.66}{\rho_a} \text{ for } CO_2 \\ \\ \dfrac{1.6}{\rho_a} \text{ for } H_2O \end{array} \right\} \text{ when } \rho = 1.$$

From equation (13.4b), hypothetical compression of the vapour to a volume v_v, such as to bring it to air pressure (and temperature) gives its concentration in parts per million by volume (vpm) as

$$\text{vpm} = 10^6 \times \frac{v_v}{v} = 10^6 \times \frac{p}{p_a} = \frac{10^6}{p_a} \text{ when } p = 1.$$

Also, from Eq. (13.6a), when $\rho = 1$,

$$\text{vpm} = \left\{ \begin{array}{l} \dfrac{6.6 \times 10^5}{\rho_a} \text{ for } CO_2 \\ \\ \dfrac{1.6 \times 10^6}{\rho_a} \text{ for } H_2O \end{array} \right.$$

and when $\rho = \rho_a$,

$$\text{vpm} = \left\{ \begin{array}{l} 6.6 \times 10^5 \text{ for } CO_2 \\ 1.6 \times 10^6 \text{ for } H_2O \end{array} \right.$$

The foregoing relationships, and others derived from them, form the basis of Table 13.7.2.2. They can be used to construct additional conversion factors where required, and to adjust those given below for temperature or pressure where a high degree of accuracy is necessary. The tabulated factors involve only the most popularly employed units, and are rounded values based where relevant on an air density of 1.2×10^{-3} g cm^{-3}.

13.7.2.2 | Concentration of gases and vapours, particularly CO_2 and water vapour

Specification	Formula	Unit		Equivalent concentration in air			
				[g cm^{-3}]	[g/g]	[vpm]	[mb]
Absolute density	ρ	1 g cm^{-3} air	CO_2	1	8.3×10^{2}	5.5×10^{8}	$1\,890T$
			H_2O	1	8.3×10^{2}	1.3×10^{9}	$4\,620T$
Specific concentration	$\frac{\rho}{\rho_a}$	1 g/g air	CO_2	1.2×10^{-3}	1	6.6×10^{5}	$0.66p_a$
			H_2O	1.2×10^{-3}	1	1.6×10^{6}	$1.6\ p_a$
Volumetric concentration	$10^6\frac{p}{p_a} = 10^6\frac{M_a}{M}\frac{\rho}{\rho_a}$	1 vpm [= cm^3 m^{-3}]	CO_2	1.8×10^{-9}	1.5×10^{-6}	1	$10^{-6}p_a$
			H_2O	7.4×10^{-10}	6.2×10^{-7}	1	$10^{-6}p_a$
Partial pressure or Vapour pressure	$\rho\frac{R}{M}T$ (T in K)	1 mb	CO_2	$1/1\,890T$	$1.5/p_a$	$10^6/p_a$	1
			H_2O	$1/4\,620T$	$0.62/p_a$	$10^6/p_a$	1

13.7.2.3 | Energy content of air

Unit	Equivalent			
	cal cm^{-3}	cal g^{-1}	mW s cm^{-3}	mW s g^{-1}
1 cal cm^{-3} air	1	8.3×10^{2}	4.2×10^{3}	3.5×10^{6}
1 cal g^{-1} air	1.2×10^{-3}	1	5.0	4.2×10^{3}
1 mW s cm^{-3} air	2.4×10^{-4}	0.20	1	8.3×10^{2}
1 mW s g^{-1} air	2.9×10^{-7}	2.4×10^{-4}	1.2×10^{-3}	1

1 W s m^{-3} air = 10^{-3} mW s cm^{-3} air = 1 J m^{-3} air
1 mW s g^{-1} air = 1 J kg^{-1} air

13.7.2.4 | Flux of CO_2, water and energy

The energy equivalents of the fluxes of CO_2 given below are based on $\epsilon = 10^7$ mW s g^{-1}. Those of water vapour are based on $L = 2.4 \times 10^6$ mW s g^{-1}. Conversions between energy units *per se* can be made from the entries in the bottom right-hand corner of the table.

Unit		Equivalent flux					
		g cm^{-2} s^{-1}	g m^{-2} h^{-1}	mm H_2O h^{-1}	mW cm^{-2}	cal cm^{-2} s^{-1}	cal cm^{-2} min^{-1}
1 g cm^{-2} s^{-1}	CO_2	1	3.6×10^7	—	10^7	2.4×10^3	1.4×10^5
	H_2O	1	3.6×10^7	3.6×10^4	2.4×10^6	5.7×10^2	3.4×10^4
1 g m^{-2} h^{-1}	CO_2	2.8×10^{-8}	1	—	0.28	6.6×10^{-5}	4.0×10^{-3}
	H_2O	2.8×10^{-8}	1	10^{-3}	6.7×10^{-2}	1.6×10^{-5}	9.6×10^{-4}
1 mm H_2O h^{-1}	CO_2	—	—	—	—	—	—
	H_2O	2.8×10^{-5}	10^3	1	67	1.6×10^{-2}	0.96
1 mW cm^{-2}	CO_2	10^{-7}	3.6	—	1	2.4×10^{-4}	1.4×10^{-2}
	H_2O	4.2×10^{-7}	15	1.5×10^{-2}	1	2.4×10^{-4}	1.4×10^{-2}
1 cal cm^{-2} s^{-1}	CO_2	4.2×10^{-4}	1.5×10^4	—	4.2×10^3	1	60
	H_2O	1.7×10^{-3}	6.3×10^4	63	4.2×10^3	1	60
1 cal cm^{-2} min^{-1}	CO_2	7.0×10^{-6}	2.5×10^2	—	70	1.67×10^{-2}	1
	H_2O	2.9×10^{-5}	1.05×10^3	1.05	70	1.67×10^{-2}	1

1 kg m^{-2} s^{-1} = 10^{-1} g cm^{-2} s^{-1}
1 W m^{-2} = 10^{-1} mW cm^{-2}
1 W = J s^{-1}

13.7.3 | *Psychrometric parameters*

Parameters for fully-ventilated thermometers at 1 000 mb ambient pressure (based on Chart MP 1 of Slatyer & McIlroy 1961):

T^* [°C]	s [(°C)$^{-1}$]	$\frac{s+\gamma}{\gamma}$	$\frac{\gamma}{s+\gamma}$	T^* [°C]	s [(°C)$^{-1}$]	$\frac{s+\gamma}{\gamma}$	$\frac{\gamma}{s+\gamma}$
0	2.7×10^{-4}	1.7	0.59				
1	2.9×10^{-4}	1.7	.58	21	9.7×10^{-4}	3.3	0.30
2	3.1×10^{-4}	1.8	.56	22	10.2×10^{-4}	3.4	.29
3	3.4×10^{-4}	1.8	.55	23	10.8×10^{-4}	3.5	.28
4	3.7×10^{-4}	1.9	.53	24	11.4×10^{-4}	3.7	.27
5	3.9×10^{-4}	1.9	.52	25	12.0×10^{-4}	3.8	.26
6	4.2×10^{-4}	2.0	.50	26	12.7×10^{-4}	4.0	.25
7	4.4×10^{-4}	2.0	.49	27	13.3×10^{-4}	4.1	.24
8	4.7×10^{-4}	2.1	.48	28	14.0×10^{-4}	4.3	.23
9	5.0×10^{-4}	2.2	.46	29	14.8×10^{-4}	4.5	.22
10	5.3×10^{-4}	2.3	.44	30	15.6×10^{-4}	4.6	.22
11	5.7×10^{-4}	2.3	.43	31	16.4×10^{-4}	4.8	.21
12	6.0×10^{-4}	2.4	.41	32	17.2×10^{-4}	5.0	.20
13	6.4×10^{-4}	2.5	.40	33	18.1×10^{-4}	5.2	.19
14	6.7×10^{-4}	2.6	.39	34	19.0×10^{-4}	5.4	.18
15	7.0×10^{-4}	2.7	.37	35	$20\ \times10^{-4}$	5.6	.18
16	7.4×10^{-4}	2.8	.36	36	$21\ \times10^{-4}$	5.8	.17
17	7.8×10^{-4}	2.9	.35	37	$22\ \times10^{-4}$	6.0	.17
18	8.3×10^{-4}	3.0	.33	38	$23\ \times10^{-4}$	6.3	.16
19	8.8×10^{-4}	3.1	.32	39	$24\ \times10^{-4}$	6.5	.15
20	9.3×10^{-4}	3.2	.31	40	$25\ \times10^{-4}$	6.8	.15

$\gamma \approx 4.2\times10^{-4}$(°C)$^{-1}$

* When using Eqs. (13.14), (13.15) and (13.21), or others analogous to them, T in this table should be taken as T_w at the height of determination of $\delta T_w/\delta z$, or as the average of T_w between the heights defining ΔT_w. In practice, it will often be sufficiently accurate to take values from the table at a wet-bulb temperature measured at a convenient reference height. Where wet-bulb depressions are small enough, even a dry-bulb reference temperature may sometimes be permissible.

13.8 | References

Allen, L. H., Jr.: Turbulence and wind speed spectra within a Japanese larch plantation. – J. appl. Meteorol. 7: 73-78, 1968a.

Allen, L. H.: A study of the carbon dioxide concentration monitored over an agricultural field near Ithaca, N.Y. – Tech. Report ECOM 2-681-3, 1968b.

Angus, D. E.: Instruments for micrometeorological research. Solar and terrestrial radiation. – In: Agricultural Meteorology. Pp. 203-218. Bureau of Meteorology, Australia 1968a.

Angus, D. E.: Instruments for micrometeorological research. Temperature and humidity. – In: Agricultural Meteorology. Pp. 231-242. Bureau of Meteorology, Australia 1968b.

Baumgartner, A.: Meteorological approach to the exchange of CO_2 between the atmosphere and vegetation, particularly forest stands. – Photosynthetica 3: 127-149, 1969.

van Bavel, C. H. M.: Potential evaporation: The combination concept and its experimental verification. – Water Resources Res. 2: 455-467, 1966.

Bradley, E. F.: A shearing stress meter for micrometeorological studies. – Quart. J. roy. meteorol. Soc. 94: 380-387, 1968.

Brooks, F. A., Pruitt, W. O.: Investigation of energy, momentum, and mass transfer near the ground. – Univ. California-Davis, Final Rep., U.S. Army Electronics Command Grant DA-AMC-28-043-65-G12, 259 pp., 1965.

Brown, K. W., Covey, W.: The energy-budget evaluation of the micro-meteorological transfer processes within a cornfield. – Agr. Meteorol. 3: 73-96, 1966.

Collins, B. G.: An integrating temperature and humidity gradient recorder. – In: Wexler, A. (ed.): Humidity and Moisture. Vol. I, pp. 83-94. Reinhold Publ. Corp., New York 1965.

Deacon, E. L.: The measurement and recording of the heat flux into the soil. – Quart. J. roy. meteorol. Soc. 76: 479-483, 1950.

Deacon, E. L., Swinbank, W. C.: Comparison between momentum and water vapour transfer. – In: Climatology and Microclimatology. Pp. 38-41. UNESCO, Paris 1958.

Denmead, O. T.: A strip net radiometer. – Aust. J. Instr. Control 23: 61, 1967.

Denmead, O. T.: Carbon dioxide exchange in the field: Its measurement and interpretation. – In: Agricultural Meteorology. Pp. 445-482. Bureau of Meteorology, Australia 1968.

Denmead, O. T.: Comparative micrometeorology of a wheat field and a forest of *Pinus radiata*. – Agr. Meteorol. 6: 357-371, 1969a.

Denmead, O. T.: Discussion to Lemon, E.: Gaseous exchange in crop stands. – In: Eastin, J. D., Haskins, F. A., Sullivan, C. Y., van Bavel, C. H. M. (ed.): Physiological Aspects of Crop Yield. Pp. 137-140. American Society of Agronomy, Madison 1969b.

Denmead, O. T.: Transfer processes between vegetation and air: Measurement, interpretation and modelling. – In: Prediction and Measurement of Photosynthetic Productivity. Pp. 149-164. PUDOC, Wageningen 1970.

Denmead, O. T., McIlroy, I. C.: Measurement of non-potential evaporation from wheat. – Agr. Meteorol. 7: 285-302, 1970.

Dyer, A. J.: The adjustment of profiles and eddy fluxes. – Quart. J. roy. meteorol. Soc. 89: 276-280, 1963.

Dyer, A. J., Hicks, B. B., King, K. M.: The Fluxatron – a revised approach to the measurement of eddy fluxes in the lower atmosphere. – J. appl. Meteorol. 6: 408-413, 1967.

Farrell, D. A., Greacen, E. L., Gurr, C. G.: Vapor transfer in soil due to air turbulence. – Soil Sci. 102: 305-313, 1966.

Fontan, J., Birot, A., Blanc, D., Bouville, A., Druilhet, A.: Measurement of the diffusion of radon, thoron and their radioactive daughter products in the lower layers of the Earth's atmosphere. – Tellus 18: 623-632, 1966.

Fritschen, L. J.: Evapotranspiration rates of field crops by the Bowen ratio method. – Agron. J. 58: 339-342, 1966.

Fuchs, M., Tanner, C. B.: Evaporation from a drying soil. – J. appl. Meteorol. 6: 852-857, 1967.

Fuchs, M., Tanner, C. B., Thurtell, G. W., Black, T. A.: Evaporation from drying surfaces by the combination method. – Agron. J. 61: 22-26, 1969.

Funk, J. P.: Improved polythene-shielded net radiometer. – J. sci. Instr. 36: 267-270, 1959.

Hicks, B. B.: A simple instrument for the measurement of Reynolds stress by eddy correlation. – J. appl. Meteorol. 8: 825-827, 1969.
Inoue, E.: An aerodynamic measurement of photosynthesis over a paddy field. – Proc. 7th Japan National Congr. Appl. Mechanics, pp. 211-214, 1957.
Inoue, E.: The environment of plant surfaces. – In: Evans, L. T. (ed.): Environmental Control of Plant Growth. Pp. 23-31. Academic Press, New York 1963.
Inoue, E., Tani, N., Imai, K., Isobe, S.: The aerodynamic measurement of photosynthesis over the wheat field. – J. agr. Meteorol. (Tokyo) 13: 121-125, 1958.
Inoue, E., Uchijima, Z., Udagawa, T., Horie, T., Kobayashi, K.: Studies of energy and gas exchange within crop canopies (2) – CO_2 flux within and above a corn plant canopy. – J. agr. Meteorol. (Tokyo) 23: 165-176, 1968.
Inoue, E., Uchijima, Z., Saito, T., Isobe, S., Uemura, K.: The "Assimitron" a newly devised instrument for measuring CO_2 flux in the surface air layer. – J. agr. Meteorol. (Tokyo) 25: 165-171, 1969.
Lemon, E. R.: Photosynthesis under field conditions. II. An aerodynamic method for determining the turbulent carbon dioxide exchange between the atmosphere and a corn field. – Agron. J. 52: 697-703, 1960.
Lemon, E. R.: Energy and water balance of plant communities. – In: Evans, L. T. (ed.): Environmental Control of Plant Growth. Pp. 55-78. Academic Press, New York 1963.
Lemon, E.: Aerodynamic studies of CO_2 exchange between the atmosphere and the plant. – In: San Pietro, A., Greer, F. A., Army, T. J. (ed.): Harvesting the Sun. Pp. 263-290. Academic Press, New York–London 1967.
Lemon, E.: Gaseous exchange in crop stands. – In: Eastin, J. D., Haskins, F. A., Sullivan, C. Y., van Bavel, C. H. M. (ed.): Physiological Aspects of Crop Yield. Pp. 117-137. American Society of Agronomy & Crop Sci. Soc. Amer., Madison 1969.
Lemon, E. R., Wright, J. L.: Photosynthesis under field conditions. XA. Assessing sources and sinks of carbon dioxide in a corn (*Zea mays* L.) crop using a momentum balance approach. Agron. J. 61: 405-411, 1969.
Lemon, E. R., Wright, J. L., Drake, G. M.: Photosynthesis under field conditions. XB. Origins of short-time CO_2 fluctuations in a cornfield. – Agron. J. 61: 411-413, 1969.
Lourence, F. J., Pruitt, W. O.: Flexible bags collect gas samples. – Control Eng. 14(9): 105, 1967.
Lumley, J. L., Panofsky, H. A.: The Structure of Atmospheric Turbulence. – Interscience, New York 1964.
Lundegårdh, H.: Carbon dioxide evolution of soil and crop growth. – Soil Sci. 23: 417-452, 1927.
McIlroy, I. C.: An instrument for continuous recording of natural evaporation. – Agr. Metereol. (In press), 1971.
McIlroy, I. C.: Evaporation and its measurement. Part B. Energy balance and combination methods. – In: Agricultural Meteorology. Pp. 409-431. Bureau of Meteorology, Australia 1968.
McIlroy, I. C., Angus, D. E.: The Aspendale multiple weighed lysimeter installation. – CSIRO (Australia) Div. Met. Phys. Tech. Paper 14: 1-27, 1963.
McIlroy, I. C., Angus, D. E.: Grass, water and soil evaporation at Aspendale. – Agr. Meteorol. 1: 201-224, 1964.
Meteorological Office: The Meteorological Glossary. – Her Majesty's Stationery Office, London 1957.
Millington, R. J., Peters, D. B.: Exchange (mass transfer) coefficients in crop canopies. – Agron. J. 61: 815-819, 1969.
Monteith, J. L.: The heat balance of soil beneath crops. – In: Climatology and Microclimatology. – Pp. 123-128. UNESCO, Paris 1958.
Monteith, J. L.: Measurement and interpretation of carbon dioxide fluxes in the field. – Netherlands J. agr. Sci. 10: 334-346, 1962.
Monteith, J. L., Szeicz, G.: The carbon dioxide flux over a field of sugar beet. – Quart. J. roy. meteorol. Soc. 86: 205-214, 1960.
Monteith, J. L., Szeicz, G., Yabuki, J.: Crop photosynthesis and the flux of carbon dioxide below the canopy. – J. appl. Ecol. 1: 321-337, 1964.

Möriköfer, W.: Radiation instruments and measurements. – Ann. int. geophys. Year 5 (Part 6), pp. 365-466. Pergamon Press, New York 1958.

Pasquill, F.: Eddy diffusion of water vapour and heat near the ground. – Proc. roy. Soc. A 198: 116-140, 1949.

Perrier, A.: Approche théorique de la microturbulence et des transferts dans les couverts végétaux en vue de l'analyse de la production végétale. – Météorologie (Paris) 1: 527-550, 1967.

Philip, J. R.: The theory of local advection: I. – J. Meteorol. 16: 535-547, 1959.

Philip, J. R.: The damping of a fluctuating concentration by continuous sampling through a tube. – Aust. J. Phys. 16: 454-463, 1963.

Priestley, C. H. B.: Turbulent Transfer in the Lower Atmosphere. – University of Chicago Press, Chicago 1959.

Pruitt, W. O., Angus, D. E.: Large weighing lysimeter for measuring evapotranspiration. – Trans. Amer. Soc. agr. Eng. 3: 13-15, 1960.

Rider, N. E.: Evaporation from an oat field. – Quart. J. roy. meteorol. Soc. 80: 198-211, 1954.

Rider, N. E., Philip, J. R., Bradley, E. F.: The horizontal transport of heat and moisture – a micrometeorological study. – Quart. J. roy. meteorol. Soc. 89: 507-531, 1963.

Slatyer, R. O., McIlroy, I. C.: Practical Microclimatology. – UNESCO, Paris 1961.

Slavík, B. *et al.*: Methods of Studying Plant Water Relations. – Springer-Verlag, Berlin–Göttingen –New York 1972. (In press.)

Suomi, V. E., Franssila, M., Islitzer, N. F.. An improved net radiation instrument. – J. Meteorol. 11: 276-282, 1954.

Sutton, O. G.: Micrometeorology. – McGraw Hill, New York 1953.

Swinbank, W. C.: The measurement of vertical transfer of heat and water vapor by eddies in the lower atmosphere. – J. Meteorol. 8: 135-145, 1951.

Swinbank, W. C.: An experimental study of eddy transports in the lower atmosphere. – CSIRO (Australia) Div. Met. Phys. Tech. Paper 2: 1-30, 1955.

Tanner, C. B.: Energy balance approach to evapotranspiration from crops. – Soil Sci. Soc. Amer. Proc. 24: 1-9, 1960.

Tanner, C. B.: Basic Instrumentation and Measurements for Plant Environment and Micrometeorology. – Soils Dept. Bul. 6. Univ. Wisconsin 1963.

Thornthwaite, C. W., Holzman, B.: The determination of evaporation from land and water surfaces. – Monthly Weath. Rev. 67: 4-11, 1939.

Udagawa, T.: Variation of aerodynamical characteristics of a barley field with growth. – J. agr. Meteorol. (Tokyo) 22: 7-13, 1966.

Wadsworth, R. M. *et al.* (ed.): The Measurement of Environmental Factors in Terrestrial Ecology. – Blackwell sci. Publ., Oxford–Edinburgh 1968.

Webb, E. K.: Aerial microclimate. – Meteorol. Monographs 6: 27-58, 1965.

Wexler, A. (ed.): Humidity and Moisture. Vols. I-IV. Reinhold Publ. Corp., New York 1965.

W.M.O. (World Meteorological Organization): Agricultural Meteorology. Vols. 1-2. Bureau of Meteorology, Australia 1968.

Wright, J. L., Brown, K. W.: Comparison of momentum and energy balance methods of computing vertical transfer within a crop. – Agron. J. 59: 427-432, 1967.

Wright, J. L., Lemon, E. R.: Photosynthesis under field conditions. VIII. Analysis of windspeed fluctuation data to evaluate turbulent exchange within a corn crop. – Agron. J. 58: 255-261, 1966a.

Wright, J. L., Lemon, E. R.: Photosynthesis under field conditions. IX. Vertical distribution of photosynthesis within a corn crop. – Agron. J. 58: 265-268, 1966b.

14 | ASSESSMENT OF LEAF AREA AND OTHER ASSIMILATING PLANT SURFACES

14.1 | General principles

Estimation of the area of leaves and of the surface of other assimilating plant organs is an essential part of classical growth analysis (see Chapters 10 and 11) and is necessary in many plant physiological studies (see, *e.g.* Donald & Black 1958). While this Chapter attempts to review the principal methods suitable for estimating the size of all plant assimilatory surfaces, the main emphasis lies on methods of measuring the area of the leaves.

Several different principles have been applied to leaf area determination and a great variety of methods have been developed. The choice of methods for an investigation will depend on the main purpose of the measurement (*e.g.*, whether it should be destructive or non-destructive, and whether the total leaf area or that of individual leaves is required), on the required degree of accuracy, on sample size, on the morphology of the leaves and on the technical equipment and amount of time and labour available (see also Section 14.5).

Leaf surfaces are only rarely completely flat, but as most techniques for leaf area measurement are planimetric, the leaves have to be flattened before being measured. Usually, sufficient flattening is achieved by putting the leaves between two sheets of glass or other transparent material. Wilting grass leaves tend to fold or curl inwards; they should, therefore, be measured when turgid. On the other hand, certain curled leaves are flattened more easily when they are just slightly wilted. Some leaves must be cut into pieces, and each piece must be flattened separately. Certain types of leaves cannot be flattened at all (*e.g.*, needles of conifers, trifacial leaves of many *Ericaceae*, succulent leaves) and the investigator can either calculate their surface as that of a geometric body or measure only their projected area. It is highly desirable to find a coefficient of mutual transformation between different kinds of measurement. A transformation coefficient should also be given whenever more than one method of leaf area measurement is used in the course of an experiment.

The assimilatory surface area of other assimilating plant organs is usually estimated by calculation from linear measurements (*e.g.*, the surface of the green portion of a stem is often calculated as that of a cylinder, taking its length and diameter half-way along its length). Geyger (1964) reviews some methods applicable to measuring the often complicated surfaces of three-dimensional assimilating plant organs. Useful information on assessing the surface area relations in plants is also given by Whittaker & Woodwell (1967). Common sense must be applied here as in all methods of measuring assimilatory surfaces. In most instances, for example, the term 'leaf area' denotes one half of the total leaf surface assuming that a leaf receives light mainly from one direction. In other instances, *e.g.* with monofacial and/or amphistomatic, and upright leaves, taking the total area of leaf surface may be more justified (*e.g.* for the leaves of *Iris* or the long spirally twisted leaves of *Typha*). The meaning of terms such as 'leaf area' or 'assimilatory surface' should always be clearly stated. Comparisons between different types of plants and stands (of *LAI*, see Chapter 10) would be facilitated if the values for the leaf area and for the surface area of other assimilating organs (*e.g.*, stems) were indicated separately.

Leaf anatomy strongly influences specific leaf area (leaf area: leaf dry weight ratio) which is frequently estimated in a subsample and then used to calculate the total leaf area from total leaf weight (see Sections 10.5.4. and 14.3.2). As a rule, specific leaf area tends to be highly variable, and so representative subsampling of leaves is essential for determining the total leaf area of a plant or stand. Some suitable subsampling procedures are mentioned in Sections 10.10 and 10.13. Others consist in pooling the leaves stripped off from all plants in a sample, and in measuring a known portion of the leaves, in measuring only every i^{th} leaf (counted from base to apex of a shoot), *etc.*

Petioles are physiologically closer to stems than to leaves; in most cases, therefore, 'leaf area' refers only to leaf laminae. Stipules and cotyledons, on the other hand, are mostly measured together with the true leaves. In grasses, the surface of the leaf sheaths usually forms part of the stem surface and is calculated accordingly. The method of estimating the surface of green parts of the flowers and inflorescences must be selected individually in each case. In many instances, the assimilatory surface of these plant parts is negligible in comparison with that of the leaves and stems, and their measurement would be unnecessary for most purposes. However, this assumption can only be made after careful consideration and preferably after experimental verification.

Most of the methods of estimating leaf area are applicable not only to fresh leaves but also to their images whether drawn, recorded photographically on film or paper, or as blueprints or colour images. Such recording allows the area measurements, which are usually relatively time-consuming, to be postponed to a more convenient time. Colour images are usually negative leaf images obtained by putting the leaves on a sheet of paper covered with a loose net, and spraying with a dilute dye (Šetlík, unpublished). This technique is especially suited to large leaves. A non-destructive version of this technique, using a very dilute solution of a non-toxic dye, was devised by Hořavka (1953).

14.2 | Survey of methods of assessing leaf area

Early reviews of methods for the determination of leaf area have been made by Thoday (1909), Darrow (1932), Frear (1935), Miller (1938), Lal & Subba Rao (1951) and Milthorpe (1956). The present survey is based on the relatively recent reviews by Květ, Nečas & Kubín (1966) in Šesták, Čatský *et al.* (1966), Marshall (1968b) and de Parcevaux & Čatský (1970). A modified classification from Marshall's (1968b) review is used in this survey. Many of the methods listed below require destructive sampling.

14.2.1 | Leaf outline on graph paper

The leaf is placed on graph paper or on a grid and its margin outlined. The area is then obtained by counting the squares within the outline (Goodall 1947;

Winter *et al.* 1956). In a field modification of this method, a grid is marked on a clear piece of acrylic plastic against which the leaf is held, the squares blocked out by the leaf being counted (Vyvyan & Evans 1932). The accuracy of this method depends on leaf shape: for highly divided or compound leaves this kind of leaf area measurement is impracticable.

14.2.2 | Planimetric method

The leaf is measured directly, or an outline of the leaf is obtained by tracing or by printing on a photosensitive paper. The area within the outline is measured using a hand planimeter (Brown & Escombe 1905; Clements & Goldsmith 1924; Scheibe 1927; Stocker 1929; Graf-Marin 1934; Frear 1935; Miller 1938; Ellenberg 1939; Polster & Reichenbach 1958; Paquin & Coulombe 1959, and numerous other authors). Planimetering is repeated at least twice (with the arms of the instrument in different positions) and the mean of the values indicated by the counter is then recorded. Measurements with a hand planimeter are relatively most accurate when the angle between the two arms of the instrument deviates from 90° as little as possible (Kranz 1964). The method is therefore best suited to measuring leaves, or sets of leaves, in which the widths are fairly similar to the lengths (orbicular, elliptic, cordate, ovate leaves, *etc.*). Lanceolate, spathulate, linear and other leaves of this kind are less easy to measure and it is better to cut them into segments before measurement. Very small leaves can be projected, using a photographic enlarger, onto drawing or photographic paper, by which copies several times larger are obtained (*e.g.* de Parcevaux & Massin 1970, for flax). Hand planimetry is often used as a standard technique by which other methods of leaf area measurement are calibrated. Its accuracy, however, should not be taken for granted without checking. Some aspects of the planimetric method have been evaluated byJeško (1966) who also adapted the method for measuring narrow leaves stuck with a self-adhesive strip to a sheet of paper and air-dried afterwards (shrinkage by about 5%). Suitably arranged sets of leaves or their copies can be planimetered together (Ellenberg 1939; Möller 1945).

14.2.3 | Gravimetric method

An outline of the leaf is traced, or a print is made, on a paper which has a uniform weight distribution with area. The leaf shape is cut from the paper and weighed. The leaf area is then calculated from the weight to area relationship of the paper, established by weighing pieces of paper of known area (Ramann 1911; Henrici 1918; Lüdin 1927; Maximov 1929; Frear 1935; Miller 1938; Vareschi 1951; Ruck & Bolas 1956). Cutting out the leaf copies can be extremely tedious. This can be obviated by tracing the leaf outlines on the paper with 5% sulphuric acid using a glass pen. After slight heating, the sulphuric acid becomes concentrated, attacks the paper and the copy falls out. The shape of the copies is satisfactorily preserved if thin but tough paper is used (Václavík 1955).

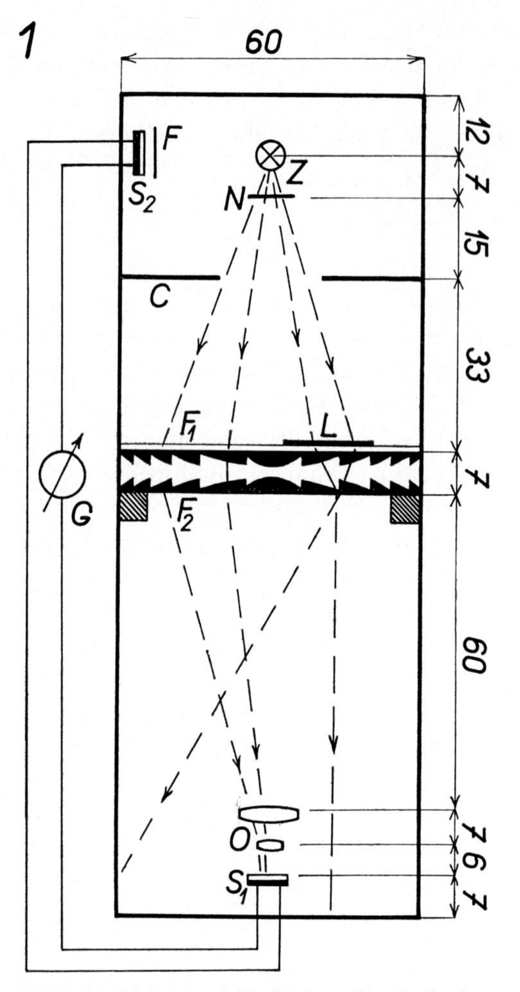

Fig. 14.1 Two types of simple photoelectric planimeters after Kubín, Květ & Šetlík (from Šetlík & Kubín 1966). Diagram *1* shows the design of the modified photoelectric planimeter devised by Miller, Shadbolt & Holm (1956). Light from a tungsten lamp Z passes through a density correction filter N and a diaphragm C which intercepts scattered light; the leaves L are placed on a transparent support immediately above the collimating Fresnel lens F_1. The condenser lens F_2 allows only those light beams, which have not been scattered by the leaves, to reach the measuring photocell S_1 in front of which a compound lens O is placed. The reference photocell S_2 protected by a neutral filter F (with approximately 2% transmission), compensates for small random variations in light flux due to voltage fluctuations in the mains. The electrical circuitry including a galvanometer G is not presented in detail.

14.2.4 | Dot counting method

A distinctive modification of the method described in Section 14.2.1 which is suitable for field use employs a grid of regularly spaced dots. The number of dots obscured by the leaf is counted (Negisi, Satoo & Yagi 1957; Henicke 1963). The measurement is repeated with the leaf in different positions, and the mean value is recorded. The most suitable distance between the dots depends on leaf size; a 1 cm × 1 cm spacing is most common. Negisi, Satoo & Yagi (1957) showed that

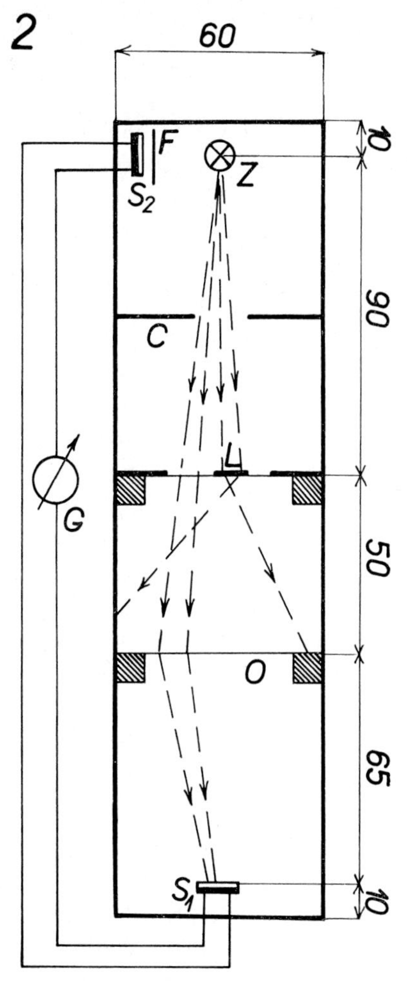

Diagram *2* shows the design of the simplified version of the photoelectric planimeter designed by Kubín, Květ and Šetlík in which Fresnel lenses are not employed. Light beams from the source *Z* which reach the light-scattering screen *O* are confined to a narrow angle; therefore, only a negligible proportion of the light scattered by the leaves *L* placed between two transparent glass sheets falls on the screen *O*. The resulting luminance of the screen is measured by the photocell S_1; when the distance of the leaf-supporting screen from the screen *O* is chosen appropriately the difference in current becomes proportional to the area of the leaves. The walls of the instrument case above *O* are painted black, thus absorbing most of the scattered light; the walls below *O* are painted white, thus homogenizing the illumination of the photocell S_1. The role of the reference photocell S_2 and the design of the circuitry not shown in the drawing are the same as in the diagram *1* (p.520).

the only slightly increased accuracy obtained by closer spacing (0.5 cm) was not commensurate with the extra time spent on counting the dots. Bachmann & Keller (1965) used an electronic device which recorded the number of holes (= dots) covered by the leaves. (This method is also relevant to Section 14.2.5.) The accuracy of the dot-counting method is subject to limitations similar to those of the point quadrat method used for estimating vegetation cover in the field (Goodall 1952; Kemp & Kemp 1956).

14.2.5 | *Interception of light or other types of radiation*

Methods based on light interception are those most commonly used for indirect measurements of leaf area. The instruments employed are called photoelectric planimeters. The common principle on which they are based is that the intensity of light emitted from a constant source and reaching a detector is proportional to the area of material (leaves) placed between the light source and the detector. The detector is usually a photovoltaic cell, the output of which is measured directly, or, preferably, against the constant output from a reference photocell under standard illuminance. Early applications of this principle include those of Gerdel & Salter (1928); Frear (1935); Withrow (1935); Mitchell (1936); Hibbard, Grisby & Keck (1937); Kramer (1937) and Milthorpe (1942). These authors established numerous features of the method, including requirements for a light-proof housing, an even illumination at the level of the inserted leaves, cooling of the light source in some instances, protection of the photocell(s) from strong illumination, and the desirability of knowing details of the light source emission spectrum and that of photocell sensitivity. Recent trends in the design of various types of photoelectric planimeters may be followed in the papers by Miller, Shadbolt & Holm (1956); Donovan, Magee & Kalbfleisch (1958); Pilet & Meylan (1958); Šanda (1958); Batyuk, Rybalko & Okanenko (1959); Gavrilov & Eremenko (1959); Voisey & Mason (1963); Geyger (1964); Hughes (1964); Kranz (1964); Kallio (1965); Brandt & Akopov (1966); Davis *et al.* (1966); Květ, Nečas & Kubín (1966); Moelker (1966); Šetlík & Kubín (1966); Marshall (1968a); Kornher & Rodskjer (1969); Lieth in Vanseveren (1969). Fig. 14.1 shows two successful modifications of the Miller, Shadbolt & Holm (1956) type of planimeter, constructed by Kubín, Květ & Šetlík (from Šetlík & Kubín 1966).

Photoelectric planimeters can be of any required size. Large planimeters can be adjusted to accommodate small samples by inserting black paper masks with openings of suitable size. The resulting reduction in illuminance may require compensation by increasing the sensitivity of the photocells in some way. There are several sources of error in photoelectric planimetry (see, *e.g.* Kranz 1964; Marshall 1968a), and it is desirable that the design of the planimeter reduces these to a realistic level in relation to errors associated with leaf sampling *etc.* Even illumination over the area on which the leaves are to be positioned ('active area') is essential. It is achieved if the light source is a bank of fluorescent tubes (Kranz 1964), incandescent lamps (Grigor'ev & Metreveli 1958) or a luminescent panel (Voisey & Kloek 1964). If the light is evenly scattered before reaching the leaf surfaces then even illuminance may also be obtained by inserting an opaque glass sheet between the light source and the leaves and by multiple reflection from the planimeter walls. With point or near-point light sources, the differences in the illuminance of the central part and that of the edges of the 'active area' are compensated by differential neutral filters inserted either above or below the leaves. The filter may be simply a glass sheet dotted differentially with Indian ink (this being done empirically so that the same reduction of photocell output is brought about by the same area of black paper positioned in different parts of the 'active area'), or it may be a suitably graded negative image of the light field at the 'active area' level, or concentric circles drawn on a glass sheet (Laisk 1965). Another problem is that of light transmission by the leaves. Photoelectric planimeters can be classified as being either 'selective' or 'non-selective' with respect to the differences in light transmission by the leaves. Most of the modern photoelectric planimeters are non-selective, the error due to differential light transmission by the leaves being less than 3 % or even 1 %. With scattered light, the error due to transmission can be greatly reduced by using very weak light – 162 lux at the 'active area' level according to Mitchell (1936). Another way of nearly eliminating differential light transmission is to use a coloured filter in the system (its exact position in the system is theoretically immaterial) which absorbs the wavelengths of the light transmitted by the leaves, to which the photocell is sensitive (see, *e.g.*, Gavrilov & Eremenko 1959; Kranz 1964; Hurd & Rees 1966). Using a light source and photocell whose emission and sensitivity, respectively, do not overlap within the range of wavelength transmission by the leaves would be another possibility.

Photoelectric planimeters using point or near-point sources emitting beams of light are mostly derived from the type described by Miller, Shadbolt & Holm (1956). They are non-selective, as their design makes use of the principles of geometrical optics, and the measuring photocell records only those beams that have not changed their pre-determined pathways. The optical equipment of these planimeters involves lenses – usually Fresnel lenses in the larger apparatus, and condenser lenses in the smaller ones (Miller, Shadbolt & Holm 1956; Kubín & Bartoš in Šesták, Čatský *et al.* 1966; Kubín, Květ & Šetlík – see Fig. 14.1-*1*) or mirrors (*e.g.*, Voisey & Mason 1963). Both lenses and mirrors have the advantage of shortening the pathway of the light beams, but practically non-selective planimeters, based on the same principle, have also been constructed without using any condensor lenses or mirrors. In such an apparatus designed by Kubín, Květ & Šetlík (see Fig. 14.1-*2*), the maximum error due to differential light transmission by the leaves does not exceed 3 %. However, the apparatus requires the use of a relatively strong light source and sufficiently sensitive photocells and galvanometer, because the pathway of the light beams is rather long.
Batyuk, Rybalko & Okanenko (1959) describe another non-selective design using two identical chambers, a control chamber and an operating one. The difference in photocell output from the two chambers is amplified and indicated on a meter calibrated directly in leaf area units. Maggs (1957) employed a similar principle, with half of the 'active area' being first obscured by a screen. After inserting the leaves, the photocell output is brought back to the original level by removing a part of the screen, with an area equal to that of the leaves.
In most photoelectric planimeters, a sensitive galvanometer of the order of 10^{-6} to 10^{-9} A is used for recording the current generated by the photocells. With two photocells, a measuring and a reference one, null-point measurements are, on the whole, preferable to those in which the galvanometer deflection (proportional to leaf area) is recorded. A simple and effective compensating electric circuitry is described by Grigor'ev & Metreveli (1958).
The use of non-selective photoelectric planimeters is recommended wherever possible. If, however, only a selective instrument is available, a transmission correction factor should be determined by measuring the photocell output for the same areas of leaf tissue and of black paper or other opaque material (Kramer 1937).

Alternatively, the light transmitted by the measured leaves can be established directly (Withrow 1935).

Calibration of the instrument should be checked during measurements in most types of photoelectric planimeters. The elaborate models are suited only for laboratory measurements of sets of relatively large leaves. Loading the instrument with very small leaves is too time-consuming, in addition to which wilting can become a problem, as can the condensation of water evaporating from the leaves on the glass sheets between which they are pressed.

The present trend in the development of photoelectric planimeters is towards small instruments suitable for field use (Stout 1963; Voisey & Kloek 1964; Woodwell & Bourdeau 1965) or towards instruments suitable for measuring photographic leaf images. Fig. 14.2 shows a successful planimeter of this type constructed by Marshall (1968a), suitable for measuring light interception by photographic images of leaves on transparent film. A similar technique is used by Schwabe (1951), Geyger (1964) and Hughes (1964). The main advantages of this combination method are that permanent records of leaf shape are produced and a wide range of both individual leaf and leaf sample sizes, once photographed, can be measured with a relatively small apparatus. The upper limit of sample size largely depends on the size of leaf photography table which can be accommodated. A detailed account of the errors associated with the combination method is given by Marshall (1968a).

Photoelectric planimeters in which the whole active area (in some instances only a narrow slot across which the leaves are moved at a constant speed) is scanned by a small flying light spot and the resulting current is measured digitally and integrated, represent another recent development in non-selective photoelectric planimetry. The first apparatus of this kind was constructed by Orchard (1961) while the latest development is represented by a highly efficient automatic apparatus designed by Murata & Hayashi (1967). This apparatus is manufactured commercially by *Hayashi Denko Comp. Ltd.* (Tokyo, Japan), under the name *Automatic Area Meter, Model AAM-4*. Another apparatus of a similar type is in use at the Agriculture Department, Univ. of Oxford, England (G. E. Blackman, personal communication).

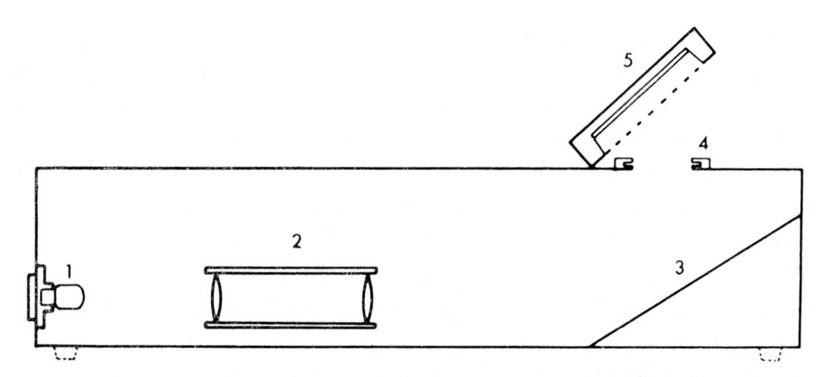

Fig. 14.2 Photoelectric planimeter for use with 35 mm film (semi-diagrammatic). *1:* light source, *2:* collimator, *3:* mirror, *4:* film carrier, *5:* photocell housing which, when lowered, operates a microswitch to turn on the light. The photocell output is fed to a galvanometer. (From Marshall 1968a.)

The automatic digital instruments are free from most of the defects of the other photoelectric planimeters caused by susceptibility to changes in voltage, and are entirely non-selective with respect to leaf thickness and colour. The performance of the Japanese light-scanning apparatus, for instance, is highly satisfactory, with an error of $\pm$ 1.5% and a sensitivity of 4 mm^2. It is capable of handling 1.2 m^2 of leaf area per hour, even when the leaves are cut into small pieces.

The errors of measurement with different photoelectric planimeters are not always indicated by the authors. Miller, Shadbolt & Holm (1956) quote 1.5% as the highest coefficient of variation for their measurements. Maggs (1957) claims an error of $\pm$ 1 cm^2 for his instrument. Similarly, Kubín, Květ & Šetlík give the error of their instrument (see Fig. 14.1-*2*) as $\pm$ 10 cm^2 when the 'active area' is 1000 cm^2. Kranz (1964) compared photoelectric and hand planimetry and statistically analysed the variation of measurements with his own type of photoelectric planimeter which was slightly selective. The random variation was mainly due to the random errors in galvanometer readings. Apart from the variation caused by differential transmission of the leaves, the systematic variation was mainly caused by uneven photocell sensitivity and its decline with time. Voisey & Kloek (1964) claim only 1% difference in output from different places on the large photocell they use (about 7 cm × 7 cm).

Alpha radioactive rays are a type of radiation other than light which has been employed in leaf area measurement (Fojtík 1969). Nátr (1968) suggested the use of '*Quantimet*', an apparatus manufactured by *Metals Research Ltd.* (Melbourn, Royston, Herts., England). The leaves or, preferably, their photographic images are recorded by a television camera and projected on a monitor. The camera can be combined with a microscope or epidiascope for use with small objects. A built-in computer evaluates the leaf area as a percentage of the total area recorded.

14.2.6 | Air flow interception and analogous measurements

Jenkins (1959) constructed an airflow planimeter in which the leaves are interposed between a bulk source of air and a receiver (vacuum line). The resistance to air flow offered by the leaves is measured by balancing the flow in a second flow line, the balancing device being calibrated in leaf area units. This method is best suited for measuring sets of evenly distributed, detached small leaves (of clover, flax, grasses, *etc.*) or pieces of them, rather than for large leaves. The leaves are pressed on to the 'active area' (a perforated plate with densely and evenly spaced small holes) automatically by air suction, which makes loading the instrument and measurement less time-consuming than with a photoelectric planimeter. This type of planimeter has also been used by Oyama (1960).

Modified versions of the airflow planimeter have been described by Bell & Smith (1965) and de Parcevaux & Grebet (1970). With pear leaves, the error of this instrument was $\pm$ 4.6%, when calibrated against hand planimetry, and the accuracy of the airflow technique was found to be greater than that of the gravimetric method (Section 14.2.3) and the estimation of leaf area from linear measurements (Section 14.3.1).

In many forage plants, in which leaf area is most conveniently measured with an airflow planimeter, separation of the leaves from the stems is very tedious. This procedure is facilitated by using a mechanical device described by Troelsen & Hanel (1969).

Jones (1961) measured the retardation by the leaves of the flow of very fine sand instead of air. In his instrument, however, the area : circumference ratio seems to be a more important source of error than in the airflow planimeter. The small-ball counting type (Iyama 1963) apparently has similar limitations.

Thomas & Lazenby (1967) compared airflow planimetry with the assessment of leaf area index by the inclined point quadrat method in swards of *Festuca arundinacea* (see also Section 12.7.3). In 5 out of 6 cases the airflow-planimeter estimates of leaf area were higher than those from inclined point quadrats.

14.3 | Estimation methods

These methods are based on a statistically defined mathematical relationship between some leaf characteristic(s) and leaf area.

14.3.1 | Relationships between linear measurements and leaf area

Estimation of leaf area from linear measurements is possible with both leaves and their images, almost always also without destroying the leaves (Section 14.4). Images of small leaves must be enlarged before sufficiently accurate measurements can be taken (de Parcevaux & Massin 1970). The most frequently used leaf characteristics to be measured and related to leaf area (A) are leaf length (L) and leaf breadth (B), either the maximum breadth, or the breadth at a specified fraction (1/2; 2/3; etc.) of the leaf length behind the leaf tip (which sometimes has to be defined arbitrarily, *e.g.* in some grass leaves with thread-like dry tips). The method can be applied to leaves of various shapes wherever these allow suitable and well-defined linear measurements to be taken.

The general form of relationship: $A = b \cdot LB$ has been found satisfactory by many authors, where b is a coefficient which requires checking from time to time, especially when leaf shape changes with position on the plant and with plant age (Clements & Goldsmith 1924; Darrow 1932; Graf-Marin 1934; Johnston & Miller 1940; Goodall 1947; Winter *et al.* 1956; Chatterjee & Dutta 1961; Stickler, Wearden & Pauli 1961; Carleton & Foote 1965; Larsen 1965; Lazarov 1965; Stoy 1965; Baker & Meyer 1966; Jain & Misra 1966; Shevtsov 1966; Hodáňová 1967; Golovin & Migunov 1968, and other authors).

A similar relationship, derived by Lal & Subba Rao (1950a, b, 1951) for cereals, relates leaf area (A), length (L) and breadth (B) by

$\log A = \log L + \log B - \log b$

where B is measured at $L/2$ and the constant $b = LB/A$. The mean coefficients of variation for b were 2.9, 3.3, 6.6 and 1.0% for barley, rice, maize and wheat, respectively. Langer (1956) modified this relationship by taking B as the mean of breadths measured at 1/4 and 3/4 of L but the extra effort involved does not seem worthwhile. Anikiev & Kutuzov (1961) provide further mathematical treatment of the relationship between leaf length and breadth and leaf area. Kemp (1960), having reviewed the previous literature on the subject, examined the use of linear measurements for estimating leaf area in grasses and arrived at $A = 0.905.\ LB$ for

Lolium perenne, *Dactylis glomerata*, *Festuca pratensis* and *Phleum pratense*, with B taken at $L/2$. The variation accounted for by this value of b was over 99%. Tejawani, Ramakrishna Kurup & Ven Kataraman (1957) examined the use of linear measurements for estimating leaf area in tobacco, and Suggs, Beeman & Splinter (1960) found the relationship $A = b\,LB$ satisfactory, with B the maximum breadth and b ranging from 0.613 to 0.675 in large leaves, according to the tobacco variety and irrigation treatment. In small leaves, $b = 0.703$.

Although the above relationships are simple and often also sufficiently accurate, the full form of the linear equation $y = bx + a$ is also frequently used, in which y represents leaf area, and a and b are constants. Relationships have been examined in which x has been leaf length (L), leaf breadth (B), their product LB, and $L + B$ (Batens & Muncie 1943; Boynton & Harris 1950; Ruck & Bolas 1956; Ackley, Crandall & Russell 1958; Chatterjee & Dutta 1961; Turrell 1961; Epstein & Robinson 1965; Kryukovskiĭ 1966; Nečas, Zrůst & Partyková 1967; Savchenko 1967; Singh 1967; Wendt 1967; Wendt, Haas & Runkles 1967; Ondok 1968 *etc.*). Ackley, Crandall & Russell (1958) examined the relationship for x representing various values derived from L and B and also determined the smallest number of leaves required to obtain a reliable relationship. R. E. Marshall (1933) describes a device for estimating the areas of strawberry leaves, having first found the relationship between linear dimensions of the terminal leaflet and total leaf area. Linear measurements have been used to estimate the area of leaves which are compound or otherwise have variable shapes, by Gregory (1921, 1928) and Volkov & Selevtsev (1959) in cucumber, Möller (1945) in beech, Goodall (1945) in tomato, Black (1958) in clover, Spencer (1962) in cassava and Peneva (1968) in *Pyrethrum* and *Artemisia*. The leaf areas of cotton (Baker & Meyer 1966), *Ricinus* (Jain &

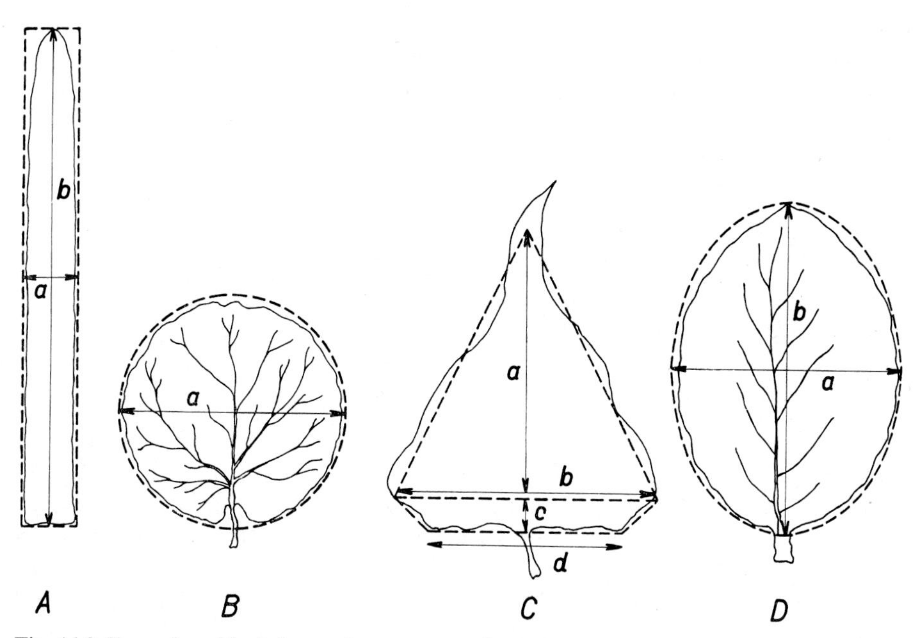

Fig. 14.3 Examples of leaf shapes that are approximated by geometric shapes, the areas within which are calculated from linear dimensions of the leaves (*A*, *B*, *C*, *D*). (From Nichiporovich *et al.* 1961.)

Misra 1966), soybean (Golovin & Migunov 1968), *Oxalis* and *Tephrosia* (Basu 1969) and of several tree species (Kryukovskiĭ 1966) have also recently been estimated from linear measurements. Tirén (1927) estimated the surface of pine needles from linear measurements. Ondok's (1968) regression equations for *Phragmites* account for the change of the relationship $A : LB$ with the position of the leaf on the stem, thus making the area estimation more precise. In potato plants, Nečas, Zrůst & Partyková (1967) studied varietal differences in the regression of leaf area on leaf length.

Many leaf shapes can be approximated by geometric shapes the areas of which are calculated using appropriate formulae. Fig. 14.3, drawn after Nichiporovich *et al.* (1961), shows several examples. The precision of the leaf area estimate is sometimes increased by introducing a correction factor obtained empirically by comparing the calculated value with that obtained by another method, usually by use of a hand planimeter. Hopkins (1939) and Ondok (1968) suggest a precise method for measuring the area of grass leaves, based on considering a grass leaf as a row of trapezia with a triangle at the tip.

Bistrup (1943) and Polster & Reichenbach (1958) examined the effect of leaf shape

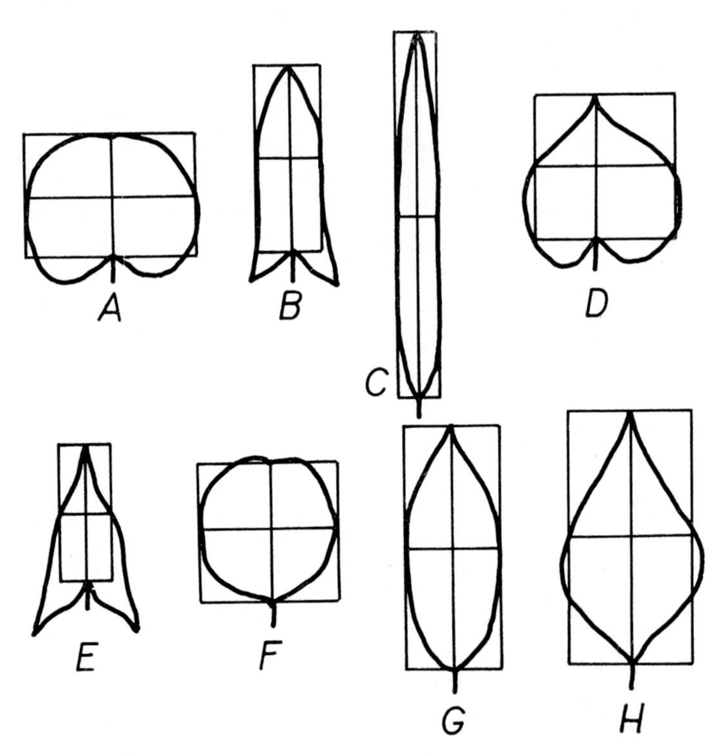

Fig. 14.4 Effect of leaf shape on the approximate value of the coefficient used to transform the product of leaf length times leaf breadth at half length (rectangle area) into leaf area. The following coefficients apply to the different leaf shapes sketched above:

A:	0.982	*E:*	1.226 (!)
B:	0.921	*F:*	0.769
C:	0.857	*G:*	0.654
D:	0.856	*H:*	0.612

(From Polster & Reichenbach 1958.)

Table 14.1 Examples of coefficients b used for converting the product of leaf length (L) and maximum leaf breadth (B) (unless otherwise stated) into leaf area (A) by $A = bLB$ in various species.

Species	b	Author(s)	Remark
Phragmites communis	0.50–0.64	Ondok (1968)	b depending on shoot age and leaf position
Barley	0.64	Lazarov (1965)	
Sudan grass	0.645	Lazarov (1965)	
Wheat	0.65	Lazarov (1965)	
	0.65–0.81	Hodáňová (1967)	Different crop densities
	0.78–0.95	Owen (1968)	Two varieties, different L classes of leaves
Oats	0.655	Lazarov (1965)	
Rice	0.66	Lazarov (1965)	
	0.702–0.943	Owen (1968)	Different L and B classes of leaves
Maize	0.71–0.81	Lazarov (1965)	Different varieties
	0.72–0.80	V. Ross (1967)	b increasing with LB
Sorghum	0.80–0.86	V. Ross (1967)	b increasing with LB
Meadow grasses	0.905	Kemp (1960)	B taken at $L/2$
Grasses in general	2/3	Anikiev & Kutuzov (1961)	Only for approximate estimates
Artemisia maritima var. *salina*	0.23–0.40	Peneva (1968)	Mean b increasing with plant age
Pyrethrum cinerariaefolium	0.28–0.49	Peneva (1968)	Mean b increasing with plant age
Mentha arvensis	0.59–0.77	Chatterjee & Dutta (1961)	No relation of b to leaf size class!
Sunflower	0.61–0.76	Lazarov (1965)	Different classes of L
	0.68	Aston (1967)	
	0.69	Šesták in Květ, Nečas & Kubín (1966)	
	0.70–0.76	V. Ross (1967)	b increasing with LB
Tobacco	0.61–0.69	McKee & Yocum (1970)	
	0.62–0.70	Suggs, Beeman & Splinter (1960)	Different varieties
Sugar beet	0.64–0.77	Birke (1965)	Different treatments and years
	0.74–0.78	Lazarov (1965)	
	0.76–0.90	Shevtsov (1966)	Different varieties
Cotton	0.69	V. Ross (1967)	
Lucerne	0.71	Lazarov (1965)	
Clover	0.725	Lazarov (1965)	
Kale	0.746-0.797	Čatský (unpublished)	B at $L/2$; mean = 0.765
	0.764	Šesták in Květ, Nečas & Kubín (1966)	
Pear tree	0.63	de Parcevaux (unpublished)	var. 'Beurré Hardy'
	0.675	Rubin & Danilevskaya (1957)	

Table 14.1 (cont.)

Species	b	Author(s)	Remark
Cherry tree	0.67	Rubin & Danilevskaya (1957)	
Apple tree	0.681–0.735	Gladyshev (1969)	Six varieties
	0.69–0.70	Rubin & Danilevskaya (1957)	
Populus robusta	0.758–0.848	Polster & Reichenbach (1958)	B at $L/2$; mean = 0.796 2

Table 14.2 Examples of regression equations used for estimating leaf area (A) from leaf length (L) and/or maximum leaf breadth (B) (unless otherwise stated). In some cases, with regression coefficients (r) for 95% probability level or with their standard deviations.

Species	Equation	Author(s)	Remarks
Sorghum 8 varieties	$\log A = 1.497 \log L = 0.406$	Wendt (1967)	$r = 0.94$
Phragmites communis, individual leaves	$A = (0.633\,4 - 0.009\,6\,Y) - LB$	Ondok (1968)	Y – number of leaf from base
Tobacco, whole plants	$A = 2.113\,B + 0.621\,LB - 11.308$	Suggs, Beeman & Splinter (1960)	Close spacing
	$A = -1.191\,B + 0.716\,LB + 3.345$		Wide spacing
	$A = 1.255\,B + 0.623\,LB - 2.122$		Irrigated
Potato var. Rajka, whole plants	$A = -0.474 + 1.178\,L$	Nečas, Zrůst & Partyková (1967)	Glass-house
	$A = -0.293 + 0.927\,L$		Field
Potato var. Cardinal, whole plants	$A = -0.272 + 0.767\,L$		Glass-house
	$A = -0.247 + 0.744\,L$		Field
Cucumber, groups of varieties of similar leaf shape	$A = 1/2(LB + 0.06\,LB)$	Volkov & Selevtsev (1959)	Round leaves
	$A = 1/2(LB + 0.19\,LB)$		Triangular or pentagonal leaves
	$A = 1/2(LB + 0.04\,LB)$		Triangularly or pentagonally lobed leaves
Cotton, 10 varieties	$\log A = 1.863 \log L + 0.006$	Wendt (1967)	$r = 0.95$
Cotton var. Gregg	$\log A = 2.046 \log L - 0.119$		$r = 0.99$
Cotton, rough leaf type	$\log A = 1.910 \log L + 0.045$		$r = 0.98$
Cassava var. Congo, sets of leaves	$LB = 0.407\,A + 11.38$	Spencer (1962)	
Prosopis glandulosa, all leaves of a tree	$\log A = 1.697 \log L_s - 0.465$	Wendt, Haas & Runkles (1967)	$r = 0.96$ ($s = 0.148$), L_s = sum of lengths of rachises

on the coefficient relating LB (B taken at $L/2$) to leaf area. Fig. 14.4 and Table 14.1 may serve as an approximate guide for those trying to establish relationships of this kind in various plant species. Some of the values presented in Table 14.1 also illustrate change of the coefficient with variety and plant age or leaf size. On the other hand, Rubin & Danilevskaya (1957) found that the ratio of LB to leaf area of a given fruit tree variety was practically constant. Table 14.2 gives a few examples of the full regression equations used for estimating leaf area.

Rapid estimation of leaf area is needed in vegetational analysis. Cain *et al.* (1956) and Cain & de Castro (1959) found the relationship $A = 2/3\,LB$ to suit most species in the tropical rain forest. Cooper (1960), working in a temperate woodland community, concluded that the $2/3\,LB$ relationship could be used to assign most of the species to Raunkiaer's (1916) leaf-size classes. For lobed leaves, the factors of 1/2 and 1/3 are recommended, depending on the size and number of sinuses. This approach may be sufficient in rapid estimates of leaf area index in communities comprising many species but its accuracy should be verified empirically, at least with the dominant species.

Linear measurements other than leaf length and breadth have sometimes also been used. In cotton, Moreshet (1965) found a high correlation between leaf area and the square of the length of one of the main veins adjacent to the central vein, but this correlation required to be established anew for each variety.

Linear coordinates of one or more well-defined points at the edge of the leaf blade can also be related to leaf area. Owen's (1957) application of this technique to leaves of sugar beet is shown in Fig. 14.5. Leaf area is calculated from $A = b.LB$, where b is the regression coefficient between the leaf area and the product of the coordinates LB. Employing a similar principle, Freeman & Bolas (1956), Freeman (1958) and Fulga (1961, 1965a, b) use rectangular grids for direct estimation of the area of fruit-tree leaves whose shape approaches an ellipse, with

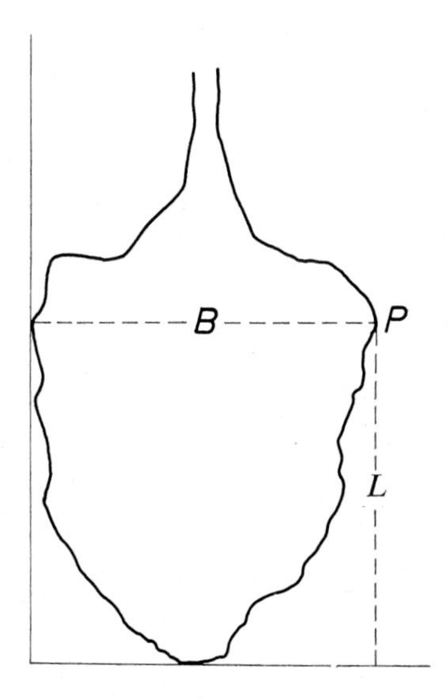

Fig. 14.5 Rapid estimation of the area of a sugar beet leaf from the co-ordinates L and B of point P, defined as the intersection of maximum leaf width with leaf edge. (From Owen 1957.)

individual cross-points of the grid calibrated in values of LB. To indicate leaf area directly in cm^2, the unit linear dimension of the grid must be $b^{-1/2}$.

Derco's (1961) measuring scale for rapid and accurate estimation of the area of sunflower leaves in the field is based on a similar principle, as well as Owen's (1968) scale for measuring areas of cereal leaves.

Any worker who has decided to use linear measurements for estimating leaf area should find the exact form and fiducial limits of the regression valid for his own plant material. Other authors' coefficients can serve only as useful guides, as the ratio of leaf length to breadth is often affected by environmental factors (see, *e.g.* Suggs, Beeman & Splinter 1960; Wassink 1961, 1965). In sugar beet, Birke (1965) found that the ratio of LB to A was appreciably different in two successive years. In some instances, it is possible to calculate the mean linear leaf dimensions and to multiply their product by the correction coefficient. This rapid procedure is, of course, somewhat less accurate than calculating the area for each leaf separately. However, it has been employed with satisfactory results by Lal & Subba Rao (1950a, b, 1951) and, in an improved version, by Langer (1956) in cereals, and by Lyon (1948) in tomato var. Bonny Best, in which the total area of a large set of leaves was calculated as the square of the sum of all leaf lengths multiplied by 0.1551. An analogous method has been proposed for maize leaves and stems by Dorovskaya (1964).

In some plants, especially in grasses or sedges with filamentous or very narrow leaves, leaf length is the only parameter which can be recorded with sufficient accuracy (see, *e.g.*, Smetánková 1959). This value is difficult to convert into leaf area. The conversion may be possible only if a row of turgid leaf segments of known length can be arranged closely alongside one another on a strip of self-adhesive tape, thus making a rectangle of measurable breadth, made up of a known number of leaf segments (Květ, unpublished).

Linear measurements are also employed in calculating the surface areas of three-dimensional plant organs (stems, conical and trifacial leaves, *etc.*), as already discussed in Section 14.1. In grasses, the assimilatory area of a leaf sheath can often be calculated as that of a rectangle. The length of the leaf sheath may be correlated with that of the leaf lamina but this relationship seems to be affected by the environment (Enyi 1962). Needles of some conifers (*e.g.*, *Abies alba*, *Taxus baccata*, *Tsuga canadensis*) can be regarded as being flat, without introducing an appreciable error. In other conifers (*e.g.*, *Pinus*), the needle thickness should be considered when converting the projected area to the actual needle surface area (*e.g.* Kozlowski & Schumacher 1943; Möller 1945; Rutter 1957). Ronco (1969) suggested that photosynthesis in conifers could be expressed on a leaf volume basis, and constructed an apparatus for determining the volume of conifer foliage. A mechanical instrument for measuring leaf thickness was devised by Meidner (1952); its construction enables continuous measurement in the field. Stickland (1969) constructed a special device for accurate measurements of plant diameters.

14.3.2 | The leaf-weighing method

This method, which depends on the leaf area : leaf weight ratio, is frequently used in growth analysis of plant stands in which it would be technically impossible to measure the area of the whole foliage. The leaf area : leaf weight ratio is estimated in a representative foliage subsample, using any convenient method of leaf area measurement. By means of this ratio, the weight of the whole sample is converted into leaf area. The usually great variation in specific leaf area within one stand, plant and even one leaf must be taken into account when preparing the subsample to avoid larger errors. (See also Chapters 9 and 10.)

14.3.2.1 | Measuring and weighing of whole leaves

The relationship between leaf area and leaf fresh weight has been used, *e.g.* by Watson (1937), Winter *et al.* (1956), Turrell (1961), Alekseenko (1965) and Nečas, Zrůst & Partyková (1967), in determining leaf area. Leaf dry weight, which is usually easier to determine in a comparable way, has been used more frequently.

Table 14.3 Leaf area : leaf weight ratio [cm^2 g^{-1}] in different grassland species, leaf weight being taken as leaf fresh weight, air-dry weight or oven-dry weight. *n:* number of estimates; *M:* arithmetic mean; *m:* standard error; *m*%: standard error as a percentage of *M*. (From Alekseenko 1965.)

Species		Leaf area : leaf weight ratio [cm^2 g^{-1}]					
	n	fresh weight		air-dry weight		oven-dry weight	
		$M \pm m$	$m\%$	$M \pm m$	$m\%$	$M \pm m$	$m\%$
Trifolium pratense	48	71.3 ± 2.8	3.9	278.9 ± 15.8	5.6	318.1 ± 19.8	6.2
T. medium	17	64.8 ± 2.3	3.6	231.2 ± 4.2	1.8	—	—
Lathyrus pratensis	22	74.8 ± 2.0	2.7	172.2 ± 7.4	4.3	193.9 ± 12.9	6.7
Vicia cracca	22	68.6 ± 1.8	2.6	203.2 ± 17.5	8.6	219.5 ± 3.7	1.7
Medicago sativa	40	59.1 ± 2.0	3.3	187.3 ± 5.7	3.0	—	—
Phleum pratense	61	64.8 ± 1.5	2.4	204.6 ± 4.6	2.2	214.7 ± 5.8	2.7
Dactylis glomerata	23	65.4 ± 4.2	6.4	258.9 ± 14.3	5.5	—	—
Festuca pratensis	22	53.4 ± 4.5	8.5	247.1 ± 30.5	12.3	—	—
Bromus inermis	21	93.2 ± 4.2	4.5	253.4 ± 9.4	3.7	293.1 ± 24.1	8.2
Carex gracilis	18	44.9 ± 1.5	3.3	124.7 ± 3.5	2.8	—	—
C. inflata	18	65.7 ± 3.3	5.0	178.3 ± 9.9	5.5	—	—
Geum rivale	18	57.8 ± 1.4	2.4	173.5 ± 7.5	4.3	—	—
Alchemilla sp.	18	58.8 ± 1.9	3.2	167.8 ± 6.6	3.9	—	—
Geranium pratense	21	68.1 ± 2.6	3.8	209.8 ± 16.8	8.0	246.4 ± 7.5	3.0
Filipendula ulmaria	23	47.6 ± 5.8	12.0	102.9 ± 8.5	8.3	117.5 ± 9.8	8.4
Sanguisorba officinalis	20	75.5 ± 3.3	4.4	184.8 ± 13.3	7.2	233.7 ± 27.7	11.8
Plantago media	20	48.8 ± 1.3	2.6	229.3 ± 19.2	8.4	261.8 ± 18.3	7.0
Taraxacum officinale	20	65.4 ± 4.1	6.3	337.3 ± 13.8	4.1	374.4 ± 14.6	3.9
Ptarmica vulgaris	20	51.6 ± 1.4	2.7	149.1 ± 20.5	13.7	195.8 ± 12.7	6.5
Caltha palustris	20	66.5 ± 7.3	11.0	197.5 ± 20.4	10.3	249.6 ± 14.7	5.9
Thalictrum simplex	20	63.7 ± 3.1	4.8	157.3 ± 16.5	10.5	184.2 ± 18.3	9.9
Galium boreale	20	62.3 ± 5.4	8.6	167.0 ± 17.5	10.5	180.0 ± 19.0	10.6
Ranunculus acer	20	48.3 ± 1.9	4.0	138.2 ± 5.7	4.1	148.0 ± 6.0	4.1
Campanula glomerata	20	48.6 ± 2.9	5.9	162.2 ± 15.4	9.5	176.4 ± 14.1	8.0
Average	—	62.0 ± 2.3	3.6	196.5 ± 10.8	5.5	225.4 ± 16.1	7.2

(For references see most instances of growth analysis of stands quoted in Chapter 10.) This method has been used for both broad-leaved and coniferous woodland stands, *e.g.* by Burger (1942), Möller (1945), Müller (1954); Müller & Nielsen (1965). Vareschi (1951) used the method for estimating the leaf area index of whole communities, as did Květ (1962) and Geyger (1964). In these studies, variation in specific leaf area or leaf area ratio (leaf area : shoot dry weight) due to habitat and season was taken into account. Leaf area ratio can also be used in estimating leaf area when the leaf weight accounts for all or most of the shoot

Table 14.4 Ranges or means of leaf area : leaf dry weight ratio (specific leaf area) and of stem surface area : stem dry weight ratio found in various meadow species. (After Geyger 1964)

Species	Leaf area : leaf dry weight ratio [$cm^2\ g^{-1}$]	Stem surface area : stem dry weight ratio [$cm^2\ g^{-1}$]
Phragmites communis	160–220	37– 45
Calamagrostis epigeios	166–271	54– 80
Bromus erectus	231	68
Alopecurus pratensis	239	100
Phalaris arundinacea	257–301	51– 65
Glyceria maxima	288	72
Arrhenatherum elatius	226–359	86–192
Calamagrostis canescens	313	196
Dactylis glomerata	256–382	121–251
Agrostis alba	350	180
Poa trivialis	388–390	129–155
Festuca rubra	383–440	—
Carex fusca	152	—
Carex gracilis	166	—
Carex acutiformis	171	—
Tanacetum vulgare	172–220	41 –100
Veronica longifolia	192–249	29 – 99
Filipendula ulmaria	220–265	37 – 51
Heracleum sphondylium	247–268	81 –105
Trifolium repens	367	—
Vicia cracca	300	239
Cirsium oleraceum	317–336	144–150
Plantago lanceolata	337	—
Achillea millefolium	378	—
Polygonum bistorta	399	—
Taraxacum officinale	402	—
Anthriscus silvestris	435	—
Ranunculus repens	420–501	—
Angelica silvestris	498	—
Myosotis palustris	550	—
Equisetum arvense	533–640	—
Glechoma hederacea	624	—
Galium palustre	660	—
Rumex acetosa	662	—

Table 14.5 Examples of values of leaf area : leaf dry weight ratio (specific leaf area) or of leaf area : shoot dry weight ratio (leaf area ratio) used in estimating leaf area of woodland herbaceous plants. (After Květ 1962.)

Species	[$dm^2 g^{-1}$]	Species	[$dm^2 g^{-1}$]
Carex digitata	1.6–3.2	*Lamium galeobdolon*	2.2–4.4*
Carex pilosa	2.8	*Primula elatior*	2.9–3.9
Luzula nemorosa	1.6–2.0*	*Anemone nemorosa*	1.2–2.7*
Fragaria elatior	1.1–4.3		3.2–3.9
Asarum europaeum	1.6–2.4	*Stellaria holostea*	1.7–3.3*
Aegopodium podagraria	1.7–3.3	*Viola silvatica*	2.3–3.0*
Hepatica nobilis	2.1–3.0	*Pulmonaria obscura*	2.0–3.5*
Pulmonaria obscura		*Stachys silvatica*	
in clearing	2.00	in clearing	2.96
in wood	4.45	in wood	5.64
Urtica dioica		*Circaea lutetiana*	
in clearing	2.05	in clearing	3.00
in wood	4.52	in wood	7.01

* indicates leaf area ratio.

weight (Květ 1962). Alekseenko (1965), working in grassland communities, studied the variation in the leaf area : leaf weight ratio, taking leaf weight as fresh weight, air-dry weight, or oven-dry weight. The method was calibrated against that of weighing leaf copies on paper (see Section 14.2.3). Some of the results are presented in Table 14.3. These results seem to indicate that leaf fresh weight would be the least variable reference basis, provided it is assessed in a strictly comparable and reliable way. Unless this condition can be fulfilled it is safer to relate leaf area to leaf oven-dry weight. In lucerne in Arizona, Robison & Massengale (1967) found that the seasonal changes in both total leaf area and size of individual leaves had hardly any influence on the constancy of the leaf area : leaf oven-dry weight ratio, the mean value of which was 331.5 $cm^2 g^{-1}$. The findings of Geyger (1964), Hughes (1965), Blackman (1968), Květ (1971) and others indicate that leaves of different species differ in the adaptability of their specific leaf area to environmental conditions (see also Tables 14.4 and 14.5). Consequently, the estimation of leaf area from the regression of leaf area on leaf weight requires careful checking in each type of plant material, similar to that by Nečas, Zrůst & Partyková (1967) for three potato varieties differing in leaf shape. These authors concluded that differences between the varieties, both in the slopes of the regression lines and in their standard errors, had to be taken into account in detailed studies of individual plants while for serial field work a single regression between leaf area and the fresh weight of whole leaves, either with or without the main petioles, was sufficient (see Fig. 14.6).

Attempts have also been made to relate the leaf area and the surface area of ears in cereals to the amount of chlorophyll contained in them (Strebeyko, Bacławska & Skośkiewicz 1966a, b). This approach requires further examination but it may be of use under certain circumstances.

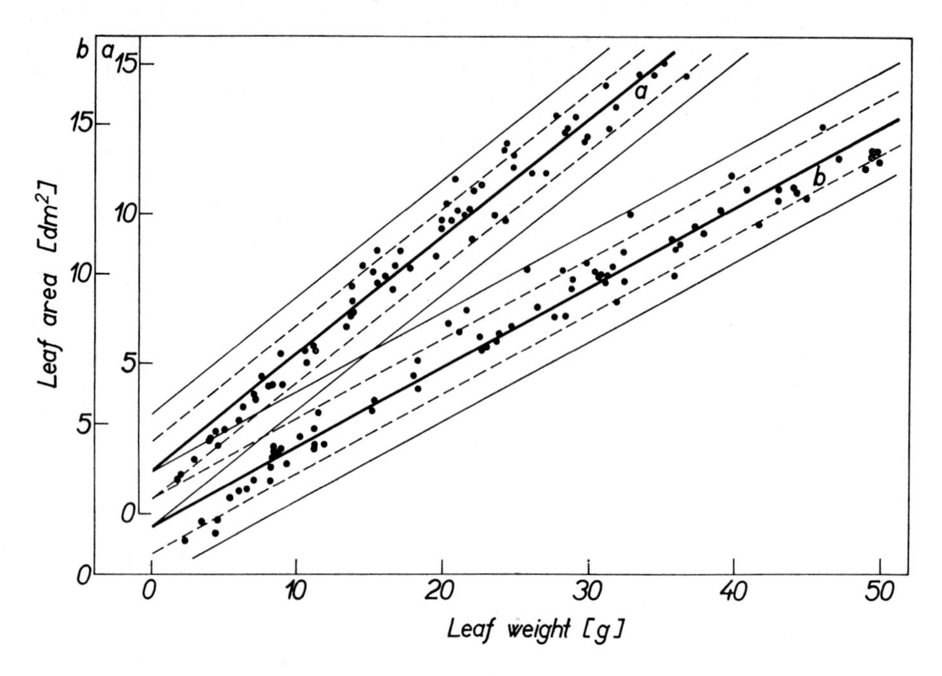

Fig. 14.6 Regression lines for the relation between the area of leaves and the weight of whole leaves (*b*) and the weight of leaflets without main petioles (*a*) in the Rajka potato variety in glass-house culture; ---- limits corresponding to *s* (standard deviation), ——— limits corresponding to 2 *s*. (From Nečas, Zrůst & Partyková 1967.)

14.3.2.2 | Measuring and weighing parts of the leaf tissue

This variant of the leaf-weighing method consists in weighing dried discs, squares or segments of known area cut from the leaves. It is applicable only to those leaves whose size and shape permit a sufficient number of large enough tissue samples to be taken. Total leaf area is calculated by multiplying the area: weight ratio found in the tissue samples by total leaf weight (Thoday 1909; Frear 1935 ; Brougham 1956; Watson 1958; Slatyer & McIlroy 1961; Larsen 1965; Květ & Svoboda 1970, and other authors). This method requires either uniformly thick leaves (*e.g.* Newton & Květ, unpublished, found that in *Mercurialis perennis* the difference between results of this method and photoelectric planimetry was not significant), or adequate precautions must be taken to ensure unbiased sampling. Sampling discs from leaves with thick vascular bundles or midribs is particularly liable to large errors (Frear 1935; Slatyer & McIlroy 1961). Larsen (1965) excluded the midribs from sampling in sugar-beet leaves. The discs or segments can be cut from the leaves with a cork-borer or with special punching devices (see Chapter 9). Watson & Watson (1953), working with leaves of sugar beet, proposed a modification of this technique enabling more rapid sampling: a number of leaves are put flat on top of one another and the whole pile is punched at once. Prior to drying and weighing, all the complete and part discs with an area of more than 1/2 the complete disc area are counted, while the smaller ones are not. In cassava, Spencer (1962) found it satisfactory to include only complete discs in the sample.

14.3.2.3 | Relationship of leaf area and leaf water content

Leaf area has been shown to be linearly related to absolute leaf water content (leaf fresh weight – leaf dry weight) for four dicotyledonous species and for rye grass when $A = a + bW$ where A is total leaf area and W is the absolute leaf water content (Hughes, Cockshull & Heath 1970). The authors consider their method to be of adequate accuracy for the purposes of growth analysis. The material used to establish the linear relationships was grown in controlled environment growth cabinets or glasshouses and so the relationship would certainly appear to merit consideration for similarly cultured material. However, further testing is required before the method can be considered suitable for field grown material, other species, and purposes which demand a higher degree of accuracy than growth analysis.

14.3.3 | The leaf-counting method

The mean area of one leaf or of a set of a known number of leaves is assessed in a representative subsample, and total leaf area is obtained by multiplying this mean value by total number of leaves in the sample. This method is likely to give unbiased results only when the area of individual leaves fluctuates within a relatively narrow range, and the leaves are easy to count. This method may also be employed in vegetational analysis (Ellenberg 1939), or in rapid surveys where an approximate estimation of leaf area index is all that is needed.

14.3.4 | Rating methods

The destructive versions of these methods evolved from an originally non-destructive technique, and are therefore described in Section 14.4.2.

14.4 | Non-destructive methods

Some of the methods in this category are derived from laboratory methods, while others were developed for application to intact plants although their application to detached leaves is usually also possible.

14.4.1 | Methods adapted for field use

The variants included here have already been presented in some of the previous sections: Hořavka's (1953) technique for obtaining leaf copies in a non-destructive way in Section 14.1, the measuring techniques of Vyvyan & Evans (1932) in Section 14.2.1; Negisi, Satoo & Yagi (1957) and Henicke (1963) in Section 14.2.4; Stout (1963); Voisey & Kloek (1964); Woodwell & Bourdeau (1965) in Section 14.2.5, and practically all methods based on linear measurements of leaves in Section 14.3.1.

14.4.2 | Methods using leaf shapes and geometric shapes (rating methods)

The early versions of these methods used outline traces or photographs of the entire range of leaf shape and size of a species. The areas of these images are then measured or calculated and for each shape a series of images (usually about 10) is selected representing a scale of leaf sizes, the increase being derived either empirically or following an arithmetic or geometric progression (Darrow 1932; Bald 1943; Williams 1954; Thorne & Watson 1955; Humphries & French 1963; Williams, Evans & Ludwig 1964). The area of every leaf of an intact plant can then be rated according to its similarity to a member of the appropriate series. The leaf area of one or more plants is estimated when the leaf area value represented by each member of the series is multiplied by the number of leaves selected to match it and the resulting products are added. This procedure is fairly rapid but the technique requires considerable preparation and training in rating in order to avoid both systematic and subjective errors. The method is suitable for use in large-scale field experiments or observations.

Humphries & French (1963, 1964) analysed the use of this method and (1964), suggested the use of standards of different geometric shapes (including ellipses, squares and circles) instead of actual leaf images. This brings the rating method nearer to some of the modifications of methods using linear measurements (see Section 14.3.1). Shapes arranged in a geometric progression underestimated the true leaf area while those in an arithmetic progression overestimated it. The geometric series had a smaller deviation, but the differences between the two progressions mattered little for practical purposes. The mean leaf area of six sugar beet or potato plants was estimated with a deviation from planimeter measurements of 3% to 1% using circles or squares as standards, while with the leaf images the deviation found for a large sample of potato leaves was about 7% (Winter *et al.* 1956).

Geyger (1964) modified the rating method by using as standards a series of 4 to 5 rectangular sheets of paper with evenly distributed black copies of leaves of a species (or group of species with similar leaf shapes) covering different proportions, according to species, of the total area of the rectangle. The series is such that the percentage of cover increases arithmetically by 5%. Sheets evenly covered with the sampled leaves are compared to these standards. In large leaf samples, and with a trained observer, the mean deviation of this area estimation from an accurate measurement was about 3%, increasing only rarely beyond 4 to 6% in individual estimates. Geyger (1964) provides scales suitable for various meadow grasses and forbs. The method has been further developed in the IBP 'Solling-Projekt' in the Federal Republic of Germany and scales for various other species are available at the Botany Department, University of Göttingen (Prof. H. Ellenberg). This modification of the rating method is easy to use in a destructive way, but it is well suited for relatively rapid field estimates of leaf area index in species-rich communities.

14.4.3 | Non-destructive estimates of leaf area index (LAI)

Overall and stratified *LAI* (see Chapters 10 and 12) can be estimated non-destructively in two ways. One is Warren Wilson's (1963, 1965) inclined point-quadrat method, which is derived from the standard point-quadrat method of estimating plant cover in vegetational analysis (Goodall 1952; Kemp & Kemp 1956; Winkworth & Goodall 1962). The other method is hemispherical photography, invented by Hill (1924) and applied by Coombe & Evans (1960); Anderson (1964a, b, c); Bonhomme (1970) and others. The last author, making use of Chartier's (1966) theoretical considerations, points out that estimation of *LAI* from hemispherical photographs taken with a 'fish-eye' camera is possible if the stand canopy is closed and if the distribution of leaf azimuths in it is random. MacArthur & Horn (1969) use a similar method.

Both the inclined point-quadrat method and hemispherical photography are discussed in detail in Chapter 12.

14.5 | Choice of method

An investigator's choice of the method(s) depends largely on the following factors:

- morphological and anatomical features of the leaves and/or other assimilatory organs to be measured;
- amount of material to be measured;
- required degree of accuracy;
- manpower and technical equipment available;
- time available; and
- whether retention of a permanent record is necessary.

Table 14.6 may serve as a guide, although most of the above factors are mutually dependent. The time requirement of any of the methods depends primarily on the kind of leaves to be measured. In photoelectric planimetry, for example, the critical limiting stage is usually loading the apparatus with the leaves. To cover an area of 1000 cm^2 with oak leaves takes 1 to 3 min, while the same operation with *Anemone* leaves takes 15 to 20 min. Covering an area of 350 cm^2 with tiny leaves (*e.g.*, of flax) takes about 30 min.

The estimation of leaf area in trees or stands of trees is particularly difficult. Leaf area is usually estimated on a few felled sample trees in which allometric relationships are established between total leaf area and characteristics which are easier to determine such as crown diameter, crown volume, tree height and trunk diameter. See, *e.g.* Turrell (1961), Müller & Nielsen (1965), Kira, Shinozaki & Hozumi (1969). Further references are given by these authors.

Ellenberg (1939) and Vanseveren (1969) estimated the leaf area index of tree canopies in temperate deciduous woodlands from measurements of areas of freshly shed off leaves, and Vanseveren (1969) found the reduction in their area due to shrinkage to be about 10% of the area of living green leaves. The dry weight of the fresh litter and the proportions of leaves of different tree species in it were assessed in a sufficiently large number of randomly selected sample plots of 1 m^2, 0.5 m^2 or 0.25 m^2. The leaf area : leaf dry weight ratio was estimated in representative subsamples of leaves, separately for each species, and the appropriate correction was then applied to make the ratio valid for living green leaves. This method, in spite of its obvious drawbacks, is perhaps the one best suited for large-scale estimates and comparisons of leaf area index in different types of deciduous tree stands. The shrinkage of the leaves in the litter should be checked whenever this method is used.

Table 14.6 Summarized presentation of the principal methods available for leaf area measurement and estimation.

Type of method and no. of relevant Section	Technical equipment required	Most suitable for:	Upper limit of error	Advantages	Disadvantages	Remarks
Counting squares (14.2.1)	Millimeter paper	Individual leaves	$\pm$ 25 mm^2	Accurate	Tedious	Suitable for calibrating other methods
Hand-planimetry (14.2.2)	Hand planimeter	Individual leaves or sets of leaves of simple shape	3% (mean of at least 2 replicates)	Accurate	Only for detached small leaves, tedious	Suitable for calibrating other methods
Gravimetric method (14.2.3)	Precise balances, good-quality heavy paper	Leaves of simple shape	5%	Accurate	Tedious	Check homogeneity of paper used!
Dot counting (14.2.4)	Regularly dotted sheet of paper or acrylic plastic	Broad and relatively short leaves or sets of them	10%	Simplicity, suitable also for field use	Bias depending on area: circumference ratio	Usual spacing of dots 1 cm × 1 cm. Dots as small as possible
Photoelectric planimetry (14.2.5)	Photoelectric planimeter, galvanometer, voltage stabilizer and/or regulator	Sets of relatively large leaves, large individual leaves	5% of 'active area'	Relatively rapid, suitable for any leaf shapes	Technically complicated, not suited for tiny leaves	Non-selective instruments recommended, frequent calibration necessary, some modifications suitable for field use
Photographic-photoelectric planimetry (14.2.5)	Leaf photographing table, photoelectric planimeter to take film, galvanometer, voltage stabiliser and/or regulator	Leaves of variable size and number	less than $\pm$ 3%	Relatively rapid, simple, flexible, accurate, separates leaf photographing from later area measurement, provides permanent record of leaves	Only for detached leaves	Absolutely contrasting leaf image and background on negative preferable by adjusting spectral emission, transmission and sensitivity of light source, filter and film, respectively.

Radiation planimetry (14.2.5)	Radiation source and detector	Sets of relatively large leaves, large individual leaves	5%	Relatively rapid, suitable for any leaf shape, non-selective	Radioactivity	—
Airflow planimetry (14.2.6)	Airflow planimeter	Sets of small leaves	5%	Rapid loading	Only for detached leaves	Precise design and construction essential
Linear measurements (14.3.1)	Ruler or scale, calculating machine	Sets of leaves	10%	Suitable for field use	Specificity with respect to material	Check effect of habitat, season leaf position and size!
Leaf weighing (14.3.2)	Balances, drying oven	Sets of leaves, foliage of stands	15%	Suitable for large samples	Destructive, frequent calibration by another method	Truly representative sub-sampling essential!
Leaf counting (14.3.3)	Calculating machine	Sets of leaves, mixed plant communities	15%	Rapid, suitable for field surveys	Frequent calibration by another method	Truly representative sub-sampling essential!
Rating method (14.4.2)	Calculating machine; series of leaf images or geometric shapes	Sets of leaves, foliage of stands, preferably samples of broad leaves	15%	Rapid, suitable for large samples and non-destructive leaf area estimates	Liable to bias due to subjective errors	Check effect of even small differences in leaf shape on ratings!
Inclined point quadrats (14.4.3)	Device for inserting pins at certain angles	Stands, assessment of canopy structure	15%	Non-destructive	Leaf shape and pin diameter affect results	Assumes random distribution of leaf azimuths
Hemispherical photography (14.4.3)	Hemispherical camera with 'Fish eye' lens	Stands, assessment of canopy structure	15%	Rapid measurement *in situ*	Applicable only to closed canopies; evaluation complex	Assumes random distribution of leaf azimuths

14.6 | Characterisation of foliage configuration

The photosynthetic production of a canopy depends not only on the amount of leaves present but also on the configuration of the leaves making up the canopy (see, *e.g.* Warren Wilson 1961; Loomis & Williams 1963; Monteith 1965; de Wit 1965; Duncan *et al.* 1967; Nil'son 1968, and numerous references in Chapter 12). The configuration of the foliage that is most efficient in intercepting and utilizing incoming solar radiation is not yet established. The latest presentation of the problems of modelling photosynthetic production in plant stands may be found in the volume 'Prediction and Measurement of Photosynthetic Productivity' (1970). Much of the recent work has been developed from the earlier findings of Japanese workers who pioneered studies of the relationship between the structure of a foliage canopy and the penetration of radiation into it (Monsi & Saeki 1953; Kasanaga & Monsi 1954; Iwaki 1959; Kuroiwa 1960; Saeki 1963; and numerous other authors, see also Chapter 12), and the effect of position in a canopy on the rate of photosynthesis of a leaf and its share in the overall net photosynthetic production of the stand (Saeki 1960; Ludwig, Saeki & Evans 1965; and others).

The following information, additional to that on total leaf area index (LAI, see Chapter 10) is usually needed to characterize a canopy:

a. The vertical profile of *LAI*. This is usually obtained by a technique of stratified harvesting (but *cf.* Warren Wilson 1959, 1961, 1965) described partly in Chapter 12 and also in Section 14.6.1, and discussed in the volume 'Prediction and Measurement of Photosynthetic Productivity' (1970).

b. The arrangement of the leaves, defined in terms of the distribution of their orientation (azimuth) and inclination (angle from a vertical or horizontal plane) within the whole canopy or finite layers of it. Techniques suitable for estimating these characteristics are presented in Section 14.6.2.

c. The reflection and transmission of light by the leaves, controlled also by their thickness (see Meidner 1952). A detailed account of this problem is given by Brandt & Tageeva (1967) for example (see also Gates *et al.* 1965).

d. The photosynthetic characteristics of the leaves in different parts of the canopy. These are assessed by techniques described in Chapters 3 to 9.

14.6.1 | Stratified harvesting

This technique consists in harvesting a plant stand in a stratified manner by removing successive layers of foliage of a certain thickness depending upon the size of the plants. Leaf area index, leaf and stem dry weight and often also other characteristics – described in detail in Chapter 10 – are assessed separately for each layer. If stratified harvests are taken at regular time intervals through the growth cycle, the overall growth analysis is usefully supplemented by a dynamic picture of canopy development. This information can be complemented by data on light penetration into the stand (see Chapter 12) and on the distribution of shoots of different heights and leaves of different insertion levels within the stand. (For references see most of the papers mentioned in this Section as well as references in Chapters 10 and 12, and Hodáňová 1967; Květ, Svoboda & Fiala 1969.)

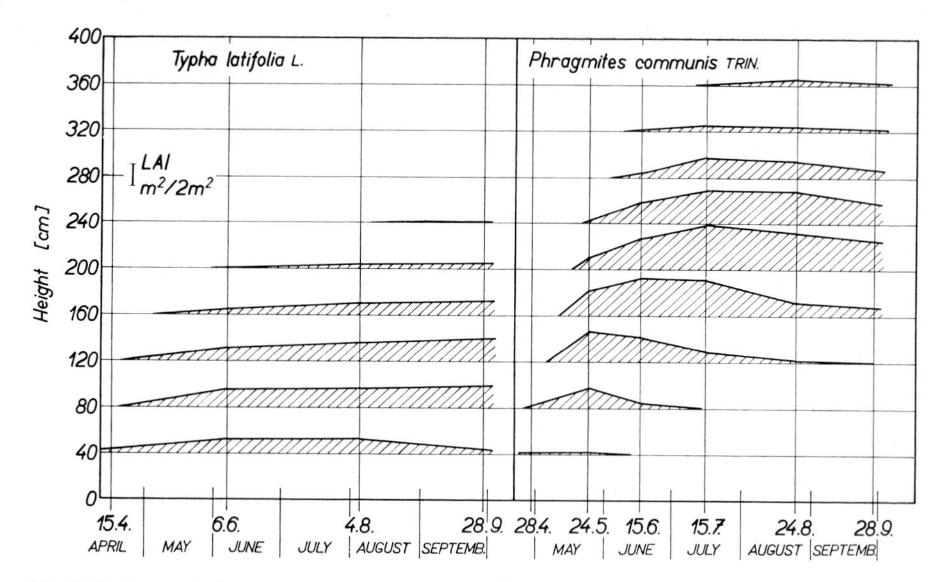

Fig. 14.7 Seasonal changes of leaf area index (*LAI*) stratified by 40 cm layers in stands of *Typha latifolia* and *Phragmites communis*. (From Květ, Svoboda & Fiala 1969).

Fig. 14.7 shows the seasonal changes in *LAI* stratified into 40 cm thick layers in two stands of very different foliage configuration.

The usual method of stratified harvesting is described in Chapter 12: This method is practicable only if the stand is not too tall and the sample plot is not too large. In tall stands, such as reeds *(Phragmites)*, or trees, the sample can be stratified after having been harvested from a plot of known size (Květ, Svoboda & Fiala 1969). Alternatively, branches can be removed from single sample trees in a stand whorl by whorl in a stratified manner from below, especially if the branches are more or less horizontal (Stephens 1969). However, after harvest it may be difficult to return the leaves to their original inclinations.

Another procedure applicable to harvested material consists of dividing the stem into sections of chosen length and taking the level of the point of insertion of each branch, petiole or leaf as the criterion for including it into a canopy layer (see, *e.g.* Hodáňová 1967). This method is best suited to stands with largely horizontal or nearly horizontal branches or leaves, as the systematic error involved increases with increasing inclination of the leaves, and branches from the horizontal plane. This technique can enable quite thin canopy layers to be examined in some stands (10 cm thick layers by Hodáňová 1967, 4 cm by W. A. Williams 1963), by recording values found on a representative sample of specimen shoots.

Specimen trees are often also sampled in forest stands whereas in a dense shrub vegetation it may be easier to 'cut out' a block of the canopy the vertical projection of which corresponds to the sample area (Lieth 1965). The problems of assessing the structure of forest canopies have recently been stated by Newbould (1967) and Kira, Shinozaki & Hozumi (1969).

14.6.2 | *Techniques for assessing leaf inclination and orientation*

Both these terms refer to leaf angles but there has been some confusion as to their use. Recently, it has been stated that inclination denotes the angle between the plane or axis of a leaf lamina and the vertical or horizontal plane, while orientation refers to the azimuth of the horizontal projection of the leaf axis (usually measured clockwise from the North).

De Wit (1965) characterized the positions of the leaves in a canopy by the cumulative frequency distribution of leaf inclination. Such a distribution function can be represented by plotting the cumulative frequency of occurrence of leaf inclinations against inclination, from 0° for a horizontal leaf to 90° for a vertical one. Four canopy types can be distinguished:

a. planophile canopies with largely horizontal or nearly horizontal leaves;
b. erectophile canopies with largely vertical or nearly vertical leaves;
c. plagiophile canopies with largely oblique leaf inclination;
d. extremophile canopies with most of the foliage having either horizontal or vertical inclinations.

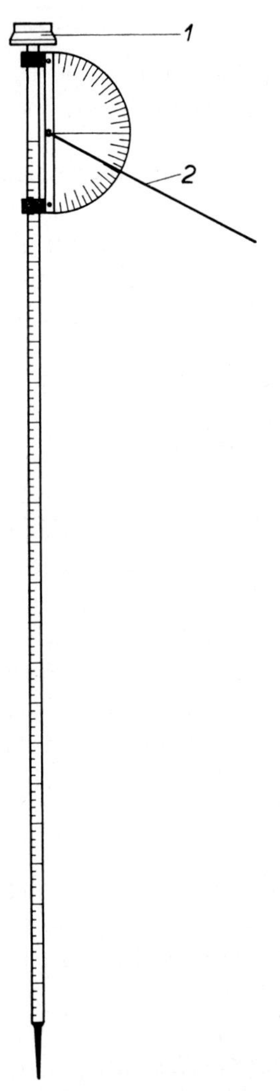

Fig. 14.8 Simple protractor with a compass (*1*) and a movable arm (*2*) for measuring leaf inclinations and orientations (after Hodáňová, unpublished).

A special case of an erectophile distribution is the spherical distribution in which the relative frequency of leaf inclinations is the same as that of the inclination of the surface elements of a sphere. Nichiporovich (1961) assumes this distribution to be particularly advantageous and has found it in the foliage of grasses and some cereals, but de Wit (1965) was not able fully to confirm this.

De Wit's (1965) classification of leaf canopies can sometimes be applied visually but accurate measurements of leaf angles must be taken in any detailed investigations. Nichiporovich (1961) measured leaf inclination with a leaf graduator consisting of 2 protractors, 1 cm apart, and a freely moving pointer suspended at the axis passing through their centres. The base of one of the protractors is kept parallel to the leaf or leaf section to be measured so that the leaf inclination can be directly read from the position of the pointer. Measuring the inclinations of about 400 leaves or leaf sections was sufficient to obtain smooth distribution functions of leaf inclination within a canopy. These measurements are usually taken in a representative subsample of either individual plants or several small sample plots. If necessary, the distribution functions of leaf inclination can be established in a stratified manner, *i.e.* separately for individual canopy layers (see Section 14.6.1 and Chapter 12). While de Wit (1965) claims that this is unnecessary for most purposes, Loomis & Williams (1969) have found it useful. Ross & Nil'son (1967) find it more precise and better suited for mathematical interpretation to define leaf inclination in terms of the angle between the normal to the leaf lamina at a given point and the horizontal or vertical plane.

The protractor of Laisk (1965) is an improved version of that of Nichiporovich (1961). It is combined with a compass, thus enabling a simultaneous reading of leaf inclination and orientation. It also enables estimation of the inclination of the normal to the leaf lamina at different points. Hodáňová (unpublished) has used a similar simple device for measuring the heights of leaf insertion, leaf inclination and orientation; it is shown in Fig. 14.8. The protractor enables the mean inclination of segments of the leaf laminae to be recorded separately. The areas of these segments can be measured, using any convenient method. The result is a breakdown of the overall *LAI* into parts of different inclination.

Loomis *et al.* (1968), working with maize, recorded the position of each leaf by drawing the projection of its midrib onto a grid and measured the inclination of each segment of the lamina off this schematic drawing.

As the distribution of leaf inclination within a canopy is closely linked with the distribution of light, de Wit's (1965) technique of measuring light distribution can also be applied to measuring leaf inclination, provided the inclination of the sun at the time of measurement is known. Alternatively, an artificial light source of a standard inclination might be employed. De Wit's (1965) device consists of two copper spheres each 15 mm in diameter, 10 cm apart, attached to a pole which supports the spheres about 50 cm above the canopy. The pole with the spheres is moved at random. When the sun is shining one sphere casts a shadow on a leaf, whereas the shadow of the other sphere is made to fall onto a piece of cardboard which is graduated in millimetres, and is held parallel to the leaf section of interest. The length of the shadow on the cardboard is measured and the sine of the angle between the leaf concerned and the sun's rays is calculated by dividing the diameter of the sphere by the length of the shadow.

Květ, Svoboda & Fiala (1967) describe a device suitable for measuring the inclination of longer leaves. The horizontal deviation of the lamina from a vertical pole is recorded on movable horizontal beams and the tangent of the mean inclination of the whole lamina or a section of it is calculated from the deviation and the length of the corresponding section of the pole.

Leaf orientation with respect to the four cardinal points is usually measured with any convenient compass. It may be of advantage to attach the compass to the device with which leaf inclinations are measured, as shown in Fig. 14.8 or by Laisk (1965).

The measurements of both leaf inclination and orientation recorded are usually grouped by 5° to 15° to obtain the relative frequency of different leaf positions in a canopy. The distribution of leaf inclination within a stand is affected both by the type of stand and the environment while that of leaf orientations seems to be random in many canopies. However, it may be non-random in some cases.

Warren Wilson's (1959, 1961, 1965) inclined point quadrat method, as described in Chapter 12, may be used to determine leaf inclinations. The whole question of foliage configuration and its effects on productivity has been recently discussed by Loomis & Williams (1969) where numerous further references can be found. Ross and his co-workers treat mathematically the whole problem of light interception and utilization for photosynthetic production, giving due consideration to foliage configuration and optical properties of the leaves.

Both the foliage configuration and the distribution of *LAI* among canopy layers affect the leaf area density, *i.e. LAI* per unit volume of canopy. This characteristic often employed by Japanese authors, can have a considerable influence on productivity (see Loomis & Williams 1969; Kira, Shinozaki & Hozumi 1969). The latter authors show that forest stands have a smaller leaf area density than herbaceous vegetation. Leaf area density clearly has a great effect on the interception of incoming solar radiation by canopies (see Chapter 12).

Leaf pattern is often related to the pattern of vegetation on the ground. Most patterns in nature are contagious; regular patterns exist perhaps only in crops. Greig-Smith (1964) and Kershaw (1964) summarize several techniques for assessing the type of pattern. An improved statistical treatment of stand pattern and its relation to productivity is provided by Ondok (1970a,b).

14.7 | References

Ackley, W. B., Crandall, P. C., Russell, T. S.: The use of linear measurements in estimating leaf areas. – Proc. Amer. Soc. hort. Sci. 72: 326-330, 1958.

Alekseenko, L. N.: Vesovoï metod opredeleniya listovoï poverkhnosti lugovykh rasteniï i lugovykh soobshchestv. [Weight method of leaf area determination of meadow plants and meadow communities.] – Bot. Zh. 50: 205-208, 1965.

Anderson, M. C.: Light relations of terrestrial plant communities and their measurement. – Biol. Rev. 39: 425-486, 1964a.

Anderson, M. C.: Studies of the woodland light climate. I. The photographic computation of light conditions. – J. Ecol. 52: 27-41, 1964b.

Anderson, M. C.: Studies of the woodland light climate. II. Seasonal variation in the light climate. – J. Ecol. 52: 643-663, 1964c.

Anikiev, V. V., Kutuzov, F. F.: Novyï sposob opredeleniya ploshchadi listovoï poverkhnosti u

zlakov. [A new method of leaf area determination of cereals.] – Fiziol. Rast. 8: 375-377, 1961.
Aston, J. M.: The relationship between transpiration and water uptake of sunflower (*Helianthus annuus* var. Advance) in relation to some environmental factors. – Ph.D. Thesis, Univ. California, Davis 1967.
Bachmann, P., Keller, B.: Messeinrichtung zur Bestimmung von Blattoberflächen. – Schweiz. Z. Forstwes. 116: 623-625, 1965.
Baker, D. N., Meyer, R. E.: Influence of stand geometry on light interception and net photosynthesis in cotton. – Crop Sci. 6: 15-19, 1966.
Bald, J. G.: Estimation of the leaf area of potato plants for pathological studies. – Phytopathology 33: 922-932, 1943.
Basu, P. K.: A rapid method for the determination of the leaf area of *Oxalis corniculata* L. and *Tephrosia purpurea* (Linn.) Pers. – Ann. Bot. N.S. 33: 77-82, 1969.
Batens, W. D., Muncie, J. H.: A new method for computing sugar beet leaf areas. – Phytopathology 33: 1071-1075, 1943.
Batyuk, V. P., Rybalko, E. F., Okanenko, A. S.: A photoelectric planimeter for measuring leaf area. – Biol. Plant. 1: 167-175, 1959.
Bell, R. D., Smith, R. S.: Modified construction of Jenkins' air flow planimeter. – J. sci. Instr. 42: 428-429, 1965.
Birke, J.: Über die Abhängigkeit des Zuckerrübenertrages von der Entwicklung des Assimilationsapparates. – Albrecht-Thaer–Arch. (Berlin) 9: 715-729, 1965.
Bistrup, C.: Bladarealer. – Dansk Skovforen. Tidskr. 28: 1-10, 1943.
Black, J. N.: Competition between plants of different initial seed sizes in swards of subterranean clover (*Trifolium subterraneum* L.) with particular reference to leaf area and light microclimate. – Austr. J. agr. Res. 9: 229-318, 1958.
Blackman, G. E.: The application of the concepts of growth analysis to the assessment of productivity. – In: Eckardt, F. E. (ed.): Functioning of Terrestrial Ecosystems at the Primary Production Level. Pp. 243-259. UNESCO, Paris 1968.
Bonhomme, R.: Application de la technique des photographies hémisphériques *in situ* à la mesure de l'indice foliaire. – In: Techniques d'Étude des Facteurs Physiques de la Biosphère. Pp. 501-505. I.N.R.A., Paris 1970.
Boynton, D., Harris, E. W.: Relationships between leaf dimensions, leaf area and shoot length in the McIntosh Apple, Elberta Peach, and Italian Prune. – Proc. Amer. Soc. hort. Sci. 55: 16-20, 1950.
Brandt, A. B., Akopov, E. I.: Avtomaticheskiĭ fotoelektricheskiĭ izmeritel' plotnosti odnokletochnykh vodorosleĭ. [An automatic photoelectric device for measuring density of unicellular algae.] – Mikrobiologiya 35: 369-373, 1966.
Brandt, A. B., Tageeva, S. V.: Opticheskie Parametry Rastitel'nykh Organizmov. [Optical Parameters of Plant Organisms.] – Nauka, Moskva 1967.
Brougham, R. W.: Effect of intensity of defoliation on regrowth of pasture. – Austral. J. agr. Res. 7: 377-387, 1956.
Brown, H., Escombe, F.: Researches on some of the physiological processes of green leaves. – Proc. Roy. Soc. B 76: 29-111, 1905.
Burger, H.: Holz, Blattmenge und Zuwachs. VI. Ein Plenterwald mittlerer Standortsgüte. – Mitt. schweiz. Centralanst. forstl. Versuchswesen 22: 377-445, 1942.
Cain, S. A., de O. Castro, G. M.: Manual of Vegetation Analysis. – Harper and Brothers, New York 1959.
Cain, S. A., de O. Castro, G. M., Pires, J. M., da Silva, N. T.: Application of some phytosociological techniques to Brazilian rain forest. – Amer. J. Bot. 43: 911-941, 1956.
Carleton, A. E., Foote, W. H.: A comparison of methods for estimating total leaf area of barley plants. – Crop Sci. 5: 602-603, 1965.
Chartier, P.: Étude théorique de l'assimilation brute de la feuille. – Ann. Physiol. vég. 8: 167-195, 1966.
Chatterjee, B. K., Dutta, P. K.: A simple method of determining leaf area in *Mentha arvensis* L. – J. sci. ind. Res. 20 C: 359-360, 1961.
Clements, F. E., Goldsmith, G. W.: The Phytometer Method in Ecology. – Carnegie Inst. Washington Publ. 356, Washington 1924.

Coombe, D. E., Evans, G. C.: Hemispherical photography in studies of plants. – Med. biol. Illustr. 10: 68-75, 1960.
Cooper, A. W.: A further application of length-width values to the determination of leaf-size classes. – Ecology 41: 810-811, 1960.
Darrow, G. M.: Methods of measuring strawberry leaf areas. – Plant Physiol. 7: 745-747, 1932.
Davis, R. G., Roberson, G. M., Johnson, W. C., Wiese, A. F.: A modified optical planimeter for measuring leaf area. – Agron. J. 58: 106-107, 1966.
Derco, M.: Rýchla metóda na určenie veľkosti listovej plochy u slnečnice ročnej – *Helianthus annuus* L. [A quick method of establishing the area of the leaf surface of the sunflower *Helianthus annuus* L.] – Poľnohospodárstvo 8: 171-182, 1961.
Donald, C. M., Black, J. N.: The significance of leaf area in pasture growth. – Herbage Abstr. 28: 1-5, 1958.
Donovan, L. S., Magee, A. I., Kalbfleisch, W.: A photoelectric device for measurement of leaf areas. – Can. J. Plant Sci. 38: 490-494, 1958.
Dorovskaya, I. F.: K metodike opredeleniya razmerov assimiliruyushcheï poverkhnosti kukuruzy. [Method of determining the assimilating surface area in maize.] – Tr. Sev.-Osetinsk. sel'skokhoz. Inst. 22: 97-103, 1964.
Duncan, W. G., Loomis, R. S., Williams, W. A., Hanau, R.: A model for simulating photosynthesis in plant communities. – Hilgardia 38: 181-205, 1967.
Ellenberg, H.: Über Zusammensetzung, Standort und Stoffproduktion bodenfeuchter Eichen- und Buchen-Mischwaldgesellschaften Nordwestdeutschlands. – Mitt. florist.-soziol. Arb. gem. Niedersachsen 5: 3-135, 1939.
Enyi, B. A. C.: Dependence of length of leaf lamina on length of leaf sheath in the rice plant. – Nature 196: 1115-1116, 1962.
Epstein, E., Robinson, R. R.: A rapid method for determining leaf area of potato plants. – Agron. J. 57: 515-516, 1965.
Fitoaktinometricheskie Issledovaniya Rastitel'nogo Pokrova. [Phytoactinometric Investigations of Plant Stands.] – Valgus, Tallin 1967.
Fojtík, L.: The use of nuclear radiation for leaf area measurement. – Photosynthetica 3: 316-319, 1969.
Fotosinteticheskaya Produktivnost' Rastitel'nogo Pokrova. [Photosynthetic Productivity of Plant Stands.] – Estonian Acad. Sci., Tartu 1969.
Francis, C. A., Rutger, J. N., Palmer A. F. E.: A rapid method for plant leaf area estimation in maize (*Zea mays* L.). – Crop Sci. 9: 537-539, 1969.
Frear, D. E. H.: Photoelectric apparatus for measuring leaf areas. – Plant Physiol. 10: 569-574, 1935.
Freeman, G. H.: A comparison of methods of measuring leaf areas in the field. – Ann. Rep. East Malling Res. Sta. 1957: 83-86, 1958.
Freeman, G. H., Bolas, B. D.: A method for the rapid determination of leaf areas in the field. – Ann. Rep. East Malling Res. Sta. 1955: 104-107, 1956.
Fulga, I. G.: Uproshchennyï metod dlya opredeleniya ploshchadi list'ev yabloni. [A simplified method of measuring apple-tree leaf area.] – Fiziol. Rast. 8: 255-257, 1961.
Fulga, I. G.: Opredelenie ploshchadi listev u plodovykh kul'tur. [Leaf area determination in fruit trees.] – Fiziol. Rast. 12: 1104-1107, 1965a.
Fulga, I. G.: K metodike opredeleniya ploshchadi listev u plodovykh derevev. [On the methods of leaf area determination in fruit trees.] – Tr. Mold. nauch.-issled. Inst. Sadovodstva, Vinograd., Vinodeliya (Kishinev) 10: 239-247, 1965b.
Gates, D. M., Keegan, H. J., Schleter, J. C., Weidner, V. R.: Spectral properties of plants. – Appl. Optics 4: 11-20, 1965.
Gavrilov, N. I., Eremenko, L. L.: Pribor dlya izmereniya ploshchadi list'ev. [An instrument for measuring leaf areas.] – Fiziol. Rast. 6: 508-512, 1959.
Gerdel, R. W., Salter, R. M.: Measurement of leaf area using the photoelectric cell. – J. Amer. Soc. Agron. 20: 635-642, 1928.
Geyger, E.: Methodische Untersuchungen zur Erfassung der assimilierenden Gesamtoberflächen von Wiesen. – Ber. geobot. Forsch.-Inst. Rübel 35: 41-112, 1964.
Gladyshev, N. P.: K metodike opredeleniya ploshchadi list'ev yabloni. [On the methods of determination of the area of apple tree leaves.] – Bot. Zh. 54: 1571-1575, 1969.

Golovin, V. V., Migunov, V. S.: Opredelenie ploshchadi lista soi po parametram. [Leaf area determination in soybeans by means of parameters.] – Vestn. sel'skokhoz. Nauki 13(12): 90-91, 1968.
Goodall, D. W.: The distribution of weight change in the young tomato plant. I. Dry weight changes of the various organs. – Ann. Bot. N.S. 9: 101-139, 1945.
Goodall, D. W.: Diurnal changes in the area of Cacao leaves. – Ann. Bot. N.S. 11: 449-451, 1947.
Goodall, D. W.: Some considerations in the use of point quadrats for the analysis of vegetation. – Austr. J. sci. Res., Ser. B 5: 1-41, 1952.
Graf-Marin, A.: Studies on powdery mildew of cereals. – Cornell Univ. Agr. exp. Sta., Memoir 157: 1-48, 1934.
Gregory, F. G.: Studies on the energy relations of plants. I. – Ann. Bot. 35: 93-123, 1921. II. – Ann. Bot. 42: 469-507, 1928.
Greig-Smith, P.: Quantitative Plant Ecology. 2nd Ed. – Butterworths, London–Washington 1964.
Grigor'ev, V. R., Metreveli, S. G.: K metodike izmereniya ploshchadeĭ fotoelektricheskim putem. [On the method of photoelectric measuring of leaf areas.] – Bot. Zh. 43: 828-830, 1958.
Henicke, D. R.. Note on estimation of leaf area and leaf distribution in fruit trees. – Can. J. Plant Sci. 43: 597-598, 1963.
Henrici, M.: Chlorophyllgehalt und Kohlensäureassimilation bei Alpen- und Ebenenpflanzen. – Verh. Naturforsch. Ges. Basel 30: 43-136, 1918.
Hibbard, R. P., Grisby, B. H., Keck, W. G.: A low light intensity photoelectric device for the measuring of leaf areas. – Pap. Mich. Acad. Sci. 23: 141-147, 1937.
Hill, R.: A lens for whole sky photographs. – Quart. J. roy. meteorol. Soc. 50: 227-235, 1924.
Hodáňová, D.: Development and structure of foliage in wheat stands of different density. – Biol. Plant. 9: 424-438, 1967.
Hopkins, J. W.: Estimation of leaf area in wheat from linear dimensions. – Can. J. Res. C 17: 300-304, 1939.
Hořavka, B.: Přístrojek na seriové zjišt'ování listové plochy. [A small device for measurements of leaf area in series of leaves.] – Československá Biol. (Praha) 2: 239-241, 1953.
Hughes, A. P.: Some modifications of Schwabe's photometric apparatus for leaf measurement. – Ann. Bot. N. S. 28: 473-474, 1964.
Hughes, A. P.: Plant growth and the aerial environment IX. A synopsis of the autecology of *Impatiens parviflora*. – New Phytol. 64: 399-413, 1965.
Hughes, A. P., Cockshull, K. E., Heath, O. V. S.: Leaf area and absolute leaf water content. – Ann. Bot. N.S. 34: 259-265, 1970.
Humphries, E. G., French, S. A. W.: The accuracy of the rating method for determining leaf area. – Ann. appl. Biol. 52: 193-198, 1963.
Humphries, E. G., French, S. A. W.: Determination of leaf area by rating in comparison with geometric shapes. – Ann. appl. Biol. 54: 281-284, 1964.
Hurd, R. G., Rees, A. R.: Transmission error in the photometric estimation of leaf area. – Plant Physiol. 41: 905-906, 1966.
Iwaki, H.: Ecological studies on interspecific competition in a plant community. I. An analysis of growth of competing plants in mixed stands of buckwheat and green grams. – Jap. J. Bot. 17: 120-138, 1959.
Iyama, J.: [A leaf-area meter using small balls.] – Nogyō-oyobi-engei 38: 127-128, 1963.
Jain, T. C., Misra, D. K.: Leaf area estimation by linear measurements in *Ricinus communis*. – Nature 212: 741-742, 1966.
Jenkins, H. V.: An airflow planimeter for measuring the area of detached leaves. – Plant Physiol. 34: 532-536, 1959.
Ješko, T.: Príspevok k meraniu listovej plochy polárnym planimetrom. [Measurement of leaf area using the polar planimeter.] – Biológia (Bratislava) 21: 904-908, 1966.
Johnson, R. E.: Comparison of methods for estimating cotton leaf area. – Agron. J. 59: 493-494, 1967.
Johnston, C. O., Miller, E. C.: Modification of diurnal transpiration in wheat by infections of *Puccinia triticina*, – J. agr. Res. 61: 427-444, 1940.
Jones, R. I.: A simple apparatus for estimating the area of detached leaves. – South African J. agr. Sci. 4: 531-542, 1961.

Kallio, A.: A photoelectric device for measuring leaf area. – Sci. Alaska – Proc. Alaskan sci. Conf. 16: 26, 1965.

Kasanaga, H., Monsi, M.: On the light-transmission of leaves, and its meaning for the production of matter in plant communities. – Jap. J. Bot. 14. 304-324, 1954.

Kemp, C. D.: Methods of estimating the leaf area of grasses from linear measurements. – Ann. Bot. N.S. 24: 491-499, 1960.

Kemp, C. D., Kemp, A. W.: The analysis of point quadrat data. – Austr. J. Bot. 4: 167-174, 1956.

Kershaw, K. A.: Quantitative and Dynamic Plant Ecology. – Academic Press, London 1964.

Kira, T., Shinozaki, K., Hozumi, K.: Structure of forest canopies as related to their primary productivity. – Plant Cell Physiol. 10: 129-142, 1969.

Kornher, A., Rodskjer, N.: Ein photoelektrisches Planimeter zur Bestimmung von Blattflächen nach einem Kompensationsverfahren. – Angew. Bot. 42: 263-269, 1969.

Kozlowski, T. T., Schumacher, F. X.: Estimation of stomated foliar surface of pines. – Plant Phys. 18: 122-127, 1943.

Kramer, P. J.: An improved photoelectric device for measuring leaf areas. – Amer. J. Bot. 24: 375-376, 1937.

Kranz, A. R.: Ein Beitrag zur Methodik der photoelektrischen Blattflächenbestimmung. – Angew. Bot. 37: 335-350, 1964.

Kryukovskiï, F. V.: Opredelenie listovoï poverkhnosti u drevesnykh porod. [Determination of leaf surface in different tree species.] – Bot. Zh. 51: 678-681, 1966.

Kuroiwa, S.: Intraspecific competition in artificial sunflower communities. – Bot. Mag. (Tokyo) 73: 300-309, 1960.

Květ, J.: Produkční ekologie bylinného patra lesních společenstev. [Production ecology of the herbaceous layer in woodlands.] – CSc. Thesis, Inst. Bot., Czechosl. Acad. Sci., Průhonice and Brno 1962.

Květ, J.: Reaction of woodland herbaceous plants to the removal of tree canopy. – Folia geobot. phytotax. (Praha) 6: (in press), 1971.

Květ, J., Svoboda, J.: Development of vertical structure and growth analysis in a stand of *Phragmites communis* Trin. – In: Dykyjová, D. (ed.): PT-PP Report No. 1. Pp. 84-87. Czechosl. IBP Nat. Comm., Praha 1970.

Květ, J., Nečas, J., Kubín, Š.: Měření listové plochy. [Leaf area measurements.] – In: Šesták, Z., Čatský, J. (ed.): Metody Studia Fotosynthetické Produkce Rostlin. Pp. 315-334. Academia, Praha 1966.

Květ, J., Svoboda, J., Fiala, K.: A simple device for measuring leaf inclinations. – Photosynthetica 1: 127-128, 1967.

Květ, J., Svoboda, J., Fiala, K.: Canopy development in stands of *Typha latifolia* L. and *Phragmites communis* Trin. in South Moravia. – Hidrobiologia (Bucureşti) 10: 63-75, 1969.

Laïsk, A.: Usovershenstvovannyï fotoplanimetr i prisposoblenie dlya opredeleniya orientatsii list'ev. [An improved photoplanimeter and a device for estimating leaf inclinations.] – In: Voprosy Radiatsionnogo Rezhima Rastitel'nogo Pokrova. Pp. 102-113. Akad. Nauk Est. SSR, Tartu 1965.

Lal, K. N., Subba Rao, M. S.: A new formula for estimation of leaf area in barley. – Sci. Cult. 15: 355-356, 1950a.

Lal, K. N., Subba Rao, M. S.: A rapid method of estimation of leaf area in growing maize plants. – Curr. Sci. 19: 179-180, 1950b.

Lal, K. N., Subba Rao, M. S.: A rapid method of leaf area determination. - Nature 167: 72, 1951.

Langer, R. H. M.: Measurement of leaf growth in grasses. – In: Milthorpe, F. L. (ed.): The Growth of Leaves. Pp. 197-198. Butterworths, London 1956.

Larsen, A.: Vaekstanalytiske undersøgelser af tre bederoestammer 1960-62. [Growth analytic studies on three beet strains 1960-62.] – Tidsskr. Planteavl 69: 1-37, 1965.

Lazarov, R.: Koefitsienti za opredelyane na listnata pov'rchnost pri nyakoi selksostopanski kulturi. [Coefficients for determining the leaf area in certain agricultural crops.] – Rast. Nauki (Sofia) 2(2): 27-37, 1965.

Lieth, H.: Ökologische Fragestellungen bei der Untersuchung der biologischen Stoffproduktion. I. Einführung, Definitionen und Wachstumsanalysen. – Qualitas Plant. Materiae vegetabiles 12: 241-261, 1965.

Loomis, R. S., Williams, W. A.: Maximum crop productivity: An estimate. – Crop Sci. 3: 67-72, 1963.

Loomis, R. S., Williams, W. A.: Productivity and the morphology of crops stands: Patterns with leaves. – In: Eastin, J. D. *et al.* (ed.): Physiological Aspects of Crop Yield. Pp. 27-47. Amer. Soc. Agron. Crop Sci. Soc. Amer., Madison, Wisc. 1969.

Loomis, R. S., Williams, W. A., Duncan, W. G., Dovrat, A., Nunez A., F.: Quantitative descriptions of foliage display and light absorption in field communities of corn plants. – Crop Sci. 8: 352-356, 1968.

Lüdin, H.: Untersuchungen über die Transpiration von Sonnen- und Schattenpflanzen, – Verh. nat. Ges. Basel 39: 176-215, 1927.

Ludwig, L. J., Saeki, T., Evans, L. T.: Photosynthesis in artificial communities of cotton plants in relation to leaf area. I. Experiments with progressive defoliation of mature plants. – Austr. J. biol. Sci. 18: 1103-1118, 1965.

Lyon, C. J.: A factor method for the area of tomato leaves. – Plant Physiol. 23: 634-635, 1948.

MacArthur, R. H., Horn, H. S.: Foliage profile by vertical measurements. – Ecology 50: 802-804, 1969.

Maggs, D. H.: A photometer for estimating the area of samples of detached leaves. – Annu. Rep. East Malling Res. Sta. 1956: 107-108, 1957.

Marshall, J. K.: The photographic-photoelectric planimeter combination method for leaf area measurement. – Photosynthetica 2: 1-9, 1968a.

Marshall, J. K.: Methods for leaf area measurement of large and small leaf samples. – Photosynthetica 2: 41-47, 1968b.

Marshall, R. E.: An apparatus for the ready determination of areas of compound leaves. – J. agr. Res. 47: 437-439, 1933.

Maximov, N. A.: The Plant in Relation to Water. A Study of the Physiological Basis of Drought Resistance. – London 1929.

McKee, G. W., Yocum, J. O.: Coefficients for computing leaf area in Type 41, Pennsylvania broadleaf, tobacco. – Agron. J. 62: 433-434, 1970.

Meidner, H.: An instrument for the continuous determination of leaf thickness changes in the field. – J. exp. Bot. 3: 319-325, 1952.

Miller, E. C.: Plant Physiology. – McGraw-Hill Co., New York 1938.

Miller, E. F., Shadbolt, C. A., Holm, L. G.: Use of an optical planimeter for measuring leaf area. – Plant Physiol. 31: 484-486, 1956.

Milthorpe, F. L.: A simplified photoelectric cell method for measuring leaf areas. – J. Austr. Inst. agr. Sci. 8: 27, 1942.

Milthorpe, F. L. (ed.): The Growth of Leaves. – Chapter 15, pp. 195-202. Butterworths, London 1956.

Mitchell, J. W.: Measurement of the area of attached and detached leaves. – Science 83: 334-336, 1936.

Moelker, W. H.: Photoelectric equipment for a quick determination of leaf areas. – Plant Soil 25: 305-308, 1966.

Möller, C. M.: Untersuchungen über Laubmenge, Stoffverlust und Stoffproduktion des Waldes. – København 1945.

Monsi, M., Saeki, T.: Über den Lichtfaktor in den Pflanzengesellschaften und seine Bedeutung für die Stoffproduktion. – Jap. J. Bot. 14: 22-52, 1953.

Monteith, J. L.: Light distribution and photosynthesis in field crops.– Ann. Bot. N.S. 29: 17-37, 1965.

Moreshet, S.: Calculation of cotton leaf area from a simple measurement of leaf length. – Israel J. agr. Res. 15: 155-157, 1965.

Müller, D.: Die Blätter und Kurztriebe der Buche. – Forst. Forsøgsvassen Danmark 21: 319-326, 1954.

Müller, D., Nielsen, J.: Production brute, pertes par respiration et production nette dans la forêt ombrophile tropicale. – Forst. Forsøgsvaesen Danmark 29: 69-160, 1965.

Murata, Y., Hayashi, K.: On a new, automatic device for leaf-area measurement. – Proc. Crop Sci. Soc. Jap. 36: 463-467, 1967.

Nátr, L.: Use of image analysing computer for measuring leaf area. – Photosynthetica 2: 39-40, 1968.

Nečas, J., Zrůst, J., Partyková, E.: Determination of the leaf area of potato plants. – Photosynthetica 1: 97-111, 1967.
Negisi, K., Satoo, T., Yagi, K.: [A method for the rapid measuring of leaf areas.] – J. Jap. Forest Soc. 39: 380-384, 1957.
Newbould, P. J.: Methods for Estimating the Primary Production of Forests. – IBP Handbook No. 2. Blackwell sci. Publ., Oxford–Edinburgh 1967.
Nichiporovich, A. A.: O svoïstvakh posevov rasteniï kak opticheskoï sistemy. [Properties of plant crops as an optical system.] – Fiziol. Rast. 8: 536-546, 1961.
Nichiporovich, A. A., Strogonova, L. E., Chmora, S. N., Vlasova, M. P.: Fotosinteticheskaya Deyatel'nost' Rasteniï v Posevakh. [Photosynthetic Activity of Plants in Crops.] – Izdat. Akad. Nauk SSSR, Moskva 1961.
Nil'son, T.: Ob optimal'noï geometricheskoï strukture rastitel'nogo pokrova. [On the optimum geometrical structure of plant cover.] – In: Rezhim Solnechnoï Radiatsii v Rastitel'nom Pokrove. Pp. 112-146. Inst. Fiz. Astron. Akad. Nauk EstSSR, Tartu 1968.
Ondok, J. P.: Measurement of leaf area in *Phragmites communis* Trin. – Photosynthetica 2: 25-30, 1968.
Ondok, J. P.: Growth analysis applied to the estimation of gross assimilation and respiration rate. – Photosynthetica 4: 214-222, 1970a.
Ondok, J. P.: The horizontal structure of reed stands (*Phragmites communis*) and its relation to productivity. – Preslia 42: 256-261, 1970b.
Orchard, B.: An automatic device for measuring leaf area. – J. exp. Bot. 12: 458-464, 1961.
Owen, P. C.: Rapid estimation of the areas of the leaves of crop plants. – Nature 180: 611, 1957.
Owen, P. C.: A measuring scale for areas of cereal leaves. – Exp. Agr. 4: 275-278, 1968.
Oyama, K.: [Measurement of leaf area by an airflow planimeter.] – Nogyō oyobi-engei 35: 1185-1186, 1960.
Paquin, R., Coulombe, L. J.: A simple method for measuring the area of leaves of potted plants. – Can. J. Bot. 37: 167, 1959.
de Parcevaux, S., Čatský, J.: Méthodes et techniques de mesure des surfaces foliaires. – In: Techniques d'Étude des Facteurs Physiques de la Biosphère. Pp. 493-499. I.N.R.A., Paris 1970.
de Parcevaux, S., Grebet, P.: Utilisation d'un appareil à aspiration pour la mesure de la surface foliaire. – In: Techniques d'Étude des Facteurs Physiques de la Biosphère. Pp. 507-511. I.N.R.A., Paris 1970.
de Parcevaux, S., Massin, B.: Agrandissement photographique appliqué à la détermination de la surface de petites feuilles. – In: Techniques d'Étude des Facteurs Physiques de la Biosphère. Pp. 513-515. I.N.R.A., Paris 1970.
Peneva, P.: Ispolzuvane na koefitsienti za opredelyane na listnata pov'rkhnost pri nyakoï rasteniya s nasechena petura. [Use of coefficients in determining the leaf area in certain plants with cleaved leaf blades.] – Rast. Nauki (Sofia) 5(6): 3-12, 1968.
Pilet, P. E., Meylan, A.: Une méthode de mesure de surface foliaire. – Ber. Schweiz. bot. Ges. 68: 307-314, 1958.
Polster, H., Reichenbach, H.: Bestimmung von Blattflächen *in situ* durch lineare Messungen. – Biol. Zentralbl. 77: 265-277, 1958.
Prediction and Measurement of Photosynthetic Productivity. – PUDOC, Wageningen 1970.
Ramann, E.: Blättergewicht und Blattfläche einiger Buchen. – Z. Forst-Jagdwes. 43: 916-919, 1911.
Raunkiaer, C.: Om Bladstørrelsens Anvendelse i den biologiske Plantegeografi. – Bot. Tidsskr. 33: 225-240, 1916.
Robison, G. D., Massengale, M. A.: Use of area-weight relationship to estimate leaf area in alfalfa (*Medicago sativa* L. cultivar 'Moapa'). – Crop Sci. 7: 394-395, 1967.
Ronco, F.: Volumeter for estimating quantity of conifer foliage for expressing photosynthesis on a leaf volume basis. – US Forest Serv. Res., Note RM 133: 1-2, 1969.
Ross, J. K., Nil'son, T. A.: The spatial orientation of leaves in crop stands and its determination. – In: Nichiporovich, A. A. (ed.): Photosynthesis of Productive Systems. Pp. 86-99. Israel Program of Scientific Translations, Jerusalem 1967.
Ross, V.: K voprosu opredeleniya listovoï poverkhnosti rasteniï. [On determination of leaf area.] – In: Fitoaktinometricheskie Issledovaniya Rastitel'nogo Pokrova. Pp. 150-162. Valgus, Tallin 1967.

Rubin, S. S., Danilevskaya, O. M.: Opredelenie ploshchadi list'ev plodovykh derev'ev. [Leaf area determination of fruit trees.] – Bot. Zh. 42: 728-730, 1957.
Ruck, H. C., Bolas, B. D.: Studies in the comparative physiology of apple rootstocks. I. The effect of nitrogen on the growth and assimilation of Malling apple rootstocks. – Ann. Bot. N.S. 20: 57-68, 1956.
Rutter, A. J.: Studies in the growth of young plants of *Pinus sylvestris* L. I. The annual cycle of assimilation and growth. – Ann. Bot. N.S. 21: 399-426, 1957.
Saeki, T.: Interrelationships between leaf amount, light distribution and total photosynthesis in a plant community. – Bot. Mag. (Tokyo) 73: 55-63, 1960.
Saeki, T.: Light relations in plant communities. – In: Evans, L. T. (ed.): Environmental Control of Plant Growth. Pp. 79-94. Academic Press, New York–London 1963.
Šanda, K.: Nový způsob měření listové plochy. [A new method of leaf area measurement.] – Věstník ČSAZV 9: 502-503, 1958.
Savchenko, M. P.: Zavisimost' mezhdu dlinoï i ploshchad'yu lista u pshenitsy. [Relation of leaf length and area in wheat.] – Uch. Zap. Omsk. gos. ped. Inst. 24: 64-66, 1967.
Scheibe, A.: Morphologisch-physiologische Untersuchungen über die Transpirationsverhältnisse bei der Gattung *Triticum* und deren Auswertung für Pflanzenzüchtung und Kulturpflanzenökologie. – Angew. Bot. 9: 199-281, 1927.
Schwabe, W. W.: Physiological studies in plant nutrition. XVI. The mineral nutrition of bracken. Part I. Protothallical culture and the effects of phosphorus and potassium supply on leaf production in the sporophyte. – Ann. Bot. N.S. 15: 417-446, 1951.
Šesták, Z., Čatský, J. *et al.*: Metody Studia Fotosynthetické Produkce Rostlin. [Methods of Studying Photosynthetic Production of Plants.] – Academia, Praha 1966.
Šetlík, I., Kubín, Š.: Industrialization of agriculture – a challenge to photosynthesis research. – Acta Univ. Carolinae-Biologica (Prague), 1966 (Suppl. 1/2) :77-88, 1966.
Shevtsov, I. A.: Koefitsienty ploshchi lystkovoiï poverkhni poliploïdnykh form buryakiv. [Coefficients of leaf area in polyploid beet forms.] – Ukr. bot. Zh. 23(6): 54-58, 1966.
Singh, U. S.: A new method for estimating area of intact sugarcane leaves. – Proc. Nat. Acad. Sci. India B 37: 192–196, 1967.
Slatyer, R. O., McIlroy, I. C.: Practical Microclimatology. – UNESCO, Paris 1961.
Smetánková, M.: Dry matter production and growth in length of overground parts of *Carex humilis* Leyss. – Biol. Plant. 1: 235-247, 1959.
Spencer, R.: A rapid method for estimating the leaf area of cassava (*Manihot utilissima* Pohl) using linear measurements. – Trop. Agr. 39: 147-152, 1962.
Stephens, G. R.: Productivity of red pine. 1. Foliage distribution in tree crown and stand canopy. – Agr. Meteorol. 6: 275-282, 1969.
Stickland, R. E.: A caliber for measuring plant diameter. – J. agr. Eng. Res. 14: 290-291, 1969.
Stickler, F. C., Wearden, S., Pauli, A. W.: Leaf area determinations in grain sorghum. – Agron. J. 53: 187-188, 1961.
Stocker, O.: Eine Feldmethode zur Bestimmung der momentanen Transpirations- und Evaporationsgrösse. – Ber. deut. bot. Ges. 47: 126-136, 1929.
Stout, N. B.: A portable optical planimeter for measuring leaf area. – Ohio J. Sci. 63: 103-105, 1963.
Stoy, V.: Photosynthesis, respiration and carbohydrate accumulation in spring wheat in relation to yield. – Physiol. Plant. 18 (Suppl. 4): 1-125, 1965.
Strebeyko, P., Bacławska, Z., Skośkiewicz, K.: Próby mierzenia powierzchni asymilacyjnej liści i kłosów pszenicy na podstawie ich świezej masy i zawartości chlorofilu. [Measuring assimilatory surface of wheat leaves and ears based on their fresh weight and chlorophyll content.] – Hodowla Rośl. Aklim. Nasien. 10: 175-182, 1966a.
Strebeyko, P., Bacławska, Z., Skośkiewicz, K.: Próby oznaczania powierzchni asymilacyjnej kłosów pięciu odmian pszenicy na podstawie ilości zawartogo w nich chlorofilu. [Determination of ear assimilatory surface in five wheat cultivars based on quantity of chlorophyll.] – Hodowla Rośl. Aklim. Nasien. 10: 361-367, 1966b.
Suggs, C. W., Beeman, J. F., Splinter, W. E.: Physical properties of green Virginia-type tobacco leaves. III. Relation of leaf length and width to leaf area. – Tobacco Sci. 4: 194-197, 1960.
Tejawani, K. G., Ramakrishna Kurup, C. K., Ven Kataraman, K. V.: Measurements of leaf area in tobacco. – Ind. J. Agron. 2: 36-39, 1957.

Thoday, D.: Experimental researches on vegetable assimilation and respiration. V. A critical examination of Sachs' method for using increase of dry weight as a measure of carbon dioxide assimilation in leaves. – Proc. Roy. Soc. B 82: 1-55, 1909.
Thomas, W. D., Lazenby, A.: Some comparisons of inclined point quadrat and airflow planimeter methods for measuring leaf-area index of grass swards. – J. Brit. Grassland Soc. 23: 268-273, 1967.
Thorne, G. N., Watson, D. J.: The effect on yield and leaf area of wheat of applying nitrogen as a top-dressing in April or in sprays at ear emergence. – J. agr. Sci. 46: 449-456, 1955.
Tirén, L.: Om barrytans storlek hos tallbestånd. – Medd. Statens Skogsförsöksanst. Stockholm 23: 295-336, 1927.
Troelsen, J. E., Hanel, D. J.: Mechanical separation of leaves and stems of forage plants. – Can. J. Plant Sci. 49: 645, 1969.
Turrell, F. M.: Growth of the photosynthetic area of *Citrus*. – Bot. Gaz. 122: 284-298, 1961.
Václavík, J.: Vliv vnějších faktorů na stav průduchů. [Effect of environmental factors on the status of stomata.] – Thesis, Faculty of Biology, Charles Univ., Praha 1955.
Vanseveren, J. P.: L'index foliaire et sa mesure par photoplanimétrie. – Bull. Soc. roy. bot. Belg. 102: 373-385, 1969.
Vareschi, V.: Zur Frage der Oberflächenentwicklung von Pflanzengesellschaften der Alpen und Subtropen. – Planta 40: 1-35, 1951.
Voisey, P., Mason, W.: Note on an improved device for measuring leaf areas. – Can. J. Plant Sci. 43: 247-251, 1963.
Voisey, P. W., Kloek, M.: A portable leaf area measuring instrument. – Can. J. Plant Sci. 44: 389-391, 1964.
Volkov, V. Ya., Selevtsev, V. F.: Raschet ploshchadi assimilyatsionnoï poverkhnosti ogurtsov. [Calculation of the area of the assimilation surface of cucumber plants.] – Fiziol. Rast. 6: 619-622, 1959.
Voprosy Radiatsionnogo Rezhima Rastitel'nogo Pokrova. [Problems of Radiation Regime in Plant Stands.] – Estonian Acad. Sci., Tartu 1965.
Vyvyan, M. C., Evans, H.: The leaf relations of fruit trees. 1. A morphological analysis of the distribution of leaf surface on two nine-year old apple trees (Laxton superb). – J. Pomology 10: 228-270, 1932.
Warren Wilson, J.: Analysis of the spatial distribution of foliage by two-dimensional point quadrats. – New Phytol. 58: 92-101, 1959.
Warren Wilson, J.: Influence of spatial arrangements of foliage area on light interception and pasture growth. – Proc. 8th Int. Grassland Congr., pp. 275-279, 1961.
Warren Wilson, J.: Estimation of foliage denseness and foliage angle by inclined point quadrats. – Austr. J. Bot. 11: 95-105, 1963.
Warren Wilson, J.: Stand structure and light penetration. I. Analysis by point quadrats. – J. appl. Ecol. 2: 383-390, 1965.
Wassink, E. C.: The effect of light intensity on growth and development of *Gladiolus*. – In: Christensen, B. C., Buchmann, B. (ed.): Progress in Photobiology. Pp. 371-378. Elsevier Publ. Co., Amsterdam–London–New York–Princeton 1961.
Wassink, E. C.: Light intensity effects in growth and development of tulips, in comparison with those in *Gladiolus*. – Meded. Landbouwhogeschool Wageningen 65(15): 1-21, 1965.
Watson, D. J.: The estimation of leaf area in field crops. – J. agr. Sci. 27: 474-483, 1937.
Watson, D. J.: The dependence of net assimilation rate on leaf-area index. – Ann. Bot. N.S. 22: 37-54, 1958.
Watson, D. J., Watson, M. A.: Comparative physiological studies on the growth of field crops – III. The effect of infection with beet yellows and beet mosaic viruses on the growth and yield of the sugar beet crop. – Ann. appl. Biol. 40: 1-37, 1953.
Wendt, C. W.: Use of a relationship between leaf length and leaf area to estimate the leaf area of cotton (*Gossypium hirsutum* L.), castors (*Ricinus communis* L.) and sorghum (*Sorghum vulgare* L.) – Agron. J. 59: 484-486, 1967.
Wendt, C. W., Haas, R. H., Runkles, J. R.: Area measurement of mesquite *(Prosopis glandulosa)* leaves by using leaf-length measurements. – Bot. Gaz. 128: 22-24, 1967.

Whittaker, R. H., Woodwell, G. M.: Surface area relations of woody plants and forest communities. – Amer. J. Bot. 54: 931-939, 1967.
Williams, R. F.: Estimation of leaf area for agronomic and plant physiological studies. – Austr. J. agr. Res. 5: 235-246, 1954.
Williams, R. F., Evans, L. T., Ludwig, L. J.: Estimation of leaf area for clover and lucerne. – Austr. J. agr. Res. 15: 231-233, 1964.
Williams, W. A.: Competition for light between annual species of *Trifolium* during the vegetative phase. – Ecology 44: 475-485, 1963.
Winkworth, R. E., Goodall, D. W.: A crosswire sighting tube for point quadrat analysis. – Ecology 43: 342-343, 1962.
Winter, E. J., Salter, P. J., Stanhill, G., Bleadsdale, J. K. A.: Some methods of measuring leaf area. – In: Milthorpe, F. L. (ed.): The Growth of Leaves. Pp. 195-197. Butterworths, London 1956.
de Wit, C. T.: Photosynthesis of leaf canopies. – Agr. Res. Rep. (Wageningen) 663: 1-57, 1965.
Withrow, R. B.: A photoelectric device for the rapid measurement of leaf area. – J. agr. Res. 50: 637-643, 1935.
Woodwell, G. M., Bourdeau, P. F.: Measurement of dry matter production of the plant cover. – In: Eckardt, F. E. (ed.): Methodology of Plant Eco-physiology. Pp. 519-527. Unesco, Paris 1965.

15 | DETERMINATION OF STOMATAL APERTURE

15.1 | Introduction

Stomata represent a major resistance to the diffusion of carbon dioxide into photosynthesizing leaves. The diffusive resistance of stomata is a function of their aperture. Estimation of the diffusive resistance is discussed in Chapter 16 in detail. A short review is given here, in the form of Table 15.1, of methods for the determination of stomatal aperture. Further information on methods of estimating stomatal aperture is given by Meidner & Mansfield (1968) and Slavík *et al.* (1972).

Table 15.1 Review of methods of stomatal aperture determination

	Method	What is measured	Procedure	Equipment	Advantages and usefulness	Disadvantages and limitations	References
1	Direct observation						
1.1	Direct microscopy on living material	Number (per mm^2), shape and size (length, width in μm) of stomatal guard cells and apertures.	Microscopy using medium magnification unless special lenses with long working distances are used.	Microscope with medium magnification.	Living material. By focusing, the shape of stomatal aperture may be observed. The same stoma may be repeatedly observed.	Limited number of stomata observed. Difficult with hairy leaves and very small stomata.	Stålfelt (1939, 1956)
			Leaf segments in liquid paraffin, no cover glass, high magnification.	Microscope with high magnification.		Possible effect of external conditions during determination.	
1.2	Direct microscopy on fixed epidermis	As in 1.1	Epidermis stripped off and fixed, high magnification and immersion may be used	Microscope with high magnification	Very simple for suitable material	Leaves with easily stripped epidermis only. Possible changes in aperture and size due to fixation.	Lloyd (1908); Ashby (1931)
1.3	Direct, still and time-lapse micro-photography	As in 1.1		Special camera adaptation (expensive) using medium magnification.	As in 1.1	As in 1.1 Effect of changed light conditions very critical, especially in time lapse photography.	Elkins & Williams (1962)

Table 15.1 (cont.)

Method		What is measured	Procedure	Equipment	Advantages and usefulness	Disadvantages and limitations	References
2	Indirect microscopy or microphotography of leaf surface reprints (impressions)						
2.1	using dissolved compounds	As in 1.1	Leaf surface smeared with solution of collodion (or metacrylate or cellulose acetate), dried reprints peeled off by means of a transparent tape and stored. Subsequent measurements under the microscope, possibly using microscope projection.		Simple and rapid technique suitable for use in the field and for quantitative evaluation of surface anatomy. Large number of stomata may be measured.	Results depend on the viscosity of the liquid: how far the pore is penetrated, so that the reprints do not necessarily represent the aperture itself. Cannot be repeated on the same spot. Stomatal aperture may be affected by the organic solvent and/or by excessive cooling of the leaf due to its vaporization. Unreliable with apertures of less than about 1 μm.	Buscalioni & Pollacci (1901a,b); Long & Clements (1934); Shmueli (1953); Sampson (1961); Horanic & Gardner (1967); Aubert (1968)
2.2	using silicon rubber negatives	As in 1.1	Silicon rubber polymerized when smeared on leaf surface. Afterwards collodion positives are made for microscopic examination.		As in 2.1	As in 2.1	Zelitch (1963)

3	Infiltration by low surface tension liquids						
3.1	Infiltration under atmospheric pressure	Resistance of stomata plus intercellular spaces to viscous flow of the liquid. Relative values only.	Drops of liquids with different viscosity and surface tension are placed on the leaf surface. The time and kind of infiltration observed.		Simple and rapid method yielding relative values.	Objective evaluation, cannot be repeated on the same leaf. Results are not comparable for different plant species. Useless in leaves with damaged cuticles (*e.g.* by pests). Wettability and solubility of leaf surface may interfere.	Molisch (1912); Schorn (1929); Shmueli (1953); Dale (1961); de Parcevaux (1963); Oppenheimer & Engelberg (1965)
3.2	Pressure infiltration	As in 3.1	Infiltration of a known liquid is observed under application of increasing and measured pressure.	Special, inexpensive equipment with small pressure bomb.	Values representing large number of stomata. Useful for field work, and also for linear (needle) leaves and both hypostomatous (or epistomatous) and amphistomatous leaves.	As in 3.1	Froeschel (1953); Fry & Walker (1967)
4	Porometry						
4.1	Diffusion porometry	Diffusive resistance of the leaf to model gases which may be recalculated for CO_2 [s cm^{-1}].	Diffusion of hydrogen (Gregory & Armstrong 1936; Spanner 1953; Louguet 1965), nitrous oxide, N_2O (Slatyer & Jarvis 1966) or radioactive argon (Moreshet, Stanhill & Koller 1968) across an amphistomatous leaf is measured under the absence of any mass flow (no pressure difference across the leaf).	Usually leaf chambers on both sides of a leaf are used; the concentration of the gas is measured by elaborate and expensive equipment.	A useful laboratory method yielding directly values of diffusive resistance.	Expensive laboratory equipment needed. Only for amphistomatous leaves. Includes the intercellular space resistance through the leaf.	Section 16.4.3.4 Gregory & Armstrong (1936); Spanner (1953); Louguet (1965); Slatyer & Jarvis (1966); Moreshet, Stanhill & Koller (1968)

Table 15.1 (cont.)

Method		What is measured	Procedure	Equipment	Advantages and usefulness	Disadvantages and limitations	References
4.2	Viscous flow porometry (mass flow)	Viscous flow conductivity c_v (or resistance) of the leaf, usually to air.	A viscous flow of the air across the leaf is induced by pressure difference across the leaf lamina.			The calculation of diffusive resistance is not simple: the relationship of viscous flow conductivity (resistance) to diffusive conductivity (resistance) also depends on the geometry of the stomatal aperture. Includes the intercellular space resistance through the leaf.	Section 16.4.3.2 Meidner & Spanner (1953); Waggoner (1965); Jarvis, Rose & Begg (1967); Milthorpe & Penman (1967)
4.2.1	Viscous flow rate measurements	Viscous flow rate measured, viscous resistance calculated	Viscous flow rate of the air measured by means of flowmeters.	Leaf chambers, flowmeter.	Useful for field measurements.	Pressure difference (if high) may cause artifacts and change stomatal aperture.	Bierhuizen, Slatyer & Rose (1965); Raschke (1965a); Solarová (1965); Strebeyko (1965a, b); Weatherley (1966); Williams & Sinclair (1969)
				Sophisticated laboratory devices.	Precise laboratory determinations which can be recorded.		Heath & Mansfield (1962); Raschke (1965b)

4.2.2	Pressure drop measurements	Viscous conductance (resistance) may be calculated from pressure drop, time and volume of the porometer chamber.	Time necessary for a certain pressure drop in a one sided leaf chamber is measured.	Mostly simple devices using leaf chamber(s).	Useful for field measurements.	High pressure difference may cause artifacts.	Alvim (1965); Shimshi (1967); Peaslee & Moss (1968)
4.2.3	Resistance porometers	Viscous flow resistance directly measured.	Resistance of an amphistomatous leaf compared with known resistances.	Laboratory equipment with leaf chambers.	Laboratory methods		Gregory & Pearse (1934); Wilson (1942); Heath & Russel (1951); Spanner & Heath (1951); Moreshet (1964)
4.3	'Transpiration porometry'	A sum of boundary layer resistance plus transpiration resistance, *i.e.* diffusive resistance to water vapour of stomata, intercellular spaces and cuticle. To some extent this may be recalculated for CO_2.	Part of the leaf surface is adpressed to an aperture opening into a chamber containing a humidity and temperature sensor. The rate of change in humidity and temperature of the leaf are recorded. The boundary layer resistance is defined by the construction of the instrument (presence or absence of artificial ventilation, shape, volume of the chamber). It must be determined previously during calibration using wet filter paper instead of leaf with known diffusive resistances (*e.g.* tubes increasing the diffusion pathway or – better – millipore membranes).	Equipment for measuring rate of change of humidity and air and leaf temperature in a leaf chamber.	Yields diffusive resistance values for water vapour which may be recalculated for CO_2. See Disadvantages.	Includes the flux of water through the cuticle. Thus recalculation for CO_2 is limited by the presence of this parallel resistance of the cuticle to water vapour transfer.	Section 16.4.3.3b. Wallihan (1964); van Bavel, Nakayama & Ehrler (1965); Slatyer (1966); Kaufmann (1967); Knipling (1968); Kanemasu, Thurtell & Tanner (1969); Byrne, Rose & Slatyer (1970); Djavanchir (1970)

Table 15.1 (cont,)

Method		What is measured	Procedure	Equipment	Advantages and usefulness	Disadvantages and limitations	References
5	Calculation of transpiration resistances and hence stomatal resistance from the determination of transpiration rate and the gradient of water vapour pressure	Transpiration rate from a leaf surface, leaf temperature and ambient water vapour pressure may be recalculated to the transpiration resistance values and diffusive resistance values for CO_2 respectively.	Transpiration rate of a leaf surface is measured in comparison to the evaporation rate of wet (green) filter paper under the same conditions (irradiation, surface temperature, ventilation).	Equipment for gasometric measurements of transpiration rate using leaf chambers. Leaf and air temperatures must be measured simultaneously.	Useful with simultaneous gasometric measurements of CO_2 exchange in controlled conditions. As in 4.3.	As in 4.3	Section 16.4.3.3a. Gaastra (1959); Meidner & Spanner (1959)

15.2 | References

Alvim, P. de T.: A new type of porometer for measuring stomatal opening and its use in irrigation studies. – In: Eckhardt, F. E. (ed.): Methodology of Plant Eco-Physiology. Pp. 325-329. UNESCO, Paris 1965.

Ashby, E.: Comparison of two methods of measuring stomatal aperture. – Plant Physiol. 6: 715-719, 1931.

Aubert, B.: Étude préliminaire des phénomènes de transpiration chez le bananier. Application à la détermination des besoins en irrigation dans les bananeraies d'Équateur. – Fruits 23: 357-381, 483-494, 1968.

van Bavel, C. H. M., Nakayama, F. S., Ehrler, W. L.: Measuring transpiration resistance of leaves. – Plant Physiol. 40: 535-540, 1965.

Bierhuizen, J. F., Slatyer, R. O., Rose, C. W.: A porometer for laboratory and field operation. – J. exp. Bot. 16: 182-191, 1965.

Buscalioni, L., Pollacci, G.: L'applicazione delle pellicole di collodio allo studio di alcuni processi fisiologici nelle piante ed in particolar modo alla traspirazione. – Atti Ist. bot. Pavia, 2a Ser. 7: 83-94, 1901a.

Buscalioni, L., Pollacci, G.: Ulteriori ricerche sull'applicazione delle pellicole di collodio allo studio di alcuni processi fisiologici delle piante ed in particolar modo della traspirazione vegetale. – Atti Ist. bot. Pavia, 2a Ser. 7: 127-170, 1901b.

Byrne, G. F., Rose, C. W., Slatyer, R. O.: An aspirated diffusion porometer. – Agr. Meteorol. 7: 39-44, 1970.

Dale, J. E.: Investigations into the stomatal physiology of upland cotton. 2. Calibration of the infiltration method against leaf and stomatal resistances. – Ann. Bot. 25: 94-103, 1961.

Djavanchir, A.: Mise au point d'une chambre de transpiration pour mesurer la résistance stomatique. – Oecol. Plant. 5: 301-318, 1970.

Elkins, C. B. Jr., Williams, G. G.: Still and time-lapse photography of plant stomata. – Crop Sci. 2: 164-166, 1962.

Froeschel, P.: Das Druckstomatometer, ein neuer pflanzenphysiologischer Apparat zur Messung der Apertur der Stomata. – Cellule 56: 63-70, 1953.

Fry, K. E., Walker, R. B.: A pressure-infiltration method for estimating stomatal opening in conifers. – Ecology 48: 155-157, 1967.

Gaastra, P.: Photosynthesis of crop plants as influenced by light, carbon dioxide, temperature, and stomatal diffusion resistance. – Meded. Landbouwhogeschool Wageningen 59(13): 1-68, 1959.

Gregory, F. G., Armstrong, J. I.: The diffusion porometer. – Proc. Roy. Soc. London, Ser. B, 121: 27-42, 1936.

Gregory, F. G., Pearse, H. L.: The resistance porometer and its application to the study of stomatal movement. – Proc. Roy. Soc. London, Ser. B 114: 477-493, 1934.

Heath, O. V. S., Mansfield, T. A.: A recording porometer with detachable cups operating on four separate leaves. – Proc. Roy. Soc. London, Ser. B 156: 1-13, 1962.

Heath, O. V. S., Russel, J.: The Wheatstone bridge porometer. – J. exp. Bot. 2: 111-116, 1951.

Horanic, G. E., Gardner, F. E.: An improved method of making epidermal imprints. – Bot. Gaz. 128: 144-150, 1967.

Jarvis, P. G., Rose, C. W., Begg, J. E.: An experimental and theoretical comparison of viscous and diffusive resistances to gas flow through amphistomatous leaves. – Agr. Meteorol. 4: 103-117, 1967.

Kanemasu, E. T., Thurtell, G. W., Tanner, C. B.: Design, calibration and field use of a stomatal diffusion porometer. – Plant Physiol. 44: 881-885, 1969.

Kaufmann, M. R.: Water relations of pine seedlings in relation to root and shoot growth. – Ph.D. Thesis, Duke University, Durham, N.C. 1967.

Knipling, E. B.: A hygrometer for measuring the transpiration resistance of leaves. – U.S. Army Cold Regions Res. and Engin. Lab. Hannover, N.H. 1968.

Lloyd, F. E.: The physiology of stomata. – Carnegie Inst. Washington Publ. 82: 1-142, 1908.

Long, F. L., Clements, F. E.: The method of collodion films for stomata. – Amer. J. Bot. 21: 7-17, 1934.

Louguet, P.: Sur une méthode d'étude du mouvement des stomates utilisant la diffusion de l'hydrogène à travers les feuilles. – In: Eckardt, F. E. (ed.): Methodology of Plant Eco-Physiology. Pp. 307-316. UNESCO, Paris 1965.
Meidner, H., Mansfield, T. A.: Physiology of Stomata. – McGraw-Hill, London 1968.
Meidner, H., Spanner, D. C.: The differential transpiration porometer. – J. exp. Bot. 10: 190-205, 1959.
Milthorpe, F. L., Penman, H. L.: The diffusive conductivity of the stomata of wheat leaves. – J. exp. Bot. 18: 422-457, 1967.
Molisch, H.: Das Offen- und Geschlossensein der Spaltöffnungen veranschaulicht durch eine neue Methode (Infiltrationsmethode). – Z. Bot. 4: 106-112, 1912.
Moreshet, S.: A portable Wheatstone bridge porometer for field measurements of stomatal resistance. – Israel J. agr. Res. 14: 27-30, 1964.
Moreshet, S., Stanhill, G., Koller, D.: A radioactive tracer technique for the direct measurement of the diffusion resistance of stomata. – J. exp. Bot. 19: 460-467, 1968.
Oppenheimer, R. R., Engelberg, N.: Mesure du degré d'ouverture des stomates de coniferes. Méthodes anciennes et modernes. – In: Eckardt, F. E. (ed.): Methodology of Plant Eco-Physiology. Pp. 317-323. UNESCO, Paris 1965.
de Parcevaux, S.: Transpiration végétale et production de matière sèche. Essai d'interprétation en fonction des facteurs du milieu. – Ann. agr. 14: 655-742, 1963.
Peaslee, D. E., Moss, D. N.: Stomatal conductivities in K-deficient leaves of maize (*Zea mays*, L.). – Crop Sci. 8: 427-430, 1968.
Raschke, K.: Das Seifenblasenporometer (zur Messung der Stomaweite an amphistomatischen Blättern). – Planta 66: 113-120, 1965a.
Raschke, K.: Eignung und Konstruktion registrierender Porometer für das Studium der Schliesszellenphysiologie. – Planta 67: 225-241, 1965b.
Sampson, J.: A method of replicating dry or moist surfaces for examination by light microscopy. – Nature 191: 932-933, 1961.
Schorn, M.: Untersuchungen über die Verwendbarkeit der Alkoholfixierung und der Infiltrationsmethode zur Messung der Spaltöffnungsweite. – Jb. wiss. Bot. 71: 783-840, 1929.
Shimshi, D.: Some aspects of stomatal behavior, as observed by means of an improved pressure-drop porometer. – Israel J. Bot. 16: 19-28, 1967.
Shmueli, E.: Irrigation studies in the Jordan Valley. I. Physiological activity of the banana in relation to soil moisture. – Bull. Res. Counc. Israel 3: 228-247, 1953.
Slatyer, R. O.: *In situ* measurements of stomatal resistance. – Proc. Conf. Instrumentation Plant Environment Measurements. Soc. Inst. Technol., Australia, pp. 5-6, 1966.
Slatyer, R. O., Jarvis, P. G.: Gaseous–diffusion porometer for continuous measurement of diffusive resistance of leaves. – Science 151: 574-576, 1966.
Slavík, B. *et al.*: Methods of Studying Plant Water Relations. – Springer-Verlag, Berlin–Heidelberg–New York 1972. (In press.)
Solarová, J.: Stomata reactivity in leaves at different insertion during wilting. – In: Slavík, B. (ed.): Water Stress in Plants. Pp. 147-154. Publ. House Czechosl. Acad. Sci., Prague, and Dr. W. Junk, The Hague, 1965.
Spanner, D. C.: On a new method for measuring the stomatal aperture of leaves. – J. exp. Bot. 4: 283-295, 1953.
Spanner, D. C., Heath, O. V. S.: Experimental studies of the relation between carbon assimilation and stomatal movement. II. The use of the resistance porometer in estimating stomatal aperture and diffusive resistance. Part 2. Some sources of error in the use of the resistance porometer and some modifications of its design. – Ann. Bot. N.S. 15: 319-331, 1951.
Stålfelt, M. G.: Neuere Methoden zur Ermittlung des Öffnungszustandes der Stomata. – Abderhalden's Handb. biol. Arbeitsmethoden, Abt. XI, Teil 4, 1: 167-192, 1939.
Stålfelt, M. G.: Die stomatäre Transpiration und die Physiologie der Spaltöffnungen. – In: Ruhland, W. ed.): Handbuch der Pflanzenphysiologie III. Pp. 351-426. Springer-Verlag, Berlin–Göttingen–Heidelberg 1956.
Strebeyko, P.: Air passage capacity in leaves. – Acta Soc. Bot. Pol. 34: 191-198, 1965a.
Strebeyko, P.: The theory of porometer. – Physiol. Plant. 18: 725-729, 1965b.

Waggoner, P. E.: Calibration of a porometer in terms of diffusive resistance. – Agr. Meteorol. 2: 317-329, 1965.
Wallihan, E. F.: Modification and use of an electric hygrometer for estimating relative stomatal apertures. – Plant Physiol. 39: 86-90, 1964.
Weatherley, P. E.: A porometer for use in the field. – New Phytol. 65: 376-387, 1966.
Williams, C. N., Sinclair, R.: A sensitive porometer for field use. – J. exp. Bot. 20: 81-83, 1969.
Wilson, C. C.: The porometer method for the continuous estimation of stomata. – Plant Physiol. 22: 582-589, 1942.
Zelitch, I.: The control and mechanisms of stomatal movement. – In: Zelitch, I. (ed.): Stomata and Water Relations in Plants. Connecticut agr. exp. Sta. Bull. 664: 18-42, 1963.

16 | THE ESTIMATION OF RESISTANCES TO CARBON DIOXIDE TRANSFER

16.1 | Introduction

The ease with which carbon dioxide moves into a leaf in the process of photosynthesis and the ease with which water vapour moves out of a leaf in the process of transpiration are clearly of great significance to the rates of these processes and to the response of the processes to the environment at any particular time. The resistances encountered by molecules of carbon dioxide in moving into the leaf from the source in the ambient air to the sink at the sites of reaction in the chloroplasts may be used to describe quantitatively specific anatomical and physiological responses to environment which in many circumstances limit the rate at which photosynthesis proceeds. Similarly, the resistances to the transfer of water through the leaf from the source, which can be considered to be at the termination of the xylem, to the sink in the ambient air, first as a liquid and then as a vapour, describe adaptations and responses of the leaf to control water loss at any particular time.
Along the transfer pathways we can identify several more or less discrete segments characterised by position or transfer mechanism. A number of methods are available for estimating the resistances to transfer, or the transfer coefficients, in the different segments of the pathway. Several segments of the pathway are common to both water vapour and carbon dioxide transfer. Use is made of this in deriving certain of the resistances to carbon dioxide transfer, since the resistances to water vapour transfer are more easily estimated.

16.2 | Definition of resistance

A generalised transfer equation can be written for the transfer of a property such as water vapour or carbon dioxide in air as follows. The net flux of mass per unit area and time, q_v[1], anywhere in the pathway is proportional to the gradient of the partial pressure or, at normal atmospheric pressure, the concentration of the property, $\mathrm{d}C/\mathrm{d}z$, so that

$$q_v = -K_v \cdot \frac{\mathrm{d}C}{\mathrm{d}z} \tag{16.1}$$

where K_v [$\mathrm{m^2\ s^{-1}}$] is a generalised transfer coefficient for the property. In circumstances where transfer is by molecular diffusion, $K_v = D_v$ where D_v is the effective molecular diffusivity of water vapour or CO_2 in air. Alternatively, K_v may be a turbulent diffusion coefficient. This equation and those that follow is not valid if appreciable mass transfer occurs as a result of temperature gradients (Bernard 1968).

1. A list of extensively used symbols and their dimensions is given in Section 16.6.

The transfer resistance, r_v, is defined by

$$r_v = \int_{z_1}^{z_2} \frac{dz}{K_v} \quad [\mathrm{s\ m^{-1}}] \tag{16.2}$$

and hence

$$q_v = \frac{C_1 - C_2}{r_v} \, [\mathrm{kg\ m^{-2}\ s^{-1}}] \tag{16.3}$$

Equations (16.2) and (16.3) imply that, over the same pathway, the transfer resistances of carbon dioxide and water vapour (or any other mass property such as heat, nitrous oxide, argon, hydrogen, helium *etc.*) are related by their transfer coefficients such that:

$$r_{v,1} = r_{v,2} \frac{K_{v,2}}{K_{v,1}} \tag{16.4}$$

Hence for a pathway in which transfer is solely by free molecular diffusion, we may write for carbon dioxide and water vapour (see also Parkinson & Penman 1970):

$$r_{CO_2} = r_{H_2O} \frac{D_{H_2O}}{D_{CO_2}} \tag{16.5}$$

On the other hand, along a pathway in which transfer is by fully turbulent diffusion, such as between the vicinity of the leaf and the reference level above the canopy (Section 16.3.1), $K_{v,1} = K_{v,2}$ and

$$r_{CO_2} = r_{H_2O} \tag{16.6}$$

(see Lemon 1967, 1968 and Chapter 13).
In the leaf boundary layer, where transfer grades from molecular diffusion through a transition region to fully turbulent diffusion, $K_v \sim D_v{}^{2/3}$ in the laminar layer which largely restricts transfer (Pohlhausen 1921; Kusuda 1965; Thom 1968; Parlange, Waggoner & Heichel 1970; de Parcevaux & Perrier 1970). Hence

$$r_{CO_2} = r_{H_2O} \left(\frac{D_{H_2O}}{D_{CO_2}} \right)^{\frac{2}{3}} \tag{16.7}$$

It may be noted in passing that equation (16.7) has rarely been used. Gaastra (1959) appreciated that equation (16.5) was unsatisfactory for the boundary layer, but he and successive workers have used equation (16.5) for the boundary layer 'because the choice of any other proportionality factor would have been more arbitrary' (Gaastra 1959). Recently, however, Thom (1968) has satisfactorily demonstrated experimentally the validity of equation (16.7). The error introduced into most earlier calculations by using equation (16.5) for the boundary layer instead of equation (16.7) is likely to be small where the boundary layer resistance

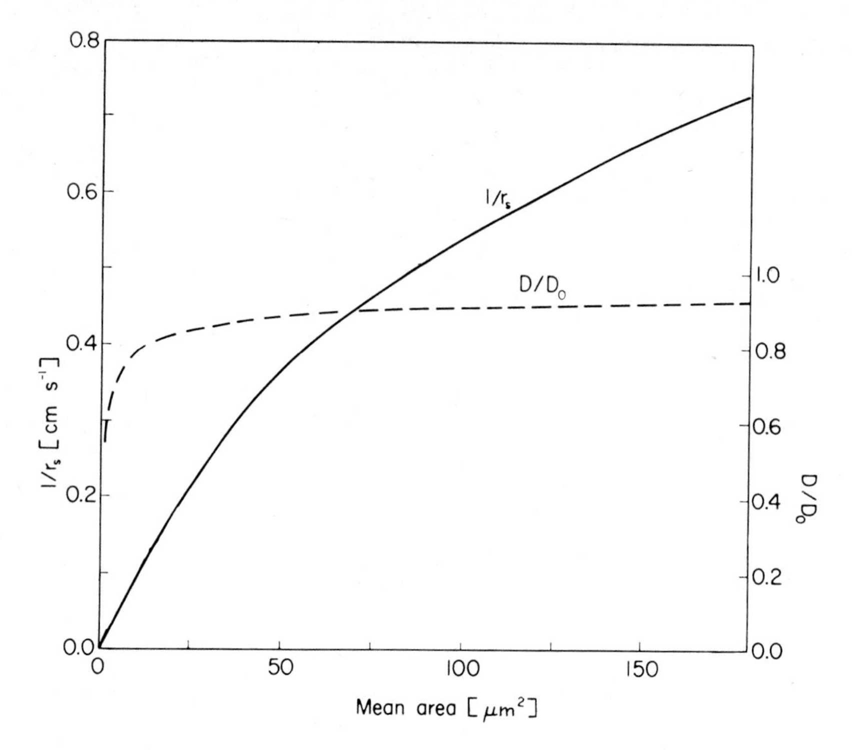

Fig. 16.1 The relationship between stomatal conductance ($1/r_s$) per cm^2 of lower surface of a wheat leaf and mean cross-sectional area of the pore together with the diffusion coefficient for water vapour as a fraction of that in free air (D/D_o). From Cowan & Milthorpe (1968a).

has been kept small in relation to the other resistance in the pathway, as in well stirred leaf chambers.

At a surface, molecular slip of diffusing molecules is incomplete so that the actual diffusion coefficient is less than the coefficient for free diffusion. In small pores or slits, such as the narrow part of the stomatal opening, with dimensions of the order of 0.01 to 10 μm, the reduction in diffusion coefficient can be appreciable and is a function of the aperture of the stomata (Milthorpe & Penman 1967). This is shown in Figure 16.1 taken from Cowan & Milthorpe (1968a). Hence, in calculating the diffusion of a property, such as carbon dioxide or water vapour, through a stomatal pore, the diffusion coefficient appropriate to the pore dimension must be used. The effective coefficient (D_v) is related to the free diffusion coefficient (D^0) and that for narrow channels (D^1) by $1/D_v = 1/D^0 + 1/D^1$ (Carman 1956):

$$D^1 = \frac{8}{3} h \frac{\delta}{k_1} \left(\frac{2\,RT}{M} \right)^{\frac{1}{2}}.$$

where h is the mean hydraulic radius and δ and k_1 are shape factors to which appropriate values are assigned (see Cowan & Milthorpe 1968a). Very fortunately, as Milthorpe and Penman point out (1967, p. 447), for water vapour and carbon dioxide the following relationship between the free diffusion coefficients, D^0, and molecular weights, M, holds approximately:

$$D^0_{H_2O}\, M_{H_2O}^{\frac{1}{2}} \approx D^0_{CO_2}\, M_{CO_2}^{\frac{1}{2}}$$

and hence the ratio of the stomatal resistances is very close to the inverse ratio of the free diffusion coefficients, so that equation (16.5) may be used even within the narrow section of the pore.

Considerable uncertainty exists as to the precise values of D_{H_2O} and D_{CO_2}, and the exact nature of their temperature dependence. Values of 0.14 $cm^2\ s^{-1}$ and 0.24 $cm^2\ s^{-1}$ for D_{CO_2} and D_{H_2O}, respectively, as given in recent editions of the Handbook of Chemistry and Physics (Weast 1968, for example) have frequently been used, giving a ratio of D_{H_2O}/D_{CO_2} of 1.714[1]. However, the sources on which these values are based are old and have been uncritically accepted. Furthermore, one value is for 0 °C and the other for 8 °C and no information on temperature dependence is provided. The values cannot be said to be satisfactory.

A critical appraisal of estimates of D_{H_2O} and its dependence on temperature has been made by Lee and Wilke (1954). They considered values obtained at different temperatures by a number of workers, including the sources given in the Handbook of Chemistry and Physics, and provide additional experimental data of their own. They conclude that a value of 0.257 $cm^2\ s^{-1}$ at 25 °C is likely to be fairly correct, but are unable definitively to settle the question of the temperature dependence. Similar values are given by List (1958, pp. 394–395), de Vries & Krueger (1967) and Bernard (1968). The temperature coefficients given by all these authors range from n = 1.7 to 2.9, for $(T/273)^n$, with the majority around 1.8. Bernard also gives an approximate temperature coefficient of n = 2 for D_{CO_2}.

In the light of these circumstances, Slatyer and Jarvis (1966) estimated the ratio D_{H_2O}/D_{CO_2} experimentally, using the bilateral leaf chamber (Chapter 2) with a small area of finely perforated metal membrane in the centre plane. They obtained a value of 1.68 at 28 °C.

Recently, Fuller, Schettler and Giddings (1966) have developed an easily applied method for predicting binary gas-phase diffusivities based on the use of special diffusion volumes. The method has been developed from a least squares analysis of extensive experimental data (340 data points) and gives an average difference between observed and predicted values of only 4.3 %. The final equation selected for use is as follows:

$$D_{AB} = \frac{1.00 \times 10^{-3}\, T^{1.75}\, (1/M_A + 1/M_B)^2}{p[(\Sigma_A\, v_i)^{\frac{1}{3}} + (\Sigma_B\, v_i)^{\frac{1}{3}}]^2}$$

where M_A, M_B is the molar mass [gram/mol], p is pressure [bar], v_i are special atomic diffusion volumes [= 20.1 for air, 26.9 for CO_2, 12.7 for water vapour]. From this equation the ratio D_{H_2O}/D_{CO_2} is obtained equal to 1.605 and independent of temperature and pressure. This value is somewhat lower than those used previously but may be more appropriate.

The driving force for the flow of liquid water in cell walls is the water potential,

1. For convenience of size, cm and s are usually taken as the working units for diffusivities and transfer resistances.

Ψ, most probably largely the matric potential component, so that the flow along any part of the gradient $d\Psi/dz$ is

$$q_l = -K_l \frac{d\Psi}{dz} \quad [\text{kg m}^{-2}\ \text{s}^{-1}] \tag{16.8}$$

where K_l is the liquid flow or hydraulic conductivity [s]. The hydraulic resistance r_H is then defined by

$$r_H = \int_{z_1}^{z_2} \frac{dz}{K_l} \quad [\text{m s}^{-1}] \tag{16.9}$$

and

$$q_l = \frac{\Psi_1 - \Psi_2}{r_H} \quad [\text{kg m}^{-2}\ \text{s}^{-1}] \tag{16.10}$$

r_v is related to r_H through the thermodynamic expression

$$\Psi = \frac{RT}{V_w} \ln \left(\frac{C}{C_0}\right) \quad [\text{bar}] \tag{16.11}$$

where R is the gas constant, T the Kelvin temperature, V_w the molal volume of water, C_0 the water vapour concentration at the saturation vapour pressure at T and C the water vapour concentration in equilibrium with liquid water in the system, so that

$$r_H = r_v \frac{RT}{V_w} \frac{\ln C_1 - \ln C_2}{C_1 - C_2} \tag{16.12}$$

It is clear that this relationship is not unique but depends upon the vapour pressure gradient (Philip 1966).

16.3 | The pathways of transfer

The following segments of the transfer pathways can be identified (see also Fig. 8.1).

16.3.1 | Transfer to the vicinity of the foliage[1]

Transfer to or from the vicinity of the foliage is from a source or sink at a reference level in the biosphere usually located several metres above the vegetation surface and largely beyond the short term influence of the vegetation. Transfer through this segment of the pathway is by a process of turbulent mixing, or eddy exchange

1. See Chapter 13 for a fuller discussion of the processes involved.

(see, for example, Brutsaert 1965a), in which molecules and heat are rapidly transferred from one eddy to another, the net transfer of the property being in the direction of the concentration gradient. Since transfer by turbulent mixing is generally very effective, the resistance to transfer per unit length of pathway is very small in comparison with resistances elsewhere in the pathway where transfer is by molecular diffusion. Although the pathway is very long in comparison with the path length within the leaf the total resistance is also very small by comparison. Typically one finds a drop in carbon dioxide concentration of not more than 10 to 20 $\mu l \, l^{-1}$ over a distance of the order of 10 metres between the source above an actively photosynthesising canopy to the vicinity of the most active leaves in the canopy (*e.g.* Monteith 1963a, 1965, 1968; Lemon 1967; Inoue 1968). Transfer coefficients for this pathway are of the order of 10 to 10^4 $cm^2 \, s^{-1}$ (*e.g.* Brown & Covey 1966), which is equivalent to transfer resistances of 0.01 to 10 s cm^{-1} for a 1 metre path length.
The estimation of transfer coefficients or resistances in this segment of the pathway can be made using micrometeorological techniques in the field and is discussed in Section 16.5. The resistance is a function of windspeed, atmospheric stability, and canopy structure.

16.3.2 | Transfer across the leaf boundary layer

The velocity of air movement increases with distance away from the leaf surface from zero at the leaf-air interface until it is indistinguishable from the bulk air movement around the leaf. The leaf boundary layer thus consists of a thin layer of air close to the surface, in which movement of the air is by laminar flow, and a transition region to the fully turbulent conditions in the ambient air (Sutton 1953). Transfer of carbon dioxide and water vapour is by molecular diffusion and by a mixture of molecular and eddy diffusion across the transition region, passing into fully turbulent transfer beyond the immediate influence of the leaf.
The thickness of the boundary layer is often defined, for convenience, as the effective thickness across which a uniform concentration gradient, equal to that at the leaf-air interface, would have to exist to give the same total drop in concentration (*e.g.* Slatyer 1967, pp. 241–242). It is a function of windspeed and leaf dimension, anatomy and orientation, increasing at lower windspeeds,and with larger leaves or leaves orientated with the larger dimension parallel to the direction of bulk air flow (see, for example: Powell 1940; Raschke 1956, 1958, 1960; Kuiper 1961; Milthorpe 1961; Gates 1962, 1963; Gates & Benedict 1963; Bouchet 1964; Gates, Tibbals & Kreith 1965; Monteith 1965; Thom 1968; Landsberg & Ludlow 1970).
The boundary layer resistance is in series with other resistances which are under physiological control. Clearly then, in leaf chamber studies of the physiological response of shoots and individual leaves to environmental conditions, it is vital that the boundary layer resistance should be maintained small in relation to the leaf resistances, if physiological responses are to be observed sensitively. In leaf chambers in which the air is well stirred, usually by an internal fan (see Chapter 2), typical values of the boundary layer resistance to CO_2 transfer are 0.5 to 2.0 s cm^{-1} (Holmgren, Jarvis & Jarvis 1965; Jarvis & Slatyer 1966; Begg & Jarvis 1968;

Holmgren 1968). Values for vegetation in the field, obtained by micrometeorological methods, are usually somewhat less and in the region of 0.1 to 0.3 s cm^{-1} (Aston 1963; Monteith 1963a, b, 1965; Denmead 1965; Rutter 1967, 1968; Cowan & Milthorpe 1968a, b). This difference may result from the greater degree of turbulence occurring in natural conditions than is attained in leaf chambers, but may also depend upon the rather different methods used in the estimation of the boundary layer resistance in the field and in the laboratory, and the multiple sources effectively linked in parallel in the field (see *e.g.* Section 16.5.1.1).

16.3.3 Transfer across the cuticle

The precise location of the liquid-air interface in the cuticle is not known. It probably lies close to the surface of the leaf amongst the cuticular wax extrusions. Thus the pathway of carbon dioxide transfer through the cuticle probably consists of only a short distance in the gas phase followed by a relatively long, high resistance pathway in the liquid phase. The liquid phase path length is long because epidermal cells, apart from guard cells, do not usually contain chloroplasts. Hence carbon dioxide molecules (or some reaction product, see Section 16.3.5) must traverse at least one cell width before entering the cell in which they will be assimilated.

There have been few attempts to measure cuticular photosynthesis at normal physiological carbon dioxide concentrations and the data available are somewhat at variance. This probably results from the difficulties encountered in obtaining complete stomatal closure and in knowing that this has occurred. Combinations of darkness and high carbon dioxide concentrations often lead to an impression of stomatal closure but the degree of closure cannot be guaranteed and frequently is not complete or as effective as that induced by a moisture stress (*e.g.* Begg & Jarvis 1968).

Working on the non-stomatal surface of hypostomatous leaves of several species, Holmgren, Jarvis & Jarvis (1965) found practically no carbon dioxide uptake and concluded that the cuticular resistance to carbon dioxide uptake was so large that the pathway could be neglected. However, Freeland (1948) and Dorokhov (1963) have shown appreciable uptake through non-stomatal leaf surfaces of other species at normal ambient carbon dioxide levels so that it would seem necessary to evaluate the resistance in this pathway for the treatment and species concerned. Relative values of cuticular photosynthesis can be readily measured with ^{14}C at abnormally high carbon dioxide concentrations (*e.g.* Dugger 1952).

The cuticular resistance to water transfer is probably also largely a liquid phase resistance but the pathway is clearly not the same as that for carbon dioxide. A wide range of cuticular resistances have been measured (see Holmgren, Jarvis & Jarvis 1965; Whiteman & Koller 1967b), and in some cases it is possible to see a relationship between development of the cuticle and retardation of evaporation. Removal of the soft external wax cuticle results in a several-fold increase in evaporation rate (Skoss 1955; Hall & Jones 1961; Horrocks 1964; Radler 1965). Recently Grncarevic and Radler (1967) have demonstrated that hydrocarbons, long chain alcohols, aldehydes and probably esters are the active components of grape cuticular wax which reduce evaporation. Thus it seems likely that the greater part of the cuticular resistance to water transfer is a hydraulic resistance to the mass transfer of liquid water and is located in the outer part of the cuticle and the cuticular epidermal cell walls.

If this is so, it is incorrect to express this resistance as a diffusive resistance to water vapour transfer as has been done in the past. This obscures the difference in mechanism. The driving force for the mass transfer of liquid water in small pores is the hydrostatic pressure or matric potential component of water potential and the resistance is a hydraulic resistance (Philip 1966). However, in the past it has seemed convenient to express the cuticular resistance in similar units to the vapour phase resistances for comparative purposes. In these units, cuticular resistances of the order of 10 to 10^3 s cm^{-1} have been measured (Holmgren, Jarvis & Jarvis 1965; Waggoner 1967; Whiteman & Koller 1967b). Such estimates can be converted to hydraulic resistances by equation (16.12).

There is some evidence for the dependence of the cuticular resistance on temperature and irradiance (Holmgren, Jarvis & Jarvis 1965), leaf water content (Hygen 1951, 1953; Slavík 1958; Bannister 1964) and vapour pressure deficit (Oppenheimer 1960).

16.3.4 | Transfer through the stomatal pore and intercellular spaces

Transfer of carbon dioxide and water vapour through the stomatal pore and intercellular spaces is generally considered to be by molecular diffusion. However, the possibility of a mass transfer should not be excluded, particularly in the case of fluttering amphistomatous leaves. Experiments with bilateral leaf chambers (*e.g.* that of Jarvis & Slatyer 1966, described in Chapter 2) show that small pressure differentials across an amphistomatous leaf will induce a significant mass flow of air through it. The influence of the pore dimension upon the diffusion coefficient is considered in Section 16.2.

Measured diffusive resistances to carbon dioxide transfer through the stomatal pore and intercellular spaces range from minimum values of about 0.6 to 20 s cm^{-1} for different species in varying physiological conditions with the stomata at maximum opening, up to values approaching infinity at smaller stomatal apertures (*e.g.* Gaastra 1959; Kuiper 1961; Slatyer & Bierhuizen 1964; Whiteman & Koller 1964a, b, 1967a, b; Holmgren, Jarvis & Jarvis 1965; Knoerr 1967; Miller & Gates 1967; Ting, Dean & Dugger 1967; Ting, Thompson & Dugger 1967; Waggoner 1967; Ehrler & van Bavel 1968).

Stomatal pore resistance and intercellular space resistance are usually considered together because the usual method of estimation from the water vapour flux does not distinguish between them. Estimation of the diffusive resistance of the pore alone by calculation from pore dimensions using Fick's law leads to somewhat lower values than are obtained by methods based on water vapour flux (see Holmgren, Jarvis & Jarvis 1965; Whiteman & Koller 1967b; Cowan & Milthorpe 1968a).

The stomatal resistance is a function of many environmental and physiological properties including previous history and current levels of irradiation, temperature, carbon dioxide concentration, vapour pressure deficit, photoperiod, leaf water status, age and general physiological condition (see Heath 1959; Raschke

1960, 1965a; Ketellapper 1963; Meidner & Mansfield 1965, 1968; Slatyer 1967; Ting, Thompson & Dugger 1967).

Few estimates of the intercellular space resistance to CO_2 transfer have been made and the values available are clearly influenced by the methods used to obtain them. For cotton leaves, calculation and experiment yield a value of about 3 s cm^{-1} for the resistance through the mesophyll from one epidermis to the other (Jarvis, Rose & Begg 1967; Jarvis & Slatyer 1970). A similar figure for wheat leaves calculated from data given by Milthorpe & Penman (1967) is 0.5 s cm^{-1}. Milthorpe (1961) quotes values of 0.2 s cm^{-1} for wheat and 0.4 s cm^{-1} for *Zebrina pendula* (from Bange 1953).

The intercellular space resistance is a function of the thickness of the leaf and the tortuosity and cross-sectional area of the voids and consequently it is also a function of leaf water content. Moderate desiccation of comparatively rigid leaves, such as mature leaves of holly, *Ilex aquifolia*, leads to little change in thickness but to a reduction in cell volume with concurrent increase in void volume. On the other hand, cell and void volume and leaf thickness decrease as a result of desiccation in the leaves of cotton and other mesophytic species (see Figure 16.2, and Kennedy & Booth 1958). Meidner (1955) found an increase in intercellular resistance in leaves of *Psychotria capensis* and *Scolopia mundii* as a result of desiccation.

16.3.5 | *Liquid phase transfer within the cell wall and the cell*

Carbon dioxide passes into solution at the liquid-air interface in the surface of the mesophyll cell walls. Transfer thereafter to the reaction sites in the chloroplasts is in the liquid phase. The liquid-air interface should be located at the morphological surface of the cell wall. Recent considerations of the hypothesis of incipient drying, first put forward over 60 years ago by Livingstone (1906), suggest that retraction of liquid-air menisci into the cell wall is most unlikely under physiological conditions (Slatyer 1966a; Jarvis & Slatyer 1970).

Transfer of carbon dioxide from the liquid-air interface to the reaction sites in the chloroplasts is a complex process. Consequently the mesophyll resistance, as the transfer resistance along this pathway has come to be called, also contains a complexity of components. It contains components of CO_2 absorption, and both diffusive and mass transfer components. Transfer within the cell is probably greatly facilitated by the rapid protoplasmic streaming and organelle movement common in living plant cells. As a result of the methods used to derive it, the mesophyll resistance may also contain components, more properly classed as parts of the photosynthetic process, which are attributable to the primary carboxylation and photochemical reactions (Gaastra 1959; Monteith 1963a; Woolhouse 1967–68; Whiteman & Koller 1968; Troughton & Slatyer 1969) (see Section 16.4.6).

Clearly therefore it is strictly incorrect for the mesophyll resistance to be expressed as a diffusion resistance but this is normally done to allow comparison with other resistances in the pathway. The length of the pathway is variable and under physiological control. It is frequently kept short by the arrangement of the chloroplasts around the periphery of the cell but chloroplasts may move and realign themselves in relation to the irradiance.

 Carbon dioxide transfer from the liquid-air interface across the cell wall is presumably by molecular diffusion. It is of interest that the diffusion coefficients of CO_2 in water (0.16×10^{-4} cm^2 s^{-1} at 15 °C) and HCO_3^- in water (*ca.* 0.14×10^{-4} cm^2 s^{-1}) are about four orders of magnitude smaller than the diffusion coefficient for CO_2 in air. Consequently the diffusive resistance per unit length of pathway would be 10^4 larger in water than in air. However, this is more than adequately compensated for by the short path length across the wall (about 0.3 μm) and by the much larger area of internal cell wall surface in relation to leaf surface (about 10 times, Turrell 1936, 1942). A rough calculation (using an equation similar to 11 in Jarvis, Rose & Begg 1967) leads to an estimate of the cell wall resistance to CO_2 or HCO_3^- diffusion of about 0.2 s cm^{-1} per unit of leaf surface area, as compared with a figure of 1 to 2 s cm^{-1} for stomatal resistance. There is some evidence that an increase in the mass and surface area of mesophyll and palisade cells leads to a reduction in mesophyll resistance (Holmgren 1968) and in this connection it should also be noted that in general the palisade cells expose a far larger area of surface to the intercellular spaces than do the spongy parenchyma (Esau 1965).

Diffusion of carbon dioxide across the cell wall into the cell is opposed by the mass flow of water carrying with it dissolved carbon dioxide and bicarbonate in the reverse direction up to the liquid-air interface. It might be thought that this counter flow of carbon dioxide would contribute significantly to the mesophyll resistance. It can readily be shown that this is unlikely. If a leaf is transpiring very rapidly at 5×10^{-6} g cm^{-2} (external surface) s^{-1}, and the average concentration of carbon dioxide dissolved in the cell wall is 200 μl l^{-1}, and the ratio of internal to external surface area is 10, then the average liquid phase mass transfer of carbon dioxide towards the liquid-air interface is 10^{-8} cm^3 cm^{-2} (internal surface) s^{-1}. If the diffusive resistance of the wall is taken as 0.5 s cm^{-1}, a rather larger figure than calculated above, and the drop in CO_2 concentration across the wall is 50 μl l^{-1}, the diffusive flux of CO_2 into the cell is 10^{-4} cm^3 cm^{-2} s^{-1}. That is to say, the diffusive flux of carbon dioxide away from the liquid-air interface is likely to be at least 10^4 times larger than the mass transfer of carbon dioxide in the transpiration stream towards the interface.

When carbon dioxide goes into solution the following equilibria are established

$$H_2O + CO_2 \rightleftharpoons H_2CO_3$$
$$H_2CO_3 \rightleftharpoons HCO_3^- + H^+$$
$$HCO_3^- \rightleftharpoons CO_3^{--} + H^+$$

The ionization constants are as follows (Kern 1960):

$$[H_2CO_3]/[CO_2] = 1.66 \times 10^{-3}$$
$$[H^+][HCO_3^-]/[H_2CO_3] = 2.5 \times 10^{-4}$$
$$[H^+][CO_3^{--}]/[HCO_3^-] = 4.8 \times 10^{-11}$$

From these constants the relative proportions of the ionic species present at different pH can be calculated (see Table 16.1).

The diffusive transport of dissolved carbon dioxide would be expected to be enhanced by the conversion of carbon dioxide to other ions and the consequent

Table 16.1 The relative proportions of the ionic species of carbon dioxide in solution at three levels of pH.

	pH		
	3	5	8
$[CO_2]$	0.998	0.960	0.023
$[HCO_3^-]$	4.17×10^{-4}	4.02×10^{-2}	0.972
$[CO_3^{--}]$	2.00×10^{-11}	1.93×10^{-7}	4.71×10^{-3}
$[H_2CO_3]$	1.66×10^{-3}	1.60×10^{-3}	3.92×10^{-5}

diffusion of several species instead of one. In solutions in which there are no electrical fields and in which no net flux of charge occurs, this expectation is realised. The additional diffusion of the bicarbonate ion leads to a greater total transfer of carbon dioxide. For an increase in pH from 6.5 to 9.0, Enns (1967) showed a doubling in rate of carbon dioxide transfer across a film of water in an artificial system.

The reversible reaction of carbon dioxide with water to form bicarbonate ions is greatly facilitated by the presence of the enzyme carbonic anhydrase. The addition of carbonic anhydrase in suitable amounts results in an increase in CO_2 transfer across the membrane of over two orders of magnitude for the same increase in pH (Enns 1967). In a similar artificial system in which HCO_3^- transfer was associated with a net transfer of charge, the carbon dioxide flux was less than doubled by the addition of carbonic anhydrase (Longmuir, Forster & Woo 1966). Enns also demonstrated that carbonic anhydrase can facilitate CO_2 transfer in the absence of HCO_3^- transfer, possibly by increasing the solubility of carbon dioxide.

Carbonic anhydrase occurs in leaves (see Steemann Nielsen 1960; Hesketh, Muramoto & El-Sharkawy 1965). Larger concentrations are found in the leaves of species in which the Calvin cycle is operative, where the enzyme is largely located in the chloroplasts, than in the leaves of species with the C_4-dicarboxylic acid pathway, where the enzyme is cytoplasmic (Everson & Slack 1968).

Therefore one may suggest that carbonic anhydrase contributes to the mesophyll resistance in species with the Calvin cycle by facilitating the transfer of carbon dioxide across the chloroplast membrane (Everson 1969) or, in some way not fully understood, by offsetting the low affinity of ribulose diphosphate carboxylase for CO_2 (see Section 16.3.6). The low level of carbonic anhydrase present in the cytoplasm of species with the C_4-dicarboxylic acid pathway may contribute to lowering of the mesophyll resistance by facilitating carbon dioxide transfer across the cytoplasm up to the chloroplast, and by the provision of substrate for carboxylation by phosphoenol-pyruvate carboxylase (Everson & Slack 1968). Species with the C_4-dicarboxylic acid pathway have much lower apparent mesophyll resistance, *ca.* 0.5 s cm^{-1}, than do species with the Calvin cycle, which have a resistance of *ca.* 3 s cm^{-1} or more (Ludlow 1969).

Values of mesophyll resistance of from 0.5 to 40 s cm^{-1} have been reported (*e.g.* Gaastra 1959, 1963; Bierhuizen & Slatyer 1964; Whiteman & Koller 1964a, b, 1967a, b, 1968; Holmgren, Jarvis & Jarvis 1965; Gale, Kohl & Hagan 1966;

Begg & Jarvis 1968; Ludlow 1969). Many of the higher values probably result from conceptual or methodological errors in determination (see Section 16.4.6 and Lake 1967b). It seems that the mesophyll resistance to carbon dioxide transfer, when determined with proper care and safeguards, has values of about 0.5 to 10 s cm^{-1} for healthy leaves of many species and somewhat larger values for ageing leaves and leaves of plants in poor physiological condition.

There is little satisfactory evidence as to the influence of environment upon mesophyll resistance. Bierhuizen & Slatyer (1964), Whiteman & Koller (1967a) and Ludlow (1969) have shown an apparent increase in mesophyll resistance at low irradiance, but this very probably merely reflects limitation of photosynthesis by the photochemical partial process and does not show unequivocally an effect of irradiance on the carbon dioxide transfer process. A similar apparent increase in mesophyll resistance is obtained at above normal ambient carbon dioxide concentrations when photosynthesis is no longer limited by transfer processes but is limited by dark reactions such as the carboxylation (*e.g.* Whiteman & Koller 1968). Apparent effects of temperature (Kuiper 1965) and of vapour pressure deficit and soil water potential (Gale, Kohl & Hagan 1966) on mesophyll resistance have also been shown. Such apparent effects of light, carbon dioxide, temperature and vapour pressure in many cases result from the method of estimation of the resistance and do not necessarily indicate an effect on the transfer process itself (see also Troughton & Slatyer 1969; Gifford & Musgrave 1970). The phase change in evaporation occurs at the liquid-air interface in the surface of the mesophyll cell walls. Liquid water moves to the interface along a gradient of water potential from the xylem terminations through either the mesophyll cell walls or the symplasm.

At least since 1906, when Livingstone advanced the concept of incipient drying, there has been discussion as to the presence and significance of an additional resistance in the water vapour transfer pathway either in the liquid or in the vapour phase, close to the liquid-air interface. The problem has been reviewed recently by Slatyer (1966a) and Jarvis & Slatyer (1970).

Evidence accumulating suggests a considerable reduction in water potential or vapour pressure at the liquid-air interface. Shimshi (1963) estimated the interface water potential to be about −80 bar in moderately stressed maize leaves and Whiteman & Koller (1964b) estimated considerably lower values in some xeromorphic desert species.

There are several possible explanations for such reductions in water potential, including solute accumulation at the interface, additional diffusive resistance in the vapour phase as a result of withdrawal of the interface menisci in incipient drying, and the existence of an appreciable hydraulic resistance to mass transfer of liquid water through the cell wall, as discussed in relation to the leaf cuticle earlier.

Slatyer (1966a, 1967) finds the first two possibilities unlikely and Jarvis and Slatyer (1970) interpret their data in terms of the presence of an hydraulic resistance which may be identified morphologically with an apparent cuticular layer on the surface of the mesophyll cells. In cotton leaves this hydraulic resistance is equivalent to a diffusive resistance which can reach 2 s cm^{-1}, and is partially dependent on transpiration rate and leaf water potential.

In leek *(Allium porrum)*, Fischer (1968) obtained a mesophyll wall resistance to water transfer of about 0.1 s cm^{-1} for turgid tissue rising to over 1 s cm^{-1} with extreme desiccation. The data of Shimshi (1963) for unwilted maize yield estimates lying within the same range. Milthorpe (1961) also quotes low values of about 0.2 s cm^{-1} for *Antirrhinum* and for wheat *(Triticum)*. The resistance is generally included in the stomatal resistance as normally estimated from the flux of water vapour. Since it has no counterpart in the CO_2 transfer pathway, the deviation of the stomatal resistance to CO_2 transfer from the vapour transfer resistance, using equation (16.5), yields an overestimate, and hence an underestimate of the mesophyll resistance. Clearly if the hydraulic resistance is appreciable, as it may be, significant errors in the carbon dioxide transfer resistances result.

16.3.6 | *The so-called excitation and carboxylation resistances*

In some conditions, transfer of carbon dioxide to the reaction sites in the chloroplasts is not the most important factor limiting the rate of photosynthesis. When the irradiance is insufficient to saturate the photochemical reaction, for example, the rate of photosynthesis is largely determined by the supply of light and to a lesser extent by the supply of CO_2 to the chloroplasts. When light and carbon dioxide supply is adequate, the rate of photosynthesis is determined by the concentration and activity of the enzymes which reduce carbon dioxide and synthesise a variety of carbon-containing products. To evaluate, on a comparative basis, the relative magnitudes of the restrictions imposed on photosynthesis by the several partial processes which might simultaneously be limiting, Monteith (1963a) proposed that the excitation and carboxylation partial processes should be considered as resistances in series with the genuine transfer resistances and expressed in the same units. Chartier (1966) has adopted this approach. He defines the carboxylation resistance as $1/A_0 \cdot k_1$ where k_1 is the rate constant for the irreversible combination of CO_2 with an acceptor:

$$CO_2 + A \xrightarrow{k_1} A\,CO_2$$

and $A_0 = [A] + [ACO_2]$ which is assumed to be constant. Whilst clearly recognising that such excitation and carboxylation resistances do not have a physical identity consistent with resistances to transfer of mass as defined in Section 16.3, this approach has a certain advantage. It allows rapid appraisal at any moment of the various partial processes which might be limiting photosynthesis and evaluation of their relative importance as limiting factors.

This approach also has serious inherent dangers. Because these 'resistances' are of different kinds to the previously considered transfer resistances, 'flow' across them will not be related to resistance in the same way as for the transfer resistances. Consequently it is not possible to predict quantitatively what effect a change in resistance elsewhere in the catena will have upon the rate of the overall process. In general it may be said that precise quantitative predictions can not be made using models in which resistances of different kinds, with different driving forces across them, are mixed. At best such models serve to demonstrate relative magnitudes at any time.

It is not pertinent here to go into the biophysics of the photochemical reaction

or the biochemistry of the carboxylation and succeeding reactions. However certain points should be made.
The efficiency of the photochemical process, and hence the excitation resistance, is given by the slope of the straight line portion of the curve relating net photosynthesis to irradiance[1], at very low levels of irradiance (in the region of net photosynthesis equal to zero) (*e.g.* Björkman & Holmgren 1963). The photochemical efficiency varies two to three-fold amongst species and as a result of pretreatment, age, physiological condition *etc.* (*e.g.* Bourdeau & Laverick 1958; Mooney & Billings 1961; Keller & Koch 1962; Björkman & Holmgren 1963, 1966; Hesketh 1963; Hiesey & Milner 1965; Björkman 1966, 1968a, b, c; Hiesey, Björkman & Nobs 1967; Gauhl 1969; Ludlow 1969). Very precise measurements of net photosynthesis around compensation irradiance are required to detect quite large changes in the slope of the curve and hence in photochemical efficiency. The measurements made with many systems have not been sufficiently accurate to describe precisely the slope and shape of the curve in this region. In some cases where accurate detailed studies have been made, it is clearly shown that the curve is a straight line over an appreciable length in the region of the abscissa (*e.g.* Björkman & Holmgren 1963; Begg & Jarvis 1968). In estimates of the CO_2 transfer resistances, it is usual to eliminate from consideration the excitation resistance by saturating photosynthesis with light. If this is not done, an undefined component of excitation resistance appears in the estimate of mesophyll resistance when this is estimated as a residual resistance (see Section 16.4.6).
Gaastra (1959, 1963) showed that at light saturation and at normal ambient carbon dioxide concentrations of around 300 $\mu l\ l^{-1}$, the rate of photosynthesis was strongly dependent upon the ambient carbon dioxide concentration and largely independent of temperature. He therefore concluded that the carboxylation and other biochemical reactions capable of occurring in the dark were not limiting the rate of photosynthesis to any significant extent, and that photosynthesis could be considered as entirely limited by the *supply* of carbon dioxide to the reaction sites. Others (*e.g.* Pisek & Winkler 1959; Björkman & Holmgren 1963; Murata & Iyama 1963; Hiesey, Nobs & Björkman 1967) have also shown a rather small dependence of net photosynthesis upon ambient temperature; whereas in other cases, especially the tropical grasses, a much more marked dependence upon temperature has been demonstrated (Murata & Iyama 1963; El-Sharkawy & Hesketh 1964; Murata, Iyama & Honma 1965; Mooney & Shropshire 1967; El-Sharkawy, Loomis & Williams 1968; Kriedemann 1968; Ludlow 1969).
In considering evidence of this kind, one point emerges clearly. If the response of photosynthesis to temperature is to be taken as the criterion for limitation by carboxylation and other 'dark' reactions, it is gross photosynthesis in relation to temperature which should be considered. With the techniques in normal use, this is not possible. Gaastra (1959) purported to do this and shows curves relating gross photosynthesis to temperature and other environmental parameters. This was achieved by displacing the abscissa downwards on his diagrams so that the curves passed through zero on both axes. That is to say, he effectively added dark

1. Strictly the abscissa should be in terms of the *absorbed* irradiance of photosynthetically useful radiation.

respiration to all his data points, thus tacitly assuming equality of respiration in darkness and in light. The observed response of net photosynthesis to temperature is the sum of the separate and different responses of photosynthesis and photo-respiration. Without knowledge of the response of photorespiration to temperature, it is therefore not possible to conclude whether or not photosynthesis shows a dependence upon temperature characteristic of limitation by the 'dark' reactions. Hence on this basis it cannot be said with any certainty whether or not a component of carboxylation resistance is included in the mesophyll resistance, when the latter is estimated as the residual term (Section 16.4.6). Estimation of photorespiration is hedged about with all kinds of difficulties (Chapter 8). If one accepts some of the equivocal methods such as CO_2 efflux into CO_2- free air in light, or photosynthesis in the presence and absence of oxygen, the dependence of photorespiration upon temperature would seem to be similar to that of dark respiration, although with a somewhat smaller temperature coefficient (*e.g.* El-Sharkawy & Hesketh 1964; Holmgren & Jarvis 1967; Björkman 1968c; Hofstra & Hesketh 1969).

Carbon dioxide is incorporated into the Calvin cycle by carboxylation of ribulose–1,5–diphosphate in the presence of the enzyme carboxydismutase, or ribulose diphosphate carboxylase, as it is also called. This carboxylation reaction appears to be the predominant CO_2 fixation reaction in most dicotyledons (excluding plants with Crassulacean type metabolism). In some monocotyledons, especially tropical grasses of the Panicoid group (*e.g.* maize, sorghum, sugar cane, sudan grass) and members of the *Amaranthaceae*, carbon dioxide seems to be largely fixed into sugars *via* the C-1 of a C_4-dicarboxylic acid with the aid of the enzyme phosphoenol-pyruvate carboxylase (PEP carboxylase) (Hatch & Slack 1966; Hatch, Slack & Johnson 1967; Johnson & Hatch 1968). There is some evidence (*e.g.* Graham & Whittingham 1968) that the potential for both pathways of CO_2 fixation exists in the same organism but that internal and external environmental conditions determine which system predominates[1].

The rate of the carboxylation reaction (and hence the carboxylation resistance) might be expected to limit photosynthesis if the carboxylation enzymes present are of either very low activity or in very small concentrations.

The activity of the carboxylation enzymes is generally expressed in terms of Michaelis-Menten kinetics. Estimates of activity must be determined *in vitro* on either the isolated enzyme, chloroplasts or cells. Consequently such estimates are extremely sensitive to the extraction procedures and composition of the solution and may well not represent the *in vivo* activity. For example, Walker (1966) states that an ambient concentration of 6% CO_2 (60 000 $\mu l\ l^{-1}$) is required for maximum rate of carboxylation by carboxydismutase.

It has generally been assumed that the species of carbon dioxide active in the carboxylation is bicarbonate, and $NaHCO_3$ is usually added as substrate. The concentration of $NaHCO_3$ (K_m) required to half-saturate the carboxylation of ribulose diphosphate in the presence of isolated carboxydismutase is in the range 5 to 30 mM (Weissbach, Horrecker & Hurwitz 1956; Paulsen & Lane 1966;

1. Since this was written, convincing evidence of the presence of both systems in higher plant leaves has been obtained, for example by O. Björkman at the Carnegie Institution, Stanford, Cal., USA.

Björkman 1967; McMahon & Bogorod 1967; Kieras & Haselkorn 1968). This is equivalent to equilibrium CO_2 concentrations in the gas phase of about 15×10^4 to 90×10^4 $\mu l\ l^{-1}$. However, in whole cells and intact chloroplasts, a lower K_m of 0.3 to 0.6 mM is obtained (Jensen & Bassham 1966; Gibbs *et al.* 1967). The level of bicarbonate required to half-saturate carboxylation by isolated phosphoenolpyruvate carboxylase is 0.2 to 0.4 mM (Walker 1957; Maruyama *et al.* 1966; Everson & Slack 1968). A concentration of 0.3 mM $NaHCO_3$ in solution is equivalent to an equilibrium concentration of about 9 000 $\mu l\ l^{-1}$ CO_2 in the gas phase[1], which is still far in excess of the normal ambient concentration!

If these estimates of bicarbonate K_m *in vitro* represent the *in vivo* activity of the enzyme, either the carboxylation resistance must have a large limiting effect on carbon dioxide fixation and comprise the major part of the mesophyll resistance, when the latter is determined as a residue, or a carbon dioxide 'pump' of some kind must exist at the chloroplast to raise the concentration of carbon dioxide prior to the carboxylation. In this connection, it is interesting to note that both Bassham & Jensen (1967) and Slack (1968) have shown, respectively, a strong rapid response of carboxydismutase and PEP-carboxylase to irradiation; carboxylation activity increases rapidly upon irradiation and decreases rapidly with the onset of darkness. However, the basic premise that bicarbonate is the species of carbon dioxide active in the carboxylation may be at fault. A recent elegant combination of theory and experiment leads to the conclusion that CO_2 is the active species in carboxylation by extracted carboxydismutase (Cooper *et al.* 1969). Correction of the K_m for bicarbonate to the concentration of carbon dioxide in solution results in a K_m about 1/50 of the previous values, yielding values similar to those reported for intact chloroplasts. It is also of considerable interest that Cooper *et al.* found that the presence of carbonic anhydrase greatly reduced the rate of carboxylation, as would be expected if CO_2 is the active species. It remains to be seen whether the active species for *intact* chloroplasts is also CO_2. If this is found to be the case, the carboxylation resistance will assume less importance as a limiting factor.

Evidence that the carboxylation step can limit photosynthesis is provided by Woolhouse (1967–68), Björkman (1968a, b), Wareing, Khalifa & Treharne (1968), Eagles & Treharne (1969). Björkman found a very close correlation between the *in vitro* activity of carboxydismutase preparations, in a standard assay, and the *in vivo* maximum rates of photosynthesis amongst a number of sun and shade species grown in their natural habitats (1968a) and amongst sun and shade ecotypes of *Solidago virgaurea* when grown in high and low irradiation environments (1968b). Similar correlations between rates of photosynthesis and activity of carboxydismutase have been found with leaves of *Phaseolus vulgaris* (Wareing, Khalifa & Treharne 1968) and *Dactylis glomerata* (Eagles & Treharne 1969). Wareing, Khalifa & Treharne also showed a correlation between the *in vivo* rate of photosynthesis in maize and the *in vitro* PEP-carboxylase activity.

There have been very few attempts to express the limiting effect of carboxylase activity in terms of a transfer resistance as proposed by Monteith (1963b). How-

1. These calculations are based on the data in Table 16.1 for pH 8 and 25 °C and the assumption that equilibrium is reached between CO_2 in the gas phase and *all* ionization products of CO_2 in solution.

ever if the carboxylation resistance does often limit photosynthesis, a large part of the mesophyll resistance (when determined as a residue) may properly be ascribed to the carboxylation reaction. With a method designed specifically to estimate the carboxylation resistance, Chartier, Chartier & Čatský (1970) obtained the small figure of about 0.2 s cm^{-1} for leaves of bean *(Phaseolus vulgaris)*. Troughton & Slatyer (1969) and Gifford & Musgrave (1970) concluded that environmentally induced variations in CO_2 influx were independent of the carboxylation resistance and were solely functions of stomatal behaviour.

16.4 | Determination of resistances: laboratory techniques

Resistances may be determined directly for the property concerned, in this case carbon dioxide, or they may be estimated from the resistance over the same pathway for another property such as water vapour, heat or another gas such as hydrogen or nitrous oxide, with the aid of relationships like equations (16.5) and (16.7).

They may be determined by steady state or non-steady state methods.

In those cases where the transfer process can be considered to be diffusive, the transfer resistance may be estimated from the dimensions of the pathway and diffusion theory.

16.4.1 | Determination of the boundary layer resistance, r_a

16.4.1.1 | Determination from carbon dioxide transfer

Gaastra (1959) attempted to determine the boundary layer resistance to carbon dioxide transfer from the steady state rate of absorption of CO_2 by a leaf replica saturated with KOH solution and identical in size, shape, roughness and exposure to the leaf. An equation like Eq. (16.3) was used, in which C_1 is the CO_2 concentration at the interface between the air and KOH solution, assumed equal to zero, C_2 is the concentration in the ambient air outside the boundary layer and q_v is the rate of CO_2 absorption measured with an infra-red gas analyser.

Unsatisfactorily high values were obtained for r_a. Gaastra (1959, p. 53) suggested as an explanation, that absorption of CO_2 may not have been complete at the interface, so that the carbon dioxide concentration there was not zero as assumed, and consequently some component of a liquid phase diffusion resistance was included in r_a. His data suggest that the liquid phase component of resistance increases with increase in the flux of carbon dioxide to the absorber. Consequently this technique can only be expected to provide reliable estimates of r_a at very low CO_2 fluxes which are difficult to measure accurately. Extrapolation to zero CO_2 flux or zero liquid phase resistance might avoid the problem, but this has not been attempted.

On the evidence available this method cannot be recommended.

16.4.1.2 | Determination from water vapour transfer

 This is the most widely used method and is described in detail since the methods for stomatal and cuticular resistance are similar in many respects. The boundary layer resistance to carbon dioxide transfer towards the leaf is usually determined from the resistance to water vapour transfer away from the leaf in evaporation, using equation (16.5) or (16.7). The latter is more appropriate but has rarely been used. The evaporation of other liquids can equally well be used but rarely has been. Thom (1968) made use of evaporation of bromobenzene and methylsalicylate. One advantage in using the evaporation of such molecules is that the ambient partial pressure is effectively zero.

The resistance to water vapour transfer is determined from an equation like Eq. (16.3) in which C_1 is the water vapour concentration or absolute humidity at the liquid-air interface [kg m^{-3}], C_2 is the water vapour concentration in the ambient air at some reference site outside the boundary layer, and q_v is the flux of water vapour [kg m^{-2} s^{-1}] evaporated from a free water surface, identical in size, shape, roughness and exposure to the leaf. It is assumed that the vapour pressure at the liquid-air interface is equal to the saturation vapour pressure at the temperature (T_1) of the interface, $e_1(T_1)$. C_1 is then derived from

$$C_1 = \frac{e_1}{p} \frac{273}{T_1} \rho_v \quad [\text{kg m}^{-3}] \tag{16.13}$$

where e and p are, respectively, the partial water vapour pressure and atmospheric pressure in the same units, and ρ_v is the density of water vapour (0.018/0.022 4 = 0.804 kg m^{-3}). Similarly, C_2 is derived from the ambient water vapour pressure, e_2, and ambient temperature, T_2.

The following measurements are required to solve equation (16.3):
- evaporation rate per unit area, q_v [kg m^{-2} s^{-1}]
- shoot or replica surface area [m^2]
- ambient water vapour pressure, e_2 [mbar]
- ambient temperature, T_2 [K]
- temperature of the liquid-air interface, T [K].

In some circumstances it may be possible to convert the leaf surface to a free water surface by spraying it with water containing a wetting agent. Rutter (1967) successfully determined r_a in the forest, from the rate of evaporation of water from wet pine foliage after rain. In general, however, the high contact angles made by water droplets on plant leaves (see for example Troughton & Hall 1967) do not allow the use of this method. The coverage of the surface of linear leaves with a water film may be improved by removing the surface waxes with organic solvents, or by coating the leaves with hygroscopic substances (Landsberg & Ludlow 1970).

The technique most widely used has been to expose a water-saturated replica of the leaf, made of a coarsely structured, inert matrix, such as blotting paper or filter paper (*e.g.* Whatman No. 1) in the leaf chamber in the same position as the leaf. Powell (1940) showed that evaporation from such a surface was similar to evaporation from a free water surface.

Replicas of broad leaves can be made to suitable shape, size and exposure. However, such replicas cannot simulate the surface roughness of the leaf caused by the presence of hairs, vein protrusions, glands *etc.* Shaving the hairs from soya bean leaves demonstrates the common assertion that the hairs contribute significantly to r_a (Woolley 1964). Preparation of replicas of succulent, linear or dissected leaves borne on shoots of complicated leaf arrangement, becomes difficult if not impossible. However, the boundary layer resistance of such shapes is small compared with broad leaves (Powell 1940; Raschke 1960; Milthorpe 1961) and in the presence of forced ventilation might be considered insignificant and neglected without serious detriment. This view gains support also because many such species have relatively high minimal stomatal resistances (Lee & Gates 1964; Miller & Gates 1967; Ting, Dean & Dugger 1967; Whiteman & Koller 1967b; Jarvis & McKerron unpublished; Ludlow & Jarvis 1971).

Some care is required in obtaining a reasonable estimate of interface temperature (see also Chapter 17). An accuracy of 0.1 °C should be aimed at since this represents about 1% relative humidity or about 0.20 mbar vapour pressure difference in the normal ambient temperature range. Small probes such as fine wire thermocouples ($\approx$ 36 to 44 s.w.g.), small thermistors or diodes are often used. In such cases it is important that the wires leading up to the sensor be well within the boundary layer and in contact with the surface for several centimetres. In a well stirred chamber, a high rate of evaporation, with consequent large reduction in interface temperature below air temperature, can occur in determinations of r_a. The resulting temperature gradient can lead to large errors in the measured surface temperature as a result of heat conduction along the wires. A reduction in vapour pressure gradient and hence in evaporation rate will reduce the size of the error but may well increase other errors in the determination of q_v and $(C_1 - C_2)$. A sandwich replica with the thermocouple and wires between the two surfaces largely eliminates this error in this case but does not eliminate the problem, which recurs in the estimation of stomatal resistance.

16.4.1.3 | Determination from sensible heat transfer

The boundary layer resistance to CO_2 transfer can be determined from the equivalent resistance to sensible heat transfer and the thermal diffusivity of air, D_h, using equation (16.7) (with r_h and D_h in place of r_{H_2O} and D_{H_2O}, respectively). Rewriting equation (16.1) for sensible heat transfer by forced convection

$$q_h = -c_p \rho_a K_h \frac{dT}{dz} \tag{16.14}$$

where c_p is the specific heat of air (1013 $kg^{-1}K^{-1}$), ρ_a the density of air (1.20 $kg\ m^{-3}$) and K_h a turbulent transfer coefficient ($m^2\ s^{-1}$). In the boundary layer, $K_h \alpha D_h^{2/3}$ as discussed earlier with regard to water vapour (Thom 1968); $D_h \approx 0.22\ cm^2\ s^{-1}$.

The diffusive resistance to heat transfer across the boundary layer is then defined by

$$r_h = \int_{z_1}^{z_2} \frac{dz}{K_h}$$

so that

$$q_h = \frac{c_p \rho_a (T_1 - T_2)}{r_h} \quad [\text{W m}^{-2}]$$

$$= k_h(T_1 - T_2) \qquad (16.15)$$

where k_h is a heat transfer coefficient in W $m^{-2}K^{-1}$. In conditions of forced convection at least, Thom (1968) has shown by experiment that

$$r_h = r_v \left(\frac{D_v}{D_h}\right)^{\frac{2}{3}}$$

For objects of rectangular geometric shape and dimension exposed in a wind tunnel with a specific orientation, k_h can be determined from heat transfer theory for conditions of free and forced convection and for the upper and lower surfaces (Gates 1962; Hsu 1963; Gates, Tibbals & Kreith 1965; Parkhurst *et al.* 1968). The heat transfer coefficients are functions of dimension, temperature difference and wind speed:

$$k_h \alpha \frac{1}{X}(X^3 \cdot \Delta T)^{0.25} \quad \text{for free convection,}$$

$$k_h \alpha \frac{1}{X}(X \cdot u)^{0.5} \quad \text{for forced convection with laminar flow,}$$

$$k_h \alpha \frac{1}{X}(X \cdot u)^{0.8} \quad \text{for forced convection with turbulent flow,}$$

where X is the effective dimension of the object in the direction of the air flow and u is the bulk air windspeed. Such expressions also contain empirical constants relating to the orientation of the object in relation to the temperature difference, for free convection, or the air flow, for forced convection. They have been applied to leaves by Gates and his colleagues.

Recently Parkhurst *et al.* (1968) have successfully predicted heat transfer coefficients from heat transfer theory for irregular, flat, compound leaf models differently orientated in a wind tunnel in both free and forced convection, using a weighted mean dimension. At present it is not possible to predict reliable values of k_h from engineering equations for compound leaves and shoots of complex geometry, such as conifer shoots, and in such cases k_h must be individually determined. Gates, Tibbals & Kreith (1965) have developed a simple method for determining the heat transfer coefficients of complex biological structures, using an elegant technique to prepare accurate silver replicas of structures such as pine shoots (see also Drake, Raschke & Salisbury 1970). Even simple real leaves differ in shape and surface flatness and roughness from the models on which the engineering heat transfer equations are based so that empirical relationships for k_h for leaves differ somewhat from the equivalent engineering expressions (Martin 1943; Raschke 1956, 1958). Furthermore, in stirred and ventilated assimilation chambers, and in canopies, and unknown degree of mixing occurs resulting in a non-direction-

al, partly turbulent air flow quite unlike the air stream in an experimental wind tunnel. Hence, in all probability the application of heat transfer coefficients derived from heat transfer theory or wind tunnel experimentation is unjustified and it is necessary to determine k_h or r_h for the particular object and circumstances (*cf.* Aston, Millington & Peters 1969).
Explicit statements of empirical equations for the determination of k_h or r_h from heat transfer theory may be found in Gates (1962, 1963, 1968a, b); Gates, Tibbals & Kreith (1965); Cowan (1968); Cowan & Milthorpe (1968a, b); Parkhurst *et al.* (1968).
Similar empirical equations can also be derived from experiments on evaporation from objects of different shapes, sizes and orientation in wind tunnels (*e.g.* Powell & Griffiths 1935; Powell 1940). They have the same limitations with regard to general application, but can be useful in model situations (*e.g.* Milthorpe 1961).

16.4.1.4 | Determination from energy balance considerations

The boundary layer resistance can be derived from a *change* in the energy balance of individual leaves or shoots in an assimilation chamber or freely exposed in the field (see Section 16.5.2.3) from a knowledge of leaf and air temperature and evaporation rate. Alternatively, if evaporation rate is not known, it may be determined from the change in the energy balance, and the sum of the resistances to water vapour transfer determined.
The relevant observations relating to the change in energy balance can be made simultaneously on two initially identical samples, one of which has been manipulated to have a different energy balance. Alternatively, the observations can be made sequentially on the same sample. The former approach is most suitable in the field (Impens 1966; Impens *et al.* 1967; Hunt & Impens 1968) (see Section 16.5.2.3). The latter approach is most appropriate to assimilation chambers. When sequential observations are made on the same sample in an assimilation chamber the energy balance of the leaf can be altered by manipulation of the transpiration rate without recourse to polythene tape or antitranspirants such as have been used in the field. The energy balance of leaf or shoot in an assimilation chamber with constant irradiance and ventilation at two rates of evaporation, E_1 and E_2, can be written as follows:

$$Q_s + Q - 2\,\varepsilon\sigma T_1^4 = LE_1 + (T_1 - T_a)c_p\,\rho_a/r_a \quad [\mathrm{W\,m^{-2}}]$$
$$Q_s + Q - 2\,\varepsilon\sigma T_2^4 = LE_2 + (T_2 - T_a)c_p\,\rho_a/r_a \quad [\mathrm{W\,m^{-2}}]$$

where Q_s is the net short-wave irradiance, Q is the thermal radiation influx from the chamber walls, T is the leaf temperature, T_a is air temperature, ε is the thermal radiation emittance of the leaf, σ is the Stefan-Boltzmann constant, L is the latent heat of vaporization, and c_p and ρ_a are the specific heat and density of moist air, respectively. By subtraction

$$2\,\varepsilon\sigma(T_1^4 - T_2^4) + L(E_1 - E_2) + (T_1 - T_2)c_p\,\rho/r_a = 0 \tag{16.16}$$

writing

$$2\,\varepsilon\sigma(T_1^4 - T_2^4) \approx \varepsilon\sigma\, 8\overline{T}^3(T_1 - T_2)$$

where $\bar{T}$ is the mean of T_1 and T_2

$$r_a = -\frac{c_p \rho_a (T_1 - T_2)}{\varepsilon\sigma\, 8\, \bar{T}^3 (T_1 - T_2) + L(E_1 - E_2)} \qquad (16.17)$$

This solution of the energy balance equation yields r_a alone from simultaneous measurements of a change in evaporation rate and leaf temperature, both of which are usually measured in assimilation chamber work. It is immaterial whether a change in stomatal resistance occurs so long as the energy balance component of latent heat transfer is changed. Hence the required change can be induced by changes in ambient water vapour pressure or carbon dioxide concentration. The accuracy of the method is clearly limited by the accuracy with which the *change* in leaf temperature can be determined. This method has a considerable advantage over that of Linacre (referred to below), in that steady state observations are made (see also Idle 1970).

Linacre (1967) has described a non-steady state method which can be used for estimating the heat transfer coefficient of a leaf that is freely transpiring. The method is based on the change in temperature which occurs when the radiation balance of the leaf is suddenly altered. The theory of the method is too extensive to allow presentation here and the reader is referred to the original paper.

16.4.2 | Determination of the cuticular resistance, r_c

Methods utilizing equation (16.3) for the determination of the total resistance to water or carbon dioxide transfer can be used for the determination of cuticular resistance in the absence of a flux through the stomata.

16.4.2.1 | Water vapour transfer

There is no problem in making determinations on non-stomatal surfaces such as the adaxial surface of hypostomatous leaves. However, it is extremely difficult to be certain that no flux is occurring through the stomata of surfaces which possess them. For example, Begg and Jarvis (1968) found the apparent cuticular resistance of *Stylosanthes humilis* after a night in darkness at normal ambient carbon dioxide concentration to be 8 to 36 s cm^{-1}.

Raising the ambient carbon dioxide concentration to 1 % gave estimates as low as 5 to 6 s cm^{-1}. Progressive desiccation of the leaves resulted in r_c increasing from about 14 to 17 s cm^{-1}, when stomatal closure was thought to have occurred from the shape of the water loss curve (Hygen 1951; Solarová 1965), to values of 24 to 36 s cm^{-1} two hours later. It would seem that in many estimates of cuticular resistance or photosynthesis of stomatal surfaces, complete stomatal closure may not have occurred (*e.g.* Williams & Amer 1957; Milthorpe 1961; Čatský 1965).

The cuticular resistance is generally determined from the rate of cuticular evaporation from a leaf in a leaf chamber or controlled environment using an equation like Eq. (16.3), in which C_1, C_2 and q_v have the same meaning as was elaborated in connection with the determination of the boundary layer resistance (Section 16.4.1.2). In this case, $r_v = r_a + r_c$. Since r_a is usually small and r_c large, $r_v \approx r_c$.

The cuticular resistance to the transfer of water determined in this way cannot be applied to carbon dioxide transfer by the use of equation (16.5) because, as discussed earlier (Section 16.3.3), the pathways of water and carbon dioxide transfer through the cuticle do not have the same length or permeability for the two properties.

16.4.2.2 | Carbon dioxide transfer

The cuticular resistance to carbon dioxide transfer, as such, has never been estimated, because rates of cuticular photosynthesis are extremely small (*e.g.* Holmgren, Jarvis & Jarvis 1965). In principle one may write, in the absence of stomatal photosynthesis, that

$$\Sigma r_{CO_2} = r_a + r_c + r_m$$

and determine r_c by difference. The estimation of Σr_{CO_2} and r_m is discussed in Section 16.4.4. The boundary layer resistance can certainly be neglected and since r_c is likely to be of the order of 10^2 or 10^3 s cm^{-1}, r_m can also probably be neglected.

16.4.3 | Determination of the stomatal resistance, r_s

A considerable number of methods have been used to obtain information about the resistance of the stomata to the diffusive transfer of water vapour and carbon dioxide, and the number is increasing[1]. In many methods the stomatal and intercellular resistances are determined together as one segment of the pathway, and in some methods other resistances are also included. Few of the methods determine the resistance of the stomatal pore alone and few have been used to determine the resistance to carbon dioxide directly. Both steady state and non-steady state methods have been used. In many cases the main features of the methods have been determined by the desire for techniques which can be used in the field, often for irrigation control. The following methods will be discussed:

1. calculation from pathway dimensions,
2. mass flow porometry,
3. water vapour exchange (also called 'Transpiration porometry').
4. gas diffusion porometry,
5. leaf energy balance.

Reference may also be made to the electrical analogue model used by de Parcevaux (1964, 1968) to investigate the relative rôles of stomata and boundary layer in controlling mass transfers.

16.4.3.1 | Calculation from pathway dimensions

With adequate knowledge of the geometry and dimensions of the pathway through the stomatal pore, it is possible, using diffusion theory, to calculate the diffusive

1. A comprehensive list is given in Chapter 15.

resistance of a stoma and hence the diffusive resistance of the stomatal pathway for an area of leaf. Various levels of approximation and of sophistication have been used in making the calculation. The ultimate has perhaps been reached in the recent treatment by Milthorpe and Penman (1967) of diffusion through wheat stomata. Simpler, more approximate calculations have been made by Heath & Penman (1941); Penman & Schofield (1951); Bange (1953); Lee & Gates (1964); Waggoner (1965); Jarvis, Rose & Begg (1967).

The data required are the length of the various segments of the pathway through the pore, the width and shape of the pore, and the approaches to it, and the number of stomata per unit area of leaf. The pathway may be considered in several segments if the geometry warrants it. The pore itself may be treated as a slit or ovoid of constant length and varying breadth, or with both dimensions variable.

It is not proposed to describe a general theory here. The reader is referred to the papers cited above (see also Parlange & Waggoner 1970).

This method is not suitable as a routine but is appropriate to special investigations. The changes in dimension cannot be obtained continuously or even easily by sampling. Sampling techniques such as the various methods of obtaining stomatal imprints (*e.g.* Sampson 1961) do not usually penetrate to the narrowest parts of the pore, especially at small apertures (Gloser 1967; Solarová 1968) and direct observation is not usually possible.

16.4.3.2 | Mass flow porometry

Mass flow porometers have been used extensively, since the time of Darwin right up to the present day (*e.g.* Raschke 1965b), to obtain relative, quantitative information about stomatal aperture. Extremely sophisticated designs of porometer were developed by Gregory and Heath and their associates for laboratory experiments (Gregory & Armstrong 1936; Heath 1939; Heath & Penman 1941; Gregory *et al.* 1950a, b; Heath & Russell 1951) and more recently there has been a resurgence of interest in simple types which can be used in the field (Moreshet 1964; Shimshi 1964; Alvim 1965; Bierhuizen, Slatyer & Rose 1965; Raschke 1965b; Weatherley 1966).

In mass flow porometry, a pressure difference is applied across a leaf and the resulting viscous flow of air through the leaf is taken as a measure of stomatal aperture.

Mass flow porometers have several limitations. In passing through the leaf, the air flows through three resistances in series – two sets of stomatal pores and the intercellular spaces. Thus the flow of air can be limited by one of these resistances if it is much larger than the others[1]. The intercellular resistance is generally small in relation to the stomatal resistance except when the stomata are wide open, but it can vary in relation to leaf water content (Meidner 1955). In hypostomatous leaves the intercellular pathway is imprecisely defined, as is the effusive stomatal pathway, since the air must flow out of the leaf on the same surface as it went in, but outside the porometer cup. Care must be taken in using the technique as the stomata

1. See Turner (1970) for a good example of errors arising in this way.

respond to the applied pressure if it is more than about 10 cm of water, by a change in aperture (Raschke 1965b). Changes in stomatal aperture may also result from flushing the intercellular spaces of the leaf with air of a different carbon dioxide concentration, or from allowing unusual carbon dioxide concentrations to develop in the porometer cup.

Perhaps the biggest disadvantage of mass flow porometry is that a viscous flow of air is measured whereas the exchanges of carbon dioxide and water vapour through the stomata are diffusive in character. Several attempts have been made to establish empirical relationships between the two processes (*e.g.* Gregory & Armstrong 1936; Meidner & Spanner 1959), and the theory of diffusive and viscous flow has earlier been developed (*e.g.* Maskell 1928; Heath & Penman 1941; Penman 1942). More recently, attempts have been made to relate the experimentally observed diffusive and viscous resistances to each other and to stomatal aperture through the dimensions of the pathways, so that the adequacy of the diffusive and viscous flow theory can be assessed, and generalisations can be made about the relationship between the two, in terms of specific anatomical properties of the pathways in the leaf (Waggoner 1965; Jarvis, Rose & Begg 1967; Milthorpe & Penman 1967).

It is clear that a satisfactory calibration between the viscous flow resistance and the diffusive resistance, or stomatal aperture, can be made for particular leaf types and that this calibration can be generalised with information about the nature of the pathway. However the labour involved in doing this is considerable. A simple generalisation from the last three papers referred to is that $r_s \propto \Omega^n$ where Ω is the viscous flow resistance [$\text{kg m}^{-2} \text{s}^{-1}$] and n has a value of about 0.4.

16.4.3.3 | Estimation from water vapour exchange

(a) Steady state methods

In leaf chambers it is usual now to estimate the total resistance to water vapour efflux out of a leaf from the flux density of water vapour in transpiration using equation (16.3). In this case, C_1 is the water vapour concentration at the liquid-air interface within the leaf and C_2 ($= C_a$) the mean water vapour concentration in the leaf chamber. The total resistance to net water vapour loss (r_v) is then partitioned into several components and the resistance through the stomatal pore and intercellular spaces obtained by difference. Raschke (1956, 1958) treated this subject exhaustively. Subsequently similar methods have been used by many others (*e.g.* Gaastra 1959; Kuiper 1961; Zelitch & Waggoner 1962; Slatyer & Bierhuizen 1964; Whiteman & Koller 1964a, 1967a, b; Holmgren, Jarvis & Jarvis 1965; Gale, Kohl & Hagan 1966; Slatyer 1967).

The total resistance, r_v, may be partitioned into several components depending upon the objectives and methods available (*e.g.* Bange 1953; Milthorpe 1961). It is usual to separate the boundary layer and cuticular resistances from it, leaving a residual resistance (r_s) which includes the resistance to diffusion through the stomatal pore and the intercellular spaces, and some properties of the liquid-air interface. This resistance (r_s) is frequently called the stomatal resistance, although it clearly also contains other components. The stomatal resistance is considered to be in parallel with the cuticular resistance (r_c,) and both of these resistances are in series with the boundary layer resistance (r_a). The boundary layer and cuticular resistances are determined by methods already described. For any leaf surface, a leaf resistance (r_l) may be defined:

$$r_l = r_v - r_a$$

The stomatal and cuticular resistances may be considered to be in parallel:

$$\frac{1}{r_l} = \frac{1}{r_s} + \frac{1}{r_c}$$

and

$$r_s = \frac{r_l \cdot r_c}{r_c - r_l} \tag{16.18}$$

Since the terms on the right hand side of equation (16.18) can all be determined, r_s can be found. This approach may be satisfactorily applied to a leaf with uniform distribution of stomata over the entire surface, *i.e.* on both sides of a broad leaf. However a biased result will occur if the stomatal frequencies are widely different on the two leaf surfaces, as is frequently found, unless this analysis is applied to each surface separately (Raschke 1958).

Considering now the two surfaces of a leaf separately:

$$\frac{1}{r_v} = \frac{1}{r_{ab}} + \frac{1}{r_{ad}}$$

where r_{ab} and r_{ad} are the total resistances of the abaxial and adaxial surfaces, respectively (Raschke 1958).

For the abaxial surface of a hypostomatous leaf:

$$r_{ab} = r_{l,ab} + r_{a,ab} = \frac{r_s \cdot r_{c,ab}}{r_s + r_{c,ab}} + r_{a,ab}$$

and hence

$$r_s = \frac{r_{l,ab} \cdot r_{c,ab}}{r_{c,ab} - r_{l,ab}} \tag{16.19}$$

For the adaxial surface

$$r_{ad} = r_{l,ad} + r_{a,ad} = r_{c,ad} + r_{a,ad}$$

and

$$r_{c,ad} = r_{ad} - r_{a,ad}$$

With amphistomatous leaves, r_s cannot usually[1] be derived for each surface using

1. Separate estimates of $r_{s,\,ab}$ and $r_{s,\,ad}$ can be made with amphistomatous leaves using bilateral assimilation chambers, as described in Chapter 2 (see Gale, Poljakoff-Mayber & Kahane 1967; Jarvis & Slatyer 1970).

equation (16.19) because the transfer resistance for each surface cannot be evaluated separately. Sealing one leaf surface may have large effects, difficult to evaluate, on the internal carbon dioxide concentration and the aperture of the stomata in the other surface. The considerable difficulties in determining r_c for amphistomatous leaves have already been discussed (Section 16.4.2).
Hence for amphistomatous leaves an average leaf resistance may be calculated:

$$r_l = \frac{C_1 - C_a}{q_v} - r_a \tag{16.20}$$

The values of r_l so obtained are correct when $r_{l,ab} = r_{l,ad}$ or when $r_a = 0$, and diverge from the values obtained from separate analysis for each surface as $r_{l,ab}$ diverges from $r_{l,ad}$ or as r_a increases (Raschke 1958; Gale & Poljakoff-Mayber 1968; Moreshet, Koller & Stanhill 1968).
Accuracy in the determination of r_s thus depends upon the accuracy with which r_l, r_c and r_a are obtained. The cuticular (r_c) and boundary (r_a) resistances have already been discussed. Since r_c is in parallel with r_s and is usually large in relation to r_s, it may vary considerably without appreciably affecting the estimate of r_s. Intentionally, r_a is usually kept small in leaf chambers by internal stirring, so that changes in r_s can be measured sensitively. Hence, small errors in the determination of r_a do not appreciably affect the estimate of r_s; r_a is also usually constant for any one experiment and in some leaf chambers is always constant.
The greatest source of error in the determination of r_s lies in the estimation of C_1, the water vapour concentration at the liquid-air interface. C_1 is usually taken to be equivalent to the saturation vapour pressure at the temperature of the leaf ($= C_s(T_s)$). We may briefly consider this assumption.
Because of the strong dependence of the saturation water vapour pressure on temperature, the temperature of the leaf must be determined with considerable precision, say to about 0.1 °C. Certain difficulties in attaining this have already been discussed in connection with the determination of the boundary layer resistance (Section 16.4.2). The same difficulties apply, though to a lesser extent, with real leaves as with wet leaf replicas. Because of the presence of the stomatal resistance, the leaf temperature has a lesser tendency than the replica temperature to fall below air temperature. Small leaves with a moderate stomatal resistance, *e.g.* conifer needles, are usually at a temperature which is close to air temperature, so that heat transfer problems are small. However, large leaves of low stomatal resistance (*e.g.* sunflower) behave in a very similar way to wet replicas, with all the associated problems, and a similar problem also arises when the stomata are closed and the leaf temperature well above air temperature. With leaves, the problem is further exacerbated by the appreciable variation in surface temperatures from point to point (for a full discussion see Chapter 17).
It is usual to speak of leaf temperature in this context. However, the temperature required is that of the liquid-air interface. Because of the low thermal capacity and high thermal conductivity of most leaves it can be shown in theory and practice that temperature gradients both across a leaf and across the pathway leading to the interface are extremely small and not significant (see Chapter 17).

Because of the difficulties in precisely determining the temperature of the liquid-air interface discussed earlier, and because of the uncertainty regarding the assumption that the vapour pressure at the interface is the saturation vapour pressure, discussed below, an alternative method for the routine determination of the vapour pressure at the liquid-air interface is desirable. Whiteman & Koller (1964b) estimated the interface vapour pressure in desert xerophytes by extrapolating the relationship between transpiration and ambient vapour pressure back to zero transpiration and a method of this kind may prove useful. We have found that such estimates are frequently much lower than those obtained from temperature measurements with fine wire thermocouples, especially with dissected material, where the conduction error in the temperature determination is unavoidably large[1].

Assuming that a *small* change in evaporation rate does not appreciably alter the temperature and vapour pressure of the liquid-air interface, the interface vapour concentration, C_1 ($= C_s(T_s)$), can be eliminated by solving simultaneous equations for evaporation from the leaf (equation 16.3):

$$q_v = \frac{C_s(T_s) - C_a}{r_v}, \text{ and}$$

$$q_v' = \frac{C_s(T_s) - C_a'}{r_v}$$

By subtraction

$$r_v = \frac{C_a - C_a'}{q_v' - q_v} = \frac{\Delta C_a}{\Delta q_v} \tag{16.21}$$

Clearly $C_s(T_s)$ is not constant, as implied above, leading to an error in r_v. This error is, however, more acceptable in many cases than the error in the temperature measurement. Furthermore it makes the determination of r_v independent of the absolute value of $C_s(T_s)$ and hence of the assumption that the water vapour pressure at the liquid-air interface is equivalent to the saturation vapour pressure at interface temperature.

This assumption, although usually made, is open to question. There are at least three reasons why it may be incorrect. The water vapour pressure may be reduced below the saturation vapour pressure by the water potential within the cell walls, by the accumulation of solutes at the interface, and by a hydraulic resistance to liquid water flow within the cell wall. The water in the cell walls is under tension and will possess a matric potential related to the water potential within the mesophyll cells. Milthorpe (1961) considered this possibility in some detail (Table 16.2). The second column shows the ratio between the actual vapour pressure at the liquid-air interface, e, when the cells have the water potentials shown in the first column, and the saturation vapour pressure at 25 °C, e_s. The last three columns show the influence of the reduction in water potential on the vapour pressure gradient between the interface and ambient air (vapour pressure, e_a) at different ambient humidities. It is apparent that in the range of water potentials normally

1. An indirect estimation of interface temperature, T_s, from the amount of water transpired has been developed and tested by Lake & Slatyer (1970).

Table 16.2 Water potential, ratio between the actual vapour pressure and the saturation vapour pressure, and vapour pressure gradients at different ambient humidities. (After Milthorpe 1961.)

Water potential	e/e_s	$(e-e_a)/(e_s-e_a)$ at 25 °C and relative humidity of		
[bar]	(25 °C)	80%	50%	20%
0	1.000	1.00	1.00	1.00
−5	0.996	0.98	0.99	0.99
−20	0.985	0.92	0.96	0.98
−50	0.963	0.82	0.93	0.95
−100	0.929	0.64	0.86	0.91

occurring in mesophytes (0 to −20 bar) and at humidities of around 50%, the reduction in vapour pressure at the interface is small and the effect on the gradient can be ignored. At lower water potentials or at higher humidities a correction for the reduction in vapour pressure would seem to be warranted if great accuracy in r_s is required.

Leaf water potentials below about −50 bar kill the cells of many plants and only a few xerophytes are known to survive water potentials below −100 bar (see Jarvis & Jarvis 1963). Yet in some instances, estimates of water potential at the liquid-air interface yield much lower values (*e.g.* Whiteman & Koller 1964b). It has generally been assumed, as a result of studies on cell permeability (*e.g.* Philip 1958), that rapid equilibrium would be attained between water potential within the cell and that in the cell wall (*e.g.* Slatyer 1966a). However this question needs re-examination: it may be that under steady state conditions an appreciable gradient can be maintained between cell and cell wall, so that the interface water potential is appreciably below the water potential in the neighbouring cells.

The water potential at the interface may also be reduced by the accumulation there of salts carried up in the transpiration stream. This has always been a popular idea. It was recently re-examined by Slatyer (1966a) who calculated that solutes brought to the interface would be transported away again by back diffusion at the same rate for an increase in concentration at the interface of only 13% above that in the transpiration stream. Jarvis & Slatyer (1970) were unable to detect an effect of feeding salts to cotton plants on the vapour pressure of the liquid-air interface. A significant reduction in vapour pressure at the interface has been found using diffusion porometry by Jarvis & Slatyer (1970) and Gale, Poljakoff-Mayber & Kahane (1967). This has been interpreted as resulting from the presence in the wall of a hydraulic resistance to the flow of liquid water across the wall (R_h). This resistance is not a constant but appears to vary in relation to transpiration rate and water stress. At the moment there is no way of separating this resistance from the other resistances included in r_s in normal routine leaf chamber work. This resistance may be *equivalent* to a water vapour diffusive resistance of up to *ca.* 2 s cm^{-1}.

 Consequently r_s, as defined above, contains the resistance to diffusion through the stomatal pore and intercellular spaces together with a hydraulic resistance to liquid water flow across the cell wall and also possibly other less well defined indeterminate components leading to small additional reductions in vapour pressure at the liquid-air interface.

(b) Non steady state methods

In recent years portable diffusion porometers have been developed in many laboratories for estimating the resistance to water transfer from leaves. These porometers have been developed largely as field instruments (*e.g.* van Bavel 1967; van Bavel, Newman & Hilgeman 1967; Kanemasu, Thurtell & Tanner 1969) but they clearly have considerable uses in the laboratory in whole plant chambers, wind tunnels and phytotron rooms and cabinets (*e.g.* Ehrler & van Bavel 1968). The instruments currently in widespread use have been developed from apparatus described by Wallihan (1964), van Bavel, Nakayama & Ehrler (1965) and Grieve & Went (1965); see also Meidner (1970), Monteith & Bull (1970), Stiles (1970), and Turner & Parlange (1970).

A small chamber (about 100–500 cm^3) containing a hygrometer, a desiccant which can be switched in or out, and one or more thermocouples or thermistors, is attached to a leaf for a short period of 30 seconds or less. The time taken for the humidity in the chamber to rise from say 10 to 20% relative humidity is recorded and the leaf and air temperature during this period noted. As with viscous flow porometers of the Alvim type, the cup size, length of exposure and, in this case, humidity interval can be adjusted to suit the material and degree of stomatal opening.

Transpiration is calculated from the increase in humidity per unit time and area. In a standard porometer for broad-leaved species, the area of leaf exposed is a constant and an estimate of resistance per unit area readily obtained. In the prototypes of Wallihan (1964) and van Bavel, Nakayama & Ehrler (1965) and in many others in use today, the geometrical arrangement and distance between hygrometer and leaf is critical. The boundary layer resistance and instrument calibration is obtained from diffusion theory by step function increases in the distance between the humidity source and the detector using tubes of various lengths (see van Bavel, Nakayama & Ehrler 1965) or plates with a variable number of holes (Kanemasu, Thurtell & Tanner 1969).

An obvious modification made by Slatyer and his associates (Slatyer 1966b; Byrne, Rose & Slatyer 1970), was to include stirring in the porometer by introducing a small fan, as in stirred leaf chambers. This makes the instrument design largely independent of distance and arrangement of leaf and hygrometer in the chamber, and eliminates internal buoyancy effects which have been found to be troublesome with unstirred porometers in hot climates. The boundary layer resistance, r_a, is reduced to a small reproducible level and can be determined by the wet replica method described in Section 16.4.2.

The flux of water vapour transpired by the leaf at any instant is:

$$q_v = \frac{C_s(T_s) - C_a}{r_v} \tag{16.22}$$

Over the interval, t, during which the humidity rises from C_1 to C_2

$$q_v = \frac{(C_2 - C_1)V}{A\ t} \tag{16.23}$$

where V is the chamber volume, and A the area of sample exposed. As the humidity in the chamber rises, the rate of change in humidity falls so that the average humidity in the chamber can be taken from:

$$\ln \bar{C} = 0.5(\ln C_1 + \ln C_2)$$

Assuming that (T_s) remains constant and substituting $\bar{C}$ for C_a in equation (16.22) gives

$$r_v = \frac{(C_s(T_s) - \bar{C})t\ A}{(C_2 - C_1)V}$$

r_v can then be partitioned into r_l and r_a. The assumption that $C_s(T_s)$ is constant is certainly not correct but the error arising from this assumption for a small change in evaporation rate is small in relation to the probable errors in the determination of the initial and final absolute values of $C_s(T_s)$[1]. A real practical difficulty arises because all electric and solid state hygrometers have an appreciable response time, so that, under the dynamic conditions of operation, the relationship between humidity in the chamber and meter reading is not precisely defined. An empirical solution is to calibrate the meter under dynamic conditions simulating the conditions of normal operation. This may be done by replacing the leaf with a small, rapidly responding, wet bulb which is well ventilated by the fans and from which water evaporates at rates comparable with evaporation from leaves. Alternatively, precisely known volumes of air of known humidity (*e.g.* saturated at room temperature) may be introduced into the chamber at constant, variable rates. This can be done using a motor-driven syringe (Byrne, Rose & Slatyer 1970) or, if larger volumes are required, by displacement of saturated air from a reservoir by the addition of known volumes of water at different rates.
Inclusion of stirring allows further modification of the method for irregular, linear leaves, as in heaths and conifers. The leaves or shoots are included in the chamber protected by a gauze from the fan(s) and hygrometer. After the observation has been made the material must, however, be removed for determination of surface area.

16.4.3.4 | Gas diffusion porometry

A gas not normally present in the air is introduced into the chamber on one side of the leaf and a concentration gradient is established through the leaf from one side to the other. The flux of the gas along this gradient is determined from the rate

1. In many instruments in current use, it is assumed that T_s equals the air temperature in the instrument.

of its appearance in the chamber on the other side. The resistance to transfer along the pathway is then determined from an equation such as equation (16.3), where now C_1 is the concentration of the gas in the source chamber, C_2 is the concentration in the sink chamber, q_v is the flux between the two chambers and r_v is the sum of resistances in the pathway:

$$r_v = r_{a,ab} + r_{s,ab} + r_i + r_{s,ad} + r_{a,ad} \quad (16.24)$$

where r_i is the intercellular resistance.

Special bilateral leaf chambers have been made for experiments along these lines (Gregory & Armstrong 1936; Heath 1939; Jarvis & Slatyer 1966; Gale, Poljakoff-Mayber & Kahane 1967; Milthorpe & Penman 1967). In general the object of such chambers is to provide close independent control of the environment near to both the abaxial and adaxial surfaces of the leaf, and to allow continuous monitoring of the gas concentrations in each chamber and in some cases too of the fluxes of carbon dioxide and water vapour to and from each leaf surface (see Section 2.7.3).

Rearranging equation (16.24)

$$r_{s,\,ab} + r_{s,\,ad} + r_i = r_v - r_{a,ad} - r_{a,ad}$$

and all the terms on the right hand side can be determined.

As with the mass flow porometer, the flux of gas across the leaf is controlled by three resistances in series and the same restrictions apply (see Section 16.4.3.2). If one of these resistances is much larger than the others, the flux will be small and largely independent of the other two resistances. The method does not therefore necessarily give an estimate which is useful in interpreting the response of the stomata in relation to carbon dioxide uptake. In the extreme case the stomata in one epidermis may be completely closed whereas they are wide open in the other (it is known that the stomata in the two surfaces may oscillate out of phase, *e.g.* Slatyer & Jarvis 1966). The flux across the leaf would be zero although the capacity to photosynthesise might only be reduced by about half.

The intercellular resistance, r_i, has previously been discussed in relation to mass flow porometry (Section 16.4.3.2) and the same comments are applicable here (see also Section 16.4.4).

A number of gases have been used, *e.g.* hydrogen by Gregory & Armstrong (1936), Gregory *et al.* (1950a, b), Louguet (1965), Milthorpe & Penman (1967); helium by Gale, Poljakoff-Mayber & Kahane (1967); nitrous oxide by Slatyer & Jarvis (1966), Jarvis & Slatyer (1966, 1970); and radioactive argon (^{41}A) by Moreshet, Stanhill & Koller (1968). The gas should be physiologically and chemically inert, of low solubility in water, not present in the normal ambient air in significant amounts, and readily analysed quantitatively, and preferably continuously, without disturbance of the leaf environment. In the above examples, hydrogen was determined with a thermal conductivity meter, helium with a gas chromatograph fitted with a thermal conductivity detector, nitrous oxide with an infra-red gas analyser and ^{41}A with a crystal scintillation counter. The determination of helium and ^{41}A involved collecting samples; the determination of hydrogen was semi-continuous and that of nitrous oxide completely continuous. It is also desirable that the coefficient of diffusion of the gas in air be firmly established.

The resistances to diffusion of the gas may be converted to carbon dioxide or water vapour diffusion resistances by the use of equations (16.5) or (16.7). The use of equation (16.5) will be inaccurate in small pores unless $D \, . \, M^{\frac{1}{2}}$ is approximately the same for the gases concerned because of the differences in slip shown by the molecules (Milthorpe & Penman 1967).

16.4.3.5 | Leaf energy balance

The stomatal resistance of leaves in an assimilation chamber can be readily determined from a *change* in the energy balance if the boundary layer resistance is independently known. For constant net short-wave radiation and incoming thermal radiation, an induced change in the latent heat exchange results in a change in leaf temperature and *vice versa* (equation 16.16). The water vapour exchange can be written as a transfer equation in the form of equation (16.3):

$$E = \frac{C_s(T_s) - C_a}{r_a + r_l}$$

Substituting this transfer equation into equation (16.16) for E_1 and E_2 yields the following expression which can be solved for r_l if r_a is known.

$$r_a + r_l = \frac{L[C_s(T_1) - C_s(T_2) + C_a^2 - C_a^1]}{(T_2 - T_1)\left(\varepsilon\sigma \, 8\overline{T}^3 + \frac{c_p \rho_a}{r_a}\right)}$$

The accuracy of this method is clearly limited by the accuracy with which the change in leaf temperature can be determined and it is unlikely to be useful for narrow and dissected leaves (see also Idle 1970).

A variation of this approach was used by Miller & Gates (1967) both in the laboratory and in the field. They determined the evaporation rate (E_2) of an excised shoot in a potometer. The difference in the energy balance of the excised shoot and of a similarly exposed shoot, *in situ* on the plant, was used to estimate the evaporation rate of the intact shoot (E_1) from E_2:

$$E_1 = \frac{C_s(T_1) - C_a^1}{r_a + r_l} = E_2 + \frac{(T_2 - T_1)\left(\varepsilon\sigma \, 8\overline{T}^3 + \frac{c_p \rho_a}{r_a}\right)}{L}$$

The boundary layer resistance, r_a, was included as the heat transfer coefficient for an appropriate size and shape of leaf using an engineering heat transfer equation (see Section 16.4.1.3, and also Taylor & Gates 1970), but can be estimated in a parallel series of measurements by the replica method, in both field and laboratory.

16.4.4 | Determination of the intercellular space resistance, r_i

This resistance is not a constant but, like its mass flow counterpart, is a function of the dimensions of the voids within the leaf, their cross-sectional area, length and tortuosity, and hence of leaf water content (Meidner 1955). In Figure 16.2 are shown changes in void volume in two different kinds of leaf in relation to the development of low relative water content as the leaves dry out.

The intercellular space resistance may be calculated from the dimensions of the voids within the leaf (*e.g.* Jarvis, Rose & Begg 1967; Milthorpe & Penman 1967). It may also be estimated for amphistomatous leaves using kinetic methods (Gale, Poljakoff-Mayber & Kahane 1967; Milthorpe & Penman 1967; Jarvis & Slatyer 1970). From equation (16.24), r_i may be derived if $r_{s,ab}$ and $r_{s,ad}$ are independently known. Jarvis & Slatyer (1970) used the bilateral leaf chamber (Chapter 2) as a N_2O diffusion porometer and made simultaneous estimates of stomatal resistance in each leaf surface from the water vapour fluxes. They assumed that at low transpiration rates and high leaf water contents, the wall resistance component of r_s could be ignored. Under these conditions, substitution of values of $r_{s,ab}$ and $r_{s,ad}$ obtained from equation (16.19) into equation (16.24) gave an estimate of the intercellular space resistance to diffusion of CO_2 through the mesophyll of a cotton leaf, 200 μm across from epidermis to epidermis, of about 3 s cm^{-1}. This value closely agreed with the value obtained by calculation from void dimensions by Jarvis, Rose & Begg (1967).

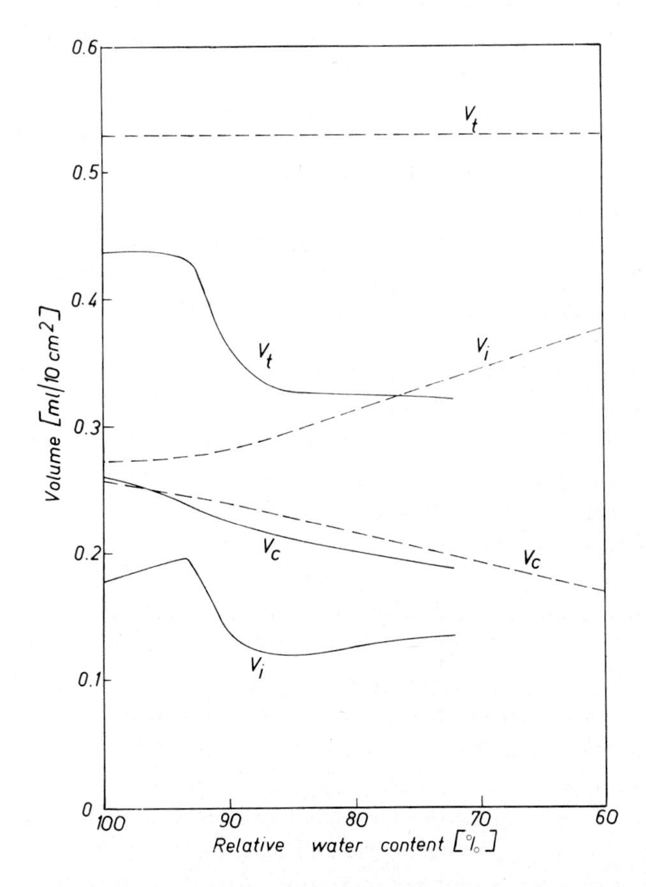

Fig. 16.2 The relationship between tissue volume (V_t), intercellular space volume (V_i), and cell volume (V_c) per unit area of leaf, and relative water content in leaves of cotton (solid line) and holly, *Ilex aquifolia* (dashed line).

16.4.5 | *Estimation of the cell wall resistance to water transfer*

An estimate of $r_{s,ab}$ and $r_{s,ad}$ including the stomatal pore, intercellular space and wall resistance is obtained from the water vapour transfer out of each surface of the leaf using equation (16.3) as described in Section 16.4.3.3.
An estimate of $r_{s,ab}$ and $r_{s,ad}$ including the stomatal pore and intercellular space resistances but *not* the wall resistance is obtained using the diffusion porometer as described in the previous section (16.4.4).
The difference between the two independent estimates of r_s gives the wall resistance as an equivalent vapour transfer resistance. This may be converted to an hydraulic resistance by equation (16.12) and the reduction in vapour pressure at the liquid-air interface calculated. Studies of this kind have been made on bean (Gale, Poljakoff-Mayber & Kahane 1967) and on cotton (Jarvis & Slatyer 1970).

16.4.6 | *Determination of the mesophyll resistance, r_m*

To some extent, the mesophyll resistance to carbon dioxide transfer is defined by the methods available for its determination (*cf.* Section 16.3.5.1). As the liquid phase resistance to carbon dioxide transfer from the liquid-air interface to the reaction sites in the chloroplasts, it has been defined as a residual term as follows:

$$r_m = \Sigma r_{CO_2} - r_s - r_a \tag{16.25}$$

Σr_{CO_2} is the sum of the resistances to carbon dioxide transfer from the ambient air to the reaction sites in the chloroplasts along the stomatal pathway. Since the cuticular conductance to carbon dioxide is assumed zero, Σr_{CO_2} is the total resistance to carbon dioxide influx; r_s is the diffusive resistance through the stomatal pore up to the liquid-air interface and r_a the boundary layer resistance to carbon dioxide.
The definition of mesophyll resistance as a residual term in this way is conceptually unsatisfactory, although practically expedient. As a residual term it contains all that is not accounted for by the stomatal and boundary layer resistances and includes photochemical and biochemical processes unrelated to the transfer of CO_2 through the cell. Because of this, misinterpretations and misconceptions can arise. For example, it is readily shown (*e.g.* Bierhuizen & Slatyer 1964; Whiteman & Koller 1968) that mesophyll resistance determined as a residual term is strongly dependent on irradiance, if photosynthesis is not light saturated. This result is inevitable if photosynthesis is limited by the photochemical partial process and says nothing about the dependence upon irradiance of the partial process of carbon dioxide transfer across the mesophyll. Yet the literature now contains references to the effect that the resistance to carbon dioxide transfer across the mesophyll is light dependent.
From a theoretical view point, the mesophyll resistance is better defined as a transfer resistance, without photochemical and biochemical overtones, in relation to the pathway of transfer as outlined in Section 16.3.5.1. That is to say, it is the transfer resistance between the liquid-air interface in the cell wall and the site at which carboxylation occurs in the chloroplasts. Such a definition clearly emphasises

the difficulties involved in the measurement of mesophyll resistance. If misconceptions are not to arise, the limitation of the existing methods must be clearly appreciated and new, more adequate methods sought.

16.4.6.1 | Calculation from pathway dimensions

If it is assumed that carbon dioxide diffuses in aqueous solution from the liquid-air interface to a site within the chloroplasts, an estimate of diffusive resistance can be made from the length and area of the pathway. This approach has been applied by Rackham (1966) and yields estimates of 0.3 to 4 s cm^{-1} depending upon the thickness of the chloroplasts. These estimates are low because the path length is short (about 0.5 to 3 μm), and the cross-sectional area large (the internal cell surface area is an order of magnitude larger than the external surface area of the leaf).
However, the assumption that carbon dioxide transfer to the reaction sites may be considered in terms of the diffusive transfer of CO_2 through water is an improbable oversimplification. This may be a reasonable model for transfer of CO_2, H_2CO_3 or HCO_3^- across the cell wall but its validity across membranes and within the cytoplasm would seem doubtful (see also Section 16.3.5.1).

16.4.6.2 | Estimation from carbon dioxide exchange

The determination of r_m from equation (16.25) rests on our ability to estimate Σr_{CO_2}. The estimation of r_a and r_s for carbon dioxide is discussed in Sections 16.4.1 and 16.4.3.
Frequently the mesophyll resistance has been estimated from

$$r_m = \Sigma r_{CO_2} - \Sigma r_{H_2O} \left(\frac{D_{H_2O}}{D_{CO_2}} \right)$$

where Σr_{H_2O} is the total leaf resistance to water vapour as described in Section 16.4.3.3. This equation as it stands makes the assumption that the cuticular conductance to water is zero, but it can readily be modified to take water transfer through the cuticle into account if the resistance is known. It becomes

$$r_m = \Sigma r_{CO_2} - (r_s + r_a) \left(\frac{D_{H_2O}}{D_{CO_2}} \right)$$

where r_s and r_a are the water vapour transfer resistances along the stomatal pathway and through the boundary layer. This equation has also frequently been used. As pointed out in Section 16.3.2, it is more appropriate to use $r_a(D_{H_2O}/D_{CO_2})^{\frac{2}{3}}$. Furthermore, in the application of this expression, r_s has almost always been determined from water vapour exchange, as described in Section 16.4.3.3 and hence includes components of resistance which are additional to the diffusive vapour transfer resistances between the boundary layer and the liquid-air interface and which result from the reduction in vapour pressure at the liquid-air interface and the cell wall resistance. An estimate of r_s which contained only the resistance to diffusion of water vapour from the liquid-air interface through the stomatal pore to the leaf surface would be more appropriate. The relevant expression would then be

$$r_m = \Sigma r_{CO_2} - r_s^1 \left(\frac{D_{H_2O}}{D_{CO_2}}\right) - r_a \left(\frac{D_{H_2O}}{D_{CO_2}}\right)^{\frac{2}{3}}$$

where r_s^1 is now the true transfer resistance between the liquid-air interface and the leaf surface (see also Parkinson & Penman 1970).

The estimation of Σr_{CO_2} from carbon dioxide fluxes is rendered difficult by the simultaneous production of carbon dioxide in respiration and consumption in photosynthesis with a consequent internal circulation both within the cell and *via* the intercellular spaces. This problem has stimulated a number of recent papers. The treatment by Lake (1967a, b) would seem to be the best to date, although other models have also appeared (*e.g.* Samish & Koller 1968a,b). Lake demonstrates that the estimates of r_m by the techniques currently in use may all be overestimates, because they fail adequately to take photorespiration into account.

When photosynthesis is light saturated, the rate of influx of carbon dioxide is linearly proportional to the ambient CO_2 concentration over quite a wide concentration range (Figure 16.3), and in many species has little or no dependence upon leaf temperature over an appreciable range (but *cf.* Section 16.3.5). Under these conditions, photosynthesis would seem to be rate-limited by the supply of carbon dioxide to the reaction sites in the chloroplasts.

When carbon dioxide supply is limiting the rate of CO_2 influx, the total resistance to carbon dioxide transfer may be estimated using an equation like equation (16.3). Gaastra (1959, 1963), and others since, have written:

$$P_G = F + R = \frac{C_a - C_c}{r_a + r_s + r_m} \qquad (16.26)$$

where P_G is the gross rate of CO_2 fixation in photosynthesis; F ($= q_v$) is the rate of net CO_2 influx; R is the respiratory efflux of CO_2 in the dark; and C_c ($= C_2$) is the carbon dioxide concentration at the sites of carboxylation in the chloroplasts, assumed equal to zero. Simultaneous estimates of r_a and r_s then permit the equation to be solved for r_m.

This approach can be criticised on several grounds. For example, the estimation of gross photosynthesis by adding the same value of dark respiration to net photosynthesis, measured at various levels of irradiances, tacitly makes the assumption of equality between light and dark respiration and the independence of respiration upon irradiance. The assumption that $C_c = 0$ is also open to criticism since the K_m of the primary carboxylation reaction is relatively high-suggesting the need for an appreciable CO_2 substrate concentration at the chloroplast to make the reaction go (see Section 16.4.7 for a more detailed discussion). Alternative methods of calculating r_m using the methods described later lead to estimates of C_c equivalent to gas phase concentrations of about 10 to 50 $\mu l\ l^{-1}$. By assuming $C_c = 0$, the carboxylation resistance is implicitly included in the estimate of r_m.

Consider the fluxes of CO_2 in a leaf as depicted in Figure 8.1. The flux of CO_2

through the stomatal and boundary layer resistances, $r_s + r_a$, is F. If the flux through r_{rw} is in the direction of the intercellular spaces, the flux through the mesophyll resistance, r_m, is $(F + B_i + \beta B_r)$ and that through the carboxylation resistance, r_x, is $(F + B_i + B_r)$. β is a dimensionless coefficient ($\leqslant 1$) depending in part upon the ratio between the two resistances to carbon dioxide transfer, r_{rw} and r_{rc}, located between the site of photorespiration and the intercellular spaces and the sites of photorespiration and carboxylation, respectively. The magnitude of β is not known since no estimates of photorespiration adequately include the flux through r_{rc} (Chapter 8). It is suggested that β may be quite small, perhaps about 0.2. B_i is the rate of CO_2 production, probably *via* the Krebs cycle, from cells without chloroplasts in both light and darkness. B_r is the rate of CO_2 production from chlorophyll-containing cells in the light. It now seems probable that in cells with chlorophyll, Krebs cycle respiration is inhibited in the light and replaced by a process possibly linked to glycolate metabolism and located in the peroxisomes (see Chapter 8). Consequently the total dark respiration is $(B_i + \alpha B_r)$, where α is a dimensionless coefficient equal to the ratio between the rates of CO_2 production in dark and light in cells with chlorophyll. Experimental evidence suggests that α is about 0.5 or less (*e.g.* Holmgren & Jarvis 1967; Lake 1967a; Begg & Jarvis 1968; Brix 1968; Jolliffe & Tregunna 1968; Ludlow 1969).

At light saturation:

$$F = \frac{C_a - C_i}{r_s + r_a} \quad (16.27a)$$

$$F + B_i + \beta B_r = \frac{C_i - C_c}{r_m} \quad (16.27b)$$

$$F + B_i + B_r = \frac{C_c}{r_x} \quad (16.27c)$$

Because of the parallel sources of carbon dioxide, it is not possible to treat this system as a simple catena as Gaastra did. Recombination of the above equations (16.27) does *not* result in a simple overall equation such as (16.26) even if a number of simplifying assumptions are made such as $C_c = 0$, $B_i = B_r = R$, and r_{rc} is infinite. From equations (16.27a, b):

$$r_m = \frac{C_a - C_c - r_m(B_i + \beta B_r)}{F} - (r_s + r_a) \quad (16.28a)$$

$$= \frac{C_i - C_c}{F + B_i + \beta B_r} \quad (16.28b)$$

These expressions for r_m may be compared with the analogous equations used by Gaastra (1959):

$$r_m = \frac{C_a - C_c}{F + R} - (r_s + r_a)$$

$$= \frac{C_i - C_c + R(r_s + r_a)}{F + R} \quad (16.28c)$$

where $R = B_i + \alpha B_r$. Since α and β may be about the same size, the main difference between equations (16.28b) and (c) is the presence of the large term $R(r_s + r_a)$ in the numerator of (16.28c). This leads to an overestimate of r_m by Gaastra's method as pointed out by Lake (1967a). Thus the magnitude of the difference between the two estimates of r_m increases with increasing stomatal and boundary layer resistance.

Substitution for C_c from equation (16.27c) into equation (16.28b) yields an expression for r_m and r_x in terms of C_i, F, B_i, B_r and β:

$$r_m = \frac{C_i}{F + B_i + \beta B_r} - r_x \left(\frac{F + B_i + B_r}{F + B_i + \beta B_r} \right)$$

F is readily measured and C_i calculated from equation (16.27a). Chartier (1970) and Chartier, Chartier & Čatský (1970) have used an approach similar to this to estimate r_m and r_x. They made an approximate estimate of $(B_i + B_r)$ and assumed $\beta = 0$. By setting up several similar equations, each containing the two unknowns, r_m and r_x, using data collected at just less than full light saturation, they were able to obtain graphical solutions for both r_m and r_x (see also Section 16.4.7.2). Their method clearly has great possibilities. It depends upon knowledge of all the fluxes of CO_2 in photorespiration including the intracellular reassimilation flux through r_{rc}. As emphasised in Chapter 8, this information is not easily obtained. Since some estimates of photorespiration which do not include the flux through r_{rc} suggest that photorespiration may be twice dark respiration (*i.e.* $\alpha = 0.5$), the real value of photorespiration may be very much larger. However, as the above equation shows, r_m is relatively insensitive to changes or uncertainty in B_r.

To avoid having to assign a value to C_c or to relate light to dark respiration, Holmgren, Jarvis & Jarvis (1965) attempted to estimate r_m from the slope of the linear portion of the curve shown in Figure 16.3. Differentiating equation (16.28a), with C_c and $(B_i + \beta B_r)$ assumed constant or zero, over the relevant range of q_v $(= F)$ and C_a, yields, in finite form:

$$r_m + r_s + r_a = \frac{\Delta C_a}{\Delta q_v}$$

Lake (1967b) points out that $(B_i + \beta B_r)$ would be expected to increase with q_v at least over part of the range and hence that r_m is overestimated. In fact, evidence is steadily accumulating to show that photorespiration is closely coupled to photosynthesis (see discussion in Ch. 8) so this is very probable. A more serious criticism is that C_c cannot be zero by definition since there is the carboxylation resistance between C_c and the end of the catena, and it cannot be constant, since, if not zero, it must be a function of C_a. Substituting for C_c from Eq. (16.27c) into Eq. (16.28a) and differentiating with $(B_i + \beta B_r)$ assumed constant yields:

$$r_m + r_x + r_s + r_a = \Delta C_a / \Delta q_v \qquad (16.28d)$$

thus emphasising that the estimate of r_m obtained by Holmgren, Jarvis & Jarvis also includes r_x.

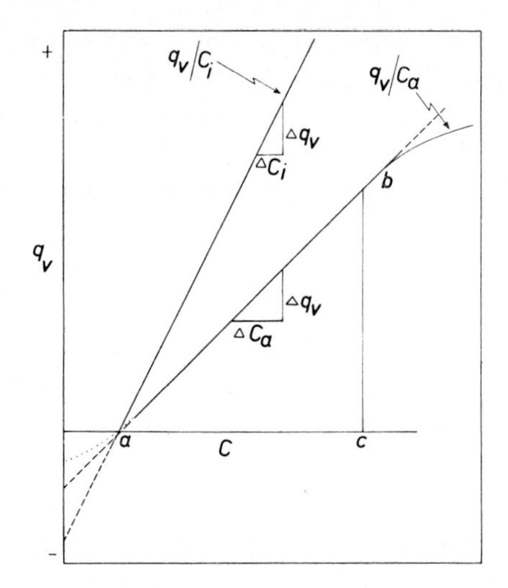

Fig. 16.3 Diagrammatic representation of the relationship between carbon dioxide concentration, C (C_a is ambient and C_i intercellular concentration) and the flux of CO_2 in photosynthesis, q_v.

In the absence of photorespiration, this equation reduces to the finite form of the differential:

$$r_m + r_x + r_s + r_a = C_a/q_v$$

for the slope of the line between $q_v = q_v$ and $q_v = 0$ at which $C_a = \Gamma = 0$. In the presence of photorespiration, $\Gamma > 0$, and the expression becomes

$$r_m + r_x + r_s + r_a = (C_a - \Gamma)/q_v$$

This expression is identical with that used by Whiteman & Koller (1964a, 1967a and b, 1968) and the same criticisms apply as levied above. Effectively, they use the larger triangle a, b, c in Figure 16.3, the intercept with the abscissa being taken as the extrapolated carbon dioxide compensation concentration. This method has a practical advantage over that of Holmgren, Jarvis & Jarvis (1965) in that it is not necessary that $(r_m + r_s + r_a)$ remain constant in the determination of the carbon dioxide compensation concentration. However, widespread use of the method using the compensation concentration as a constant and another fixed point at about 300 $\mu l\ l^{-1}$ ambient carbon dioxide concentration is to be avoided. Both the compensation concentration and the linearity of the q_v/C_a response curve over an extended range are variables under physiological control and should be checked in relation to the preconditioning and experimental treatments. In many cases the q_v/C_a relationship significantly departs from linearity before normal ambient levels of carbon dioxide are reached and before the compensation concentration is reached. Joining the two end points of the line can then lead to an appreciable reduction in slope and overestimation of r_m.

A considerable improvement on the method of Holmgren, Jarvis & Jarvis (1965), which removes the requirement for constant $(r_s + r_a)$ during the determination of the response curve, is obtained by working with the intercellular space carbon dioxide concentration, C_i, according to equation (16.28b). This can be done in practice by flushing the intercellular spaces with air of known carbon dioxide concentrations using a bilateral leaf chamber (Lake & Slatyer 1970) or by calculation from equation (16.27a) (Troughton & Slatyer 1969; Parkinson & Penman 1970; Ludlow & Jarvis 1971). Then, by similar derivation to equation (16.28 d),

$$r_m + r_x = \Delta C_i / \Delta q_v$$

again on the assumption that $(B_i + \beta B_r)$ is constant. This relationship is linear over a wider range of ambient carbon dioxide concentrations than the relationship between q_v and C_a because part of the departure from linearity results from the influence of carbon dioxide on stomatal aperture.

Thus the minimum requirements for the determination of r_m by these methods are estimates of photosynthesis at two different ambient (or intercellular) carbon dioxide concentrations, under conditions of light saturation and rate-limitation solely by the supply of carbon dioxide. Departure from these two conditions leads to overestimates of r_m which can be considered artifacts, or at best attributable to other causes such as limitation by the rate of carboxylation or the photochemical reaction. Whether rate limitation solely by CO_2 does in fact ever occur is debatable. The evidence offered in all cases so far is far from satisfactory and it seems likely that some component of carboxylation resistance is always included in the mesophyll resistance.

16.4.7 | *Determination of the carboxylation resistance, r_x*

Most methods of determining mesophyll resistance include the carboxylation resistance as part of the mesophyll resistance. Separation of the carboxylation resistance is difficult and has rarely been attempted although, as indicated in Section 16.3.6, the carboxylation resistance may be a major part of the mesophyll resistance, at least in some circumstances.

16.4.7.1 | Determination as the last resistance in the catena

If a reliable estimate of mesophyll resistance alone can be made from the methods as described in Section 16.4.6, a carbon dioxide concentration at the sites of carboxylation can be calculated from equation (16.27b), making certain assumptions about $(B_i + \beta B_r)$. The carboxylation resistance, r_x, may then be calculated from equation (16.27c). From equations (16.27b and c), the size of the carboxylation resistance relative to the mesophyll resistance may be estimated as about 1 : 5. As pointed out earlier, reliable estimation of r_m alone is difficult to obtain and hence this method is impractical.

16.4.7.2 | Determination of r_x from the relationship between photosynthesis and irradiance

Using a somewhat simpler model than that described in Section 16.4.6, Chartier (1966, 1970) and Chartier, Chartier & Čatský (1970) have derived an expression relating r_m and r_x to rate of CO_2 influx, rate of photorespiration and ambient CO_2 concentration.

Neglecting B_i and assuming that $\beta = 0$, the flux of CO_2 through r_m is equal to F and the flux through r_x is $(F + B_r)$. Since on this model all respiratory carbon dioxide goes direct to the sites of carboxylation, the system can be treated as a simple catena so that:

$$F = \frac{C_a - C_i}{r_a + r_s} = \frac{C_i - C_c}{r_m} = \frac{C_a - C_c}{r_a + r_s + r_m} \tag{16.29a}$$

and

$$F + B_r = C_c/r_x \tag{16.29b}$$

Hence at light saturation:

$$F = \frac{C_a - r_x \ B_r}{r_a + r_s + r_m + r_x} = \frac{C_i - r_x \ B_r}{r_m + r_x} \tag{16.30}$$

or

$$F + B_r = \frac{C_i - r_m \ F}{r_x}$$

These equations cannot be solved for r_m and r_x separately but can be solved for r_x if r_m is independently known.

On the basis of enzyme kinetics (Chartier 1966), and by analogy with the response of net photosynthesis to irradiance, the relation between the photochemical and biochemical processes of photosynthesis and irradiance may be assumed to approximate to a rectangular hyperbola, so that

$$F + B_r = \frac{bI \cdot \dfrac{C_c}{r_x}}{bI + \dfrac{C_c}{r_x}} \tag{16.31}$$

where I is irradiance (400–700 nm) and b is the maximum efficiency of light energy conversion as given by the initial slope of the curve relating photosynthesis to irradiance.

From equations (16.29) and (16.31), at less than saturating irradiance

$$F + B_r = \frac{C_a - F(r_a + r_s + r_m)}{\dfrac{1}{bI}[C_a - F(r_a + r_s + r_m)] + r_x}$$

or

$$= \frac{C_i - r_m F}{\dfrac{1}{bI}(C_i - r_m \ F) + r_x} \tag{16.32}$$

If a satisfactory estimate of B_r can be obtained, equation (16.32) can be solved at successive values of I to yield a series of linear regressions relating r_c and r_m. These can then be solved graphically to yield average values for r_c and r_m. This method of solution assumes that r_m, r_c and B_r are independent of irradiance over the range of I used and that the hyperbolic relationship of equation (16.31) applies. As it stands, the method assumes that $\beta = 0$ and it neglects the respiratory flux from the cells without chlorophyll, thus assuming that the flux of carbon dioxide through r_m is equal to F. The consequence of some of these assumptions have been examined by Chartier, Chartier & Čatský (1970) and found to be of only little significance to the end result. As indicated in Section 16.4.6, the method could be easily modified to embrace a more satisfactory model. The greatest difficulty with the method lies in obtaining a satisfactory estimate of B_r. As stressed earlier and in Chapter 8, the majority of methods for estimating photorespiration fail completely to take the intracellular respiratory flux into account. However, as equation (16.30) shows, the method is not very sensitive to inaccuracies in B_r.

16.4.8 | *Determination of the excitation resistance, r_e*

The excitation resistance, r_e, may conveniently be determined as the increase in mesophyll resistance associated with a reduction in irradiance below radiant energy saturation (I_s):

$$r_e = r_m(I) - r_m(I_s)$$

This presupposes no direct effect of irradiance upon the mesophyll resistance to the actual transfer of CO_2. Should there be such an effect, there will be a proportionate error in r_e.

16.5 | Determination of resistances: techniques primarily for use in the field

In recent years, several methods have been developed for the determination of boundary layer and stomatal resistances in the field. Some field methods are adaptations of laboratory methods previously described; others by their nature utilise observations which can only be made in the field and must consequently be considered in a separate category[1].

16.5.1 | *Estimates of resistances for the canopy as a whole*

16.5.1.1 | Extrapolation from the laboratory

The resistance of a population of leaves forming a canopy can be considered as the parallel sum of the resistances of the individual leaves (Monteith, Szeicz & Waggoner 1965). An approximate estimate of resistance is then obtained from $R_v = r_v/L'$, where R_v is the canopy resistance, r_v the individual leaf resistance, stomatal

1. In this Section, R is used for the transfer resistance of the canopy or a major part of it, and r for that of individual leaves or shoots, as previously.

or boundary layer or both, and L' the leaf area index. This relationship may be derived as follows:
Summing the resistance of individual leaves in parallel

$$\frac{1}{R_v} = \frac{1}{r_1} + \frac{1}{r_2} + \dots \frac{1}{r_n}$$

and hence

$$E_c = \frac{\Delta C_1}{r_1} + \frac{\Delta C_2}{r_2} + \dots \frac{\Delta C_n}{r_n} \quad [\text{kg s}^{-1}\ \text{m}^{-2}\ (\text{of ground})]$$

where E_c is the rate of evaporation from the canopy, ΔC is the gradient in absolute humidity between leaf and ambient air, and n the number of leaves of unit leaf area per unit ground area.
If

$$\Delta C_1 = \Delta C_2 = \Delta C_n$$

and

$$r_1 = r_2 = r_n$$

$$E_c = \frac{n\Delta C}{r_v}$$

and hence

$$\frac{\Delta C}{E_c} = \frac{r_v}{n} = R_v.$$

Only an approximate estimate is obtained in this way because of the assumption that all leaves in the canopy contribute equally to the total evaporation rate of the canopy. In practice, large variations in stomatal resistance, boundary layer resistance, humidity gradient and transfer coefficient lead to wide variations in evaporation rate within the canopy (see *e.g.* Lemon 1967).

16.5.1.2 Determination of boundary layer and stomatal resistances using excised shoots

In principle, the boundary layer and stomatal resistances can be estimated directly from equation (16.3). Rutter (1967) used simple techniques to obtain the necessary data in a pine canopy. A sampling procedure was adopted and the evaporation rate was determined by weighing excised shoots both when the needle surface was wet after rain and when dry. Ambient humidity, temperature above the canopy and the difference between leaf and air temperature were recorded and the resistances calculated from equation (16.3). Observations were made on a number of

days through the growing season under varying conditions of weather, including wind, canopy wetness and soil moisture deficit.
The simplicity of this method has obvious advantages although the labour involved is considerable. However, estimation of evaporation from loss of weight of a sample of excised shoots is conceptually and practically unsatisfactory (Eckardt 1960), although in this case careful tests showed that excision did not significantly affect the rate of water loss over several minutes. Accurate estimate of leaf temperatures on a scale sufficient to characterize the canopy is difficult and especially prone to errors with small leaves (see Chapter 17).
Rutter (1967) assumes in this and the following method that the rate of evaporation from foliage after it has been wetted by rain can be used to calculate boundary layer resistance. This assumption supposes that the surface of the needles is completely covered with a film of water. However, needles and leaves of most species are covered with wax deposits, often well-defined rods or plates of wax, and exhibit large contact angles to water droplets (*e.g.* Troughton & Hall 1967). Furthermore, evaporation occurs from all wet surfaces, including the surfaces of the twigs and branches, so that the resulting boundary layer resistance is not specifically relevant to the gas and vapour exchange of needles and leaves. It seems therefore that the estimate of boundary layer resistance obtained cannot be clearly related physically to the leaf surface.

16.5.1.3 Determination of the boundary layer resistance from the water balance of the canopy

By solving the water balance equation for the canopy between showers of rain, Robins & Rutter (personal communication) have obtained estimates of evaporation from the canopy from which the boundary layer resistance can be determined. After a shower of rain, the canopy is saturated. It loses water by evaporation and by drip (U) until the next shower occurs, when evaporation virtually ceases. When this second shower occurs, water is retained in the canopy until the amount lost by evaporation and drip has been replaced, by which time considerable through-fall and stem-flow (J) occurs.
The amounts of precipitation (P) and through-fall + stem-flow (J) are recorded, the first with rain gauges above the canopy or in glades, the second with a sampling network of troughs and rain gauges beneath the canopy and with collars on the trees. Constant rates of drip after the first shower (t_1) and after the second shower (t_2) are taken to indicate equal canopy water contents (respectively, w_1 and w_2). Then

$$w_1 - (E' + U) + (P - J) = w_2 \quad [\mathrm{kg\ m^{-2}}]$$

where E' is the amount of evaporation occurring between t_1 and t_2.
Hence when $w_2 = w_1$

$$\bar{E}_c = E'/(t_2 - t_1) = [P-(J + U)]/(t_2 - t_1)\ [\mathrm{kg\ m^{-2}\ s^{-1}}]$$

 where $\bar{E}_c$ is the mean rate of evaporation between the showers. Evaporation so estimated is then substituted for q_v in equation (16.3) to estimate r_a. As with the previous method, assumptions are made about the wetness and definition of the wet surface. During the period between t_1 and t_2, evaporation varies considerably and so must $C_1(= C_s(T_s))$ and C_2 $(= C_a)$, especially with the onset of the second shower. To a large extent then, the method depends upon the satisfactory integration of T_s and C_a during the period between t_1 and t_2.

16.5.1.4 | Determination of stomatal and boundary layer resistances with the aid of the wind profile

An ingenious method has been developed by Monteith (1963b, 1965) for the determination of the average boundary layer and surface resistance ($\approx$ stomatal resistance when there is complete cover) of a canopy from standard micrometeorological measurements.
In principle, equation (16.3) is applied as follows:
For the average boundary layer resistance in the canopy

$$R_a = \frac{C_0 - C_a}{q_v} \tag{16.33}$$

for the average surface resistance in the canopy

$$R_l = \frac{C_s(T_0) - C_0}{q_v} \tag{16.34}$$

where C_a is the absolute humidity at a reference height above the canopy, C_0 and T_0 are the absolute humidity and the temperature at the leaf surface and C_s is the absolute humidity equivalent to the saturation vapour pressure at T_0. q_v is the water vapour flux away from the canopy – the evaporation rate – which can be determined in one of several ways. For example, q_v may be determined from energy balance or wind profile considerations, or from an approach combining the two as in the Penman equation or similar equations of the same kind (Slatyer & McIlroy 1961; van Bavel 1966; Penman, Angus & van Bavel 1967; Lemon 1968; Tanner & Fuchs 1968). For details of some methods – see Chapter 13.
The ingenuity of Monteith's approach arises in the determination of C_0 and T_0 both of which are difficult to measure directly. By extrapolation of the logarithmic wind profile, Monteith defines a hypothetical plant surface in the canopy at which the windspeed $u = 0$. Relationships between T and u, and C and u are then plotted and extrapolated to $u = 0$ to yield values of T_0 and C_0 for the surface. Substitution of these values for T_0 and C_0, together with C_a and q_v into equations (16.33) and (16.34) yields estimates of R_a and R_l.
Further elaboration of Monteith's approach requires some elaboration of turbulent transfer theory (see Priestley 1959; Brutsaert 1965a; Monteith 1965; Lemon 1967, 1968, for example). In essence, Monteith calculates q_v from estimates of momentum transfer derived from the wind profile and substitutes it into equations

(16.33) and (16.34). Transfer of a property along a gradient can be described by the following equations in conditions close to adiabatic (see Chapter 13):

$$q_v = -K_v\left(\frac{dC}{dz}\right) \text{ for water vapour [kg m}^{-2}\text{ s}^{-1}]$$

$$\tau = -K_m\rho_a\left(\frac{du}{dz}\right) \text{ for momentum [N m}^{-2}]$$

where ρ_a is the density of air, q_v the flux of water vapour down the gradient of humidity (dC/dz), τ the momentum flux, or shearing stress, down the gradient of windspeed (du/dz), and K is the turbulent transfer coefficient [m^{-2} s^{-1}].
If the water vapour flux from the canopy, q_v, is to be derived from the wind profile, the assumption is made that

$$K_m = K_v = K$$

Then

$$q_v = -\frac{\tau}{\rho_a}\left(\frac{dz}{du}\right)\left(\frac{dC}{dz}\right)$$

But, from wind profile theory,

$$\tau = -\rho_a k^2 z^2\left(\frac{du}{dz}\right)^2$$

where k is von Kármán's constant.
Hence

$$q_v = -k^2 z^2\left(\frac{du}{dz}\right)\left(\frac{dC}{dz}\right)$$

which on integration gives

$$q_v = \frac{u\,k^2(C_0 - C_a)}{\left(\ln\frac{z}{z_0}\right)^2} \tag{16.35}$$

where C_0 and C_a are as described previously in this section and z_0 is the height at which the logarithmic profile of windspeed extrapolates to $u = 0$[1].
Thus from equation (16.33), $R_a = \{(\ln(z/z_0))^2\}/U^2k$ and R_l is obtained from equations (16.34) and (16.35).
In addition to the work of Monteith, cited above, this method has been used by

1. If the displacement of the zero plane (d) is appreciable, z must be replaced with (z–d).

Conaway & van Bavel (1966), van Bavel (1967), van Bavel, Newman & Hilgeman (1967), van Bavel & Ehrler (1968) and Szeicz, Endrödi & Tajchman (1969).
This method has been severely criticised on theoretical grounds (see the discussion following Monteith's 1963 paper; Philip 1966; Cowan 1968; Tanner & Fuchs 1968). The principal criticisms relate to the definition of a plant surface within the canopy from the wind profile above the canopy, and the derivation of temperature and humidity properties of the surface by extrapolation of the wind profile from above the canopy. Although the transfer of mass properties and momentum may be closely related above the canopy, within the canopy, mass and momentum transfer would be expected to be differently affected. For example, the distribution and strengths of the radiation sinks will largely affect transfer of mass properties, whereas the distribution and strength of surface drag forces will largely affect momentum transfer, so that the sources of water vapour and sinks of momentum will not be identical. Furthermore, the assumption that the mass transfer coefficients equal the momentum transfer coefficient also seems doubtful. In the last few years considerable evidence has accumulated that this assumption is incorrect (*e.g.* Brutsaert 1965b; Record & Cramer 1966; Businger *et al.* 1967; Swinbank & Dyer 1967; Wright & Brown 1967).

16.5.1.5 | Determination of stomatal and boundary layer resistances from the energy balance

The stomatal and/or the boundary layer resistance can be determined continuously on a single untreated sample (*cf.* Section 16.5.2.3) from the following (*e.g.* Hunt, Impens & Lemon 1968):

$$R_N = \frac{L(C_s(T_s) - C_a)}{R_l + R_a} + \frac{(T_s - T_a)c_p\rho_a}{R_a} + G$$

Measurements of the radiation balance of the canopy, R_N, vegetation mean surface temperature, T_s, and ambient temperature, T_a, and humidity, C_a, are required. If the soil heat flux, G, is appreciable, it should be known also. If the vegetation is sampled for R_l with the diffusion porometer, for example, R_a is found. Alternatively, if R_a is determined by another method, such as described in Section 16.5.1.4, the equation can be solved for R_l.
If evaporation is also known, by lysimetry or micrometeorological methods, for example, it can be substituted in place of the vapour transfer term. The equation can then be solved explicitly for R_a if the leaf surface temperature is known. R_a can then be substituted into the vapour transfer term to yield R_l (*e.g.* van Bavel & Ehrler 1968).

16.5.1.6 | Determination of stomatal resistance from combination methods

In the previous method, and in several others in this and the following section, information is needed on the temperature and vapour pressure at the liquid-air interface within the leaf or at the leaf surface. These data are not easily determined accurately, yet accurate knowledge of them is crucial to the reliable determination of stomatal and boundary layer resistances.

In several equations widely used for the estimation of evaporation, these parameters have been eliminated algebraically and replaced by more easily measurable parameters. The best known such equation is that derived by Penman (1948, 1956; van Bavel 1966; Penman, Angus & van Bavel 1967; Tanner & Fuchs 1968). The original Penman equation provides an estimate of evaporation from a free water surface. Over the years it has undergone a number of modifications to make it applicable to vegetation (*e.g.* Penman & Schofield 1951; Penman, Angus & van Bavel 1967). Monteith rederived it to include the identifiable components of boundary layer and stomatal resistance (Monteith 1963b, 1965; Monteith, Szeicz & Waggoner 1965). The form of the equation relevant to our considerations is as follows:

$$E_c = \frac{\omega R_N/L + (C_s(T_a) - C_a)/R_a}{\omega + 1 + R_l/R_a} \tag{16.36}$$

where ω is the increase in latent heat content with increase in sensible heat content of saturated air at ambient temperature, T_a. It is frequently written as Δ/γ where Δ is the slope of the curve relating the saturation vapour pressure to temperature and γ is the psychrometric constant. Van Bavel (1966) tabulates values of ω for 0° to 60°C at half degree intervals (see also Section 13.7.3).

The Penman equation is usually considered to give accurate estimates of evaporation over periods of days or weeks. However, van Bavel (1966) has demonstrated a reasonable degree of agreement between calculated and measured rates of evaporation over hourly periods using a modified Penman equation. By substitution into the Penman equation, van Bavel and his colleagues have obtained apparently useful mean daily and hourly values of R_l or R_a (van Bavel 1967; van Bavel, Newman & Hilgeman 1967).

Solution of equation (16.36) for R_l and R_a requires knowledge of the rate of evaporation. This may be obtained from a soil water balance or, over shorter periods, from lysimeters. The equation can be solved for R_a if R_l is found by sampling the canopy with the diffusion porometer, for example (*e.g.* van Bavel & Ehrler 1968). Alternatively, it may be solved for R_l, if R_a is found by another method, *e.g.* that described in Section 16.5.1.4.

In the absence of stomatal control of evaporation, equation (16.36) is simplified to yield the potential evaporation from the canopy, E_o:

$$E_o = \frac{\omega R_N/L + [C_s(T_a) - C_a]/R_a}{\omega + 1}$$

One may then write that

$$R_l = R_a(\omega + 1)(E_o/E_c - 1)$$

This form of computation has been used by van Bavel (1966) and van Bavel & Ehrler (1968), for example.

This method has recently been criticised by Tanner & Fuchs (1968) because it 'assumes that the flux density at the surface . . . is independent of the distribution of heat sources and sinks and vapour sources'. Since the distribution of these sources and sinks vary in space and time *within* the canopy, 'apparently reasonable relations between stomatal resistance and canopy resistance that may result from the inapplicable model . . . seem to be fortuitous. It seems clear that canopy models that consider the spatial distribution of heat sources and transfer coefficients are necessary'. The alternative models proposed by Tanner and Fuchs unfortunately require knowledge of leaf or canopy temperature and therefore fail where Penman succeeds. In principle, they are similar to others presented here, *e.g.* Section 16.5.2.1, although containing some of the Penman algebra.

16.5.2 | *Estimates of resistances for parts of the canopy*

Micrometeorological techniques have been developed in recent years for the study of physiological and exchange processes within the canopy. In current practice it is usual to treat the canopy as a number of layers, each of which is regarded as homogeneous (see, for example, Lemon 1967, 1968). Several techniques have been developed for the derivation of average stomatal and boundary layer resistances for layers of a canopy from standard microclimatological methods.

16.5.2.1 | Determination of boundary layer, stomatal and total CO_2 transfer resistances using the energy balance

The source or sink strengths for water vapour, sensible heat and carbon dioxide are derived for layers of finite thickness in the canopy from considerations of the energy balance at the boundaries of the layers. Combination of the source and sink strength equations with simple transfer equations such as equation (16.3) lead to estimates of the transfer resistances (*e.g.* Denmead 1965).
Consider a horizontal plane within or at the surface of a canopy. Energy fluxes towards the plane are defined as positive and those away from it as negative. The energy balance of the plane is then as follows:

$$\pm R_N \pm G \pm S \pm LE \pm H \pm \gamma F = 0 \quad [\mathrm{W\,m^{-2}}]$$

where R_N is the flux of radiation absorbed below the plane, G is the soil heat flux, S is change in heat storage in the vegetation, LE is the flux of latent heat, H is the flux of sensible heat, γF is the equivalent flux of energy as the result of metabolism [F is the flux of CO_2 and γ the thermal energy of CO_2 assimilation (Lemon 1967)]. The fluxes of latent, sensible and metabolic heat can be written as energy transfer equations as follows:

$$LE = -LK_v \frac{\mathrm{d}C}{\mathrm{d}z} \quad [\mathrm{W\,m^{-2}}]$$

$$H = -c_p \rho_a K_h \frac{\mathrm{d}T}{\mathrm{d}z} \quad [\mathrm{W\,m^{-2}}]$$

$$\gamma F = -\gamma \rho_c K_c \frac{d[CO_2]}{dz} \quad [W\ m^{-2}]$$

where ρ_c is the density of CO_2.
If $K_v = K_h = K_c = K_{z_1}$

$$-K_{z_1} = \frac{R_N - G - S}{L\frac{dC}{dz} + c_p\rho_a\frac{dT}{dz} + \gamma\rho_2\frac{d[CO_2]}{dz}} \quad [m^2\ s^{-1}] \qquad (16.37)$$

The flux of water vapour through the plane is then given by

$$E = q_{v_{z_1}} = -K_{z_1}\left(\frac{dC}{dz}\right)_{z_1} \quad [kg\ m^{-2}\ s^{-1}]$$

and similarly for sensible heat and carbon dioxide.
Consider now a second plane in the canopy some finite distance from the first:

$$q_{v_{z_2}} = -K_{z_2}\left(\frac{dC}{dz}\right)_{z_2} \quad [kg\ m^{-2}\ s^{-1}]$$

where K_{z_2} is not likely to be identical with K_{z_1} and is separately determined by solution of equation (16.37) for the second plane.
The source or sink strengths for water vapour, sensible heat and carbon dioxide in the layer between the two planes are given, respectively, by the following:

$$q_v = q_{v_{z_1}} - q_{v_{z_2}} = K_{z_2}\left(\frac{dC}{dz}\right)_{z_2} - K_{z_1}\left(\frac{dC}{dz}\right)_{z_1} \quad [kg\ m^{-2}\ s^{-1}]$$

$$q_h = q_{h_{z_1}} - q_{h_{z_2}} = c_p\rho\left(K_{z_2}\left(\frac{dT}{dz}\right)_{z_2} - K_{z_1}\left(\frac{dT}{dz}\right)_{z_1}\right) \quad [W\ m^{-2}]$$

$$q_c = q_{c_{z_1}} - q_{c_{z_2}} = \rho_c\left(K_{z_2}\left(\frac{d[CO_2]}{dz}\right)_{z_2} - K_{z_1}\left(\frac{d[CO_2]}{dz}\right)_{z_1}\right) \quad [kg\ m^{-2}\ s^{-1}]$$

Within a layer, the fluxes of water vapour, sensible heat and carbon dioxide can be described by equations of the form of equation (16.3), in which R is now the average resistance for the layer.
Thus for water vapour

$$R_l + R_a = \frac{C_1 - C_a}{q_v} \quad [s\ m^{-1}]$$

for sensible heat

$$R_a = c_p\frac{\rho_a(T_1 - T_a)}{q_h} \quad [s\ m^{-1}]$$

for carbon dioxide

$$\Sigma R = \frac{([CO_2]_a - [CO_2]_1)}{q_v} \quad [s\ m^{-1}]$$

where q_v, q_h and q_c are given by the preceding set of equations. The suffix a indicates ambient concentrations within the layer and the suffix 1 defines the other end of the pathway at or within the leaf. Thus C_1 is the absolute humidity corresponding to the saturation vapour pressure at T_1. In the case of carbon dioxide, $[CO_2]_1$ is not easily defined (see Sections 16.3.5 and 16.3.6 or 16.4.6 and 16.4.7). This method requires estimations of source and sink strengths within layers using the energy balance. For this, profiles are required of net radiation, air and plant temperatures, humidity and carbon dioxide concentration. The soil heat flux and the components of net radiation at the surface of the vegetation are also desirable. For the calculation of leaf resistances from the source and sink strengths, knowledge of leaf temperatures is also necessary and in the case of carbon dioxide some physiological information such as the CO_2 compensation concentration.
The piece of vegetation under study should be located within a large area of similar, uniform vegetation and the site should, as far as possible, be flat. More detailed considerations of the theory and assumptions involved lead to more precise evaluation of site requirements (see, for example, Monteith 1968) and the errors involved (see Chapter 13).
The method appears to be without serious conceptual drawbacks (see, for example, Dyer 1967) but great practical difficulties arise in the determination of the gradients of net radiation, temperature, water vapour, and CO_2 concentrations with sufficient accuracy to lead to reliable estimates of source and sink strength (Chapter 13) and hence resistances. Another considerable difficulty arises in the determination of leaf temperature in each layer. Some resistances calculated in this way from data of Brown (1964, see also Brown & Covey 1966) for maize are tabulated by Cowan & Milthorpe (1968a, Table X).

16.5.2.2 | Determination of resistances using the wind profile

In method described in Section 16.5.2.1, the energy balance is used to derive estimates of the transfer coefficient, K, so that fluxes of mass properties can be calculated from their gradients.
The transfer coefficient, K_m, for momentum can be derived from the wind profile, as in Section 16.5.1.4. If the assumption is then made that $K_m = K_v = K_h = K_c = K$ within the canopy, the fluxes of mass properties can be determined as in the preceding case. In this case, considerations of the energy balance are replaced by considerations of the wind profile. A larger, uniform, flat site is required so that a proper logarithmic wind profile can develop above the canopy (see Chapter 13 for more details).
This procedure is open to the objections outlined in Section 16.5.1.4 that K_m diverges appreciably from the mass transfer coefficients within the canopy. Estimates of fluxes of mass properties obtained by substituting K_m into the transfer equations have not in practice proved very successful (*e.g.* Mukammal, King &

Cork 1966) and systematic differences between K_m and K_v have emerged (Wright & Brown 1967).

16.5.2.3 Determination of stomatal and boundary layer resistances from the energy balance of individual leaves and shoots

The transpiration rate and hence $(r_a + r_l)$ can be determined from a change in the energy balance of individual leaves or shoots in the field, from a knowledge of leaf and air temperature and ambient vapour pressure. With a knowledge of r_l, obtained, for example, with a diffusion porometer (Section 16.4.3.3), r_a can be found. Alternatively, if r_a is known or can be neglected, r_l is found (see also Idle 1970).

Impens (1966) described the use of an artificially induced change in the energy balance of one leaf of a pair, assumed initially to have identical sensible and latent heat exchanges, to yield an estimate of $(r_l + r_a)$ in the field. Transpiration of one leaf, or set of leaves, is prevented and the rate of evaporation calculated from the difference in temperature between the transpiring and non-transpiring leaves. The method by which transpiration is prevented must not interfere with other components of the energy balance, *e.g.* short- and long-wave exchange and sensible heat transfer. Impens (1966) and Impens *et al.* (1967) wound thin, self-adhesive polythene tape around leaves to prevent transpiration. Thin polythene has only small effects on radiation exchange (see Chapter 2) but the effects of the adhesive are unknown. More seriously, however, it is extremely probable that the boundary layer resistances of the taped and untaped leaves were significantly different. Recognising these and other disadvantages, Hunt & Impens (1968), using a similar approach, changed transpiration by spraying leaves with an anti-transpirant.

In contrast with the conditions obtainable in assimilation chambers, in the field the radiation fluxes are not constant and the evaporation is not usually known. Hence either the radiation balance must be measured, or simultaneous observations, as opposed to sequential observations, made on transpiring and non-transpiring samples (*cf.* Sections 16.4.1.4 and 16.4.3.5).

Substituting an expression for water vapour transfer into equation (16.16) yields the following solution of the energy balances of two *similarly exposed* samples transpiring *simultaneously* at different rates when E is not known:

$$\varepsilon\sigma\, 8\, \overline{T}^3 (T_1 - T_2) + \frac{L(C_s(T_1) - C_a)}{r_{l,1} + r_a} - \frac{L(C_s(T_2) - C_a)}{r_{l,2} + r_a} + (T_1 - T_2)c_p\rho_a/r_a = 0$$

r_a can be evaluated by iteration or by solution of the cubic polynomial (Hunt & Impens 1968) if the leaf and air temperatures, ambient humidity and two sets of stomatal resistances are known. The stomatal resistances may, for example, be determined by diffusion porometry.

If E_2 is zero, as when polythene tape is used or the stomata are closed, the third term in the equation is eliminated and r_l can then be estimated if r_a is known or can be approximated (Taylor & Gates 1970).

r_a can be estimated from parallel measurements using the replica method (Section 16.4.1.2).

16.5.2.4 | Empirical estimates

Philip (1964) proposes that the boundary layer resistance of leaves can be related to the eddy transfer coefficient empirically, as follows:

$$R_a \approx \frac{1}{aK} \times 10^{-2} \quad [\mathrm{s\ cm^{-1}}]$$

where a $[\mathrm{m^{-1}}]$ is a coefficient which takes into account, among other things, foliage distribution and dimensions and the anisotropy and spatial variability of the transfer processes. A value of a of about 5 gives estimates of R_a which are consistent with observed leaf-air temperature differences (Denmead 1965).
From considerations of forced convection, laminar flow theory and from empirical observations on evaporation from leaf models in wind tunnels (*e.g.* Powell & Griffiths 1935; Powell 1940), Monteith (1965) derived the following empirical relationship for the determination of the boundary layer resistance of single leaves in a canopy to water vapour transfer:

$$r_a \approx 6.5\left(\frac{X}{u}\right)^{\frac{1}{2}} \times 10^{-3} \quad [\mathrm{s\ cm^{-1}}]$$

where X is the width of the leaf [m] and u the bulk air flow $[\mathrm{m\ s^{-1}}]$. The data on which equation (17.18) is based were found by Monteith to be compatible with the above expression which has been independently verified by Parlange, Waggoner & Heichel (1971) in the laboratory.
From similar considerations, Cowan (1968) and Cowan & Milthorpe (1968a) derive a similar equation for randomly orientated leaves in a canopy:

$$R_a \approx 2.6\,\frac{A^{\frac{1}{4}}}{u^{\frac{1}{2}}} \times 10^{-2} \quad [\mathrm{s\ cm^{-2}}]$$

where A is the area of the leaf in $\mathrm{m^2}$.
From his own experiments with model leaves in a wind tunnel, Thom (1968) derives the following empirical equation for the boundary layer resistance to water vapour transfer of a leaf in a canopy where forced convection occurs:

$$r_a = 1.84\left(\frac{X}{u}\right)^{\frac{1}{2}}\left(\frac{D_v}{\nu}\right)^{\frac{2}{3}} \times 10^{-2} \quad [\mathrm{s\ cm^{-1}}]$$

where ν is the kinematic viscosity of air $[\mathrm{m\ s^{-1}}]$.
These equations have not been adequately tested in practice. Monteith's was compared recently with the heat transfer method of Linacre and the energy balance method of Impens (Section 16.4.1.3) and found to yield much larger values (Hunt, Impens & Lemon 1968).

16.6 | Symbols and their dimensions

The most widely used symbols in their general form are listed below. In a number of cases, the convenient working units used in the text are several orders of magnitude smaller than the fundamental dimensions which are given below.

A leaf surface area [m^2]
B_i rate of production of CO_2 in respiration by achlorophyllous cells [$kg\ m^{-2}\ s^{-1}$]
B_r rate of production of CO_2 in respiration by chlorophyllous cells during irradiation [$kg\ m^{-2}\ s^{-1}$]
C, C_a, C_c, C_s, C_i concentration of gas or vapour [$kg\ m^{-3}$]
D_h, D_v, D_{H_2O}, D_{CO_2} effective molecular diffusion coefficients of heat, gas or vapour [$m^2\ s^{-1}$]
E flux density of water vapour in evaporation from leaves [$kg\ m^{-2}\ s^{-1}$]
E' amount of evaporation from the canopy between t_1 and t_2 [$kg\ m^{-2}$ ground area]
E_c flux density of water vapour in evaporation from a canopy [$kg\ m^{-2}\ s^{-1}$]
E_o potential flux density of water vapour from a canopy ($R_s = 0$) [$kg\ m^{-2}\ s^{-1}$]
F net flux density of CO_2 during irradiation [$kg\ m^{-2}\ s^{-1}$]
G flux density of heat into the soil [$W\ m^{-2}$]
H flux density of sensible heat to or in a canopy [$W\ m^{-2}$]
I irradiance [$W\ m^{-2}$]
I_s irradiance at which F is independent of I ("saturating" irradiance) [$W\ m^{-2}$]
J amount of through — fall and stem — flow occurring between t_1 and t_2 [$kg\ m^{-2}$ ground area]
$\mathrm{K_m}$ Michaelis-Menten constant for the carboxylation system
K_c, K_h, K_m, K_v turbulent transfer coefficients [$m^2\ s^{-1}$]
K_l liquid flow, hydraulic conductivity [s]
L latent heat of vaporization of water [$2.450 \times 10^6\ J\ kg^{-1}$ (20 °C)]
L' leaf area index [m^2 leaf area/m^2 ground area]
M, M_{H_2O}, M_{CO_2} molar mass [$kg\ mol^{-1}$]
P amount of precipitation falling between t_1 and t_2 [$kg\ m^{-2}$ ground area]
Q flux density of thermal radiation incident on both leaf surfaces [$W\ m^{-2}$]
Q_s net flux density of short-wave radiation incident on both leaf surfaces [$W\ m^{-2}$]
R Universal Gas Constant [$8.31\ J\ K^{-1}\ mol^{-1}$]
R respiratory efflux density of CO_2 in the dark [$kg\ m^{-2}\ s^{-1}$]
R_a, R_l, R_v resistances to transfer of heat, gas or vapour in the canopy [$s\ m^{-1}$]
R_N net flux density of short-wave and thermal radiation [$W\ m^{-2}$]
S flux density of heat into storage in the vegetation [$W\ m^{-2}$]
T, T_s, T_l, T_a temperature [°C or K]
U amount of canopy drip occurring between t_1 and t_2 [$kg\ m^{-2}$ ground area]

V volume [m^3]
V_w partial molal volume of water [m^3 mol^{-1}]
X leaf dimension in the direction of horizontal air flow [m]

b maximum efficiency of light energy conversion ($\Delta F/\Delta I$) [mol CO_2 fixed/Einstein absorbed]
c_p specific heat of air [1 013 J kg^{-1} K^{-1} (20 °C)]
e partial pressure of water vapour [bar]
e_s saturation vapour pressure over water [bar]
k von Kármán's constant (0.41)
k_h heat transfer coefficient [W m^{-2} K^{-1}]
p atmospheric pressure [bar]
q_c, q_v mass flux density of gas and vapour [kg m^{-2} s^{-1}]
q_h flux density of heat [J m^{-2} s^{-1}, W m^{-2}]
q_l mass flux density of liquid water [kg m^{-2} s^{-1}]
r_v, r_{H_2O}, r_{CO_2} resistance to transfer of gas and vapour [s m^{-1}]
r_{ab} total gas or vapour transfer resistance for the abaxial leaf surface [s m^{-1}]
r_{ad} total gas or vapour transfer resistance for the adaxial leaf surface [s m^{-1}]
r_a resistance to transfer across the boundary layer [s m^{-1}]
r_c equivalent diffusive resistance to transfer across the cuticle [s m^{-1}]
r_e equivalent excitation resistance [s m^{-1}]
r_i resistance to diffusive transfer through the intercellular spaces [s m^{-1}]
r_l average transfer resistance for a leaf [s m^{-1}]
r_s resistance to diffusive transfer through the stomata [s m^{-1}]
r_m equivalent diffusive resistance to transfer in the mesophyll [s m^{-1}]
r_x equivalent carboxylation resistance [s m^{-1}]
r_H hydraulic resistance to flow of liquid water [m s^{-1}]
t time [s]
u windspeed [m s^{-1}]
w water content of the canopy [kg m^{-2} ground area]
z length of segment of transfer pathway [m]

Γ ambient CO_2 concentration at which $F = 0$ ("compensation" concentration) [m^3 CO_2/m^3 air]
Ψ water potential [bar]
α ratio between rate of CO_2 production during irradiation and in darkness in chlorophyllous cells
β proportion of photorespired CO_2 reaching the intercellular spaces
γ thermal energy of CO_2 assimilation [$\approx 10^7$ J kg^{-1}]
ε thermal radiation emittance
ν kinematic viscosity of air [0.15×10^{-4} m^2 s^{-1} (20 °C)]
ρ_a density of air [1.20 kg m^{-3} (20 °C)]
ρ_c density of carbon dioxide [≈ 1.84 kg m^{-3} (20 °C)]
ρ_v density of water vapour [0.75 kg m^{-3} (20 °C)]
σ Stefan-Boltzmann constant [5.67×10^{-7} J m^{-2} K^{-4} s^{-1}]

τ flux density of momentum (shearing stress) $[\mathrm{N\ m^{-2}}]$

ω increase in latent heat content with increase in sensible heat content of saturated air $\left[\frac{de_s}{dT_a}\ \frac{1}{\gamma}\right]$ where γ is the psychrometric constant

16.7 | References

Alvim, P. de T.: A new type of porometer for measuring stomatal opening and its use in irrigation studies. – In: Eckardt, F. E. (ed.): Methodology of Plant Eco-Physiology. Pp. 325-329. Unesco, Paris 1965.

Aston, A. R., Millington, R. J., Peters, D. B.: Radiation exchange in controlling leaf temperature. – Agron. J. 61: 797-801, 1969.

Aston, M. J.: Resistance to water loss from plants. – In: Investigation of Energy and Mass Transfers near the Ground, including the Influences of the Soil-Plant-Atmosphere System. – Pp. 191-201. Univ. California, Davis 1963.

Bange, G. G. J.: On the quantitative explanation of stomatal transpiration. – Acta bot. neerl. 2: 255-297, 1953.

Bannister, P.: Stomatal responses of heath plants to water deficits. – J. Ecol. 52: 151-158, 1964.

Bassham, J. A., Jensen, R. G.: Photosynthesis of carbon compounds. – In: San Pietro, A., Greer, F. A., Army, T. J. (ed.): Harvesting the Sun. Pp. 79-110. Academic Press, New York-London 1967.

van Bavel, C. H. M.: Potential evaporation: the combination concept and its experimental verification. – Water Resources Res. 2: 455-467, 1966.

van Bavel, C. H. M.: Changes in canopy resistance to water loss from alfalfa induced by soil water depletion. – Agr. Meteorol. 4: 165-176, 1967.

van Bavel, C. H. M., Ehrler, W. L.: Water loss from sorghum field and stomatal control. – Agron. J. 60: 84-88, 1968.

van Bavel, C. H. M., Nakyama, F. S., Ehrler, W. L.: Measuring transpiration resistance of leaves. – Plant Physiol. 40: 535-540, 1965.

van Bavel, C. H. M., Newman, J. E., Hilgeman, R. H.: Climate and estimated water use by an orange orchard. – Agr. Meteorol. 4: 27-37, 1967.

Begg, J. E., Jarvis, P. G.: Photosynthesis in Townsville lucerne (*Stylosanthes humilis* H. B. K.). – Agr. Meteorol. 5: 91-109, 1968.

Bernard, E. A.: Théorie des échanges gazeux et énergétiques entre la végétation et l'air. – In: Eckardt, F. E. (ed.): Functioning of Terrestrial Ecosystems at the Primary Production Level. Pp. 67-83. Unesco, Paris 1968.

Bierhuizen, J. F., Slatyer, R. O.: Photosynthesis of cotton leaves under a range of environmental conditions in relation to internal and external diffusive resistances. – Aust. J. biol. Sci. 17: 348-359, 1964.

Bierhuizen, J. F., Slatyer, R. O., Rose, C. W.: A porometer for laboratory and field operation. – J. exp. Bot. 16: 182-191, 1965.

Björkman, O.: The effect of oxygen concentration on photosynthesis in higher plants. – Physiol. Plant. 19: 618-633, 1966.

Björkman, O.: Carboxydismutase activity in relation to light-saturated rate of photosynthesis in plants from exposed and shaded habitats. – Carnegie Inst. Year Book 65: 454-459, 1967.

Björkman, O.: Carboxydismutase activity in shade-adapted and sun-adapted species of higher plants. – Physiol. Plant. 21: 1-10, 1968a.

Björkman, O.: Further studies on differentiation of photosynthetic properties in sun and shade ecotypes of *Solidago virgaurea*. – Physiol. Plant. 21: 84-99, 1968b.

Björkman, O.: Further studies of the effect of oxygen concentration on photosynthetic CO_2 uptake in higher plants. – Carnegie Inst. Washington Year Book 66: 220-228, 1968c.

Björkman, O., Holmgren, P.: Adaptability of the photosynthetic apparatus to light intensity in ecotypes from exposed and shaded habitats. – Physiol. Plant. 16: 889-914, 1963.

Björkman, O., Holmgren, P.: Photosynthetic adaptation to light intensity in plants native to shaded and exposed habitats. – Physiol. Plant. 19: 854-859, 1966.

Bouchet, R. J.: Évapotranspiration réelle, évapotranspiration potentielle, et production agricole. – Ann. agr. 14: 743-824, 1963, or in: L'eau et la Production Végétale. Pp. 151-232. I.N.R.A. Paris 1964.

Bourdeau, P. F., Laverick, M. L.: Tolerance and photosynthetic adaptability to light intensity in white pine, red pine, hemlock and ailanthus seedlings. – Forest Sci. 4: 196-267, 1958.

Brix, H.: Influence of light intensity at different temperatures on rate of respiration of Douglas-fir seedlings. – Plant Physiol. 43: 389-393, 1968.

Brown, K. W.: Vertical fluxes within the vegetative canopy of a corn field. – Interim Report 64-1 DA Task 1-A-0-11001-B-021-08. 91 pp. Ithaca, N.Y. 1964.

Brown, K. W., Covey, W.: The energy-budget evaluation of the micro-meteorological transfer processes within a cornfield. – Agr. Meteorol. 3: 73-96, 1966.

Brutsaert, W.: A model for evaporation as a molecular diffusion process into a turbulent atmosphere. – J. geophys. Res. 70: 5017-5024, 1965a.

Brutsaert, W.: Equations for vapour flux as a fully turbulent diffusion process under diabatic conditions. – Bull. I.A.S.H. 10: 11-21, 1965b.

Businger, J. A., Miyake, M., Dyer, A. J., Bradley, E. F.: On the direct determination of the turbulent heat flux near the ground. – J. appl. Meteorol. 6: 1025-1032, 1967.

Byrne, G. F., Rose, C. W., Slatyer, R. O.: An aspirated diffusion porometer. – Agr. Meteorol. 7: 39-44, 1970.

Carman, P. C.: Flow of Gases Through Porous Media. – Butterworth, London 1956.

Čatský, J.: Water saturation deficit and photosynthetic rate as related to leaf age in the wilting plant. – In: Slavík, B. (ed.): Water Stress in Plants. Pp. 203-209. Publ. House Czechoslovak Acad. Sci., Prague and Dr. W. Junk N.V., The Hague 1965.

Chartier, P.: Étude théorique de l'assimilation brute de la feuille. – Ann. Physiol. vég. 8: 167-195, 1966.

Chartier, P.: A model of CO_2 assimilation in the leaf. – In: Prediction and Measurement of Photosynthetic Productivity. Pp. 307-315. PUDOC, Wageningen 1970.

Chartier, P., Chartier, M., Čatský, J.: Resistances for carbon dioxide diffusion and for carboxylation as factors in bean leaf photosynthesis. – Photosynthetica 4: 48-57, 1970.

Conaway, J., van Bavel, C. H. M.: Evaporation from a wet soil surface calculated from radiometrically determined surface temperatures. – J. appl. Meteorol. 6: 650-655, 1966.

Cooper, T. G., Filmer, D., Wishnick, M., Lane, M. D.: The active species of 'CO_2' utilized by ribulose diphosphate carboxylase. – J. biol. Chem. 244: 1081-1083, 1969.

Cowan, I. R.: Mass, heat and momentum exchange between stands of plants and their atmospheric environment. – Quart. J. roy. meteorol. Soc. 94: 523-544, 1968.

Cowan, I. R., Milthorpe, F. L.: Plant factors influencing the water status of plant tissues. – In: Kozlowski, T. T. (ed.): Water Deficits and Plant Growth 1: 137-193. Academic Press, New York 1968a.

Cowan, I. R., Milthorpe, F. L.: Physiological responses in relation to the environment within the plant cover. – In: Eckardt, F. E. (ed.): Functioning of Terrestrial Ecosystems at the Primary Production Level. Pp. 107-130, Unesco, Paris 1968b.

Denmead, O. T.: Evaporation from plant surfaces and the significance of diffusive resistances. – In: Water Transport through Surfaces. Univ. Tasmania 1965.

Dorokhov, B. L.: O vozmozhnosti vneustichnogo kutikulyarnogo fotosinteza u nekotorykh rasteniï. [About the possibility of cuticular photosynthesis in some plants.] – Bot. Zh. 48: 893-896, 1963.

Drake, B. G., Raschke, K., Salisbury, F. B.: Temperatures and transpiration resistances of *Xanthium* leaves as affected by air temperature, humidity and wind speed. – Plant Physiol. 46: 324–330, 1970.

Dugger, W. M.: The permeability of non-stomate leaf epidermis to carbon dioxide. – Plant Physiol. 27: 489-499, 1952.

Dyer, A. J.: The turbulent transport of heat and water vapour in an unstable atmosphere. – Quart. J. Roy. Meteorol. Soc. 93: 501-508, 1967.

Eagles, C. F., Treharne, K. J.: Photosynthetic activity of *Dactylis glomerata* L. in different light regimes. – Photosynthetica 3: 29-38, 1969.
Eckardt, F. E.: Eco-physiological measuring techniques applied to research on water relations of plants in arid and semi-arid regions. – Arid Zone Res. 15: 139-171, 1960.
Ehrler, W. L., van Bavel, C. H. M.: Leaf diffusion resistance, illuminance, and transpiration. – Plant Physiol. 43: 208-214, 1968.
El-Sharkawy, M. A., Hesketh, J. D.: Effects of temperature and water deficit on leaf photosynthetic rates of different species. – Crop Sci. 4: 514-518, 1964.
El-Sharkawy, M. A., Loomis, R. S., Williams, W. A.: Photosynthetic and respiratory exchanges of carbon dioxide by leaves of the grain amaranth. – J. appl. Ecol. 5: 243-251, 1968.
Enns, T.: Facilitation by carbonic anhydrase of carbon dioxide transport. – Science 155: 44-47, 1967.
Esau, K.: Plant Anatomy. – John Wiley & Sons Inc., New York 1965.
Everson, R. G.: Bicarbonate equilibria and the apparent K_m (HCO_3^-) of isolated chloroplasts. – Nature 222: 876, 1969.
Everson, R. G., Slack, C. R.: Distribution of carbonic anhydrase in relation to the C_4 pathway of photosynthesis. – Phytochemistry 7: 581-584, 1968.
Fischer, R. A.: Resistance to water loss in the mesophyll of leek *(Allium porrum)*. – J. exp. Bot. 19: 135-145, 1968.
Freeland, R. O.: Photosynthesis in relation to stomatal frequency and distribution. – Plant Physiol. 23: 595-600, 1948.
Fuller, E. N., Schettler, P. D., Giddings, J. C.: A new method for prediction of binary gas-phase diffusion coefficients. – Ind. eng. Chem. 58(5): 18-27, 1966.
Gaastra, P.: Photosynthesis of crop plants as influenced by light, carbon dioxide, temperature and stomatal diffusion resistance. – Meded. Landbouwhogesch. Wageningen 59(13): 1-68, 1959.
Gaastra, P.: Climatic control of photosynthesis and respiration. – In: Evans, L. T. (ed.): Environmental Control of Plant Growth. Pp. 113-140. Academic Press, New York 1963.
Gale, J., Poljakoff-Mayber, A.: Resistances to the diffusion of gas and vapor in leaves. – Physiol. Plant. 21: 1170-1176, 1968.
Gale, J., Kohl, H. C., Hagan, R. M.: Mesophyll and stomatal resistances affecting photosynthesis under varying conditions of soil, water and evaporation demand. – Israel J. Bot. 15: 64-71, 1966.
Gale, J., Poljakoff-Mayber, A., Kahane, I.: The gas diffusion porometer technique and its application to the measurement of leaf mesophyll resistance. – Israel J. Bot. 16: 187-204, 1967.
Gates, D. M.: Energy Exchange in the Biosphere. – Harper & Row, New York 1962.
Gates, D. M.: Leaf temperature and energy exchange. – Arch. Meteorol. Geophys. Bioklimatol. B. 12: 321-336, 1963.
Gates, D. M.: Transpiration and leaf temperature. – Annu. Rev. Plant Physiol. 19: 211-238, 1968a.
Gates, D. M.: Energy exchange in the biosphere. – In: Eckardt, F. E. (ed.): Functioning of Terrestrial Ecosystems at the Primary Production Level. Pp. 33-43. Unesco, Paris 1968b.
Gates, D. M., Benedict, C. M.: Convection phenomena from plants in still air. – Amer. J. Bot. 50: 563-573, 1963.
Gates, D. M., Tibbals, E. C., Kreith, F.: Radiation and convection for Ponderosa pine. – Amer. J. Bot. 52: 66-71, 1965.
Gauhl, E.: Differential photosynthetic performance of *Solanum dulcamara* ecotypes from shaded and exposed habitats. – Carnegie Inst. Year Book 67: 482-487, 1969.
Gibbs, M., Latzko, E., Everson, R. G., Cockburn, W.: Carbon mobilization by the green plant. – In: San Pietro, A., Greer, F. A., Army, T. J. (ed.): Harvesting the Sun. Pp. 111-130. Academic Press, New York – London 1967.
Gifford, R. M., Musgrave, R. B.: Diffusion and quasi-diffusion resistances in relation to the carboxylation kinetics of maize leaves. – Physiol. Plant. 23: 1048-1056, 1970.
Gloser, J.: Some problems of the determination of stomatal aperture by the microrelief method. – Biol. Plant. 9: 28-33, 1967.
Graham, D., Whittingham, C. P.: The path of carbon during photosynthesis in *Chlorella pyrenoidosa* at high and low carbon dioxide concentrations. – Z. Pflanzenphysiol. 58: 418-427, 1968.
Gregory, F. G., Armstrong, J. I.: The diffusion porometer. – Proc. Roy. Soc. London, Ser. B, 121: 27-42, 1936.

Gregory, F. G., Milthorpe, F. L., Pearse, H. L., Spencer, H. J.: Experimental studies of the factors controlling transpiration. I. Apparatus and experimental technique. – J. exp. Bot. 1: 1-14, 1950a.
Gregory, F. G., Milthorpe, F. L., Pearse, H. L., Spencer, H. J.: Experimental studies of the factors controlling transpiration. II. The relation between transpiration rate and leaf water content. – J. exp. Bot. 1: 15-28, 1950b.
Grieve, B. J., Went, F. W.: An electric hygrometer apparatus for measuring water vapour loss from plants in the field. – In: Eckardt, F. E. (ed.): Methodology of Plant Eco-Physiology. Pp. 247-258. Unesco, Paris 1965.
Grncarevic, M., Radler, F.: The effect of wax components on cuticular transpiration – Model experiments. – Planta 75: 23-27, 1967.
Hall, D. M., Jones, R. L.: Physiological significance of surface wax on leaves. – Nature 191: 95-96, 1961.
Hatch, M. D., Slack, C. R.: Photosynthesis by sugar-cane leaves. A new carboxylation reaction and the pathway of sugar formation. – Biochem. J. 101: 103-111, 1966.
Hatch, M. D., Slack, C. R., Johnson, H. S.: Further studies on a new pathway of photosynthetic carbon dioxide fixation in sugar-cane and its occurrence in other plant species. – Biochem. J. 102: 417-422, 1967.
Heath, O. V. S.: Experimental studies of the relation between carbon assimilation and stomatal movement. I. Apparatus and technique. – Ann. Bot. N.S. 3: 469-495, 1939.
Heath, O. V. S.: The water relations of stomatal cells and the mechanisms of stomatal movement. – In: Steward, F. C. (ed.): Plant Physiology: A Treatise. – Vol. 2, pp. 193-250. Academic Press, New York–London 1959.
Heath, O. V. S. (with an Appendix by Penman, H. L.): Experimental studies of the relation between carbon assimilation and stomatal movement. II. The use of the resistance porometer in estimating stomatal aperture and diffusive resistance. Pt. I. A critical study of the resistance porometer. – Ann. Bot. N.S. 5: 455-500, 1941.
Heath, O. V. S., Russell, J.: The Wheatstone bridge porometer. – J. exp. Bot. 2: 111-116, 1951.
Hesketh, J. D.: Limitations to photosynthesis responsible for differences among species. – Crop Sci. 3: 493-496, 1963.
Hesketh, J., Muramoto, H., El-Sharkawy, M.: Carbonic anhydrase and photosynthesis in leaves among species. – Arizona agr. exp. Sta. Dep. Plant Breeding Report 2 on Photosynthesis. Pp. 1-5. 1965.
Hiesey, W. M., Milner, H. W.: Physiology of ecological races and species. – Annu. Rev. Plant Physiol. 16: 203-216, 1965.
Hiesey, W. M., Björkman, O., Nobs, M. A.: Light-saturated rates of photosynthesis in *Mimulus cardinalis*. – Carnegie Inst. Year Book 65: 461-464, 1967.
Hiesey, W. M., Nobs, M. A., Björkman, O.: Photosynthetic rates of *M. lewisii* and *M. cardinalis* in comparison with their F_1 hybrid. – Carnegie Inst. Year Book 65: 464-468, 1967.
Hofstra, G., Hesketh, J. D.: Effects of temperature on the gas exchange of leaves in the light and dark. – Planta 85: 228–237, 1969.
Holmgren, P.: Leaf factors affecting light-saturated photosynthesis in ecotypes of *Solidago virgaurea* from exposed and shaded habitats. – Physiol. Plant. 21: 676-698, 1968.
Holmgren, P., Jarvis, P. G.: Carbon dioxide efflux from leaves in light and darkness. – Physiol. Plant. 20: 1045–1051, 1967.
Holmgren, P., Jarvis, P. G., Jarvis, M. S.: Resistances to carbon dioxide and water vapour transfer in leaves of different plant species. – Physiol. Plant. 18: 557-573, 1965.
Horrocks, R. L.: Wax and the water vapour permeability of apple cuticle. – Nature 203: 547, 1964.
Hsu, S. T.: Engineering Heat Transfer. – Van Nostrand, Princetown, N.J. 1963.
Hunt, L. A., Impens, I. I.: Use of antitranspirants in studies of the external diffusion resistance of leaves. –Œcol. Plant. 3: 1-6, 1968.
Hunt, L. A., Impens, I. I., Lemon, E. R.: Estimates of the diffusion resistance of some large sunflower leaves in the field. – Plant Physiol. 43: 522-526, 1968.
Hygen, G.: Studies in plant transpiration. I. – Physiol. Plant. 4: 57-183, 1951.
Hygen, G.: Studies in plant transpiration. II. – Physiol. Plant. 6: 106-133, 1953.
Idle, D. B.: The calculation of transpiration rate and diffusion resistance of a single leaf from

micrometeorological information subject to errors of measurement. – Ann. Bot. N.S. 34: 159-176, 1970.
Impens, I.: Leaf wetness, diffusion resistances and transpiration rates of bean leaves (*Phaseolus vulgaris* L.) through comparison of 'wet' and 'dry' leaf temperatures. –Œcol. Plant. 1: 327-334, 1966.
Impens, I. I., Stewart, D. W., Allen, L. H., Lemon, E. R.: Diffusive resistances at, and transpiration rates from leaves *in situ* within the vegetative canopy of a corn crop. – Plant Physiol. 42: 99-104, 1967.
Inoue, E.: The CO_2-concentration profile within crop canopies and its significance for the productivity of plant communities. – In: Eckardt, F.E. (ed.): Functioning of Terrestrial Ecosystems at the Primary Production Level. Pp. 359-366. Unesco, Paris 1968.
Jarvis, P. G., Jarvis, M. S.: The water relations of tree seedlings. IV. Some aspects of the tissue water relations and drought resistance. – Physiol. Plant. 16: 501-516, 1963.
Jarvis, P. G., Slatyer, R. O.: A controlled-environment chamber for studies of gas exchange by each surface of a leaf. – C.S.I.R.O. Div. Land Res. tech. Paper 29: 1-16, 1966.
Jarvis, P. G., Slatyer, R. O.: The role of the mesophyll cell wall in leaf transpiration. – Planta 90: 303-322, 1970.
Jarvis, P. G., Rose, C. W., Begg, J. E.: An experimental and theoretical comparison of viscous and diffusive resistances to gas flow through amphistomatous leaves. – Agr. Meteorol. 4: 103-117, 1967.
Jensen, R. G., Bassham, J. A.: Photosynthesis by isolated chloroplasts. – Proc. Nat. Acad. Sci. U.S. 56: 1095-1101, 1966.
Johnson, H. S., Hatch, M. D.: Distribution of the C_4-dicarboxylic acid pathway of photosynthesis and its occurrence in dicotyledonous plants. – Phytochemistry 7: 375-380, 1968.
Jolliffe, P. A., Tregunna, E. B.: Effect of temperature, CO_2 concentration, and light intensity on oxygen inhibition of photosynthesis in wheat leaves. – Plant Physiol. 43: 902-906, 1968.
Kanemasu, E. T., Thurtell, G. W., Tanner, C. B.: Design, calibration and field use of a stomatal diffusion porometer. – Plant Physiol. 44: 881-885, 1969.
Keller, T., Koch, W.: Der Einfluß der Mineralstoffernährung auf CO_2-Gaswechsel und Blattpigmentgehalt der Pappel. I. Teil. Stickstoff, II. Teil. Eisen. – Mitteil. Schweiz. Anstalt forstliche Versuchswesen 38: 253-318, 1962.
Kennedy, J. S., Booth, C.O.: Water relations of leaves from woody and herbaceous plants. – Nature 181: 1271-1272, 1958.
Kern, D. M.: The hydration of carbon dioxide. – J. chem. Educ. 37: 14-23, 1960.
Ketellapper, H. J.: Stomatal physiology. – Ann. Rev. Plant Physiol. 14: 249-270, 1963.
Kieras, F. J., Haselkorn, R.: Properties of ribulose-1,5-diphosphate carboxylase (carboxydismutase) from chinese cabbage and photosynthetic microorganisms. – Plant Physiol. 43: 1264-1270, 1968.
Knoerr, K. R.: Contrasts in energy balances between individual leaves and vegetated surfaces. – In: Sopper, W. E., Lull, H. W. (ed.): Forest Hydrology. Pp. 391-401. Pergamon Press, Oxford 1967.
Kriedemann, P. E.: Some photosynthetic characteristics of *Citrus* leaves. – Austr. J. biol. Sci. 21: 895-905, 1968.
Kuiper, P. J. C.: The effects of environmental factors on the transpiration of leaves, with special reference to stomatal light response. – Mededel. Landbouwhogeschool Wageningen 61(7): 1-49, 1961.
Kuiper, P. J. C.: Temperature dependence of photosynthesis of bean plants as affected by decenylsuccinic acid. – Plant Physiol. 40: 915-918, 1965.
Kusuda, T.: Calculation of the temperature of a flate plate wet surface under adiabatic conditions with respect to the Lewis relation. – In: Wexler, A. (ed.): Humidity and Moisture. Vol. 1. Pp. 16-32. Reinhold Publ. Co., New York 1965.
Lake, J. V.: Respiration of leaves during photosynthesis. I. Estimates from an electrical analogue. – Austr. J. biol. Sci. 20: 487-493, 1967a.
Lake, J. V.: Respiration of leaves during photosynthesis. II. Effects on the estimation of mesophyll resistance. – Austr. J. biol. Sci. 20: 495-499, 1967b.
Lake, J. V., Slatyer, R. O.: Respiration of leaves during photosynthesis. III. Respiration rate

and mesophyll resistance in turgid cotton leaves with stomatal control diminished. – Austr. J. biol. Sci. 23: 529-535, 1970.
Landsberg, J. J., Ludlow, M. M.: A technique for determining resistance to mass transfer through the boundary layers of plants with complex structures. – J. appl. Ecol. 7: 187-192, 1970.
Lee, C. Y., Wilke, C. R.: Measurements of vapor diffusion coefficient. – Ind. eng. Chem. 46: 2381-2387, 1954.
Lee, R., Gates, D. M.: Diffusion resistance in leaves as related to their stomatal anatomy and micro-structure. – Amer. J. Bot. 51: 963-975, 1964.
Lemon, E.: Aerodynamic studies of CO_2 exchange between the atmosphere and the plant. – In: San Pietro, A., Greer, F. A., Army, T. J. (ed.): Harvesting the Sun. Pp. 263-290. Academic Press, New York – London 1967.
Lemon, E. R.: The measurement of height distribution of plant community activity using the energy and momentum balance approaches. – In: Eckardt, F. E. (ed.): Functioning of Terrestrial Ecosystems at the Primary Production Level. Pp. 381-389. Unesco, Paris 1968.
Linacre, E. T.: Further studies on the heat transfer from a leaf. – Plant Physiol. 42: 651-658, 1967.
List, R. J.: Smithsonian Meteorological Tables. 6th rev. Ed. – Smithsonian Miscellaneous Collections 114, 1958.
Livingstone, B. E.: The relation of desert plants to soil moisture and the evaporation. – Carnegie Inst. Washington Pub. 50: 1-78, 1906.
Longmuir, I. S., Forster, R. E., Woo, C-Y.: Diffusion of carbon dioxide through thin layers of solution. – Nature 209: 393-394, 1966.
Louguet, P.: Sur une méthode d'étude du mouvement des stomates utilisant la diffusion de l'hydrogène à travers les feuilles. – In: Eckardt, F. E. (ed.): Methodology of Plant Eco-Physiology. Pp. 307-316. Unesco, Paris 1965.
Ludlow, M. M.: Growth and photosynthesis of tropical pasture plants. – Ph.D. Thesis, Univ. Queensland, Australia 1969.
Ludlow, M. M., Jarvis, P. G.: Photosynthesis in Sitka Spruce (Bong.) Carr. I. General characteristics. – J. appl. Ecol. 8: in press, 1971.
Martin, E. V.: Studies of evaporation and transpiration under controlled conditions. – Carnegie Inst. Wash. Pub. No. 550, 1943.
Maruyama, H., Easterday, R. L., Chang, H.-C., Lane, M. D.: The enzymatic carboxylation of phophoenolpyruvate. I. Purification and properties of phophoenolpyruvate carboxylase. – J. biol. Chem. 241: 2405-2412, 1966.
Maskell, E. J.: Experimental researches on vegetable assimilation and respiration. XVIII. The relation between stomatal opening and assimilation. A critical study of assimilation rates and porometer rates in cherry laurel. – Proc. Roy. Soc. B 102: 488-533, 1928.
McMahon, D., Bogorad, L.: Some kinetic studies of ribulose-1,5-diphosphate carboxylase (carboxydismutase) from races of *Mimulus cardinalis*. – Carnegie Inst. Year Book 65: 459-461, 1967.
Meidner, H.: Changes in the resistance of the mesophyll tissue with changes in the leaf water content. – J. exp. Bot. 6: 94-99, 1955.
Meidner, H.: A critical study of sensor element diffusion porometers. – J. exp. Bot. 21: 1060-1066, 1970.
Meidner, H., Mansfield, T. A.: Stomatal responses to illumination. – Biol. Rev. 40: 483-509, 1965.
Meidner, H., Mansfield, T. A.: Physiology of Stomata. – McGraw-Hill, London 1968.
Meidner, H., Spanner, D. C.: The differential transpiration porometer. – J. exp. Bot. 10: 190-205, 1959.
Miller, P. C., Gates, D. M.: Transpiration of plants. – Amer. Mid. Nat. 77(1): 77-85, 1967.
Milthorpe, F. L.: Plant factors involved in transpiration. – Arid Zone Res. 16: 107-115, 1961.
Milthorpe, F. L., Penman, H. L.: The diffusive conductivity of the stomata of wheat leaves. – J. exp. Bot. 18: 422-457, 1967.
Monteith, J. L.: Gas exchange in plant communities. – In: Evans, L. T. (ed.): Environmental Control of Plant Growth. Pp. 95-112. Academic Press, New York 1963a.
Monteith, J. L.: Calculating evaporation from diffusive resistances. – In: Investigation of Energy and Mass Transfers near the Ground Including the Influences of the Soil-Plant-Atmosphere System. Pp. 177-189. Univ. California, Davis 1963b.

Monteith, J. L.: Evaporation and environment. – Symp. Soc. exp. Biol. 19: 205-234, 1965.
Monteith, J. L.: Analysis of the photosynthesis and respiration of field crops from vertical fluxes of carbon dioxide. – In: Eckardt, F. E. (ed.): Functioning of Terrestrial Ecosystems at the Primary Production Level. Pp. 349-358. Unesco, Paris 1968.
Monteith, J. L., Bull, T. A.: A diffusive porometer for field use. II. Theory, calibration and performance. – J. appl. Ecol. 7: 623-638, 1970.
Monteith, J. L., Szeicz, G., Waggoner, P. E.: The measurement and control of stomatal resistance in the field. – J. appl. Ecol. 2: 345-355, 1965.
Mooney, H. A., Billings, W. D.: Comparative physiological ecology of arctic and alpine populations of *Oxyria digyna*. – Ecol. Monographs 31: 1-29, 1961.
Mooney, H. A., Shropshire, F.: Population variability in temperature-related photosynthetic acclimation. –Œcol. Plant. 2: 1-13, 1967.
Moreshet, S.: A portable Wheatstone bridge porometer for field measurements of stomatal resistance. – Israel J. agr. Res. 14: 27-30, 1964.
Moreshet, S., Koller, D., Stanhill, G.: The partitioning of resistances to gaseous diffusion in the leaf epidermis and the boundary layer. – Ann. Bot. N.S. 32: 695-701, 1968.
Moreshet, S., Stanhill, G., Koller, D.: A radioactive tracer technique for the direct measurement of the diffusion resistance of stomata. – J. exp. Bot. 19: 460-467, 1968.
Mukammal, E. I., King, K. M., Cork, H. F.: Comparison of aerodynamic and energy budget techniques in estimating evaporation from a cornfield. – Arch. meteorol. geophys. Bioklimatol. B. 14: 384-395, 1966.
Murata, Y., Iyama, J.: Studies on the photosynthesis of forage crops II. Influence of air-temperature upon the photosynthesis of some forage and grain crops. – Proc. Crop Sci. Soc. Japan 31: 315-322, 1963.
Murata, Y., Iyama, J., Honma, T.: Studies on the photosynthesis of forage crops IV. Influence of air-temperature upon the photosynthesis and respiration of alfalfa and several southern type forage crops. – Proc. Crop Sci. Soc. Japan 34: 154-158, 1965.
Oppenheimer, H. R.: Adaptation to drought: xerophytism. – Arid Zone Res. 15: 105-138, 1960.
de Parcevaux, S.: Calcul de la résistance stomatique et mesures de la résistance dans la couche limite grâce aux analogies électriques: cas de la vapeur d'eau. – Wiss. Z. (Leipzig) 4: 877-880, 1964.
de Parcevaux, S.: Application des analogies rhéo-électriques à la determination de la résistance à la diffusion gazeuse dans la couche limite et calcul de la résistance stomatique: cas de la vapeur d'eau. – In: Eckardt, F. E. (ed.): Functioning of Terrestrial Ecosystems at the Primary Production Level. Pp. 421-427. Unesco, Paris 1968.
de Parcevaux, S., Perrier, A.: Bilan énergétique de la feuille. Application de l'étude des cinétiques de température à la détermination des résistances aux flux gazeux. – Preprint, Symp. Plant Response to Clim. Factors. Unesco, Uppsala 1970.
Parkhurst, D. F., Duncan, P. R., Gates, D. M., Kreith, F.: Wind-tunnel modelling of convection of heat between air and broad leaves of plants. – Agr. Meteorol. 5: 38-47, 1968.
Parkinson, K. J., Penman, H. L.: A possible source of error in the estimation of stomatal resistance. – J. exp. Bot. 21: 405-409, 1970.
Parlange, J.-Y., Waggoner, P. E.: Stomatal dimensions and resistance to diffusion. – Plant Physiol. 46: 337-342, 1970.
Parlange, J.-Y., Waggoner, P. E., Heichel, G. H.: Boundary layer resistance and temperature distribution on still and flapping leaves. – Plant Physiol. 47: (in press), 1971.
Paulsen, J. M., Lane, M. D.: Spinach ribulose diphosphate carboxylase. I. Purification and properties of the enzyme. – Biochemistry 5: 2350-2357, 1966.
Penman, H. L.: Theory of porometers used in the study of stomatal movements in leaves. – Proc. Roy. Soc. B 130: 416-434, 1942.
Penman, H. L.: Natural evaporation from open water, bare soil and grass. – Proc. Roy. Soc. A 193: 120-145, 1948.
Penman, H. L.: Evaporation: an introductory survey. – Neth. J. agr. Sci. 4: 9-27, 1956.
Penman, H. L., Schofield, R. K.: Some physical aspects of assimilation and transpiration. – Symp. Soc. exp. Biol. 5: 115-129, 1951.
Penman, H. L., Angus, D. E., van Bavel, C. H. M.: Microclimatic factors affecting evaporation and transpiration. – Agronomy 11: 483-505, 1967.

Philip, J. R.: The osmotic cell, solute diffusibility, and the plant water economy. – Plant Physiol. 33: 264-271, 1958.
Philip, J. R.: Sources and transfer processes in the air layers occupied by vegetation. – J. appl. Meteorol. 3: 390-395, 1964.
Philip, J. R.: Plant water relations: some physical aspects. – Annu. Rev. Plant Physiol. 17: 245-268, 1966.
Pisek, A., Winkler, E.: Licht- und Temperaturabhängigkeit der CO_2-Assimilation von Fichte (*Picea excelsa* Link), Zirbe (*Pinus cembra* L.) und Sonnenblume (*Helianthus annuus* L.). – Planta 53: 532-550, 1959.
Pohlhausen, E.: Der Wärmeaustausch zwischen festen Körpern und Flüssigkeiten mit kleiner Reibung und kleiner Wärmeleitung. – Z. angew. Math. Mech. 1: 115-121, 1921.
Powell, R. W.: Further experiments on the evaporation of water from saturated surfaces. – Trans. Inst. chem. Eng. 18: 36-55, 1940.
Powell, R. W., Griffiths, E.: The evaporation of water from plane and cylindrical surfaces. – Trans. Inst. chem. Eng. 13: 175-198, 1935.
Priestley, C. H. B.: Turbulent Transfer in the Lower Atmosphere. – Chicago Univ. Press 1959.
Rackham, O.: Radiation, transpiration, and growth in a woodland annual. – In: Bainbridge, R., Evans, G. C., Rackham, O. (ed.): Light as an Ecological Factor. Pp. 167-185. Blackwell Sci. Pub., Oxford 1966.
Radler, F.: The surface waxes of the sultana vine (*Vitis vinifera* cv. Thompson seedless). – Austral. J. biol. Sci. 18: 1045-1056, 1965.
Raschke, K.: Mikrometeorologisch gemessene Energieumsätze eines *Alocasia*-Blattes. – Arch. Meteorol. Geophys. Bioklimatol. 7: 240-268, 1956.
Raschke, K.: Über den Einfluß der Diffusionswiderstände auf die Transpiration und die Temperatur eines Blattes. – Flora 146: 546-578, 1958.
Raschke, K.: Heat transfer between the plant and the environment. – Annu. Rev. Plant Physiol. 11: 111-126, 1960.
Raschke, K.: Die Stomata als Glieder eines schwingungsfähigen CO_2-Regelsystems. Experimenteller Nachweis an *Zea mays* L. – Z. Naturforschung 20b: 1261-1270, 1965a.
Raschke, K.: Das Seifenblasenporometer (zur Messung der Stomaweite an amphistomatischen Blättern). – Planta 66: 113-120, 1965b.
Record, F. A., Cramer, H. E.: Turbulent energy dissipation rates and exchange processss above a non-homogenous surface. – Quart. J. roy. meteorol. Soc. 92: 519-561, 1966.
Rutter, A. J.: An analysis of evaporation from a stand of Scots pine. – In: Sopper, W. E., Lull, H. W. (ed.): Forest Hydrology. Pp. 403-417. Pergamon Press, Oxford 1967.
Rutter, A. J.: Water consumption by forests. – In: Kozlowski, T. T. (ed.): Water Deficits and Plant Growth. Vol. 2. Pp. 23-84. Academic Press, New York–London 1968.
Samish, Y., Koller, D.: Photorespiration in green plants during photosynthesis estimated by use of isotopic CO_2. – Plant Physiol. 43: 1129-1132, 1968a.
Samish, Y., Koller, D.: Estimation of photorespiration of green plants and of their mesophyll resistance to CO_2 uptake. – Ann. Bot. N.S. 32: 687-694, 1968b.
Sampson, J.: A method of replicating dry or moist surfaces for examination by light microscopy. – Nature 191: 932-933, 1961.
Shimshi, D.: Effect of soil moisture and phenylmercuric acetate upon stomatal aperture, transpiration and photosynthesis. – Plant Physiol. 38: 713-721, 1963.
Shimshi, D.: The use of a field porometer for the study of water stress in plants. – Israel J. agr. Res. 14: 137-143, 1964.
Skoss, J. D.: Structure and composition of plant cuticle in relation to environmental factors and permeability. – Bot. Gaz. 117: 55-72, 1955.
Slack, C. R.: The photoactivation of a phosphopyruvate synthese in leaves of *Amaranthus palmeri*. – Biochem. biophys. Res. Comm. 30: 483-488, 1968.
Slatyer, R. O.: Some physical aspects of internal control of leaf transpiration. – Agr. Meteorol. 43: 281-292, 1966a.
Slatyer, R. O.: *In situ* measurements of stomatal resistance. – Proc. Conf. Instr. Plant Environment Measurements, Aspendale, 23: 88-89, 1966b.
Slatyer, R. O.: Plant-Water Relationships. – Academic Press, London – New York 1967.

Slatyer, R. O., Bierhuizen, J. F.: Transpiration from cotton leaves under a range of environmental conditions in relation to internal and external diffusive resistances. – Aust. J. biol. Sci. 17: 115-130, 1964.

Slatyer, R. O., Jarvis, P. G.: Gaseous-diffusion porometer for continuous measurement of diffusive resistance of leaves. – Science 151: 574-576, 1966.

Slatyer, R. O., McIlroy, I. C.: Practical Microclimatology. – UNESCO, Paris 1961.

Slavík, B.: The influence of water deficit on transpiration. – Physiol. Plant. 11: 524-536, 1958.

Solarová, J.: Stomata reactivity in leaves at different insertion level during wilting. – In: Slavík, B. (ed.): Water Stress in Plants. Pp. 147-154. Czechoslov. Acad. Sci. Prague and Dr. W. Junk N.V., The Hague 1965.

Solarová, J.: Unzuverläßlichkeit des Abdruckverfahrens bei der Bestimmung des Spaltöffnungszustandes. – Photosynthetica 2: 178-183, 1968.

Steemann Nielsen, E.: Uptake of CO_2 by the plant. – In: Ruhland, W. (ed.): Encyclopedia of Plant Physiology. Vol. 5/1. Pp. 70-84. Springer Verlag, Berlin–Göttingen–Heidelberg 1960.

Stiles, W.: A diffusive resistance porometer for field use. I. Construction. – J. appl. Ecol. 7: 617-622, 1970.

Sutton, O. G.: Micrometeorology. – McGraw-Hill Publ. Co. Ltd., London 1953.

Swinbank, W. C., Dyer, A. J.: An experimental study in micro-meteorology. – Quart. J. roy. meteorol. Soc. 93: 494-500, 1967.

Szeicz, G., Endrödi, G., Tajchman, S.: Aerodynamic and surface factors in evaporation. – Water Resources Res. 5: 380–394, 1969.

Tanner, C. B., Fuchs, M.: Evaporation from unsaturated surfaces: A generalized combination method. – J. geophys. Res. 73: 1299-1304, 1968.

Taylor, S. E., Gates, D. M.: Some field methods for obtaining meaningful leaf diffusion resistances and transpiration rates. – Oecol. Plant. 5: 103-112, 1970.

Thom, A. S.: The exchange of momentum, mass, and heat between an artificial leaf and the airflow in a wind-tunnel. – Quart. J. roy. meteorol. Soc. 94: 44-55, 1968.

Ting, I. P., Dean, M. L., Dugger, W. M. Jun.: Leaf resistance in succulent plants. – Nature 213: 526-527, 1967.

Ting, I. P., Thompson, M.-L. D., Dugger, W. M. Jr.: Leaf resistance to water vapor transfer in succulent plants: Effect of thermoperiod. – Amer. J. Bot. 54: 245-251, 1967.

Troughton, J. H., Hall, D. M.: Extracuticular wax and contact angle measurements on wheat (*Triticum vulgare* L.). – Aust. J. biol. Sci. 20: 509-526, 1967.

Troughton, J. H., Slatyer, R. O.: Plant water status, leaf temperature, and the calculated mesophyll resistance to carbon dioxide of cotton leaves. – Aust. J. biol. Sci. 22: 815-827, 1969.

Turner, N. C.: Response of adaxial and abaxial stomata to light. – New Phytol. 69: 647-653, 1970.

Turner, N. C., Parlange, J.-Y.: Analysis of operation and calibration of a ventilated diffusion porometer. – Plant Physiol. 46: 175–177, 1970.

Turrell, F. M.: The area of the internal exposed surface of dicotyledon leaves. – Amer. J. Bot. 23: 255-264, 1936.

Turrell, F. M.: A quantitative morphological analysis of large and small leaves of alfalfa with special reference to internal surface. – Amer. J. Bot. 29: 400-415, 1942.

de Vries, D. A., Krueger, A. J.: On the value of the diffusion coefficient of water vapour in air. – In: Phénomènes de transport avec changement de phase dans les milieux poreux ou colloïdaux. – Coll. int. C.N.R.S. No. 160: 61-72, Edit. C.N.R.S., Paris 1967.

Waggoner, P. E.: Calibration of a porometer in terms of diffusive resistance. – Agr. Meteorol. 2: 317-329, 1965.

Waggoner, P. E.: Moisture loss through the boundary layer. – Biometeorology 3: 41-52, 1967.

Walker, D. A.: Physiological studies on acid metabolism. 4. Phosphoenolpyruvic carboxylase activity in extracts of crassulacean plants. – Biochem. J. 67: 73-79, 1957.

Walker, D. A.: Carboxylation in plants. – Endeavour 25: 21-26, 1966.

Wallihan, E. F.: Modification and use of an electric hygrometer for estimating relative stomatal apertures. – Plant Physiol. 39: 86-90, 1964.

Wareing, P. F., Khalifa, M. M., Treharne, K. J.: Rate-limiting processes in photosynthesis at saturating light intensities. – Nature 220: 453-457, 1968.

Weast, R. C. (ed.): Handbook of Chemistry and Physics. 49th Ed. – Chemical Rubber Co., Cleveland, Ohio 1968.
Weatherley, P. E.: A porometer for use in the field. – New Phytol. 65: 376-387, 1966.
Weissbach, A., Horrecker, B. L., Hurwitz, J.: The enzymatic formation of phosphoglyceric acid from ribulose diphosphate and carbon dioxide. – J. biol. Chem. 218: 795-810, 1956.
Whiteman, P. C., Koller, D.: Environmental control of photosynthesis and transpiration in *Pinus halepensis*. – Israel J. Bot. 13: 166-176, 1964a.
Whiteman, P. C., Koller, D.: Saturation deficit of the mesophyll evaporating surfaces in a desert halophyte. – Science 146: 1320-1321, 1964b.
Whiteman, P. C., Koller, D.: Interactions of carbon dioxide concentration, light intensity and temperature on plant resistances to water vapour and carbon dioxide diffusion. – New Phytol. 66: 463-473, 1967a.
Whiteman, P. C., Koller, D.: Species characteristics in whole plant resistances to water vapour and CO_2 diffusion. – J. appl. Ecol. 4: 363-377, 1967b.
Whiteman, P. C., Koller, D.: Estimation of mesophyll resistance to diffusion of carbon dioxide and water vapour. – In: Eckardt, F. E. (ed.): Functioning of Terrestrial Ecosystems at the Primary Production Level. Pp. 415-419. Unesco, Paris 1968.
Williams, W. T., Amer, F. A.: Transpiration from wilting leaves. – J. exp. Bot. 8: 1-19, 1957.
Woolhouse, H. W.: Leaf age and mesophyll resistance as factors in the rate of photosynthesis. – Hilger J. 11: 7-12, 1967-8.
Woolley, J. T.: Water relations of soybean leaf hairs. – Agron. J. 6: 569–571, 1964.
Wright, J. L., Brown, K.W.: Comparison of momentum and energy balance methods of computing vertical transfer within a crop. – Agron. J. 59: 427-432, 1967.
Zelitch, I., Waggoner, P. E.: Effect of chemical control of stomata on transpiration and photosynthesis. – Proc. Nat. Acad. Sci. U.S. 48: 1101-1108, 1962.

17 | LEAF TEMPERATURE MEASUREMENT

17.1 | Introduction

17.1.1 | Temperature and biological processes

In photosynthesis or in any physico- or chemico-biological processes concerning growth, development or general plant life, temperature has various effects: qualitative or quantitative, direct or indirect. Three zones of temperature can be recognised:

a. The zone of median temperature, which more or less favours plant development or growth (about 0 to 40 °C) (Durand, de Parcevaux & Roche 1967).

b. The zone of high temperature which may bring about injury or cause death (between 35 and 55 °C) (Levitt 1962).

c. The zone of low temperature which may affect development (*e.g.* by causing inhibition or by inducing dormancy) or have lethal effects (near 0 °C and below) (Levitt 1956).

Because of large variability in the definition of these zones and in their effects according to species, plant organs and temporal variation in temperature, it is necessary:

– first, to define and to localise exactly the temperature to be measured in relation to the phenomena studied,

– secondly, to increase the number of measurements in a given period and, as far as possible, to record them, when a rapid temperature fluctuation affects a biological processes.

17.1.2 | List of symbols

h	height of the crop [m]
$\mathrm{d}h$	thickness of layer of the crop [m]
L	length of leaf [m]
l	width of leaf [m]
L_0	mean dimension of leaf [m]
e	thickness of leaf [m]
δ_F, δ'_F, δ'_{FC}	thickness parameters of diffusion path [m]
x, y, z	rectangular coordinates for L, l, e
S	leaf area (one surface) [m^2]
V	leaf volume [m^3]
t	time [s]
U	windspeed [$m\ s^{-1}$]
T	temperature (indexes a, s, v, d, 0, 1 . . . n for air, surface, mean leaf temperature, dewpoint, reference temperature, and junctions, respectively) [°C]

Φ energy flux (indexes R, L, S, T, B for net radiation, latent heat, sensible heat, emitted radiation, biochemical energy) [W m^{-2}]
ρ, ρ_0 density (air and body) [kg m^{-3}]
C, C_p heat capacity (air and body) [J kg^{-1} °C^{-1}]
L_v latent heat of vaporization [J kg^{-1}]
λ thermal conductivity of a body [W m^{-1} °C^{-1}]
Λ diffusion time [s]
Δ first derivative of saturation vapour pressure [kg m^{-1} s^{-2} °C^{-1}]
γ psychrometric constant [kg m^{-1} s^{-2} °C^{-1}]
ν kinematic viscosity of air [m^2 s^{-1}]
ε emittance of body
σ Stefan Boltzmann constant [W m^{-2} K^{-4}]
λ_1, λ_2 wavelengths [m]
E, E_0 e.m.f. and reference e.m.f. for T_0 [V]
I current intensity [A]
R resistance (indexes T, C, G, 0, m, a, b, 1, 2 for thermometers, thermocouples, galvanometer, reference resistance at T_0, and resistances in the bridge) [Ω]
r, r_x, r_y resistances [Ω]
a, b, c, d coefficients for output of thermocouples, resistance thermometers and thermistors as functions of T
D galvanometer deviation [m]
β sensitivity of galvanometer [m A^{-1}]
α galvanometer coefficient for temperature measurement [m °C^{-1}]
$C(\lambda_1, \lambda_2)$ luminescence parameter of colour
$P(\lambda_1)$ luminescence parameter of phosphorescence
A_0 data supplied by I. R. thermometer [mV]
A thermal radiation measured by I.R. thermometer [W m^{-2}]
B incident thermal (long-wave) radiation [W m^{-2}]

17.1.3 | Leaf temperature

The temperature of any body is difficult to define when it is not a homogeneous body. According to the scale on which the analysis of photosynthesis or dry matter production is effected (*e.g.* canopy – vegetation layer – leaf) different temperatures will be considered:
1. average temperature of a canopy (*i.e.* all the leaves) or the upper leaves (*e.g.* surface temperature of a canopy),
2. average temperature of a vegetation layer (height h, thickness dh),
3. average temperature of a leaf which is the primary site of exchanges and transfers between plant or crop and air.
In the last case, it is moreover necessary to define what we call 'leaf temperature'. Owing to leaf geometry and the spatial variability of the terms of the leaf energy budget which determine temperature, each point on the leaf attains its own local temperature.
The leaf can be represented schematically as an approximately elliptic plate of various dimensions (length L, width l, and thickness e). The temperature at any

point is defined by its position given by two co-ordinates, x ($0 \leqslant x \leqslant L$) and y ($0 \leqslant y \leqslant l$) in the leaf plane and another co-ordinate z ($0 \leqslant z \leqslant e$) indicating thickness (*i.e.* with axis perpendicular to leaf plane). Surface temperatures $T(x, y, z\ (z = 0 \text{ or } e))$ result from the budget of energy exchanges between leaf and environment; they determine the internal temperature $T(x, y, z)$ which influences biological processes. Since the natural variations in temperature from point to point can reach several degrees (Raschke 1956a, b; Takechi & Haseba 1962, 1963; Takechi *et al.* 1962; Perrier 1968), it is important to keep in mind that different mean temperatures are defined as a result of integrations or averaging of local temperatures:

1. mean internal temperature for a small cylindrical element of a leaf

$$T = \frac{1}{e} \int_{0}^{z=e} T(x, y, z)\mathrm{d}z;$$

2. mean surface temperature of the leaf

$$T_S = \frac{1}{S} \int_{0}^{x=L} \int_{0}^{y=l} T(x, y, z)\mathrm{d}x\,\mathrm{d}y \quad (z = 0 \text{ or } e);$$

3. mean temperature for the whole leaf

$$T_v = \frac{1}{V} \int_{0}^{x=L} \int_{0}^{y=l} \int_{0}^{z=e} T(x, y, z)\mathrm{d}x\,\mathrm{d}y\,\mathrm{d}z.$$

Because of the spatial heterogeneity of temperature in the plane of the leaf and perpendicular to the plane of the leaf in the leaf thickness, it is not easy to interpret the significance of temperature measured at a point. Moreover, this interpretation must be made without forgetting that leaf temperature is also the result of physical and biochemical factors which are related as follows:

$$\rho_o C_p \frac{\partial T(x, y, z)}{\partial t} =$$

$$= \lambda\left(\frac{\partial^2 T}{\partial x^2} + \frac{\partial^2 T}{\partial y^2} + \frac{\partial^2 T}{\partial z^2}\right) \begin{array}{l} + \Phi_L(x, y, z\ (z = 0 \text{ and } e)) \\ + \Phi_S(x, y, z\ (z = 0 \text{ and } e)) \\ + \Phi_R(x, y, z\ (z = 0 \text{ and } e)) \\ + \Phi_B(x, y, z) \end{array} \quad [\mathrm{W\ m^{-2}}] \qquad (17.1)$$

where

ρ_o is density [kg m^{-3}]
C_p heat capacity [J kg^{-1} °C^{-1}]
λ thermal conductivity of the body [W m^{-1} °C^{-1}]
t time [s]
T temperature [°C]

Φ_L latent heat flux (function of cuticular and stomatal resistances, surface temperature and environmental characteristics) [W m^{-2}]
Φ_S sensible heat flux (function of surface temperature and environmental characteristics) [W m^{-2}]
Φ_R net radiation flux including incident, reflected, diffused, transmitted and emitted fluxes (energy exchanges which are supposed to be localised at the level of the two leaf surfaces) [W m^{-2}]
Φ_B energetic flux of a biological nature; it is generally negligible when compared with the other fluxes over a period of several hours (1 or 2%; in the most propitious case, *e.g.* in maize with very good conditions, 5% for a few minutes) [W m^{-2}]
The conductive flux between the leaf and the other parts of the plant can be neglected, as well as the lateral fluxes within the tissues of a leaf (generally, only the term $\partial^2 T/\partial z^2$ plays a significant role). In fact the heat conductivity of mesophyll is small, about 0.15 W m^{-1} $°C^{-1}$ (Perrier 1968). With regard to exchange between surface and air, the lateral flux is small even with a gradient of about 100 to 400 °C m^{-1} which is the maximum possible lateral gradient. However, between the two surfaces, the flux is more important (gradients of 1 000 or 3 000 °C m^{-1} are observed) because of the difference between the two surfaces in the term ϕ_R and sometimes in the term ϕ_L, for dissymmetric leaves (*i.e.* leaves differing in the structure of the abaxial and adaxial leaf sides).

17.2 | Fundamental criteria for leaf temperature measurement

These criteria depend on the temperature to be measured (T, T_s or T_v), on the structure of the leaf and on the methodology of measurement.
To measure leaf temperature it is necessary, as far as possible, not to disturb the physiological properties and life of the plant and the energy exchanges with the environment (equation 17.1). Any method must always be considered from both of these points of view. Such considerations justify the utilisation of remote sensing (Section 17.5).
For a certain application, the method used must possess appropriate characteristics with regard to spatial dimension of measurement (*i.e.* local temperature or mean temperature) and time or frequency of measurement (*i.e.* continuous or intermittent measurement). For experiments in the field, it is necessary to consider other characteristics of the method such as the handling properties, portability, environmental resistance, volume and weight of the instrument.
With regard to the measurement itself the following five criteria should be considered (Idrac 1968):
1. Scale of measurement: in natural environments, leaf temperature is generally within the range from −10 °C to +50 °C with a fluctuation of about ± 10 to 15 °C around air temperature during the day, and with an instantaneous thermal heterogeneity of a few degrees.
2. Sensitivity: if the mean temperature of a canopy, a layer or a leaf is to be determined, a sensitivity of the order of ± 1 °C is sufficiently accurate for analysis of growth or development. However, a sensitivity of the order of ± 0.1 °C is required to measure leaf temperature with sufficient precision for determination of thermal gradients, of heterogeneities, and of heat transfers.

3. Accuracy: this is defined as the total uncertainty which appears in the determination of the temperature of a body, including the sensitivity and measurement errors. It varies considerably with methods and techniques and it must reach a suitable degree for a given purpose.

4. Thickness of the sensor: this is an important factor which determines the disturbance resulting from the introduction of the sensor. For leaves, the main disturbance is a thermal one (disturbance of the boundary layer and vapour flux, energetic gain or loss by conduction or radiation, *etc.*).

5. Response time constant: this is defined as the time necessary to obtain a record. It is an important factor in the analysis of unsteady states and the kinetics of cooling or heating.

Each method will be characterised and compared with other methods on the basis of this set of criteria, which generally allow one to define the range of a method and type of temperature for which it is best fitted, the kind of recording (*e.g.* continuous, semicontinuous, or intermittent) and the handiness of the method (Section 17.7 and Table 17.7).

17.3 | Different methods of thermometry

Leaf temperature is not usually equal to air temperature (except as a mean and approximate value over a period of 24 h) (Papadakis 1965), although the difference may be very small for leaves of small boundary layer thickness and moderate vapour flux such as conifer needles. In certain conditions, however, with a particular value of stomatal resistance such as $\delta'_F + \delta_F = (\Delta/(\Delta + \gamma))\ \delta'_{FC}$ (see Section 17.6 and Fig. 17.10), equal air and leaf temperatures can be found (Daudet & Perrier 1968).

Hence many kinds of methods have been adopted for the measurement of leaf temperatures. The fragility, thinness and low heat capacity of leaves do not facilitate accurate measurement.

The first measurements of leaf temperature were done either with classical instruments (*e.g.* a small mercury thermometer, placed close to the leaf, or on which the leaf was rolled) (Hirsch 1957) or with microcalorimetric methods (Shrewe 1914). The latter requires a range of measurement from 1 to 10 calories with an accuracy of at least 10%. These methods destroy the organ; they are intermittent and present some difficulties when employed in the field.

By using the melting points of different compounds, it is possible to obtain the approximate leaf temperature (Kreeb 1954). Leaf temperature is given by the first compound to melt, the compounds being taken in decreasing order of their melting points (Geiger 1957). This method requires much time and several manipulations of the leaf and is generally of low accuracy. These historical methods are not practical for modern applications. Nowadays many alternative methods are available (for reviews see Chapter III of the manual Techniques d'Étude des Facteurs Physiques de la Biosphère. I.N.R.A. Paris 1970).

Firstly, electrical methods can be employed. Some are based upon thermoelectric effects, *e.g.* thermocouples (Miller & Saunders 1923; Huber 1937, 1956; Wallace & Clum 1938). Others are based on the variability of electrical resistance with temperature, *e.g.* the resistance of metal (Tranquillini 1955) and metallic oxides

(*i.e.* thermistors) (Platt & Wolf 1950). These methods require a sensor close to the leaf. The sensor possesses specific properties related to its dimensions, physical characteristics of heat capacity, conductivity and resistance, and location.
Secondly, methods based upon radiant properties of the leaf can be used. They are based on the fundamental laws of radiation and thermal emission of bodies (Aldrich 1922). The sensor for these methods can be placed at a distance from the surface to be measured.
It is possible to use infra-red thermometry, *e.g.* the I.R. thermometer of Stoll & Hardy (1952), or I.R. thermography (Barnes 1967), or luminescence thermometry (Perrier 1966). These methods are more or less indirect. Elimination or evaluation of reflected radiation from the surroundings must be carried out and, moreover, when using I.R. thermometry the emittance of the leaves or vegetation must be known.

17.4 | Electrical methods of thermometry

These methods have been fundamental to the development of investigations on leaf temperature. A disadvantage is that the presence of the sensor and of lead wires between sensor and meter disturbs the environment and decreases the accuracy. (To the 'theoretical' accuracy of the apparatus the error of the perturbation is added.)

17.4.1 | Thermocouples

First experience of thermoelectric effects was obtained in 1821 by Seebeck. He observed that if a circuit consists of two dissimilar metallic conductors A and B, with junctions at different temperatures, a current flows through the circuit (Fig. 17.1*a*).

17.4.1.1 | Basic principles of thermocouples

The basic principles of thermocouples as given by Finch (1962) are as follows:
1. A thermal gradient applied along a homogeneous wire cannot create an electric current (law of homogenous circuit).

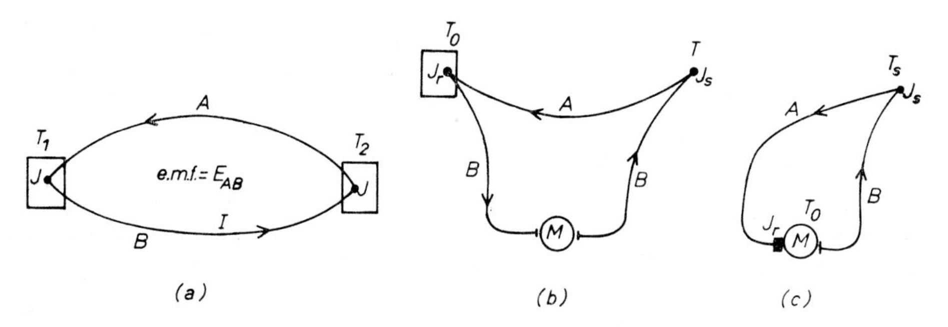

Fig. 17.1 Thermocouple circuits. T_0: reference temperature (for example 0 °C), T, T_1, T_2, T_s: different temperatures, A, B: two metals with opposite e.m.f., J: junction, J_r: reference junction, J_s: measuring junction (sensor), M: meter.

2. If the e.m.f. (E_{AC} and E_{BC}) of two metals (A and B) as related to a third metal (C) are known, the e.m.f. E_{AB} between A and B is the algebraic sum ($E_{AC} + E_{BC}$) (law of intermediate metals).
3. If E_{AB} ($T_2 - T_1$) is the thermoelectric e.m.f. of two metals A and B with metal junctions at T_1 and T_2, and similarly E_{AB} ($T_3 - T_2$) is the e.m.f. for these junctions at T_2 and T_3, the total e.m.f. E_{AB} ($T_3 - T_1$) between T_1 and T_3 for the two metals concerned will be E_{AB} ($T_3 - T_2$) + E_{AB} ($T_2 - T_1$) (law of successive and intermediate temperatures).
Hence by measuring the e.m.f. of a thermoelectric circuit (Fig. 17.1*b*) where the junctions are at temperatures of T_0 and T, a single value of ($T - T_0$) can be obtained. Only the junction temperatures have to be considered; no part is played by the temperature along the conductors or by the connections resulting from the presence of a meter in the circuit, if these two connections are at the same temperature. (The junction temperature and hence the measured temperature may, however, be influenced by the conduction of heat along the conductors to the junction; see Section 17.4.1.6.)

17.4.1.2 | Measuring circuit

The e.m.f. of a thermoelectric circuit with the reference junction at a standard temperature (for example 0 °C given by a water-ice mixture) is given by the formula:

$$E = E_0(T - T_0)^a \quad [T \text{ in } ^\circ\text{C}, E \text{ in volts}] \tag{17.2}$$

where E_0 is the change in e.m.f. per unit change in temperature at the reference temperature (T_0) [V °C^{-1}], a is a constant (for T_0 near 0 °C for thermocouples such as copper-constantan, $a \approx 1$).
Equation (17.2) (Platt & Griffiths 1964) can be replaced with a linear expression ($E = E_0$ ($T - T_0$)) for small differences (say 10 °C) and for the usual kinds of thermocouples. For the greatest accuracy it is necessary to determine the calibration curve relating E to T experimentally.
Measurement of the e.m.f. can be made with a potentiometer (null-point system) or with a galvanometer, in which case the estimate depends on the resistance of the circuit (Fig. 17.1 *b*). Using a potentiometer, the e.m.f. is measured by comparison with a reference e.m.f.; when equilibrium is obtained there is no current flowing in the circuit so that the resistance of the thermocouple wires does not affect the measurement. On the other hand, with a galvanometer, the e.m.f. is given by the intensity of the current flowing through the galvanometer, so that the resistance of the wires is important if it is larger than the internal resistance of the galvanometer.
For accurate measurements ($< \pm 1$ °C), the connection at the inlet of the instrument (Fig. 17.1 *c*) cannot be taken as the reference junction. A junction placed in known steady conditions (*e.g.* a water-ice mixture) is much more suitable than a cold junction compensator.
Thermocouples may be connected in a series arrangement of n thermocouples (e.m.f. is n times as great as a single thermocouple) (Fig. 17.2*a*), or in a circuit of n thermocouples connected in parallel (Fig. 17.2*b*).

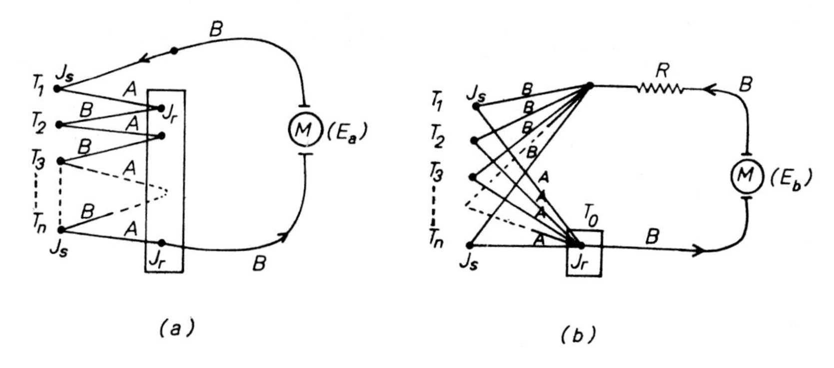

Fig. 17.2 Multiple thermocouple connections: *a:* in series, *b:* in parallel. T_0: reference temperature, $T_1, T_2 \ldots T_n$: different temperatures, *A, B:* two metals with opposite e.m.f., J_r: reference junction, J_s: measuring junction (sensor), *M:* meter, E_a, E_b: electromotive force ($E_a = nE_b$), *R:* resistance,

$$\frac{T_1 + T_2 + \ldots + T_n}{n} = \frac{E_a}{kn}; \qquad \frac{T_1 + T_2 + \ldots + T_n}{n} = \frac{E_b}{k}.$$

1. With a *series* circuit, sensitivity may be increased if n junctions are at the same temperature (temperature T which can be detected $T = T_1 = T_2 = \ldots = T_n$) or a mean temperature of the n values may be obtained (mean temperature of n leaves or mean temperature of n points on a leaf).
2. A circuit of thermocouples in *parallel* directly supplies the mean temperature if a resistance R of high value ($> 100\ R_C$, for example), when compared with each thermocouple resistance R_C, is introduced into the circuit.

For any circuit, the use of a potentiometer is always more suitable (null-point system) because circuit characteristics such as the length and resistance of the wires then have no influence. However this kind of measurement generally requires a lapse of time for equilibrium and it is not possible to make very quick readings of, for instance, the cooling and heating kinetics of the leaf. With a good potentiometric recorder, the response time for a null-point system is small (about several tenths of a second) and with an electronic recorder (the principle is different from a null-point system) the response time falls to a few 1/100 s. Although the equilibration time constant of a galvanometer is much smaller, its internal resistance R_G and the couple resistance R_C influence the measurement. So for each couple and each galvanometer, it is necessary to determine the coefficient α which relates deviation D of the galvanometer with temperature T. According to equation (17.2) with $a \sim 1$ and $T_0 = 0$°C it follows that:

$$E = E_0 T \qquad [\mathrm{V}]$$

$$E = (R_C + R_G)I \quad [\mathrm{V}]$$

where I is current intensity in amperes and R resistances in ohms. The galvanometer deviation, D, is:

$$D = I\beta \quad [\mathrm{m}]$$

$$D = \alpha T \quad [\mathrm{m}]$$

where β is the sensitivity of the galvanometer [m A^{-1}] and hence

$$\alpha = E_0\beta/(R_C + R_G) \quad [\text{m } °\text{C}^{-1}] \tag{17.3}$$

Coefficient α is necessary to determine temperatures obtained with a given couple (E_0 and R_C) and a given galvanometer (β and R_G). It also enables one to know if the galvanometer employed permits temperature to be measured with the required accuracy (*i.e.* the deviation ΔD must be correctly read to detect suitable ΔT°C).

17.4.1.3 | Reference temperature and thermocouple calibration

The accuracy of measurement depends mainly upon the reference temperature and the calibration curve relating E to T. Both factors must be defined with twice the accuracy required for the measured temperature (errors made in each term will be added); hence, to obtain an accuracy of 0.1 °C, one has to proceed very carefully (Roeser & Lonberger 1958).
The reference temperature can be easily obtained with a thermostatic bath (0.1 or 0.01 °C) or with a Dewar flask containing a homogeneous water-ice mixture or possibly with a cold junction compensator (Gordon & Seay 1948). The accuracy of a thermostatic bath mainly depends on the contact thermometer used (0.01 °C is not a limit). For a water-ice mixture a precision better than 0.1 °C can be obtained with good mixing and by periodically removing water and introducing some ice. The advantage of the water-ice mixture is the precision of the reference temperature and lack of drift during a period of 24 h (with a good Dewar flask). Actually it is easy to keep a good reference temperature with a water-ice mixture if a small cooling element and agitator as well as a pressure sensor are used in a hermetically closed Dewar flask. When a certain amount of ice has melted, the pressure sensor in the air above the mixture detects the reduced pressure and switches on the cooling element. It is also possible to use systems with temperature compensation but a precision better than 0.1 °C requires very expensive systems.
It can be advantageous to set the reference temperature near the measured temperature because a higher sensitivity of the recorder can be used. A thermometer placed at a depth of one or two meters in the soil supplies a good reference temperature which is very stable and almost constant during a day. It is also possible to use a Dewar flask containing oil at a temperature close to the ambient temperature, but it is necessary to measure the oil temperature several times a day.
In practice, when making thermocouples it is necessary to set up a calibration curve for the wires employed. For a thermocouple of two given metals, this precise calibration is done in a thermostatic bath with a reference thermocouple (Pt-PtRd) or a precision thermometer reading to 1/100 °C. A corrected calibration suitable for any thermocouple is obtained by fitting a curve to four or five calibration points.
Manufactured thermocouples increasingly offer the desired characteristics (in particular, sensitivity and small size). They can be used directly, thanks to the calibration tables which are provided with them (Shenker *et al.* 1955). However the precision required for industrial purposes is usually less than for plant temperatures.

17.4.1.4 | Choice and construction of some thermocouples

The choice of the two metals depends first on the e.m.f. they can produce, as it is responsible for the accuracy. The choice may be modified in relation to linearity of response and other features may be taken into consideration, such as physical characteristics of the metals or alloys (see Table 17.1), conductivity, emittance, heat capacity, electrical or mechanical resistance, chemical properties and possible reaction with environment (Caldwell 1962). These characteristics may be summarised as follows:

1. the e.m.f. produced must be as large as possible to ensure the highest accuracy of measurement, and it must increase continuously with increasing temperature over the range used,
2. the e.m.f. must not change after calibration during use, *e.g.* by chemical contamination, oxidation, corrosion or mechanical effects,
3. the thermocouples must be reproducible and easily obtainable in a uniform quality.

When making a thermocouple, two pairs of wires are joined to provide the reference junction and the measuring junction which has to be made with much care and is usually very small. The joins can be made with well-known solders (with tin or silver) or with special low thermal solder and resin or other low thermal flux. Arc-welding can be easily carried out especially with very small thermocouples, using an electrical circuit for resistance welding (Platt & Griffiths 1964).

Several practical hints for making thermocouples. The best thermoelectric junction between two metals is certainly made by *welding*; this ensures perfect connection

Table 17.1 Main thermocouples

Copper - constantan	e.m.f. ~ 40 μV °C^{-1}	Practical, but low resilience of Cu and small variation of e.m.f. with wires of different casting	Tin soldering is very practical and easy ø > 0.2 mm*
Iron - constantan	e.m.f. ~ 50 μV °C^{-1}	Good resilience, high e.m.f.	Tin soldering ø > 0.05 mm
Chromel - alumel	e.m.f. ~ 40 μV °C^{-1}	Good resilience	ø > 0.1 mm
Chromel - constantan	e.m.f. ~ 60 μV °C^{-1}	Very high e.m.f., good resilience	ø from 0.05 to 0.1 mm
Platinum - platinum rhodium	e.m.f. ~ 7 μV °C^{-1}	High resilience, unalterable, great fidelity	ø > 0.025 mm

(Arc-welding or silver soldering may be used for each couple; *cf.* Section 17.4.1.4.)

* When the diameter of the thermocouple is thinner than the values given above, direct utilisation without protection such as with resin or glass is impossible because the strength and resilience of the wires is insufficient.

of the metals over a small depth. Welding is done either with a blow-pipe or by arc-welding. If a blow-pipe with a narrow orifice (about 0.4 mm) is used, it is necessary to heat the tips of the wires rapidly and put them in borax or in a mixture of fluorspar and borax before welding. The blow-pipe should be fixed (45°) to enable easy manipulation of the wires, and a neutral flame to avoid carburation is indispensable. For iron-constantan, chromel-constantan and chromel-alumel junctions, *e.g.* an oxygen-acetylene blow-pipe is usually used; for Pt-PtRd junctions, an oxygen-hydrogen one is preferable.

For thin wires (< ∅ 0.1 mm), however, *arc-welding* is more practical. In one method a condenser is charged from a battery (60 V d.c.). The condenser is then discharged through the wires to be welded, forming the junction. This is done by bringing the tips of the wires together under oil to prevent oxidation. Alternatively, the carbon rod is made the negative electrode, and the two wires, held together by one or two twists (Fig. 17.3 *a*) or by a slight pressure from the bend of wires (Fig. 17.3 *b*, *c*), form the positive electrode. Current flows through the circuit when the two electrodes are in contact: if the electrodes are separated several tenths of mm, the high temperature of the arc welds the wires. The suitable current intensity for a good weld without harm to the metals should be found experimentally.

The second way is to *solder* with a third metal. There are many solders but the most practical are tin (*e.g.* for Cu-Cst) or silver (*e.g.* for chromel-Cst). Tin soldering is very easy when using a small soldering iron to heat the wires twisted at their tips (Fig. 17.3 *a*) or in the middle to obtain directly two thermocouples (Fig. 17.3 *d*); the amount of tin used should be as small as possible. Often it is necessary to cut the tip of the junction to reduce the dimension of the thermocouple (Fig. 17.3 *a*, *b*, *d*). Silver soldering is very advantageous for thin thermocouples (*e.g.* chromel-Cst 0.05 mm in diameter). The tip of the twisted wires is cleaned in borax moistened with water and then put in silver powder, which forms a layer on it. The tip is then placed for several seconds above a small flame (alcohol burner, candle, match), and left to redden. The junction is then shortened to a suitable length.

The *cleaning of thermocouples* after manufacture is important. After soldering, the thermocouples should be boiled in several rinses of distilled water to remove

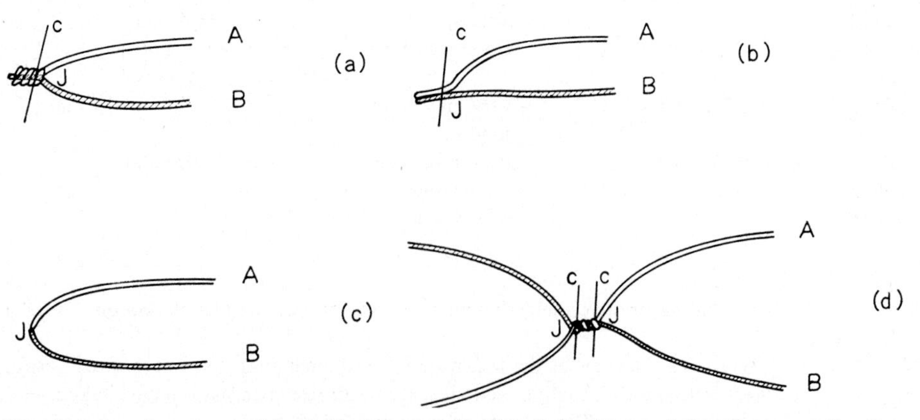

Fig. 17.3 Junction prepared for soldering. *A:* soft wire, *B:* hard wire, *J:* junction, *c:* section for cutting.

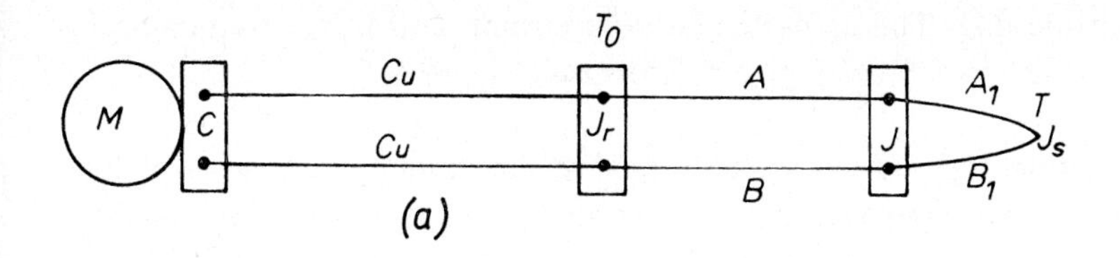

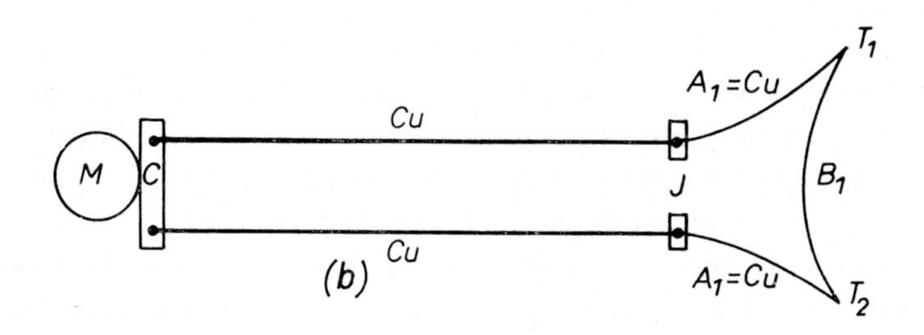

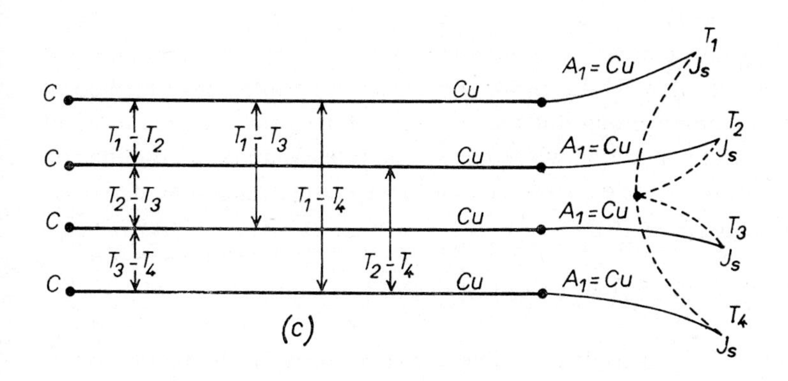

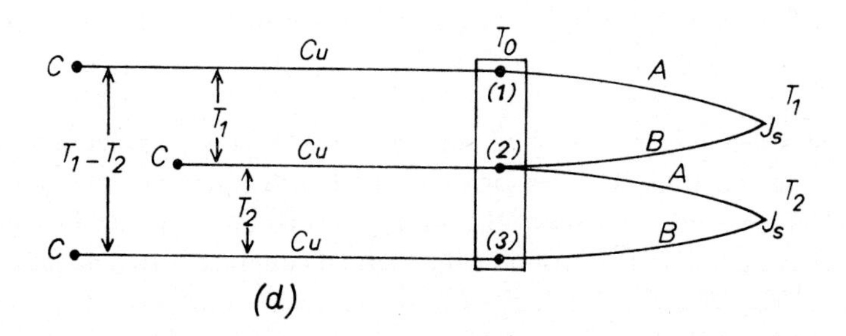

Fig. 17.4 Usual circuit for measuring leaf temperature. T_0: reference temperature (*e.g.* 0 °C), T, T_1, T_2, T_3, T_4: different temperatures of sensors, J_r: reference junction, J_s: measuring junction (sensor), *J:* junction, *A*, *B:* two metals with opposite e.m.f., A_1, B_1: the same metals of smaller diameter, *C:* connection with meter, *Cu:* lead wire of copper.

completely all the flux. This is particularly important with fluxes containing inorganic ions , which if left may give rise to specious e.m.fs.

Kinds of connection. Fig. 17.4 *a* shows a simple scheme commonly used to make a thermocouple for leaf temperature measurement (metals *A* and *B*). The sensor is composed of two wires of thin section connected with wires of thicker section (to give greater resilience) originating from the same cast. The two connecting junctions must be isolated electrically and kept at the same temperature to remove any parasitic e.m.f. It is advisable (for reasons of cost, low resistance, ease of supply) to make the lead wires between thermocouple and inlet of meter of copper (shielded leads must be employed for a long distance on the ground). Moreover leads of copper suppress possible parasitic e.m.fs appearing at the level of connection with the meter, if their temperatures are perceptibly different (Fig. 17.4 *a*). If the soldered junctions between *A*-Cu and *B*-Cu are at the same temperature T_0, they act at the same time as compensating junctions (T_0) for the thermocouple. In the same way, for example, Fig. 17.4 *b* shows a suitable circuit which allows one to measure directly the difference between two temperatures without a bath at reference temperature (T_0), if wires A_1 are of copper and B_1 of constantan. This scheme avoids the error in the determination of the reference temperature, but gives differences only. Fig. 17.4 *c* shows, for example, an alternative method of measuring directly multiple and differential temperatures (only if wires *A* are of Cu). Another type of connection which allows one to measure both absolute and differential temperatures (*e.g.*, leaf- and air temperatures and the difference between them) is presented in Fig. 17.4 *d*.

17.4.1.5 | Techniques for the measurement of leaf temperature

Two possibilities can be considered: either a contact between the thermocouple and leaf surface (*i.e.* surface temperature) or introducing the thermocouple into the leaf (*i.e.* internal temperature). The latter leads to unavoidable damage and biological reactions producing in the long run local necrosis or death of tissues but in the short term may give a better estimate of leaf temperature.

a. Contact measurement. Such a method supposes steady, close contact between leaf and measuring junction. The sensor must reach a temperature as near as possible to leaf temperature, in spite of the air which surrounds the junction and in spite of the unavoidable imperfection of the thermal coupling between leaf and junction (Idle 1968) (Section 17.4.1.6). Many technical solutions have been suggested (Fig. 17.5 *a*, *b*, *c*) but gluing the measuring junctions onto the leaf is not to be recommended because of the resulting local decrease in or inhibition of evaporation. Some useful approaches are:
1. Winding the wires of the thermocouple along the petiole and positioning the thermoelectric junction with a loop acting as a spring (Palmer 1966 – Fig. 17.5 *a*). Thus it is possible to fix the thermocouple and also to minimize disturbance of temperature at the measuring site, but with this technique, the contact remains free and is not always perfect. Furthermore the loop of wire is coupled to air tem-

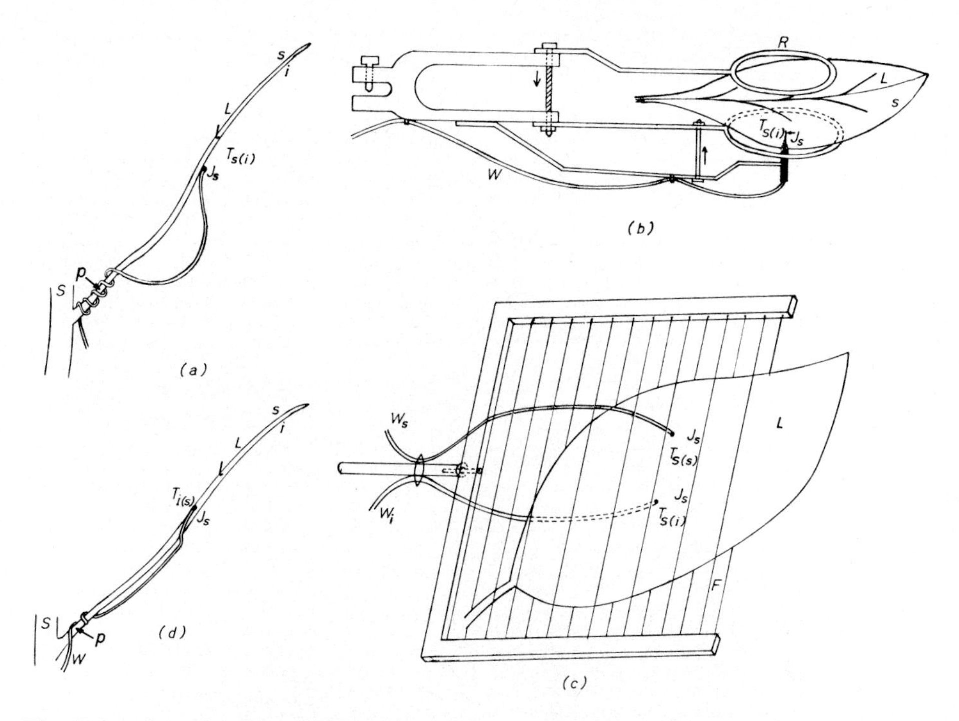

Fig. 17.5 *a*, *b*, *c*, *d* Devices for the measurement of leaf temperature. *L:* leaf (*l:* lamina, *p:* petiole), $T_{s(s)}$*:* upper surface temperature of the leaf, $T_{s(i)}$*:* lower surface temperature, $T_{i(s)}$*:* inner temperature of upper layers of the leaf, J_s*:* measuring junction (sensor), *W:* thermocouple wires, *S:* stem, *F:* thread, *R:* clamping rings, *s:* adaxial surface, *i:* abaxial surface. (Only the dimensions of the thermoelement and the thickness of the leaf blade are drawn to correct scale.)

perature and it is not possible to lead a significant length of wire along the surface isotherm within the boundary layer.

2. *Attachment of the thermocouple* by means of a *clip* (Lange 1965) (Fig. 17.5*b*) ensures good thermal contact but at the expense of some disturbance to the energy exchanges at the leaf. The clip and thermocouple alter the characteristics of the boundary layer, thus influencing convective exchange of sensible and latent heat, disturb the radiative exchanges and introduce conduction along a body with an appreciable heat capacity (*cf.* also Gale, Manes & Poljakoff-Mayber 1970).

A recent modification to the arrangement shown in Fig. 17.5*b* is shown in Fig. 17.5 *e*. A fine thermocouple embedded in *Araldite* with some mm of wire each side of the junction parallel to the leaf is ground down to yield an extremely thin junction exposed against the leaf (Schulze 1970).

Such thermocouples are held against the leaf by the pressure of a spring attached to the clip. A common danger with such an arrangement is that too much pressure is applied, thus causing closure of the stomata in the immediate vicinity of the thermocouple and a significant rise in temperature.

An appreciable conduction error may occur with the perpendicular thermocouple shown in Fig. 17.5 *b*. This error is largely eliminated by placing the wires adjacent to the thermocouple within the boundary layer and by using fine wires as in Fig. 17.5 *e*.

3. *Using a frame with a net* of thin wires (some 0.01 mm) (Perrier 1966) allows

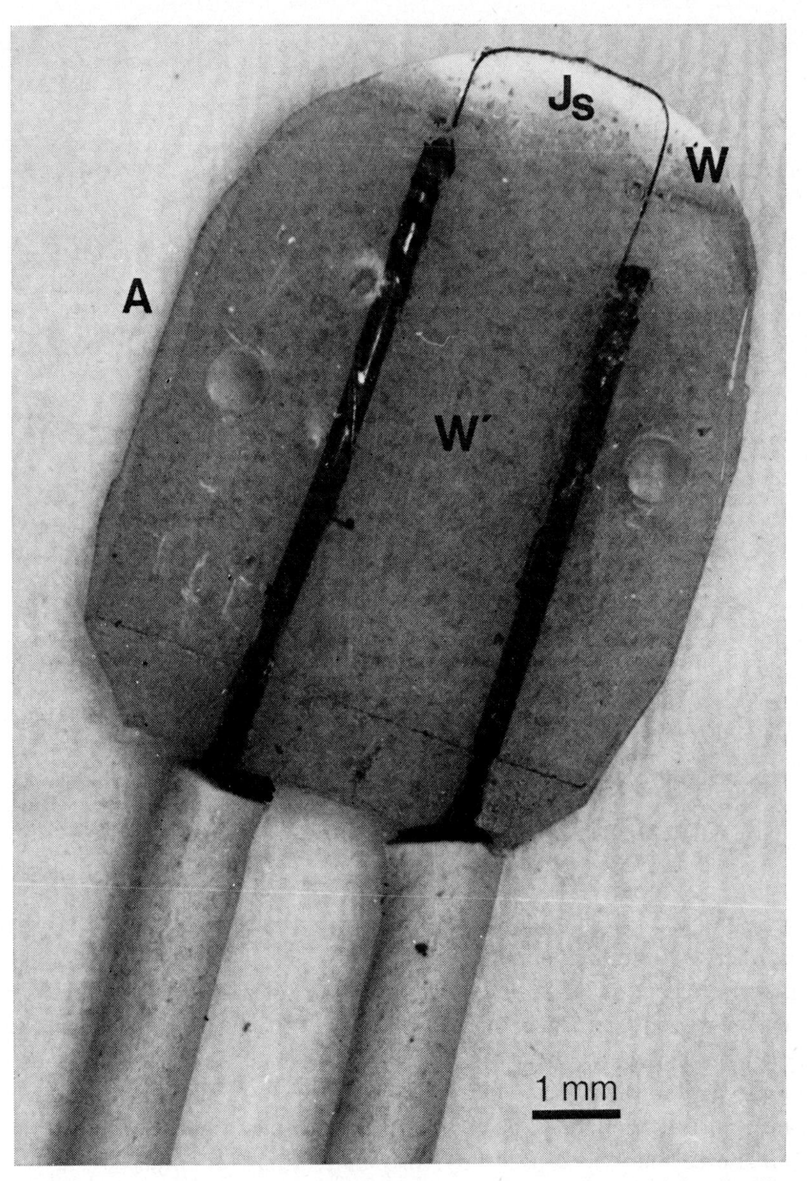

Fig. 17.5 *e* Photograph of the thermoelement used by Schulze (1970) for the clip-system. *W:* thin wire (copper, constantan 0.05 mm in diameter), *W′:* wire (copper, constantan), J_s*:* measuring junction, *A:* Araldite mass (2 to 3 mm).

relatively good fixation for small thermocouples (0.05 to 0.1 mm) and a low local disturbance (Fig. 17.5*c*).

b. Measurement by penetration. This method is difficult for leaves which do not exceed 0.1 mm in thickness as it requires a thin and frail thermocouple. Generally with a thin thermocouple and a thick leaf (0.3 mm), the temperature measured is near to the temperature of the tissue around the junction but location of the measuring junction in this case presents some difficulties (*e.g.* what temperature exactly is measured – upper or lower surface, internal temperature *etc.*).

However, biological disturbances, injuries and thermal perturbations (*e.g.* evaporation at the wound) may occur. Trials seem to show that the evaporation rate at the wound has no influence (Section 17.4.1.6) if the measuring junction inside the leaf lamina is localized 3 or 4 mm away from the wound (Fig. 17.5 *d*). Biological reactions are generally very slow, allowing a measuring period of at least 24 hours, except when necrosis appears. A significant and fast thermal disturbance of biological origin is not likely apart from stomatal regulation or death of cells. Local changes in stomatal aperture just above the inserted thermocouple do result in significant errors in the leaf temperature measurement.

17.4.1.6 | Analysis of errors

Some errors of electrical origin arising in the sensor, in the connection of the sensor to the recording instruments, and in the instruments themselves, can be avoided or compensated but errors due to the location of the sensor are more or less unavoidable (Rizika & Rohsenow 1953).

a. Parasitic e.m.fs: They appear in junctions of metals of dissimilar composition or wires of different diameters, in the sensor (galvanic e.m.f.) and along leads if they are not shielded. They may also arise from the presence of ions at the junction which should therefore be carefully cleaned and sealed before insertion into tissue.

b. Resistance of circuit: This is an important problem when using a galvanometer. To the resistance of the thermocouple, which has already been stressed (Section 17.4.1.2), the resistance of the lead wires must be added (copper wires of low resistance are suitable). However, resistance variations with temperature always exist and are significant (a variation of 24 °C leads to a variation of 10% in a copper resistance). This variation must be minimised; otherwise constantan wires or temperature-compensated leads should be used.

c. Thermal effects at the level of the sensor: They depend on the thermal coupling of sensor to leaf, conduction along wires, absorbed radiation and evaporation at the wound when introducing the sensor (Molnar & Rosenbaun 1962).

Thermal coupling. A thermocouple is closely coupled to a leaf thermally if it is in close contact with the leaf and if it is small and within the boundary layer (Table 17.2). Coupling is improved by larger pressure and area of contact and by blackening the wires to increase their emittance (Idle 1968). The pressure of the thermo-

Table 17.2 Difference between surface temperature (T_s) determined by thermoluminescence and with a thermocouple in contact with the surface (T) (*cf.* Fig. 17.5*c*). After Perrier (1966). (Chromel-constantan couple ø = 0.2 mm; young leaf of maize with $T_a \sim 24$ °C and irradiance of 1 000 W m^{-2}.)

	Windspeed [m s^{-1}]					
	5.5	2.5	2.0	1.5	1.0	0.7
T_s	34.7	37.4	39.5	41.6	46.3	54.7
$T_s - T$	4.6	4.5	3.9	2.9	1.5	1.7

Table 17.3 Arbitrary coupling factors (defined by $(T_s - T)/(T_s - T_a)$) for 2 thermocouples of differing thickness under different conditions of application to a standard surface (after Idle 1968).

Conditions	Wire diameter [mm]	
	0.5	0.12
1. Thermocouple tip only in contact with surface of block	0.8	0.6
2. Wires laid flat along surface for 3 mm behind the junction	0.4	0.27
3. Wires as in (2), blackened with paint of high emissivity in the infra-red	0.34	0.14
4. Wires as in (3), dipped in silicone oil before placing on the surface	0.23	0.05

junction on the leaf should not be so great as to close the stomata or damage the leaf in the vicinity of the thermojunction. Coupling can also be improved with a drop of silicone oil but this may not be desirable for physiological reasons. Table 17.3 (Idle 1968) shows variation of the ratio $(T_s - T)/(T_s - T_a)$, which must be as low as possible (T_s is real surface temperature, T thermocouple temperature, T_a air temperature).

Thermal conduction. When temperature gradients along a leaf can reach 1 or 2 °C cm^{-1} and when irradiance is high (> 300 W m^{-2}) appreciable thermal conduction along the wires to the measuring junction may occur, especially with high conductive wires such as copper (conductivity ~ 390 W m^{-1} °C); this phenomenon becomes less marked when using iron, chromel and alumel (~ 80 W m^{-1} °C) and vanishes with constantan (~ 25 W m^{-1} °C).

The error is frequently reduced by combining a stout constantan wire, to give the strength and resilience necessary, with a very much thinner copper wire. This conduction error practically disappears when the measuring junction is introduced into the leaf a distance of 3 to 5 mm because of the high heat capacity of the leaf in comparison to the wires and junction, and also in the case of thin wires ($\varnothing \leqslant$ 0.1 mm).

In the case of contact measurements it is desirable that the lead wires to the thermo-

Table 17.4 Temperature excess (°C) for various diameters of thermocouple wire (King's formula) with solar radiation of 700 W m^{-2} as a function of wind speed (after Platt & Griffiths 1964).

Wind speed [m s^{-1}]	Diameter of wire [cm]			
	10^{-3}	10^{-2}	10^{-1}	10^{0}
1	0.2	0.6	1.9	6.0
2	0.15	0.4	1.3	4.1
10	0.08	0.2	0.6	1.9

Table 17.5 Example of differences observed between surface temperature (T_s) determined by thermoluminescence and with a thermocouple placed inside the leaf lamina through the upper surface of the leaf (T_1) and the lower surface (T_2). After Perrier (1966).

	Solar radiation [W m^{-2}]		
	1 000	700	500
$T_s - T_1$	−1.2	−0.8	−0.4
$T_s - T_2$	$\simeq 0$	$\simeq 0$	$\simeq 0$

Table 17.6 Example of differences observed between surface temperature determined by thermoluminescence (T_s) and by a thermocouple badly introduced into the leaf lamina (T) (with natural convection, relative humidity 40%, air temperature 20 °C, and solar radiation of 200 to 1000 W m^{-2}). After Perrier (1966).

T_s	23.7	30.3	37.5	42.5
$T_s - T$	1.4	1.8	2.3	2.7

junction be within the boundary layer for *ca.* 1 cm to minimise this error. The exact length depends on their thermal conductance, the temperature gradient and the accuracy required.

The radiation absorbed by wires is one of the more important sources of error (Table 17.4). Therefore the thermocouple must be attached to the underside of the leaf (Fig. 17.5 *d*) even if the measuring junction is put close to the upper surface (Table 17.5). Blackening the wires to increase their emittance also reduces this error.

Evaporation at the wound causing differences of about 1 to 3 °C as shown in Table 17.6 (Perrier 1966) is an important factor which has been already stressed. It can be avoided by introducing the measuring junction sufficiently deeply into the tissue (3 to 4 mm, see Fig. 17.5 *d*).

d. Localisation of the measuring junction: To avoid errors which can play a significant part in some measurements, the temperature required must be precisely defined. By an accurate analysis of the relations between the measuring junction and its environment it is possible to determine whether the measured temperature is more representative of a surface temperature, a tissue temperature, a vein temperature or mean leaf temperature.

17.4.2 | Electrical resistance methods

The change in resistance of certain metals or of semi-conductors (*e.g.* thermistors) with temperature provides a suitable method for the measurement of temperature because of their large temperature coefficient. However the relatively large size of wire-wound, metal resistance thermometers (usually of Pt or Ni) makes them unsuitable for the measurement of leaf temperature. Thermistors, on the other hand, are now available in sufficiently small sizes to have been used for certain leaf temperature measurements.

17.4.2.1 | Basis and scheme for measurement

a. With a resistance thermometer: the variation of resistance with temperature can be written as follows:

$$R_T = R_0[1 + b(T - T_0) + c(T - T_0)^2] \quad [\Omega] \qquad (17.4)$$

where T, T_0 are temperatures [K], R_0 resistance at the temperature T_0 [Ω], and b, c coefficients varying with the nature of the metal [K^{-1} and K^{-2}]. Temperature is obtained by measurement of this resistance with a Wheatstone bridge (Fig. 17.6 *a*). In practice, it is preferable to obtain a response which is linear with temperature, at least for small intervals (*e.g.* 20 to 50 °C); this is almost the case for wire wound resistance thermometers (c is very small and $c(T-T_0)^2$ is negligible for a small difference $(T-T_0)$).

b. With a thermistor: the change in resistance with temperature is given by

$$R_T = R_0\, e^{d\left(\frac{1}{T} - \frac{1}{T_0}\right)} \quad [\Omega] \qquad (17.5)$$

where T, T_0 are temperatures [K], R_0 resistance at temperature T_0 [Ω], and d the coefficient of the thermistor [K].
The exponential variation of thermistor resistance can be linearised with appropriate circuits (Beakley 1951). For instance, it is possible as an approximation, to represent part of the exponential curve as a part of an hyperbola. Thus a suitable resistance R_I in parallel with R_T can be adjusted to obtain a measured resistance r [$r = (R_T\, R_I)/(R_T + R_I)$] which linearly varies with T (Durand, unpubl.).
There is another way to linearise the change in resistance by considering a series expansion (Droms 1962):

$$\log x = 2\frac{x-1}{x+1} + \frac{1}{3}\left(\frac{x-1}{x+1}\right)^3 + \dots \qquad (17.6)$$

(with $x = R_T/R$ and $0.3 < R_T < 3$).
At equilibrium the bridge gives $R_T/R = (R_m - r)/r$ and considering only the first term of the series expansion $\{2(x-1)/(x+1)\}$, this relation becomes $\log R_T/R = 2 - 4\, r/R_m$ (see Fig. 17.6 *b*).
The measured variation of r (Fig. 17.6 *b*) (deviation D of galvanometer) is linear with $\log R_T$ (thus $\log R_T$ is a first power linear function of D).
The nominal manufacturing tolerance for thermistors is about 20% for the resistance value R_0 and 5% for the coefficient d. Hence each thermistor should be individually calibrated. The circuit (Fig. 17.6 *c*) allows these variations (R_0, d) to be compensated in such a way that each thermistor of the same type can be adjusted to a single calibration curve (Droms 1962). In fact, resistance R_1 allows

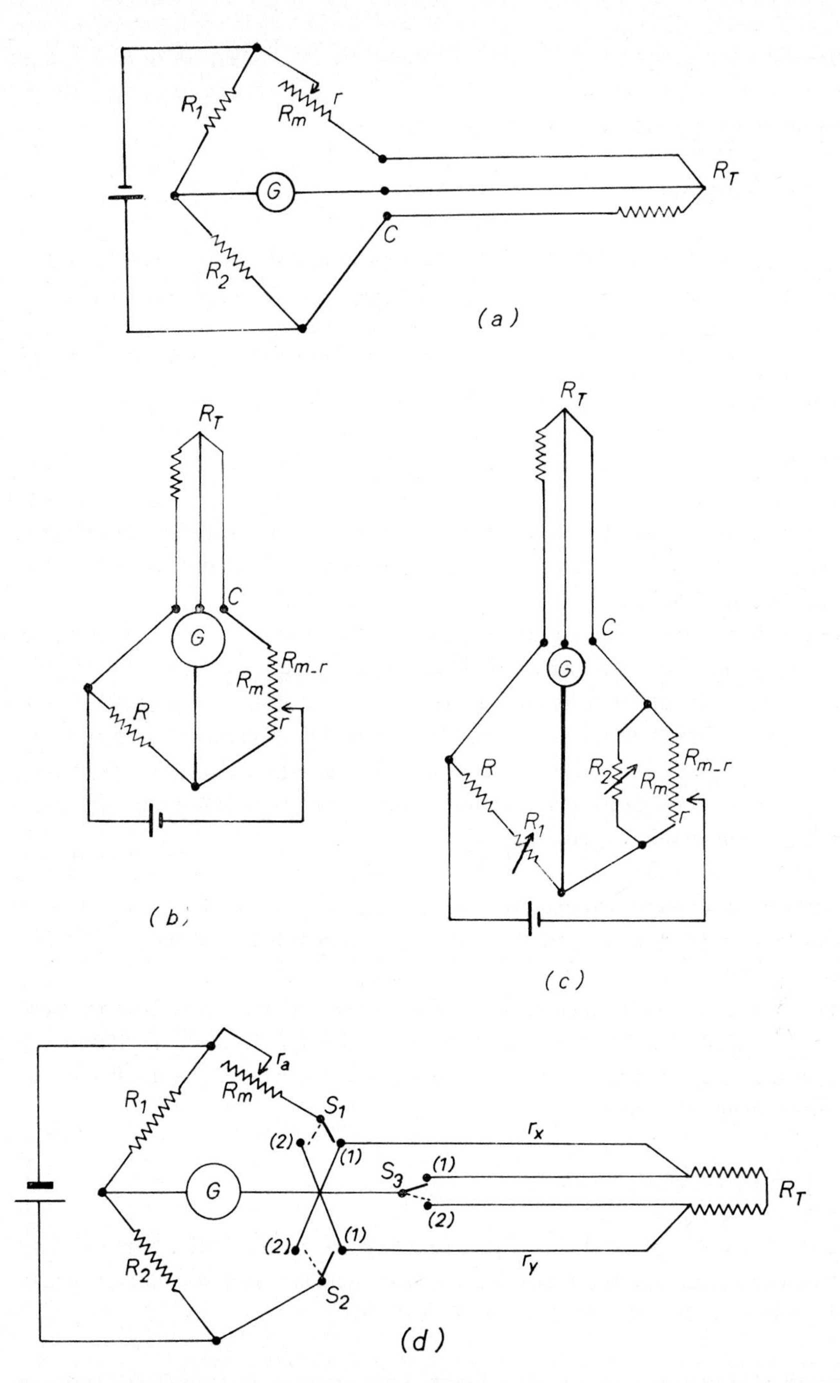

Fig. 17.6 Modified Wheatstone bridge for resistance thermometers. (*a*): Wheatstone bridge for thermoelement (resistance R_T), (*b*): ratio type of thermistor bridge, (*c*): compensated thermistor bridge circuit, (*d*): Kelvin bridge for 4 wire thermoelement (resistance R_T). R_T: compensating resistance thermometer, *C*: connection, *G*: galvanometer, R, R_1, R_2, R_m, r, r_x, r_y: different resistances in the circuit, S_1, S_2, S_3: switches.

compensation for variation in R_0 and resistance R_2 for variation in d; R_2 is an added resistance in parallel which plays the role of a resistance in series with R_m without changing the linearity of r with log R_T.

17.4.2.2 | Calibration

Accuracy depends on the calibration and on good linearisation. Each resistance thermometer or each thermistor should be either calibrated (see Section 17.4.1.3) or adjusted for 2 or 3 points to the standard calibration curve using the circuit described above. The calibration of thermistors should be frequently checked since it changes continuously as they age.

17.4.2.3 | Use of resistance thermometers and thermistors

Manufactured wire-wound resistance thermometers have smaller temperature coefficients than thermistors but they have greater stability and uniformity (Becker, Green & Pearson 1947).

If it is easy to make a thermocouple oneself, it is more difficult to build resistance thermometers, and only commercially available thermistors should be used. It is possible to get a batch of resistance thermometers with characteristics (R_0 and coefficients b, c) which are in practice extremely close, all giving the temperature with the desired precision (0.1 °C for example) in the same conditions. It is more difficult in the case of thermistors to find many elements giving good agreement and such a batch is very expensive.

Resistance thermometers and thermistors require much care and in practice a good calibration for each element. Also it is more difficult to work with n resistance thermometers or thermistors either in series or in parallel than with n thermocouples.

Generally, the size of resistance sensors allows only contact measurements. Such a sensor has been widely used and is described by Lange (1965). Platinum is especially suitable for small and very steady sensors which are unaffected by chemical reactions (Smith 1912).

17.4.2.4 | Analysis of errors

Resistance thermometers and thermistors have many of the same errors as occur with thermocouples, but thermal effects which increase with the size of sensor assume greater importance (Platt & Griffiths 1964).

a. Errors due to the resistance of the circuit. The variation of circuit and lead wire resistance with temperature ($< 0.1\%$ °C^{-1}) is almost negligible in relation to the resistance of thermistors (resistance of some thousand ohms and variation from 3 to 4% °C^{-1}). However in the case of resistance thermometers (a few ohms and variation from 0.5% °C^{-1}) a compensating system (circuit with 3 or 4 wires) is then necessary (Fig. 17.6 *a*, *b*, *c*, *d*).

A Kelvin bridge is probably the best solution for avoiding, without particular precautions, all errors resulting from the resistance of the circuit. A resistance thermometer (R_T) with four wires is used (Fig. 17.6 *d*). In this case two successive measurements (R_a and R_b) are made, the three switches (S_1, S_2, S_3) connecting respectively in the position one and two, and if R_1 is equal R_2 the two relations obtained are:

$$R_a + r_x = R_T + r_y$$
$$R_b + r_y = R_T + r_x$$

or

$$R_T = (R_a + R_b)/2$$

But with this system, it takes longer to obtain a record because two measurements are made and the result requires a mean.

b. Errors at the level of the sensor. Radiative, conductive and coupling effects increase with the size of sensor. In the first place, perfect thermal coupling of sensor and leaf is not obtainable (Section 17.4.1.6) and this results in a measured temperature which is different from leaf temperature. Secondly, the sensor integrates not only leaf temperature but also the temperature of the surrounding air (Ramdas & Paranjpe 1936; Gates & Benedict 1963). Hence, the temperature of the sensor becomes further from leaf temperature as its dimensions increase in comparison with the thickness of the leaf and the boundary layer (Raschke 1958, 1960; Bouchet 1964).
This error can be reduced (but not eliminated) if the temperature difference between leaf and air is measured with a surface sensor calibrated against the known real surface temperatures of an artificial similar body and the air temperature.
The use of all flattened, plate-like surface sensors (sides of 2 to 5 mm) which disturb all the terms of energy budget (equation 17.1) is to be avoided.
Resistance thermometers and thermistors may have an appreciable heat capacity and a thermal time constant of several tenths to several seconds. Significant thermal dissipation occurs mostly with small sensors. According to the resistance of the sensor and the e.m.f. used in the circuit this effect disturbs the measurement of leaf temperature (*e.g.* in still air, dissipation constants can reach from 0.1 to 10 mW °C^{-1}).

17.5 | Radiation thermometry

In this alternative way to measure temperature, the sensor is not in contact with the leaf or vegetation. Such indirect methods require the measurement of the reference temperature of a body with known temperature and emittance. Unfortunately, these methods present great difficulties and at present they are insufficiently accurate for the determination of actual absolute temperatures.

17.5.1 | Infra-red thermometry

First introduced by Aldrich (1922), then used by many since Monteith & Szeicz

(1962), Stoll (1962), Gates (1963) and Fimpel (1964), infra-red thermometry has been developed by miniaturization of the thermometer and the incorporation of methods allowing corrections to be made to give the real surface temperature. The estimated radiative temperature has to be corrected for the emittance of the surface and for the incident and reflected thermal radiation from the surroundings (Raschke 1956a, b; Fuchs & Tanner 1966).
In this method the mean temperature of the layer of air up to 20 to 40 μm from the leaf surface is determined; this gives a good measure of leaf temperature.

17.5.1.1 | Basic principles of infra-red thermometers

Thermal radiation of a body (Φ_T) follows the Stefan-Boltzmann black body law, with an appropriate coefficient ε for the emittance ($\leqslant 1$)

$$\Phi_T = \varepsilon\sigma T_s^4 \quad [\mathrm{W\,m^{-2}}] \tag{17.7}$$

where T_s is the temperature of the surface [K], and σ is the Stefan-Boltzmann constant [5.674×10^{-8} W m^{-2} °C^{-4}].
Surface temperature, T_s, can then be calculated from this equation if surface emittance is known and the flux of thermal radiation emitted is measured. Radiometers with two types of sensor can be used for this measurement.
Radiometers such as *bolometers* and *thermopiles* are composed of a *heat sensor*. This is always a black surface, the temperature variation of which is measured by a detector (*e.g.* by resistance thermometer or thermocouple). Another type of radiometer includes a sensor which is a *quantum detector* (PbS, CdSe or InSb are generally used).
Schematically the sensor receives energy from the measured surface through the optics which define the field of view by use of a diaphragm, lens and sometimes a mirror, and bring localized surface areas into focus. It is necessary to select the waveband of thermal energy emitted by the surface from the total energy (0.4 to 40 μm)[1] received by the sensor and originating at the surface. Therefore a filter with a sharp bandpass in the infra-red is used generally to eliminate the short-wave radiation: the bandpass 8 to 13 μm is particularly suitable. In fact this selected bandpass includes the peak of black body emission at normal temperature (9–10 μm) so that the maximum energy is measured. Moreover, water does not absorb radiation in this band, so that the effect of water vapour on the measurement is minimized. But that part of the long-wave radiation emitted by the surroundings and reflected by the surface in this waveband cannot be eliminated directly (Fig. 17.7 *c*).
Theoretically, taking into account the approximations listed below to obtain a

1. Total energy = energy emitted by the surface + transmitted, reflected and diffused part of total radiation + radiation emitted by the surrounding and reflected by the surface.
Total radiation = long-wave radiation emitted by sky (3 to 100 μm) + global radiation (0.4 to 3 μm).
Global radiation = direct radiation of sun + radiation originating from sun and diffused in the air.

simple integration of the relation representing the response of I.R. thermometers, it can be written:

$$A = \varepsilon\sigma T_s^4 + (1 - \varepsilon)B \quad [\mathrm{W\,m^{-2}}] \tag{17.8}$$

where A is the flux of long-wave radiation from the surface being radiated in 2π-steradian, T_s the real temperature of the surface (leaves or vegetation), B total incident long-wave (or thermal) radiation; $(1 - \varepsilon)B$ is the reflected component influencing the thermometer output, ε the surface emittance, σ Stefan-Boltzmann constant.

It is supposed (see Fuchs & Tanner 1966 for more details) that ε is independent of T_s over a narrow range (-15 to 60 °C), and is independent of wavelength over a narrow waveband (8 to 13 μm); this condition is important only in the second term $(1 - \varepsilon)B$. It is supposed also that the filter function is practically independent of the temperature T_s (0 to 40 °C) and the temperature of the filter is constant. As a first approximation, since ε and B are unknown, by assuming that ε is close to unity (generally, for leaves $0.94 < \varepsilon < 0.98$, Gates & Tantraporn 1952), the real surface temperature (T_s) can be estimated *(T)* (Monteith & Szeicz 1962; Gates 1963) from the relation:

$$A = \sigma T^4 \tag{17.9}$$

In this case (*cf.* equation 17.8) the calculated surface temperature *(T)* will be overestimated because the term containing B is neglected and also underestimated because ε is overestimated. This compensation between two opposed deviations leads to a small overall error in the calculation of the surface temperature *(T)*. The size of the error is given from equations (17.8) and (17.9) by:

$$(T_s - T)/T = 1 - \sqrt[4]{\varepsilon + (1 - \varepsilon)B/\sigma T^4} \tag{17.10}$$

Compensation of the errors is much better when B is close to A. If B is equal to A then T is the real surface temperature T_s. When B decreases, the error increases (the maximum error is $1 - \sqrt[4]{\varepsilon}$ for $B = 0$) and the calculated value of surface temperature is always underestimated. Experience shows that B is most often less than A and the maximum of B is reached in the evening (more scattering and reflection) or under a cloudy sky. Thus the error varies generally between 0.5 and 1.5 °C.

17.5.1.2 | Calibration

The unique relationship between the data supplied by the I.R. thermometer (A_0) (*i.e.* meter or recorder displacement) and the flux of long-wave radiation A reaching the apparatus from the surface is obtained in the laboratory by measuring A_0 for many different surface temperatures *(T)* of a reference black body. The temperature *(T)* gives the flux A (equation 17.9) so that it is possible to draw the curve relating A_0 to A or directly to T. For these measurements, the I.R. thermometer is put either close to the surface of a sphere immersed in a temperature-controlled bath (Fig.

17.7 *a*) (thus obtaining a very good black body at known temperature T) or at the top of a perfect reflecting cone placed on a reference surface (anodised aluminium) the temperature of which is controlled and varied (Fuchs & Tanner 1966) (Fig. 17.7 b). Such calibration curves relating A_0 to T are reproducible to within a range of 0.3 °C.

The reference surface with controlled surface temperature (*e.g.* D in Fig. 17.7 *b*) is important in order to evaluate B for measuring in natural conditions (following Section 17.5.1.3). In this case the emittance of the reference surface must be known

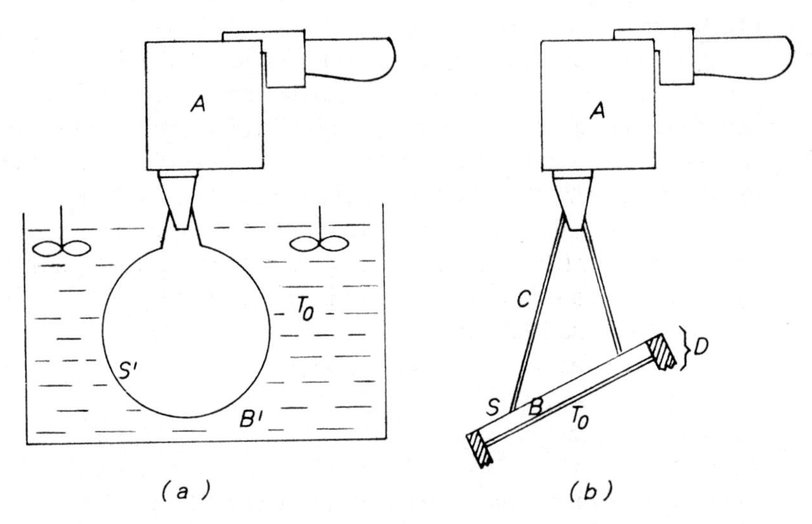

Fig. 17.7 *a*, *b* Schematic diagram of I.R. thermometer used for calibration. *A:* radiation thermometer, T_0*:* controlled temperature, *B:* aluminium block, *B′:* temperature-controlled bath, *S:* anodized aluminium surface, *S′:* spherical surface (black surface), *C:* cone (reflecting surface), *D:* reference surface system.

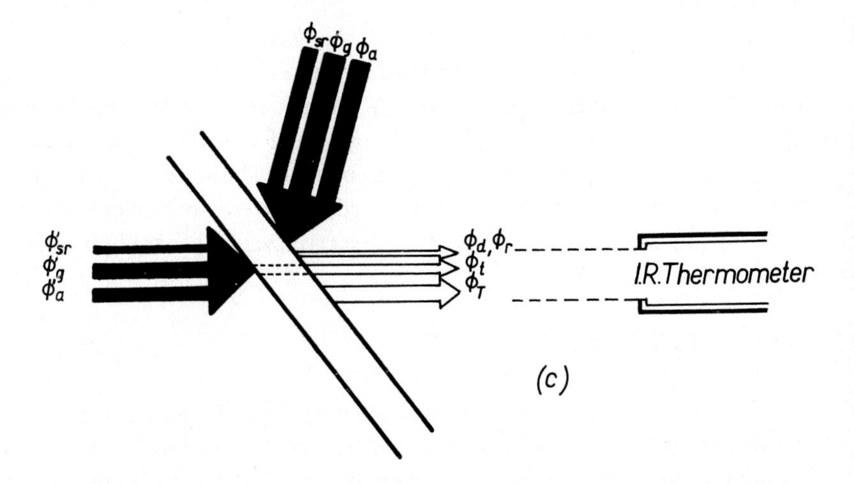

Fig. 17.7*c* Scheme of fluxes of energy. Φ_T: energy emitted by the surface, Φ_g*:* part of global radiation received by the surface, Φ_a*:* part of long-wave radiation emitted by sky and received by the surface, Φ_{sr}*:* radiation from the surroundings received by the surface, Φ_r*:* reflected part of all these radiations, Φ_d*:* diffused part of all these radiations, Φ_t*:* transmitted part.

and it is obtained by determining A at different temperatures T of the anodised aluminium block *(D)* under conditions of constant B (*e.g.* in a laboratory without windows or under clear skies). The emittance ε is then given by the slope of the straight line relationship between A and T^4 and B is the intercept on the ordinate for $T = 0$ (provided that B does not vary with T).

17.5.1.3 | Techniques of measurement

To determine the mean surface temperature T_s of a given surface (*e.g.* parts of leaves, leaves or vegetation) the I.R. thermometer is brought into focus on the surface which must cover all the viewing angle. Then, in natural conditions, from equation (17.8), the surface temperature can be calculated from ε, B, and A which is given by A_0 and the calibration curve. Hence the emittance ε must be determined for the leaves or vegetation in question and B also must be measured at intervals during the course of the measurement since it continuously varies.

Hence *determination of* B is needed before and after each measurement of the surface temperature T_s to detect eventual variation of B during the operation. With the anodised aluminium reference surface at known temperature T_0, as close as possible to T_s, and placed in the same position with the same inclination and direction and viewing angle as the thermometer, a measurement of A_0 with the I.R. thermometer is made. Then equation (17.8) permits evaluation of B since ε is known (Section 17.5.1.2), T_0 is fixed during the experiment and A is given by the calibration curve from A_0.

A *measurement of the emittance* ε of the analysed surface, even approximate, is difficult to obtain. However, under some conditions, it is possible to measure it approximately. From equation (17.8) a determination of ε requires that B is known (see above), A is determined in natural conditions with the I.R. thermometer (given by value A_0) and the term (σT_s^4) is measured. This term in the energy flux of a black body of unknown temperature T_s can be measured with the I.R. thermometer if the surface is placed in a black body cavity for a short time without significantly influencing the surface temperature T_s. By placing a reflecting cone (Fig. 17.7 *b*) on a small surface such as leaf, or quickly covering the vegetation with a larger internally reflecting hemispherical 'pop tent' lined with aluminium (Fuchs & Tanner 1966), it is possible to obtain an approximate black body cavity in natural conditions. Since covering the foliage results in a rapid change in temperature, it is advisable to do this at night. The surface temperature then remains stable for a period of about ten seconds during which the observation of A can be made.

During a clear and calm night with steady temperature a measurement of A_{01} with cone or tent supplies a value A_1. Since $\varepsilon \simeq 1$ and $(1 - \varepsilon)B$ is then negligible $(A_1 = \sigma T_s^4)$. A second measurement taken just before the emplacement or after removal of the cone or tent, gives A_{02} or A_2 $[A_2 = \varepsilon\sigma T_s^4 + (1 - \varepsilon)B]$. In these conditions, the simple ratio A_2/A_1 is almost equal to the emittance, ε, because, generally $(1 - \varepsilon)B$ can be neglected. To obtain better accuracy, it is possible to determine B and calculate ε from A_2, T_s and B which are known.

Thus precise measurement of surface temperature in this way is complex: the emittance must be determined from measurements made at night and it is impossible to detect eventual variation of ε during the day, and three measurements of A (reference surface, actual surface, then reference surface) are necessary for each determination of T_s.

However, the measurement of difference in two temperatures ΔT_s can be simpler if the two surfaces have the same high emittance and receive the same incident long-wave radiation as it is often the case in experiments (two points on a single leaf, two leaves in the same conditions, or two neighbouring areas of vegetation). Equation (17.8) can be rewritten for two surfaces 1 and 2 as follows:

$$\Delta A \simeq 4\,\varepsilon\sigma\, T_s^3\, \Delta T_s \qquad (17.11)$$

where

ΔA is $A_1 - A_2$

ΔT_s is $T_{s_1} - T_{s_2}$

T_s is $(T_{s_1} + T_{s_2})/2$

The determination of emittance is needed to calculate ΔT_s and as T_{s_1}, T_{s_2} are unknown it is possible to approximate T_s by using T_1 and T_2 provided by equation (17.9) ($A_1 = \sigma T_1^4$, $A_2 = \sigma T_2^4$). Generally, for measurements of temperature differences, ΔT_s is estimated as the difference between the apparent radiative temperature of the two surfaces ($\Delta T = T_1 - T_2$). In this case the relative error is the difference in real temperature between the two surfaces, according to equation (17.11) which becomes:

$$\Delta T \,.\, T^3 = \varepsilon\, T_s^3\, \Delta T_s$$

where

T is $(T_1 + T_2)/2$

This expression can be written in the following form:

$$\Delta(\Delta T_s)/\Delta T_s = 1 - \varepsilon \left(\frac{T_s}{T}\right)^3 \qquad (17.12)$$

The variation of this error can be calculated in the same way as the relative error of T_s (Section 17.5.1.1 and equation 17.10):

$$1 - \varepsilon^{\frac{1}{4}} < \Delta(\Delta T_s)/\Delta T_s < (1 - \varepsilon)$$

This relative error is always greater than the previous error $\Delta T_s/T_s$, but generally amounts to a small error of few tenths °C for ΔT_s if the value of ΔT_s is between 1 and 10 °C (the maximum error $(1 - \varepsilon)$ is about 5% and in this case the error for ΔT_s is from 0.05 to 0.5 °C).

17.5.1.4 | Analysis of errors

The main advantage of the radiometric method is that it eliminates errors due to disturbance of the zone of measurement. However, the electronic stability of the whole set-up, thermometer, circuit, and recorder, does not enable an accuracy of better than $\pm$ 0.1 to 0.3 °C in the determination of the radiative temperature T, defined by the relation $A = \sigma T^4$.
The main errors are due to the various manipulations required for the determination of ε and B. For instance:

$$\frac{\Delta T_s}{T_s} \simeq \frac{1}{4} \cdot \frac{\Delta \varepsilon}{\varepsilon} \tag{17.13}$$

1. An error of 2% in ε leads to an error of about 1.5 °C.
2. Neglecting B leads to an error of 0.5 to 1.5 °C.

Another error results from absorption by gases and vapours in relevant bands between the leaves and the thermometer (*e.g.* CO_2 and H_2O). This can be important if distances are large and the sensor is non-specific. The spectral sensitivity of the sensor is very important.
The determination of ε and B for a leaf is relatively easy, but it is less satisfactory for a vegetation surface, the 'pop-tent' is not a perfect black body and the reference surface is no longer representative of the actual surface. When measuring temperature of a canopy, these errors vary with viewing angle, incident angle and fields of view, and then corrections are difficult (Fuchs *et al.* 1967).

17.5.2 | Infra-red thermography

These methods of temperature measurement, which have a similar basis to I.R. thermometry, give quite different results.
In I.R. thermography, the thermal radiation emitted by a body is analysed with a quantum sensor, such as the InSb sensor, which has a very small time-delay of 10^{-6}s. So, whereas I.R. thermometry only gives a mean surface temperature, the sensitivity and the speed of this new technique allows measurement of semi-point temperatures and gives a picture of these temperatures. I.R. thermography involves scanning the whole surface, which is analysed point by point giving several pictures per second (Bowling Barnes 1968). Commercial instruments are available but they are rather expensive. In some countries they are available for hire.

17.5.2.1 | Techniques

The picture of a body is analysed point by point (at a distance of 1 m, a point represents 6 × 6 mm or 4 × 4 mm, according to scanning speed). Emitted radiation from each point is transmitted to the quantum sensor; this information is then collected onto a screen or onto film. The result is a thermal picture of the object, in black and white, or in colour (thermography, see Fig. 17.8). The temperature of the object is then determined from optical density measurements; clear zones are colder, dark zones are warmer. The relation between optical density and tempera-

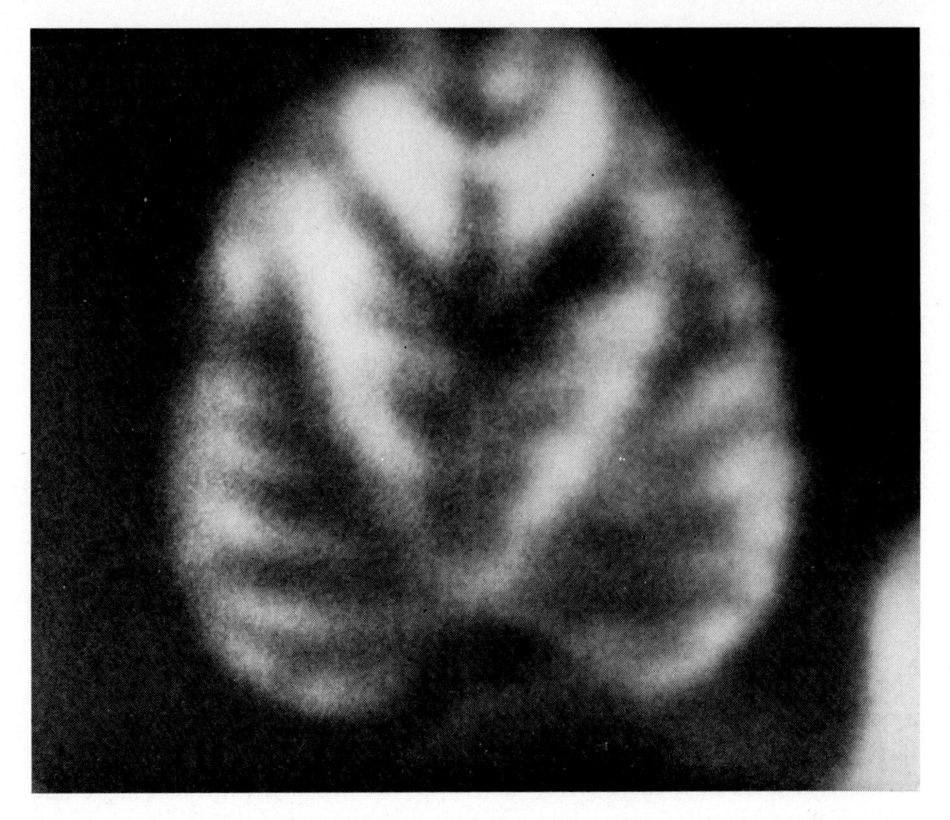

Fig. 17.8*a:* Black and white photograph of a thermogram of a sunflower leaf. Temperature range: 2 °C, resolution: 0.05 °C.

ture can be obtained by calibration against a reference black body. For natural bodies, the emittance of the surface and the reflected flux of incident thermal energy must be taken into account as in the previous section. As analysis is by points, a determination of these two terms is difficult because they may vary from one point to another.

17.5.2.2 | Applications

This method allows rapid investigation of a surface; the response immediately gives a picture of the zones with thermal heterogeneity and thermal gradients. Moreover, this fast response allows investigation of non-steady state processes such as the kinetics of cooling or heating of a leaf.

Thus, it is possible to measure differences of temperatures with an accuracy of some few percent (about 0.5 °C for a discrepancy of 10 °C, for instance), with no influence of emittance or reflected flux of incident energy (Section 17.5.1.3). The minimum difference which can be detected is about 0.05 °C.

If emittance and reflected flux of incident energy are the same for the whole surface, it is possible to draw isothermal lines immediately.

Obviously, the direct measurement of absolute temperatures is not possible (Section 17.5.1.3).

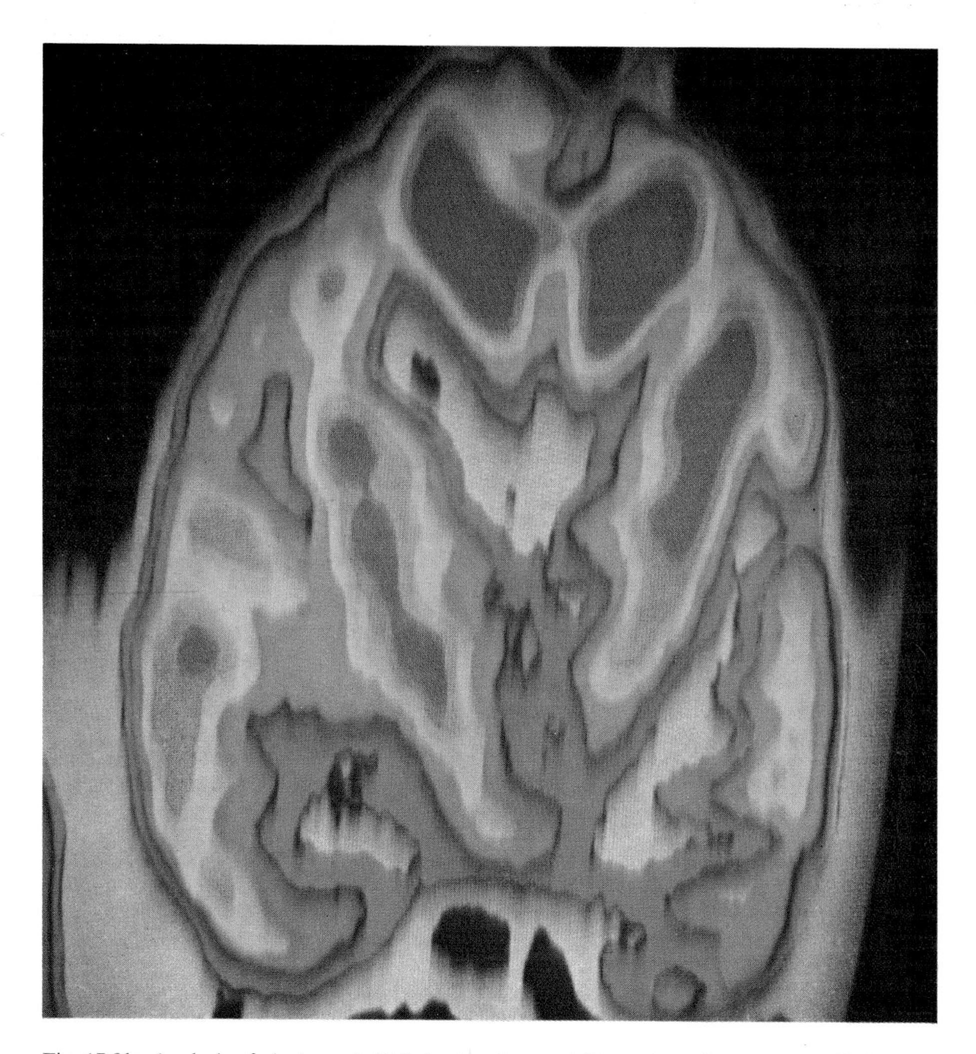

Fig. 17.8*b:* Analysis of photograph 17.8*a* by densitometry. The range of temperature (2 °C) used is divided into five zones which are arbitrarily associated to five colours – red (hottest zone), orange, yellow, green, blue (coldest zone). Light blue is out of the temperature range and cannot be evaluated in this case. (Obtained using the thermograph *TS 405 Thermorama*, with collaboration of the *Société Européenne de Matériels Spéciaux (S.E.M.S.)* and the *Institut National de la Recherche Agronomique – Service de Métrologie* and *Station Centrale de Bioclimatologie*).

17.5.3 | *Luminescence methods*

Luminescent radiation may be employed to determine surface temperature. Thin layers of a luminescent compound are deposited on the surface and emit visible radiation, some properties of which vary with temperature (Lewerenz 1950). Two methods make use of this thermal sensitivity.

17.5.3.1 | Basis and instrumentation

Two methods, which differ very little, are based on the luminescent emission of thin layers excited by U.V. radiation. The thin layer is a deposit of a mixed sulphide of Zn and Cd, activated by Mn and Au (thickness of deposit: 0.02 mm). Different powders can be used and for each batch of powder supplied by the manufacturer, a calibration curve should be prepared. A very small quantity V ($\sim$ 0.1 g) of powder is mixed with a little glue (*ca.* $V/4$) diluted in water, and a small part of the mixture is put onto the surface with a thin brush of appropriate surface dimension (Section 17.5.3.2).

The *colour method* (Thureau 1955) is based on the variation of visible waveband spectra with temperature. The thermosensitive parameter C (λ_2, λ_1) is defined as the ratio of the monochromatic luminances of the deposit at the two wavelengths λ_1 and λ_2. Calibration is necessary to establish the variation of this parameter with temperature.

The *phosphorescence method* (Leroux 1961) is based on phosphorescent phenomena which result from a delay between excitation and emission. A thermosensitive parameter P (λ_1) is then defined as the ratio between the effective value of the

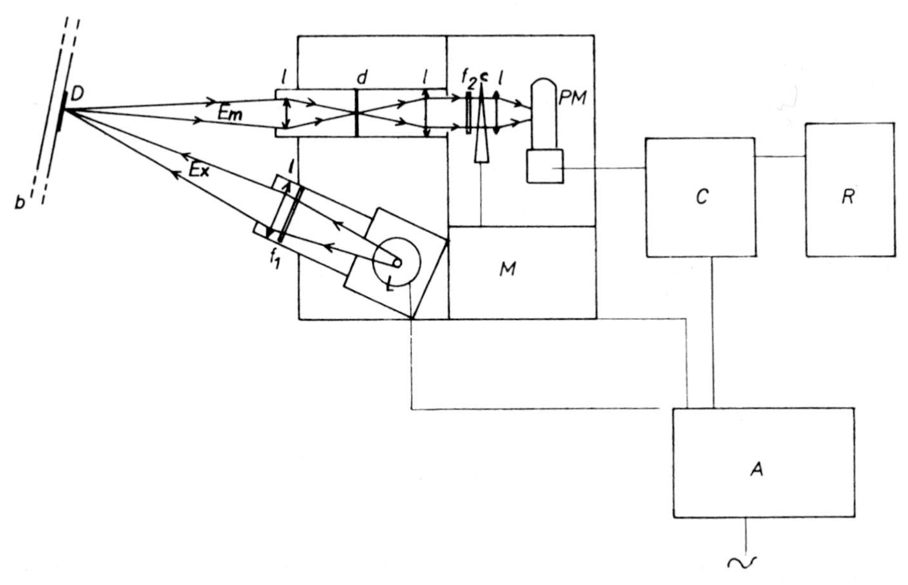

Fig. 17.9 Schematic diagram of the luminescence photothermometer (CNRS–ADRRSTME, 92-Bellevue, France). *A:* power supply (V.H.V.), *C:* control panel, *R:* recorder, *M:* regulation motor (for compensation), *L:* U.V. lamp, *PM:* photomultiplier, *Ex:* excitation light, *Em:* emission light, *D:* deposit, *b:* body, *d:* diaphragm, f_1*:* Wood's filter, f_2*:* filters which can be changed automatically, *l:* lens, *c:* compensation system.

alternative component of emission of the deposit and the mean value of the constant component of emission.
These two methods are used with the same instrumentation: a surface photothermometer (Huetz & Leroux 1964) which includes radiation source (mercury lamp) and a sensor system (diaphragm, filter λ_1 and λ_2, and photomultiplier) (Fig. 17.9).

17.5.3.2 | Techniques

The surface of the leaf must be covered with a thin deposit of a luminescent compound, covering about 0.25 mm^2 to several cm^2, depending on whether a point or mean temperature is required; this permeable layer does not significantly disturb mass transfer and energy exchanges at the leaf surface (Perrier 1966). These methods can be employed for smooth or irregular surfaces of any dimensions. The instrumentation is placed on a support with free orientation 0.5 or 1 m away from the surface for small deposits (0.25 mm^2) or several meters away for larger deposits. Measurements can be permanently recorded but it is necessary from time to time to adjust the compensation for parasitic reflected ambient light by connecting the automatically compensated system. Automatic compensation of the reflected radiation from the surroundings (without direct sunlight) and incident on the deposit is done by measuring emission without excitation of the deposit (incident U.V. radiation is suppressed) and by compensating for it. The main inconvenience is the rapid saturation of the photomultiplier when the normal amount of reflected visible radiation increases (*e.g.* in the case of reflected direct incident sunlight) because the reflected flux density of natural light in the waveband chosen to analyse luminescence emission is too high; in this case compensation is not possible.
However, this method allows measurement of actual surface temperature at all points on a leaf; this can be done alternately on both sides using a mirror (Perrier 1968). Absolute temperatures are obtained with an accuracy of $\pm$ 1 °C (over a small scale of temperature 0–30 °C or 0–40 °C) with the colour method and with an accuracy of $\pm$ 0.5 to 1 °C with the phosphorescent method, which allows measurement of differences of temperature with an accuracy of 0.3 °C.
Accuracy of the surface temperature is relatively low in spite of the direct measurement of the thermosensitive parameter although surface emittance and incident radiation from the surroundings are automatically compensated. A certain instability of the electronic system and of the luminiscence of the sulphide mixture is responsible for this relatively poor accuracy.

17.6 | Calculation of mean leaf temperature

It is possible to calculate leaf temperature from the different components of the energy budget if these are known (Raschke 1956a, b; Bouchet 1963/4). Many analyses of some of these parameters have been made (Takechi & Haseba 1962, 1963; de Parcevaux 1964; Gates 1965; Monteith 1965; Linacre 1967; Perrier 1968) and graphical solutions have been proposed (Gates 1968).
Schematically, in a steady state without storage changes, the energy budget can

be written as follows if fluxes by conduction and metabolic fluxes are neglected:

$$\Phi_L = \Phi_R + \Phi_S \tag{17.14}$$

$$\Phi_L = L_v \Lambda \Delta (T_s - T_d)(\delta_F + \delta_F')^{-1} \quad [\mathrm{W\ m^{-2}}] \tag{17.15}$$

$$\Phi_S = L_v \Lambda \gamma (T_a - T_s) \delta_F^{-1} \tag{17.16}$$

The eight parameters of the energy balance are Φ_L: latent heat flux [W m^{-2}], Φ_R: net radiation flux [W m^{-2}], Φ_S: sensible heat flux [W m^{-2}], T_a: air temperature [°C], T_d: dew point temperature of the air [°C], T_s: surface temperature [°C], δ_F: thickness parameter of diffusion path [m] (equal to $\Lambda R T r_a / M$ or $\Lambda \gamma L_v r_a' / \rho c$)[1], δ_F': supplementary thickness parameter of diffusion path [m] (equal to $\Lambda R T r_s / M$ or $\Lambda \gamma L_v r_s' / \rho c$)[1], where L_v: latent heat of water vapourisation [J kg^{-1}], Λ: time of diffusion [s], γ: psychrometric constant [kg m^{-1} s^{-2} °C^{-1}], Δ: first derivative of saturation vapour pressure for mean temperature T [Pascal/°C or kg m^{-1} s^{-2} °C^{-1}], c: heat capacity of the air [J °C^{-1} m^{-3}], ρ: specific mass of the air [kg m^{-3}].
All these constants are assumed to be constant for small variations of temperature around T_* ($T_* \simeq (T_a + T_d)/2$).
From five of the parameters it is possible to determine the other three terms, and a graphical solution has been proposed (Daudet & Perrier 1968).
The general graph presented in Fig. 17.10 gives any solution of the 3 equation system (for a mean reference temperature near to 15 °C, Δ (15 °C) and L_v (15 °C)). The graph is dimensionless because T, Φ and δ are expressed as ratios T/T_{ref}, Φ/Φ_{ref}, δ/δ_{ref} (where T_{ref} is $T_a - T_d$, Φ_{ref} is Φ_R, δ'_{ref} is δ_{FC} – see further on):

$$\delta'_{FC} = L_v \Lambda (\Delta + \gamma)(T_a - T_d) \Phi_R^{-1} \quad [\mathrm{m}] \tag{17.17}$$

The two most frequent problems will be treated here as an example:

a. *Firstly, T_a, T_d, Φ_R, δ_F' and δ_F are data which are known*: T_s, Φ_L, and Φ_S are then unknown. δ_F' can be obtained by measurement of stomatal resistance (see Chapters 15 and 16) and δ_F by measurement of wind speed, U (Fig. 17.11 for example).
1. When δ_F' is known, O_1 on the abscissa axis and O_1T can then be drawn.
2. δ_F' gives a curve of each of the two sets (dotted line set and solid line set); their intersection with O_1T gives points T_s and T_{ds} respectively, *i.e.* by projecting them onto the temperature axis: T_s – surface temperature, and T_{ds} – dew point temperature at the surface are obtained (T_{s0} or $T_{s\max}$ would represent the surface temperature of a perfectly humid or a perfectly dry leaf in the same conditions).
3. The line OT_{ds} determines latent heat flux at the intersection with the flux axis (Φ_L point) and sensible heat flux is obtained by difference from net radiation flux.

1. r_a and r_s, are respectively the boundary layer resistance and stomatal resistance to water vapour transfer [s m^{-1}], r_a' the corresponding resistance to heat transfer, and r_s' the corresponding resistance analogous to r_a'. R is the gas constant [kg m^2 s^{-2} °C^{-1}/mol] and M is mass of water mole [kg/mol].

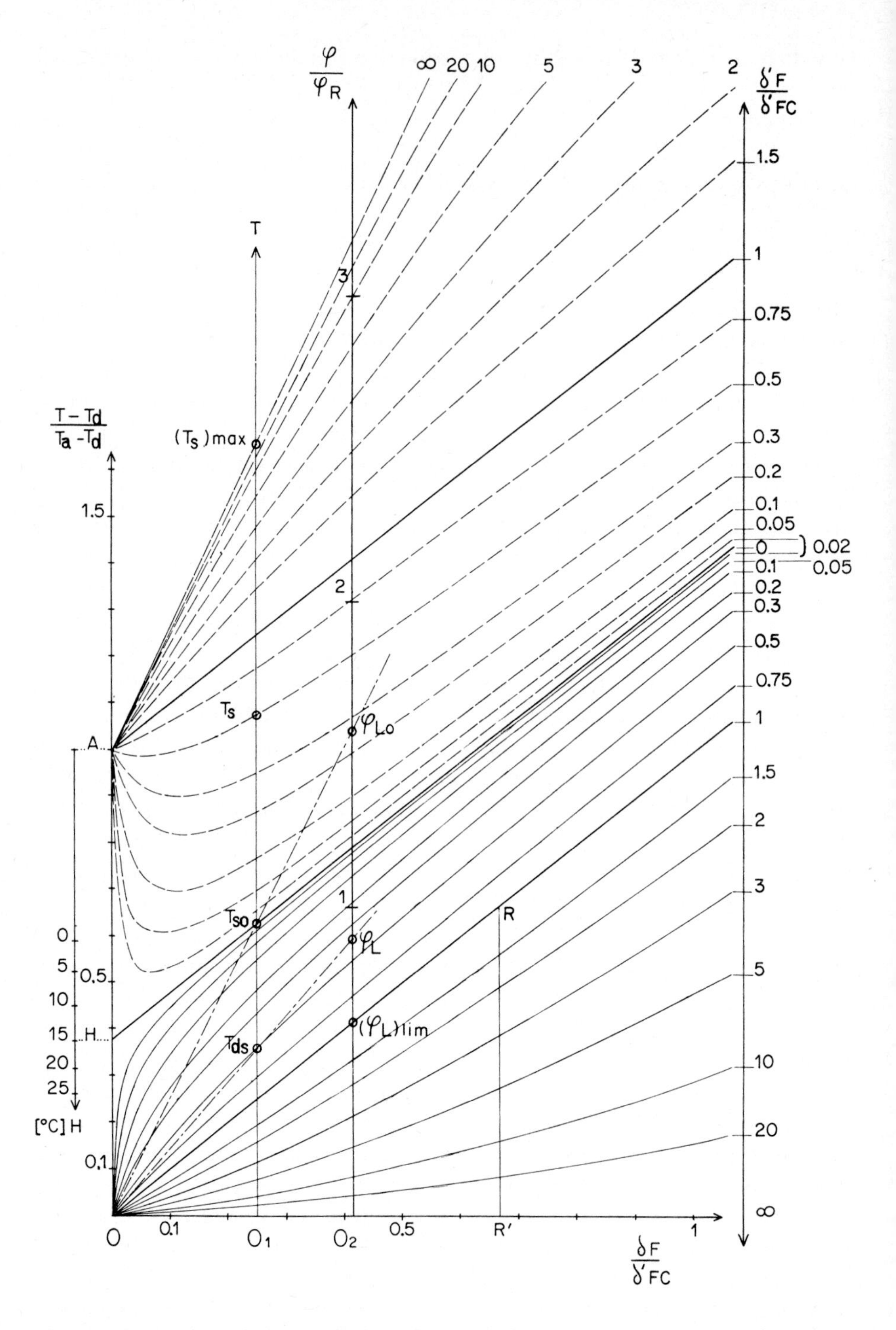

Fig. 17.10 General graph for calculation of mean leaf temperature. See the text for details. After Daudet & Perrier (1968).

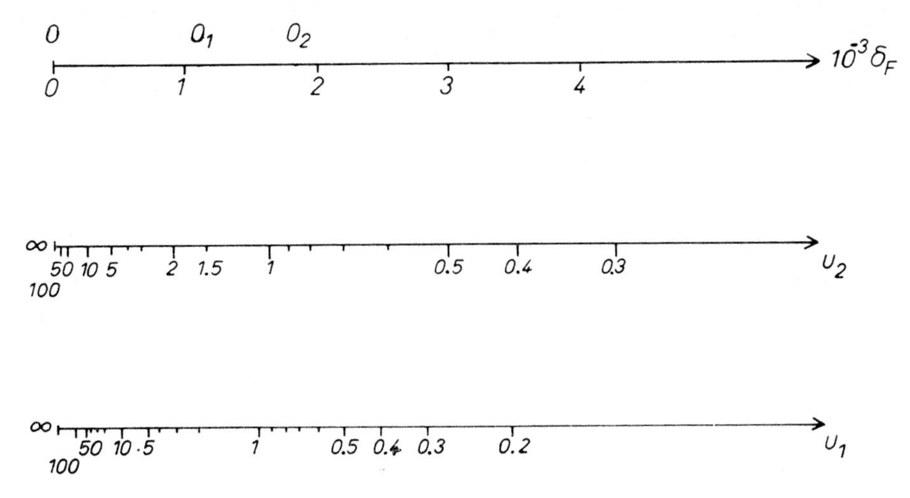

Fig. 17.11 Relation for determining the thickness parameter of the diffusion path [m] (for leaf of 5 × 3 cm) and the wind speed U [m s^{-1}]. U_1: laminar flow, U_2: turbulent flow (after Perrier, unpubl.). For explanation see text.

b. Secondly, T_a, T_d, Φ_R, δ_F, and Φ_L are known data: T_s, δ_F', Φ_s are unknown (for instance, Φ_L is measured by weighing). The problem is identically resolved:

1. The known value of δ_F gives point O_1 and fixes the O_1T axis; similarly, the point Φ_L can be obtained and the line $O\Phi_L$ determines T_{ds} at the intersection with the O_1T axis (temperature of dew point at the surface of the leaf); T_{ds} determines a curve of the set in solid lines which defines a value of δ_F'/δ_{FC}', so that finally δ_F' can be deduced.
2. The corresponding curve of the other set gives point T_s on the axis O_1T, and consequently the surface temperature can be calculated.

To furnish complementary information, a relationship between U and δ_F for a leaf of given dimensions is given in Fig. 17.11. A generalisation of this relationship has been proposed (de Vries & Venema 1954, see also Monteith 1965) as follows:

$$\delta_F = 5\, L_0 \left(\frac{U L_0}{\nu} \right)^{-0.7} \quad [\mathrm{m}] \tag{17.18}$$

where L_0 is the characteristic dimension of the leaf [*e.g.* $2/L_0 = 1/L + 1/l$], ν is kinematic viscosity of air [m^2 s^{-1}], U is windspeed [m s^{-1}].

17.7 | Range of application and comparison of methods

Fig. 17.12 is a simple diagram of the leaf zones investigated by the different methods. The size of the sensors (especially thermistors and resistance thermometers) is an importance factor causing disturbances and is in practice a limiting factor when it reaches leaf thickness or when it exceeds half the thickness of the boundary layer. Each method is more or less suitable for a certain type of temperature measurement according to its characteristics. Table 17.7 presents the main points of comparison.

Table 17.7. Comparison of methods of leaf temperature measurement.

Method	Range of measurement	Sensitivity*	Practical accuracy**	Response-time constant
Thermocouple	Common range (−20 °C, +60 °C) Good linearity	Good but depending on meter (potentiometer or galvanometer) 0.1 °C	± 0.1 °C	About 0.1 s or le according to the p tentiometer, and few μs for a gal nometer
Resistance	Good linearization obtained only with differences from 30 °C to 50 °C	Good, easily less than 0.1 °C to 0.01 °C	± 0.3 °C because of errors due to size	About 0.1 s to 1 according to Whe stone bridge, resistance equilib tion and above size
Thermistor	Linearization obtained only with differences of about 20 °C to 40 °C	Very good 0.01 °C is common	± 0.3 °C	About 0.1 s to 1 according to th mistor equilibrati and size
I.R. Thermometry	Not limited (used from 0 °C to 60 °C)	Does not exceed 0.3 °C	± 0.3 °C in best conditions	Great variability with the type, gen ally few seconds (1 3 s), sometimes l than one tenth o
I.R. Thermography	Differences of 10 °C to 20 °C	Can reach 0.05 °C	± 0.1 to 0.3 °C for differences	Very fast – 10^{-6} s
Thermo-luminescence	Only temperatures from 0 °C to 45 °C	Does not exceed 0.3 °C	± 0.5 °C to ± 0.3 °C for differences	About a few ten of s

* Values of sensitivity given here are not theoretical or technical limits, but sensiti ties which are readily obtained.

** The practical accuracy is the real uncertainty over the temperature of the le or part of leaf which cannot be reduced in various natural conditions, and wh taint a determination of the true expected temperature.

*** Different calibration curves are necessary for each channel, or it is necessary adjust every resistance to the same calibration curve (this is more difficult th checking thermocouples which will fit one calibration curve).

sturbances	Fidelity	Technical conditions	Usefulness	Application range
ther small ckness, disturb- ce varies with nditions, small ring many urs after roducing rmocouple	Good	– Easy to work up – Good handling – Potentiometer or better galvanometer necessary for fast measurements (kinetics) – Reference temperature is necessary – Recording (multi-channel if possible) – Thermocouples can be linked in series or in parallel	– Suitable for leaf temperature measurement in field or in laboratory – Investigation of leaf or canopy temperature heterogeneity is possible	Measurement of local or point temperatures
g thickness d important sturbance	Good	– Good handling – Sensors adapted to leaf temperature are difficult to make – Multi-channel recording is relatively difficult***	Insufficient definition of temperature and great disturbance causes errors in leaf investigations	Measurement of local or point surface temperatures
g thickness d important sturbance	Moderate	– Good handling – Sensors are not easily miniaturized and linearized (some are commercial) – Multi-channel recording is relatively difficult***	*id.*	*id.*
nsor at dis- nce without sturbance	Rather bad	– Difficult working up – Stability is hardly maintained – Intermittent measurement (measurement of surrounding radiation-calibration)	More convenient for large surfaces (canopy)	Measurement of mean surface temperature of canopy
nsor at dis- nce without sturbance	Rather bad	– Difficult reading – Recording on a film	Useful for gradient measurements mainly in laboratory	Measurement of thermal gradient for small surfaces
ery thin deposit, nall disturbance	Reduced	– Working up is difficult – Sufficient stability difficult to obtain – Measurements with direct radiation are impossible – Continuous recording is difficult	Well adapted as laboratory method particularly for working on a small scale	Mean or local temperature of leaf surface

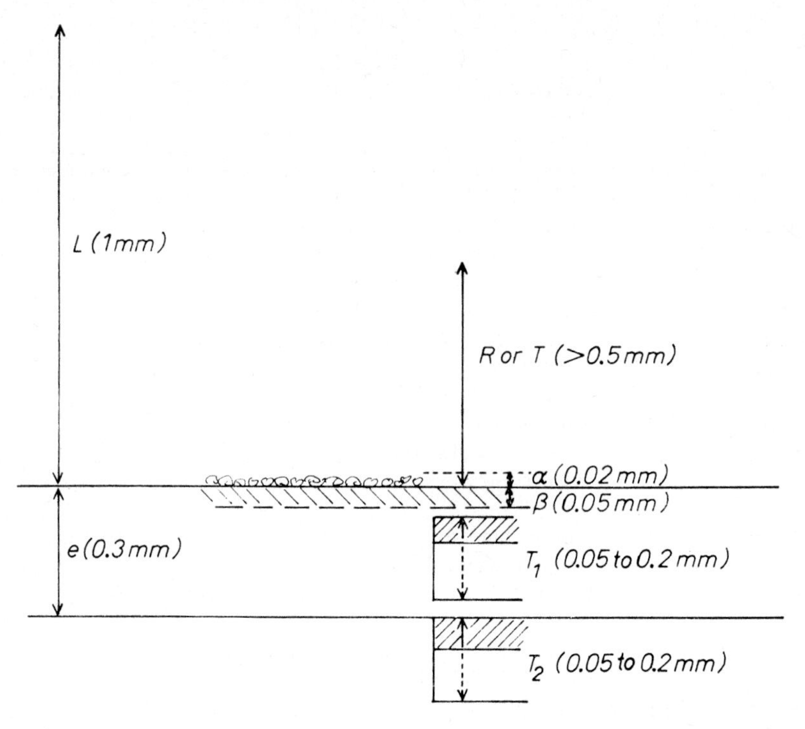

Fig. 17.12 Measuring range of different methods for determining leaf temperature. *e:* leaf thickness, *L:* leaf boundary layer mean thickness, *α:* luminescence range of measurement, *β:* maximum I.R. thermometer range of measurement, T_1, T_2: thermocouple range of measurement (junction in the leaf T_1, junction in contact with the leaf T_2), *R* or *T:* resistance thermometer or thermistor range of measurement.

17.8 | Conclusion

This review shows that the primary criteria governing the choice of a suitable method are mainly determined by the purpose and the kind of experimentation. For example: Firstly, what should be measured? Which phenomena should be demonstrated or calculated? Under what conditions will these measurements be made (environment, time . . .)?, *etc.*

Different space scales can be investigated, from temperature at the level of a chloroplast, to temperature at each point of a leaf, to temperature of a canopy. Similarly different time scales can be used from instantaneous measurement to continuous recording. These are some of the factors which will lead to the choice of a convenient method.

The current level of technology does not facilitate measurements of leaf temperature because of the precautions which must be taken either at the level of the sensor (*e.g.* with electrical methods) or at the level of the instrumentation (*e.g.* with radiative methods). Under particular conditions, which must be born in mind, thermoelectric methods allow easy, reliable and precise measurements in most cases. For particular applications in the field (*e.g.* canopy surface temperature) or in the laboratory (*e.g.* investigation of thermal field) radiative methods can be efficiently employed.

17.9 | References

Aldrich, L. B.: The melikeron – an approximately black-body pyranometer. – Smithsonian Misc. Collection 72: 1-13, 1922.

Barnes (U.S.A.): L'appareil photographique infra-rouge. – Mesures, Régulations, Automatisme (Paris) 32(5): 91, 1967.

Beakley, W. R.: The design of thermistor thermometers with linear calibration. – J. sci. Instr. 28: 176-179, 1951.

Becker, J. A., Green, C. B., Pearson, G. L.: Properties and uses of thermistors – thermally sensitive resistors. – Bell System tech. J. 26: 170-212, 1947.

Bouchet, R. J.: Évapotranspiration réelle, évapotranspiration potentielle, et production agricole. – Ann. agr. 14: 743-824, 1963; or in: L'eau et la Production Végétale. Pp. 151-232. I.N.R.A., Paris 1964.

Bowling Barnes, R.: Diagnostic thermography. – Appl. Optics 7: 1673-1695, 1968.

Caldwell, F. R.: Thermocouple materials. – In: Temperature, its Measurement and Control in Science and Industry. Part 2. Pp. 82-134. Reinhold Publ. Corp., New York 1962.

Daudet, F., Perrier, A.: Étude de l'évaporation ou de la condensation à la surface d'un corps à partir du bilan énergétique. – Rev. gén. Thermique 76: 353-363, 1968.

Droms, C. R.: Thermistors for temperature measurements. – In: Temperature, its Measurement and Control in Science and Industry. Part 2. Pp. 339-346. Reinhold Publ. Corp., New York 1962.

Durand, R., de Parcevaux, S., Roche, P.: Action de la température sur la croissance et le développement du lin. – Ann. Physiol. vég. 9: 87-105, 1967.

Fimpel, H.: Messungen der Temperatur einer Grassoberfläche mit einem Gesamtstrahlungspyrometer Meteor. – Inst. Mitteil. Univ. München 9: 98-106, 1964.

Finch, J. D.: General principles of thermoelectric thermometry. – In: Temperature, its Measurement and Control in Science and Industry. Part 2. Pp. 1-32. Reinhold Publ. Corp., New York 1962.

Fuchs, M., Tanner, C. B.: Infrared thermometry of vegetation. – Agr. J. 58: 597-601, 1966.

Fuchs, M., Kanemasu, E. T., Kerr, J. P., Tanner, C. B.: Effect of viewing angle canopy temperature measurements with infrared thermometers. – Agr. J. 59: 494-496, 1967.

Gale, J., Manes, A., Poljakoff- Mayber, A. A rapidly equilibrating thermocouple contact thermometer for measurement of leaf-surface temperatures. – Ecology 51: 521–525, 1970.

Gates, D. M.: Leaf temperature and energy exchange. – Arch. Meteorol. Geophys. Bioklimatol. B 12: 321-336, 1963.

Gates, D. M.: Energy, plants, and ecology. – Ecology 46: 1-13, 1965.

Gates, D. M.: Transpiration and leaf temperature. – Annu. Rev. Plant Physiol. 19: 211-238, 1968.

Gates, D. M., Benedict, C. M.: Convection phenomena from plants in still air. – Amer. J. Bot. 50: 567-573, 1963.

Gates, D. M., Tantraporn, W.: The reflectivity of deciduous trees and herbaceous plants in the infra-red to 25 microns. – Science 115: 613-616, 1952.

Geiger, R.: The Climate near the Ground. – 2nd Ed. Harvard Univ. Press, Cambridge, Mass. 1957.

Gordon, W. E., Seay, P. A.: Compensation of temperature elements. – Bull. Amer. meteorol. Soc. 29: 41-42, 1948.

Hirsch, G.: Zur Klimatologie und Transpiration an Vegetationsgrenzen. – Beitr. Biol. Pfl. 33: 371-422, 1957.

Huber, B.: Mikroklimatische und Pflanzentemperatur-Registrierungen mit dem Multithermographen von Hartmann-Braun. – Jahrb. wiss. Bot. 84: 671-709, 1937.

Huber, B.: Die Temperatur pflanzlicher Oberflächen. – In: Ruhland, W. (ed.): Handbuch der Pflanzenphysiologie. Vol. 3. Pp. 285-292. Springer, Berlin–Göttingen–Heidelberg 1956.

Huetz, J., Leroux, J. P.: Étude sur la mesure des températures de surface. – Rapport A.D.R.S.T. M.E. No. 3 & 4, ref. 6434305 00 480 75 01, 1964.

Idle, D. B.: The measurement of apparent surface temperature. – In: The Measurement of Environmental Factors in Terrestrial Ecology. Pp. 47-57. Blackwell sci. Publ., Oxford–Edinburgh 1968.

Idrac, J.: Caractéristique d'une chaîne de mesure. – In: Eckardt, F. E. (ed.): Functioning of Terrestrial Ecosystems at the Primary Production Level. Pp. 151-175. Unesco, Paris 1968.

Kreeb, K.: Eine neue Methode für Temperaturmessungen an Pflanzen. – Meteorol. Rundsch. 7: 13-14, 1954.

Lange, O. L.: Leaf temperatures and methods of measurement. – In: Eckardt, F. E. (ed.): Methodology of Eco-Physiology. Pp. 203-209. Unesco, Paris 1965.

Leroux, J. P.: Étude sur la détermination des températures de surface. – Thèse, Faculté de Paris, Série A, no 3693, 1961.

Levitt, J.: The Hardiness of Plants. – Academic Press, New York 1956.

Levitt, J.: Temperature effect in plants. – In: Temperature, its Measurement and Control in Science and Industry. Part 3. Pp. 131-134. Reinhold Publ. Corp., New York 1962.

Lewerenz, H. W.: Luminescence of Solids. – J. Wiley, New York 1950.

Linacre, E. T.: Further studies of the heat transfer from a leaf. – Plant Physiol. 42: 651-658, 1967.

Miller, E. C., Saunders, A. R.: Some observations on the temperature of the leaves of crop plants. – J. agr. Res. 26: 15-43, 1923.

Molnar, G. W., Rosenbaun, J. C.: Surface temperature measurement with thermocouples. – In: Temperature, its Measurement and Control in Science and Industry. Part 3. Pp. 3-11. Reinhold Publ. Corp., New York 1962.

Monteith, J. L.: Evaporation and environment. – In: The State and Movement of Water in Living Organisms. (Symp. Soc. exp. Biol. 19.) Pp. 205-234. Univ. Press, Cambridge 1965.

Monteith, J. L., Szeicz, G.: Radiative temperature in the heat balance of natural surfaces. – Quart. J. roy. meteorol. Soc. 88: 496-507, 1962.

Palmer, J. H.: A thermocouple technique of the measurement of vegetation temperature. – In: Instrumentation for Plant Environment Measurements. Pp. 15-16. C.S.I.R.O., Aspendale 1966.

Papadakis, J.: Potential Evaporation. – Buenos Aires 1965.

de Parcevaux, S.: Transpiration végétale et production de matière sèche. Essai d'interprétation en fonction des facteurs du milieu. – In: L'eau et la Production Végétale. Pp. 63-150. INRA, Paris 1964.

Perrier, A.: Mesure des températures de surface de feuilles végétales par la méthode de luminescence et application à leur bilan énergétique. Thèse 3ème cycle. Faculté des Sciences de Paris 1966.

Perrier, A.: Contribution à l'étude des échanges thermiques en biologie végétale (emploi du photothermomètre de surface pour la détermination du bilan énergétique des feuilles). – Rev. gén. Thermique 79-80: 721-740, 1968.

Platt, R. B., Griffiths, F. G.: Temperature. – In: Environmental Measurement and Interpretation. Pp. 92-113. Reinhold Publ. Corp., New York 1964.

Platt, R. B., Wolf, J. N.: General uses and methods of thermistors in temperature investigations with special reference to a technique for high sensitivity contact temperature measurement. – Plant Physiol. 25: 507-512, 1950.

Ramdas, L. A., Paranjpe, M. K.: An interferometric method of measuring temperatures and temperature gradients very close to a hot surface. – Current Sci. 4: 642, 1936.

Raschke, K.: Über die physikalischen Beziehungen zwischen Wärmeübergangzahl, Strahlungsaustausch, Temperatur und Transpiration einer Blattes. – Planta 48: 100-238, 1956a.

Raschke, K.: Mikrometeorologisch gemessene Energieumsätze eines *Alocasia*-Blattes. – Arch. Meteorol. Geophys. B 7: 240-268, 1956b.

Raschke, K.: Über den Einfluß der Diffusionswiderstände auf die Transpiration und die Temperatur eines Blattes. – Flora 146: 546-578, 1958.

Raschke, K.: Heat transfer between the plant and the environment. – Annu. Rev. Plant Physiol. 11: 111-126, 1960.

Rizika, J. W., Rohsenow, W. M.: Thermocouple thermal error. – Ind. eng. Chem. 44: 1168-1171, 1953.

Roeser, W. F., Lonberger, S. T.: Methods of testing thermocouples and thermocouple materials. – Nat. Bur. Standards Cir. 590: 1-21, 1958.

Schulze, E. D.: Der CO_2-Gaswechsel der Buche (*Fagus silvatica* L.) in Abhängigkeit von den Klimafaktoren im Freiland. – Flora 159: 177-232, 1970.

Shenker, H., Lauritzen, J. I. Jr., Corruccini, R. J., Lonberger, S. T.: Reference tables for thermocouples. – Nat. Bur. Standards Cir. 561: 1-84, 1955.
Shrewe, E. B.: The daily march of transpiration in a desert perennial. – Publ. Carnegie Inst. Washington 194: 1-64, 1914.
Smith, F. E.: Bridge methods for resistance measurements of high precision in platinum thermometry. – Phil. Mag. 24: 541-569, 1912.
Stoll, A. M.: The measurement of bioclimatological heat exchange. – In: Temperature, its Measurement and Control in Science and Industry. Part 3, Pp. 73-82. Reinhold Publ. Corp., New York 1962.
Stoll, A. M., Hardy, J. D.: A method for measuring radiant temperatures of the environment. – Appl. Physiol. 5: 117-124, 1952.
Takechi, O., Haseba, T.: Studies on the leaf temperature. (2). – J. agr. Meteorol. 18: 92-97, 1962.
Takechi, O., Haseba, T.: Studies on the leaf temperature. (3): – J. agr. Meteorol. 19: 7-10, 1963.
Takechi, O., Haseba, T., Tomari, I., Akimoto, T.: Studies on the leaf temperature. (1) – J. agr. Meteorol. 18: 89-91, 1962.
Thureau, P.: Étude d'une méthode de mesure des températures utilisant la sensibilité thermique des couleurs de fluorescence. – Thèse. Faculté de Paris 1955.
Tranquillini, W.: Die Bedeutung des Lichtes und der Temperatur für die Kohlensäureassimilation von *Pinus cembra*-Jungwuchs an einem hochalpinen Standort. – Planta 46: 154-178, 1955.
de Vries, D. A., Venema, H. J.: Some considerations on the behaviour of the Piche evaporimeter. – Vegetatio 5-6: 225-234, 1954.
Wallace, R. H., Clum, H. H.: Leaf temperatures. – Amer. J. Bot. 25: 83-97, 1938.

18 | DETERMINATION OF CHLOROPHYLLS *a* AND *b*

18.1 | Introduction

The leading role of chlorophylls in absorption of radiation and their participation in photosystems transforming the absorbed radiant energy into chemical energy is now well known. This is the main reason why photosynthetic activity is often expressed per amount of total chlorophyll ($a + b$) or chlorophyll *a* only. Carotenoids, which also participate in the absorption of short-wave, visible radiation and perhaps also in redox reactions of photosynthesis, are usually omitted. Their exact analysis is more complicated than chlorophyll determination: they are more labile, and their only absorption bands in the blue spectral region overlap with blue absorption bands of chlorophylls. Plant material contains various carotenoids differing in spectral properties: this diversity makes their determination without previous separation very difficult or impossible, and time-consuming. Therefore this Chapter deals mainly with selected methods for the determination of chlorophylls *a* and *b*[1]. Since at present there is no method for completely separating or reliably determining the biological forms of chlorophyll *a*, only the pigment that can be extracted into organic solvents will be dealt with here.

From the recent literature concerning chlorophyll analysis, the review papers by Smith & Benitez (1955), French (1960), Holden (1965) and Strain & Svec (1966), as well as the book by Sapozhnikov (1964), deserve the attention of everyone interested in details of chlorophyll estimation procedures.

18.2 | Non-destructive methods of assessing the content of chlorophyll in plants

For many research problems, a rapid, approximate method which is not injurious to the experimental plants is desirable.

A simple but inaccurate method is visual comparison of the colour of the plant material with standard colour charts (*e.g.* Munsell 1958) or with specially designed colour scales prepared individually by the gradual mixing of fundamental colours (Grime 1961). The results obtained in this way and their errors vary with the ability and experience of the investigator, the time of day, illuminance and characteristics of the plant material such as the waxiness of the surface, the presence of trichomes, leaf thickness, the distribution of chloroplasts in the cells, the ratio of chlorophyll *a* to *b*, the presence of carotenoids and anthocyanins, *etc.*

A more objective procedure is the measurement of leaf reflectance *in vivo* using an appropriate spectral colorimeter or spectrophotometer with an integrating sphere. Such equipment can give integrated values for a piece of growing turf (Birth & McVey 1968). The relation between reflectance and chlorophyll content differs amongst plant types. Hence each kind of material requires a particular

1. This book is very largely devoted to higher plants. Hence algal chlorophylls (*c* and *d*) and chlorophylls of photosynthetic bacteria are not dealt with.

calibration curve (Benedict & Swidler 1961; Turrell, Weber & Austin 1961). As reflectance is also determined by the character of the leaf surface, the structure of the cells in the epidermis and the internal arrangement of cells, the variability of values obtained is high and the error of determination reaches ± 10 to 50% (Nybom 1955).

Determination of radiation absorption by the leaf *in vivo* gives more reliable results. Inada's (1963) 'chlorophyllometer' measures the difference between absorption by the leaf at 670 and 750 nm by means of interference filters. This value is linearly related to the chlorophyll concentration per unit leaf area (the correlation coefficient for rice leaves was $r = 0.998$). A dual-monochromator spectrophotometer constructed by Birth (1960) measures the difference between absorbance at 695 and 725 nm, a fibre optic photometer of McClure (1969) the difference between 675 and 720 nm.

All these methods require a separate calibration for each material. They are not suitable for the comparative determinations frequently required in photosynthesis research. Generally reliable methods of chlorophyll analysis can only be those based on the quantitative extraction of pigments from the plant material.

18.3 | General instructions for chlorophyll estimation in extracts

To avoid decomposition of the pigments (see Table 18.1), all glassware and solvents must be free from acids, bases and reducing or oxidizing substances. Residues of acids on glassware may be washed off with a concentrated solution of sodium phosphate (Official Methods . . . 1960, p. 92). The water used must be distilled, without the addition of permanganate, in all-glass apparatus. Redistillation of solvents or use of high purity solvents is necessary.

All procedures should be performed in darkness, under a green safe-light, or at least with elimination of direct, bright light or sunlight. The extracts may be kept for a few hours at temperatures near 0 °C in darkness. An atmosphere of nitrogen is preferable, especially for chromatographic procedures. It is desirable that all steps of the analysis should be performed as rapidly as possible.

Table 18.1 Degradation products of chlorophylls in solution obtained as the result of different treatments (after Bruinsma 1963).

Treatment	Effect	Product
Chlorophyllase	Hydrolysis of phytol group	Chlorophyllides (green)
Alkali	The same, further hydrolyses	Various compounds
Weak acid	Mg dissociation	Pheophytins (brown)
Strong acid	Mg and phytol removed	Pheophorbides (brown)
Moist heat	Stimulates acid treatment; keto-enol tautomerism (?)	Pheophorbides, pheophytins Chlorophyll isomers (green)
Oxygen + alcohols	Allomerisation	Chlorophyll peroxides (green)
Photooxidation	Bleaching	Various compounds
Photoreduction	Bleaching	Mesochlorophylls, leuco compounds

18.4 | Preparation of extracts

18.4.1 | Sampling

The sample should be fully representative of the material studied if the results of the analyses are to be relevant. To achieve this, whole plants or leaves are only rarely taken for analysis. It is difficult to grind up large samples and their extraction consumes large amounts of expensive solvents. Hence a representative sub-sample is usually analysed. Prior to sampling, an appropriate unit should be chosen: this determines the size of the sub-sample and the basis on which the chlorophyll content is expressed.

The most appropriate basis on which to express chlorophyll content is leaf area, since it is closely related to the photosynthetic function of the leaf. Usually a sub-sample consisting of a number of discs of known area is taken by a cork-borer or a special cutting device. The sampling pattern should cover the whole area of the leaf, all leaves of the plant analysed and the experimental treatment, *etc.* In experiments in which the photosynthetic rate is determined simultaneously by the leaf disc method (see Chapter 9), the discs for chlorophyll determination should be taken from nearby areas of the leaf blade and in the same number as the set for photosynthesis measurement. When measuring photosynthesis by gasometric methods, chlorophylls should be determined in the same part of the leaf lamina as was used for the determination of assimilatory activity (always provided that chlorophyll was not degraded during the experiment by strong light, for example). In experiments with large symmetric leaves, chlorophyll content can be determined in the corresponding part of the non-exposed half of the leaf. When determining photosynthetic rate in a pincer-chamber (see Fig. 2.11), a simple quadrangular metal punch, of the exact size and shape of the window in the pincer chamber, can be used to obtain the specimen for analysis quickly.

The analysis of curled, small leaves of seedlings usually requires sampling a number of whole plants or their green photosynthetically active parts. Prior to analysis it is a good idea to determine their fresh weight simultaneously with the fresh weight of the same number of similar plants (or their green parts) of the same experimental treatment. After drying and weighing the parallel sample, the chlorophyll content can be expressed on the basis of either a single plant, or of fresh or dry weight.

Alternatively, the sample can be chopped or clipped into fine pieces which are then mixed. From the mixture, two samples are chosen and weighed, one of them being analysed for chlorophylls and the second dried and weighed again. This type of sampling must be done quickly to avoid large losses of water: it is therefore used more often with needles than with more mesophytic leaves.

It is always desirable to be able to express the chlorophyll content on a leaf area and a dry weight basis. The least useful basis is fresh weight because it changes with the water content of the tissues, especially in studies of the time-course of chlorophyll fluctuations, the effects of different chemical substances and environmental factors, *etc.*

In special cases (*e.g.* comparison of chlorosis types, developmental changes), it may be necessary to express the chlorophyll content per cell, per chloroplast, or per unit of chloroplast volume.

18.4.2 | Storage of samples

In principle only fresh, turgid material should be analysed. If the material cannot be analysed immediately after sampling, it should be stored in such a way as to avoid pigment destruction. Prior to storage, the sample size should be specified, because the stored material is always subject to changes in shape, water content, *etc.*

All procedures of drying in air, including mild ones (*e.g.* +50 °C), may induce destruction of as much as 50% of the chlorophylls. The pigments in monocotyledons are usually more susceptible to destruction than the pigments in dicotyledons. If, for any reason, plants must be dried, freeze drying is acceptable. Deterioration of chlorophyll also takes place in dried material. Freezing in a mixture of acetone and dry ice, or in liquid nitrogen, or liquid air in a Dewar flask is preferable. The frozen sample can be stored at −10 °C, or lyophilized.

Samples can be kept at temperatures below 0 °C for one or two days, *e.g.* in polythene bags. Stored in this way, perceptible changes only occur in the pigment composition of acid tissues, which always present difficulties in obtaining a reliable analysis.

For longer periods of storage the following method is recommended (Šesták 1959b): 10 to 15 leaf discs of 8 mm diameter in a test tube (*ca.* 10 × 100 mm) are covered with 2 ml anhydrous acetone *p.a.* and a pinch of $MgCO_3$ is added. The test tube is then half submerged in water at *ca.* + 80 °C. When the acetone begins to boil, the test tube is quickly closed with a stopper saturated with warm paraffin and cooled by submersion in cold water. The test tubes standing upright are then stored in closed boxes at temperatures below +4 °C. This procedure softens the tissues and facilitates the extraction of chlorophyll. Losses of chlorophyll are less than 3% after 1 month (sugar beet, sunflower, tobacco) and less than 10% after 3 months (the same plants and kale, clover and pumpkin).

18.4.3 | Inhibition of enzymatic activity

In addition to redox systems, the enzyme chlorophyllase may also induce pigment deterioration in living plant cells during the preparation for analysis. Chlorophyllase hydrolytically removes phytol from the IVth pyrrol ring in the chlorophyll molecule, which is thus converted to chlorophyllide, methyl chlorophyllide or ethyl chlorophyllide (in aqueous acetone, methanol or ethanol). Phytol is responsible for the lipophilic character of the chlorophyll molecule and therefore the chlorophyllides are hydrophilic. They are mainly formed during the extraction procedure (Shlyk *et al.* 1961; Šesták 1964), especially in some plant species (*e.g.* sugar beet, *Chlorophytum*, *etc.*).

The activity of chlorophyllase mainly interferes with exact chlorophyll determination in procedures which include the transfer of pigments from a polar extraction solvent (acetone, alcohol) into diethyl ether, ligroine or another non-polar solvent (see Section 18.6.5). In this case the hydrophilic chlorophyll products remain in the polar phase of the solvent system and escape determination. The same holds for the determination of chlorophylls *a* and *b* after chromatographic separation of the pigment mixture (Sections 18.7, 18.8 and 18.9) when water-soluble chlorophyll derivatives remain usually at, or near, the origin. On the other hand, the activity of chlorophyllase does not introduce errors into colorimetric or spectrophotometric determination of chlorophylls in the original, unpurified chlorophyll extract because the absorption spectra of chlorophyllides (mainly chlorophyllides *a*) are – according to Holt & Jacobs (1954) – very similar to those of chlorophylls. This general view is opposed by the studies of Rudolph (1965) who found a spectral shift of 3 nm to longer wavelengths for chlorophyllide *a* and protochlorophyllide in comparison with the respective phytolized pigments.

High enzymatic activity of some tissues can be arrested by a 30 s to 1 min (according to the thickness and infiltrability of the tissue) immersion in boiling distilled water, of neutral pH. Leaf discs are placed on a nylon net forming the bottom of a glass cylinder of diameter 2 to 3 cm. The cylinders are placed upright in a basket of aluminium netting. This ensures uniform covering of all the discs with water Reliable fixation is provided by scalding with hot steam for 2 min. Careful scalding is essential in protochlorophyll(ide) determination. The effect of scalding, on each material to be analysed should be checked. Immediately after scalding, the tissue must be cooled and dried with filter paper and then quickly extracted.

Substitution of distilled water by phosphate buffer of pH 10 (103 g Na_2HPO_4 + 12.7 g Na_3PO_4 *ad* 2 500 ml) as recommended by Maslova (1959) increases the eventual unfavourable effects of scalding in old leaves (release of some pigments into the boiling buffer, formation of chlorophyll isomers – Strain & Manning 1942).

18.4.4 | Grinding the material

Quantitative determination of chlorophylls requires complete extraction of all pigments from the material analysed. Simple chopping up of the tissue as recommended by Strain (1958) is not sufficient for the majority of plants. Blending in a *Waring Blendor* type device or in models with an overhead motor and special small flasks (*MSE*, '*Vortex*' beaker; *Bühler*, Tübingen, Germany) is satisfactory for many types of material. The rotating knives chop the tissues in the liquid into small pieces. An admixture of small glass beads (usually a mixture of beads of two diameters) prevents settling of tissue pieces on the walls of the glass flask and improves cell breakage. On the other hand the action of the beads may lower the life of the blender. Some special homogenizers vibrate the plant tissue with glass beads in a solvent to disrupt the cells (*MSK*; *B. Braun*, Melsungen, Germany). The homogenizer *Ultra Turrax TP 18/2* (*Janke & Kunkel*, Staufen in Br., Germany) consists of a double cylinder, knife system which is immersed into the liquid containing the plant tissue in a thick-walled test tube. The high speed of the motor (24 000 r.p.m.) induces sucking of the plant material to the knife. This technique prevents the material settling on the walls and permits quantitative washing of the device by a further portion of solvent (Ziegler & Egle 1965). Unfortunately the seals around the shaft are not resistant to contact with acetone. For small amounts of plant material the Potter-Elvehjem piston homogenizer can be recommended, especially if the piston is made of inert plastics instead of the traditional glass.

A procedure still commonly used is to grind the tissue with the solvent in a pestle and mortar by hand. This is more effective with the addition of quartz sand or carborundum powder. Grinding with granular anhydrous sodium sulphate (Sapozhnikov 1951) dehydrates the material at the same time, but the strong adsorption of some pigments on sodium sulphate sometimes interferes with complete extraction.

The plant material, with 1/3 to 1/4 of its volume of abrasive, is put into a china or glass mortar of adequate diameter (for 10 to 20 cm^2 of leaf area, a mortar of diameter *ca.* 6 cm is suitable). After the addition of a pinch of $MgCO_3$ *p.a.* or a few drops of dimethylaniline (fresh colourless preparation) to neutralize the acids, the mixture is just saturated with the extraction solvent. Grinding with a large volume of solvent is a lengthy job and there is a danger that some of the extract might be spilt. Grinding takes *ca.* 3 min, being finished when the slurry is homogeneous and no pieces of tissue can be distinguished.

Whatever the method, grinding should be carried out quickly and at low temperature (*e.g.* +4 °C).

18.4.5 | Extraction and clearing of the extract

Chlorophyll is usually extracted from its lipoprotein complex *in vivo* with acetone, methanol or ethanol or (to improve extraction of carotenoids) a mixture of these polar solvents with ligroine or petroleum ether (*e.g.* methanol – petroleum ether 2 : 1, Strain 1958). Although the smell of acetone makes the work more unpleasant than does the smell of ethanol, acetone does ensure better extraction from tissues containing a higher percentage of water. As early as 1913, Willstätter & Stoll found relatively sharp extraction maxima for chlorophylls from fresh higher plants with 85% acetone in water (by volume), or 90% ethanol or 100% methanol. The suitability of solvents for extraction is given, for example, by their dielectric constants: acetone (const. 21.5) is less polar than ethanol (const. 25.8) and methanol (31.2). In contrast to acetone, in alcoholic solvents allomers of the chlorophylls are formed, which are spectrally different from the chlorophylls (their red absorption peak is lower and shifted 8 nm to shorter wavelengths – Johnston & Watson 1956).

Extraction should be done at low temperature and the solvent should be cooled to 0° to −5 °C prior to extraction. Extraction with boiling solvent used by some authors stimulates pigment deterioration. Freezing, lyophilization, scalding and storage in acetone facilitate the extraction.

The mash of ground leaf material and abrasive is mixed with 2 to 5 ml of 85% acetone and the extract is decanted onto a sintered glass filter (*e.g. Schott*, Jena, *3G4*). Filtration is speeded up by the application of suction below the filter or pressure above the filter. Filtration suction of *ca.* 70 to 90 mb (50 to 70 torr) below atmospheric pressure is maintained *e.g.* by a simple mercury valve; lower pressures can induce boiling of the solvent and cause it to overflow from the test tube in the suction flask. For the quicker pressure filtration, the sintered funnel is put into a hermetically sealed perspex box with its stem projecting through the bottom of the box. After decanting the extract onto the funnel and screwing on the lid, the pressure in the box is raised by introducing nitrogen through a side-arm.

A second side-arm on the box is closed with a valve which allows pressure equilibration when the filtration is finished.
The mash in the mortar is repeatedly washed by further 2 to 5 ml aliquots of 80 to 85% acetone: these are again decanted and filtered until no more pigment can be extracted. The extract is made up to the required volume (usually 10 to 25 ml) in a graduated test tube which is stoppered by a cork (pigments in rubber stoppers are often soluble in acetone or alcohols).
The extract can also be cleared by repeated centrifugation. After decantation of the first supernatant, the sediment is mixed with a fresh portion of solvent and the centrifugation is repeated until the sediment is colourless.

18.4.6 | Transfer of pigments into the nonpolar solvent

For special purposes (*e.g.* separation from water-soluble pigments, removing solution turbidity, pretreatment for chromatographic separation, testing of preparation purity by comparison of specific absorption coefficients, *etc.*) the pigments may be transferred into a nonpolar solvent, usually diethyl ether (without peroxides), petroleum ether or ligroine. The nonpolar solvent is added to the original acetone extract in a separating funnel (in an amount equal to more than half of the initial volume). After a gentle shaking, distilled water or 10% solution of NaCl or solution of ammonium acetate is added very carefully. Two layers separate – the upper nonpolar layer contains chlorophylls and carotenoids, the lower one holds the water-soluble pigments (*e.g.* chlorophyllides, anthocyanins). The nonpolar layer is repeatedly washed dropwise with distilled water without shaking as that may induce the formation of heavy emulsions (mainly when using ligroine). Washing removes residues of acetone and salts and partially concentrates the nonpolar solution. Further evaporation of the solvent is induced by reduced pressure or blowing nitrogen over the surface of the solution. Drying with anhydrous Na_2SO_4 cannot be recommended (see Section 18.4.4); a better procedure is to freeze out the water at 0 °C.
Losses of pigments may occur during their transference to the nonpolar solvent (Kupke & Huntington 1963 give 2 to 5% losses) and therefore it should be done only exceptionally.

18.5 | Colorimetric determination of total chlorophyll amount

If a colorimeter is the sole instrument available, only the total amount of chlorophylls ($a + b$) can be determined. The rather close proximity of the red absorption peaks of both chlorophylls does not allow the separate determination of chlorophylls a and b with colorimeters without their preliminary chromatographic separation [even if the colorimeters are equipped with narrow spectral range filters as *e.g.* a *Pulfrich* photometer, or with simple diffraction gratings such as *Spekol* (*Zeiss*, Jena, DDR), *Coleman Junior* (Maywood, Ill., U.S.A.), or a *Spectronic 20* (*Bausch & Lomb*, Rochester, N.Y., U.S.A.)].
The absorbance of a clear acetone or alcohol extract is usually measured in cuvettes of 10 mm light path using a red filter cutting off radiation of wavelengths shorter than 600 nm. Water or pure solvent serves customarily as a comparative solution.

The most appropriate spectral region for colorimetric measurement of chlorophylls is near the isosbestic point, *i.e.* the wavelength of intersection of the absorption curves of chlorophylls *a* and *b* in red light. When using dark red filters, which mainly transmit wavelengths of the chlorophyll *a* absorption peak and longer, fluorescence emitted by chlorophyll *a* interferes with measurement of its absorbance and the shape of the calibration curve is exponential instead of linear. This is why orange red filters *S 64* or *S 61* are recommended for a *Pulfrich* photometer, *OG 2* for a *Lange* colorimeter, *etc.* In spectral colorimeters, the wavelength of measurement should be adjusted to that of the isosbestic point – 652 nm for 80% acetone. In comparative analyses, absorbances may serve directly as relative values, without the calculation of absolute chlorophyll amounts, only when linearity of the ratio of absorbance to dilution is ensured and checked. Such values should always be complemented with the conditions of measurement (*i.e.* volume of the extract, model of the colorimeter, filter, light path, *etc.*).

For the calculation of chlorophyll amount, a calibration curve is constructed using an extract diluted progressively with the solvent, *e.g.* 1 + 9, 2 + 8, 3 + 7 . . . 10 + 0 ml. These solutions are measured as soon as possible with both the colorimeter and a reliable spectrophotometer (see Section 18.6). Chlorophyll amounts are calculated on the basis of the two-wavelengths spectrophotometric method and then plotted against colorimetric absorbance. A colorimeter can also be calibrated with solutions prepared from weighed amounts of crystalline chlorophyll preparations (*Sandoz*, Basel, Switzerland; *Calbiochem*, Lucerne, Switzerland; *Koch – Light Lab.*, Colnbrook, England; *etc.*). The disadvantage of this method of calibration is – besides the high price of the preparations – the possible presence of pheophytins (Falk 1958), which increase with the period of storage of chlorophyll crystals. Artificial chlorophyll standards prepared from $K_2Cr_2O_7$ and Cu or Ni salts (Guthrie 1928), or organic dyes (Sprague & Troxler 1930), were designed for visual comparison without filters, and therefore their use introduces a bigger error the narrower the bandwidth transmitted by the filter (*e.g.* with Guthrie's standard and *S 64* filter the error amounted to 175%). Calibration curves constructed for a given solvent, filter, light path and instrument cannot be used for another solvent, filter, light path or instrument. Absorbances measured should not exceed 0.5; extracts of higher chlorophyll concentration must be diluted.

Examples of calibration curves for *Pulfrich* and *Lange* colorimeters were given *e.g.* by Šesták & Ullmann (1964). When using the spectral colorimeter *Spekol*, the absorbance measured at 652 nm is multiplied by 30.0 or 27.6 (Borris & Köhler 1968): this gives the amount of chlorophyll ($a + b$) in mg l^{-1} corresponding to spectrophotometric determinations based on the equations of Mackinney (Arnon 1949) or Ziegler & Egle (1965).

18.6 | Spectrophotometric determination of chlorophylls *a* and *b*

The only speedy method of determination of individual chlorophylls *a* and *b* in the extract is by spectrophotometry. Chlorophylls are measured in the red spectral range where carotenoids do not interfere. In higher plants, unlike blue-green and red algae, interference by phycobilins having absorption peaks near 600 nm is not expected and therefore an unpurified acetone or alcohol extract is measured

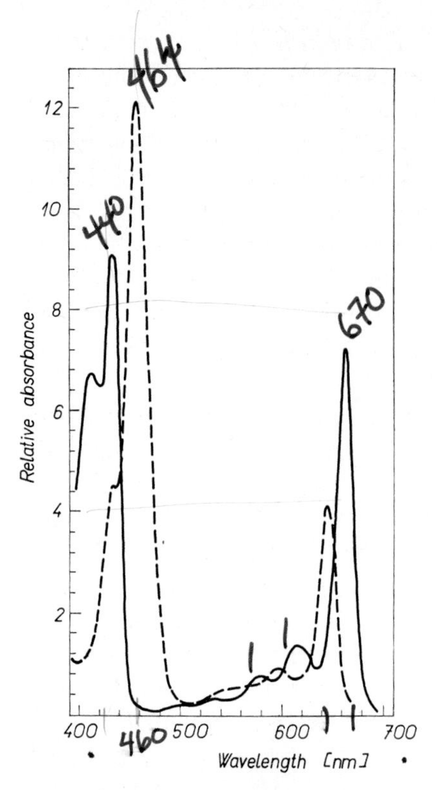

Fig. 18.1 Absorption curves of chlorophylls *a* (——) and *b* (– – –) in 100% acetone (after Comar & Zscheile 1942).

most frequently. The well-known two-wavelength method is then based on measurements of extract absorbance at the wavelengths of the absorption peaks of both chlorophylls *a* and *b* in the appropriate solvent (see Fig. 18.1).

To calculate chlorophyll amounts, the equations given by various authors, who measured more or less perfectly purified chlorophyll preparations, are used. The equations are based on the specific absorption coefficient[1] α which is the absorbance of unit amount of the pigment '*x*' measured at a given wavelength λ in a cuvette of unit light pathlength:

$$\alpha_\lambda^x = \frac{A_\lambda^x}{lc} \quad [\mathrm{l\,g^{-1}cm^{-1}}] \tag{18.1}$$

where A_λ^x = absorbance of pigment x at wavelength λ, l = length of the light path [cm], c = concentration of pigment x [g l^{-1}].

Using solutions of purified pigments in a given solvent, specific absorption coefficients are determined for chlorophyll *a* solution at wavelengths of the absorption peak of both chlorophyll *a* ($\alpha^a_{\max a}$) and chlorophyll *b* ($\alpha^a_{\max b}$), and similarly for chlorophyll *b* solution ($\alpha^b_{\max b}$, $\alpha^b_{\max a}$).

1. Specific absorption coefficient is synonymous with absorptivity.

Absorbance of a mixture of chlorophylls *a* and *b* in a solution measured at the wavelength of absorption peak of chlorophyll *a* is then given by the equation

$$A_{\max a} = \alpha^{a}_{\max a}\, c_a\, l + \alpha^{b}_{\max a}\, c_b\, l \tag{18.2}$$

A similar equation holds for absorbance at the wavelength of the absorption peak of chlorophyll *b*. Starting with this pair of equations another pair of equations is derived enabling the direct determination of concentrations of chlorophylls *a* and *b* [g 1^{-1}] in a cuvette of a standard light pathlength of 1 cm:

$$c_a = \frac{\alpha^{b}_{\max b}}{z} A_{\max a} - \frac{\alpha^{b}_{\max a}}{z} A_{\max b} \tag{18.3}$$

$$c_b = \frac{\alpha^{a}_{\max a}}{z} A_{\max b} - \frac{\alpha^{a}_{\max b}}{z} A_{\max a} \tag{18.4}$$

where

$$z = \alpha^{a}_{\max a}\, \alpha^{b}_{\max b} - \alpha^{a}_{\max b}\, \alpha^{b}_{\max a}\,.$$

Summing equations (18.3) and (18.4) the equation for concentration of chlorophyll $(a + b)$ is obtained:

$$c_{(a+b)} = \left(\frac{\alpha^{b}_{\max b} - \alpha^{a}_{\max b}}{z}\right) A_{\max a} + \left(\frac{\alpha^{a}_{\max a} - \alpha^{b}_{\max a}}{z}\right) A_{\max b} \tag{18.5}$$

By replacing the specific absorption coefficients α by molar absorption coefficients[1] ε in equations (18.1) to (18.5), equations are obtained for the calculation of moles of the pigments in one litre of solution[2]. This calculation is useful when studying synthetic or degradiation processes.

18.6.1 | *Spectrophotometers*

As the absorption peaks of both chlorophylls in the red spectral region are narrow, their maxima are sharply expressed and their distance apart is relatively small, only spectrophotometers with good resolution should be employed. The narrower the spectral band used for measurement, the more exact are the results. Therefore instruments that expand the visible spectrum and which are of sufficient luminosity to permit the use of a very narrow slit width for isolation of the smallest bandwidth are recommended.

A guide to the selection of a convenient spectrophotometer is thus the bandwidth isolated in the wavelength range from *ca.* 640 to 665 nm. Equations for the cal-

1. Molar absorption coefficient is synonymous with molar absorptivity.
2. Molecular weight of chlorophyll *a* = 893.48, chlorophyll *b* = 907.47. A list of molar absorption coefficients for chlorophyll *a* solutions in 40 solvents measured at the wavelength of the red absorption peak is given by Seely & Jensen (1965).

culation of chlorophyll amounts given in Sections 18.6.3 to 18 6.7 are based on specific absorption coefficients from Table 18.2. The most exact coefficients were determined using bandwidths smaller than 1 nm. An increase of the bandwidth to 2 nm lowers the value of specific absorption coefficients by 1% (Ziegler & Egle 1965), a further increase to 4 nm (*e.g.* with the spectrophotometer *Beckman DB*) reduces α by *ca.* 5%. The error of determination is multiplied by putting absorbances measured on an inexact spectrophotometer into the calculation equations based on very high specific absorption coefficients determined at narrow bandwidths. The equations given in Section 18.6 are suited for spectrophotometers isolating bands narrower than 1 nm in the red spectral region and are still applicable for instruments isolating bands of 2 to 3 nm (Zscheile 1947). Such spectrophotometers are *e.g. Perkin-Elmer Model 139*, *Hilger Uvispek*, *Beckman DU-2* and *DK-2*, *Unicam SP 500* and *SP 700*, *Cary Model 11*, *14*, *15* and *16*, *Optica CF 4*, *Zeiss* (Oberkochen) *PMQ II*, *Zeiss* (Jena) *Specord*, *VSU 1* and *VSU 2*, and Soviet devices *SF 4*, *SF 5* and *SF 10*. For chlorophyll analyses, instruments with glass optics are always preferable to those with quartz optics (*e.g. SF 5* is preferable to *SF 4*; spectrophotometer *PMQ II* with monochromators *M 4 G II* or *M 4 G III* to *M 4 Q II* or *M 4 Q III* – see Ziegler & Egle 1965); instruments with a perfect grating are preferable to those with a perfect prism and those with double monochromators to those with single monochromators.
None of the equations given in Section 18.6 should be used for determination of individual chlorophylls with spectral colorimeters with a simple grating *(Coleman Junior*, *Spekol*, *Spectronic 20*, *etc.)*. Even the best of them do not isolate a bandwidth narrower than 12 nm (Hoffmann & Werner 1966), thus failing to give a precise determination even with the use of special equations.
We cannot rely on the exactness of the wavelength scale in any spectrophotometer. The red spectral region is best checked by the red emission line of the deuterium lamp at 656.3 nm. If such a lamp is not available, absorbances of chlorophyll *a* or $(a + b)$ solution are measured in the range of 655 to 670 nm using intervals of 1 nm. The absorption peak found is then set equal to the theoretical wavelength of maximum absorption of chlorophyll *a* in that solvent (see Table 18.2) and other wavelengths are shifted by the same amount: *e.g.* if the maximum absorption in 80% acetone is found at 662 nm instead of 664 nm, 2 nm are added to all values of the wavelength scale in the red spectral region (the shift need not hold for the whole spectrum, *e.g.* for the blue region).
If a recording spectrophotometer is used, high speed of response and slow wavelength drive is recommended. This ensures that the exact position for reading the absorbance is found: this is mainly important for the accurate determination of chlorophyll *b*.

18.6.2 | Specific absorption coefficients

Specific absorption coefficients given by individual authors differ rather significantly (see Tab. 18.2). This is caused by differences in the purity of preparations and solvents as well as by different properties of the spectrophotometers used, as discussed in Section 18.6.1. The purer the chlorophyll preparation and the narrower the measuring bandwidth, the higher are the specific absorption coefficients calculated, and the lower are the multiplying coefficients in the calculation equations. By using equations based on α values measured with a more precise spectrophotometer, for chlorophyll calculation from absorbances found with a less precise spectrophotometer, lower than actual amounts of chlorophyll are estimated (and *vice versa*). Thus it is most appropriate to calculate chlorophyll amounts using specific absorption coefficients found with the same instrument. However, because it is difficult to obtain really pure chlorophyll preparations, specific absorption coefficients and equations given in the literature are frequently used. One set of absorbances may lead to estimates of chlorophyll amounts differing by as much as 20% when the calculations are made with equations given by different authors. The difference is smaller when the wavelength of maximum absorbance found is identified with the wavelength of chlorophyll *a* in the set of equations used and when the other wavelength is appropriately shifted.

18.6.3 Determination of chlorophylls a, b and their total amount in acetone extract

Absorption properties of chlorophyll solutions also depend – according to Kundt's rule (see Mackinney 1938; Harris & Zscheile 1943) – on the refractive index of the solvent. This is why each addition of water to acetone lowers the value of the specific absorption coefficients and shifts the position of the absorption peak of both chlorophylls to longer wavelengths (see Tab. 18.2). Thus the change in acetone concentration from 100% to 80% is reflected in a lowering of the value of α by 2 to 3.5% and a shift in the peak position by 1.5 to 2 nm (Vernon 1960; Ziegler & Egle 1965; Wintermans & de Mots 1965). For the majority of higher plants, maximum extraction is obtained with 80 to 85% acetone. The ground plant material usually only supplies 0.3 to 0.5% water to the pigment solution and this amount does not change its absorption properties.
According to Vernon (1960) the absorbance of the red maximum of a mixture of chlorophylls should lie within the limits of 0.4 to 0.7 (or in extreme cases 0.2 to 0.8) for reliable results.
To calculate the amount of chlorophyll the equations based on the specific absorption coefficients of Mackinney (1941), compiled by Arnon (1949) and checked by Bruinsma (1961), are used most frequently and taken as standard for most common spectrophotometers. Their use gives the highest results and the lowest ratio of chlorophylls *a*/*b*.
The appropriate factors derived from equations (18.3) and (18.4) using the data of Mackinney-Arnon (Arnon 1949) for 80% acetone solution[1] are as follows [mg l^{-1}]:

1. Taking the specific absorption coefficients from the original paper by Mackinney (1941), Starnes & Hadley (1965) found that the correct equations should be:
chlorophyll *a* $= 12.72\,A_{663} - 2.58\,A_{645}$
chlorophyll *b* $= 22.87\,A_{645} - 4.67\,A_{663}$
chlorophyll (*a* + *b*) $= 8.05\,A_{663} + 20.29\,A_{645}$
As the difference is very small, the equations given by Arnon (1949) are still used as the standard ones.

chlorophyll a $= 12.7\ A_{663} - 2.69\ A_{645}$
chlorophyll b $= 22.9\ A_{645} - 4.68\ A_{663}$
chlorophyll $(a + b) = 8.02\ A_{663} + 20.20\ A_{645}$

For spectrophotometers of a good resolution, the equations of Ziegler & Egle (1965) are probably most suitable. They are based on specific absorption coefficients similar to those of Vernon (1960) and Wintermans & de Mots (1965): the positions of the absorption peaks of the chlorophylls at 664 and 647 nm agree with recent findings. The appropriate factors given by Ziegler & Egle (1965) for 80% acetone solution are [mg l^{-1}]:

chlorophyll a $= 11.78\ A_{664} - 2.29\ A_{647}$
chlorophyll b $= 20.05\ A_{647} - 4.77\ A_{664}$
chlorophyll $(a + b) = 7.01\ A_{664} + 17.76\ A_{647}$

High specific absorption coefficients give evidence of the high level of purity of the preparations used by Holm (1954) in deriving equations for chlorophyll determination in 100% acetone. Hoffmann & Werner (1966) recommend these equations as being the most exact. They found that they gave chlorophyll amounts lower by 20% than those calculated by the equations of Mackinney-Arnon.

The equations given by Holm (1954) for 100% acetone solution are [mg l^{-1}]:

chlorophyll a $= 9.78\ A_{662} - 0.99\ A_{644}$
chlorophyll b $= 21.4\ A_{644} - 4.65\ A_{662}$
chlorophyll $(a + b) = 5.13\ A_{662} + 20.41\ A_{644}$

To speed up the calculation of results nomograms may be used with sufficient precision (see Fig. 18.2) (for everyday use they should be produced in a bigger scale). Instruction on how to construct a nomogram of this type based on any optional set of equations is given by Šesták (1966). A similar nomogram using Holm's (1954) data for solutions in 100% acetone and also assessing the total amount of carotenoids was published by Nybom (1955).

The wavelength scales of spectrophotometers with quartz prisms are usually only divided into segments of 5 nm in the red spectral region. In repeated measurements it is difficult to adjust to exactly the same wavelength within the marks of the scale divisions (*e.g.* 663, 644 nm). This is the reason why some authors recommend measuring at wavelengths coinciding with the marks of the scale (*e.g.* 660 and 645 nm – Medina & Lieth 1963) and use for calculation equations based on extrapolated absorption coefficients. In this case all measurements of absorbance are performed on steep parts of the absorption curves and thus a small inaccuracy in wavelength adjustment introduces a big error (see Section 18.6.8).

Total chlorophyll amount may also be determined from absorbances measured at the wavelength of intersection of the red absorption bands of chlorophylls a and b. At this isosbestic point the specific absorption coefficient is identical for both chlorophylls. Chlorophylls in 80% acetone have an isosbestic point at 652 nm. The value of $\alpha_{652}^{a,b}$ equals 34.5 (Arnon 1949), 36.0 (Bruinsma 1961) or 38.4 ± 2.6 (de Kouchkovsky 1963). The general equation for chlorophyll $(a + b)$ in a cuvette of light pathlength of 1 cm is

$$c_{(a+b)} = \frac{1000}{\alpha_{iso}^{a,b}} A_{iso} \quad [\text{mg l}^{-1}] \qquad (18.6)$$

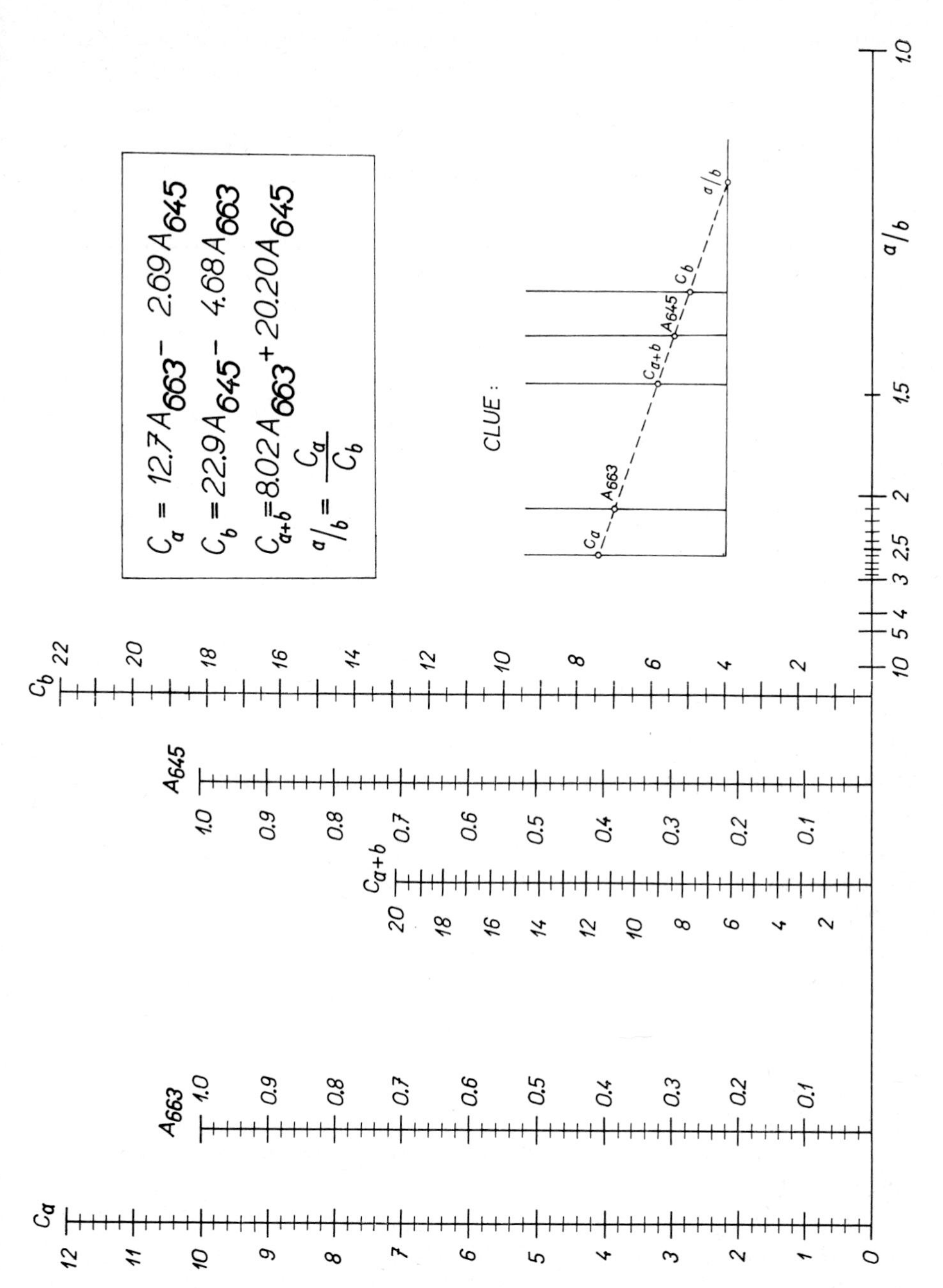

Fig. 18.2 Nomogram for determination of amount of chlorophylls *a*, *b*, (*a* + *b*) and their ratio *a*/*b* in 80% acetone extract from spectrophotometric measurement at wavelengths 663 and 645 nm in cuvettes of 10 mm lightpath. Absorbances found on the respective scales A_{663} and A_{645} are joined with a transparent ruler. On the scales C_a, C_b and C_{a+b} amounts of chlorophylls *a*, *b* and (*a* + *b*) [mg l^{-1}] are then read directly. The horizontal scale gives the ratio of chlorophylls *a*/*b*. The nomogram based on equations of Mackinney-Arnon (Arnon 1949) was constructed according to Šesták (1966).

where the factor $1000/\alpha_{iso}^{a,b}$ is 29 (Arnon 1949), 27.8 (Bruinsma 1961) or 26 (average value of de Kouchkovsky 1963). Calculation with the de Kouchkovsky factor gives values very similar to those obtained with the summary equation of Mackinney-Arnon. Simultaneous determination of absorbance at the third (isosbestic) wavelength and calculation with this equation is a valuable check on the two wavelength determination.

The measured extracts should be clear. To check this, the absorbance at 710 (or 750) nm, where chlorophylls *in vitro* do not absorb, is measured. If absorbance at this wavelength is higher than 5% of absorbance at the wavelength of the red absorption peak of chlorophyll *a*, the solution should be cleared again by filtration or centrifugation and the measurement repeated. The small absorbance found at 710 nm is simply subtracted from the absorbances at wavelengths of the absorption peaks of chlorophylls *a* and *b* prior to the final calculation.

The presence of anthocyanins in acetone extracts interferes with chlorophyll determinations. Anthocyanins may be eliminated by transferring the chlorophylls into diethyl ether or by measuring absorbance at three wavelengths (663, 645 and 550 nm in 80% acetone) and determining simultaneously the anthocyanin amount (Billot 1964).

18.6.4 | *Determination of chlorophylls a, b and (a + b) in alcohol extracts*

The calculation equations for unpurified extracts in methanol, which is the second most frequently used solvent for chlorophyll extraction, are based on the specific absorption coefficients of Mackinney (1941). The equations for extracts in 96% ethanol are given by Wintermans & de Mots (1965). Calculation with their sets of equations gives results similar to those for 80% acetone and Arnon's (1949) equations or for diethyl ether and equations of Smith & Benitez (1955) (Wintermans 1969).

The appropriate equations given by Mackinney (1941) for extracts in 100% methanol are [mg l^{-1}]:

chlorophyll *a* $= 16.5\ A_{665} - 8.3\ A_{650}$

chlorophyll *b* $= 33.8\ A_{650} - 12.5\ A_{665}$

chlorophyll $(a + b) = 4.0\ A_{665} + 25.5\ A_{650}$

Wintermans & de Mots (1965) gave the following equations for extracts in 96% ethanol [mg l^{-1}]:

chlorophyll *a* $= 13.7\ A_{665} - 5.76\ A_{649}$

chlorophyll *b* $= 25.8\ A_{645} - 7.6\ A_{665}$

chlorophyll $(a + b) = 6.1\ A_{665} + 20.04\ A_{649}$

Values for ethanol extracts may be checked using measurements at the isosbestic point 654 nm, where $\alpha_{654}^{a,b} = 39.8$:

chlorophyll $(a + b)$ [mg l^{-1}] $= 25.1\ A_{654}$

The calculation of chlorophyll amounts for ethanol extracts can be simplified by using Table 18.3 proposed by Wintermans (1969). The ratio of measured absorbances $A_{\max a}$ and $A_{\max b}$ is established first. Contents of chlorophyll *a*, *b* and $(a + b)$ are then found by multiplication of $A_{\max a}$ or $A_{\max b}$ by coefficients found on the appropriate line of the table.

Table 18.3 Table for the calculation of the amount of chlorophyll $a(C_a)$, $b(C_b)$ and $(a + b)$ (C_{a+b}) in 96% ethanol solutions. The ratio of absorbances at 665 and 649 nm in a cuvette of 10 mm path length is first calculated. On the appropriate line the coefficients are given by which to multiple A_{665} to obtain the resulting chlorophyll amounts [mg l^{-1}]. On the same line the ratio of chlorophylls a/b is read directly (Wintermans 1969).

A_{665}/A_{649}	$C_a = A_{665} \times$	$C_b = A_{665} \times$	$C_{a+b} = A_{665} \times$	$a/b =$
2.00	10.82	5.30	16.12	2.04
2.05	10.88	5.00	15.88	2.18
2.10	10.96	4.69	15.65	2.33
2.15	11.02	4.40	15.42	2.50
2.20	11.08	4.13	15.21	2.68
2.25	11.14	3.87	15.01	2.88
2.30	11.20	3.61	14.81	3.10
2.35	11.25	3.36	14.61	3.33
2.40	11.30	3.14	14.44	3.59
2.45	11.35	2.92	14.27	3.88
2.50	11.40	2.72	14.12	4.19

18.6.5 | Determination of chlorophylls a, b and (a + b) in diethyl ether solution

Transfer of pigments from the extraction solvent into diethyl ether is recommended by some authors (see Section 18.4.6). This procedure removes the hydrophilic pigments and, when executed carefully, clears turbid extracts. Moreover, specific absorption coefficients measured in diethyl ether are taken as standard values in chlorophyll analysis. These advantages are balanced by the longer time needed for analysis and the risk of pigment losses, especially in experiments with small extract volumes. The biggest errors are introduced by the washing out and loss of chlorophyllides formed by chlorophyllase action during the extraction (see Section 18.4.3). Diethyl ether must be peroxide-free and the ether solution should not contain water.

There is no general agreement on the size and wavelength of the absorption peaks of diethyl ether solutions of chlorophylls (Table 18.2). The two most frequently used sets of equations are given below.

The appropriate factors given by Comar & Zscheile (1942) for solutions in diethyl ether are [mg l^{-1}]:

$$\text{chlorophyll } a = 9.93\,A_{660} - 0.78\,A_{642.5}$$
$$\text{chlorophyll } b = 17.60\,A_{642.5} - 2.81\,A_{660}$$
$$\text{chlorophyll } (a+b) = 7.12\,A_{660} + 16.80\,A_{642.5}$$

The appropriate factors given by Smith & Benitez (1955) for solutions in diethyl ether are [mg l^{-1}]:

$$\text{chlorophyll } a = 10.1\,A_{662} - 1.01\,A_{644}$$
$$\text{chlorophyll } b = 16.4\,A_{644} - 2.57\,A_{662}$$
$$\text{chlorophyll } (a+b) = 7.53\,A_{662} + 15.39\,A_{644}$$

Table 18.4 Table for calculation of chlorophyll *a* (C_a), *b* (C_b), and ($a + b$) (C_{a+b}) amount in diethyl ether solutions using their specific absorption coefficients of Smith, Benitez & Koski (in French 1960). The ratio of absorbances at 662 and 644 nm in a cuvette of 10 mm path length is first calculated. On the appropriate line the coefficients are given by which to multiply A_{662} to obtain the resulting chlorophyll amounts [mg l^{-1}]. On the same line the ratio of chlorophylls *a*/*b* is read directly (Wintermans 1969).

A_{662}/A_{644}	$C_a = A_{662} \times$	$C_b = A_{662} \times$	$C_{a+b} = A_{662} \times$	$a/b =$
2.20	9.64	4.88	14.52	1.97
2.30	9.66	4.56	14.22	2.12
2.40	9.68	4.27	13.95	2.26
2.50	9.69	3.99	13.68	2.43
2.60	9.71	3.73	13.44	2.60
2.70	9.72	3.50	13.22	2.78
2.80	9.74	3.28	13.02	2.97
2.90	9.75	3.08	12.83	3.16
3.00	9.76	2.89	12.65	3.38
3.10	9.77	2.72	12.49	3.60
3.20	9.78	2.56	12.34	3.82
3.30	9.79	2.40	12.19	4.08

Table 18.4 proposed by Wintermans (1969) enables quick calculation of chlorophyll amounts in accordance with the equations of Smith & Benitez (1955).

18.6.6 | Determination of pheophytins

Pheophytin formation from chlorophylls is induced by contact with acids in plant cells during the extraction procedure as well as by the presence of acidic substances on the surface of laboratory glass, in solvents, *etc*. Their spectra differ from those of chlorophylls by shifts in the positions of the peaks (blue to shorter and red to longer wavelengths) and relatively low specific absorption coefficients in the red. Their presence in extracts introduces big errors into results obtained with methods described in Sections 18.6.3 to 18.6.5, because the original two-component mixture changes into a four-component one.

Following Willstätter & Stoll (1913), many authors have tried to eliminate this inaccuracy by converting all chlorophylls present in 80% ethanol solution into pheophytins by HCl action. Pheophytins are then determined by two-wavelength spectrophotometry (Wickliff & Aronoff 1962). Complications in this procedure may result from incomplete pheophytinization or further degradation of pheophytins into pheophorbides and finally to porphyrins (Zscheile, Comar & Harris 1944).

The possibility of incomplete pheophytinization is lessened by using the ion-exchanger *Dowex 50 W–X 4* in H^+ form. Pigment extract in 100% acetone is applied to the column of resin and elution with 100% and 85% acetone separates both the pheophytins then formed. Their absorbance can be measured at the red absorption peaks, or at the blue absorption peaks after shifting the absorption spectra of carotenoids to shorter wavelengths by the addition of tetracyanoethylene. The amount of separated pheophytins is calculated from

$$c = \frac{A_\lambda}{\alpha_\lambda l} \tag{18.7}$$

where c = pheophytin concentration [g l^{-1}], A_λ = absorbance at the wavelength λ, α_λ = specific absorption coefficient at the wavelength λ, l = length of the light path [cm].
It is preferable to take the mean of calculations of pheophytin amount based on measurements in the red and blue spectral regions as the final value. The appropriate specific absorption coefficients are:

pheophytin *a* $\alpha_{667}^{ph_a} = 56.6$
$\alpha_{409}^{ph_a} = 130.9$

pheophytin *b* $\alpha_{654}^{ph_b} = 35.3$
$\alpha_{436}^{ph_b} = 181.0$

The amount of chlorophylls equals 102.71% of the pheophytin amount (Wilson & Nutting 1963).
Vernon (1960) gives equations for the determination of pheophytin formed by acidifying chlorophylls in 97 ml of 80% acetone with 3 ml of a saturated solution of oxalic acid. Pheophytin amounts [mg l^{-1}] are calculated from equations based on the determination of absorbance at four wavelengths:
pheophytin *a* = $(20.15\ A_{663} - 5.87\ A_{655})$ or $(21.67\ A_{666} - 17.42\ A_{536})$
pheophytin *b* = $(31.90\ A_{655} - 13.40\ A_{666})$ or $(95.0\ A_{536} - 22.0\ A_{666})$
pheophytin $(a + b)$ = $(6.75\ A_{666} + 26.03\ A_{655})$ or $(77.58\ A_{536} - 0.33\ A_{666})$
The real value is again taken as the mean of both equations.

Pheophytinization procedures are the only methods applicable for acid plant tissues (*e.g.* leaves of *Begonia* – pH 1.3 to 1.6!). With these tissues, or stored plant material, the percentage of chlorophyll not converted into pheophytins is often determined. Vernon (1960) gives an equation based on an idea of Dietrich (1958):

$$\%\ \text{retention of chlorophyll} = \frac{2.1 - A_{536}/A_{558}}{1.26} \times 100$$

This equation holds only for the chlorophyll *a*/*b* ratio of 2.5. As the absorbances at 536 and 558 nm are very low and similar, the results of the determination present an approximation only. Furthermore the presence of anthocyanins in the tissues and extracts interferes with this procedure.
Simultaneous determination of chlorophylls and pheophytins in the same solution is always very inaccurate and is best avoided, especially in solutions containing larger amounts of pheophytins. In the case of necessity another method given by Vernon (1960) may be used: absorbances of the solutions in 80% acetone are measured at 666, 662, 655 and 645 nm prior to and after the addition of oxalic acid solution.

Analysis of complicated mixtures of chlorophylls, chlorophyllides, pheophytins and pheophorbides is performed by a triple procedure (White, Jones & Gibbs 1963): Absorbance of the original diethyl ether solution is measured at 660 and 642.5 nm. The solution is then divided into two aliquots. Chlorophyllides and pheophorbides are extracted from the first aliquot by 0.01 N KOH and discarded. The absorbance of the upper diethyl ether phase is then measured at 660 and 642.5 nm. Chlorophylls present are then converted to pheophytins by means of HCl and their absorbance measured together with the original pheophytins at 666.5 and 653 nm. Chlorophylls and chlorophyllides in the second aliquot of the initial solution are then converted to pheophytins and pheophorbides which are measured at the latter two wavelengths. The amounts of eight pigments present in the original solution are then calculated using a set of 13 equations.

18.6.7 | *Simultaneous determination of chlorophylls with protochlorophyll(ide)*

The amount of protochlorophyll together with both chlorophylls is traditionally determined after transfer of the pigments from an acetone extract into diethyl ether using a three-wavelength spectrophotometric procedure performed in darkness or weak green safe-light.
The appropriate equations given by Koski (1950) for solutions in diethyl ether are [mg l^{-1}]:

chlorophyll *a* $= 10.69\ A_{663} - 0.94\ A_{644} - 0.04\ A_{624}$
chlorophyll *b* $= 17.73\ A_{644} - 2.80\ A_{663} - 0.52\ A_{624}$
protochlorophyll $= 25.21\ A_{624} - 3.02\ A_{663} - 4.06\ A_{644}$

During the transfer of the pigment mixture to diethyl ether most of the protochlorophyllide is probably lost. Therefore direct measurements in 80% acetone extracts are recommended by Anderson & Boardman (1964). The appropriate set of equations is based on specific absorption coefficients determined for chlorophylls by Mackinney (1941) and for protochlorophyll by Koski & Smith (1948) [mg l^{-1}]:

chlorophyll *a* $= 12.67\ A_{663} - 2.65\ A_{645} - 0.29\ A_{626}$
chlorophyll *b* $= 23.60\ A_{645} - 4.23\ A_{663} - 0.33\ A_{626}$
protochlorophyll $= 29.60\ A_{626} - 3.99\ A_{663} - 6.76\ A_{645}$

Nevertheless, some authors prefer relative fluorescence (Virgin 1955) or luminescence (Kaler & Podchufarova 1965) measurements or determination after chromatographic separation.
Using the equation sets given in this Section, the amounts of protochlorophyll are calculated: if the sample contains protochlorophyllide, the calculated protochlorophyll amounts must be divided by 1.5 (the ratio of their molecular weights is 891.5/597).

18.6.8 | *Chlorophyll a and b determination with a one-wavelength hydroxylamine method*

The main source of error in the two-wavelength spectrophotometric determination of chlorophylls is the inexact adjustment of one or both wavelengths when they are interchanged. Inaccurate adjustment of the wavelength of the chlorophyll *b* peak is most serious because this wavelength corresponds to a point laying on the steep part of the absorption curve of the chlorophyll mixture. Hence a small shift results in a big difference in the absorbance value and in the amount of chlorophyll *b* which is estimated. Ziegler & Egle (1965) found that a 1 nm shift of wavelength results in only a 1.6% error in the chlorophyll *a* determination, but a 15.2% error in the chlorophyll *b* determination.

These errors can be reduced by the procedure of Ogawa & Shibata (1965). A methanolic extract is divided into two aliquots, the absorbances of which are measured at one wavelength with and without the addition of a hydroxylamine reagent. Hydroxylamine does not change the character of the absorption curve of chlorophyll *a*, but reacts with the aldehyde group of chlorophyll *b* to form a product spectrally similar to chlorophyll *a*. The red maximum of chlorophyll *b* in methanol is shifted from 653 nm to 663 nm and the Soret (blue) band from 471 to 453 nm. The resulting absorption band of the mixture is relatively wide in the red so that the amounts of chlorophylls *a* and *b* are determined from estimates of absorbance at 666 nm.

The reagent is prepared by dissolving 4 g hydroxylamine hydrochloride in 6 ml of water, adjusting the pH to 4.0 ± 0.5 with NaOH solution and adding water to make up to 10 ml.

Two 9.5 ml aliquots are pipetted from the methanolic solution of pigments. To one, 0.5 ml H_2O is added and to the other 0.5 ml of hydroxylamine reagent. After mixing and leaving for at least 5 min, both aliquots are measured at 666 nm, either absolutely or differentially. The amounts of chlorophylls [mg l^{-1}] are then calculated using the equations

chlorophyll $a = 7.2\ (2\ A_{666} - \Delta\ A_{666})$

chlorophyll $b = 25.4\ \Delta\ A_{666}$

chlorophyll $(a + b) = 14.4\ A_{666} + 18.2\ \Delta\ A_{666}$

where $\Delta\ A_{666}$ = the difference in absorbances of solutions with and without the reagent.

Even this simple method, which has an error of less than 5% induced by a 1 nm shift, does not avoid completely errors introduced by the presence of pheophytins and other degradation products in the extract. The advantage of the method is the stability of the reaction product, the absorption characteristics of which do not change during 24 h storage in darkness and cold. A disadvantage is the necessity to extract with methanol, the extraction power of which is often smaller than that of acetone, particularly with well-hydrated tissues.

18.7 | Column chromatography of chlorophylls

The amounts of chlorophylls *a* and *b* may also be determined by chromatographic separation and colorimetric determination as described in Section 18.5. The disadvantage of this procedure is its relative lengthiness and the risk of losses by firm adsorption of pigments on adsorbent particles and by the incomplete separation ('tailing') of individual pigment zones. Resulting accuracy is usually similar to that reached by two-wavelength spectrophotometry of the unpurified extract, but – from time to time – procedures including chromatographic separation are a useful check on the spectrophotometric method. The chief significance of chromatographic methods lies in the purification of chlorophylls and their isolation. They are equally as efficient and cheaper than multiple partition between immiscible solvents.

During more than 60 years of column chromatography development, probably all possible powder adsorbents have been tested. Pigment-saving adsorbents such as sucrose (usually with 3% starch added) and cellulose powder have proved best in recent procedures for chlorophyll separation. Powdered sugar can give excellent results but, unfortunately, the commercial brands vary so much that good separation cannot be guaranteed. This is why only a simple procedure using cellulose powder is recommended here.

A glass tube 30 to 35 cm long, 10 to 15 mm in diameter, fixed in a hole in a rubber stopper, is packed with *Whatman CC 41* cellulose powder. Layers of dry adsorbent *ca.* 1 cm thick are pressed down with a glass or plastic tamper until the column is *ca.* 20 to 25 cm long. The base of the column is formed by a sintered glass plate (porosity 1), glass wool or disc of filter paper and its top is covered with a 5 mm thick layer of glass beads (*ca.* 0.5 mm in diameter). The bottom of the tube is attached to a flask under suction, one or two ml of pigment solution in petroleum ether is applied and the column is developed by toluene. After the elution of all carotenoids, apart from neoxanthin, is finished, chlorophylls are further separated using 2% isopropanol in toluene. The separation of both chlorophylls is fairly good, but they are not completely free from the remainder of the carotenoids. The column is never allowed to dry out. The separated pigments are either directly eluted with the solvent mixture from the column or the zones are quickly scraped out and eluted in a beaker. After repeated chromatography the eluate is evaporated *in vacuo* and the pigments are dissolved in the required solvent.

Column chromatography is recommended for the separation of large amounts of chlorophylls. Its disadvantages are the necessity to practice to get comparable results and the lengthiness of column preparation and development. This is why the quicker methods of paper and thin-layer chromatography predominate in laboratories to-day.

18.8 | Paper chromatography of chlorophylls

In the literature a large number of modifications to paper chromatographic methods of chlorophyll separation can be found. They were reviewed in detail by Šesták (1958, 1959a, 1965). The procedure recommended here requires only simple equipment. It is quick and well-suited to the detection of pigment composition and to elution for colorimetric determination.

18.8.1 | The application of the sample

Concentrated acetone or diethyl ether solution of pigments is applied 20 mm from the margin of the short side of a *ca.* 140 × 250 mm rectangle cut from paper *Whatman No. 1* (thin - for small amounts of pigments) or *Whatman No. 3, 17,* or *31 ET* (thick - for quantitative determination of pigments). The sample is applied as a narrow streak by a calibrated capillary pipette or by a small volume syringe.

To compare different samples, streaks *ca.* 2 cm long with 0.5 to 1 cm space between them and 1 cm space from the margins are recommended.
As separation depends mainly on the adsorption principle, the R_F values of the chlorophylls increase with the amount of pigment applied per unit length of the starting line. The application of a large amount of chlorophylls results in one unseparated pigment zone near to the solvent front. Satisfactory pigment separation thus depends on the amount of pigments applied. Appropriate amounts are 2 to 5 μg chlorophyll ($a + b$) per cm of the starting line with *Whatman No. 1*, or 10 to 20 μg cm^{-1} with *Whatman No. 31 ET*. (If only chlorophylls are to be separated, this amount may be 50 to 100% higher.) When comparing several samples, the amount of chlorophylls per unit length of the starting line should be kept constant. Evaporation of the solvent is accelerated by ventilating with nitrogen, particularly with samples in acetone.

18.8.2 | Development

One-dimensional ascending development takes place in a glass tank with dimensions of *ca.* 200 × 50 × 250 mm hermetically closed with a lid. Sheets of thin paper are suspended from a glass bar fixed near the lid. Sheets of thick paper stand in the tank, their upper margin provided with a paper clip bent in the middle to prevent the paper touching the wall. The vertical inner walls of the tank may be lined with chromatographic paper; this improves the saturation of the atmosphere with diffusion solvent vapours but slows down the migration of pigment zones and thus increases the risk of the diffusion zone widening. The bottom of the tank is covered with 30 to 50 ml of the solvent system. The tank is darkened with a black cloth or cardboard box.
The choice of the solvent system depends on the character of the separation required:
1. Toluene. – Badly separated chlorophylls remain near the starting line, but carotenoids form distinct zones.
2. Toluene – methanol (400 : 1) (modified system of Chiba & Noguchi 1954). Methanol can be replaced by *n*- or *iso*-propanol. Chlorophylls and carotenoids are fairly well separated.
3. Ligroine – benzene – chloroform – acetone – isopropanol (50 : 35 : 10 : 0.5 : 0.17), the system of Hager (1955). Chlorophylls *a* and *b* are well separated, but often overlap spots of xanthophylls. The best system for elution of individual chlorophylls.
The ascending development is finished when the distance from starting line to solvent front is *ca.* 20 cm: this takes *ca.* 60 min at 20 °C.

18.8.3 | Sequence and detection of zones

After development the shape of the zones is marked with a pencil and their colour recorded.
The usual order of separated spots is shown in Fig. 18.3. The separation of carotenoids depends on the amount of oxygen atoms in the molecule. Sometimes the front of the chlorophyll zones is double, the narrow front zones being chloro-

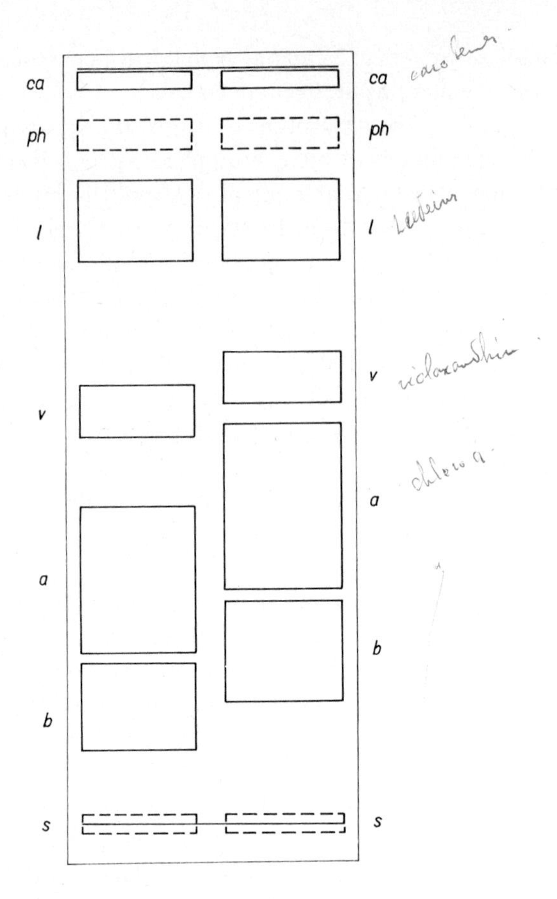

Fig. 18.3 Scheme of order of separated spots on a chromatogram of pigments from wheat leaves on paper *Whatman No. 3*. Developed with Hager's (1955) solvent system. Left row: 7.5 mg chlorophylls ($a + b$) per 1 cm of starting line, right row: 15.0 mg cm^{-1}. Symbols of pigment zones: *ca:* carotenes (near to the solvent front), *ph:* pheophytins, *l:* xanthophylls of the lutein type, *v:* xanthophylls of the violaxanthin type, *a:* chlorophyll *a* (blue green), *b:* chlorophyll *b* (yellow green), *s:* starting line with chlorophyllides and other water-soluble pigments.

phyll isomers – a' and b'. Six to seven spots of chlorophyll derivatives are characteristic of the separation of old extracts or extracts which have been exposed to extreme conditions (Bacon & Holden 1967).

Chlorophyll spots are visible; their fluorescence in ultraviolet light is red.

18.8.4 | *Elution and quantitative determination of separated pigments*

Separated spots of chlorophylls are eluted with absolute acetone and chlorophyllides with 80% acetone, carotenoids are eluted with petroleum ether or ligroine. Zones cut out with scissors are eluted in a test tube by repeated washing with the solvent and decantation for as long as the paper fluoresces in UV radiation. The resulting solution is usually very dilute.

A better method of elution is to flush the pigment out of the paper with solvent. The lower empty edge of the paper strip containing the pigment zone is cut

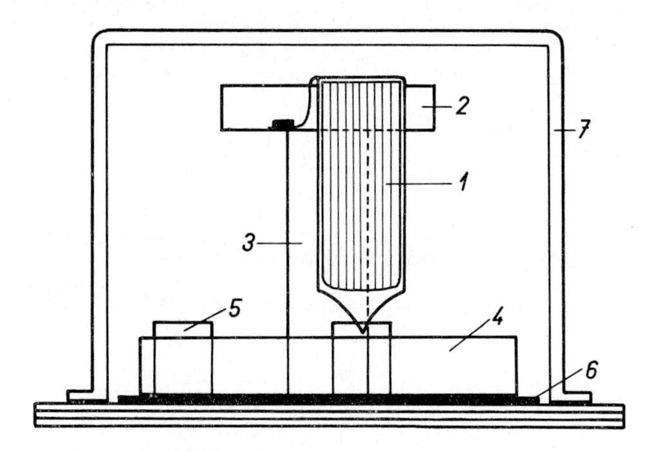

Fig. 18.4 Simple arrangement for pigment elution from paper strips with separated pigment zones. Paper strips (*1*) are immersed in the elution solvent in the smaller upper Petri dish (*2*) which is glued to a wide glass tube (*3*) which is glued to a larger lower Petri dish (*4*), in which small vessels (*5*) collecting the eluate are situated. The bottom dish is placed on a filter paper (*6*) to show any drops of pigments falling outside the vessel. The elution space is closed hermetically with a ground glass cover (*7*).

slantwise from both sides to form a tip. A piece of clean chromatographic paper is sewn onto the upper edge, to serve as a wick, and is submerged in a trough or Petri dish containing elution solvent (Fig. 18.4). The solvent flows through the paper into a small glass vessel placed below the paper tip (no contact!). If the elution proceeds well, the first drops contain the greater part of the pigment. Elution continues until all the chlorophyll has been eluted.
The eluates are made up to the required volume and their absorbances measured in a colorimeter or spectrophotometer. The accuracy of the results depends on the procedure employed: only rarely are both chlorophylls separated completely during one development. Usually chlorophyll *b* contains a small amount of chlorophyll *a* and thus a lower than real *a*/*b* ratio is obtained. Repeated development involves a risk of pigment degradation and losses. Determination of chlorophylls *a* and *b* by this method can be distorted by chlorophyllide formation, which may be avoided by scalding the plant material prior to extraction (see Section 18.4.3, and Šesták 1964).

18.9 | Thin layer chromatography of chlorophylls

Of the many modifications of thin layer chromatography of chlorophylls reviewed by Šesták (1967), only two (Hager & Meyer-Bertenrath 1966; Schneider 1966) are presented here. The first produces sharper separation of the pigment zones; the second ensures better stability of the pigments by using a neutral cellulose powder adsorbent. Recently, different pre-coated thin layer sheets have become popular and some of them appear adequate for chlorophyll separation (Sherma & Lippstone 1969). However, because of their rather high price they will not be discussed.

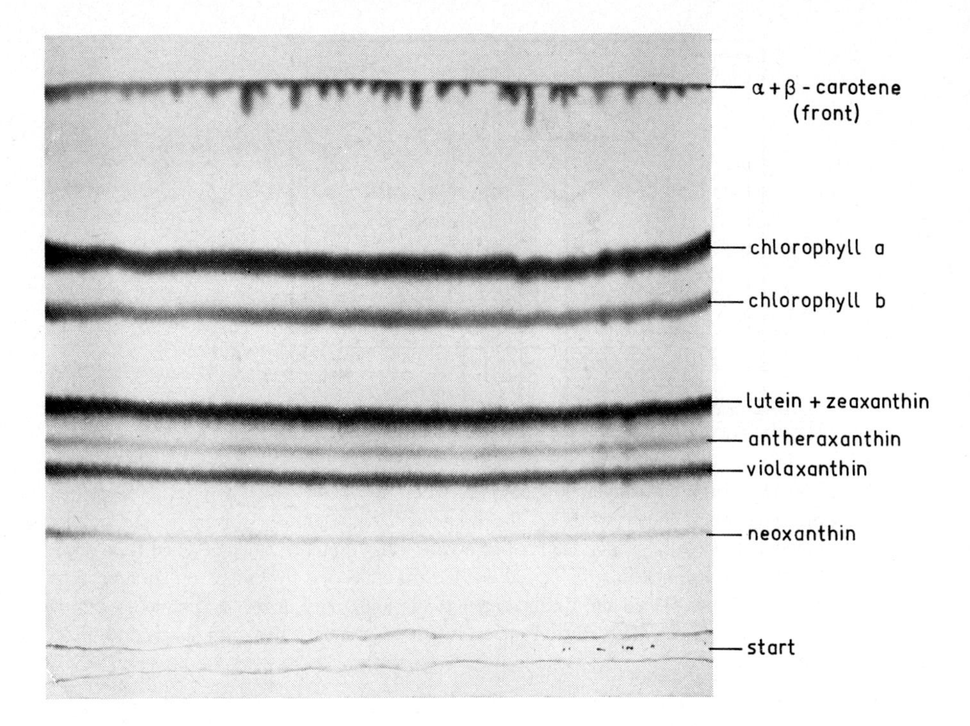

Fig. 18.5 Photograph of thin layer chromatogram of plastid pigments from *Hedera helix* L. according to the method of Hager & Meyer-Bertenrath (1966). (Original A. Hager.)

18.9.1 | Hager and Meyer-Bertenrath's method

The adsorbent mixture is prepared by mixing 12 g Kieselguhr G (*Merck* 8129), 3 g silica gel '*unter 0.08 mm*' (*Merck* 7729), 3 g $CaCO_3$ (*Merck* 2066), 0.02 g $Ca(OH)_2$ (*Merck* 2047)[1] and 50 ml 8×10^{-3} M ascorbic acid solution in water. The slurry is spread on a glass plate 200 × 200 mm or 200 × 50 mm forming a layer 0.125 or 0.25 mm thick, which is dried 90 min at 50 to 60 °C. After cooling, the plate should be used within the next few hours, otherwise destruction of the pigments occurs.

Concentrated acetone extract of the pigments is applied as a streak 2 cm from the lower margin of the plate under a stream of nitrogen, taking care not to injure the layer surface.

One-dimensional ascending development takes place in darkness in a simple closed glass chamber or in a narrow chamber formed by placing another glass plate of the same dimensions adjacent to the thin layer plate, from which it is separated by cardboard strips around the margins. In this case *ca.* 5 mm borders are scraped off three sides of the plate. The solvent system is ligroine – *iso*-propanol – distilled water (100 : 12 : 0.25); the development lasts 50 min at room temperature. The sequence of separated pigments, starting from the solvent front, is: carotenes – chlorophyll *a* – chlorophyll *b* – lutein + zeaxanthin – antheraxanthin – lutein-5,6-epoxide –

1. Calcium hydroxide keeps the pH higher than 7; it may be omitted when the pH of the slurry is 7.3 to 7.6.

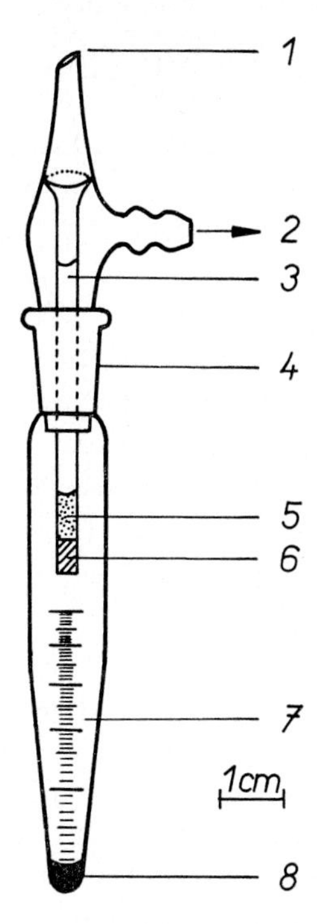

Fig. 18.6 Thin layer elution tube after Jeffrey (1968). The pigment zone is scraped off the plate by a scraping surface (*1*) under suction of a pump, which is attached to the side arm (*2*) of the upper detachable part of the device connected by a ground glass joint (*4*) to the lower graduated centrifugation tube (*7*). The scraped adsorbent with pigment (*5*) is drawn down on the top of the cotton wool plug (*6*) and after adding the elution solvent (*3*) the filtered eluate is collected at the bottom of the centrifuge tube (*8*).

violaxanthin – neoxanthin (see Fig. 18.5). As soon as development is complete the pigmented zones of the adsorbent are scraped off and the pigments eluted in acetone (chlorophylls), *n*-hexane (carotene), or 98% ethanol (xanthophylls), using the elution tube described by Jeffrey (1968) (see Fig. 18.6), for example.

18.9.2 | Schneider's method

The chemically inactive layer is made of 15 g cellulose powder *Macherey-Nagel MN 300* blended with 100 ml distilled water. The layer is spread *ca.* 0.4 mm thick and is dried for 60 min at 100 to 105 °C.

After cooling the plate, acetone extract of the pigments is applied as a streak and the chromatogram is developed with a mixture of methanol – dichloromethane – water (100 : 18 : 20) yielding the following sequence of pigment zones from the solvent front: neoxanthin – violaxanthin – lutein–5,6–epoxide – lutein – chlorophyll *b* – chlorophyll *a* – (carotenes + pheophytins).

18.10 | Evaluation of results and applicability of procedures

Before beginning a new series of chlorophyll analyses, appropriate methods and units must be chosen. The results should characterize the photosynthetic apparatus in the material studied or determine the action of environmental or artificial factors on chlorophyll synthesis or deterioration. Unfortunately, the amount of chlorophylls is often used as an ornament for a research paper, without looking for some causal connection with the processes being studied.

The results of analyses are often invalidated by insufficient care with regard to pigment lability, sampling, *etc.* Normal leaves contain 1 to 10 mg (usually 2 to 6 mg) chlorophyll ($a + b$) per dm^2 of leaf area. This amount is subject to variation with plant species and ecotype, age of leaf and part of the blade, nutrition, time of year, irradiance (smaller concentration of chlorophylls in glasshouse plants) and other factors. Chlorophyll-lacking mutants, etiolated plants and old leaves contain negligible amounts of chlorophylls. Chlorophylls usually form 0.5 to 2% of the plant's dry matter, and 5 to 10 times less when calculated on a fresh weight basis. The ratio of chlorophylls a/b is generally 1.5 to 3.5.

Differences of less than $\pm$ 5 to 10% cannot be taken as reliable unless supported by a considerable number of uniform results, because the errors inherent in the colorimetric determination of chlorophylls fall within these limits.

Using a colorimetric or spectrophotometric procedure with the unpurified acetone extract one technician can analyse *ca.* 30 to 40 samples of 5 to 6 cm^2 leaf area in 8 hours. The speed of analysis depends on the toughness of the material (*e.g.* a much smaller number of needle samples can be analysed during the same time). Quantitative transfer of pigments to diethyl ether doubles the time required.

Spectrophotometric two-wavelength methods give exact results when done on good instruments, but their results differ according to the set of equations used and hence must really be treated as relative rather than absolute. Determinations based on chromatographic separation are not more accurate, but they are more time-consuming. At least three chromatograms are required to obtain a valid mean, but 8 h are needed for the production of *ca.* eight paper or six thin layer chromatograms.

18.11 | References

Anderson, J. M., Boardman, N. K.: Studies on the greening of dark-grown bean plants. II. Development of photochemical activity. – Austral. J. biol. Sci. 17: 93-101, 1964.

Arnon, D. I.: Copper enzymes in isolated chloroplasts. Polyphenoloxidase in *Beta vulgaris*. – Plant Physiol. 24: 1-15, 1949.

Bacon, M. F., Holden, M.: Changes in chlorophylls resulting from various chemical and physical treatments of leaves and leaf extracts. – Phytochemistry 6: 193-210, 1967.

Benedict, H. M., Swidler, R.: Nondestructive method for estimating chlorophyll content of leaves. – Science 133: 2015-2016, 1961.

Billot, J.: Méthode de dosage des chlorophylles en présence d'anthocyanes. – Physiol. vég. 2: 195-208, 1964.

Birth, G. S.: Agricultural applications of the dual-monochromator spectrophotometer. – Agr. Eng. 41: 432-452, 1960.

Birth, G. S., McVey, G. R.: Measuring the color of growing turf with a reflectance spectrophotometer. – Agron. J. 60: 640-643, 1968.

Borris, H., Köhler, K.-H.: Die Bestimmung des Gesamtchlorophyllgehaltes von Laubblättern mit Hilfe des Spektralkolorimeters SPEKOL. – Jenaer Rundschau 13: 232-236, 1968.

Brown, S. R.: Absorption coefficients of chlorophyll derivatives. – J. Fisher. Res. Board Canada 25: 523-540, 1968.
Bruinsma, J.: A comment on the spectrophotometric determination of chlorophyll. – Biochim. biophys. Acta 52: 576-578, 1961.
Bruinsma, J.: The quantitative analysis of chlorophylls *a* and *b* in plant extracts. – Photochem. Photobiol. 2: 241-249, 1963.
Chiba, Y., Noguchi, I.: A new method of paper chromatography of chlorophylls. – Cytologia 19: 41-44, 1954.
Comar, C. L., Zscheile, F. P.: Analysis of plant extracts for chlorophylls *a* and *b* by a photoelectric spectrophotometric method. – Plant Physiol. 17: 198-209, 1942.
Davidson, J.: Procedures for the extraction, separation and estimation of the major fat-soluble pigments of hay. – J. Sci. Food Agr. 5: 1-7, 1954.
Determination of Photosynthetic Pigments in Sea-Water. – UNESCO, Paris 1966.
Dietrich, W. C.: Determination of the conversion of chlorophyll to pheophytin. – Food Technol. 12: 428, 1958.
Falk, H.: Ein Beitrag zur Methode der quantitativen Chlorophyllbestimmung. – Planta 51: 49-62, 1958.
French, C. S.: The chlorophylls *in vivo* and *in vitro*. – In: Ruhland, W. (ed.): Handbuch der Pflanzenphysiologie. Vol. V/1. Pp. 252-297. Springer-Verlag, Berlin–Göttingen–Heidelberg 1960.
Griffith, R. B., Jeffrey, R. N.: Determining chlorophyll, carotene, and xanthophyll in plants. – Ind. eng. Chem., Anal. Ed. 16: 438-440, 1944.
Grime, J. P.: Measurement of leaf colour. – Nature 191: 614-615, 1961.
Guthrie, J. D.: A stable colorimetric standard for chlorophyll determinations. – Amer. J. Bot. 15: 86-87, 1928.
Hager, A.: Chloroplasten-Farbstoffe, ihre papierchromatographische Trennung und ihre Veränderungen durch Aussenfaktoren. – Z. Naturforsch. 10b: 310-312, 1955.
Hager, A., Meyer-Bertenrath, T.: Die Isolierung und quantitative Bestimmung der Carotinoide und Chlorophylle von Blättern, Algen und isolierten Chloroplasten mit Hilfe dünnschichtchromatographischer Methoden. – Planta 69: 198-217, 1966.
Harris, D. G., Zscheile, F. P.: Effects of solvent upon absorption spectra of chlorophylls *A* and *B*; their ultraviolet absorption spectra in ether solution. – Bot. Gaz. 104: 515-527, 1943.
Hoffmann, P., Werner, D.: Zur spektralphotometrischen Chlorophyllbestimmung unter besonderer Berücksichtigung verschiedener Gerätetypen. – Jenaer Rundschau 11: 300-304, 1966.
Holden, M.: Chlorophylls. – In: Goodwin, T. W.: Chemistry and Biochemistry of Plant Pigments. Pp. 461-488. Academic Press, London–New York 1965.
Holm, G.: Chlorophyll mutations in barley. – Acta agr. scand. 4: 457-471, 1954.
Holt, A. S., Jacobs, E. E.: Spectroscopy of plant pigments. I. Ethyl chlorophyllides *a* and *b* and their pheophorbides. – Amer. J. Bot. 41: 710-717, 1954.
Inada, K.: Studies on a method for determining the deepness of green and color chlorophyll content of intact crop leaves and its practical applications. 1. Principle for estimating the deepness of green color and chlorophyll content of whole leaves. – Proc. Crop Sci. Soc. Japan 32: 157-162, 1963.
Jeffrey, S. W.: Quantitative thin-layer chromatography of chlorophylls and carotenoids from marine algae. – Biochim. biophys. Acta 162: 271-285, 1968.
Johnston, L. G., Watson, W. F.: The allomerization of chlorophyll. – J. chem. Soc. 1956: 1203-1212, 1956.
Kaler, V. L., Podchufarova, G. M.: Polumikrokolichestvennoe opredelenie kontsentratsii protokhlorofillida v rastitel'nom materiale. [Semi-microquantitative determination of protochlorophyllide concentration in plant material.] – In: Fiziologo-biokhimicheskie Issledovaniya Rasteniĭ. Pp. 20-26. Nauka i Tekhnika, Minsk 1965.
Koski, V. M.: Chlorophyll formation in seedlings of *Zea mays* L. – Arch. Biochem. 29: 339-343, 1950.
Koski, V. M., Smith, J. H. C.: The isolation and spectral absorption properties of protochlorophyll from etiolated barley seedlings. – J. Amer. chem. Soc. 70: 3558-3562, 1948.
de Kouchkovsky, Y.: Induction photosynthétique des chloroplastes isolés. – Physiol. vég. 1: 15-76, 1963.

Kupke, D. W., Huntington, J. L.: Chlorophyll *a* appearance in the dark in higher plants: Analytical notes. – Science 140: 49-51, 1963.
Mackinney, G.: Applicability of Kundt's rule to chlorophyll. – Plant Physiol. 13: 427-430, 1938.
Mackinney, G.: Criteria for purity of chlorophyll preparations. – J. biol. Chem. 132: 91-109, 1940.
Mackinney, G.: Absorption of light by chlorophyll solutions. – J. biol. Chem. 140: 315-322, 1941.
Maslova, T. G.: Izvlekaemost' khlorofilla petroleïnym efirom iz list'ev rasteniĭ raznykh sistematicheskikh grupp. [Extractability of chlorophyll from leaves of plants of various systematic groups by petroleum ether.] – Bot. Zh. 44: 389-394, 1959.
McClure, W. F.: Fiber-optic spectrophotometer for *in vivo* analysis of biological materials: Chlorophyll measurements. – Transactions ASAE 12: 319–321, 1969.
Medina, E., Lieth, H.: Contenido de clorofila de algunas asociaciones vegetales de Europa Central y su relación con la productividad. – Qualitas Plant. Mater. Vegetab. 9: 217-229, 1963.
Munsell, A. H.: Munsell Book of Color. Cabinet Edition. – Baltimore 1958.
Niewiadomski, H., Bratkowska, I.: Zawartość barwników grupy chlorofilu w surowych olejach rzepakowych. [Contents of chlorophyll in raw rape seed oil.] – Roczniki Technol. Chemii Żywności 12: 207-221, 1966.
Nybom, N.: The pigment characteristics of chlorophyll mutations in barley. – Hereditas 41: 483-498, 1955.
Official Methods of Analysis of the Association of Official Agricultural Chemists. - 9th Ed. Assoc. Offic. Agr. Chem., Washington 1960.
Ogawa, T., Shibata, K.: A sensitive method for determining chlorophyll *b* in plant extracts. – Photochem. Photobiol. 4: 193-200, 1965.
Parsons, T. R., Strickland, J. D. H.: Discussion of spectrophotometric determination of marine-plant pigments, with revised equations for ascertaining chlorophylls and carotenoids. – J. marine Res. 21: 155-163, 1963.
Richards, F. A., Thompson, T. G.: The estimation and characterization of plankton populations by pigment analysis. II. A spectrophotometric method for the estimation of plankton pigments. – J. marine Res. 11: 156-172, 1952.
Röbbelen, G.: Untersuchungen an strahleninduzierten Blattfarbmutanten von *Arabidopsis thaliana* (L.) Heynh. – Z. indukt. Abstammungs- u. Vererbungslehre 88: 189-252, 1957.
Rudolph, E.: Untersuchungen über den Einfluss der Photoreaktionssysteme auf die Chlorophyll-synthese. – Planta 66: 75-94, 1965.
Sapozhnikov, D. I.: Razdelenie i kolichestvennoe opredelenie fitokhromov plastidy. [Separation and quantitative determination of plastid pigments.] – Eksper. Bot. 8: 140-163, 1951.
Sapozhnikov, D. I. (ed.): Pigmenty Plastid Zelenykh Rasteniĭ i Metodika ikh Issledovaniya. [Plastid Pigments of Green Plants and Methods of their Studying.] – Nauka, Moskva–Leningrad 1964.
Schneider, H. A. W.: Eine einfache Methode zur dünnschichtchromatographischen Trennung von Plastidenpigmenten. – J. Chromatogr. 21: 448-453, 1966.
Schötz, F.: Pigmentanalytische Untersuchungen an *Oenothera*. I. Vorversuche und Analyse der Blätter und Blüten von *Oenothera suaveolens* DESF., Mutante 'Weissherz'. – Planta 58: 411-434, 1962.
Seely, G. R., Jensen, R. G.: Effect of solvent on the spectrum of chlorophyll. – Spectrochim. Acta 21: 1835-1845, 1965.
Šesták, Z.: Paper chromatography of chloroplast pigments. – J. Chromatogr. 1: 293-308, 1958. – Chromatogr. Rev. 1: 193-208, 1959a.
Šesták, Z.: A method of storage of leaf samples for chlorophyll analysis. – Biol. Plant. 1: 287-294, 1959b.
Šesták, Z.: Factors affecting the accuracy of chlorophylls *a* and *b* determination by means of their paper chromatographic separation and colorimetric measurement in eluates. – Biol. Plant. 6: 132-141, 1964.
Šesták, Z.: Paper chromatography of chloroplast pigments (chlorophylls and carotenoids) – Part 2. – Chromatogr. Rev. 7: 65-97, 1965.
Šesták, Z.: Construction of a simple nomogram for evaluating two-wavelength spectrophotometric determination of chlorophylls. – Biol. Plant. 8: 97-109, 1966.
Šesták, Z.: Thin layer chromatography of chlorophylls. – Photosynthetica 1: 269-292, 1967.

Šesták, Z., Ullmann, J.: Srovnání metod stanovení chlorofylů. I. Spektrofotometrické a kolorimetrické metody. [Comparison of methods for chlorophyll determination. I. Spectrophotometric and colorimetric methods.] – Rostlinná Výroba 10: 1197-1206, 1964.

Sherma, J., Lippstone, G. S.: Chromatography of chloroplast pigments on preformed thin layers. – J. Chromatogr. 41: 220-227, 1969.

Shlyk, A. A., Nikolaeva, G. N., Vlasenok, L. I., Godnev, T. N.: Obrazovanie khlorofillida pri ekstraktsii zelenykh list'ev vodnym atsetonom. [Chlorophyllide formation during the extraction of green leaves with aqueous acetone.] – Dokl. Akad. Nauk Belorussk. SSR 5: 364-368, 1961.

Smith, J. H. C., Benitez, A.: Chlorophylls: Analysis in plant materials. – In: Paech, K., Tracey, M. V. (ed.): Modern Methods of Plant Analysis. Vol. IV. Pp. 142-196. – Springer-Verlag, Berlin–Göttingen–Heidelberg 1955.

Sprague, H. B., Troxler, L. B.: An improved color standard for the colorimetric determination of chlorophyll. – Science 71: 666-667, 1930.

Starnes, W. J., Hadley, H. H.: Chlorophyll content of various strains of soybeans, *Glycine max* (L.) Merrill. – Crop Sci. 5: 9-11, 1965.

Strain, H. H.: Chloroplast Pigments and Chromatographic Analysis. – Pennsylvania State Univ., University Park, Pa. 1958.

Strain, H. H., Manning, W. M.: Isomerization of chlorophylls *A* and *B*. – J. biol. Chem. 146: 275-276, 1942.

Strain, H. H., Svec, W. A.: Extraction, separation, estimation, and isolation of the chlorophylls. – – In: Vernon, L. P., Seely, G. R. (ed.): The Chlorophylls. Pp. 21-66. Academic Press, New York–London 1966.

Strain, H. H., Thomas, M. R., Katz, J. J.: Spectral absorption properties of ordinary and fully deuteriated chlorophylls *a* and *b*. – Biochim. biophys. Acta 75: 306-311, 1963.

Turrell, F. M., Weber, J. R., Austin, S. W.: Chlorophyll content and reflection spectra of citrus leaves. – Bot. Gaz. 123: 10-15, 1961.

Vernon, L. P.: Spectrophotometric determination of chlorophylls and pheophytins in plant extracts. – Anal. Chem. 32: 1144-1150, 1414, 1960.

Virgin, H. I.: The conversion of protochlorophyll to chlorophyll *a* in continuous and intermittent light. – Physiol. Plant. 8: 389-403, 1955.

White, R. C., Jones, I. D., Gibbs, E.: Determination of chlorophylls, chlorophyllides, pheophytins, and pheophorbides in plant material. – J. Food Sci. 28: 431-436, 1963.

Wickliff, J. L., Aronoff, S.: Quantitative measurement of leaf chlorophylls by spectrophotometry of their pheophytins in aqueous alcoholic extracts. – Plant Physiol. 37: 584-589, 1962.

Willstätter, R., Stoll, A.: Untersuchungen über Chlorophyll. – J. Springer, Berlin 1913.

Wilson, J. R., Nutting, M.-D.: Use of ion exchange resin for conversion, separation, and determination of chlorophylls as pheophytins. – Anal. Chem. 35: 144-146, 1963.

Wintermans, J. F. G. M.: Comparative chlorophyll determinations by spectrophotometry of leaf extracts in different solvents. – Photosynthetica 3: 112-119, 1969.

Wintermans, J. F. G. M., de Mots, A.: Spectrophotometric characteristics of chlorophylls *a* and *b* and their pheophytins in ethanol. – Biochim. biophys. Acta 109: 448-453, 1965.

Ziegler, R., Egle, K.: Zur quantitativen Analyse der Chloroplastenpigmente. I. Kritische Überprüfung der spektralphotometrischen Chlorophyll-Bestimmung. – Beitr. Biol. Pflanzen 41: 11-37, 1965.

Zscheile, F. P.: Photoelectric spectrophotometry. – J. phys. coll. Chem. 51: 903-926, 1947.

Zscheile, F. P., Comar, C. L.: Influence of preparative procedure on the purity of chlorophyll components as shown by absorption spectra. – Bot. Gaz. 102: 463-481, 1941.

Zscheile, F. P., Comar, C. L., Harris, D. G.: Spectrophotometric stability of chlorophylls *a* and *b* and certain analytical considerations. – Plant Physiol. 19: 627-637, 1944.

Zscheile, F. P., Comar, C. L., Mackinney, G.: Interlaboratory comparison of absorption spectra by the photoelectric spectrophotometric method. – Determinations on chlorophyll and Weigert's solutions. – Plant Physiol. 17: 666-670, 1942.

19 | MEASUREMENT OF RADIANT ENERGY

19.1 | Fundamental terms and quantities

19.1.1 | Significant parts of the electromagnetic spectrum

All kinds of radiant energy can be defined as electromagnetic waves of a certain wavelength or frequency. The electromagnetic spectrum is spread over a wide range of wavelengths, encompassing about 20 orders of magnitude. However, only a very small part of this range influences the growth and development of green plants. The main physiological effects occur in that region of the electromagnetic spectrum which contains a large part of the *solar* radiation reaching the Earth's surface, *i.e.* the wavelength range of *ca.* 280 to 740 nm.
Radiation may have both chemical and physical effects. In the former case, the absorption of a certain amount of radiant energy results in photochemical and synthetic reactions, in the latter the result is usually heating of the irradiated plant and hence a change in the rate of various physiological processes.

Table 19.1 The main spectral regions of physiological importance to plants (after Committee on Plant Irradiation 1953).

Spectral region		Character of absorption	Physiological effect
IR	> 1000 nm	By water in tissues	Without any specific effect on photochemical and biochemical processes; converted into heat
IR	1000–720 nm	Slight	Stimulating elongation
PhAR	720–610 nm	Very strong, by chlorophylls	Large effect on photosynthesis and photoperiodism
PhAR	610–510 nm	Somewhat less	Small effect on photosynthesis; small morphogenetic effect
PhAR	510–400 nm	Very strong, by chlorophylls and carotenoids	Large effect on photosynthesis; large morphogenetic effect
UV	400–315 nm	By chlorophylls and protoplasm	Without any specific effect, small effect on photosynthesis
UV	315–280 nm	By protoplasm	Large morphogenetic effect; stimulating some biosyntheses; large effect on physiological processes
UV	< 280 nm	By protoplasm	Lethal in large doses

Committee on Plant Irradiation (1953) distinguishes eight principal wavelength ranges of physiological significance, as shown in Table 19.1. The properties of radiation change continuously in relation to its wavelength. The shorter the wavelength, the bigger is the energy of the fundamental unit, the quantum or photon. Thus the same number of quanta contain more radiant energy at shorter wavelengths than at longer ones. As the photochemical effect of radiation in photosynthesis is proportional primarily to the number of quanta which are absorbed, exact knowledge of the spectral composition of the incident radiation is very important.

Photosynthetically active radiation (Nichiporovich 1954; Bell 1955; Gaastra 1959) is that part of the electromagnetic spectrum which on absorption by pigments in the plant induces the process of photosynthesis. The approximate limits of this region are defined by wavelengths of *ca.* 380 and 740 nm. This range approximately coincides with that of light which is, however, defined in relation to the photochemical response of the human retina and is not appropriately used in connection with photosynthesis. The response of the human retina to light of different spectral composition in the visible region is usually defined by the average luminosity curve (Fig. 19.1), the peak of which is in the region of 555 nm, from where the curve drops off approximately symetrically on either side. Hence quantitative data measured in photometric units of luminous flux density, which is based on the physiological response of the human eye, have no direct relation to the amount of radiant energy or to the number of quanta. Clearly, the correct and objective evaluation of light requires a radiation detector, the spectral sensitivity of which agrees closely with the average luminosity curve of the human eye. Similarly, a sensor for measuring radiation in relation to photosynthesis should measure the spectrally integrated energy available to the plant.

Some Soviet authors have used the term 'physiological radiation' to denote the spectral region from 300 to 700 nm (Ivanov 1938; Kleschnin 1960). This term can-

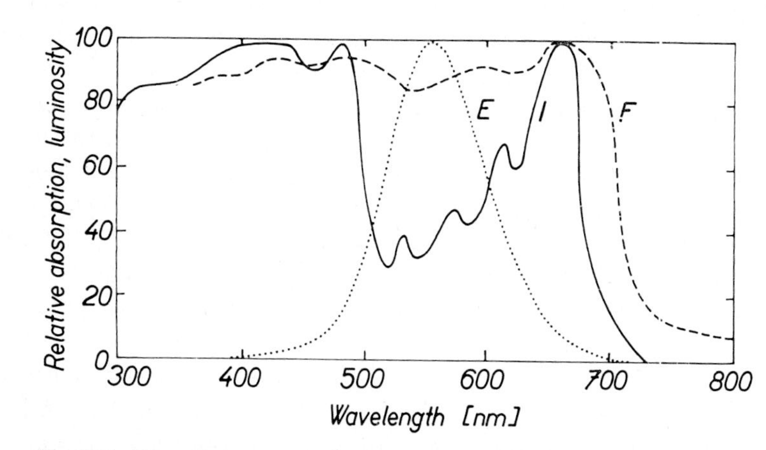

Fig. 19.1 Absorption spectra of two leaves of different anatomical structure in comparison with the average luminosity curve of the human eye.
E: the luminosity curve; *F:* absorption spectrum of a *Ficus* leaf; *I:* absorption spectrum of an *Impatiens* leaf. (From Oranje 1943; Kleschnin 1960.)

not be recommended, because it is already in use to denote the radiation emitted by some organisms and because other types of radiation may have physiological effects.

19.1.3 | *Radiometric and photometric terms and units*

As radiation is a form of energy, measurements of it should be expressed in the corresponding physical terms and units. The following review is based on the nomenclature which was suggested by Withrow (1943). This nomenclature, as well as the symbols used, also agree with the UNESCO document 'Symbols, Units and Nomenclature in Physics' (1961). For comparison, the appropriate photometric terms and symbols are always given.

a. Radiant energy is a form of energy which propagates through space in the form of electromagnetic waves. It is usually denoted by a single word – *radiation*, although this does not have precisely the same sense as radiant energy. Strictly, radiation is the emanation of radiant energy from a source as the result of a physical or chemical process. However, the term radiation has become so deep-rooted that one cannot at present object to this looseness in its usage. In order to make the above distinction, the term 'emanation' will be applied to the process by which radiant energy is generated. Light is a form of radiant energy delimited by the spectral response of the human retina as described previously. The symbols Q_e and Q have become established for quantities of radiant energy and light respectively.

b. Radiant flux, Φ_e, is the radiant energy propagated through space, regardless of the direction of the rays, the nature of the source and its orientation, and is expressed in units of power, *i.e.* by units of energy per unit time:

$$\Phi_e = \frac{Q_e}{dt} \text{ [J s}^{-1}\text{; W]} \tag{19.1}$$

In the literature one frequently encounters the use of the term 'radiation' where the radiant energy flux is meant. As above, this usage is incorrect and it should be avoided.

The analogous photometric term is the *luminous flux* of light (Φ). The unit of luminous flux is the lumen (lm) which is derived from the international conventional standard of luminous intensity – the candela (cd). The luminous flux of an ideal source of which the luminous intensity is one candela, is 4 πlm, *i.e.* 12.57 lm. Thus one lumen is defined as the luminous flux radiated by a source of which the luminous intensity is one candela, into one steradian, *i.e.* into a unit solid angle which cuts out an area of r^2 on the surface of a sphere of radius r.

c. Radiant flux density (F_e) at a given point is the radiant flux through a unit surface (of which the said point is part), orientated at right angles to the direction of the rays of the radiant flux. Hence this is a quantity which expresses the radiant flux (the amount of radiant energy per unit time) passing through a unit surface of definite orientation. The radiant flux density can also be expressed relative to a unit surface of arbitrary orientation in which case the flux density propagated

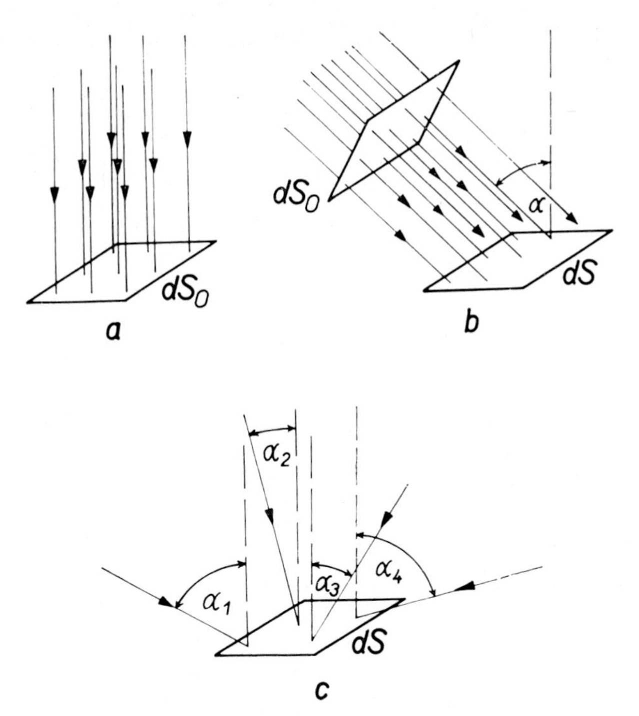

Fig. 19.2 The relation between irradiance and the cosine of the angle of incidence. *a:* perpendicular incidence of rays; *b:* a beam of parallel rays incident at the irradiated surface at an angle α; *c:* surface irradiated by dispersed rays.

through the surface is always smaller than that propagated through the surface normal to the direction of the rays. The proportionality factor is $1/\cos\alpha$ (see Fig. 19.2), where α is the angle between the direction of the rays and the normal to the arbitrarily orientated reference unit surface (*i.e.* the angle of incidence):

$$F_e = \frac{\Phi_e}{\mathrm{d}S_0} = \frac{\Phi_e}{\mathrm{d}S} \cdot \frac{1}{\cos\alpha} \; [\mathrm{J\,m^{-2}\,s^{-1};\,W\,m^{-2}}] \qquad (19.2)$$

where $\mathrm{d}S_0$ is the area of unit surface at right angles to the direction of the rays considered and $\mathrm{d}S$ is the area of a unit surface of arbitrary orientation. If the radiant flux consists of rays propagating in various directions, only this formulation may be used to express the flux density. The orientation of the reference surface may then be arbitrary, but the various inclinations of the individual rays must be taken into account:

$$F_e = \sum_{i=1}^{i=n} \frac{(\Phi_e)_i}{\mathrm{d}S} \cdot \frac{1}{\cos\alpha_i}. \qquad (19.3)$$

Hence it follows that under natural conditions (*e.g.*, in the open under an overcast sky, or inside a stand) accurate measurements of the radiant flux density are practically impossible. It can only be computed from the observed values, provided the angles between the plane of the measuring device and the incident rays of one or several beams of parallel radiation emitted by point sources, are known. If measurements are made in the field, where direct solar rays only very seldom

Table 19.2 Radiometric and photometric terms, symbols, and units (for equivalents of these units s Table 12.1).

Terms, symbols, defining equations, and units			
radiometric			photometric
Radiant energy	Q_e	J, W s	Luminous energy, light
Radiator, source, lamp			Luminator, source, lamp
Radiation			Lumination
Radiant emittance	$M_e = \frac{\Phi_e}{dS_r}$	J m^{-2} s^{-1}; W m^{-2}	Luminous emittance
Radiant flux	$\Phi_e = \frac{Q_e}{dt}$	J s^{-1}; W	Luminous flux
Radiant flux density	$F_e = \frac{\Phi_e}{dS\cos\alpha}$	J m^{-2} s^{-1}; W m^{-2}	Luminous flux density
Radiant flux intensity	$I_e = \frac{\Phi_e}{d\omega}$	J sr^{-1} s^{-1}; W sr^{-1}	Luminous flux intensity
Radiance	$L_e = \frac{\Phi_e}{d\omega(dS\cos\alpha)}$	J m^{-2} s^{-1} sr^{-1}; W m^{-2} sr^{-1}	Luminance[1] Brightness[1]
Irradiance	$E_e = \frac{\Phi_e}{dS}$	J m^{-2} s^{-1}; W m^{-2}	Illuminance
Irradiation			Illumination
Radiant exposure	$H_e = \frac{Q_e}{dS}$	J m^{-2}; W s m^{-2}	Light exposure

1. Terms used for the characterization of light sources.

constitute the entire radiant flux, it is the irradiance which is actually always observed (E_e – see paragraph *f*).
If radiation is emitted by a point source into a solid angle (ω, sr), *i.e.* if the radiant flux density decreases with the square of the distance from the source, one speaks of the *radiant flux intensity* (I_e):

$$I_e = \frac{\Phi_e}{d\omega} \quad [\text{J sr s}^{-1};\ \text{W sr}^{-1}].$$

Similar photometric terms are the *luminous flux density* (F) and the *luminous flux intensity* (I). Sometimes light intensity is used instead, but this is not correct. Luminous flux density is expressed in terms of lumens per unit area = lux.

		Concise definition
	lm s	Energy in the form of electromagnetic waves
		Device converting a certain form of energy into the radiant one (into the light)
		Process of generation of radiant (luminous) energy
$= \frac{\Phi}{\mathrm{d}S_r}$	lm m^{-2}	Radiant (luminous) flux emitted per unit area of radiating body
$\frac{Q}{\mathrm{d}t}$	lm	Rate of propagation of radiant energy (light)
$\frac{\Phi}{\mathrm{d}S \cos\alpha}$	lm m^{-2} = lux (lx)	Radiant (luminous) flux passing through a plane of unit area
$\frac{\Phi}{\mathrm{d}\omega}$	lm sr^{-1} = cd (candela)	Radiant (luminous) flux emitted by a point-like source into a unit solid angle
$\frac{\Phi}{\mathrm{d}\omega(\mathrm{d}S \cos\alpha)}$	lm sr^{-1} m^{-2} = cd m^{-2} = = 10^{-4}sb (stilb) = nt(nit)	Radiant (luminous) flux intensity per unit area in direction of emission
$\frac{\Phi}{\mathrm{d}S}$	lx	Radiant (luminous) flux intercepted per unit area
		Emission of radiant (luminous) flux, which is incident on the surface of some body
$= \frac{Q}{\mathrm{d}S}$	lx s	Amount of radiant energy (light) intercepted per unit area during a certain period

d. Radiant emittance (M_e) is the radiant energy flux emitted by a unit radiating surface S_r:

$$M_e = \frac{\Phi_e}{\mathrm{d}S_r} \qquad [\mathrm{J\,m^{-2}\,s^{-1};\ W\,m^{-2}}] \tag{19.4}$$

The analogous photometric term is the *luminous emittance (M)*.

e. Irradiation (*illumination*) is an emission of radiant (luminous) flux, which is incident on the surface of some body.

f. Irradiance (E_e) is the irradiation of unit surface area of a body. This has the same units as the radiant flux density, *i.e.* units of power relative to a unit area which may be either flat or spherical (hemispherical). For a flat surface the irradiance decreases with the cosine of the angle of incidence (see Fig. 19.2), because rays which are not normal to the surface are only incident on the projection of the surface:

$$E_e = F_e \cdot \cos\alpha = \frac{\Phi_e \cos\alpha}{dS_0} = \frac{\Phi_e}{dS} = \frac{Q_e}{dS \cdot t} \quad [\mathrm{J\,m^{-2}\,s^{-1};\,W\,m^{-2}}] \tag{19.5}$$

The second ratio can only be used in measuring irradiance with spherical radiation receivers, the readings of which are usually considered relative to the surface of a sphere one cm^2 in cross-section (see Section 19.2.1). The photometric analogue of irradiance is *illuminance (E)*. The illuminance of a flat surface is the luminous flux per unit surface area. It is also directly proportional to the cosine of the angle between the incident rays and the normal to the surface. The unit of illuminance is the lux (lx, 'meter candle'), *i.e.* the illuminance of an area of one m^2 by a luminous flux of one lumen, or normal illuminance by a source the luminous intensity of which is one candela, cd, from a distance of one m.

g. *Radiant exposure (light exposure)* is the amount of radiant energy (light) incident upon unit area of a body, during a period of irradiation. The incident radiation is not identical with the absorbed radiation since some of it is reflected and some may be transmitted. Radiant exposure is expressed in units of energy per unit area. As there is no symbol for this quantity in the UNESCO Commission document, nor is it mentioned, the symbol H_e is proposed by International Commission of Illumination (CIE):

$$H_e = E_e \cdot t = \frac{Q_e}{dS} \quad [\mathrm{J\,m^{-2};\,W\,s\,m^{-2}}] \tag{19.6}$$

Similarly, for light exposure:

$$H = E \cdot t = \frac{Q}{dS} \quad [\mathrm{lx\,s}] \tag{19.7}$$

Table 19.2 gives a summary of the radiometric and photometric terms with short definitions and the appropriate symbols. The relations between the various units of energy and illumination and between the units of irradiance are given in Figs. 19.3 and 19.4 and in Table 12.1.

19.2 | Measurement of radiant energy

The necessity for frequent and repeated measurements of the input of radiant energy results from the considerable variability of the radiant flux of the sun and of the sky and from the variety of types of artificial luminous sources, mains voltage fluctuations, and the ageing of artificial sources (the radiant emittance of some sources is strongly dependent on voltage variations; this deficiency may be removed by suitable stabilization).

The evaluation of the radiant flux emitted by a source is relatively simple. It is more difficult to evaluate the irradiance and its spectral composition both in

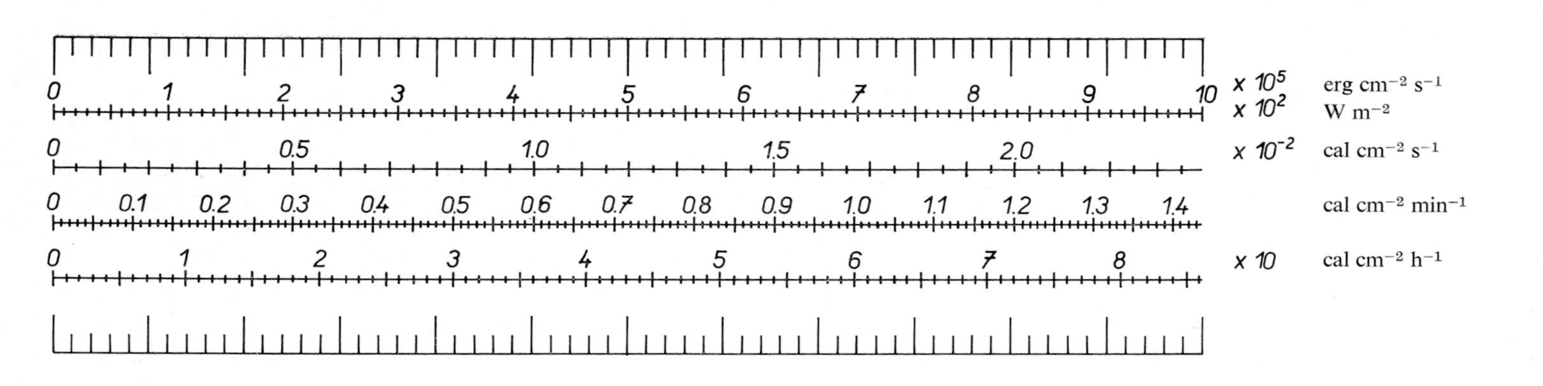

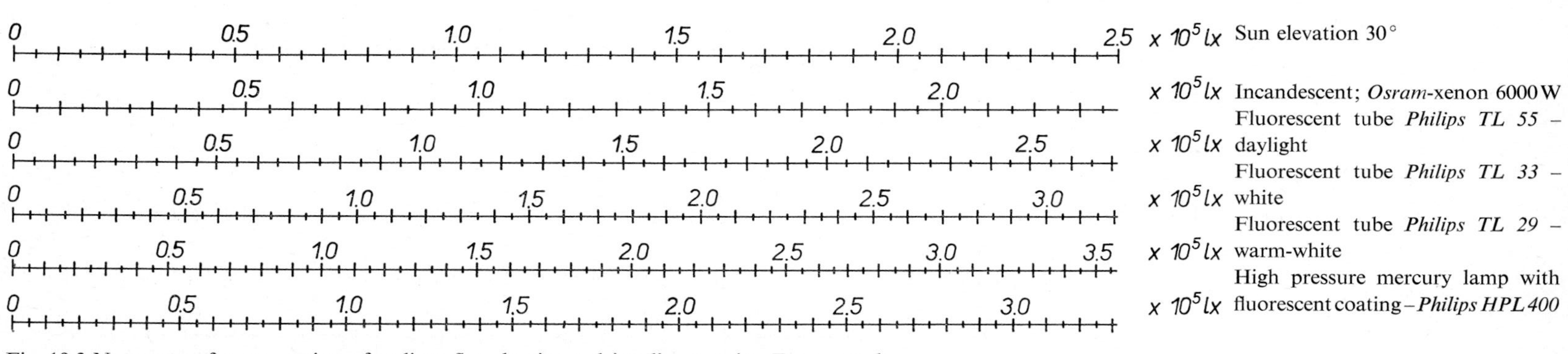

Fig. 19.3 Nomogram for conversion of radiant flux density and irradiance units. For a rough comparison, the relationships between energy units and photometric units (lux) for direct sunlight, incandescent lamp, xenon lamp, fluorescent lamps and high pressure mercury vapour lamp with fluorescent coating in the spectral region 400 to 700 nm are provided (data from Gaastra 1959).

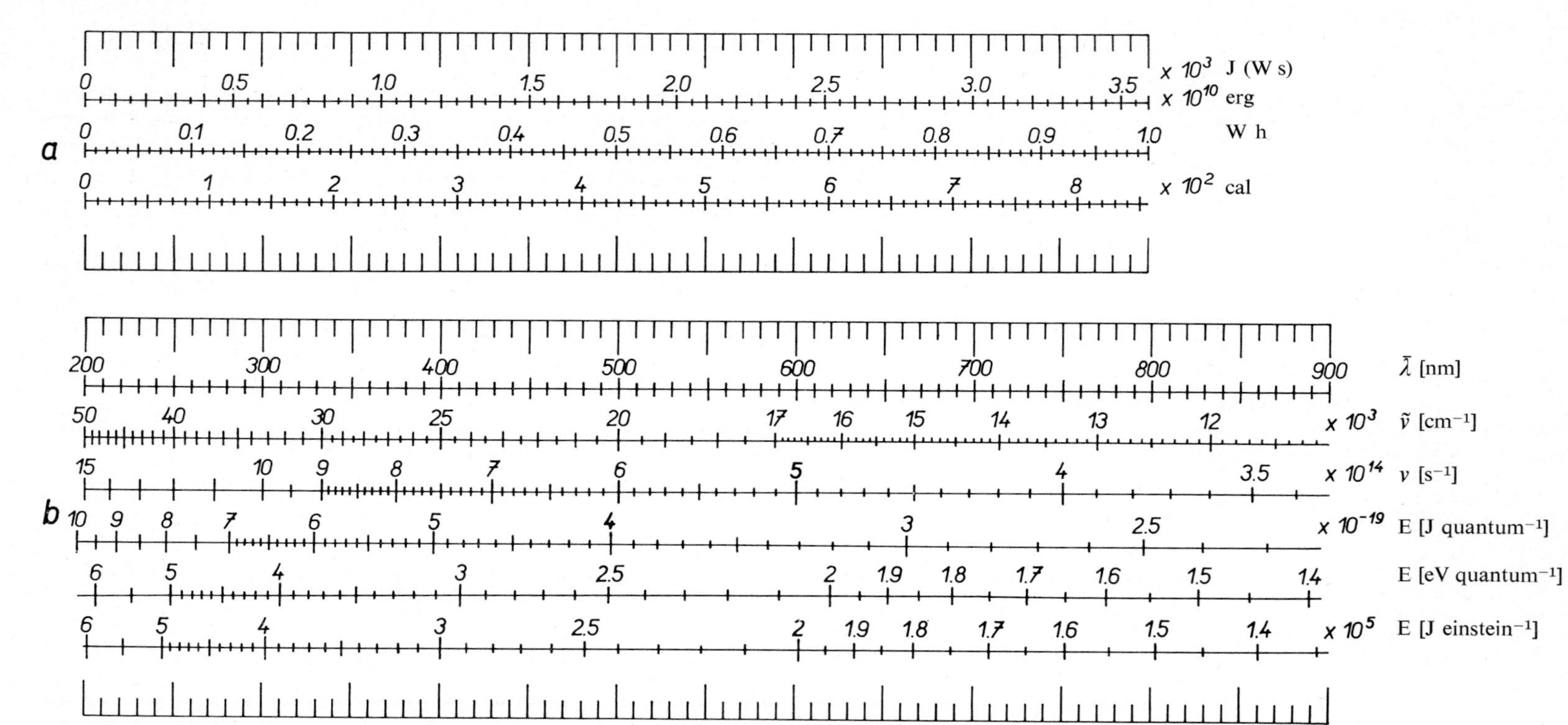

Fig. 19.4 *a:* Nomogram for conversion of units of energy. *b:* Nomogram comparing some properties of radiation.

natural conditions and in a growth room, for example. One or more radiation sources, placed at a comparatively small distance from the plants, is capable of creating a considerably heterogeneous radiant flux at the level of the highest leaves, as regards density, spectral composition and the direction of the individual rays. If one also considers the effects of mutual shading of the lower parts of the plant by the upper, the differences in the surface structure, the morphology, and the inclination and the orientation of the leaves, it is apparent why accurate measurements of the amount of radiant energy incident upon the plant are as difficult to obtain under artificial conditions as under natural ones.
Measurements of radiant energy require three fundamental elements: a receiver, a detector and a measuring instrument. To calibrate the whole system, a standard radiation source, or another measuring system capable of absolute measurements, is necessary.

19.3 | Receiver

The proportion of energy captured by the receiver from a flux of given directional properties, depends on the geometric and absorptive properties of the receiver surfaces. If the surface of the detector itself is not suitable for absorption of radiation the receiver becomes a necessary and independent part of the sensor. The radiant energy absorbed by the receiver is transmitted to the detector, which transforms it into a measureable form of energy.
Receivers are generally either flat, spherical or hemispherical. A flat receiver is suitable for beams of parallel rays, or for the global radiant flux per unit of horizontal surface. It is also suitable for all measurements in which the decrement of the irradiance, proportional to the cosine of the angle of incidence, is required. Spherical and hemispherical receivers are suitable for investigating radiant fluxes acting on solitary plants, plants growing in or below dense canopies and plants cultivated in growth-rooms equipped with many radiation sources. It is necessary to decide in each case whether one should use a flat, spherical or hemispherical receiver (Wallace 1937; Wassink & van der Scheer 1951; Giovanelli 1953; Middleton 1953; Dlugos 1958; Richardson 1959; Anderson 1964; Krochmann 1964; Eckhardt 1965). At the same time one must realise that no receiver can provide an accurate picture of the amount of radiant energy the plant or the whole stand is receiving, and that it is impossible to compare values obtained with receivers of different geometric properties and corresponding to radiant fluxes of quite different nature (Schüepp 1961; Impens 1962; Thams & Wierzejewski 1963).
As regards the quality and the function of the surface there are two types of receivers: one type absorbs radiation, converting radiant energy to heat, the other type only homogenizes the absorbed radiation by scattering (or modifying it in some other way) and transmits it to the detector. The former are usually made of thin tin plate or other material of high heat conductivity and small heat capacity, and their surface is covered by as perfectly absorbing black as possible. The other type of receiver is most frequently made of opal glass or other diffusing material without selective absorption (within the sensitivity range of the detector). Opal glass with a rough surface is more suitable than smooth or polished glass. Diaphragms and neutral filters, restricting the quantity of radiation, or coloured glass

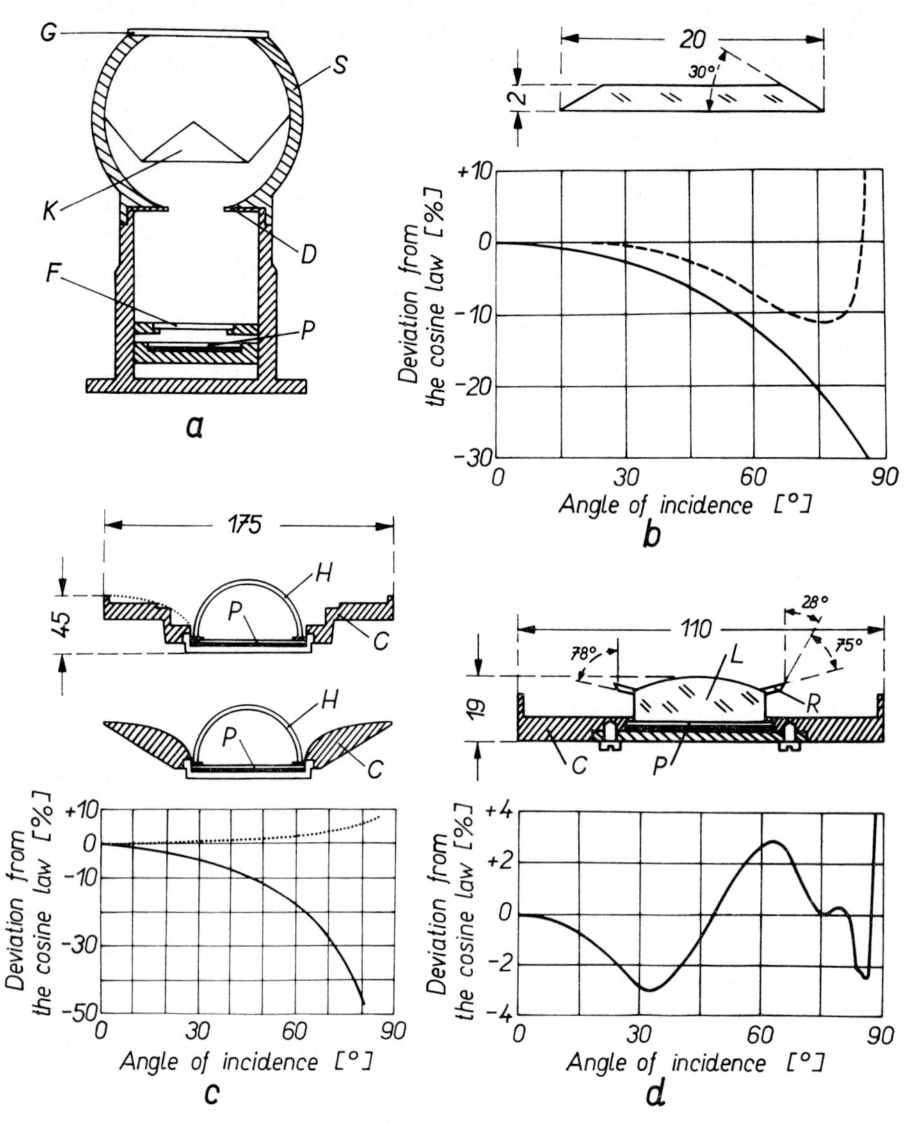

Fig. 19.5 Examples of various designs of flat radiation receivers with correction for deviations from the cosine law.
a: Modification of the Ulbricht sphere. *S:* hollow sphere with a perfectly reflecting inner surface; *G:* glass plate; *K:* conical screen; *D:* diaphragm; *F:* filter; *P:* photocell. The response of the photocell is reduced to 6% of the original value. (From Seemann 1957.)
b: Plate of opal glass, worked to the shape of a cone frustrum. Dimensions in mm. The full curve indicates the measurement error of the photocell itself; the dashed curve the error in the measurement when the photocell is fitted with a receiver.
c: Corrected luxmeter receiver, produced by *AEG*. *H:* hemispherical bowl of opal glass; *C:* screen of light metal; *P:* photocell. Dimensions in mm. The full curve indicates the measurement error of the photocell itself: the dotted line the error in measurement when the photocell is fitted with a receiver. (From Eckhardt 1965.)
d: Receiver with which the required correction was achieved by means of a screen and a convex lens, fixed directly to the photocell. *L:* lens; *C:* screen; *R:* ring fixed to the upper edge of the lens; *P:* photocell. Dimensions in mm. (From Dlugos 1958.)

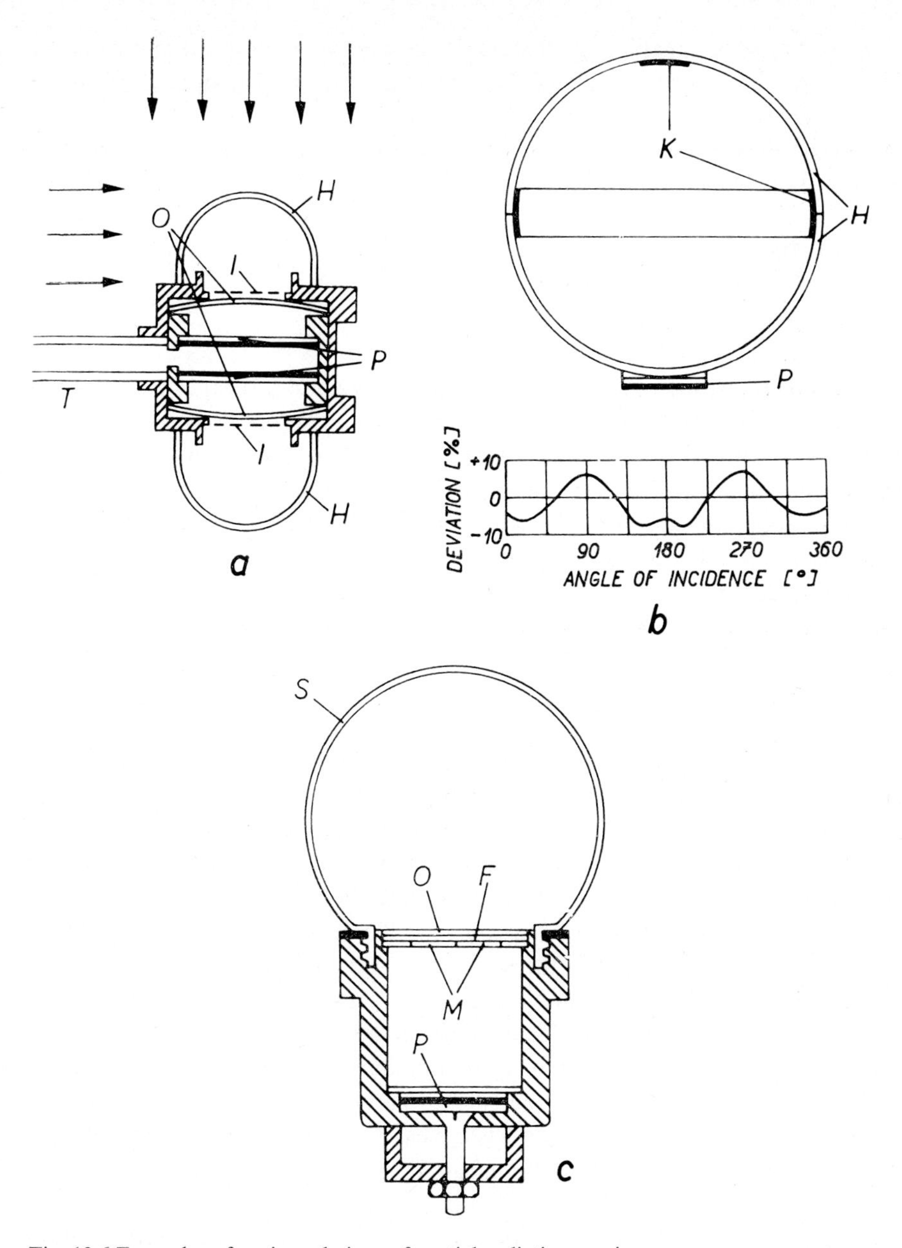

Fig. 19.6 Examples of various designs of spatial radiation receivers.
a: Spherical receiver with two selenium photocells. *H:* hemispherical domes of opal glass; *O:* convex opal glasses; *I:* iris diaphragms; *P:* photocells; *T:* tube which serves as a handle through which the connecting cables go to the measuring instrument (from Wassink & van der Scheer 1951).
b: Spherical receiver constructed using hemispherical bowls of white 'Perspex'. *H:* hemispheres; *K:* blackened surfaces; *P:* photocell. Abscissa: angle of incidence in the plane perpendicular to the photocell surface; ordinate: % deviation at constant irradiation. (From Krochmann 1964.)
c: Hemispherical receiver of a phyto-actinometer (Šetlík & Kubín 1966). *S:* opal-glass sphere; *O:* flat opal glass; *F:* *BG 21* (2 mm) filter; *M:* mosaic filter for correcting the spectral sensitivity; *P:* photocell under protective plate of clear glass.

filters modifying its quality, are frequently inserted between the receiver and the detector. As the radiant flux density, transmitted through flat opal glass, is not proportional to the cosine of the angle of incidence, various designs of flat receivers have been suggested (Fig. 19.5). Three types of spatial radiation receivers are shown in Fig. 19.6.

19.4 | Detector

19.4.1 | Functional classification of detectors

The detector transforms the absorbed radiant energy into a form of energy which can be measured by means of a specific effect, which is proportional either to the energy or to the quantum content of the radiant flux. From this point of view detectors can be divided into two groups:
a. thermal radiation detectors, the action of which is based on the transformation of the absorbed radiation into thermal energy;
b. quantum detectors, which transform the radiation into another form of energy, other than heat, proportional to the number of absorbed quanta.

19.4.2 | Absorption characteristics of detectors

Only an ideal black body absorbs all the radiation incident on it. The surface of a detector which is to measure incident radiation of all wavelengths and which is also to give the correct value of the amount of radiant energy in all parts of the spectrum, must approximate to the surface of an ideal black body. This may be largely achieved by covering it with carbon black, colloidal graphite, or a metal, evaporated onto the surface in a vacuum, *etc.* These absorbing surfaces may be considered almost unselective in the near ultraviolet and PhAR regions.
However, in the infrared region their absorptive properties may decrease with increasing wavelength of the incident radiation. From this point of view metals evaporated in a vacuum (platinum, gold, aluminium, zinc) usually absorb more effectively than some of the previously used carbon blacks. Such detectors are unselective and should be used for basic measurements. They are the only unselective detectors for measurement of infra-red radiation of over 4 μm (Pfund 1937; Blevin & Brown 1966; Harris 1967).
As the only effect common to radiation of all wavelengths is the transformation of the absorbed radiation into heat, unselective detectors are designed to measure the temperature change relative to a reference temperature which is not influenced by the observed radiation and remains close to the ambient temperature. For example, with thermocouples the radiation is transformed into heat on the surface of the detector or receiver which is composed of the hot-junctions of thermocouples connected up to form a battery. The temperature difference between the hot thermo-junctions and the cold thermo-junctions placed elsewhere, generates an electric signal which is measured or recorded.
Only a very few detectors do not require a separate measuring device and allow direct readings of the radiation effect; *e.g.*, the Bellani pyranometer, in which the measuring device is a calibrated tube in which the distilled liquid collects, and the

Robitzsch pyranometer which records the degree of curvature of a bi-metallic strip. The conversion efficiency of photoelectric and photochemical quantum detectors is wavelength dependent. These detectors are selective for one or both of the following reasons:

a. the detector only absorbs radiation in a certain range of wavelengths and reflects or transmits the others;

b. the effect of the absorbed radiation is wavelength dependent because it depends on the amount of energy contained per quantum.

The efficiency characteristic of these detectors is usually expressed by the spectral sensitivity curve. Clearly, the limits of the spectral sensitivity of the detector must at least partly correspond to the limits of the emission spectrum of the source.

19.4.3 | Detector linearity

The response of the detector should be such that a linear relationship between irradiance and the magnitude of the observed signal, is obtained over the largest irradiation range possible (usually several orders of magnitude). Most detectors now used will give a linear response in connection with a suitable measuring system. However, non-linear detectors are known and used, *e.g.* photographic paper or the human eye.

19.4.4 | Thermal radiation detectors

Thermal radiation detectors can be classified into the following types on the basis of the effect used to measure the output: thermoelectric, thermomechanical, pneumatic, distillatory.

19.4.4.1 | Thermoelectric detectors

These detectors are most frequently used as electrical indicating and recording instruments. They are currently available and enable very accurate and sensitive measurements. The irradiance absorbed by the surface of the receiver changes its temperature. The electrical signal is proportional to the detector temperature, the principle of the transformation itself being either the thermoelectric effect, or the change in a conductor or semiconductor resistance with temperature. Thus either thermocouples or bolometers can be used as thermoelectric detectors.

a. Thermocouples are the oldest radiation detectors and in many ways they are still the most reliable (Joffe 1956; Kortum 1957; Smith, Jones & Chasmar 1958; Chapter 17 of this volume). The theory and design of thermocouple circuits is discussed in Chapter 17.

Because the e.m.f. induced per degree of temperature difference is very small whatever the pair of materials used (Table 19.3), thermocouples for the measurement of radiant energy are usually connected together in series to form thermopiles to increase sensitivity.

The temperature difference between the set of hot and the set of cold (or reference) thermo-junctions indicates the irradiance directly. Because the temperature

Table 19.3 Thermoelectric e.m.f. of different materials (related to copper).

Material	$\mu V/^{\circ}C$
Ag	+ 2.9
Fe	+ 16.0
Ni	− 19.0
Sb	+ 40.0
Bi	− 60.0
Te (monocrystallic)	+436.0
Te (polycrystallic)	+376.0
constantan	− 38.0
Special alloys:	
95% Bi-5% Sn	+ 30.0
90% Bi-10% Sb	− 78.0
98.5% Te-1.5% Sb	+575.0
75% Sb-25% Cd	+112.0

difference occurring in radiation measuring instruments is small the relationship between thermocouple output and temperature can be taken as linear, but if large temperature differences are measured the non-linearity of this relationship must be taken into account (Fig. 19.7).

The hot junctions are in close contact with the surface absorbing radiant energy; the cold junctions are placed so as not to be influenced by the incident radiant energy. If the cold junctions are not located in the immediate vicinity of the hot junctions the temperature of the air around the irradiated junction may affect the accuracy and the reproducibility of the measurement. Hence, compensated thermopiles have been designed for very accurate measurements. In principle two thermocouples are connected in series, such that their thermoelectric currents are opposed. The observed radiation is incident only on the hot junction of one of the

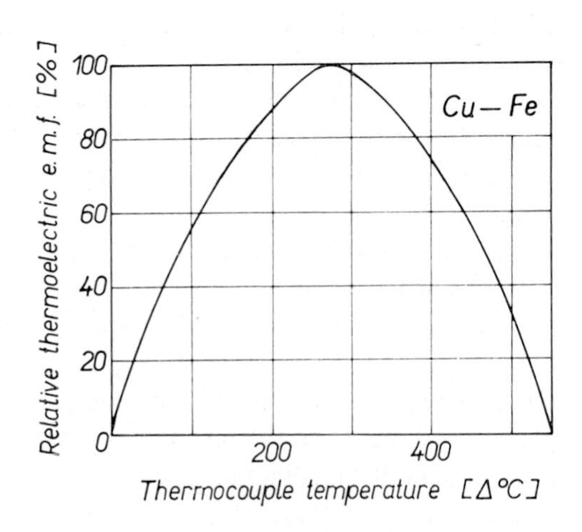

Fig. 19.7 The e.m.f. produced by an iron-copper thermocouple as a function of temperature. (From Prouty & Hardy 1950.)

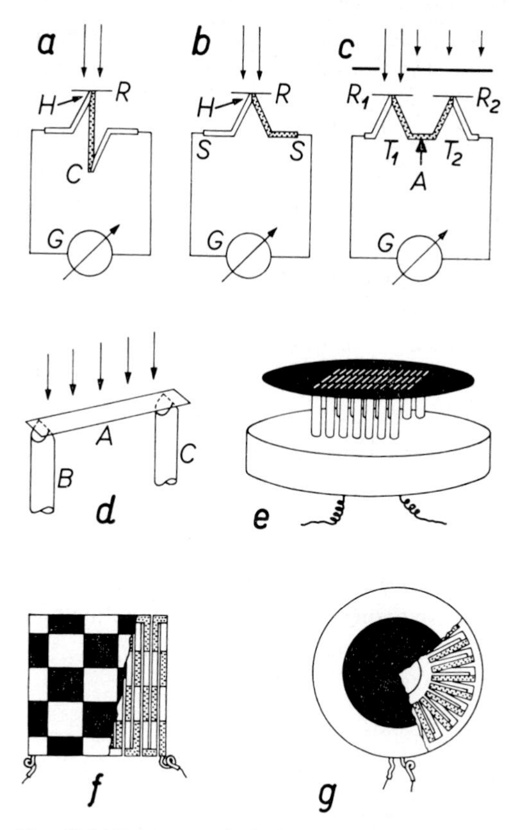

Fig. 19.8 Thermocouple design and function. An example of thermopile design.
a: Schematic illustration of a thermocouple. *R:* receiver; *H:* hot junction; *C:* cold junction; *G:* galvanometer.
b: In practice the 'cold' junction of the thermocouple is represented by its clamps *(S)* the temperature of which must be exactly the same and must remain constant during the measurements.
c: Block diagram of the compensated thermocouple. R_1: receiver of measuring thermocouple; R_2: receiver of compensating thermocouple; T_1: hot junction of measuring thermocouple; T_2: hot junction of compensating thermocouple; *A:* fictitious joint of both thermocouples; *G:* galvanometer.
d: Design of a thermocouple after Schwarz. *A:* gold foil coated with absorbing black; *B:* positive conductor of thermocouple; *C:* negative conductor of thermocouple (from Smith, Jones & Chasmar 1958).
e: Arrangement of thermocouples under the receiver of a *Kipp & Zonen* solarimeter type *CM-3*. The hot junctions are under the blackened receiver, the cold junctions are located in the brass block, which is mounted in a protecting tube.
f: Arrangement of thermocouples under the radiation receiver of the Yanishevskiĭ pyranometer. Alternating thermopile conductors are marked white and dotted (from Yanishevskiĭ 1957).
g: Star-like arrangement of thermocouples under the receiver of an actinometer. Alternating thermopile conductors are marked white and dotted (from Yanishevskiĭ 1957).

thermocouples, whereas the identical junction of the other thermocouple records the changes in ambient temperature and thus compensates for fluctuations in the output signal derived from this source (*c* in Fig. 19.8).
The sensitivity of a thermocouple is decreased considerably by heat dissipation

from its surface resulting from convection. At low irradiances heat dissipation from the surface of the irradiated thermocouple junction is quite considerable in comparison to the heating which the radiation can cause. This undesirable phenomenon can be avoided if the thermocouple is placed in a vacuum (Fig. 19.9). Such thermopiles may be enclosed in flasks of glass or silica and metal chambers with sealed windows of the same materials or of halogenides of alkaline metals, if the thermopile is designed for measurements in the far-infrared region.

Thermocouple sensitivity is usually given in two ways:

1. the e.m.f. in μV, corresponding to some radiant flux density in the plane of the receiver (*e.g.* 24 μV per 1 W m^{-2}),

2. the e.m.f. in μV, corresponding to the power of radiant energy actually absorbed by the receiver (*e.g.* 0.25 $\mu V \ \mu W^{-1}$).

To convert one to the other the area of the receiver must be known.

The thermal capacity of the conductors determines the undesirable thermal inertia of the thermocouples, which can only be limited by decreasing the total mass of the constructional elements of the receiver and of both conductors. The inertia of some modern thermocouples is now so small that they may be subjected to a light beam, modulated with a frequency of 5 to 7 Hz. A voltage signal of this frequency can be comparatively easily amplified electronically.

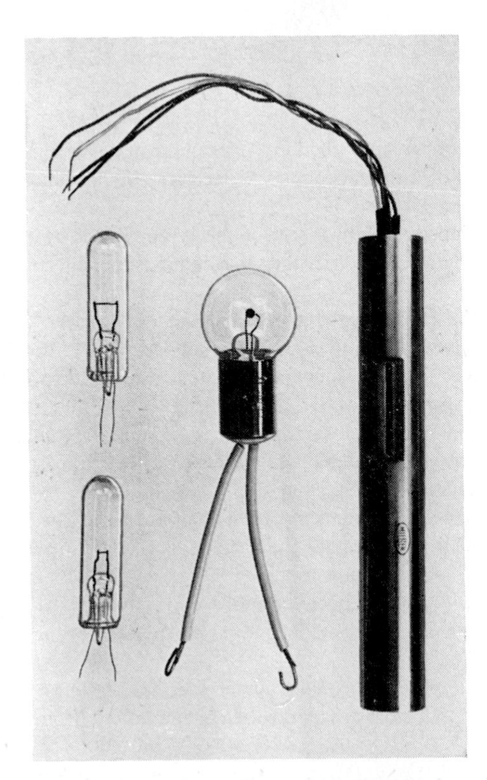

Fig. 19.9 Vacuum thermocouples of various designs. Right: compensated thermocouple made by *Hilger*, type *FT 15* (the thermocouples can be connected in series in two different ways); Middle: vacuum *Carl Zeiss-Jena* thermocouple (older design, uncompensated); left: two *Kipp & Zonen* thermocouples (older design, uncompensated).

b. A bolometer is a resistance thermometer designed to measure the changes in temperature of a thermal radiation detector. Resistance thermometers are often preferred to thermocouples for temperature measurements because changes in resistance of the measuring element can be more readily determined with robust measuring instruments than can the very small voltages obtained with thermocouples (for details of resistance thermometer design and use see Section 17.4). However, in the case of radiation measurements heating of the sensor by passage of a current is a serious disadvantage (with vacuum bolometers up to 50 °C). This effect is of no consequence if the resistance element is in contact with a large mass of a body or liquid with a considerable thermal capacity. In such a case the thermometer cannot be heated appreciably by the measured current. However, if the heating of the sensor is a measure of the irradiance and if the mass of the sensor is as small as possible, in order to reduce undesirable thermal inertia, the passage of even a small current may produce a considerable temperature difference. The more sensitive the sensor is to radiant energy the more sensitive it is to temperature fluctuations, which may result from unstable voltage in the current supply. The resistance element may be metal wire or foil (*e.g.* platinum or nickel) or it may be a semiconductor (*i.e.* a thermistor). Details of the construction and use of various kinds of resistance thermistors are given in Section 17.4.
The receivers of most bolometers are flat and they are designed in such a way that the resistance material of the detector itself is covered by one of the currently used black coatings.
Furthermore thermistors usually have surfaces with good absorptive properties. However, because of their small size and irregular shape, they are not suitable for measuring diffused radiation unless they are in contact with a receiver of geometrically defined properties.

19.4.4.2 | Thermomechanical detectors

The temperature of a thermal radiation detector can also be measured as a mechanical effect (Robitzsch 1932; Yanishevskiĭ 1957). The receiver is in close contact with a bi-metallic strip, the curvature of which is either measured visually (by a Michelson-Marten actinometer), or recorded by an instrument which mechanically amplifies the curvature with a lever (a Robitzsch pyranograph). Thermomechanical methods can only be used to advantage, provided the design of the recording or indicating instrument is perfect; this is only the case with the Michelson-Marten actinometer.

19.4.4.3 | Pneumatic detectors

The pneumatic detector of Golay (1947) is one of the most sensitive radiation detectors. The observed radiant flux is interrupted by a rotating chopper and is then incident on a thin membrane (Fig. 19.10), which is coated with an absorbant. The latter is alternately heated and cooled by the radiant energy with the frequency of the rotating chopper, so that the gas in the pneumatic chamber alternately contracts and expands corresponding to the temperature changes of the membrane. The chamber is connected by a duct with another chamber, across the window of

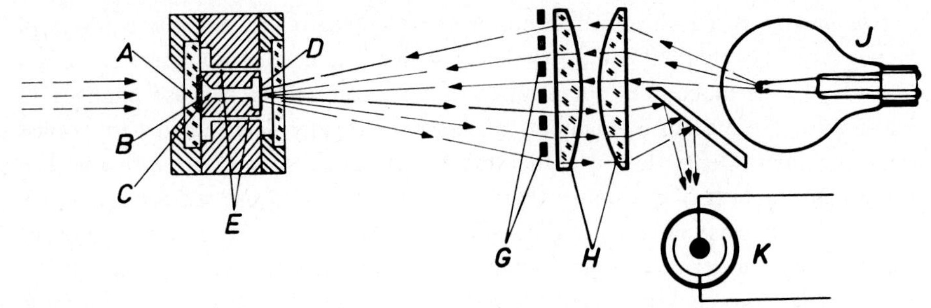

Fig. 19.10 Golay's pneumatic detector. *A:* input window (NaCl, KBr); *B:* absorbing membrane; *C:* pneumatic cell; *D:* elastic mirror membrane; *E:* ducts for compensating pressure changes; *G:* grid; *H:* condensor; *J:* lamp; *K:* photocell connected to a modulated amplifier (from Golay 1947).

which a flexible mirror is stretched. The mirror being flexible, is deflected proportionally to the amount of radiant energy absorbed by the fixed membrane of the first chamber. The mirror deflections are measured photoelectrically *e.g.*, as shown in Fig. 19.10. Although the principle of this detector is simple, its con-

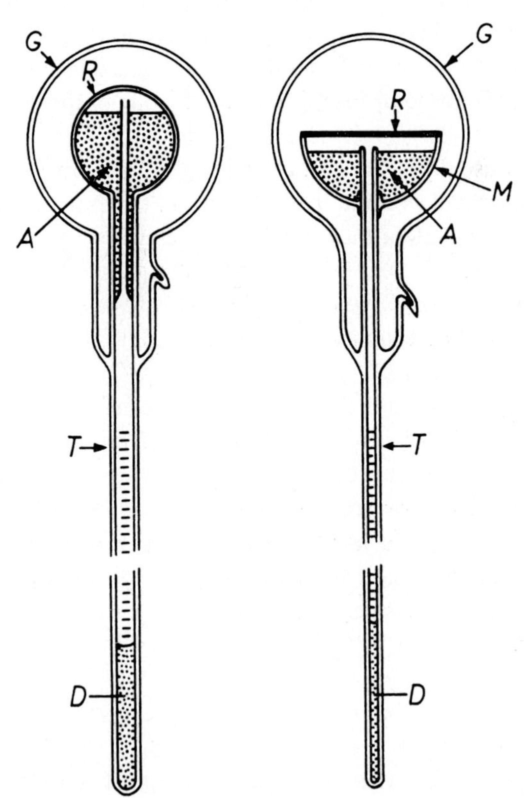

Fig. 19.11 Two modifications of the Bellani pyranometer. Left: all-glass model with a spherical receiver fitted with a non-selective absorbing layer (designed by The Physical and Meteorological Observatory, Davos); right: combined model of glass and metal with a flat receiver (design by National Institute of Agricultural Engineering, Silsoe, U.K.). *G:* outer glass vessel; *R:* receiver; *M:* metal-plated mirror surface (with flat receiver); *A:* alcohol filling; *T:* calibrated tube; *D:* distilled liquid (from Courvoisier & Wierzejewski 1954; Trickett, Moulsley & Edwards 1957).

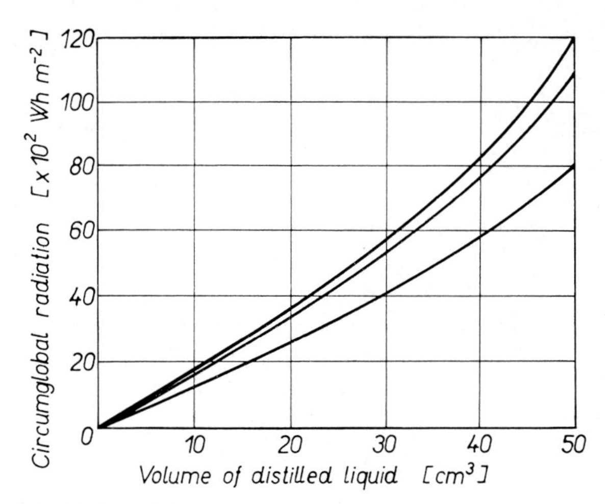

Fig. 19.12 Calibration curves of three different Bellani pyranometers (modified from Wörner 1956).

struction is complex and it cannot, therefore, be recommended for the current purpose.

19.4.4.4 | Distillation detectors

The distillation methods are based on several modifications of the Bellani pyranometer (Bellani 1836; Courvoisier & Wierzejewski 1954). This instrument is sometimes called the distillometer or the lucimeter. The integral nature of the method, the simple functional principle, and the fact that the shape of the receiver may be arbitrary (Fig. 19.11), makes this method very attractive: the simple design results in minimal breakdown and maintenance.
The inner flask of the instrument (Fig. 19.11) is filled with a liquid of low boiling point, usually with pure ethanol. The absorbed radiant energy heats the flask causing the liquid to evaporate in proportion to the absorbed energy. The vapour condenses in the cooler, graduated, lower part of the instrument and, after recording, is returned to the flask simply by inverting the instrument. The Bellani pyranometer is calibrated against some other kind of standard instrument (Fig. 19.12). Irregular cooling of the receiver by variable convection is restricted to a minimum by evacuating the space between the two flasks.

19.4.5 | Photoelectric detectors

In a substance which absorbs radiation of certain wavelengths, a certain number of electrons are released from the orbits along which they normally move, as the result of the absorption of quanta of radiant energy. With metals the incident radiation causes a state different from the usual only if the electrons completely leave the crystal lattice in which they are moving. Maximum emission from the irradiated surface is obtained with alkaline metals of the first principle group of the Mendeleev system of elements (Fig. 19.13). The free electrons are emitted from alkaline metals (in an elementary state or bound in certain compounds

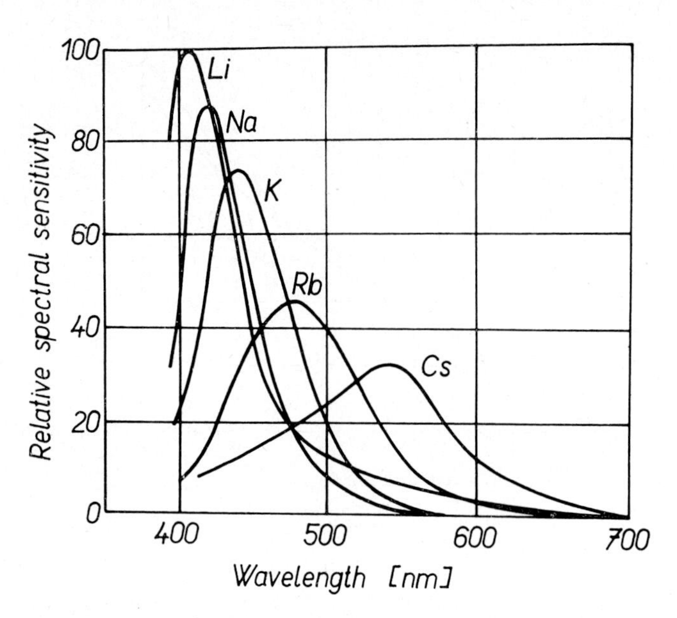

Fig. 19.13 Spectral sensitivity of emission cells in which a layer of alkaline metal was used as the photo-cathode (from Seiler 1920).

– oxides, hydrides) in a certain range of wavelengths, in proportion to the irradiance. The electron emission is considerably selective with respect to the value of the quantum energy. This phenomenon is called the external photoelectric effect. Emission photocells and photomultipliers are designed on this principle.

Electrically non-conducting materials (insulators) release only a negligible number of electrons from their crystal lattice as a result of irradiation; this is only displayed in the form of a hardly measurable surface conductivity.

A third effect is encountered with substances of a semiconductor nature, in which an internal photoelectric effect takes place. The electrons, released by radiation, can move freely in the crystal lattice of the semiconductor (similarly to the electrons in metals); however, they never attain sufficient energy to leave the lattice and the surface of the semiconductor. In order to be able to measure the number of released electrons in the semiconductor, they must be drawn off by means of an electrode, which is in close contact with its surface. In designing semiconductor photocells, therefore, the semiconductor layer is always inserted between two electrodes, of which one is usually designed to transmit the incident radiation. Either the e.m.f. which forms on the electrodes after irradiation of the semiconductor is measured (photovoltaic or rectifying photocells), or an auxiliary voltage is supplied to the electrodes and the conductivity which is created in the irradiated semiconductor by the released electrons is measured (photoconductive cells).

Thus photoelectric detectors can be divided into three large groups: photocells and photomultipliers, barrier layer photovoltaic cells, photoconductive cells.

Fundamental information on photoelectric phenomena and their practical exploitation has been surveyed, *e.g.* by Zworykin & Ramberg (1949) and Bauer (1965).

Because of the reactivity of alkaline metals, the sensitive layers of photo-emissive cells must be enclosed either in a vacuum or in an inert gas. The emissive layer itself is always distributed on a base formed by another metal, which is either a variously shaped electrode of thin tin-plate, or a layer of vacuum-evaporated metal on a part of the inner surface of the glass or silica flask. The anode which captures the released electrons is opposite the sensitive layer. This is usually a fine metal net or wire, shaped into a circle.
The current, which is spontaneously generated between the photo-cathode and the anode after irradiation is hardly measurable. The energy of the electrons, emitted from the photo-sensitive layer, is comparatively small and only a small percentage of the electrons reach the anode. The remainder return, being attracted by the positive charge of the sensitive layer. However if a voltage is introduced between the photo-cathode and the anode, the latter attracts part of the emitted electrons and the current passing through the photocell will be enhanced considerably. At constant irradiation the current in vacuum photocells increases roughly logarithmically with voltage until it has reached a constant value, which means that all emitted electrons have been captured by the anode. This state of the photocell is called saturated (Fig. 19.14). It is desirable that measurements be carried out at a slightly higher voltage than that corresponding to the saturated state, because in this way contingent fluctuations of the voltage cannot affect the measurements.
The sensitivity of vacuum photo-emissive cells is low, so that at very small irradiances they transmit currents which are on the boundaries of measurability (5×10^{-11}A per cm^2 of the photo-cathode surface, for an irradiance of 10^{-3} W m^{-2}).
The photoelectric current can be increased (about 10 to 25 times), if the flask is

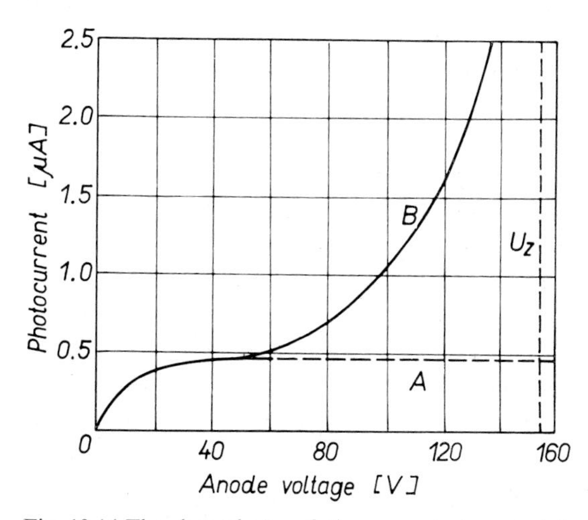

Fig. 19.14 The dependence of the current characteristic of vacuum and gas-filled photocells on the anode voltage (at constant illumination). *A:* characteristic of vacuum photocell; *B:* characteristic of gas-filled photocell. The vertical dashed line indicates the value of the ignition voltage *(U_z)* of the gas-filled photocells. (Courtesy of *Pressler*, Leipzig, GDR.)

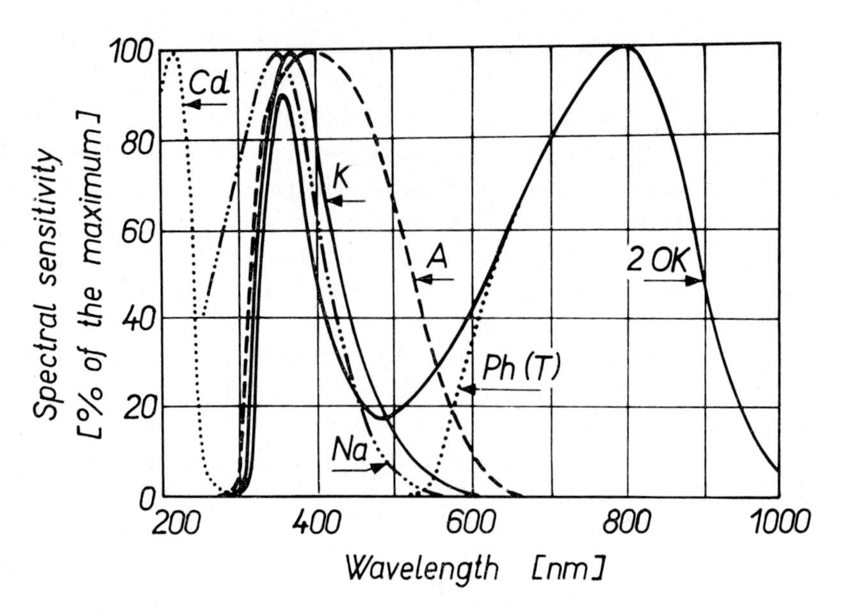

Fig. 19.15 Spectral response of photocells commercially produced by *Pressler*. *Na:* sodium photo-cathode (in a quartz vessel); *Cd:* cadmium photo-cathode; *K:* potassium photo-cathode; *A:* antimony-cesium photo-cathode; *2OK:* silver-cesium oxide-cesium photo-cathode; *Ph (T):* silver-cesium oxide-cesium photo-cathode in a vessel with a layer of red paint. (Courtesy of *Pressler*, Leipzig, GDR.)

filled with an inert gas at very low pressure. The electrons, emitted from the photo-cathode, collide with molecules of the inert gas on their way to the anode and ionize them, giving rise to other (secondary) free electrons, which are also attracted to the anode. With gas-filled photocells the dependence of the photo-current on the voltage is initially the same as with vacuum photocells. However, from a certain voltage value (depending on the kind and pressure of the gas used), the value of the photocurrent increases until it reaches ignition voltage, when a discharge occurs in the photocell, which is usually accompanied by the destruction of the sensitive layer (Fig. 19.14). That is why the manufacturers of gas photocells, apart from giving the operational voltage, also give the ignition voltage. For protection against discharge it is recommended that gas photocells be connected in series with a sufficiently large resistor to prevent the ignition voltage from becoming established on the photocell electrodes.

The spectral sensitivity of the photo-cathode (Fig. 19.15) is defined by the metal used, the thickness and the structure of the layer, its treatment (hydration, oxidation) and by additions of other elements, especially of silver and antimony. Examples of various photo-emission cells are shown in Fig. 19.16.

The photocell should only be subject to such an irradiance which will not induce an electric current density of higher than 0.5 to 1.0 $\mu A\ cm^{-2}$ with vacuum types, and 0.1 to 0.4 $\mu A\ cm^{-2}$ with gas-filled types. Vacuum photocells give a linear output. Gas-filled photocells may become non-linear at higher irradiances, and their sensitivity increases slowly with irradiance.

As the photocell is in fact a variable resistor, which has a high resistance under weak illumination or in the dark (of the order of $10^{12}\Omega$), even minute impurities

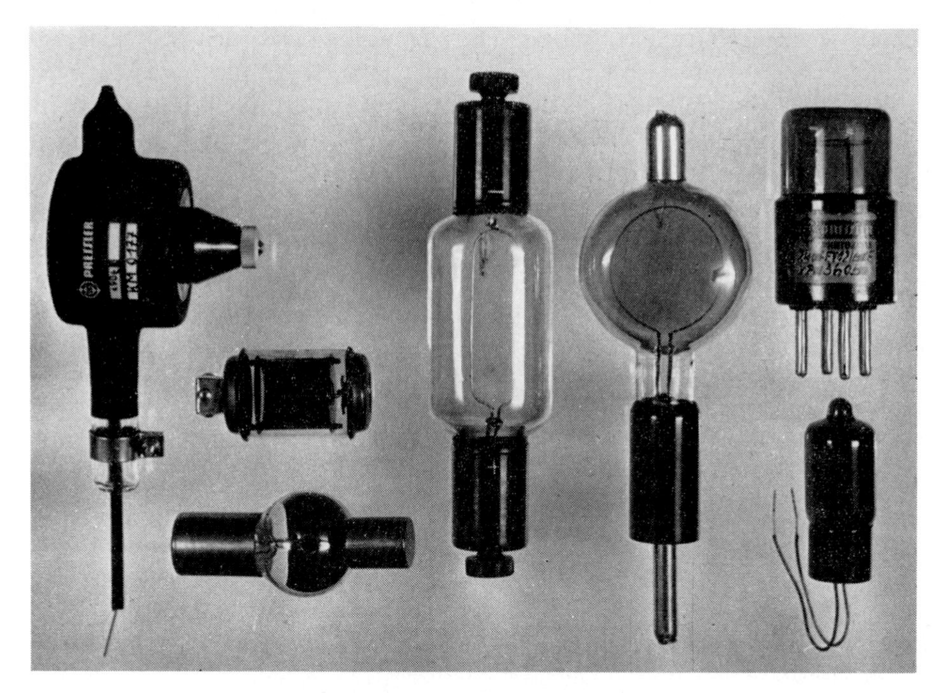

Fig. 19.16 Various types of photometric photocells of German *(Pressler)*, American *(RCA)* and Soviet origin.

in the inner and outer surfaces of the flask increase conductivity of the surfaces affecting the accuracy of the measurement unfavourably. The leads to the photocell must be perfectly insulated to limit leakage to a minimum.

For measuring very small radiation energies (*ca.* 10 mW m^{-2}) photocells with secondary electron emissions have been designed, *i.e.* photomultipliers (Chechik, Faïnshteĭn & Lifshits 1957; Fig. 19.17). The internal amplification of the photoelectric current is achieved by a system of auxiliary electrodes (dynodes), inserted between the photo-cathode and the anode (Fig. 19.18). Dynodes have a positive potential and they are designed so that its value decreases by degrees from the anode, where the potential is the highest, to the first dynode, located opposite the photo-cathode. The auxiliary electrodes are usually coated with sensitive layers which emit secondary electrons.

The electrons, emitted by the photo-cathode, impinge on the first auxiliary positive electrode and release from it a larger number of secondary electrons. By choosing a suitable shape of the electrodes one may achieve such a degree of electrostatic focusing that all the emitted electrons are captured by the next electrode, where this process is repeated. This can be done several times. The resultant amplification is directly proportional to the number of auxiliary electrodes (of which there may be up to 15) on the one hand, and to the potential difference between the individual electrodes (Fig. 19.19) on the other. The partial voltage across the individual stages is usually 50 to 100 V, exceptionally even 200 V.

An electromagnetic field may also be used to focus the secondary electrons, but is less convenient. Photomultipliers with electrostatic focusing must be perfectly shielded from the effect of alien electromagnetic fields, especially if they are A.C.

The internal amplification of the primary photoelectric current has some advantages compared with electronic amplification. The measuring device is simpler, smaller, less costly and it is possible to measure the very small photo-currents (10^{-14} to 10^{-16} A) coming from the photo-cathode itself; these cannot be amplified by current methods as they are drowned in the amplifier noise. The disadvantage of this method is that a very carefully stabilized power supply (0.6-2 kV)

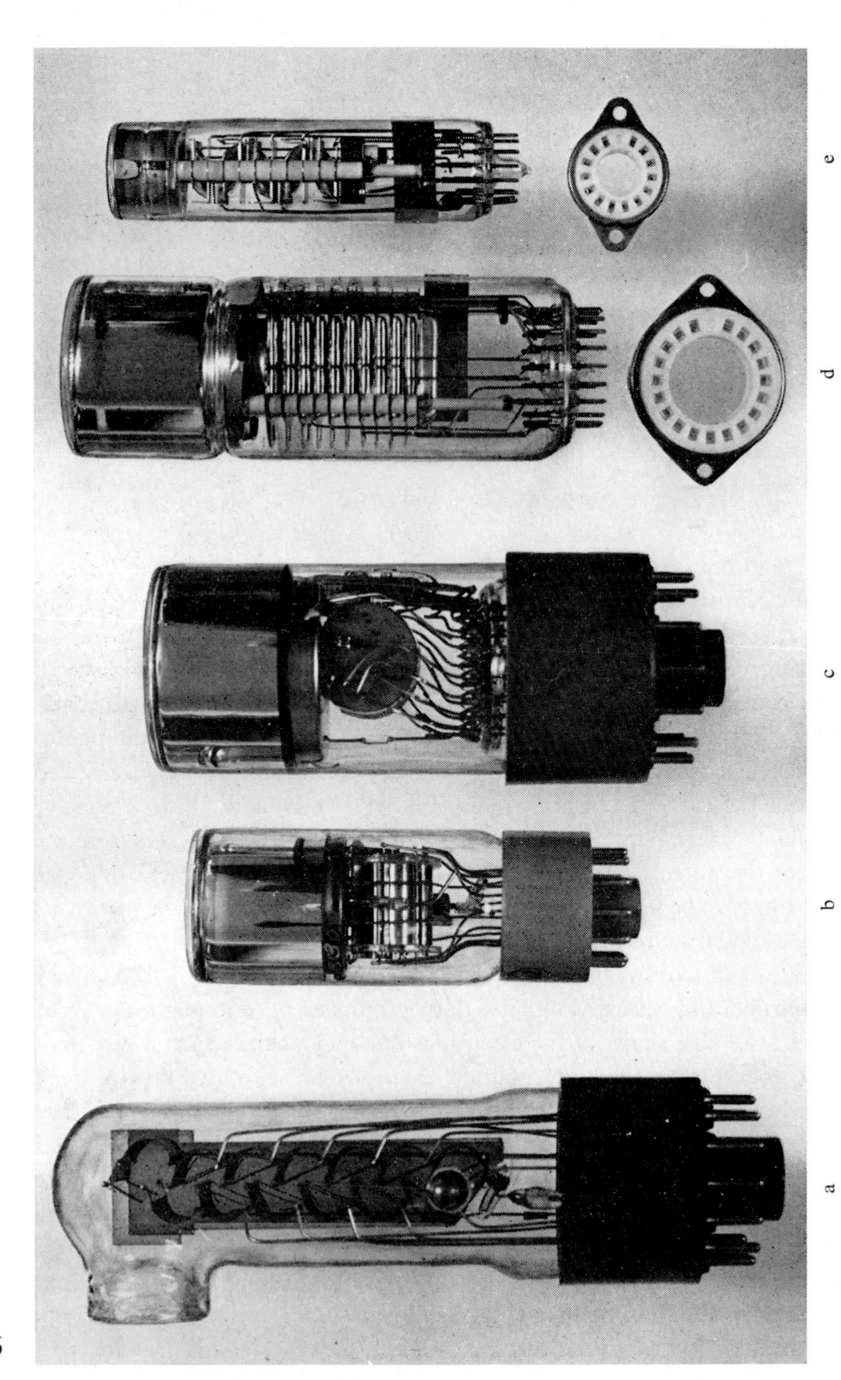

Fig. 19.17 Examples of different types of photo-multipliers. *a*: photo-multiplier with quartz window (U.S.S.R., type *FEU-18*); *b*, *c*: photo-multipliers with compact focussed structure dynode systems (*b*: *RCA*, type *7102*; *c*: *Tesla*, Prague, type *65 PK 413*); *d*: photo-multiplier with a venetian blind structure dynode systems (*EMI*, type *9558 B*); *e*: photo-multiplier with a box-and-grid structure dynode systems (*EMI*, type *9529 B*) (courtesy of *EMI Electronics Ltd*., *Electron Tube Division*, Hayes, Middlesex, England).

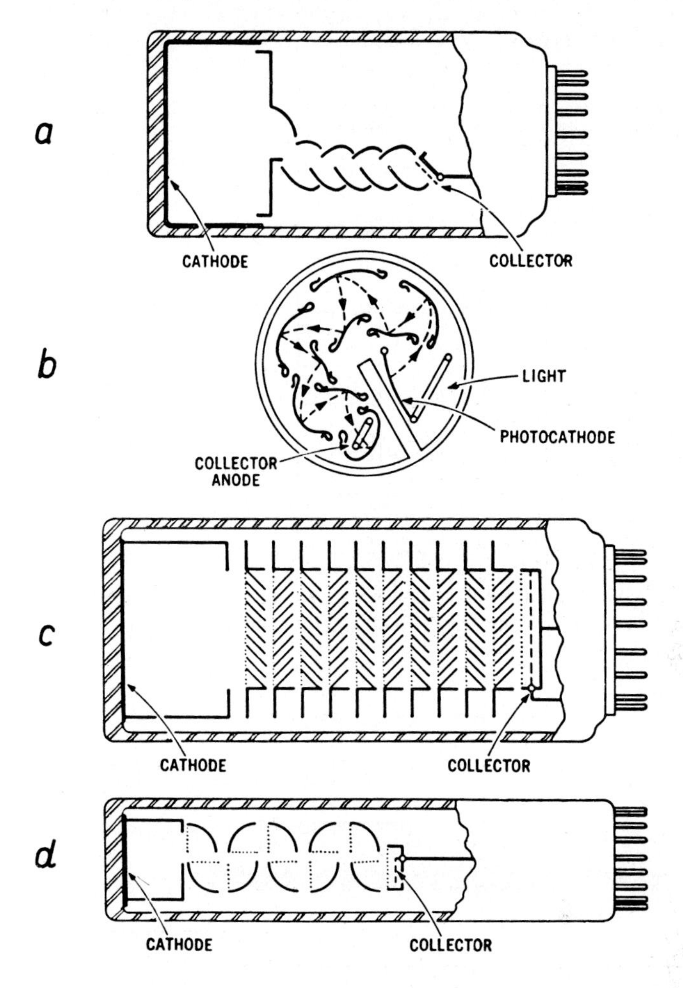

Fig. 19.18 Electrostatic dynode systems: *a:* focused structure, *b:* compact focussed structure, *c:* venetian blind structure, *d:* box-and-grid structure. (Courtesy of *EMI Electronics Ltd.*, *Valve Division*, Hayes, Middlesex, England.)

must be used. Any voltage change causes a large change in the amplification of the photo-current as it is amplified between each of the individual stages.

19.4.5.2 | Barrier layer, photovoltaic cells

Photovoltaic (rectifying) cells can have two designs (Fig. 19.20):
a. The incident radiation can be transmitted through the whole semiconductor layer and the released electrons accumulate on the semiconductor–conductor boundary, from where they pass into the conductor, which forms a mechanical frame and acts as the cathode of the photocell.
b. The radiation is only transmitted through the semi-conducting electrode, formed by a thin layer of evaporated metal, which serves as a collector of electrons released by the semiconductor. The other conductor again forms the frame of the photocell, which in this case acts as the anode.

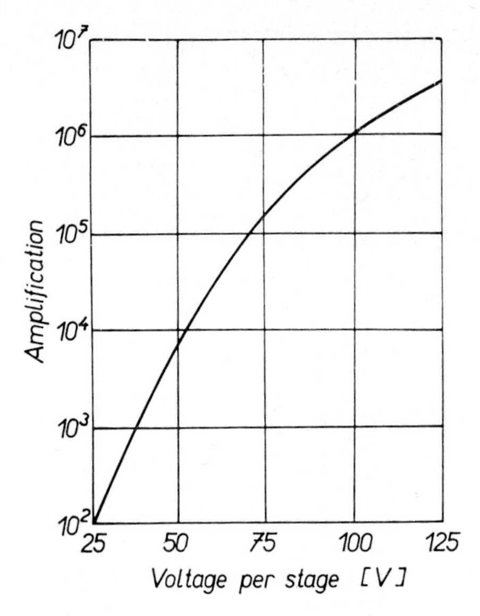

Fig. 19.19 Internal amplification of an *RCA* type *931 A* photo-multiplier versus potential gradient between the individual dynodes. (From Smith, Jones & Chasmar 1958.)

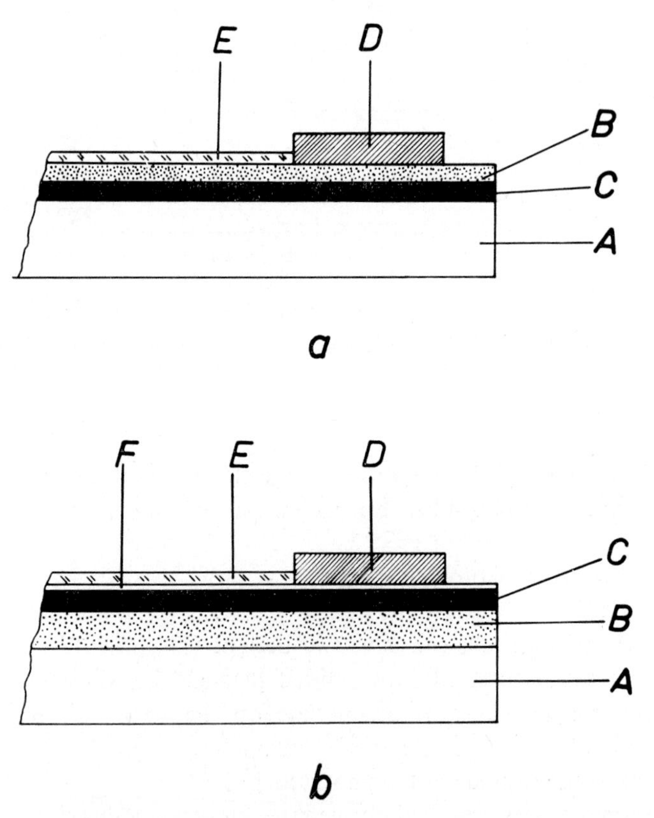

Fig. 19.20 Two possible arrangements *(a, b)* of the sensitive layers of photovoltaic cells. *A:* basic metal; *B:* semiconductor layer; *C:* semiconductor barrier layer; *E:* protective paint; *F:* transparent collector (only with the second type of photocell); *D:* collector ring.

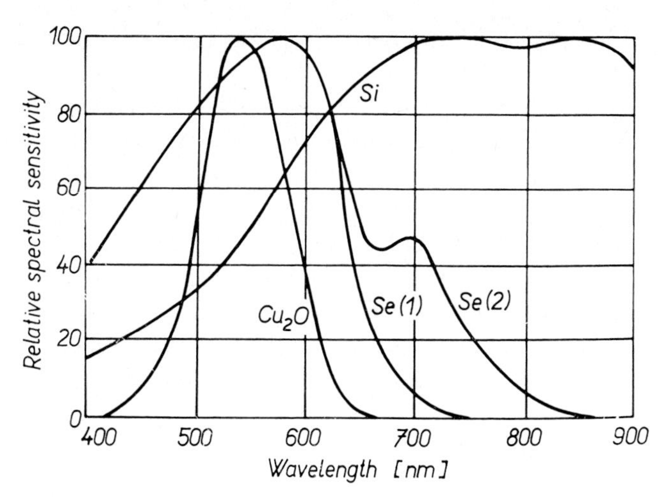

Fig. 19.21 Spectral response of photovoltaic cells. *Cu_2O:* copper-oxide photocell; *Se (1):* selenium cell of Czechoslovak production *(ČKD Modřany)*; *Se (2):* selenium cell *(Carl Zeiss*, Jena*)*; *Si:* silicon cell *(B. Lange*, West Berlin*)*.

The latter design is now used more frequently (*e.g.*, with selenium and silicon cells) because of its higher efficiency. The first design was applied to copper-oxide cells (copper-oxide sensitive layer), for example.
The spectral selectivity of photovoltaic cells is determined by the semiconductor used, its treatment and by the spectral properties of the upper collecting electrode. Fig. 19.21 shows the spectral-sensitivity curves of the most widely used photovoltaic cells. The most frequently employed are selenium cells, the spectral sensitivity of which is most akin to the average luminosity curve of the human eye. Selenium cells are manufactured in various shapes and sizes (Fig. 19.22) and are used in the most current photometric instruments – luxmeters, exposure meters and simple colorimeters. The selenium cells of *Zeiss*, Jena (GDR) have a marked secondary sensitivity maximum in the red region (Fig. 19.21), which makes them especially

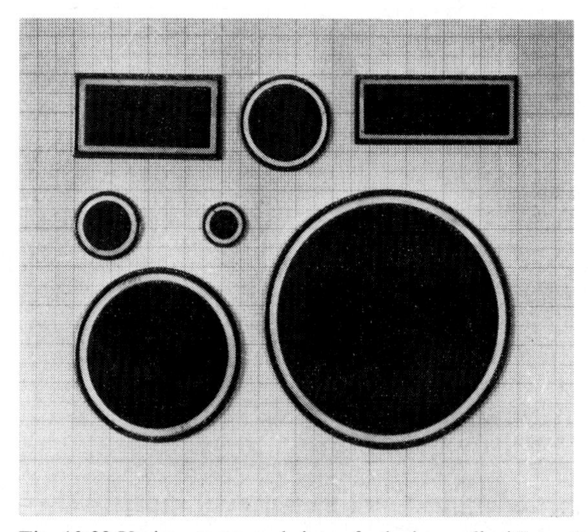

Fig. 19.22 Various types and sizes of selenium cells *(Zeiss*, Jena*)*.

suitable for use in instruments for PhAR measurements. Because of their small size and high efficiency, germanium and silicon photocells are now becoming widely used. Germanium photo-diodes are unsuitable for PhAR measurements because of their high temperature dependence and unsuitable spectral characteristics. The photocurrent of silicon diodes depends on temperature very little and they can be subjected to much higher irradiances without danger of damage or fatigue than selenium cells. Their sensitivity in the photosynthetically active region depends on the manufacturing technique (see Fig. 19.21) and is usually low in the shorter wavelengths. A silicon photo-diode with the spectral characteristic shown in Fig. 19.21 (a product of the *B. Lange*, West Berlin) could very well be used for constructing a PhAR detector, in contrast to other brands.

19.4.5.3 | Photoconductive cells

Until recently, photoconductive cells were not used as radiation detectors because dependence of the photo-current on irradiance is usually non-linear, most semiconductors usually display considerable inertia, their sensitivity decreases after long periods of operation, their resistance changes in the dark and the photoelectric phenomenon depends considerably on temperature. Fig. 19.23 shows spectral sensitivity curves of current photoconductive cells. However, their characteristics strongly depend on the manufacturing technique used.
Photoconductive cells of lead and cadmium sulphides are least prone to the deficiencies mentioned above and their properties are stable enough for radiant energy measurements in spectrophotometry where they are used. Cadmium sulphide cells are sensitive to nearly the whole of the visible region and lead sulphide cells to the IR region up to wavelengths of about 4.5 μm. Sensitive layers

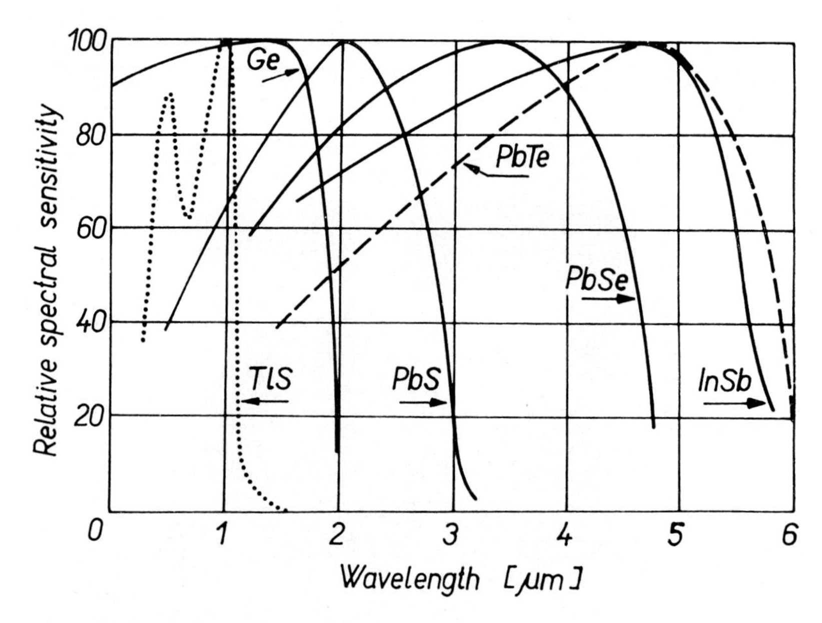

Fig. 19.23 Spectral sensitivity of some photo-conductive cells (from Kalendovský & Strnad 1949; Dragoun & Šmirous 1962).

of lead telluride and indium antimonide display a long-wave spectral sensitivity limit which has been shifted into the region around 6 μm.
In general, photoconductive cells are more suitable for technical purposes (photo-relays *etc.*) than for measuring radiant energy.

19.4.6 | Photochemical detectors

Photochemical methods of measuring radiant energy are frequently recommended for their simplicity as especially suitable for ecological work in the field. The main reasons for their application are:
- they are easy to use for integrating measurements,
- a large number of parallel measurements is possible, which would be very expensive with other methods,
- the equipment is small and light.

However, in spite of their advantages these methods can only be applied very cautiously and cannot be recommended for general use.
All photochemical reactions display considerable spectral selectivity, the maximum of the photochemical effect usually being in the short-wave region of the photosynthetically active radiation, or in the UV region. This circumstance is usually not considered (Klugh 1925; Bachman 1930; Friend 1961). Fig. 19.24 shows the absorption maximum of heliographic *Sepia Ozalid Paper No. 33 NT* which is characteristic of some diazo compounds used for these purposes. It is notable that it is markedly dissimilar to the spectral distribution of solar radiation.
Photochemical methods of measurement, in solution or on paper, have three fundamental acts in common:

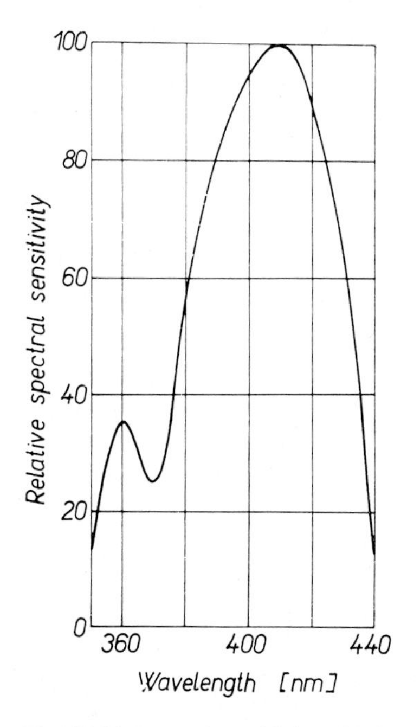

Fig. 19.24 Spectral sensitivity of heliographic *Ozalid* paper No. *33 NT* (from Friend 1961).

- preparation of the sensitive material,
- exposure,
- quantitative determination of the photochemical change (titration or photometry of solutions or development of sensitive paper and comparison with a set of standard samples).

Methods which use solutions of sensitive substances are more difficult to use than photographic methods and special care must be taken with the geometric design of the radiation receiver. In the past this care has not been exercised. The solutions of the substances used, *e.g.* anthracene polymerizing in dianthracene (Dore 1958), potassium iodide (Pearsall & Hewitt 1933), or uranyloxalate (Atkins & Poole 1930) have been enclosed into more or less arbitrary ampoules or test tubes, and exposed directly in them. However, the intensity of the absorption of incident radiation and, thus, also the rate of the photochemical reaction vary with the thickness of the layer of the solution according to the Lambert-Beer law. Furthermore, as the ampoules used were usually circular in cross-section, the observed irradiance could not be expressed in terms of unit surface. With appropriate spectral absorption for PhAR measurements, a satisfactory design of the radiation receiver would be a necessary pre-requisite for its use.

If the sensitive substance is distributed on paper, it becomes a plane radiation receiver. However, even in this case the thickness of the layer affects the non-linear dependence of the rate of the photochemical reaction on irradiance. Besides the heliographic paper mentioned above, one can use ordinary positive and negative photographic material. The positive paper is mostly only sensitive in the short-wave region of PhAR. Negative panchromatic layers are sensitive to the whole of the PhAR interval. However, the spectral sensitivity curve depends considerably on the technological treatment of the emulsion and on its age. In each series of measurements in which new material is being used (of different origin or age, a different production series or gradation) it is always necessary to re-expose a set of comparative standards at known irradiances from a source of the same spectral composition. In developing exposed photographic material the procedures used must be identical with those used for the calibration samples.

19.5 Instruments and circuits with thermoelectric and photoelectric detectors for radiation measurements

Electrical measuring instruments facilitate direct and rapid readings of the observed quantities, a simple choice of the required sensitivity range, and often also a continuous and accurate record of the variation in the observed phenomenon. The electrical signal measured is either the e.m.f. generated by radiation (thermocouple, photovoltaic cell), or the change in the detector resistance, corresponding to the absorbed radiation (bolometer, thermistor, photo-emission cell, photoconductive cell). In the former case, it is a question of measuring small currents and voltages, in the latter case, considerably larger voltages (of the order of tens to hundreds V) facilitate the circuit design.

If maximum sensitivity and stability of the measuring system is required, a sensitive galvanometer may be used in the laboratory. For field measurements robust instruments which amplify the primary signal electrically are to be preferred. They

are more complicated and may have a higher failure rate and sometimes be less accurate, but they are usually capable of operating in any position, as opposed to galvanometers and electrometers.
Electrical measuring instruments can be used to measure irradiance on a linear or logarithmic scale, according to the nature of the phenomenon observed. For example, in photometry precedence is usually given to expressing the observed values in terms of absorbance, *i.e.* on a logarithmic scale.

19.5.1 | Electrical measuring instruments

Instruments with a rotating coil located between the poles of a permanent magnet (the Depréz system) are most commonly used for direct indication of the observed signal, which is practically always D.C. (*e.g.* a change of current proportional to a change in the detector resistance, or an e.m.f.). In robust measuring instruments of low sensitivity (up to a sensitivity of the order of tens of microamperes or tens of millivolts) the rotating system is supported in bearings; with sensitive galvanometers it is fixed to, or suspended from, a thin stretched fibre.
Electrostatic measuring instruments, electrometers, are less frequently used. They may be more sensitive than galvanometers by an order or two, however, operationally they are less suitable. The evolution of effective photomultipliers has almost completely eliminated them from current practice in measuring radiant fluxes of small densities and they are now only used in integrating methods.
The sensitivity of a galvanometer is usually expressed by the current (c_I) which causes a deflection of 1 mm on a scale at a distance of 1 m. Less frequently it is expressed by the deviation in mm (the scale value – a_I) caused by a current of 1 μA on a scale at a distance of 1 m. The voltage scale value (a_u) is not usually given because it can easily be calculated from the total resistance of the circuit by means of the equation:

$$a_U = \frac{a_I}{R_g + R_t + R_x} \; [\mathrm{mm\ m^{-1}\ \mu V^{-1}}],$$

where R_g is the internal resistance of the galvanometer, R_t is the internal resistance of the detector and R_x is the resistance of the conductors, which should be of such quality as to render the resistance practically negligible. A similar equation holds for the voltage sensitivity (c_U):

$$c_U = c_I(R_g + R_t + R_x) \; [\mathrm{V\ mm^{-1}\ m^{-1}}].$$

In an ideal case the internal resistance of the detector, the e.m.f. of which is being measured, and of the appropriate conductors is equal to the critical aperiodic resistance of the galvanometer R_{ap}. If the sum of all resistances in the circuit is higher, the galvanometer must be damped by connecting a suitable resistor across its clamps. This, of course, decreases the sensitivity of the whole system. A double-coil galvanometer may be damped conveniently without loss of sensitivity, by introducing a resistor into the circuit of the second coil. In the opposite case, when the value of all external resistances is lower than R_{ap}, the galvanometer is over-damped, attainment of the final position of the rotating system is very slow and the reading may prove to be inaccurate. In this case a resistor is connected in series with the galvanometer so that the inverse value of the resultant resistance of the whole system is equal to the sum $1/R_g + 1/R_{ap}$; this again necessarily decreases the sensitivity. In this case, however, the use of a two-coil galvanometer has no advantage.

19.5.2 | Circuitry

An electrical signal can be measured in three ways:
a. by directly reading the deviation on the measuring instrument,
b. potentiometrically with the measuring instrument being used as a zero device,
c. after electronic or other amplification.

a. Robust measuring instruments (microammeters, millivoltmeters) are usually supplied by the manufacturer together with the radiation detector and the whole system has, as a rule, already been calibrated, whether the instrument in question is non-selective, or just a current luxmeter. For example, the solarimeter of the firm *Kipp & Zonen* is supplied with the following kind of calibration: an e.m.f. of 10.0 mV corresponds to an irradiance of 1.89 cal cm^{-2} min^{-1} (1.32×10^3 W m^{-2}). If the manufacturer is only supplying the detector alone, such fundamental data are given, together with the internal resistances of the instrument. These data are necessary to evaluate radiant energy in absolute units and if it is proposed to use a galvanometer for measuring the e.m.f.
In choosing a galvanometer for measuring the electrical signal generated by a thermoelectric detector, the following must be borne in mind: *1.* thermocouples and thermopiles are voltage sources with a comparatively low internal resistance (of the order of a few Ω to several tens of Ω), *2.* as very small voltages are being measured, an instrument with a high voltage scale value must be used, *3.* the measuring circuit must enable full exploitation of the detector linearity. Hence, a suitable galvanometer must comply with the following fundamental conditions: large voltage scale value, minimum internal resistance, small aperiodic resistance, sufficiently long oscillations period.
The detector itself is usually calibrated in terms of an open circuit e.m.f. This method of calibration does not limit the detector to a single measuring instrument and allows the possibility of choosing a measuring system which is most suitable for the purpose.
Thermoelectric detectors are usually calibrated in terms of a voltage corresponding to a certain irradiance. This voltage (U_t) can be computed from the observed current intensity by using Ohm's law:

$$U_t = I_g(R_t + R_g),$$

where I_g is the current flowing through the measuring instrument, R_t is the internal resistance of the thermoelectric detector and R_g is the internal resistance of the measuring instrument. If the measuring instrument is calibrated in units of voltage, a modified equation is used:

$$U_t = \frac{R_t + R_g}{R_g} U_g,$$

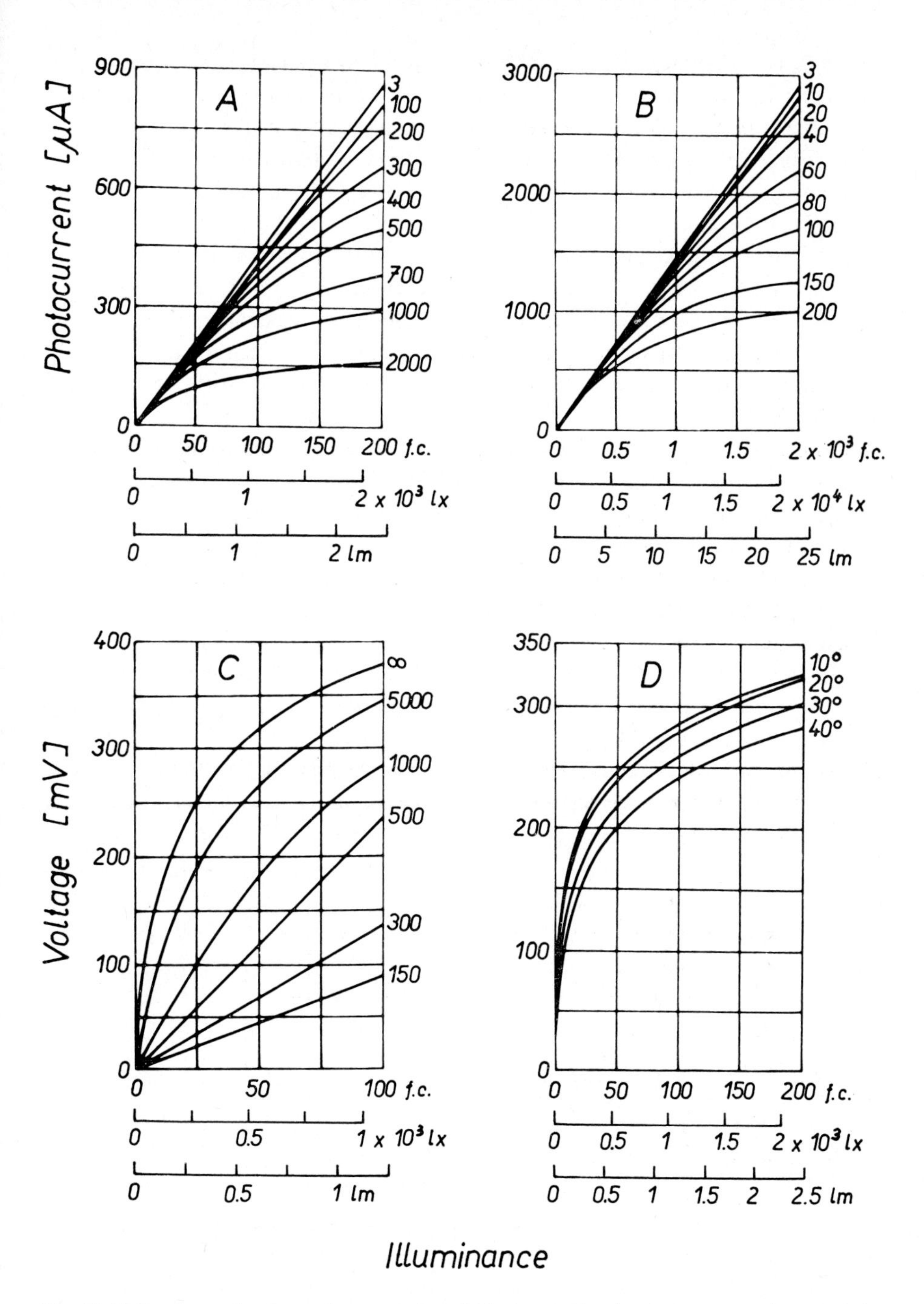

Fig. 19.25 Current and voltage characteristics of selenium cells. *A* and *B:* current characteristics of a selenium cell for weak and strong illuminance at various values of the external resistance of the measuring circuit. *C:* dependence of the voltage characteristic of a selenium cell on illuminance and on the external resistance of the measuring circuit. *D:* dependence of the voltage characteristic of a selenium cell on illuminance and on temperature with a large external resistance in the measuring circuit (from Zworykin & Ramberg 1949).

where U_g is the voltage recorded by the measuring instrument. Both equations are valid on the assumption that the resistance of the connecting conductors is negligible with respect to the other resistances in the measuring circuit.

In choosing a measuring device for an electrical signal from sensors made of selenium cells, one must allow for their electrical characteristic. The voltage generated by irradiating a selenium cell is directly proportional to the irradiance provided the resistance of the external (measuring) circuit is comparatively low, *i.e.* provided it does not exceed about 100 to 200 Ω (see Fig. 19.25). If the resistance of the measuring circuit is between 300 and 600 Ω the dependence of the photo-current on irradiance deviates from linearity, and if the resistance is high the dependence approximates to a logarithmic relation, characteristic of the e.m.f. of an open-circuit photocell.

The internal resistance of a selenium photocell changes not only with the irradiance, but also with the overall (external) resistance of the measuring circuit (Fig. 19.26). The same holds as regards fatigue phenomena (Fig. 19.27).

Furthermore the intensity of the photo-electric current from a selenium cell can be affected to a considerable extent by the detector temperature, the undesirable effect of temperature variations increasing with increasing resistance of the measuring circuit (Fig. 19.27). Hence, the resistance (internal) of the measuring circuit should be small not only to maintain linearity, but also to restrict measurement errors resulting from temperature fluctuations of the sensor. The temperature of a selenium cell should not exceed +40 °C.

The voltage across a photocell subject to an irradiance of 0.5 W m^{-2} may be about 100 to 200 mV if the resistance of the external circuit is sufficiently low for

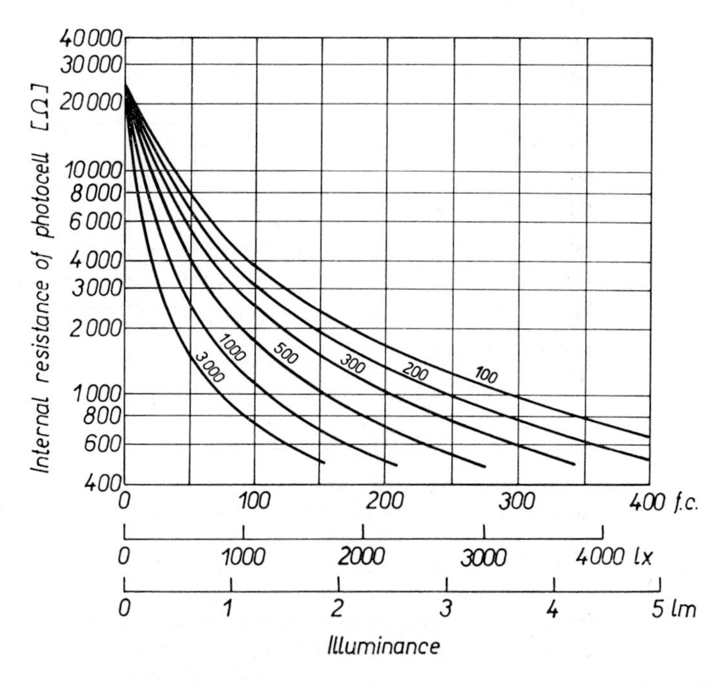

Fig. 19.26 Dependence of the internal resistance of a selenium cell on illuminance for different external resistance ([Ω], numbers by the curves) of the measuring circuit. (From Zworykin & Ramberg 1949.)

a linear dependence of the e.m.f. on the irradiance. An irradiance of 5 to 10 W m^{-2} should not be exceeded to avoid severe fatigue and ageing of the photocells (Fig. 19.27). If larger irradiances are being observed, it is convenient to include a grey glass in front of the detector. From the values mentioned above, it follows that in the range of external resistances, where the e.m.f. of the photocell depends linearly on the irradiance, a generated e.m.f. of 2 to 5 $\times$ 10^{-5} V corresponds to an irradiance of 1 $\times$ 10^{-3} W m^{-2} (Müller 1950).

In designing sensors for PhAR measurements based on selenium cells, one must also take into account that the receiver and the correction filters decrease the

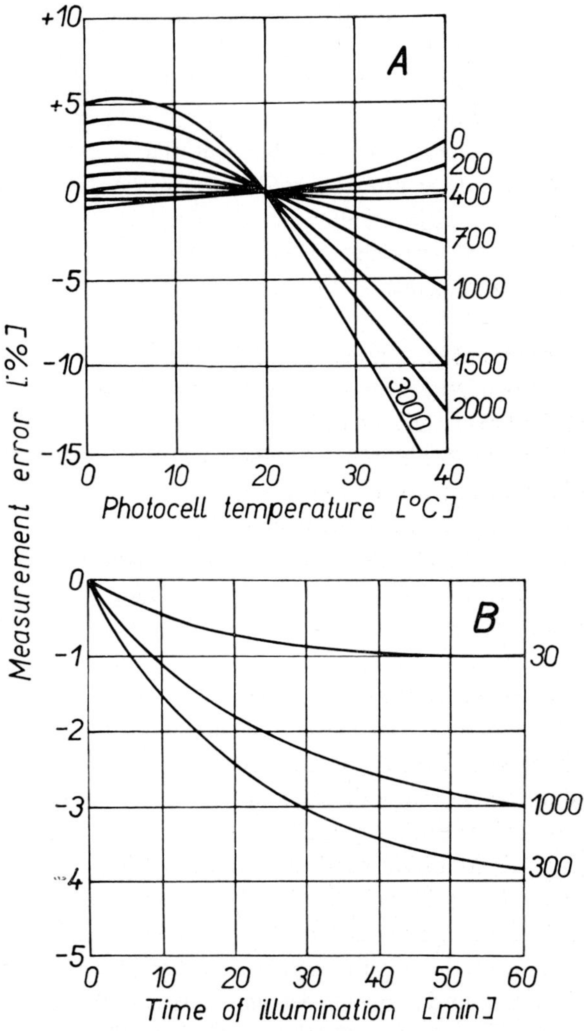

Fig. 19.27 The temperature dependence of selenium cells and their fatigue on the external resistance of the measuring circuit.

A: Dependence of the photo-current on temperature and on the external resistance ([Ω], numbers at the curves) of the measuring circuit. Illuminance of photocell 215 lx. (From Zworykin & Ramberg 1949.)

B: Fatigue of selenium cell as a function of the time of illumination and the external resistance ([Ω], numbers by the curves) of the measuring circuit. (From Zworykin & Ramberg 1949.)

irradiance of the photocell to 5–10% of the radiant density incident on the receiver. Under such circumstances a generated e.m.f. of about 1×10^{-6} V corresponds to a receiver irradiance of 10^{-3} W m^{-2}. If it is required that a division of the scale corresponds to such an irradiance, it is necessary to use a measuring instrument with a voltage scale value of 1×10^{-6} V per division. This condition is satisfied, for example, by the comparatively robust lightspot galvanometers with a sensitivity of 1×10^{-8} A mm^{-1} m^{-1} and an internal resistance of 50 to 200 Ω. Current indicating instruments with a high sensitivity cannot be used with selenium photocells because they have a comparatively high internal resistance which results in a non-linear dependence of the recorded value on the irradiance. Furthermore a full-scale reading can only be achieved at maximum irradiance values permitted for the photocell. For example, current *Metra* (Blansko, Czechoslovakia) indicating instruments with a range of 0 to 100 μA usually have an internal resistance of 2 to 5×10^3 Ω. If the e.m.f., generated by an irradiance of 5 W m^{-2} is approximately 300 mV, the current flowing through the measuring instrument has an intensity of 60 μA. At a ratio of irradiances of the detector and of the receiver surface of 1:10, as mentioned above, a deviation of 60 μA will correspond to an irradiance of 50 W m^{-2}, which may be satisfactory for a rough estimate, but not for accurate measurements.

b. Potentiometric measurement is mostly used in observing radiant energy by photovoltaic and photo-emission cells. In measuring with bolometers and thermistors, bridge circuits are usually used. This method of measurement has been used most in absorption spectrophotometry and colorimetry, as the measurement, under these conditions (using two detectors each of which is connected into a different arm of the bridge) is independent of variations in the radiant density, due, for example, to voltage fluctuations in the mains. The bridge circuit is suitable for all relative measurements; for example, for determining the gradient of the radiant flux in stands of tall plants.

c. A low-voltage signal (*e.g.* from thermocouples and photovoltaic cells) can be amplified photoelectrically or electronically. The main design problem with photoelectric amplifiers based on a galvanometer, the light signal of which is incident at a secondary photoelectric detector, is to preserve accurate proportionality between the changes in the primary and amplified signals. Reliable commercial instruments satisfying this condition, tend to be the exception (*e.g.*, the *Hilger & Watts* photoelectric amplifier). For electronic amplification the low-voltage D.C. signal is transformed to A.C., or chopped at an adequate frequency, as direct, multi-stage amplification of this type of signal is not stable. Moreover, usually even a D.C. signal of a considerably higher voltage is modulated (*e.g.* tens to hundreds of volts in measurements with photo-emission cells), as this simplifies the construction of the amplifier considerably.

19.6 | Radiant energy standards

Radiant energy standards (or luminous intensity standards) of suitable geometry and reliability are usually hard to come by and are generally only found in special-

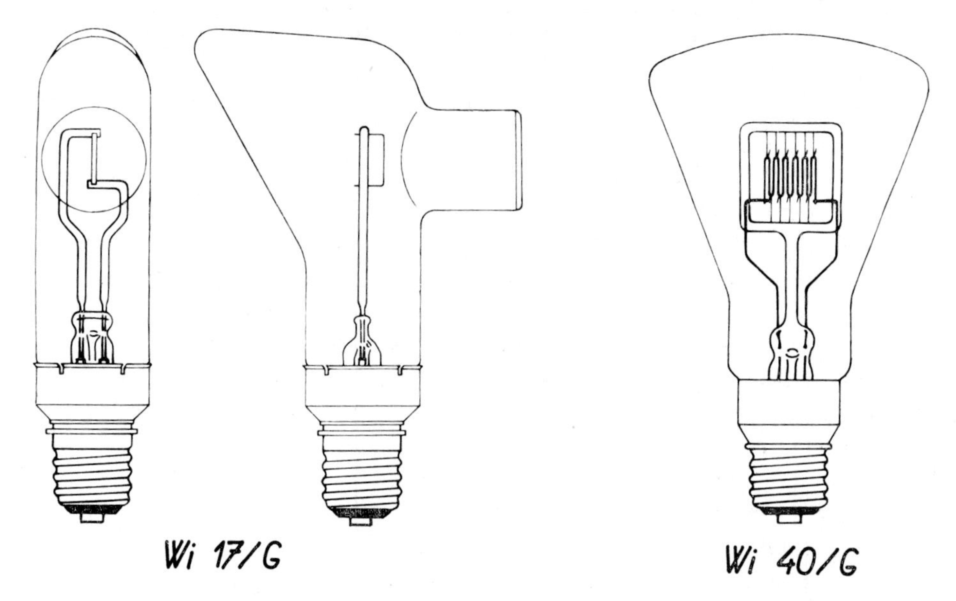

Fig. 19.28 Normal *Osram* lamps. Left: type *Wi 17/G* for 9 V and 16 A (colour temperature 2600 °K). Right: type *Wi 40/G* for 30 V and 6 A (colour temperature 2850 °K). (Courtesy of *Osram GmbH.*, Hamburg, FRG.)

ised research establishments, *e.g.* the National Bureau of Standards in Washington, D.C., U.S.A., or the National Physical Laboratory in Teddington, Great Britain. Incandescent lamps, including halogen lamps, are almost exclusively used as radiant energy standards (Stair, Schneider & Jackson 1963). The filaments are usually located in one plane and they are straight, because the emission of spiral filaments is considerably affected by even small changes in the position of the source. The bulbs are usually designed to exclude all reflections from the inner surface of their rear walls (Fig. 19.28) and, to make the properties of the source as stable as possible, the filament is not heated to a very high temperature and the bulbs are not filled with an inert gas.
In the calibration certificate of a standard lamp the following data should be included: the operational position, the direction in which the lamp was calibrated, the operational voltage, the distance at which the radiant or luminous flux density was measured, the background, and the diaphragms used in calibration. Deviations from these conditions may be the source of considerable errors.
Standard lamps are very expensive and the costs of having them calibrated are also high. They are, therefore, not used for routine measurements but only for checking secondary ('operational') standards.
For the calibration of newly made measuring instruments and for regularly checking instruments in use, secondary standards are quite adequate in plant physiology and ecology. For a secondary standard, a point-like lamp with the filament arranged in a closely spaced coil or a powerful projection lamp (operational position base down) with its filament occupying a small area in a single plane can be used (see Fig. 19.29). The input to the lamp is determined by the irradiance range required. A new lamp should be left on for a certain period prior to calibration (usually 1/10 of the nominal life) to stabilize its operational properties.

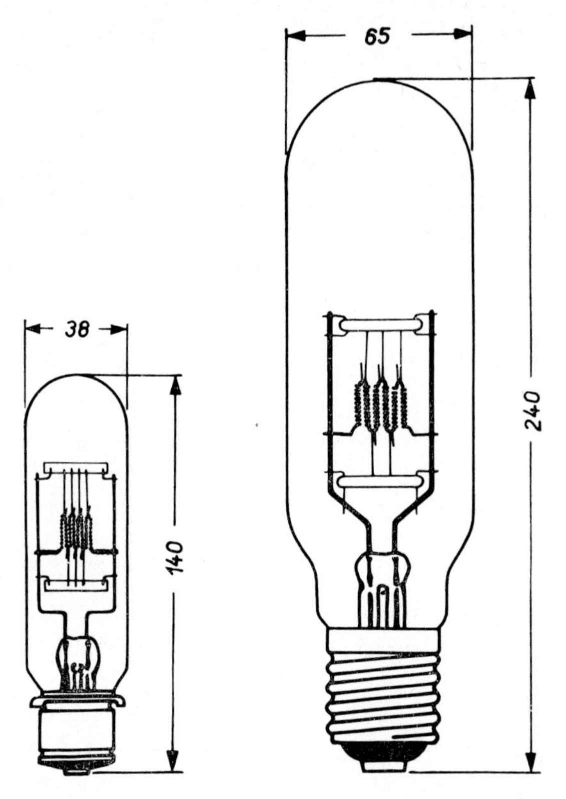

Fig. 19.29 Two different types of high-power (1000 W) incandescent lamps for projectors. The filaments are mounted in single plane. Average life: 25 h (left) and 100 h (right).

The correct calibration and use of the standard requires careful stabilization of the voltage and its accurate determination, since the radiant emittance is very dependent on voltage fluctuations. As this dependence increases very rapidly, if the voltage of the lamp is increased above the nominal value, it is convenient to work with a slightly underheated standard. In this way the life of the lamp is extended considerably, not to mention the enhancement of the accuracy of the whole calibration.

19.7 | Radiant flux density and irradiation measurements

When measuring highly variable radiation fluxes such as solar radiation, the initial decision to be made is whether to measure with instruments indicating and recording the instantaneous values of the incident radiant flux density or to use integrating instruments, which yield the radiant exposure of a given surface over a longer time interval (Anderson 1964).

The final aim of most measurements is to obtain data to relate the radiation absorbed by a plant or vegetation to its photosynthetic activity, and to determine the efficiency of utilization of the radiant energy in the photosynthetic production of plants. For general productivity studies estimates of efficiency of energy conversion over long intervals of time (hours, days, vegetative period *etc.*) are often

of interest and thus estimates of radiant exposure over the period are usually required. As the dependence of the photosynthetic rate on the density of the absorbed radiant flux is not linear and the conversion efficiency of radiation in photosynthesis decreases with increasing irradiance, estimates of instantaneous irradiance are also required in more exact studies (see also Chapter 12).
It is generally tedious to obtain the radiant exposure for a period by integrating records of instantaneous values. Furthermore, with certain types of cloudiness, irradiance changes so rapidly that reliable integration of records is practically impossible (see Fig. 19.30). This problem may be solved by employing two measuring systems one of which provides the instantaneous values and the other the integrated ones. This can be realized either by two independent instruments, or by connecting an integrator to the recorder (*e.g.* Trickett, Moulsley & Edwards 1957). Alternatively, the measuring system may integrate in such a way that the incident radiant energy is summed separately for various, predetermined levels of

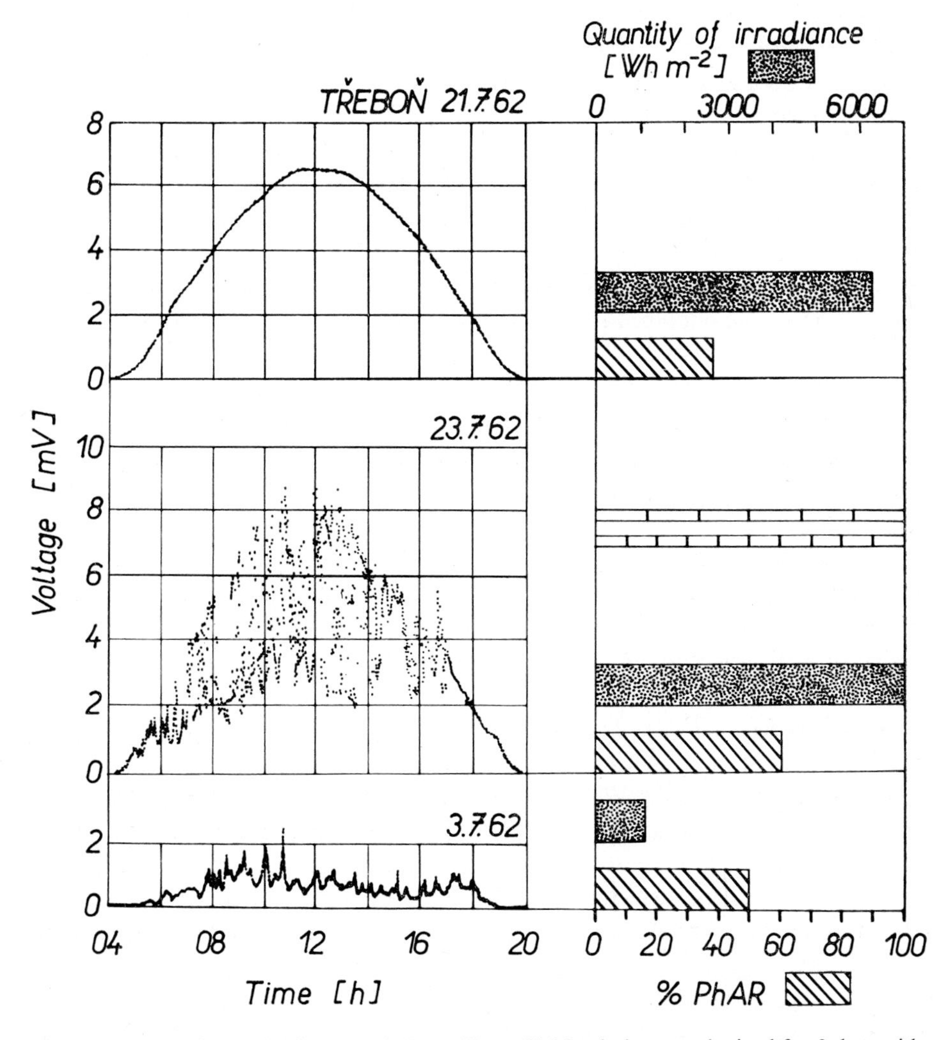

Fig. 19.30 Diurnal records of a *Kipp & Zonen* Type *CM 3* solarimeter, obtained for 3 days with different degrees of cloudiness.

radiant density, which corresponds to separate outputs of the recorder (McCree 1965; also *cf.* Section 19.8.4). Another solution is to integrate sums of incident radiant energy for short periods (*e.g.* hours) over longer periods of time (*e.g.* days) (Kubín & Hládek 1963; Czopek *et al.* 1967).
An integrating measuring instrument is especially useful in conditions in which the irradiance fluctuates widely and rapidly such as in measurements of irradiance at different levels in plant stands, and in different positions in a glasshouse during changeable weather (*e.g.* Edwards & Moulsley 1958).

19.8 | Instruments for measuring photosynthetically active radiation

The appropriate instrument depends to a large extent on the circumstances in which photosynthetically active radiation is to be measured.

a. In laboratory measurements of the irradiance of an object, the photosynthetic rate of which is observed, the geometry of the irradiated object as well as of the radiation source are more or less defined, as is the source emission spectrum. Under these circumstances it is possible to use luxmeters or other instruments, in which a selenium or some kind of photovoltaic cell is connected into the circuit of a suitable measuring instrument, and to apply conversion factors obtained from the literature (*e.g.* Bell 1956; Gaastra 1959; Kleschnin 1960 – see Table 12.2). However, since the characteristics of lamps and photocells vary with make and age, and as it is common to insert various filters and transparent materials between the lamp and irradiated object, it is vastly preferable that the conversion factor or calibration of the photocell in units of energy be determined *in situ* for each and every irradiation system.
This may be done by simultaneous measurement of irradiance in the assimilation chamber, or other plant space, with the photocell used for routine purposes and with a calibrated, thermoelectric detector such as the *Kipp & Zonen* thermopile *CA 1*. To delimit the PhAR region, it is necessary to use glass spectral filters. Unfortunately no single filter effectively absorbs IR radiation and is simultaneously capable of transmitting the PhAR region with sufficiently sharp limits. Hence, irradiance in the PhAR region must be determined from the difference between two sequential measurements. In the first a filter is used which selectively only absorbs radiation with wavelengths shorter than 400 nm (*e.g. Schott-Jena WG 1*): in the second the filter used only transmits radiation with wavelength longer than 700 nm (*e.g. Schott-Jena RG 8*). The difference between the two measurements gives the irradiance in the PhAR region. Unfortunately, the transmission of both filters in infra-red is not identical. Furthermore, both filters mentioned absorb IR radiation of wavelengths longer than 3 μm. If the radiation flux contains a large fraction of IR radiation and is intense, the filters become hot and radiate thermal radiation to the thermoelectric detector. Hence it is necessary to insert a water filter of sufficient thickness into the optical path to absorb radiation with wavelengths longer than 1.4 μm.
In many cases, thermoelectric detectors are too large to be used in assimilation chambers and small plant chambers. In these cases a small photocell can be used routinely provided that it is calibrated against a thermoelectric detector with all

appropriate filters, water-jackets and transparent materials, each of appropriate thickness, present in the optical path.

b. The measurement of solar radiation and of its photosynthetically active part provides data of fundamental importance for analysing photosynthetic production under natural conditions (Yanishevskiĭ 1957; Berger-Landefeldt 1965; Drummond 1965; Gast 1965; Gates 1965; Reifsnyder & Lull 1965). Measurement of solar radiation does not fall within the scope of this Chapter; however it is discussed for several reasons: *1.* Good quality instruments for measuring the incident solar radiation flux are produced commercially and may be directly applied to PhAR measurements by employing the appropriate filters. *2.* The fraction of PhAR in the solar radiation flux is variable within certain limits (38 to 62% within the vegetative period in Middle Europe, depending on meteorological conditions and solar elevation), but this range is not so wide as to prevent one from using the amount of PhAR as a fixed fraction of solar radiation in model calculations. Over longer periods of weeks or months PhAR is close to 45% of solar radiation on average. *3.* Many physiological and ecological problems concerning the dependence of the primary production of plants on the character of the incident radiation, require simultaneous information on both solar radiation and its photosynthetically active part.

For measuring and recording solar radiation it is most convenient to use standard instruments designed for the purpose (*e.g.* a *Kipp & Zonen* solarimeter type *CM 3* with a recording millivoltmeter). Only if a receiver of different geometrical design is required, is it worth while designing and making similar instruments (see *e.g.* Monteith 1959; Monteith & Szeicz 1962).

Similarly as in laboratory measurements it is possible to use filters with thermoelectrical detectors to measure the PhAR flux under natural conditions (Monteith 1959; Monteith & Szeicz 1962). However, if a continuous record of PhAR is required, parallel to records of solar radiation, the signal from two sensors must be recorded simultaneously, each of the sensors being equipped with the appropriate filter. The PhAR value is then obtained from the difference between the parallel records. A much more approximate approach is to equip a single non-selective thermal detector with a filter absorbing short-wave radiation with a wavelength shorter than 400 nm and with a filter absorbing IR radiation (McCree 1965, 1966; Uchijima 1968). However, the absorption limits of filters absorbing IR radiation are very imprecise and start in the PhAR region at a wavelength of 600 nm ending at 850 nm.

The most reliable instruments for measuring incident PhAR are those based on photovoltaic and photo-emission cells, with which an almost non-selective response can be achieved by means of a combination of filters in precisely defined limits of wavelengths, corresponding to the PhAR region. Silicon photovoltaic cells have proved particularly suitable for this (McPherson 1969; Norman, Tanner & Thurtell 1969). Selenium cells, on the other hand, are subject to fatigue and their sensitivity may decrease with time. Both kinds of cell are temperature dependent and require some in-built compensation for temperature changes. The output from such sensors can be simply and inexpensively integrated (see Section 19.8.5), or continuously monitored on a chart recorder.

19.8.1 | *Luxmeters*

The spectral sensitivity curve of a selenium cell is very similar to the luminosity curve of the human eye. Selenium cells, therefore, are ideal detectors for evaluating illuminance and, because of their simplicity, instruments made with them and designed for measuring illuminance have become widely used for measuring radiation in plant physiology, without regard to the marked difference between the action spectrum of photosynthesis and that of the human eye (Saeki 1963; Anderson 1964). In Section 19.4.5.2, conditions have been described under which it is possible to evaluate PhAR with sufficient accuracy with selenium cells, and Table 12.2 and Fig. 19.3 give the appropriate reduction factors by which the data recorded in photometric units can be transformed to absolute units, if the measurements were made with luxmeters, the spectral sensitivity of which has been modified by a filter to be similar to the standard luminosity curve of the human eye. It is also necessary to take into account the temperature dependence of selenium cells, which varies with the resistance of the measuring instrument (or circuit), as can be seen from Fig. 19.27, and ageing effects. Permanent changes in photocell sensitivity appear sooner if the photocells are subject to large irradiances during measurements so that if these are to be observed neutral filters or diaphragms should be used to protect the photocell. Furthermore it is necessary to check the calibration of the selenium cells at approximately annual intervals.
The voltage generated by irradiating a selenium cell is directly proportional to the logarithm of the irradiance provided the resistance of the measuring circuit is very high, *i.e.* provided the photocell operates with practically no load. This can be conveniently exploited for measuring very different irradiances, if the measuring circuit is arranged so that no current passes through the photocell. In practice, a currentless state may be achieved not only by a high external resistance, but also by the use of compensation measurements.

19.8.2 | *Phyto-actinometers*

To avoid difficulties arising from the spectral selectivity of photocells and the necessity of knowing the character of the emission spectrum of the radiation source, the solution suggested by Bell (1955) can be used. By using an appropriate filter or combination of filters, the sensitivity of a photocell can be restricted to the PhAR range and made approximately the same over the whole of the range. The spectral transmittance of the filter or filters would have to be the opposite of the spectral sensitivity curve of the photocell (Fig. 19.31). No single filter is available to do this but it can be achieved using combinations of several filters (*e.g.* Bell 1955; McPherson 1969; Norman, Tanner & Thurtell 1969). A spectrally non-selective instrument for PhAR measurements, equipped with a corrected detector, has been called a photoelectrical phyto-actinometer by Bell (1955) although PhAR detector is a name now more commonly used.
Most selenium cells are not very sensitive in the long-wave region of PhAR. Hence, their spectral correction is necessarily accompanied by a considerable loss in total average sensitivity, as correction can only be achieved by decreasing the sensitivity in the other regions of the PhAR range to that of the region of

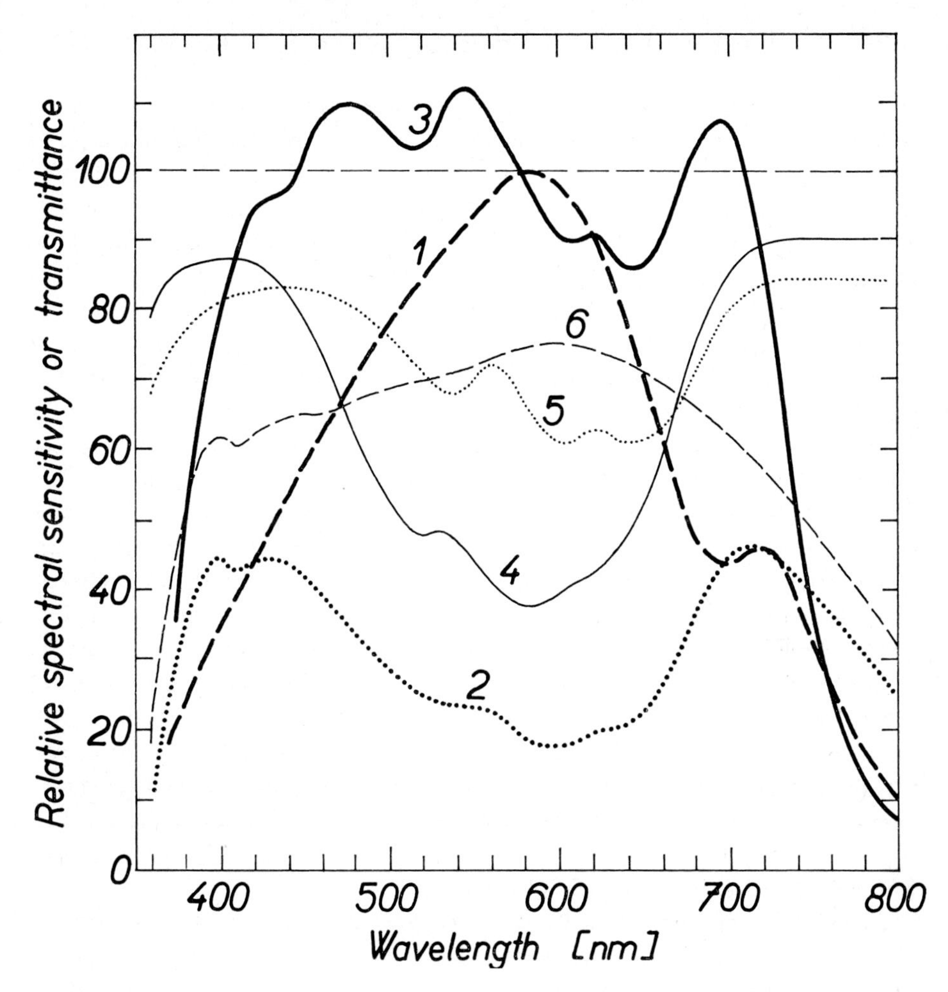

Fig. 19.31 Spectral correction of a *Carl Zeiss* (Jena) selenium cell. *1:* spectral sensitivity of the cell itself; *2:* spectral transmittance of a combined correction filter; *3:* spectral sensitivity of a complete phyto-actinometer receiver, fitted with a *BG 17* filter; *4, 5, 6:* transmittances of *BG 29* – 2 mm, *BG 33* – 0.7 mm, *BG 17* – 3 mm filters, respectively.

minimum sensitivity. The *Zeiss* (GDR) photocells, however, are several times more sensitive at about 700 nm and can be used to construct instruments with a considerably higher average sensitivity. Largely for this reason, in recent years silicon photovoltaic cells have been preferred to selenium cells in making PhAR detectors.

Detectors can be corrected either by superimposing filters (McPherson 1969; Norman, Tanner & Thurtell 1969) or by making a mosaic filter (Bell 1955). A filter for correction of *Zeiss* photocells is composed of two coloured glasses: *BG 29*, 2 mm, and *BG 33*, 0.7 mm (*Schott*, *Jena*, GDR).

However the increased sensitivity of the *Zeiss* photocell in the red region also has a disadvantage: the photocell is still sensitive in the adjacent part of the short-wave IR spectrum. Although the sensitivity in this band gradually decreases and falls off altogether before reaching 900 nm, it is necessary to minimize the undesirable effect of the IR radiation. A *BG 17* dethermal filter (*Schott, Jena*), thickness 3 mm, is suitable for this purpose (Fig. 19.31).

The receiver with a spectrally corrected selenium photocell can be used with a robust portable light-spot galvanometer to measure a minimum radiant flux density of 5×10^{-3} W m^{-2}. The corresponding deflection of the galvanometer is roughly equal to 1 mm m^{-1}, and if the scale is 200 mm long, full deflection corresponds to an observed radiation flux density of 1 W m^{-2}. For measuring the highest irradiances (approx. 400 to 500 W m^{-2} PhAR) it is therefore necessary to reduce the sensitivity of the galvanometer in a ratio of about 1:500. Galvanometer sensitivity is usually decreased by a universal shunt, which preserves the constant resistance of the external circuit connected to the galvanometer clamps, and in this way there is sufficient damping of the galvanometer oscillations. At the same time, the resistance included in the measured electric current flow is varied either continuously or in steps. In order to maintain linearity of the signal generated by irradiating the photocell, the resistance of the external photocell circuit should remain approximately constant and be within a range of 100 to 300 Ω. An independent pair of resistors for each measuring range must therefore be selected, the resistor connected across the photocell clamps being within the range 200 to 400 Ω, whereas the total resistance of the shunt (inserted between the galvanometer clamps) varies in the range 800 to 40 000 Ω. The condition of the approximately constant and low resistance in the photocell circuit is thus always satisfied, whereas the sum of the damping resistance of the galvanometer itself ($R_{ap} \simeq 800$ Ω) and the shunt resistance varies between 400 and 800 Ω, which still gives suitable overall damping of the galvanometer oscillations. Some commercially available galvanometers (*e.g.*, the *Kipp & Zonen* '*Microva*' type *AL 4*) have already been equipped with suitable sensitivity reducers of this type.

The dimensions of the phyto-actinometer receiver are determined by the size and kind of the photocell used. Selenium cells are manufactured in many sizes and shapes and some of them (*e.g.* those with diameters of 25, 16 or 12 mm) can be used to construct flat detectors of very small dimensions, which are especially suitable for measuring the irradiance in very restricted spaces, *e.g.* in assimilation chambers. Because of their much higher output, silicon cells of much smaller size (*e.g.* < 10 mm^2) can be used and are preferable in small assimilation chambers. Because the photoelectrical output of such small photocells is small, it is necessary to use measuring instruments with high voltage sensitivity to measure the generated e.m.f., *i.e.* instruments with a small internal resistance.

19.8.3 | Electrolytic integrating devices for small currents

The photoelectric current generated by photovoltaic cells, used in constructing luxmeters and PhAR detectors can be measured by integrating methods, based on coulombmetric principles. In this case, data on the amount of electricity transmitted per unit time are obtained by measuring the amount of reduced metal or liberated gas in an electrolyzer of a suitable design. Several types of integrators for small currents, based on this principle, have been designed and some of them are manufactured commercially. If it is required to measure the total amount of PhAR incident per unit time it is more convenient and more sensitive to integrate using sensors, based on photo-emission cells (see Section 19.8.5). However, for sake of completeness, descriptions of some small-current integrators are also given:

Fairbairn (1958) employed the electrolytic reduction of silver and Powell & Heath (1964) a coulombmeter for copper in order to determine the amount of electricity, generated in a photovoltaic cell by irradiation per unit time. The latter of the two instruments deserves attention because of its compactness, small size and, especially, its marked simplicity. It can be inexpensively produced in large numbers (Jackson & Slater 1967), and it should also prove suitable for inexpensive industrial series production. To obtain a record, it is necessary to remove from the instrument, dry and weigh the two electrodes of the electrolyzer and then to clean them, dry them and weigh them again before beginning another measurement. To obtain a satisfactory weighing accuracy, the amount of reduced copper must be sufficiently large. Thus the instrument can be used to advantage for measurements over intervals of time such as a week.

From the calibration curves of Powell & Heath (1964), a difference in electrode weights of 10 mg would correspond to irradiation values of between 580 and 1160 W h m^{-2} depending on the design of the instrument, and the standard error is between $\pm$ 5–10% if the integrated amount of incident radiation is about 5800 W h m^{-2}.

Small-current integrators, such as that designed by *Siemens-Schuckert* for an integrated current range of 1 μA–2 mA (see Trickett & Moulsley 1956) are less laborious. In this instrument (Fig. 19.32) the current passes through an acid solution, which is enclosed in a sealed all-glass system of two chambers and one

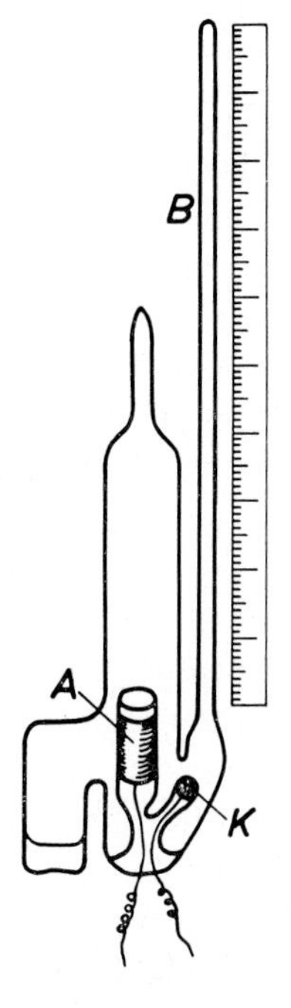

Fig. 19.32 Design of an electrolytic integrator of low currents *(Siemens-Schuckert)*. *A:* anode; *K:* cathode; *B:* calibrated tube (from Trickett & Moulsley 1956).

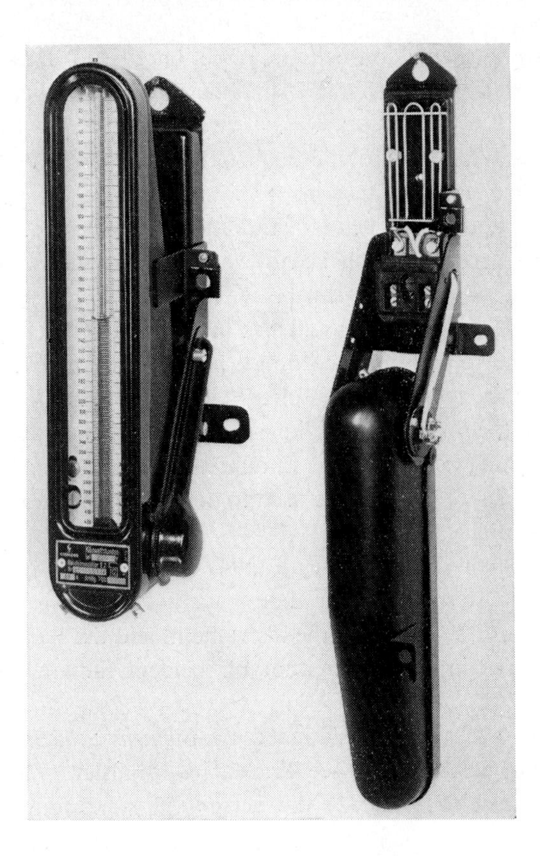

Fig. 19.33 *Siemens-Schuckert* electrolytic integrator. Left: instrument in operational position; right: instrument turned upside down for filling the tube.

vertical graduated tube, in an atmosphere of pure hydrogen (Fig. 19.33). The electrodes are of platinum, the cathode being located under the orifice of the graduated tube, and the cylindrical anode, platinum blackened, being fixed centrally in the chamber which is immediately connected with the tube.

Hydrogen is evolved from the cathode at a rate which is proportional to the current intensity and accumulates in the graduated tube which is filled initially by the electrolyte. The oxygen, released from the anode, immediately reacts with the hydrogen forming the gaseous phase of both chambers and thus balancing the pressure difference resulting from the decomposition of the electrolyte, so that the whole electrolysis outwardly appears as the transition of hydrogen from the chambers into the graduated tube. Hence the volume of hydrogen captured in the graduated tube is directly proportional to a certain amount of radiant energy.

The average internal resistance of the electrolytic integrator is about 60 Ω. The sensitivity of the measuring system is defined by the size of the photocell used and by the cross-section of the graduated tube (*e.g.* 1 scale division per hour corresponds to a current of 100 μA in the less sensitive instrument with a graduated tube of a larger cross-section, divided into 100 divisions, and 10 scale divisions correspond to the same current in the more sensitive instrument with a capillary graduated tube, divided into 250 divisions).

19.8.4 | *Instruments based on photo-emission cells*

The most suitable photo-emission cell for simple and reliable instruments for measuring photosynthetically active radiation is undoubtedly a vacuum type with a silver-cesium oxide-cesium (so-called *S 1* or double octave response) emission layer. As mentioned in Section 19.4.5.1 the signal of vacuum photo-emission cells is exactly proportional to the density of the incident radiation over a wide range (perfect response linearity), and does not change substantially with temperature and with fluctuations in the supply voltage, which do not exceed the range of the horizontal section of their characteristic. The spectral sensitivity of the silver-cesium emission layer includes the whole region of photosynthetically active radiation (see Fig. 19.15). With suitable filters it is comparatively easy to design a receiver, the response of which is proportional to the energy of the incident radiation, regardless of its spectral composition, within the whole range of wavelengths, 400–700 nm, and is not sensitive to incident radiation outside this range.
Photo-emission cells are often thought to be more complex detectors than photo-voltaic cells and to require more complicated measuring instruments with electronic amplifiers *etc.* This is not so. To measure the current passing through a photo-emission cell a simple galvanometer may be used and, if vacuum photocells are being used, even considerable fluctuations are within the limits of saturation, where the photo-current is practically independent of the anode voltage. It is, therefore, possible with a vacuum photo-emission cell, a dry battery with a voltage of 100 to 200 V (depending on the type of cell) and a sufficiently sensitive galvanometer to measure radiant energy just as easily as with selenium cells but with slightly less sensitivity.
An average vacuum photocell with a silver-cesium oxide-cesium cathode has an area of about 10 cm^2 and its nominal sensitivity is about 25 $\mu A\ lm^{-1}$ (with average vacuum photocells with a simple layer of alkaline metal the sensitivity is usually 5 times lower) whereas an average selenium cell with the same area has a sensitivity of 800 $\mu A\ lm^{-1}$. Hence an illuminance of 10 lx (equivalent to an irradiance PhAR of about 10 to 20 $mW\ m^{-2}$) will cause an emission in a vacuum cell, which will transmit about 0.25 μA, whereas with a selenium cell it will cause an e.m.f. of about 2.5 mV, which corresponds to a current of 8 μA, given an instrument resistance of 300 Ω. The resistance of a photo-emission cell, however, is about $10^8\ \Omega$, for a supply voltage of about 100 V, and a measuring instrument with an arbitrarily high resistance can be used (*e.g.* even $10^4\ \Omega$), without decreasing the transmitted current substantially. Hence an instrument measuring 0 to 20 μA, with scale divisions of 0.2 μA, can be used and the illuminance of 10 lx will correspond to one scale division. On the other hand, laboratory instruments with an internal resistance of 300 Ω usually have a minimum range of 0 to 600 μA so that an illuminance of 10 lx at a selenium cell will also induce a deflection of approximately one scale division. Therefore, the higher current sensitivity of the selenium cell is only apparent in practice.
The use of a galvanometer as in this simple system is not desirable in the field. The character of the signal, transmitted by a photo-emission cell, makes it possible in principle to construct a portable amplifier for measuring it by current electronic

means. However, stable D.C. amplifiers for high-impedance sources are very difficult to construct and transformation of the D.C. signal from the photocell to an A.C. signal which can be easily amplified, has also met with considerable difficulties, so that no suitable amplifier has become available, to make it possible to read or record the value of the signal of photo-emission cells in the field. Similar considerations also apply to electronic circuits used with photo-electrical detectors with internal amplification, such as gas-filled photocells and photomultipliers. The specific properties of photo-emission cells make it possible to measure the transmitted photo-current by a simple and reliable method, if the density of the observed radiation flux does not vary too rapidly, or if it is possible to ignore short-term fluctuations in the irradiance. The instrument which will be described below, measures the electric charge which passes through a photocell per unit time as a result of irradiation. The integral of the incident radiation flux is expressed as discrete electric charges of a certain magnitude, which are recorded by the measuring instrument. The irradiance is given by the electrical charge, read off the instrument, divided by the interval during which the charge passed through the cell. It follows that the shortest interval for which it is possible to determine the average value of the irradiance is defined by the time during which one portion is measured. The magnitude of the electrical charge is defined by the design of the instrument and can be chosen from a very wide range.

19.8.5 *The Kubín-Hládek integrating recorder for photosynthetically active radiation*

The principle of the electrical circuit on which the integrator is based has been used in measuring equipment many times in various forms, especially in instruments for UV and X-ray dosimetry. Its principle, first described by Rentschler (1930), can be seen in Fig. 19.34. A capacitor is the fundamental integrating element. This capacitor (C_1) accumulates electric charge passing through photocell V_1 and it is, therefore, charged at a rate proportional at any moment to the irradiance of the photo-emission cell (or to the intensity of the photo-current). The voltage across the capacitor is increased by charging (indirectly proportional to the capacitor capacity). This voltage also determines the trigger potential of the starting anode of the cold-cathode discharge tube (thyratron) (V_2). When it reaches the value of the ignition voltage of the auxiliary path, a discharge is

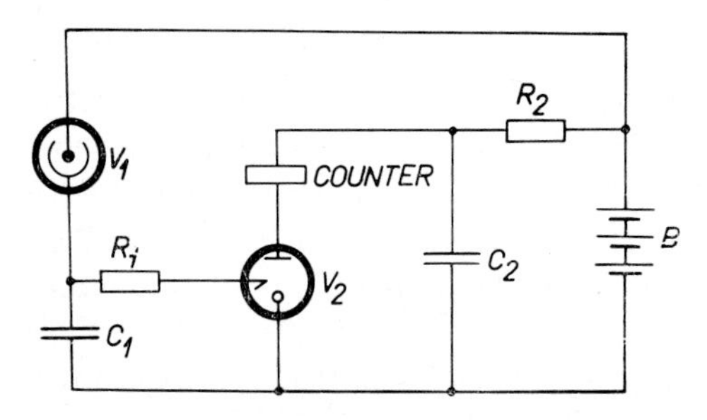

Fig. 19.34 Circuit diagram of an integrator of photosynthetically active radiation (from Rentschler 1930). (For explanation see text.)

generated across the latter, by which the spare condenser is discharged (through the current-limiting resistor R_1) down to the value of the extinction voltage of the auxiliary path of the discharge tube. The discharge across the auxiliary path ionizes the main path, which ignites and discharges another capacitor C_2. A sufficient electric charge accumulates in it between two discharges for the current impulse to actuate a five-digit non-reset electromagnetic counter, the coil of which is connected in series with capacitor C_2 (alternatively a relay may be actuated which then controls the counter). After the discharge passes, the whole system is ready for the next cycle of operation. The voltage in the circuit of the spare capacitor C_1, therefore, varies constantly between the values of the ignition and extinction voltage of the auxiliary path of the discharge.

The resolution of the integrating circuit, *i.e.* the ratio between the minimum and maximum value of the photo-current, which can still be integrated reliably, is defined by the quality of the components used, especially by the insulating properties of the spare capacitor and by the input of the counter. The electrical properties of the counter determine the value of capacitor C_2, in which the electrical energy actuating the counter is accumulated. This capacitor is discharged through resistor R_2, the value of which must be sufficiently large for the discharge tube to go extinct after capacitor C_2 is discharged. The maximum frequency of the counter, therefore, is inversely proportional to its input. On the other hand, the minimum intensity of the photo-current, which is still capable of initiating a cycle of operations in the integrator, is determined by the leakage of the spare capacitor, the photocell and the discharge tube.

As opposed to the designs hitherto described, the integration circuit presented (Fig. 19.35) has the following improvements:

1. The spare capacitor is discharged completely during each cycle of operations across one of the two pairs of contacts of the auxiliary relay, connected into the circuit of the main path of the discharge tube V_2 (contacts *c* in Fig. 19.35). In

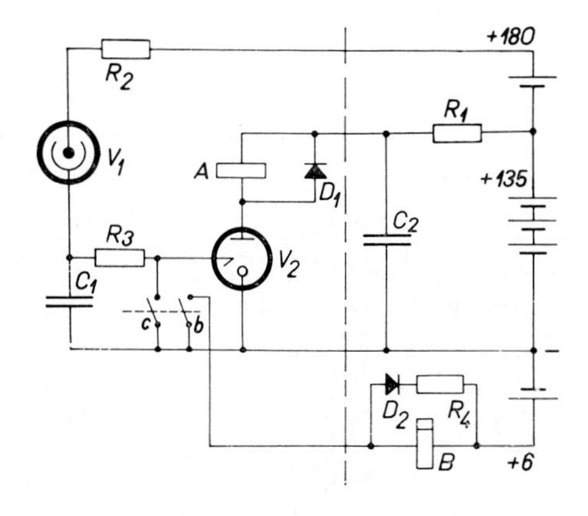

Fig. 19.35 Complete diagram of the electrical circuits of an integrator of photosynthetically active radiation made by *Laboratorní přístroje*, Prague (from Kubín & Hládek 1963): *Pressler* Type *494 PLLA GZV* photocell. Capacitors: C_1: 10 000 to 40 000 pF; C_2: 4 μF; V_2: thyratron *10 TC 9; D_1: 35 NP 75; D_2: GA 204;* Resistors: R_1: 250 kΩ; R_2: 3 MΩ; R_3: 10 kΩ; R_4: 220Ω; *A: Tesla HC 500-01; B: Tesla FE 909-08; c, b:* contacts.

this way the average voltage across the capacitor is decreased considerably, and this also restricts the average leakage.

2. The delay in the counter circuit (during the discharge period the instrument is actually out of action) is cut down to the necessary minimum by connecting a germanium junction diode in parallel with the relay coil. This diode absorbs the induction voltage peaks, which appear in the coils at the moment when the discharge is interrupted.

The modifications just described improve not only the linearity of the measuring system, but also increase the resolution of the instrument to such a degree that it may be used for relatively accurate quantitative work, as shown by the following technical data:

– maximum counting rate	1 impulse per s
– minimum counting rate	1 impulse per 15–20 min
– maximum photo-tube current	3.2×10^{-6} A
– average leakage resistance	2.5 to 3×10^{10} Ω
– minimum current required to load the spare capacitor upto trigger potential	3×10^{-9} A
– absolute resolution limits	1:1000
– resolution at 5% deviation from linearity	1:100

The integrator is designed so that the electrical circuits are divided into two independent parts (Fig. 19.36). The integrating circuit components, the insulating properties of which have to be exceptionally good, and the photocell are in a water-proof container, forming the sensing unit. In Fig. 19.35 these circuits have been encompassed by a dashed line. The counter circuits are placed in another box, together with the batteries. This is necessary for practical reasons, although from the point of view of the measurements themselves it would have been more convenient for the sensor to contain the photocell alone since it could then have been much smaller.

The flat receiver is made of a white opal glass plate, which is non-selective in the region of the wavelengths observed. The radiation detector itself is a vacuum photo-tube, the sensitivity of which is corrected by a combination of three spectral

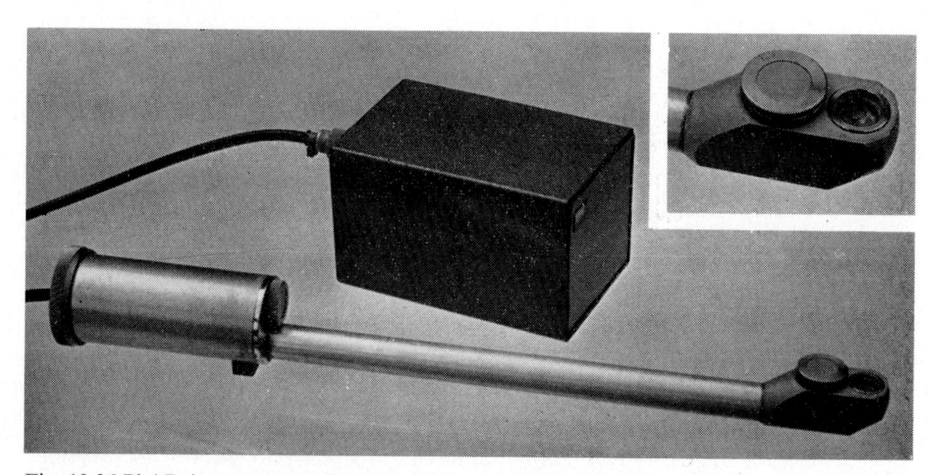

Fig. 19.36 PhAR integrator produced by *Laboratorní přístroje*, Prague. In the foreground the probe, in the background the box with the counter circuit and batteries.

filters to render it proportional to the energy of the incident radiation over the whole PhAR range. The absorptance of the combined correction filter (*Schott*, Jena, GDR: *BG 9* – 2 mm, *BG 10* – 2 mm, *BG 21* – 2 mm) and the spectral characteristics of the photocell itself and the corrected photocell are shown in Fig. 19.37. The irradiation of the photocell can be controlled by interchangeable diaphragms of various apertures, inserted between the filters and the photocell, in relation to the radiant flux observed so that the counter circuit operates at an optimum average rate *i.e.* with maximum allowable rate at maximum observed irradiance. The photocell, together with the filters, is placed in a small aluminium container, which is attached by a long duraluminium tube to the other parts of the probe (Fig. 19.38). This design makes it possible to measure in comparatively small and inaccessible spaces. The probe is water-proof, so that it can be used out-doors for long periods and it can also be used for short-term measurements under water. The probe contains a removable capsule of desiccant (silicagel), the state of which can be checked through a window.
The five-digit counter can record data over intervals of a week, but it can also be used for short-term measurements of a few minutes. If the time during which the counter records a certain number of impulses is recorded, the density of the radiant flux can be calculated.

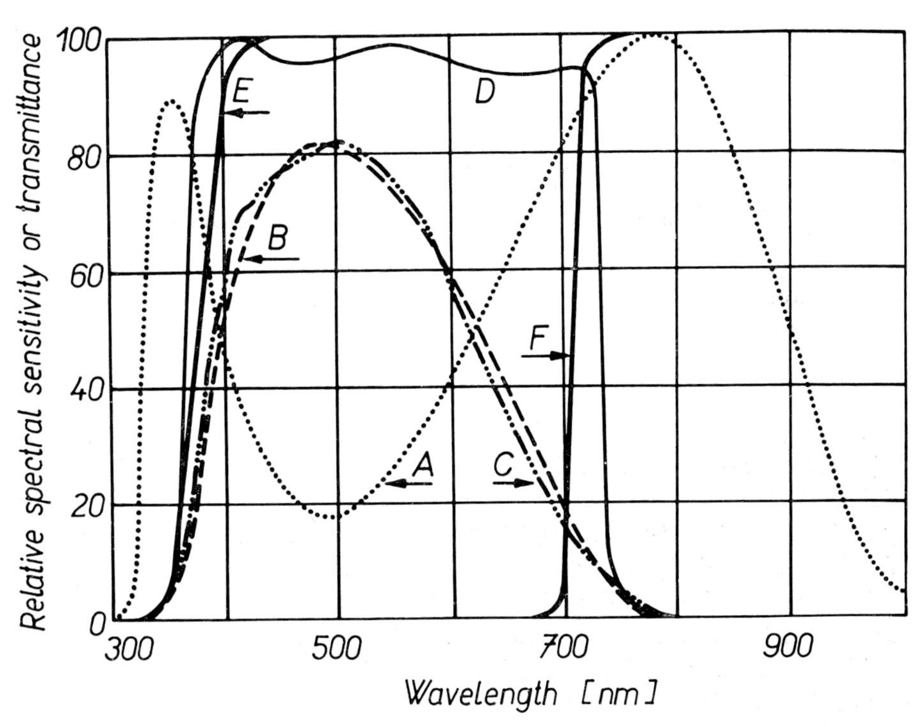

Fig. 19.37 Spectral correction of silver-cesium oxide-cesium photo-cathode (*Pressler* photocells), used for constructing PhAR integrators. *A:* spectral sensitivity of the photocell itself (if the photocell bulb is painted red, this layer has to be removed first); *B:* spectral transmittance of an ideal correction filter; *C:* spectral transmittance of a real correction filter (combination of filters *BG 9* - 2 mm, *BG 10* - 2 mm and *BG 21* - 2 mm); *D:* resultant spectral sensitivity of the complete receiver; *E:* spectral transmittance of filter *WG 1* - 2 mm; *F:* spectral transmittance of filter *RG 8* - 2 mm.

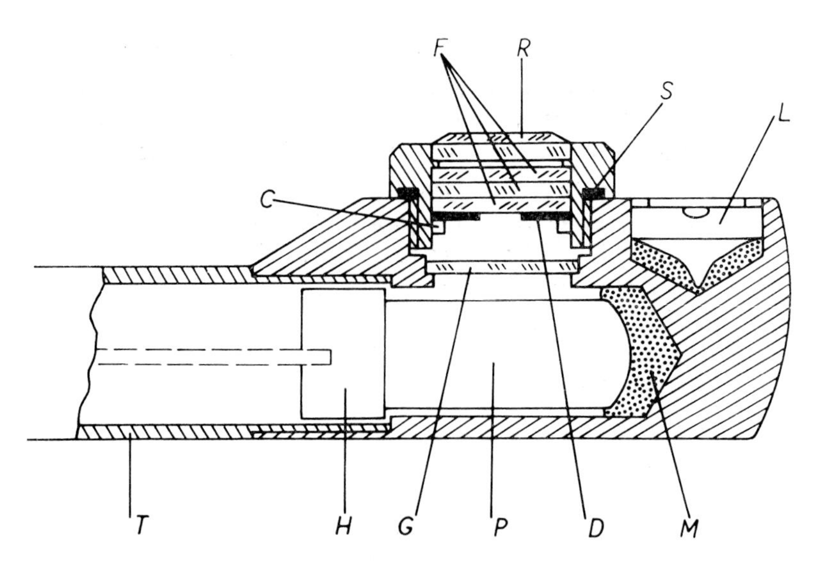

Fig. 19.38 Section of the window of the instrument probe of the PhAR integrator. *R:* opal glass receiver; *F:* combined filter; *D:* exchangeable diaphragm; *C:* diaphragm securing ring; *S:* packing; *G:* sealed glass plate which prevents humidity from getting into the instrument when the diaphragm is being exchanged; *P:* photocell; *H:* photocell base; *M:* soft polyurethane insert; *L:* level; *T:* tube, connecting photocell container with the other parts of the probe.

The power supply consists of four layer-type miniature high-tension batteries, each providing 45 V (180 V in all) and two 4.5 V batteries (9 V in all). The load on the batteries is very slight and even in continuous use of the instrument their life is practically equal to their storage life.

If work is being carried out with several instruments in one place where A.C. mains is available, a suitable rectifier can be used instead of batteries and the counter circuits of the individual instruments (capacitor C_2, the counter with the germanium diode and the current-limiting resistor R_2) can be mounted in a single unit.

The radiation integrating meters are calibrated against a non-selective detector such as a type *CA-1* compensated thermopile or a type *E 5* standard thermopile (*Kipp & Zonen* – see Figs. 19.44 and 19.45). The photosynthetically active region of the spectrum of the standard radiation source (see Section 19.6) is delimited by *WG 1* and *RG 8* cut-off filters (*Schott*-Jena, GDR, see Fig. 19.37).

With instruments designed for measuring radiant flux density of the natural PhAR during the vegetative period, a diaphragm is chosen so that one counter impulse corresponds to an irradiation of 0.40 to 0.45 W h m^{-2}. If a four-digit counter is used in constructing the integrator, its capacity is sufficient to record the daily sum of the radiation in the temperate zone, where the overall diurnal amount of PhAR does not exceed 4 kW h m^{-2}.

19.9 | Instruments for recording solar radiation

An internationally acknowledged standard instrument for measuring solar radiation is the *Kipp & Zonen* (Delft, Holland) type *CM-3* solarimeter. The

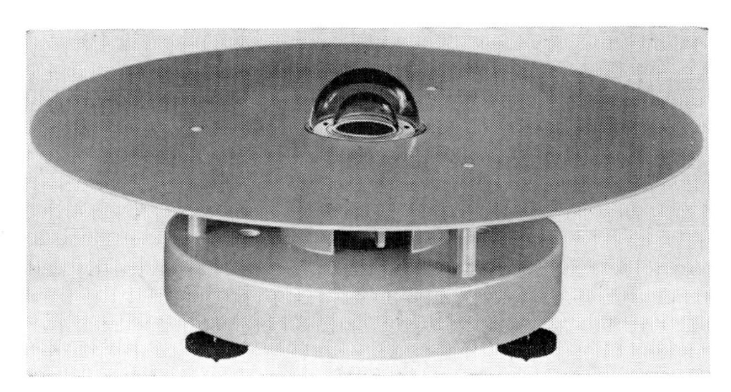

Fig. 19.39 *Kipp & Zonen* solarimeter (Delft, Holland). The flat non-selective receiver is projected by two concentric, hemispherical glass domes, transmitting in the region of 300 to 3500 nm. See also Fig. 19.8. (Courtesy of *Kipp & Zonen*, Delft, The Netherlands.)

Moll-Gorczynski thermopile is constructed of 14 thermocouples in series. Strips of silver foil, arranged in a horizontal plane, are coated with a very fine carbon black and their ends are alternately connected to the constantan and manganine elements of the thermopile. These connections form the hot ends of the thermocouples, the cold ends being placed in a brass block under the receiver (see Fig. 19.8). The flat receiver is protected from weather influences by two hemispherical

Fig. 19.40 Yanishevskiĭ pyranometer type *AS 3 × 3*. The construction allows the instrument to be turned through 180° downwards. See also Fig. 19.8.

Table 19.4 Characteristics of thermopiles, actinometers (pyrheliometers) and pyranometers.

Instrument	Model	Receiver dimensions [mm]	Number of junctions	Internal resistance [Ω]
Moll thermopile *CA 1*	compensated	10 × 10	20 + 20	60
Moll thermopile *CA 2*	non compensated, with conical reflector	ø 10	16	50
Standard thermopile *E 5*[2]	non compensated, in tube fitted with rectangular diaphragms	10 × 10	66	50
Actinometer *CM 1*	compensated, in tube fitted with circular diaphragms	ø 10	20 + 20	65
Actinometer *AT 50*	non compensated, in tube fitted with circular diaphragms	ø cca 10	26 to 36	13 to 20
Solarimeter *CM 3*	non compensated	12 × 11	14	8
Eppley pyranometer[2] (earlier development)	standard model lower sensitivity model	ø 29 ø 29	50 16	100 35
Eppley Black and White Pyranometer (recent development)	standard model, compensated lower sensitivity model higher sensitivity model		48	300
Pyranometer *3*× *3* (Albedometers *AS 3* × *3* and *AP 3* × *3*)	non compensated	30 × 30	32–40	30–50

1. No more produced.
2. Output in terms of 'open circuit' EMF.

glass domes (Fig. 19.39). A white laquered tin screen prevents the base of the instrument with the thermopile holder from being heated by radiation.
A similar instrument, produced in the USSR, is the Yanishevskiï pyranometer, type *3* × *3* (Yanishevskiï 1957; Fig. 19.40). The design of the detector differs from that of the *Kipp & Zonen* solarimeter in that both the cold and the hot ends of the thermocouples are arranged together in one plane beneath alternate white and black squares (Fig. 19.8). The whole receiver is protected by a hemispherical glass dome.
The fundamental characteristics of the *CM-3* solarimeter and of the *3* × *3* pyranometer are given in Table 19.4. Similar solar radiation measuring instruments are made in several other countries *e.g. Eppley* in the U.S.A. (see Fig. 19.41), *Stern* in the FRG.
The mechanical effects of heat have been exploited in the design of the Robitzsch-type actinometer (Robitzsch 1932; Blackwell 1953; Thams 1962). The radiation detector consists of three flat bi-metal strips, 85 × 15 × 1.5 mm, arranged parallel to each other in one plane (Fig. 19.42) and joined at one end. Both outside bi-

utput[1]		Manufacturer
V per μW	EMF per W m^{-2}	
25	5-12 μV	*Kipp & Zonen*, Delft, Holland
16	variable due to conical reflector	
13	10–12 μV	
	16 μV	
	5.5–10.0 μV	*Gruzinskiĭ sovnarkhoz, Tbilisskiĭ zavod gidrometpriborov*, Tbilisi, USSR
	11 μV	*Kipp & Zonen*, Delft, Holland
	9,5–11 μV	*The Eppley Laboratory, Inc.*, Newport, Rhode Island, U.S.A.
	3 μV	
	10.5 μV	
	3.5 μV	
	35–43 μV	
	15 μV	*Gruzinskiĭ sovnarkhoz, Tbilisskiĭ zavod gidrometpriborov*, Tbilisi, USSR

metallic strips are covered with a reflective coating such as magnesium oxide. The middle bi-metallic strip is coated with an absorptant such as zinc black. The free end of the middle bi-metallic strip is connected by a fine lever to the recorder indicator, whereas the frame with the bearings of the lever is fixed to the free ends of the white bi-metallic strips. This type of compensation eliminates effects of changes in the ambient temperature. The incident radiation, absorbed by the surface, heats the middle black bi-metallic strip, which is deformed more than the neighbouring white strips, the deflection of which only depends on the ambient temperature. The difference in deflection between the black and white strips is recorded and is directly proportional to the absorbed incident radiation. The main drawback of this instrument as currently made, is a relatively small sensitivity and considerable inertia (20 to 25 min).

Only one of the latest modifications of the Bellani pyranometer, with a horizontal receiving surface, is suitable for observing solar radiation (Trickett, Moulsley & Edwards 1957; Wierzejewski 1962); and the technical design of such instruments is being developed at the Physical and Meteorological Observatory in Davos.

Fig. 19.41 *Eppley* black and white pyranometer model *8-48*. (Courtesy of *Eppley Laboratory, Inc.*, Newport, R.I., U.S.A.)

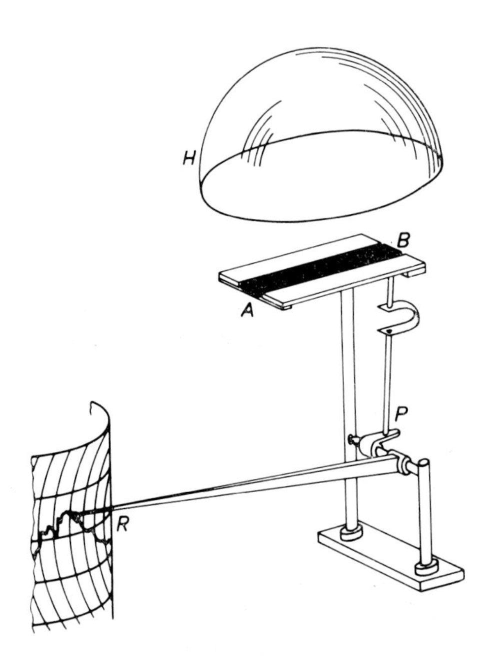

Fig. 19.42 Diagram of the Robitzsch pyranograph. *A:* connected ends of all three bi-metallic strips; *B:* free end of blackened bi-metallic strips connected to the recorder; *H:* hemispherical glass dome; *P:* lever transmission; *R:* cylinder with recording paper. The base of the glass dome is at the same level as the bi-metallic strips during measurements.

However, the theory of the instrument has not yet been elaborated sufficiently and the instrument, as opposed to the alternatives with a spherical receiver, is not being produced commercially.

The hitherto best known modification of the Bellani pyranometer is the instrument with the spherical receiver, which has been described in Section 19.4.4.4. This instrument is used to measure radiation which has been denoted as circumglobal. This name was suggested by Courvoisier & Wierzejewski (1954), to whom most credit is due for working out the instrument theory. By circumglobal radiation they understand all radiation incident at the spherical receiver, located in a given position, *i.e.* radiation coming from the upper and lower hemispheres. The spherical Bellani pyranometer really records the sum of solar radiation (*i.e.* the radiation incident at a horizontal surface from the upper hemisphere) and the radiation reflected from the base (ground, stand), above which the instrument is located. Furthermore, the response of a spherical receiver to solar radiation differs from the response of a flat receiver, as the surface receiving the individual components of solar radiation is markedly different in the two cases (see Section 19.3).

The relation between circumglobal and solar radiation and the use of the Bellani pyranometer is discussed by Courvoisier & Wierzejewski (1954), Wörner (1956) and Impens (1962).

The calibration of the Bellani pyranometer in absolute energy units, described here, is taken from Courvoisier & Wierzejewski (1954). Several instruments, the constants of which are not known, are placed for at least a week in the same environment such as over open grassland, to determine the differences in their sensitivities with an error of less than 1 %. During clear, cloudless weather, one of these instruments is exposed for the whole day so that no direct solar radiation is incident upon it *e.g.* by placing the instrument on a stand to which a clockwork driven arm about 50 cm long with a screen is fixed, constantly following the path of the sun across the sky. The other instruments remain unscreened. At the same time, a pyrheliograph is used to measure the flux density of solar radiation throughout the day. After sun-set the volume of distilled alcohol in each of the exposed instruments is recorded and, using a planimeter, the pyrheliograph record is integrated with the greatest possible accuracy. In this way two types of data are obtained which can be used to calculate the instruments constants:

a. the amount of direct solar radiation, captured by a unit surface perpendicular to the direction of the incident radiation;

b. the ratio of the direct to diffuse solar radiation.

Well constructed Bellani pyranometers are outstanding for their high operational reliability and long life. Their constants change only over a number of years as a result of the decomposition of the alcohol by the small amount of UV radiation entering the instrument. However, the alcohol can easily be exchanged. These properties and the simple method of recording the observed values, as well as the extraordinarily simple manipulation, are so important that the development of an alternative instrument with a flat receiver is highly desirable.

19.10 Thermopiles for indoor radiation measurements, actinometers and bolometers

The receivers of thermo-electric instruments for measuring solar radiation (*e.g. Kipp & Zonen* solarimeter receivers) are designed to accept radiation from a solid angle of 180°. However this is not appropriate for certain other measurements of radiant flux. Thermoelectric sensors are also available which can only accept radiation incident at the receiver perpendicularly, or at a small angle of incidence. Instruments of this type, designed solely for laboratory measurements, are also based on a thermopile composed of a number of thermocouples. The detector itself is fixed to a heavy metal base with a large thermal inertia and, together with it, it is usually enclosed in a protective cover (see Fig. 19.43). In front of the receiver plane there may be a shorter or longer tube (Fig. 19.44), which has two functions: it limits the beam of approximately parallel rays and prevents turbulent motion of the air in the immediate vicinity of the receiving surface, since this may cause fluctuations in the e.m.f. produced. Hence, open receivers almost always

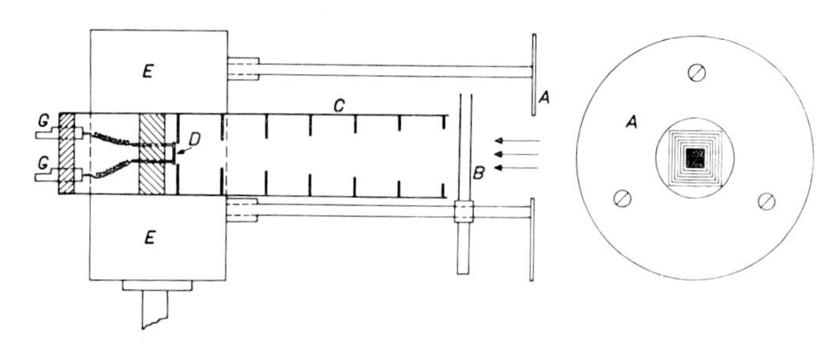

Fig. 19.43 Longitudinal section and front view of *Kipp & Zonen* standard thermopile, type *E 5*. *A:* frontal diaphragm; *B:* simple shutter; *C:* tube with a system of diaphragms; *D:* thermopile; *E:* thermostatic vessel filled with distilled water; *G:* clamps.

Fig. 19.44 *Kipp & Zonen* standard thermopile, type *E 5*.

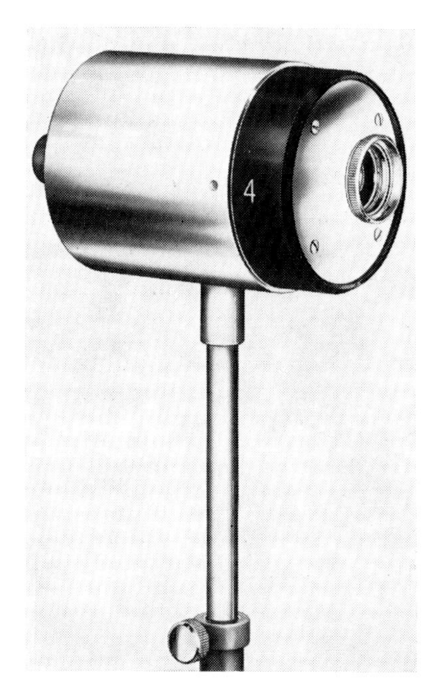

Fig. 19.45 Compensated *Kipp & Zonen* type *CA 1* thermopile. The instrument has no tube and is fitted with three interchangeable diaphragms with calibres of 8, 6 and 4 mm. (Courtesy of *Kipp & Zonen*, Delft, The Netherlands.)

have a tube, whereas receivers protected by a glass, fluoride or quartz window may not have one (see Fig. 19.45). Both functions of the tube are supplemented by a system of several co-axial diaphragms inside the tube, the calibre of which diminishes gradually towards the receiver. The surfaces of these diaphragms facing the radiation source, are chromium plated and polished in order to reflect radiation which would by-pass the receiver. The opposite sides of the diaphragms are black to prevent the reflection of radiation towards the receiver. The front end of the tube is usually equipped with a simple shutter.

Such thermopiles, designed for receiving a narrow beam of rays and used for measuring direct solar radiation, are usually called actinometers or pyrheliometers. These thermopiles are equipped with an especially long tube with a large number of diaphragms so that only the solar disc is in the field of view of the receiver, and they are either fixed to a revolving stand, making it possible to sight an arbitrary point within a solid angle of 180°, or placed on a heliostat.

The characteristics of some of the commercially produced instruments discussed above are given in Table 19.4.

A wavelength independent line operated radiometer designed as an aid to the photobiologists is manufactured by *Yellow Springs Instrument Co.*, Yellow Springs, Ohio, U.S.A. (see Figs. 19.46 and 19.47). The instrument (*YSI* model *65*) is based on a thermistor bolometer connected with amplifier. A silver target coated with a special black is used as the receiver which allows measurements in the range from 280 nm to 2.6 μm within a $\pm$ 5% accuracy. The *YSI* model *65* has seven ranges of sensitivity (from 0 to 2.5 W m^{-2} to 0 to 2 500 W m^{-2}) and includes a recorder output.

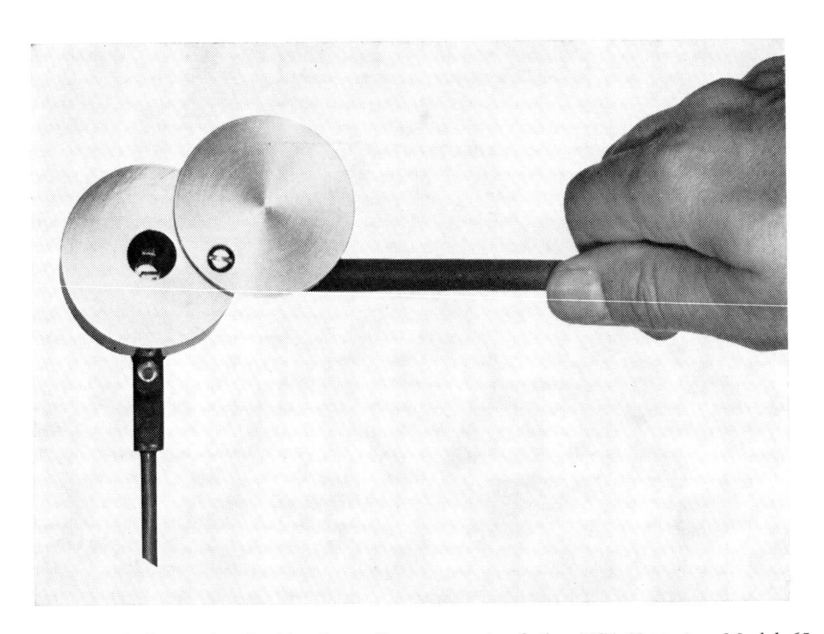

Fig. 19.46 The probe (inside the collector cone) of the *YSI Kettering Model 65* Radiometer. (Courtesy of the *Yellow Springs Instrument Co. Inc.*, Yellow Springs, Ohio, U.S.A.)

Fig. 19.47 *YSI Kettering Model 65* Radiometer. The case with amplifier, scale selector and built-in meter. (Courtesy of the *Yellow Springs Instrument Co. Inc.*, Yellow Springs, Ohio, U.S.A.)

19.11 | References

Anderson, M. C.: Light relations of terrestrial plant communities and their measurement. – Biol. Rev. 39: 425-486, 1964.
Atkins, W. R. G., Poole, H. H.: Methods for the photoelectric and photochemical measurement of daylight. – Biol. Rev. 5: 91-113, 1930.
Bachman, F.: Ein neuer Aktinograph. – Planta 9: 660-675, 1930.
Bauer, G.: Measurement of Optical Radiations. – Focal Press, London-New York 1965.
Bell, L. N.: Fotoelektricheskiĭ pribor dlya izmereniya fotosinteticheski aktivnoĭ radiatsii (fotoelektricheskiĭ fitoaktinometr). [A photo-electric device for measuring photosynthetically active radiation (photoelectric phyto-actinometer).] – Trudy Inst. Fiziol. Rast. K.A. Timiryazeva 10: 257-264, 1955.
Bell, L. N.: Ob ispol'zovanii lyuksmetrov i selenovykh fotoelementov dlya izmereniya fiziologicheskoĭ radiatsii. [On the use of luxmeters and selenium photocells for measuring physiological radiation.] – Fiziol. Rast. 3: 176-178, 1956.
Bellani, A.: Il colletore del calorico. – Ann. Sci. Regno Lombardo-Veneto 1836.
Berger-Landefeldt, U.: Radiation measurements over the plant cover. – In: Eckardt, F. E. (ed.): Methodology of Plant Eco-Physiology. Pp. 47-53. UNESCO, Paris 1965.
Blackwell, M. J.: On the development of an improved Robitzsch-type actinometer. – Meteorol. Res. Comm., Air Ministry, London, Meteorol. Res. Pamphlet No. 791, London 1953.
Blevin, W. R., Brown, W. J.: Black coatings for absolute radiometers. – Metrologia 2: 139-143, 1966.
Chechik, N. O., Faĭnshteĭn, S. M., Lifshits, T. M.: Elektronnye Umnozhiteli. [Photomultipliers.] – Gosudarstv. Izdatel'. tekhn.-teoret. Literatury, Moskva 1957.
Committee on Plant Irradiation – Nederl. Stichting Verlichtingskunde (Arnhem, Netherlands): Specification of radiant flux and radiant flux density in irradiations of plants with artificial light. – J. hort. Sci. 28: 177-184, 1953.
Courvoisier, P., Wierzejewski, H.: Das Kugelpyranometer Bellani. Beiträge zur Strahlungsmessmethodik V. – Arch. Meteorol. Geophys. Bioklimatol. (Ser. B) 5: 413-446, 1954.
Czopek, M., Starzecki, W., Łagisz, J., Motyka, B.: An automatic registrator as a supplement of an electronic integrator of photosynthetically active radiation and their adaptation to ecophysiological studies. – Photosynthetica 1: 65-68, 1967.
Dlugos, H. G.: Aus der Praxis der cos-Korrektur von Photoelementen mit Hilfe von Optiken. – Lichttechnik 10: 565-567, 1958.
Dore, W. G.: A simple chemical light-meter. – Ecology 39: 151-152, 1958.
Dragoun, Z., Šmirous, K.: Polovodiče. [Semiconductors.] – SNTL, Praha 1962.
Drummond, A. J.: Techniques for the measurement of solar and terrestrial radiation fluxes in plant biological research. A review with special reference to the arid zones. – In: Eckardt, F. E. (ed.): Methodology of Plant Eco-Physiology. Pp. 13-27. UNESCO, Paris 1965.
Eckhardt, G.: Neuzeitliche Beleuchtungsmesser. – Lichttechnik 17: 110A-113A, 1965.
Edwards, R. I., Moulsley, L. J.: Preliminary measurements of the distribution of light in a glasshouse. – J. agr. eng. Res. 3: 69-75, 1958.
Fairbairn, W. A.: Methods of light intensity measurements in forest stands. II. The use of light measurement instruments in the field. – Forestry 31: 155–162, 1958.
Friend, D. T. C.: A simple method of measuring integrated light values in the field. – Ecology 42: 577-580, 1961.
Gaastra, P.: Photosynthesis of crop plants as influenced by light, carbon dioxide, temperature, and stomatal diffusion resistance. – Meded. Landbouwhogesch. (Wageningen) 59(13): 1-68, 1959.
Gaastra, P.: Some comparisons between radiation in growth rooms and radiation under natural conditions. In: Chouard, P., de Bilderling, N. (ed.): Phytotronique I. Pp. 45-53. CNRS, Paris 1969,
Gast, P. R.: Modification and measurement of sun, sky and terrestrial radiation for eco-physiological studies. – In: Eckardt, F. E. (ed.): Methodology of Plant Eco-Physiology. Pp. 29-45. UNESCO, Paris 1965.
Gates, D. M.: Radiant energy, its receipt and disposal. Heat, radiant and sensible. Chapter I. – Meteorol. Monogr. 6: 1-26, 1965.

Giovanelli, R. G.: An omnidirectional photometer of small dimensions. – J. sci. Instrum. 30: 326–328, 1953.

Golay, M. J. E.: A pneumatic infra-red detector. – Rev. sci. Instrum. 18: 357-362, 1947.

Harris, L.: The optical properties of metal blacks and carbon blacks. – In: Massachusetts Inst. Technol. and Eppley Found. Res. Monogr. Ser. 1: 1-116, 1967.

Impens, I.: Toepassingsmogelijkheden van de sferische pyranometer naar Bellani, type Davos, in agro-biologische stralingsstudies. – Meded. Landbouwhogesch. Gent 27: 575-590, 1962.

Ivanov, A. P.: Elektricheskie Istochniki Sveta. Lampy Nakalivaniya. [Electric Light Sources. Incandescent Lamps.] – Gostekhizdat, Moskva 1938.

Jackson, J. E., Slater, C. H. W.: An integrating photometer for outdoor use particularly in trees. – J. appl. Ecol. 4: 421-424, 1967.

Joffe, A. F.: Poluprovodnikovye Termoelementy. [Semiconductors.] – Izdat. Akad. Nauk SSSR, Moskva–Leningrad 1956.

Kalendovský, J., Strnad, J.: Fotoelektrické Články a Jejich Použití v Technické Praxi. [Application of Photocells and Photoelements.] – Elektrotechnický Svaz českoslov., Praha 1949.

Kleschnin, A. F.: Die Pflanze und das Licht. – Akademie-Verlag, Berlin 1960.

Klugh, A. B.: Ecological photometry and a new instrument for measuring light. – Ecology 6: 203-237, 1925.

Kortum, H.: Leistungsfaktor und Empfindlichkeitsmessung bei Thermoelementen und Thermosäulen. – Jenaer Rundschau 2: 36-39, 1957.

Krochmann, J.: Über ein neues Raumbeleuchtungs-Messgerät. – Lichttechnik 16: 180-181, 1964.

Kubín, Š., Hládek, L.: An integrating recorder for photosynthetically active radiant energy with improved resolution. – Plant Cell Physiol. 4: 153-168, 1963.

McCree, K. J.: Light measurements in plant growth investigations. – Nature 206: 527-528, 1965.

McCree, K. J.: A solarimeter for measuring photosynthetically active radiation. – Agr. Meteorol. 3: 353-366, 1966.

McPherson, H. G.: Photocell-filter combinations for measuring photosynthetically active radiation. – Agr. Meteorol. 6: 347-356, 1969.

Middleton, W. E. K.: Spherical illumination as an ecological parameter and an improved integrator. – Ecology 34: 416-421, 1953.

Monteith, J. L.: Solarimeter for field use. – J. sci. Instrum. 36: 341-346, 1959.

Monteith, J. L., Szeicz, G.: Simple devices for radiation measurements and integration. – Arch. Meteorol. Geophys. Bioklimatol. (Ser. B) 11: 491-500, 1962.

Müller, R. H.: Filter photometers. – In: Mellon, M. G. (ed.): Analytical Absorption Spectroscopy. Pp. 161-185. J. Wiley & Sons, New York 1950.

Nichiporovich, A. A.: Fotosintez i teoriya polucheniya vysokikh urozhaev. [Photosynthesis and theory of high yields.] – Timiryazevskie Chteniya 15: 1-93, 1954.

Norman, J. M., Tanner, C. B., Thurtell, G. W.: Photosynthetic light sensor for measurements in plant canopies. – Agron. J. 61: 840-843, 1969.

Oranje, P. J.: Grundlagen, Anwendungen, Eigenschaften von Gasentladungslampen. – Philips Techn. Bibliothek, Berlin 1943.

Pearsall, W. H., Hewitt, T.: Light penetration in fresh water. II. Light penetration and changes in vegetation limits in Windermere. – J. exp. Biol. 10: 306-312, 1933.

Pfund, A. H.: The blackening of radiometers. – In: Forsythe, W. E. (ed.): Measurement of Radiant Energy. McGraw-Hill Book Co., Inc., New York 1937.

Powell, M. C., Heath, O. V. S.: A simple and inexpensive integrating photometer. – J. exp. Bot. 15: 187-191, 1964.

Prouty, L. R., Hardy, J. D.: Temperature determinations. – In: Uber, F. M. (ed.): Biophysical Research Methods. Pp. 131-173. Intersci. Publ., New York–London 1950.

Reifsnyder, W. E., Lull, H. W.: Radiant energy in relation to forests. – Tech. Bull. No. 1344 U.S. Dept. Agr., pp. 1-111. Washington 1965.

Rentschler, H. C.: An ultraviolet light meter. – Trans. Amer. Instr. Electr. Eng. 49: 576-578, 1930.

Richardson, S. D.: The use of a spherical radiation meter in woodlands. – Forestry 32: 126-137, 1959.

Robitzsch, M.: Über den Bimetallaktinographen Fuess-Robitzsch. – Beitr. Geophys. 35: 387-394, 1932.

Saeki, T.: Light relations in plant communities. – In: Evans, L. T. (ed.): Environmental Control of Plant Growth. Pp. 79-94. Academic Press, New York–London 1963.
Schüepp, W.: La conversion du rayonnement sphérique en rayonnement global. – Arch. Meteorol. Geophys. Bioklimatol. (Ser. B) 10: 311-341, 1961.
Seemann, J.: Klima und Klimasteuerung im Gewächshaus. – Bayerischer Landwirtschaftsverlag GmbH., Bonn–München–Wien 1957.
Seiler, E. F.: Color-sensitiveness of photoelectric cells. – Astrophys. J. 52: 129-153, 1920.
Šetlík, I., Kubín, Š.: Industrialization of agriculture – a challenge to photosynthesis research. – Acta Univ. Carolinae – Biologica (Prague) 1966 (Suppl. 1/2): 77-88, 1966.
Smith, R. A., Jones, F. E., Chasmar, R. P.: The Detection and Measurement of Infra-red Radiation. – Clarendon Press, Oxford 1958.
Stair, R., Schneider, W. E., Jackson, J. K.: A new standard of spectral irradiance. – Appl. Opt. 2: 1151-1154, 1963.
Thams, J. C.: Ein Beitrag zum Problem der Eichung des Bimetallpyranographen Fuess-Robitzsch. – Arch. Meteorol. Geophys. Bioklimatol. (Ser. B) 11: 501-511, 1962.
Thams, J. C., Wierzejewski, H.: Die Grösse der diffusen Zirkumglobalstrahlung. – Arch. Meteorol. Geophys. Bioklimatol. (Ser. B) 12: 47-63, 1963.
Trickett, E. S., Moulsley, L. J.: An integrating photometer. – J. agr. eng. Res. 1: 1-11, 1956.
Trickett, E. S., Moulsley, L. J., Edwards, R. I.: Measurement of solar and artificial radiation with particular reference to agriculture and horticulture. – J. agr. eng. Res. 2: 86-110, 1957.
Uchijima, Z.: A newly devised solarimeter for measuring photosynthetically active radiation. – Jap. agr. Res. Quart. 3(3): 20-22, 1968.
Wallace, R. H.: Methods of sampling visible radiation. – Plant Physiol. 12: 647-666, 1937.
Wassink, E. C., van der Scheer, C.: A spherical radiation meter. – Meded. Landbouwhogesch. (Wageningen) 51: 175-183, 1951.
Wierzejewski, H.: Ein neues integrierendes Messinstrument für Sonnen- und Himmelsstrahlung mit ebener Empfangsfläche. – Verhandl. Schweiz. naturforsch. Ges., pp. 73-75, Scuol 1962.
Withrow, R. B.: Radiant energy nomenclature. – Plant Physiol. 18: 476-487, 1943.
Wörner, H.: Eine neue Ausführung des Kugelpyranometers Bellani. – Z. Meteorol. 10: 65-75, 1956.
Yanishevskiĭ, Yu. D.: Aktinometricheskie Pribory i Metody Nablyudeniĭ. [Actinometric Instruments and Observation Methods.] – Gidrometeorol. Izdat., Leningrad 1957.
Zworykin, W. K., Ramberg, E. G.: Photoelectricity and Its Application. – J. Wiley & Sons, Inc., New York 1949.

SUBJECT INDEX

Numbers in *italics* refer to the more extensive treatments of the subject

B

C

D

I

J

Q

R

S

T

X

Y

Z

Greek alphabet:

AUTHOR INDEX

Numbers in *italics* refer to pages on which the complete reference is listed.

D

E

F

G

H

I

J

K

L

N

O

P

T

U

V

W